Alveolar Gas Exchange and Pulmonary Circulation

Main Symbols

C	concentration in a liquid
Cap	capacity
D	diffusing capacity
f	respiratory frequency
F	fraction
G	conductance
P	pressure, total or partial
Q	volume of liquid
$\dot{Q}$	flow of blood, perfusion
R	gas-exchange ratio
S	saturation
V	gas volume
$\dot{V}$	ventilation
β	slope of a dissociation curve
θ	reaction rate

Modifiers

a	arterial
A	alveolar
B	barometric
c	capillary
DS	dead space

e	effective
E	expired
I	inspired
la	left atrial
m	membrane
p	plasma
pa	pulmonary arterial
pc	pulmonary capillary
pc′	pulmonary end capillary
pv	pulmonary venous
pw	pulmonary wedge
s	shunt
t	time t
T	total
ti	tissue
v	venous
$\bar{v}$	mixed venous
va	venous admixture
0	(zero) initial value

Special Symbols

ATPD	ambient temperature and pressure, dry
ATPS	ambient temperature and pressure, saturated

BTPS	body temperature, ambient pressure, saturated with water vapor
STPD	standard temperature and pressure, dry

Examples of Combinations

$C\bar{v}_{O_2}$	concentration of O_2 in mixed venous blood
$O_2\text{Cap}$	O_2 capacity
Pa_{O_2}	partial pressure of O_2 in arterial blood
$PA_{O_2} - Pa_{O_2}$	alveolar-arterial difference in partial pressure of O_2
P_{O_2}	partial pressure of O_2
$\dot{Q}T$	cardiac output
Sa_{O_2}	saturation of hemoglobin with O_2 in arterial blood
$\dot{V}A/\dot{Q}$	ventilation-perfusion ratio
$\dot{V}E$	expired minute ventilation
$\dot{V}max_{O_2}$	maximum O_2 consumption (also $\dot{V}_{O_2 max}$)

Control of Breathing

$Pm_{0.1}$	mouth occlusion pressure 0.1 s after onset of inspiration
TE	expiratory time
TI	inspiratory time
TT	total respiratory cycle duration

See Symbols and Abbreviations, p. ix.

HANDBOOK OF PHYSIOLOGY

SECTION 3: The Respiratory System, VOLUME III, PART 1

HANDBOOK OF PHYSIOLOGY

A critical, comprehensive presentation
of physiological knowledge and concepts

SECTION 3: # The Respiratory System

Formerly SECTION 3: Respiration

VOLUME III.
Mechanics of Breathing, Part 1

Section Editor: ALFRED P. FISHMAN

Volume Editors: PETER T. MACKLEM
JERE MEAD

Executive Editor: STEPHEN R. GEIGER

American Physiological Society, BETHESDA, MARYLAND, 1986

Preface to the Section on Respiration

The intent of this *Handbook* section is to provide a scholarly, comprehensive, and critical view of contemporary respiratory physiology within the framework of respiratory biology. This has been no simple task; in the 20 years since the first edition, respiratory physiology has extended far beyond its original bounds while becoming more deeply rooted within traditional confines. In large measure this flourishing of respiratory physiology is attributable to the biochemists, anatomists, pharmacologists, pathologists, and bioengineers who have entered the field and enriched it with their approaches, knowledge, concepts, and techniques. During this period the growth of ideas, advances in technology, and accumulation of facts has been steady, with occasional punctuation by scientific upheavals that have reoriented thinking and opened new directions for exploration. To accommodate the expanded body of knowledge and its conceptual framework requires four volumes instead of the three volumes originally planned.

The increase in content, the new direction, and the broader horizons are reflected in the title of this section. The 1964–1965 edition was simply designated *Respiration*; this edition is entitled *The Respiratory System*. This change is a reminder of the complexity, organization, and integration that make respiration possible. Other parts of the body have the same characteristics, but probably in no other component are these characteristics so striking because of the phasic nature of the breathing process, the automatic adjustments of breathing to changing metabolic states, and the many provisions for interruptions in the phasic process by episodic events, such as eating, talking, coughing, straining, and vomiting.

One fruitful way to regard the living organism is to view it as a system of interrelated functional hierarchies. From this vantage a hierarchy or its components can be probed in great detail, always within the larger framework of the whole animal. In this section, one large hierarchy—the respiratory system—and its component parts are put under the microscope, leaving other large and related units, such as the circulatory system, to be considered elsewhere.

The hierarchical approach has broad implications. First, the predominant concern is with function rather than anatomy; boundaries, orderliness, and self-containment are more a matter of feedback mechanisms than of structural restraints. Second, within the framework of the whole body a hierarchy may be involved in more than one function; a single hierarchy (such as the arachidonic acid cascade) generates some substances that act locally and others that behave as circulating hormones and exert their biological effects in remote corners of the body. Third, large systems (such as the respiratory and circulatory systems) are closely interlinked and interdependent; as a rule the larger systems modulate the activities of smaller hierarchies within them. Fourth, at the level of the cell and organelle, hierarchies are exceedingly minute, yet they retain complexity and integration as cardinal features; in this realm, structure gives way to molecular interactions as the basis for function. Finally, the living body could not operate effectively as a conglomeration of hierarchies without sophisticated methods for information transfer to ensure integrated performance.

Currently much physiological experimentation is concerned with information transfer and control mechanisms. Not very long ago this aspect of physiology dealt almost exclusively with nerves and neurohumoral transmitters. Visionaries such as Bernard, Cannon, Barcroft, Henderson, and Sherrington constructed grand schemes to explain the complicated biological interplays that automatically adjust the body at rest, during exercise, on exposure to unsettling environments, and during the fight-or-flight reaction. Their legacy is a body of monumental concepts epitomized by rubrics such as "Homeostasis," "The Architecture of Physiologic Function," and "The Wisdom of the Body."

Although the integrated responses of the whole body continue to be intensely researched, within the hierarchies of the body there is apparently much more to information transfer than nerves, neurohumoral substances, and feedback mechanisms. Individual cells could not do their job without self-replenishing receptors at their surfaces for signal transduction, which triggers biochemical events that activate and regulate the activities of the cells. Endothelial cells that line blood vessels communicate by elaborate biological machinery with smooth muscle cells in the vascular walls. Electrical stimuli conveyed by nerves link events at the cellular level with humors in the central nervous system. An elaborate system for maintaining acid-base balance ensures a background of stability in hydrogen ion concentration so that background noise does not interfere with message centers or media in a hierarchical system that relies so heavily on uninterrupted information transfer for its survival, operation, and propagation.

The respiratory system is currently being explored as a component of the entire organism and in terms of its constituent parts: the perspective of overall integration is exemplified by the exploration of the control of breathing; that of molecular biology is exemplified by the study of macromolecular transport across special domains on the plasma membrane of the pulmonary capillary endothelial cell. The broad sweep of research on the respiratory system and its components and the ways in which the system relates to other systems during rest, activity, stress, and adaptation are the mainstays of this *Handbook* section.

For convenience the section has been subdivided into four volumes: *Circulation and Nonrespiratory Functions, Control of Breathing, Mechanics of Breathing*, and *Gas Exchange*. The hierarchies vary from chapter to chapter in size, complexity, regulatory mechanisms, and machinery for information transfer. The volumes devoted to the circulation and nonrespiratory functions of the lungs and gas exchange give high priority to organization and operation at the cellular level. Those concerned with the control and mechanics of breathing are more inclined toward integrating mechanisms at the level of the whole body. Full understanding of the respiratory system requires reconciliation of its materials and design with its effectiveness in performance under ordinary and under trying conditions. No matter how meticulously and successfully each component of the system is probed, in the last analysis the responsibility of physiology is to restore the isolated component to its proper place in the operations of the respiratory system and to reconcile the respiratory system with the other inner workings of the entire organism.

My debt to the volume editors and authors is self-evident: without them there would be neither content, organization, nor style (in fact, no books). Less evident is my obligation to those in my organization, particularly Jayne Pickard, who managed—by prompting and cajoling authors and editors and by unremitting devotion to the cause—to ensure proper review in my office while maintaining an uninterrupted flow of manuscripts to the Society's publications office.

This was a large effort. One can only hope that the product lives up to the expectations and needs of the readers.

ALFRED P. FISHMAN
Section Editor

Preface

It is appropriate to introduce such a formidable tome with equally impressive generalizations, and we have found it remarkably easy to come up with one important concept that we can actually take seriously: the understanding of respiratory mechanics has benefited enormously from a multidisciplinary approach. Indeed this generalization prompted the design of this volume and embodies our hopes for it as well.

No other topic in mammalian physiology approaches respiratory mechanics in terms of the breadth of knowledge required. Consider the walks of life that have contributed to its understanding: physicians, anatomists, and physiologists, to begin with; followed by engineers, including specialists in fluid dynamics, solid mechanics, acoustics, and systems analysis; but also physicists, applied mathematicians, surface chemists, immunologists, cell biologists, neurophysiologists, psychologists, and more to come! Although the overriding purpose of these volumes must be to present to the world a useful summary of the current status of knowledge in physiology, a particular aim of this volume is to facilitate communication among these varied disciplines. More than anything else, we hope that the experts we have assembled have made themselves clear to nonexperts: for example, engineers to immunologists, and immunologists to neurophysiologists.

Thus we offer our one weighty generalization, but we would also like to confront another. It is currently popular to regard much of physiology as history. If so, those of us interested in respiratory mechanics have been left behind. We are still just beginning to describe breathing adequately, let alone understand it. We have only the vaguest notion as to the relative importance of tissue and surface forces in lung recoil. We appear to have no idea at all about the physiological role of airway smooth muscle. We have yet to agree on the actions of the respiratory muscles, and the ghost of Hamberger is back among us. Clearly we have much to do before the topic can be laid to rest. These chapters should be regarded as working papers to that end.

Nevertheless, since the original American Physiological Society *Handbook* on respiration (published in 1964 and 1965), there has been an enormous growth of knowledge in the field of respiratory mechanics. The original two volumes covered this subject with 174 pages written by 12 authors, whereas this volume consists of 784 pages written by 58 authors.

To determine the subjects to be covered in this volume we had an informal meeting with a number of experts in respiratory mechanics at which the contents were fleshed out in general. However, we take full responsibility for the final development, with any omissions, areas of overlap, or overemphasis that may have resulted. In some instances overlap has been deliberate to allow the same subject to be presented from different points of view.

We attempted to select the individuals most qualified to write on the topics that are covered. The authors we chose made our task enormously easier by providing us with scholarly and up-to-date reviews. If this *Handbook* is a success it is due to the time and effort they put into ensuring contributions of excellence. Having chosen authors who provided us with outstanding contributions, there was little left for us to do. We are very grateful to them.

JERE MEAD
PETER T. MACKLEM

Symbols and Abbreviations

In the summer of 1977 at the International Union of Physiological Sciences Congress in Paris, the Commission of Respiratory Physiology established a committee to improve the glossary of terms and symbols used in respiratory physiology. Shortly thereafter the American Physiological Society decided to publish the new *Handbook* series on respiratory physiology. To incorporate the IUPS symbols into these books, a committee consisting of one of the editors of each *Handbook* was established, namely Leon E. Farhi, Alfred P. Fishman, Peter T. Macklem (chairman), and John G. Widdicombe, along with Curt von Euler and Peter Scheid. The symbols and abbreviations chosen by this committee were approved by the Commission on Respiratory Physiology at the Budapest Congress in 1980 and subsequently approved for publication in the *Handbook of Physiology* by the Publications Committee of the American Physiological Society.

SYMBOLS IN RESPIRATORY PHYSIOLOGY

Main Symbols

The main symbol indicates the nature of the variable and usually appears in the form of a single large capital letter. More rarely it is denoted by a Greek letter, a lowercase letter, or a combination of capital and lowercase letters. Exceptions are the subdivisions of lung volume and symbols for measurements of forced respiratory maneuvers for which accepted usage has been followed.

The main symbol can be modified by a character that appears over the symbol itself (bar for a mean or average value, single dot for the first time derivative, two dots for the second time derivative).

Modifiers

Main symbols are further clarified by the addition of one or more modifiers, usually small capitals for the gas phase, standard chemical symbols for the chemical species, and lowercase letters in most other instances. Modifiers denote locations, anatomic structures, media in which the measurements are made, respiration phases, types of resistance to motion, chemical species, and so forth. The first modifier appears directly after the main symbol. Subsequent modifiers are either separated from the other modifiers by commas or more rarely appear as subscripts. Chemical species always appear as subscripts and follow all other modifiers used (the only exception is the symbol for capacity of a gas). Modifiers denoting time (t or 1.0 s) or numerical designations (0, 1, 2, 3, . . .) appear as subscripts.

The symbols have been divided into three main groups: *1*) respiratory mechanics, *2*) alveolar gas exchange and pulmonary circulation, and *3*) control of breathing. Rather than introduce entirely new symbols to replace those that have gained widespread acceptance, the committee that prepared this guide feels that greater clarity is achieved by some symbols having different meanings and some words more than one symbol. Thus $\dot{V}$ in respiratory mechanics usually means flow, whereas in gas exchange it usually means ventilation. The symbol C can have one of three meanings: compliance in mechanics of breathing, capacity in the subdivisions of lung volume, and concentration in a liquid in gas exchange. In gas exchange, capacity is represented by the symbol Cap. The symbol R signifies respiratory exchange ratio or resistance. The meaning of the symbols should be clearly understood from the context. (*See* endpapers.)

PETER T. MACKLEM

Contents

CHAPTER 1

History of respiratory mechanics

ARTHUR B. OTIS | *Department of Physiology, University of Florida, Gainesville, Florida*

CHAPTER CONTENTS

MANY BOOKS AND ARTICLES have been written about the development of concepts concerned with the chemical aspects of respiration. From this literature one can gain a reasonably clear picture of the evolution of our present appreciation of respiration as gas exchange and intracellular oxidation from which biologically useful energy is derived. On the other hand, relatively little has appeared regarding our understanding of respiration as a mechanical process, and no comprehensive historical work on the topic has been published. This brief account is intended to help the student who wishes to acquire an introduction to the history of respiratory mechanics. It is in no way exhaustive, critical, or definitive (for background reading see refs. 14, 18, 25, 26, 30, 52, 60).

Mechanics of breathing is concerned with one basic question: how does air get into and out of the lungs? The history of the subject reveals two somewhat separate but complementary approaches. The first, and earliest to arise, concerns the arrangement and action of indvidual muscles and is based largely on detailed anatomical knowledge and visual observation. The second approach, which could develop only with the emergence of the concepts and laws of physics, is more quantitative, abstract, and mathematical and is based on the measurements of forces and magnitudes (usually pressures and volumes and their changes with time). It originated as iatromechanics and might now be regarded as biophysics or bioengineering.

History deals with people, events, and concepts. Because events may be influenced by past or contemporary occurrences but not future ones, it is reasonable to outline history chronologically. Table 1 lists the names of some individuals and hints as to their contributions to our understanding of the mechanics of breathing. The list is not complete and other names might have been chosen. Because of space limitations not all those listed are discussed in the text. Likewise the figures illustrating this chapter show only portraits not included in the excellent account by Perkins (45) in the 1964 edition of the *Handbook* section on respiration. Some of the men in Table 1 were primarily physicists rather than physiologists. Their contributions may be indirect, but our understanding of the mechanics of breathing could hardly proceed faster than development of the basic principles of mechanics.

RESPIRATORY MECHANICS FROM ANCIENT TIMES THROUGH THE SEVENTEENTH CENTURY

Although names and dates may form a necessary framework of history, a more interesting and difficult aspect deals with the development of ideas and concepts. That air moves in and out of the nose or mouth must have been an early observation. Because this movement is to some extent subject to voluntary control, just as the movements of arms or legs, recognition of breathing as a muscular activity must also have been made. Who first made this important discovery we shall never know. Erasistratus, who has been called the "father of physiology," thought the diaphragm was the only muscle of breathing (ref. 26, p. 20).

Galen recognized that the diaphragm and intercostal and accessory muscles are involved and realized that the lung is moved by action of the chest rather than the chest by the lung as Herophilus had believed. In *Galen on the Usefulness of the Parts of the Body*, Galen says, "In all animals that inhale through the mouth from the atmosphere and exhale into it again, the lung, which is an instrument of both the voice and respiration, fills the thoracic cavity. The source of its motion is the thorax" (ref. 27, p. 279). He also had some understanding of the action of the larger airways: "For when the whole thorax expands in inspiration ... and then causes the entire lung to expand to fill the space left vacant, the membranous parts of ... [the trachea and its branches] readily increase in breadth

TABLE 1. *Contributors to Respiratory Mechanics*

Alcmaeon of Croton	ca. 500 B.C.	Goats breathe through their ears
Erasistratus of Chios	ca. 300 B.C.	"Father of Physiology"; believed diaphragm was the only muscle of respiration
Galen	A.D. 130–200 (?)	Intercostal and accessory muscles as well as diaphragm are concerned with breathing
Leonardo da Vinci	1452–1519	Lungs expand like a bellows
Andreas Vesalius	1514–1564	Made "pleural window" and saw movements of lungs; punctured pleura and lungs collapsed
Fabricius ab Aquapendente	ca. 1533–1619	Described action of respiratory muscles in *De respiratione et ejus instrumentis*; teacher of William Harvey
Galileo Galilei	1564–1642	Laws of motion
René Descartes	1596–1650	Living matter subject to physical laws; man is a machine; *De homine liber* (1662)
Otto von Guericke	1602–1686	Constructed first vacuum pump
Evangelista Torricelli	1608–1647	Made first mercury barometer; "We live submerged at the bottom of an ocean of the element of air, which by unquestioned experiments is known to have weight" (ref. 15, p. 35)
Giovanni Alfonso Borelli	1608–1679	Pioneer iatromechanist; *De motu animalium*
Franciscus de Le Boe Sylvius	1614–1672	Lungs do not move by themselves but follow motion of thorax and diaphragm
Thomas Willis	1621–1675	Noted constriction of bronchioles in asthma
Blaise Pascal	1623–1662	Understood barometer as a mechanical balance; with his brother-in-law demonstrated variation of barometric pressure with altitude
Robert Boyle	1627–1691	Demonstrated "spring of the air"; PV = constant
Marcello Malpighi	1628–1694	Microstructure of the lung
Richard Lower	1631–1691	Division of phrenic nerves made a dog "breathe like a broken-winded horse" (ref. 45, p. 46)
Robert Hooke	1635–1703	Laws of springs
Jan Swammerdam	1637–1680	Plethysmographic techniques
Isaac Newton	1642–1727	Discovered calculus; formulated laws of motion
John Mayow	1640–1679	Lucid description of mechanics of breathing
Stephen Hales	1677–1761	Measured intrapleural and inspiratory pressure
Georg E. Hamberger	1697–1755	External intercostal muscles are inspiratory; internal intercostal muscles are expiratory
Albrecht von Haller	1708–1777	Generally accurate description of breathing movements
James Carson	1772–1843	Measured elastic recoil of lungs
François Magendie	1783–1855	Abdominal contents act as fulcrum for action of diaphragm
Jean Leonard Marie Poiseuille	1799–1869	Law of fluid flow
Guillaume Benjamin Amand Duchenne	1806–1875	Demonstrated action of respiratory muscles by electrical stimulation
John Hutchinson	1811–1861	Applications of spirometry; pressure-volume curves of chest and lungs
Franciscus Cornelius Donders	1818–1889	Measured elastic forces of lungs
Hermann von Helmholtz	1821–1894	Laws of thermodynamics
Max Cloetta	1868–1940	Pressure-volume relationships
Arthur Keith	1886–1955	Description of respiratory muscle action
Kurt von Neergaard	1887–1947	Surface forces in the lung
Fritz Rohrer	1888–1926	Formulation of quantitative respiratory mechanics
Karl Wirz	1896–1978	Analysis of pleural pressure
Wallace O. Fenn	1893–1971	Elaboration of pressure-volume relationships; *Studies in Respiratory Physiology Chemistry and Mechanics of Pulmonary Ventilation*

and length" (ref. 27, p. 338–339). Galen also understood the action of the "wonderful lids" (ref. 27, p. 373) that directed food and drink down the esophagus and excluded them from the trachea. However, he did believe that a small amount of liquid was allowed to pass, just enough to keep the walls of the airways moist. Of the fine structure of the lung he of course knew nothing and was able only to speculate on the relationship between gas and blood. Recognizing the diaphragm as having unique features, Galen (ref. 27,

p. 599–600) was impressed with the manner in which nature had innervated it:

In a very wonderful way she has brought down to the diaphragm nerves from the spinal medulla in the neck and has conducted nerves to the intercostal muscles from each of the vertebrae touching them. Now the diaphragm differs from all other muscles not only in shape, but also in position and action; for its shape is circular and its position oblique, since its anterior and upper parts reach the sternum and it passes thence back and down farther and farther till it touches the spine, with which it unites at the loins. Its head, the point to which in all muscles the fibers are attached, is not, as one might suppose, in the region near the sternum, nor is it in the lumbar region, but in the sinewy center of the whole diaphragm. Accordingly, the nerves moving its fibers must come down from some source above and reach this point in order to extend the action equally to every part.... This is the reason why the diaphragm alone of the parts below the clavicles receives nerves from the cervical region of the spinal medulla, and not a one of the others does likewise. For when it was possible to send nerves in from parts near by, to bring them from a long distance would be the act of a Creator ignorant of what is better.

Galen clearly was a remarkable man who made many keen observations and demonstrated unusual insight. During the many centuries after Galen until the Renaissance, respiratory mechanics, like all other branches of science, made little progress. One light that glowed from the darkness was Leonardo da Vinci, who among his many remarkable activities made drawings of the respiratory muscles and attempted to analyze their action. He noted that the lungs draw in air like a pair of bellows (37). This analogy, which is still useful, had been made even earlier by Aristotle. But the man to reestablish scientific experiment as a method of elucidating respiratory mechanics was Andreas Vesalius, who in 1543 removed part of a rib and surrounding tissues from a living dog, leaving the pleura through which he could see the movements of the lungs. Puncturing the pleura, he observed the lungs collapse. Vesalius recognized the diaphragm as a muscle of inspiration because it elevated and extended the lower ribs, but mistakenly believed that in producing this action the diaphragm ascended into the thoracic cavity (25).

Almost a century later there was an individual who had a long-lasting impact on the development of physiology by broadening its outlook to encompass not only the facts of anatomy but also the concepts of physics. This was René Descartes, born in France in 1596, died in Stockholm in 1650; mathematician, physicist, and philosopher; amateur anatomist and physiologist. His 1662 book, *De homine liber*, is called by Michael Foster "the first Text-Book of Physiology" (ref. 25, p. 57). He was in no way an experimentalist or researcher but rather a thinker and interpreter. It had become clear to Descartes that the universe worked like a machine in a mathematically predictable fashion in conformity with physical laws. His premise was that such laws might even be applied to living matter, that man might also be regarded as a machine. Although he was wrong in many details, his important notion that living matter has many properties of mechanical systems and can be so analyzed had a lasting influence on the direction of physiological thought.

A contemporary of Descartes was Galileo, a physicist who made major contributions to the development of laws of motion and who appreciated the effects of gravitational loading on biological systems (18a). One of Galileo's admirers was Giovanni Alfonso Borelli, who is sometimes credited with having founded the iatromechanical or iatrophysical school (biophysics). Borelli was born in Naples, studied mathematics in Rome (where he and Torricelli were fellow pupils), and about 1640 became professor of mathematics at Messina. It is not clear how his attention was turned to biological applications of mathematics and physics, but he may have been influenced by his teacher in Rome, Father Bendetto Castelli, who was a mathematician, friend and disciple of Galileo, and author of a treatise on vision. Borelli went from Messina to Florence to see Galileo, but the latter died before they could meet. Borelli returned to Messina but in 1656 was appointed professor of mathematics at Pisa, where he became closely associated with Malpighi.

The association between biological and physical scientist, although ending in a falling-out, was a fruitful one for both, and each provided much stimulation and encouragement to the other. Malpighi was the first to describe the microscopic structure of the lungs. Whereas Galen supposed the lungs to be fleshy, Malpighi was able to say: "Instead of being constructed of flesh or parenchyma, the lungs of man and the other perfect animals called sanguineous are composed of extremely thin membranes propagated from the trachea and loosened up and stretched to form sinuses and cellules [that is to say, spaces and small chambers], so that there is an open avenue for air entering or leaving" (ref. 1, p. 173). Borelli's great two-volume treatise on animal motion, *De motu animalium*, was published only after his death. This beautifully illustrated work analyzes in geometric fashion all types of animal movements. As regards breathing, Borelli seems to have realized that it is the pressure of the atmosphere that drives air into the lungs as the chest expands. Although he may have been mistaken regarding some details of the action of the diaphragm, he did much to show that breathing (and other bodily movements) was amenable to analysis in terms of mechanics.

Also in the seventeenth century, Englishman John Mayow provided a lucid and generally correct description of the mechanism of breathing (41). He understood that both pressure and elasticity of gas are important factors in the inward movement of air that occurs when the chest is expanded. As to the muscles involved, he argued that both internal and external intercostal muscles elevate the ribs and therefore expand the chest. Mayow recognized the importance of the diaphragm and that "ordinary inspiration seems to be mainly caused by it" (ref. 41, p. 195). He felt it "probable ... that, in expiration, the parts of the thorax return, by a movement of restitution, to their natural position without any aid from the muscles" (ref. 41, p. 193). It is not certain that Mayow was aware of the importance of elastic forces in the lungs because he states, "clearly the lungs do not subside of themselves, but follow the movement of the thorax" (ref. 41, p. 201). On the other hand, he seems to have had a considerable appreciation of the mechanics of a pneumothorax.

Mayow pointed out that the diaphragm is curved with its concavity directed toward the abdomen and even in its most contracted state could not become convex in that direction as had been supposed by "the eminent Dr. Willis" (ref. 41, p. 288). [Dr. Thomas Willis was a prominent physician, author, and Oxford professor (19), remembered today for the circular arrangement of cerebral arteries that bears his name.] Mayow also understood the role of the abdominal muscles in active expirations and in acts such as sneezing, coughing, and laughing, and pointed out that laughter does not consist of repeated contractions of the diaphragm "as this learned man [Thomas Willis] supposed" but proceeds "on the contrary, from its diastole" (ref. 41, p. 202).

Although many similar analogues have since been devised (43), Mayow may have been the first to describe the construction of a model of the chest and lungs by enclosing inside a bellows a bladder with the neck connected to the outside. The upper side of the bellows was fitted with a glass window so that an observer could watch the bladder inflate and deflate when the bellows was operated (Fig. 1).

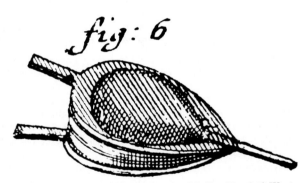

FIG. 1. Plate from John Mayow's 1674 *Medico-Physical Works* (ref. 41, p. 186–187) showing his bellows model of the chest and lungs.

But we may illustrate the inflation of the lungs in this way by yet another example. Let us then suppose that a bladder is enclosed in the cavity of a pair of bellows, and that its neck is so fixed to the pipe of the bellows which is placed in it, that air blown into the pipe can pass only into the bladder, as is seen in Plate II., Fig. 6. (But to ensure this result, the bladder should be fitted in that manner to the pipe before the latter is attached to the bellows.) Further, let the hole be made not as is usual in the lower blade of the bellows, but in the upper one, and let it be of considerable size. Let it also be perfectly closed by a plate of glass, attached to the blade by a suitable cement, so that the bladder shut up within may be seen through the glass as through a window. When these preparations have been made, you will see, if the bellows are opened by drawing the blades apart, the bladder swell and extend into the enlarged cavity of the bellows, as is shown in the figure referred to. And indeed it is plainly in the same way that the inflation of the lungs in the dilated chest is produced.

RESPIRATORY MUSCLES AND THEIR ACTION

The eighteenth century is not remarkable for great advances in respiratory mechanics, but two men deserve comment. One is Hamberger, who in 1748 published *De respirationis mechanismo et usu genuino dissertatio*, in which he presented a geometric model representing the action of the intercostal muscles. Although his analysis has been controversial, it is still found to have some merit (ref. 2, p. 381). The other is Albrecht von Haller, a man of many talents: investigator, scholar, teacher, poet, and author of textbooks. He disagreed with Hamberger's view on the action of the internal intercostal muscles and maintained that they were inspiratory in function.

The American edition of von Haller's *First Lines of Physiology* must have been one of the few physiology textbooks available in the United States in the early nineteenth century, and these excerpts from his chapter on respiration give some impression of what was presented to the student of that day (ref. 54, p. 110–120):

This air, which surrounds the earth on all sides, being compressed by its incumbent columns, perpendicularly and laterally, enters with great force wherever it meets with less resistance, as appears from experiments made in vacuo, and from the phenomena of the air-pump; so that its pressure on the human body is not less than 30,000 pounds.

. . . .

Therefore, that the air may enter the lungs, they must make a less resistance to it than before; namely, the air, which is already in the cellular fabric of the lungs, must be rarefied: but this effect will be produced, if the cavity of the breast, which is filled by the lungs, be dilated. The air, which is always in the lungs, expands into this increased space, by which, being weakened in its spring, it makes less resistance to the external air; consequently a portion of external air descends into the lungs, sufficient to restore to the air, now contained in the lungs, the same density with that of the external air.

. . . .

Almost all authors agree, that they [external intercostals] elevate the ribs.... [Internal intercostals] Therefore their action is disputed ... however, they elevate the ribs notwithstanding this.

. . . .

But this dilatation is neither sufficient for healthy respiration, nor is it almost observable in men; although even then, the intercostal muscles, by retaining and elevating the ribs, very much assist the inspiration in a secondary way, by affording a fixed point to the diaphragm, so that the whole force of that muscle may be spent, not in depressing the ribs, but in lowering itself. The greater part, therefore, of the space which the thorax gains in inspiration, arises from the action of the diaphragm.

. . . .

The diaphragm almost alone performs the office of respiration in a healthy man who is at rest.

. . . .

Is air contained between the lungs and the thorax?...
[The answer is no, except in birds.] But in these there is
a manifest space betwixt the lungs and the pleura.

Von Haller (ref. 54, p. 122–123) speaks of the elasticity
of ribs and the lungs:

Hence expiration is performed more easily and quickly
than inspiration.... In violent respiration ... the more
powerful expirations derive assistance from some other
causes, as the sacrolumbalis, longissimus and quadratus
muscles. By this force, leaden bullets, weighing above a
dram, may be blown to the distance of 363 feet; which
force is equal to a third part of the pressure of the
atmosphere.

French physiologist François Magendie, writing in
the early nineteenth century, found von Haller's opinions "far from satisfactory" (ref. 40, p. 392). He differed with von Haller regarding the mobility of the
first rib and on the importance of the intercostal
muscles in elevating the ribs. Magendie (ref. 40, p.
394) emphasized the importance of the diaphragm in
this action:

when it [the diaphragm] contracts, it forces down the
abdominal viscera, but, in order to do this, the sternum
and ribs must present a resistance sufficient to counteract
the effort made in the opposite direction. Now this resistance can be but imperfect, inasmuch as all these parts
are moveable; for this reason, every time that the diaphragm contracts, it must elevate the thorax more or
less. In general, the extent of the elevation will be in
direct proportion to the resistance of the abdominal viscera, and the mobility of the ribs.

In 1843 Beau and Maissiat (7) published a comprehensive review on the mechanism of respiratory movements in which they considered and evaluated various
views on the action of the diaphragm and intercostal,
abdominal, and accessory muscles of breathing as well
as the elastic forces involved. Among the elastic forces
they included intestinal gas as an important factor.
Beau and Maissiat espoused and may have originated
the popular but controversial notion that men breathe
with the abdomen, whereas women breathe with the
rib cage.

Guillaume Duchenne (Fig. 2), described by Sir Arthur Keith as "one of the most remarkable characters
in medical biography" (ref. 36, p. 94), was a French
physician who spent much of his career studying the
action of muscles by observing their behavior when
stimulated electrically. He also applied his knowledge
to diagnosis and treatment. His important 1867 book,
Physiology of Motion, includes a section on the muscles
of respiration in which he presents a brief but critical
historical review in addition to describing his own
experiments. Duchenne, who coined the term *faradi-
zation*, applied currents from an induction coil to the
phrenic nerve in humans by placing electrodes over
the spot where the nerve crosses the anterior scalenus
muscle. He found that the "*diaphragmatic ribs of the*

FIG. 2. Guillaume Benjamin Amand Duchenne de Boulogne
(1806–1875). Clinician and investigator, he used transcutaneous
electrical stimulation in the diagnosis and treatment of disease and
for elucidation of the physiological action of individual muscles and
muscle groups, including those involved in respiration. [Photogra-
phie Félix Nadar. (C). Arch. Phot. Paris—Paris/Spalden. Courtesy
of Pierre Dejours.]

stimulated side elevated and moved outward." Simultaneous stimulation of both phrenics "*produced the
same expansion of the two sides and an elevation of the
epigastric region*" (ref. 21, p. 449). The anteroposterior
diameter also increased. In one instance he repeated
the experiment with the mouth and nostrils of the
patient closed and again saw the elevation of the ribs
and enlargement of the lower half of the chest, but
noted that "the patient felt a very strong pain at the
base of the thorax on the stimulated side" (ref. 21, p.
450). Duchenne also performed experiments on animals and demonstrated that continued stimulation of
the phrenic nerve in dogs led to asphyxia within a few
minutes.

In accord with Magendie's notion that the viscera
act as a fulcrum permitting the diaphragm to lift the
ribs, Duchenne noted that in eviscerated animals the
base of the chest is circumferentially contracted rather
than expanded by diaphragmatic contraction, although the long diameter of the chest is still increased

by downward movement of the diaphragm. He also found that even with maximal contraction the diaphragm is a truncated cone upwardly directed. The diaphragm had been previously reported to be convex downward by some authors, including von Haller, but Duchenne was unable to substantiate this.

Duchenne noted that in contraction of the diaphragm by electrical stimulation of the phrenic nerve the expansion of the base of the thorax is greater in living animals than in dead animals. He also observed that living animals maintain tension in the abdominal muscles, whereas in dead animals these muscles are completely relaxed. Duchenne (ref. 21, p. 460) concluded:

Whatever the explanation may be, this observation obviously demonstrates that the distention of the inferior ribs produced by the contracture of the diaphragm increases in direct ratio to the resistance of the viscera or abdominal walls. This resistance opposes the descent of the diaphragm and prevents or interferes with the increase of the vertical diameter of the thoracic cavity; the transverse expansion which then occurs forms a sort of compensation. If one reflects on the frequent causes which may resist the lowering of the diaphragm, and consequently interfere with breathing, it may be appreciated (as was mentioned by Galen in the Usu partium), how wise and farsighted nature was in providing the diaphragm with the ability of increasing the thoracic cavity in width almost as much as it loses in height.

Coleman observed that "the textbook is often the truest key to the state of scientific knowledge in a given period" (ref. 14, p. 31). With reference to the understanding of intercostal muscle action a century ago, this statement is exemplified by a footnote in Carpenter's textbook (ref. 11, p. 370–371):

There is probably no point in the whole range of physiology respecting which such different opinions have been entertained by good observers as upon the action of the intercostal muscles, and it may be instructive to give the following enumeration of them, drawn from Beau and Massiat (Archiv. Gén. de Méd., 1842), Küss (Physiologie, 1873, p. 343), Budge (Compendium de Physiol. Humain, 1874, p. 55), and Colin (Traité de Physiologie Comparée, 1873, p. 251 et seq.): 1. Both the external and internal intercostals are *inspiratory muscles* (Borelli, Senac, Boerhaave, Winslow, Haller, Cuvier, Colin, Wündt, Duchenne, Duval). Duchenne supports his opinion by reference to a case in which all the respiratory muscles were paralyzed except the intercostals, and yet in which respiration was maintained; Duval rests his upon experiments made on decapitated criminals shortly after death. 2. Both sets of muscles are *expiratory* (Vesalius, Diemerbröck, Sabatier, Beau and Massiat, Longet). This view rests on the fact that in vivisections the muscles may be seen to contract in forced expiration, as in coughing or crying out. Moreover, the intercostals are present in Birds, in which the act of expiration alone is due to muscular effort. 3. The *external* intercostals are *expiratory*, the *internal, respiratory* muscles (Galen, Bartholinus). 4. The *external* intercostals are *inspiratory*. The *internal, expiratory* muscles (Spigelius, Vesling, Hamberger, and, with some modification, Sibson, Herrmann, and Cleland). According to Sibson the external intercostals are inspiratory, except at their anterior part, in the five inferior intercostal spaces; the internal intercostals are inspiratory in the anterior part of the five first spaces, but have elsewhere an expiratory action. Herrmann observes that the external muscles are *inspiratory* where they are attached to the osseous portions of the ribs, the internal where attached to the cartilaginous portions; but as this corresponds to the chief action of the two sets of fibres both may be regarded as inspiratory muscles. Cleland (Letter to Editor) remarks similarly that the external and anterior fibres of the internal intercostals are most advantageously disposed for elevating the ribs, and that the remaining intercostals are most advantageously placed for depressing the ribs; but that all the intercostals are capable of giving some assistance in inspiration, as also in forced expiration, whilst ordinary expiration is accomplished altogether by elasticity, and not by muscular effort at all. Aeby (Lehrbuch, 1871, p. 379) holds that both sets of muscles approximate the adjoining ribs, but whether this occasions an elevation or depression of the whole series is dependent on the coincident action of other muscles. 5. Mayo and Magendie regarded both sets of muscles as at once expiratory and inspiratory in their action. Lastly, Van Helmont, Arantius, Cruveilhier, Küss, and Jobelin considered that both sets of muscles are passive in the movements of respiration, and simply form an immovable wall to the chest, or rather they contract, not to produce the movements of inspiration or expiration, but to resist at both periods the pressure either of the external or of the internal air.

This controversy regarding the intercostal muscles is not completely resolved in all details even today [(10); see also the chapter by De Troyer and Loring in this *Handbook*]. However, it now receives less attention in most textbooks of medical physiology, which tend to emphasize pressure-volume and pressure-flow relationships rather than the action of individual muscles.

An especially valuable contribution, integrating knowledge of the respiratory muscles and summarizing their action, was published in 1909 by Sir Arthur Keith, an anatomist (Fig. 3). His essay (35) was based on his own careful observations and those of other authors. This thoughtful, lucid presentation shows the considerable insight Keith had regarding the problem and is worthy of perusal today by workers in the field. Among other points he recognized that: *1*) the lungs do not, within the chest, expand equally in all directions; *2*) the bronchial musculature may help regulate the distribution of blood and air in the lungs; and *3*) the effect produced by contraction of the intercostal muscles, as well as that of the diaphragm, depends on the nature of the simultaneous action occurring in antagonistic muscles. Keith also stated that "the diaphragm is made up of two parts which are different in

FIG. 3. Sir Arthur Keith (1866–1955). An anatomist whose careful observations and logical, imaginative mind produced a qualitative but accurate and comprehensive description of the action of the respiratory muscles. (Courtesy of the National Library of Medicine.)

origin, different in their nerve supply, and different in their action" (ref. 35, p. 199).

LUNG ELASTICITY AND PLEURAL PRESSURE

What seem to be the first measurements of pulmonary elasticity were reported in 1819 by Scottish physician James Carson, who connected a water manometer to the trachea of a recently killed animal and then opened the thorax. "In calves, sheep, and in large dogs, the resiliancy of the lungs was found to be balanced by a column of water varying in height from one foot to a foot and a half, and in rabbits and cats, by a column of water varying in height from six to ten inches" (ref. 12, p. 42). In colorful prose, Carson (ref. 12, p. 43) set forth a physiological role for pulmonary elasticity:

Two powers are therefore concerned in regulating the movements and in varying the dimensions and form of the diaphragm, the elasticity of the lungs, and the contractile power of the muscular fibres of the diaphragm. Of these powers the one is permanent and equable, the other variable and exerted at intervals. The contractile power of the diaphragm, when fully exerted, is evidently much stronger than its antagonist, the resilience of the lungs; but the latter not being subject to exhaustion, takes advantage of the necessary relaxations of the former, and rebounding, like the stone of Sisyphus, recovers its lost ground, and renews the toil of its more powerful opponent.

Breathing is in a great measure the effect of this interminable contest between the elasticity of the lungs and the irritability of the diaphragm.

Carson's experiments must be regarded as a pioneer venture in pulmonary mechanics, because very few quantitative measurements had been made previously. His interest in the problem may be related to the fact that he was a proponent and perhaps the originator of induced pneumothorax as a therapy for pulmonary tuberculosis.

Similar demonstrations of pulmonary elasticity were performed on rabbits and human cadavers by Donders (20, 59) in 1853. He proposed that in life the retractile force of the lungs is ~25% greater than after death, because in the former condition tonus is present in addition to passive elastic forces. Donders was aware of the fluctuations of intrapleural pressure with breathing movements and was particularly interested in the effect these might have on the circulation. The first actual measurement of fluctuations of intrapleural pressure during breathing movements is attributed by Wirz (59, 62) to Ludwig, who in 1847 made graphic recordings using a water-filled balloon inserted in the intrapleural space and connected to a mercury manometer. Stephen Hales (28) had visually observed such fluctuations more than a century earlier by means of a manometer tube containing wine.

The first measurements relating elastic forces of the lung to volume were made in 1882 when Heynsius (29) removed the lungs from dogs and rabbits and enclosed them in a glass chamber. Although he did not plot pressure-volume curves, some of his data yield respectable relationships when so represented. He found his results were more consistent when he inflated the lungs by external negative pressure than by positive pressure applied to the trachea. Subsequent investigators who related elastic forces of the lung to volume were van der Brugh (53) and Cloetta (13).

The first direct measurement of intrapleural pressure on a healthy human was reported by Aron (5) in 1900, although the actual experiments had been performed some four years previously. Aron (4) had already made such measurements in a patient being treated for emphysema with suction drainage and obtained graphic records of the fluctuations occurring with breathing movements. Even earlier, Quincke (47) had measured intrapleural pressure in patients during withdrawal of pleural transudates or exudates.

The first comprehensive, conceptual analysis of pleural pressure and its significance to the mechanics of breathing was presented in 1923 by Wirz (59, 62). This clear and carefully reasoned article also contains a detailed historical review of the subject.

PRESSURE-VOLUME RELATIONSHIPS

In his *Statical Essays Containing Vegetable Staticks*, Stephen Hales (ref. 28, p. 270–271) noted:

> For tho' a man by a peculiar action of his mouth and tongue may suck *Mercury* 22 inches, and some men 27 or 28 high; yet I have found by experience, that by the bare inspiring action of the *Diaphragm*, and dilating *Thorax*, I could scarcely raise the *Mercury 2* inches. At which time the *Diaphragm* must act with a force equal to the weight of a *Cylinder* of *Mercury*, whose base is commensurate to the area of the *Diaphragm*, and its height 2 inches, whereby the *Diaphragm* must at that time sustain a weight equal to many pounds. Neither are its counteracting muscles, those of the *Abdomen*, able to exert a greater force.

John Hutchinson (31–33) is widely known for his extensive pioneering studies of vital capacity and other lung volumes by use of his "breathing machine" or spirometer. With an "inspirator" (mercury manometer fitted with a nosepiece) he also measured respiratory "power," i.e., the pressure developed when a subject makes an inspiratory or expiratory effort. Hutchinson (31) classified individuals according to the maximal pressures they developed into eight categories ranging from "weak" (expiratory pressure, 2 inches Hg; inspiratory pressure, 1.5 inches Hg) to "very extraordinary" (expiratory pressure, 10 inches Hg; inspiratory pressure, 7 inches Hg). He also obtained on a cadaver some measurements showing that elastic recoil of the chest and lung increases with increasing volume.

The first data on relaxation pressure in living humans were published by Jaquet (34) in 1908, and the first complete pressure-volume curves for both relaxation and maximal effort were carried out three years later by Bernoulli (8). Both of these Swiss investigators used a chamber similar to one that an American physician, Herbert Williams, designed for a therapeutic procedure he called pneumatic differentiation (61). No further measurements of pressure-volume relationships appear to have been reported until publication of a paper in 1916 by Swiss physician and physiologist Fritz Rohrer (50, 59). Rohrer, in his doctoral dissertation (49, 59) submitted to the faculty at Zurich, had already conceptually outlined and theoretically examined the problem of flow resistance in the airways. Although von Recklinghausen (58) had made an earlier attempt in this area, Rohrer's study is far more penetrating and comprehensive and still a standard of reference.

INTEGRATED VIEW OF RESPIRATORY MECHANICS

Duchenne and Keith were masters of the anatomical approach based on keen observation and logical analysis but little quantitative measurement. Fritz Rohrer was the man who led the way to a comprehensive, conceptually quantitative but more abstract way of looking at respiratory mechanics. Rohrer's publications (49–51, 59) in the decade of 1915–1925, together with those of his associates von Neergaard and Wirz (55–57, 59, 62), have provided paradigms for research in the field even to the present day. He explained the basis for his approach as follows:

> Few data are available on the magnitude of the forces acting in respiration (muscular, elastic, etc.), and the concepts of their correlation are little developed. This is, in my opinion a shortcoming, for—as repeatedly revealed in the history of physics—when facing complicated movements, the insight into the course of the process gains in depth, and often its representation also gains in simplicity, through the knowledge of the forces involved and of their interaction (ref. 59, p. 68).

> In the study of the physiology of respiration, it is important to work out maximally clear, quantitatively developed concepts on mechanical respiratory interrelations; these can serve as a basis for clinical considerations. In this way it will also gradually become possible to replace the many qualitative viewpoints in the pathology of respiration—often difficult to judge, and in contradiction with one another—by reliable quantitative considerations (ref. 59, p. 101).

FIG. 4. Karl Wirz (1896–1978). His career as a physiologist was a brief but brilliant 2 years as a fellow at Rohrer's laboratory in Basel. Wirz subsequently completed his clinical training and took up general practice in Basel. Portrait excerpted from a group photograph taken shortly after his fellowship in physiology. (Courtesy of Mrs. Wirz and Professor H. Bachofen.)

FIG. 5. Kurt von Neergaard (1887–1947). He made important studies of lung elasticity and flow resistance with Wirz. Independently he published a classic paper on surface forces in the lung. Like Wirz, von Neergaard spent only a relatively brief period in physiology and devoted his later life to clinical practice at the Institute of Physical Therapy in Zurich. (Courtesy of the National Library of Medicine.)

mechanics not set forth by Rohrer, yet which has yielded bountiful results, was introduced in 1929 by Rohrer's associate von Neergaard. This concept is the importance of surface tension as a retraction force in the lung. Von Neergaard even foresaw the discovery of pulmonary surfactant when he wrote, "The possibility exists that surface tension of the alveoli decreases in comparison to the other physiologic solutions by becoming enriched with surface-active substances, according to the Gibbs-Thomson law" (ref. 59, p. 290). For a fascinating account of the surface tension story see Comroe (16).

Why did the work of Rohrer and his associates have so little impact at the time? And why, in contrast, was that of Fenn so immediately accepted? No simple answer to these questions seems adequate. Transmission of an idea requires a clear statement and receptive audience, and if either factor is lacking no effective communication can occur. Perhaps respiratory physiologists of Rohrer's day were unprepared through training or interest to accept what he had to say.

In 1975 Mead said, "Rohrer's intentional simplification of the complex motions and forces of respiration to single variables—volumes and pressures—is the basis of most of the advances in the field of respiratory mechanics of the past 50 years" (ref. 59, p. 1).

Rohrer's impact on the study of respiratory mechanics was not immediate, however. Except within his own laboratory, where his associates Wirz and von Neergaard (Figs. 4 and 5) made their fundamental contributions, the period of 1925–1945 seems to have been little influenced by him. For example, Bayliss and Robertson (6) in their 1939 paper on viscoelastic properties of lungs do not recognize the Swiss authors. Dean and Visscher (17), writing two years later on kinetics of lung ventilation, cite von Neergaard and Wirz but do not mention Rohrer. The work and writings of Rohrer and his colleagues began to receive wide attention only after publication of work by the group headed by Wallace Fenn (Fig. 6) at the University of Rochester (23, 44, 48).

The period since this time has been one of great activity in the field of respiratory mechanics and is perhaps too recent to be relegated to history. For perspective refer to reviews by Mead (42), Agostoni (3), and Macklem (38), the book by Campbell et al. (10), Comroe's essays (16) and editorial comments (15, 15a), and Fenn's (24) chapter in the 1964 edition of the *Handbook* section on respiration. The contents of this *Handbook* are of course an indicator of the current state of the subject and may be considered living history. Most of the work during the past 35 years has been along the lines prescribed by Rohrer and Fenn, but one important concept of respiratory

FIG. 6. Wallace Osgood Fenn (1893–1971). Professor of physiology at the University of Rochester, he was an outstanding leader in the development, clarification, and application of principles of respiratory mechanics. One of the most versatile and widely respected physiologists of this century, Fenn had previously made important contributions to the physiology of muscle and electrolyte exchange. He also provided wise and dedicated leadership to such organizations as the American Physiological Society, the American Institute of Biological Science, and the International Union of Physiological Sciences. (Photograph by M. Dvorak.)

Perhaps Fenn (23) was better able to indicate the practical value of the analytic approach to respiratory mechanics. Perhaps language (English vs. German) was a factor. Perhaps the increased availability of convenient instrumentation played a part. At any rate, Fenn had an international audience of eager listeners, many of whom went on to make important contributions of their own (44).

INSTRUMENTATION

Recent studies of respiratory mechanics have been greatly abetted by remarkable technical advances in instrumentation. A history of instrumentation important to respiratory mechanics could itself fill a book. Key items are the barometer, vacuum pump, U-tube manometer, spirometer, membrane manometer of Marey that wrote on a kymograph, optical manometer, and body plethysmograph. Introduction of the pneumotachograph by Fleisch in 1925 and popularization of the esophageal balloon by Buytendijk in 1949 allowed rapid advances in the study of dynamic aspects of respiratory mechanics (15). The potential of these devices was much enhanced by the development of pressure transducers. With remarkable ease their electrical outputs can be amplified and displayed on screens, recorded on paper, printed in digital form, or coupled with computers that can process the information in any desired fashion. Today this sort of instrumentation is taken for granted. Only those who have worked without benefit of stable, high-gain amplifiers and direct writing recorders can truly appreciate such equipment.

LITERATURE OF RESPIRATORY MECHANICS

Respiratory physiology, like other disciplines, is not confined to one country or language. Those who do not readily read several languages often become frustrated in pursuing the history of the subject because so much material is thus unavailable. Translations such as those of the Alembic Club (41), May (27), and Kaplan (21) and those appearing in the volumes edited by Comroe (15, 15a) and West (59) are invaluable to those who read only English. English translations of Borelli's (9, 9a) great work, *De motu animalium*, and

Hamberger's *Dissertatio* would be welcome contributions.

CONCLUSION

Among the numerous investigations published, only a few can be regarded as brilliant or highly original. But the many plodding researchers who make no outstanding discoveries, or even those who make erroneous conclusions from data honestly obtained, may in the long run contribute to the development of a science merely because they keep a problem or an idea alive. They may not kindle new fires but they keep the torch burning.

Sometimes a potentially important idea is conceived but not effectively transmitted because the author mentions it only incidentally or inadvertently distracts the reader by emphasizing other points that may in the long run be less important. Such an example concerning frequency-dependent compliance has been pointed out by Macklem (39). Another example is found in a paper published in 1892 by Einthoven (22), in which he suggested the possibility of dynamic flow limitation in the airways during expiration. Einthoven's paper received little attention, and the notion was born again some 60 years later.

There appears to be a current trend in respiratory mechanics to give more attention to the action of individual muscles or groups of muscles rather than to merely lump them together as a pressure generator. This is not a return to the predominately descriptive, anatomical method but rather a synthesis of it with the biophysical approach. It is hoped that this marriage results in a better understanding not only of the purely mechanical aspects of breathing but also of factors such as neural control and fatigue, and of sensory processes by which perturbations of normal breathing mechanics are detected.

There are still many unsolved problems of respiratory mechanics, but we seem to have come a long way since the time of Alcmaeon, who thought that goats breathe through their ears (ref. 26, p. 18).

I acknowledge support of Grants from the National Institutes of Health (HL-23515 and HL-28263) during the period in which this chapter was written. I thank Theresa MacFadden for editorial assistance and Jerline Galloway for typing.

REFERENCES

1. ADELMANN, H. B. *Marcello Malpighi and the Evolution of Embryology.* Ithaca, NY: Cornell Univ. Press, 1966.
2. AGOSTONI, E. Action of respiratory muscles. In: *Handbook of Physiology. Respiration,* edited by W. O. Fenn and H. Rahn. Washington, DC: Am. Physiol. Sr , 1964, sect. 3, vol. I, chapt. 12, p. 377–386.
3. AGOSTONI, E. Mechanics of the pleural space. *Physiol. Rev.* 52: 57–128, 1972.
4. ARON, E. Ueber einen Versuch, den intrapleuralen Druck am lebenden Menschen zu messen. *Virchows Arch. Pathol. Anat. Physiol.* 126: 517–533, 1891.
5. ARON, E. Der intrapleurale Druck beim lebenden gesunden Menschen. *Virchows Arch. Pathol. Anat. Physiol.* 160: 226–234, 1900.
6. BAYLISS, L. E., AND G. W. ROBERTSON. The visco-elastic properties of the lungs. *Q. J. Exp. Physiol.* 29: 27–47, 1939.
7. BEAU, J. H. S., AND J. H. MAISSIAT. Recherches sur le mécanisme des mouvements respiratoires. *Arch. Gen. Med.* 15, Ser.

3: 397–420, 1842; 1, Ser. 4: 265–295, 1843; 2, Ser. 4: 257–282, 1843; 3, Ser. 4: 249–284, 1843.

8. BERNOULLI, E. Zur Mechanik der Atembewegungen. *Arch. Exp. Pathol. Pharmakol.* 66: 313–333, 1911.

9. BORELLI, G. *De motu animalium.* Rome: Bernabò, 1680, vol. 1.

9a. BORELLI, G. *De motu animalium.* Rome: Bernabò, 1681, vol. 2.

10. CAMPBELL, E. J. M., E. AGOSTONI, AND J. NEWSOM DAVIS. *The Respiratory Muscles: Mechanics and Neural Control* (2nd ed.). London: Lloyd-Luke, 1970.

11. CARPENTER, W. B. *Principles of Human Physiology* (8th ed.). Philadelphia, PA: Lea, 1876. (New Am. ed. by F. G. Smith.)

12. CARSON, J. On the elasticity of the lungs. *Philos. Trans. R. Soc. London* 110: 29–44, 1820.

13. CLOETTA, M. Untersuchungen über die Elastizität der Lunge und deren Bedeutung für die Zirkulation. *Pfluegers Arch. Gesamte Physiol. Menschen Tiere* 152: 339–364, 1913.

14. COLEMAN, W. *Biology in the Nineteenth Century.* London: Cambridge Univ. Press, 1977.

15. COMROE, J. H., JR. (editor). *Pulmonary and Respiratory Physiology.* Stroudsburg, PA: Dowden, Hutchinson & Ross, 1976, vol. 5, pt. 1. (Benchmark Papers in Human Physiology.)

15a. COMROE, J. H., JR. (editor). *Pulmonary and Respiratory Physiology.* Stroudsburg, PA: Dowden, Hutchinson & Ross, 1976, vol. 6, pt. 2. (Benchmark Papers in Human Physiology.)

16. COMROE, J. H., JR. *Retrospectroscope: Insights into Medical Discovery.* Menlo Park, CA: Von Gehr, 1977.

17. DEAN, R. B., AND M. B. VISSCHER. The kinetics of lung ventilation. *Am. J. Physiol.* 134: 450–468, 1941.

18. DEBUS, A. G. *Man and Nature in the Renaissance.* London: Cambridge Univ. Press, 1978.

18a. Dedication [to Galileo]. *Physiologist* 24(6), Suppl.: S-ii, 1981.

19. DEWHURST, K. (editor). *Thomas Willis's Oxford Lectures.* Oxford, UK: Sanford, 1980.

20. DONDERS, F. C. Beiträge zum Mechanismus der Respiration und Circulation im gesunden und kranken Zustande. *Z. Rat. Med.* 3: 287–319, 1853.

21. DUCHENNE, G. B. *Physiology of Motion,* translated by E. B. Kaplan. Philadelphia, PA: Lippincott, 1949. (Translated from *Physiologie des mouvements démontrée à l'aide de l'expérimentation électrique et de l'observation clinique, et applicable à l'étude des paralysies et des déformations.* Paris: Ballière, 1867.)

22. EINTHOVEN, W. Ueber die Wirkung der Bronchialmuskeln, nach einer neuen Methode untersucht, und über Asthma nervosum. *Pfluegers Arch. Gesamte Physiol. Menschen Tiere* 51: 367–445, 1892.

23. FENN, W. O. Mechanics of respiration. *Am. J. Med.* 10: 77–90, 1951.

24. FENN, W. O. Introduction to the mechanics of breathing. In: *Handbook of Physiology. Respiration,* edited by W. O. Fenn and H. Rahn. Washington, DC: Am. Physiol. Soc., 1964, sect. 3, vol. I, chapt. 10, p. 357–362.

25. FOSTER, M. *Lectures on the History of Physiology.* London: Cambridge Univ. Press, 1901.

26. FRANKLIN, K. J. *A Short History of Physiology* (2nd ed.). London: Staples, 1949.

27. GALEN. *Galen on the Usefulness of the Parts of the Body,* translated by M. T. May. Ithaca, NY: Cornell Univ. Press, 1968. (Translated from *De usu partium.*)

28. HALES, S. *Statical Essays Containing Vegetable Staticks* (3rd ed.). London: Innys and Manby, 1738.

29. HEYNSIUS, A. Ueber die Grösse des negativen Drucks im Thorax beim ruhigen Athmen. *Pfluegers Arch. Gesamte Physiol. Menschen Tiere* 29: 265–310, 1882.

30. HUNTER, M. *Science and Society in Restoration England.* London: Cambridge Univ. Press, 1981.

31. HUTCHINSON, J. Lecture on vital statistics, embracing an account of a new instrument for detecting the presence of disease in the system. *Lancet* 1: 567–570, 594–597, 1844.

32. HUTCHINSON, J. On the capacity of the lungs, and on the respiratory movements, with the view of establishing a precise and easy method of detecting disease by the spirometer. *Lancet* 1: 630–632, 1846.

33. HUTCHINSON, J. Researches on the function of the intercostal muscles and on the respiratory movements with some remarks on muscular power in man. *Abstr. Pap. Printed Philos. Trans. R. Soc. London* 5: 591–693, 1847.

34. JAQUET, A. Zur Mechanik der Atembewegungen. *Arch. Exp. Pathol. Pharmakol.* 59, Suppl.: 309–316, 1908.

35. KEITH, A. The mechanism of respiration in man. In: *Further Advances in Physiology,* edited by L. Hill. London: Arnold, 1909.

36. KEITH, A. *Menders of the Maimed.* London: Frowde, 1919. (Reprint. Huntington, NY: Krieger, 1975.)

37. MacCURDY, E. (editor). *The Notebooks of Leonardo da Vinci.* New York: Reynal & Hitchcock, 1938.

38. MACKLEM, P. T. Airway obstruction and collateral ventilation. *Physiol. Rev.* 51: 368–436, 1971.

39. MACKLEM, P. T. Relationship between lung mechanics and ventilation distribution. *Physiologist* 16: 580–588, 1973.

40. MAGENDIE, F. *An Elementary Treatise of Human Physiology,* translated by J. Revere. New York: Harper, 1844. [Translated from *Précis elémentaire de physiologie* (5th ed.), 1838.]

41. MAYOW, J. *Medico-Physical Works,* translated by A. Crum Brown and L. Dobbin. Edinburgh: Alembic Club Reprints, no. 17, 1907. (Translated from *Tractatus quinque medico-physici,* 1674.)

42. MEAD, J. Mechanical properties of lungs. *Physiol. Rev.* 41: 281–330, 1961.

43. OTIS, A. B. Man's urge to model. *Bull. Physio-Pathol. Respir.* 8: 181–198, 1972.

44. OTIS, A. B., AND H. RAHN. Development of concepts in Rochester, New York, in the 1940s. In: *Pulmonary Gas Exchange,* edited by J. West. New York: Academic, 1980, vol. 1, chapt. 2, p. 33–66.

45. PERKINS, J. F., JR. Historical development of respiratory physiology. In: *Handbook of Physiology. Respiration,* edited by W. O. Fenn and H. Rahn. Washington, DC: Am. Physiol. Soc., 1964, sect. 3, vol. I, chapt. 1, p. 1–62.

47. QUINCKE, H. Ueber den Druck in Transudaten. *Dtsch. Arch. Klin. Med.* 21: 453–468, 1878.

48. RAHN, H. Wallace Osgood Fenn (1893–1971). *Biogr. Mem. Natl. Acad. Sci.* 50: 141–173, 1979.

49. ROHRER, F. Der Strömungswiderstand in den menschlichen Atemwegen und der Einfluss der unregelmässigen Verzweigung des Bronchialsystems auf den Atmungsverlauf in verschiedenen Lungenbezirken. *Pfluegers Arch. Gesamte Physiol. Menschen Tiere* 162: 225–299, 1915.

50. ROHRER, F. Der Zusammenhang der Atemkräfte und ihre Abhängigkeit von Dehnungszustand der Atmungsorgane. *Pfluegers Arch. Gesamte Physiol. Menschen Tiere* 165: 419–444, 1916.

51. ROHRER, F. Physiologie der Atembewegung. In: *Handbuch der normalen und pathologischen Physiologie,* edited by A. Bethe, G. von Bergmann, G. Embden, and A. Ellinger. Berlin: Springer, 1925, vol. 2, p. 70–127.

52. STICKNEY, J. C., AND M. F. WILSON. *An Annotated Bibliography of the Physiology of Respiratory Mechanics and its Application in Health and Disease.* Morgantown: West Virginia Univ., 1968, 308 p. (Bull., ser. 68, no. 10-2.)

53. VAN DER BRUGH, J. P. Ueber eine Methode zur Messung des intrapleuralen Druckes. *Pfluegers Arch. Gesamte Physiol. Menschen Tiere* 82: 591–602, 1900.

54. VON HALLER, A. *First Lines of Physiology* (1st Am. ed.). Troy, NY: Penniman, 1803. (Translated from 3rd Latin ed.)

55. VON NEERGAARD, K. Neue Auffassungen über einen Grundbegriff der Atemmechanik. Die Retraktionskraft der Lunge, abhängig von der Oberflachenspannung in den Alveolen. *Z. Gesamte Exp. Med.* 66: 373–394, 1929.

56. VON NEERGAARD, K., AND K. WIRZ. Über eine Methode zur Messung der Lungenelastizität am lebenden Menschen, insbesondere beim Emphysem. *Z. Klin. Med.* 105: 35–50, 1927.

57. VON NEERGAARD, K., AND K. WIRZ. Die Messung der Strömungswiderstände in den Atemwegen des Menschen, insbesondere bei Asthma und Emphysem. *Z. Klin. Med.* 105: 51–82,
1927.

58. VON RECKLINGHAUSEN, H. Ueber die Athmungsgrösse des
Neugeborenen. *Pfluegers Arch. Gesamte Physiol. Menschen
Tiere* 62: 451–493, 1896.

59. WEST, J. B. (editor). *Translations in Respiratory Physiology.*
Stroudsburg, PA: Dowden, Hutchinson & Ross, 1975.

60. WESTFALL, R. S. *The Construction of Modern Sciences: Mechanisms and Mechanics.* London: Cambridge Univ. Press, 1977.

61. WILLIAMS, H. F. Pneumatic differentiation and the pneumatic
differential process. Its definition and general suggestions for
its application. *J. Am. Med. Assoc.* 8: 509–512, 1887.

62. WIRZ, K. Das Verhalten des Druckes im Pleuraraum bei der
Atmung und die Ursachen seiner Veränderlichkeit. *Pfluegers
Arch. Gesamte Physiol. Menschen Tiere* 199: 1–56, 1923.

General principles of respiratory mechanics

The general principles of respiratory mechanics illustrate the points we made in the preface. A remarkable number of disciplines have contributed to our understanding of the mechanics of breathing, including the application of elasticity theory to describe the distribution of stresses within the lung; basic principles of aerodynamics to the study of pressure-flow relationships in the airways; wave-speed theory to understand the mechanism of expiratory flow limitation; stereology to quantify lung structure; and principles of acoustics and systems analysis to improve the methods used to measure pressure, flow, and volume and to understand the oscillation mechanics of the respiratory system.

These are subjects not generally taught in physiology departments or medical curricula. A major purpose here is to make these frequently complex topics understandable to the average physiologist, who like ourselves has never had formal training in these disciplines. The authors of these chapters reflect our objectives. Thus many are written by an engineer, physicist, or mathematician jointly with a physiologist in the hope that the basic principles described will be understandable to a nonspecialist in the field.

PETER T. MACKLEM
JERE MEAD

CHAPTER 2

Principles of measurement: applications to pressure, volume, and flow

JAMES P. BUTLER

DAVID E. LEITH

ANDREW C. JACKSON

Department of Physiology, Harvard School of Public Health, Boston, Massachusetts

California Primate Research Center, University of California, Davis, California

CHAPTER CONTENTS

A MEASUREMENT HAVING BEEN MADE, an investigator is confronted with the task of determining what that measurement means. All branches of science share the attendant questions and problems associated with extracting desired information from a given measurement. These fall under several broad areas. This chapter gives an overview of the principles underlying the entire measurement process, as schematically represented in Figure 1, while drawing some illustrative examples from the specific field of measurements in respiratory mechanics. More specific aspects of methodology are treated in the chapter by Mead and Milic-Emili (21) in the 1964 edition of the *Handbook* section on respiration.

Principles concerning four of these categories appear rather naturally in sequence. Consider a system with some physical quantity of interest. That unmea-sured quantity represents a kind of Truth that one may trace as the measurement is being made. The first question arises when an instrument is connected to the system. The very coupling itself constitutes a loading phenomenon; the Truth has been modified to some degree. The extent to which this is a problem is a function of the system characteristics (which are often unknown) and the input characteristics of the measuring instrument. Second, the instrument itself has some characteristic response. Whatever modified (loaded) version of the Truth is presented to the instrument, its output systematically deviates from the ideal. It is often possible to characterize the instrument response, but correcting for it may be a difficult and delicate task. This brings up the third broad area, the general problem of signal processing. Both analog and digital processing techniques appear at this stage. The basic idea of such processing is to undo the undesirable effects of loading, system response, and noise. The extent to which this is successful depends on many factors, most of which relate essentially to the information content of the basic signal itself. Fourth, the investigator must use the measurements in a suitable and appropriate interpretation of the physical system in question. This latter area is not properly a question of measurement per se, but often arises when the physical quantity of interest is not itself measurable. One then must rely on indirect measurements and infer the desired results.

These four areas appear sequentially as the Truth is traced to its final interpretation. Three other broad areas are crucial to consider; they overlap this sequence in many ways. The first is noise, defined here as the contamination of what one wishes to measure with unwanted effects. Noise has many guises and many sources both within and external to the biological system under study. It is sometimes a difficult task to unravel signal from noise, and much of the success (or lack thereof) of a particular measurement

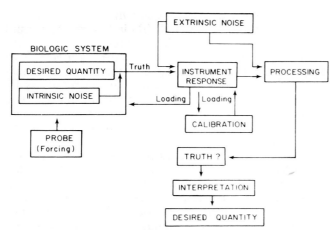

FIG. 1. Schematic diagram of the entire measurement process.

technique depends on carefully dealing with noise. Second, there is the problem of calibration. Conceptually this is simple: use the real instrument to measure something that is known. The final output is then calibrated (defined) by the known input. However, this simple procedure assumes that something known can be generated and characterized. For some quantities, standards (either primary or secondary) can indeed be found that suffice, but for other quantities, constructing standards can be problematical. Third, the measurement structure described above attempts to measure a preexisting physical quantity, a process that might be called passive. By contrast, other measurements are active in the sense that the system is artificially challenged and its response to that probe is the desired result. In these circumstances the characteristics of the probe or forcing function are important; the system must be probed with sufficient energy to ensure that the information content of the signal is adequate relative to the noise, and the intervention must probe the system in a manner appropriate to the questions being asked.

PRELIMINARY CONSIDERATIONS

Before embarking on a systematic treatment of the general areas and principles, some preliminary groundwork must be laid. This section presents a summary of some of the common concepts from linear systems analysis (29). These have been successfully used in respiratory mechanics for many years and are convenient for analyzing the various problems encountered later in this chapter. Certain aspects of nonlinear behavior are addressed in LINEAR VERSUS NONLINEAR SYSTEMS, p. 31. It must be emphasized that the following remarks only apply to systems that are linear; i.e., apart from scaling, there is no direct amplitude dependence of the system's characteristics. The APPENDIX, p. 31, treats this concept and defines Fourier and Laplace transforms in some detail.

The most important concept used freely in this chapter is the notion of the frequency or Fourier domain. Although measurements are perforce made in the time domain, it is often problematic how best to characterize them. Because in the time domain the system is usually governed by complicated differential or integral equations, there may be no convenient way to display the system's generalized characteristics as distinguished from its temporal responses over a range of different circumstances. This problem is avoided in the frequency domain. For example, with sinusoidal input and output at a given frequency, the actual time-varying curves of input and output are unnecessary to characterize the system; a pair of numbers suffices to describe completely the relationship of the output to the input at that frequency. This pair is commonly given as the ratio of the magnitudes of the sinusoids together with the phase difference between them. Equivalently, the pair is sometimes simply given as the complex number with the given magnitude and phase. Finally, a description of how this pair of numbers varies with frequency yields a complete description of the system. This relationship is called the system transfer function and is labeled $T(\omega)$, where, at frequency f, ω is the angular frequency $2\pi f$. Throughout this chapter input and output functions, when transformed to the frequency domain, are written with a circumflex.

In the special case where input is a flow-type variable and output is the associated stress-type variable (e.g., pressure drop or voltage drop), the transfer function is called the impedance and is denoted by $Z(\omega)$. Note that impedance is not the ratio of pressure to flow in the time domain. It is defined only in the frequency domain. Of course, if the system is driven at a single frequency, a temporal measurement of amplitude ratio and phase difference is a direct measure of the impedance at that frequency. However, small amounts of signal at other frequencies may markedly compromise such a direct measurement.

The concept of equivalent circuits is often helpful conceptually. Idealized mechanical elements in physiology have analogous electrical elements when their respective transfer functions are identical. The manner in which the mechanical elements are related can then be displayed as an equivalent electrical circuit, with appropriate substitutions of electrical elements. Three basic passive system elements are commonly used: resistance, compliance (or capacitance), and inertance (or inductance). The impedances of these elements are given in APPENDIX, p. 31.

LOADING

This section describes some of the ramifications and potential problems associated with the modification of the desired quantity of interest (the Truth) in consequence of coupling a measuring instrument to a biological system. Such coupling is commonly called loading. All biological systems change or adjust their underlying behavior in response to external loading. Such changes may be undesired and interfere with the signals of interest (see *Intrinsic Noise*, p. 26) or they may be desired and elicited on purpose. That is, the load is an experimental intervention designed to generate responses of interest (see PROBES, p. 29). This section, however, explicitly assumes no such change in the underlying behavior of the biological system and considers only the way in which the external load makes the measured Truth differ from that present in the unloaded system.

For simplicity, consider the quantity to be measured to be some pressure or voltage. A real system has some internal source impedance Z_S, and a real measuring device has an input impedance Z_L. Here the system is considered to be a source, and the device to be a load. Figure 2 represents pressure or voltage loading (Fig. 2A) and the "dual" of this, flow or current loading (Fig. 2B). In voltage loading, instrument coupling constitutes a voltage divider. If the impedances are resistive ($Z_S = R_S$, $Z_L = R_L$), the actual voltage presented to the device is not E_0, but rather E_1, which equals $R_L/(R_L + R_S)E_0$, where R_L is the input resistance of the device and R_S is the source resistance. Thus the extent to which the device "sees" E_0 is simply the extent to which R_L is large compared with R_S. Even if there is substantial alteration of E_0 by the

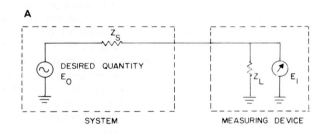

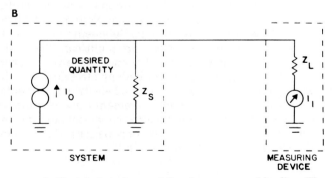

FIG. 2. Electrical analogue of the phenomenon of loading. The biological system has a source impedance Z_S, whereas the measuring device has an input impedance that is functionally a load Z_L. A: pressure or voltage loading. The measured value E_1 systematically deviates from the desired value E_0 by virtue of a nonzero Z_S and a finite Z_L. B: flow or current loading. The measured value I_1 systematically deviates from the desired value I_0 by virtue of a finite Z_S and a nonzero Z_L.

loading presented by the measuring device, one can in principle correct for it if R_L/R_S is known. The input resistance for typical devices is often known, but the driving (or source) resistance is often unknown. This implies that one must be able to measure, or at least estimate, R_S itself. One approach to this is to vary R_L (possibly to the extremes of zero or infinity) and observe the behavior of the measured E. The dependence of E on R_L then suffices to determine R_S and hence the Truth E_0.

This problem would present little difficulty if measurements were performed with devices that had either high input impedances for pressure or voltage measurements, or low impedances for flow or current measurements. Whether the device impedance is high or low is determined by comparison with the source impedance. Real physical devices such as pressure or flow transducers and body plethysmographs may not have impedance magnitudes sufficiently high or low to avoid significant loading.

Consider some physiological examples of loading. If the desired quantities were volumes and flows in spontaneous breathing, any added resistance and inertance of a pneumotachometer would by definition alter the system's behavior from that in the unloaded state. Therefore it is important to minimize the load as much as possible (though quantifying that may be difficult). A somewhat ironic example arises in measurements of lung mechanics in small animals due to fresh gas bias flows introduced into the external equipment. These are used to wash out equipment dead space to avoid rebreathing effects and thus minimize the effective load to gas exchange; however, their introduction may present a pressure offset to the airway opening and thus load the mechanical properties.

Loading of body surface pressure is another example. In one type of pressure plethysmograph, typically used for small animals, a subject within a closed box breathes air from outside the box (18). Volume changes of the subject are by Boyle's law associated with pressure changes in the box, with a magnitude ratio inversely proportional to box volume. Large boxes therefore have relatively small pressure excursions for a given volume change and thus present a small load to the subject but a more difficult pressure measurement. Small boxes have good signal-to-noise characteristics but may excessively load the subject in studies dealing with spontaneous breathing. In addition to size considerations, changes in temperature or humidity can present large static pressure loads. These can affect the subject's relaxation volume and the time course of relaxed expiration, among other static and dynamic variables. Periodic "bleeding" of box pressure to room air often solves this.

In a DuBois plethysmograph (6), in which the subject breathes within the box, the considerations discussed above are negligible. However, pressure drifts can load the sensitive box pressure transducer to an unacceptable degree and constitute a form of noise. A long time constant leak from box to room usually suffices to prevent this.

Esophageal pressures measured with highly compliant balloons (19) are often used to infer pleural pressures (see the chapter by Anthonisen in this *Handbook*). Apart from balloon-transducer characteristics and esophageal contributions, there is in principle a systematic error introduced by lung distortion. If the balloon volume were excessively large, the locally distorted lung would have a local recoil lower than that of the lung as a whole.

D'Angelo et al. (5) and Agostoni and Miserocchi (1) used a novel technique to measure pleural pressures in which no loading was involved. Parietal pleural "windows" freed of overlying tissue exhibit elastic distortion due to local lung recoil. If one assumes a flat, preexisting pleural configuration, the applied (external) pressure necessary to eliminate the distortion from that assumed configuration is a load-nulling measure of the preexisting pleural pressure.

INSTRUMENT RESPONSE

Dynamic properties of real measuring instruments are often usefully characterized by their frequency response. Consider measuring a pressure or voltage. If E_{in} is what is actually presented to the device (either a loaded Truth or a calibration signal that effectively has zero source impedance) and E_{out} is the device output, the instrument's response characteristics are defined in terms of the relationship between E_{out} and E_{in}. Over some range of signal amplitudes, many devices may be described as linear. In this circumstance an appropriate characterization of the device is $T(\omega) = \hat{E}_{out}(\omega)/\hat{E}_{in}(\omega)$ (see **PRELIMINARY CONSIDERATIONS**, p. 16, and **APPENDIX**, p. 31). If output measurements are then made sequentially at different frequencies (with sufficient time allowed for the system's transients to decay), knowledge of the transfer function suffices to infer the actual input (the desired quantity).

To illustrate the frequency response of a device, consider the dynamic behavior of a commonly used pressure transducer (10). Most pressure transducers work on the principle that a volume delivered to the chamber changes its pressure and causes a displacement of a diaphragm that in turn is reflected in the output voltage. That is, $P_{out} = (1/C)V$, where C is effective compliance of the diaphragm and gas compression, if any, P_{out} is the estimated pressure, and V is the delivered volume. The transducer is connected to some place at which a pressure measurement is desired; pressure there is P_{in}. If the transducer is used within its linear range, if changes in P_{in} occur sufficiently slowly (quasi-static conditions), and if sufficient volume is available at the measurement site, then P_{out} is an accurate estimate of P_{in}. If P_{in} is rapidly changing with time, this picture may change depending on the physical connection between the transducer

and P_{in}. This connection is usually made with a tube or catheter that has compliance C (lumped with transducer C noted above), resistance R, and inertance I with respect to transmitting volume changes. In the Fourier domain, these have pressure drops associated with them of $i\omega R\hat{V}$ and $-I\omega^2\hat{V}$, respectively, where i = $\sqrt{-1}$. Thus under dynamic conditions the volume delivered to the transducer is related to $\hat{P}_{in}$ by

$$\hat{P}_{in}(\omega) = (1/C + i\omega R - I\omega^2)\hat{V}(\omega)$$

or

$$\hat{P}_{out}(\omega)/\hat{P}_{in}(\omega) = (1 + 2i\zeta\omega/\omega_0 - \omega^2/\omega_0^2)^{-1}$$

where ζ is the damping coefficient, conventionally defined as $\frac{1}{2}R(C/I)^{\frac{1}{2}}$, and ω_0 is the natural frequency of the system, defined by $\omega_0^2 = 1/IC$.

This expression is the classic result for second-order response (29). (This terminology arises from the second-order differential equation governing behavior in the time domain or, equivalently, the quadratic character of the transfer function of ω in the Fourier domain.) Its characteristics may be displayed in a so-called Bode plot, where the logarithm of $|T(\omega)|$ and the phase of $T(\omega)$ are plotted against the logarithm of frequency. Figure 3 shows the characteristics of general second-order systems as a function of normalized frequency and as families in the damping coefficient ζ. For $\zeta > (1/\sqrt{2})$, the system is called overdamped, and $\hat{P}_{out}$ always systematically underestimates $\hat{P}_{in}$. The magnitude of this error asymptotically increases as the square of the frequency. For $\zeta < (1/\sqrt{2})$, the system is called underdamped and resonance phenomena may be observed, wherein for some frequency range $\hat{P}_{out}$ actually overestimates $\hat{P}_{in}$. Critical damping is defined as when $\zeta = 1/\sqrt{2}$ and corresponds to optimal response characteristics ("flattest") for a given ω_0. At $\omega = \omega_0$ the phase shift is 90°, regardless of damping, and the amplitude is monotonically decreasing with increasing damping, with a value of 0.707 for critical damping. The term *resonance* usually refers to the frequency at which a 90° phase shift is observed, although occasionally it is associated with the lower frequency at which the amplitude reaches a peak in the underdamped situation. For completeness, first-order characteristics are included in Figure 3. The magnitude and phase response for the transfer function correspond to the characteristics of simple resistance-compliance systems. The abscissa must be read as $\omega\tau$, for τ (the time constant of the system) = RC (the uniform limit of $1/\omega_0$ as I → 0).

The response of the physical transducer plus connector system is dependent on properties of both the transducer and the connector. Thus frequency-response curves, or specifications provided by manufacturers for transducers, do not necessarily represent the response characteristics of the system in use. The dramatic effect of representative connections on the response of a transducer is illustrated in Figure 4. If

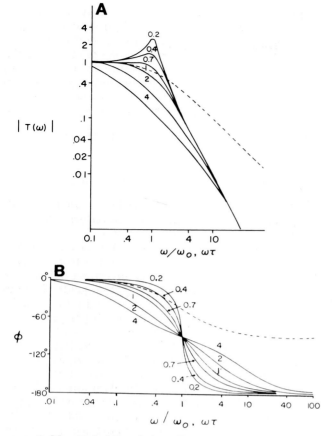

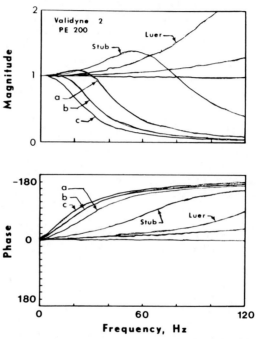

or expansion of box gas. The rate of change of thoracic gas volume is denoted by $\dot{V}$. At low frequencies, virtually all of $\dot{V}$ goes through the pneumotachometer and Pbox is close to $\dot{V}R$. The integral of Pbox is then proportional to the change in the subject's lung volume. At high frequencies, however, much of the change in thoracic volume may be accounted for by compression of box gas. Therefore Pbox/R systematically underestimates $\dot{V}$ (and introduces a phase shift). These relationships may be quantified by writing the transfer function

$$\hat{V}(\omega) = (1/R)(1 + i\omega RC)\hat{P}box(\omega)$$

Thus as $\omega \to 0$, $\dot{V}$ is adequately measured by Pbox/R. For $\omega \gtrsim 1/RC$, both the amplitude and phase relation-

FIG. 3. Magnitude (A) and phase (B) of the second-order transfer function $T(\omega) = [1 + 2i\zeta\omega/\omega_0 - (\omega/\omega_0)^2]^{-1}$ as a function of normalized frequency, as a family in the damping coefficient ζ; ω is the angular frequency $2\pi f$. *Dotted line* shows the response of a first-order transfer function $T(\omega) = (1 + i\omega\tau)^{-1}$, where τ is the time constant of the system. Abscissa for the second-order transfer function is ω/ω_0, whereas that for the first-order is $\omega\tau$. [Adapted from Shearer et al. (29).]

the response characteristics of a particular measurement are critical, it is important that the response of the total system, including all connectors, tubing, and transducer, be measured. This should be done in a physical configuration as close as possible to that which is used. (Identical configurations may not always be possible. The distribution of volume in an esophageal balloon is different in situ from that when its volume-pressure characteristics are measured prior to use.)

Pressure transducers are often used in conjunction with other devices such as pneumotachometers or plethysmographs. As an example of a first-order system, consider an integrated-flow plethysmograph (12, 17). The analogue electrical network for this system is shown in Figure 5. The subject is placed inside the plethysmograph breathing outside air. Changes in thoracic gas volume cause changes in box pressure (Pbox), which in turn are supported by a flow-resistive pressure drop across a box flowmeter and by compression

FIG. 4. Effect of connectors on the amplitude and phase response of a Validyne MP-45 transducer with 2-cmH$_2$O sensitivity. Unlabeled lines: minimum attachments; Luer: male-male Luer slip fitting; Stub: needle stub adapter; a, b, c: 15-cm, 30-cm, and 45-cm PE-200 air-filled catheters, respectively. [From Jackson and Vinegar (17).]

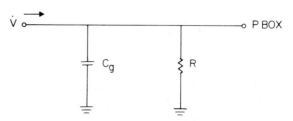

FIG. 5. Electrical analogue of a flow plethysmograph. C$_g$, box gas compliance; R, flow resistance of a pneumotachograph; Pbox, box pressure; $\dot{V}$, flow rate. Note that ground for resistor is atmospheric pressure, and ground for capacitor is zero pressure. These 2 points nevertheless represent a common virtual ground for the signals of interest.

ships between $\hat{\dot{V}}$ and $\hat{P}box$ become frequency dependent. Except for a constant factor of 1/R, the $\hat{P}box/\hat{\dot{V}}$ transfer function is precisely the one shown by the dotted line in Figure 3 as the first-order system. Consider using such a device to measure volume changes. The integral of Pbox as an estimate of V is likewise compromised by effects of gas compliance, and pressure compensation may be indicated. This is properly an example of analog signal processing and is discussed in the next section.

An example of first- and second-order plethysmograph characteristics is treated by Sinnett et al. (31). A maximal expiratory maneuver where flow falls exponentially in time (after an instantaneous rise to peak) would be displayed as a straight line in a flow-volume plot. The effect of first-order devices on such a measurement is shown in Figure 6A. The shape of the measured flow-volume curve depends on how fast the measurement system is relative to the lung. Even if the transducer is as much as 10 times faster, there can still be a substantial alteration of the Truth. Figure 6B shows one example of the same curve, measured with a second-order underdamped system. (Inertance is either in the flowmeter or the pressure transducer connections.) The rapid rise of flow at the onset of the maneuver leads to a substantial "bounce" in the measured curve. Clearly it is important to consider the instrument's response characteristics in interpreting such measurements.

Two other problems may arise in connection with the response characteristics of physical devices. First, even with low-amplitude signals, measuring devices may behave nonlinearly. Pneumotachometers may have different pressure–mass flow characteristics during inspiration and expiration if gas temperature, humidity, and composition are different in the two phases. Even if the response is linear on both sides of zero mass flow, this asymmetry is a source of nonlinearity in the overall response of the instrument. Although the basic idea of bias flows is to minimize rebreathing effects, they are also used, together with heating, to run the device in a linear region and to reduce the nonlinearities themselves. Second, even if the device is strictly linear (and therefore completely characterizable by its transfer function) there may still be substantial problems with the signal-to-noise ratio. For example, consider the measured response E_{out} of systems probed with nonperiodic drives E_{in}. (Impulse and step drives are typical of this class.) Because these nonperiodic drives contain contributions at all frequencies, the system's response also contains all frequencies. This broadband signal is then presented to the measuring device. In the frequency domain the device essentially multiplies the signal by $T(\omega)$. If resonances in the device are excited in frequency ranges not of interest, the signal-to-noise ratio in the range of interest may be compromised. Some

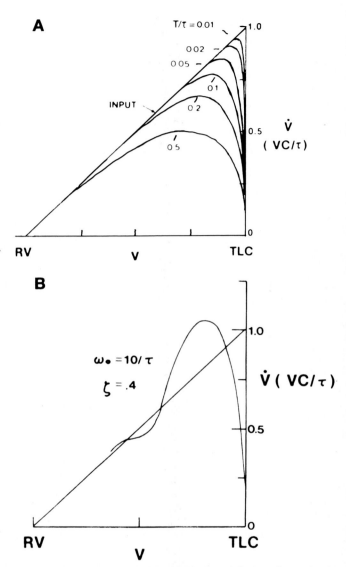

FIG. 6. Modification of a hypothetical straight-line flow-volume curve. A: effect of first-order transducer system with various time constants (T); τ is the lung time constant for exponential flow decay. B: effect of second-order transducer system that is slightly underdamped, showing the characteristic "bounce" that accompanies rapid flow onset. Note that flow is shown in units of vital capacities per lung time constant (VC/τ). RV, residual volume; TLC, total lung capacity; ω_0, natural frequency; ζ, damping coefficient. [From Sinnett et al. (31).]

methods of dealing with this are outlined in the next section and in PROBES, p. 29.

SIGNAL PROCESSING

In continuing to sequentially trace the measurement procedure, the Truth, altered by the loading of the system by the instrument and further altered by the instrument response itself, is now presented to the investigator. Depending on the degree of loading and the instrument response, the first task is somehow to undo these effects. The second task is related to whether the measured quantity is the one of interest or if a derived quantity is desired.

If the response of the instrument is linear, it may (depending on the availability of suitable calibration devices) be described by a transfer function. That is, the Fourier transform of the output of the device is uniquely related (multiplicatively) to the Fourier transform of the input to the device. If the device itself does not introduce a substantial amount of noise into the signal, the effects of the inherent transfer function of the device may be compensated for by simply working in the Fourier domain. In principle, the input magnitude is given by the measured output magnitude divided by the transfer-function magnitude, and the input phase is given by the measured output phase minus the transfer-function phase. In practice, however, one must take care that the ratio of signal (or information) to noise is not unduly compromised by this procedure.

Why is this a problem? Consider the measured output as a function of time, $E_{out}(t)$. The transfer function of the device, $T(\omega)$, is known ex hypothesi; we wish to go backward and compute $E_{in}(t)$. The forward problem is specified by an operator (T_{op}), typically involving integrals and derivatives (see APPENDIX, p. 31)

$$E_{out}(t) = T_{op} E_{in}(t)$$

or in the frequency domain

$$\hat{E}_{out}(\omega) = T(\omega)\hat{E}_{in}(\omega)$$

The formal inverse procedure is then specified by solving for $E_{in}(t)$

$$E_{in}(t) = \mathcal{F}^{-1}\hat{E}_{in}(\omega)$$
$$= \mathcal{F}^{-1}[\hat{E}_{out}(\omega)/T(\omega)]$$

where $\mathcal{F}^{-1}$ denotes the inverse Fourier transform. In essence, the fact that $T(\omega)$ typically drops off at high frequencies and appears here in the denominator implies that the higher-frequency noise contributions present in $\hat{E}_{out}(\omega)$ are artifactually amplified, and the resulting estimates of $E_{in}(t)$ contain an abnormally large contamination of noise. Indeed in many applications a naive attempt to invert this basic problem leads to the signal being completely swamped by the noise.

There are several approaches that may be exploited to circumvent this problem. First, the measured signal itself may be filtered sufficiently strongly so that it drops off more steeply with frequency (and perhaps at a lower frequency) than the denominator $T(\omega)$. Second, $E_{in}(t)$ may be more judiciously chosen. It may be possible to "tailor" $E_{in}(t)$ to provide maximal information in some frequency band of interest relative to

the noise level. See PROBES, p. 29, for a consideration of various probes. Third, the frequency-response characteristics of various intermediate stages within the device may be altered intentionally to make the overall $T(\omega)$ flatter. Thus unwanted rising or falling frequency responses at some point in the system may sometimes be compensated for by opposite characteristics elsewhere in the system. The advantage of such a trick is that one does not have to deal with the problems inherent to the inverse procedure outlined above and can directly infer the physical quantities of interest from the measured outputs.

A classic example of this is the so-called pressure compensation for integrated-flow plethysmographs (18). As noted in INSTRUMENT RESPONSE, p. 18, naively using Pbox as a measure of flow may lead to substantial error at frequencies above the inverse time constant of the box. If volumes are the primary quantity of interest, one needs in the Fourier domain

$$\hat{V}(\omega) = (1/i\omega)\hat{\dot{V}}(\omega)$$
$$= (1/i\omega R + C)\hat{P}box(\omega)$$

or in the time domain

$$V(t) = (1/R) \int^t Pbox(t')dt' + C\, Pbox(t)$$

That is, if a judicious amount of the pressure itself (determined by gas compliance) is simply added to the integrated pressure signal, formally one has a perfect measure of $V(t)$ itself. In other words, by analog means, the transfer function is artificially changed to one that approaches the ideal unity.

As another example, Sinnett et al. (31) considered the coupling of box characteristics to transducer characteristics in plethysmographs for small mammals. In general, the response of the box (chamber and flowmeter) fell with frequency, but as noted in INSTRUMENT RESPONSE, p. 18, the transducer's characteristics can be substantially modified by choice of connectors and tubing. The box behavior could thus be at least partially compensated by using a transducer configuration that was underdamped and whose output rose proportionately as the box response fell. Figure 7 shows the magnitude of the transfer functions for the box, transducer, and combined system. It is clear that this mechanical tailoring can produce an overall transfer function (the only one that matters) that is close to the ideal unity.

The other common problem of signal processing arises in the situation where the only practical measurement is related, but not identical, to the quantity of interest. For example, one may want flows given a primary measurement of volumes, or vice versa. One may want the impulse (or step) response of a system when probed with an approximate impulse (or step). Indeed one may simply want a procedure by which to

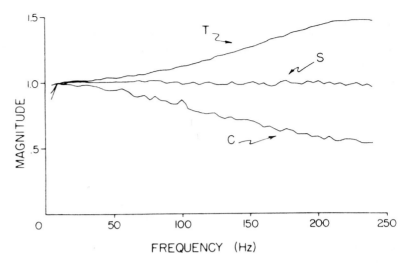

FIG. 7. Magnitude-frequency plot showing partial compensation of chamber characteristics (C) by judicious choice of transducer characteristics (T). Overall response of the system (S) is remarkably flat. [From Sinnett et al. (31).]

smooth the primary measurements so that additional derivations or manipulations are possible.

It is important in these problems to consider whether the problem is well conditioned or ill conditioned (sometimes called well posed or ill posed). For example, because the differentiation operator is equivalent in the Fourier domain to multiplication by frequency $i\omega$, one sees immediately that the high-frequency components of the signal and whatever noise is present get proportionately amplified. In a 1-Hz volume signal contaminated by 5% noise at 60 Hz, pure differentiation to obtain flow results in 300% noise in the flow signal. In general, if the signal's spectrum decays in some smooth fashion (as is typically the case), the pure differentiator ultimately pays undue attention to the noise (which often persists in its spectral contributions). Differentiating devices (analog) or procedures (digital) must therefore be constructed with great care, with particular attention to the noise level and spectral structure. These problems associated with differentiation are characteristic of ill-conditioned problems.

Integration, by contrast, is a well-conditioned procedure. Given primary measurements of flow, it is reasonably simple to infer volumetric changes. The perfect integrator (operator) in the Fourier domain is equivalent to dividing by frequency $i\omega$; thus high-frequency components of both the signal and the noise tend to be reduced. The only real problem that the investigator must deal with is that of drift. That is, although integration per se may not be a terribly delicate issue, existence of a nonzero offset to the input of the integrator when the Truth is actually zero causes a runaway condition in the integrator. This offset may arise from less-than-perfect devices (transducers and electronics) or from real physiological drifts in the system under test (particularly thermal and water vapor effects). This kind of issue is typically dealt with on the basis of the comparison of the time scale of the drift versus the time scale of the measure-

ment desired. If the drifts are very slow in comparison to the time scales in question, a simple reset capability often suffices. If the time scales are comparable and traceable to the instrumentation, a higher-grade device may be indicated. On the other hand, if the comparable time-scale drifts are inherent to the system (mechanical examples include thermal and water vapor effects; gas-exchange drifts may arise from the respiratory exchange ratio not being unity), they may be considered a type of intrinsic noise (see *Intrinsic Noise*, p. 26).

Intermediate between the differentiating and integrating procedures is that of simply smoothing a set of measurements (typically as a function of time or perhaps volume). In this procedure the investigator anticipates that the underlying phenomenon is being contaminated with noise that carries well into frequencies higher than the region of interest. Most of the schemes that deal with this situation are variations on a low-pass filter. For example, the moving time average, the rectangular or boxcar filter, and the polynomial (e.g., linear or quadratic) filters all essentially fulfill the function of passing the frequencies of interest while rejecting at various levels contributions from frequencies above or below certain values (the cutoff or break frequencies).

Finally, it must be noted how one gets into (and out of) the frequency domain. The discrete Fourier transform is the most common method in use. A sequence of points is sampled in the time domain and then transformed into the complex frequency domain. The advent of the Cooley-Tukey algorithm, now known as the fast Fourier transform (FFT), meant that calculations that were previously time consuming and laborious could be done quickly and easily with digital computers. Details of how the FFT works are not relevant here; suffice to say that it computes N points of the transform (forward or inverse) with computation time essentially proportional to $N \ln N$; this is sufficiently fast to bring the FFT into general laboratory use. Bracewell (2) gives an excellent introduction to Fourier analysis, and Rabiner and Gold (27) provide a thorough and complete account of the FFT and its relatives. See also Roth (28) for other digital techniques.

A few properties of the FFT deserve some attention. The first is that it is equally well conditioned whether transforming from time to frequency or frequency to time. This distinguishes the Fourier transform from its Laplace counterpart most dramatically, the latter being extremely well conditioned in the forward direction but correspondingly ill conditioned in its inverse. The second property is sometimes called the Nyquist criterion. Because one is measuring a time signal that is finite in length and has a finite number of sampled points, the question arises regarding uniqueness of the transform (or of the reconstructed time function). The Nyquist criterion states that if the underlying signal is band limited (i.e., there is no contribution at frequencies above some characteristic frequency), sampling that signal at any rate faster than twice that characteristic frequency is sufficient to obtain exact spectra in principle. Violating this leads to errors known as aliasing. The chapter by Loring and Bruce in this *Handbook* deals with this phenomenon in some detail. Therefore the investigator must be careful to sample at sufficiently high rates so that the Nyquist criterion is at least approximately satisfied.

INTERPRETATION OF MEASUREMENTS

Questions of interpretation of measurements generally fall into two broad categories. First, a wide variety of physiologically important variables is not directly measurable, and one must rely on indirect means or inference. This may obtain even when the system variables in question are quite simple conceptually. Alveolar pressure and pleural pressure are clear examples of the kind of quantity that is not directly accessible to measurement. It is important to realize that the success of the inference to a great extent depends on the type of indirect means used to make the transition from what can be measured to what is desired. The second broad category of interpretation arises when the investigator tries to put the pure observations into a kind of coherent framework. This often comes under the rubric of modeling. That is, a series of measurements is made; one of the interpretive goals is to reduce these data to functional forms dictated by the model. That picture then gives the essence of the underlying phenomena, and the data serve to fix the parameters that characterize the picture (or model). Such a reduction is useful because it gives a clearer idea of the essential physics and physiology and provides a powerful base from which to make comparisons between individuals and among species.

Indirect Measurements (Inference)

As noted above, the extent to which indirect estimation is successful is directly a function of the means of estimation. That is, one looks for some auxiliary quantity that is accessible to measurement and that furthermore is uniquely related to the quantity of interest by a known relationship. Under such circumstances the indirect measurement succeeds. The problems encountered are clearly related to the uniqueness of the relationship between the desired and measurable quantities and to the extent to which that relationship can be known.

Consider the problem of estimating alveolar pressure during measurement of airway resistance in a plethysmograph. This has been explored by many authors since DuBois (6) and in essence relies on the measurability of pressure in a body plethysmograph and a presumed unique relationship between that pressure and alveolar pressure using Boyle's law. Problems encountered include a number of assumptions. First, one is implicitly assuming that there is a single value for alveolar pressure and that distributional effects and regions other than alveoli (e.g., abdominal gas) may be neglected. Second, the relationship between pressure and volume is affected by the thermodynamic characteristics of the system. Typically one treats the box as adiabatic. Thoracic gas is taken to be isothermal and saturated. At normal breathing frequencies this is not a problem, but as higher frequencies are investigated one must be aware of potential difficulties. Other problems may arise from the assumption that the expirate is at body temperature, ambient pressure, saturated with water vapor, whereas the box gas is at ambient temperature and pressure. At sufficiently high frequencies or in circumstances of large tidal volumes even this assumption may be problematic, because the thermodynamic relationship between inspired and expired gas may change.

Another example is the difficult problem of inferring pleural pressure, treated in detail in the chapter by Anthonisen in this *Handbook*. One standard technique is to use the pressure in an esophageal balloon as an estimate of pleural pressure. Again one must assume that esophageal pressure is determined solely by pleural pressure and that, in addition, the esophageal characteristics are known. In particular the esophagus is typically taken to have a region of zero transmural pressure adjacent to the balloon and, assuming negligible resistive and inertial effects, therefore a measurement of esophageal pressure itself suffices to determine pleural pressure. Note that there exists a pleural pressure gradient due to gravity and other regional nonuniformities and that esophageal pressure is at best a measure of some representative value of pleural pressure.

Finally, the measurement of lung volume deserves

some remarks (see the chapter by Anthonisen in this *Handbook* for a complete discussion). Body plethysmography during panting against an obstructed airway is commonly used to measure thoracic gas volume (3, 13). This requires the assumption that there is a unique relationship between changes in body volume (as measured, e.g., by box pressure in a pressure plethysmograph) and alveolar pressure measured at the mouth. What about the presence of gas in the abdomen? This affects total body volume and hence the pressure in the box, but gas spaces that are not in communication with the mouth do not directly affect alveolar pressure. Thus the uniqueness of the box pressure–mouth pressure relationship can be compromised, and the resulting indirect measurement is in error. Measurement of lung volumes that by definition are in communication with the mouth may be done by gas-dilution techniques. If the tracer is not soluble, in principle one can indeed measure that volume of gas (but regions that have excessively long time constants or that open and close may lead to errors). Real gases, however, have nonzero solubilities and in this context can raise problems.

Models

Modeling biological systems and using measurements to estimate parameter values are potentially extremely powerful tools. On the other hand, their power has led to some misconceptions about the nature of the modeling procedure itself. This section attempts to delineate some of the major features of modeling. In particular it stresses some of the reasons why modeling can be so useful and under what circumstances it is an appropriate tool.

Before beginning, however, consider a procedure that is not strictly modeling but is instructive as an introduction to modeling. Suppose one has a sequence of measurements that results in some large number of data points. These raw data comprise so many numbers that they are unwieldy at best. Some reduction to a manageably small number of parameters would clearly be of value in organizing and manipulating the data. Indeed the interpretation of the data is greatly facilitated if such a reduction can be done. How may this be effected? One method may be described generically as curve fitting. That is, the data per se "look" like some familiar curve that is parameterized by some small set of numbers. By using various statistical techniques, those numbers are estimated and the data are said to have been fitted by that curve. It is generally true that the more parameters used, the closer the resulting fit. However, other statistical criteria may be used to determine when adding more parameters does not significantly improve the fit. Having completed such a fitting or parameterization procedure, one is left with the question of further interpretation. That is, although the data have been successfully reduced to a manageable number of parameters, the

interpretation of those values is sometimes problematic. The raw curve-fitting procedure is essentially a convenient characterization of the data, but has no physical or physiological content per se. (Of course, such an empirical reduction may lead to suggestive relationships that point toward other experiments and interpretations; therein lies a hidden value over simply looking at the data and wondering about the relationships they represent.)

This section describes some features of modeling. Virtually no measurements are ever taken blindly; the investigator usually has preconceptions about the underlying principles governing the behavior of the system. That is, although the actual values of some parameters may be essentially unknown prior to the measurements, the investigator typically has some guess as to the internal structure of the system. For example, knowledge that the lungs are passive and collapse on opening the chest implies an elastic structure. Furthermore gas flow into and out of the lung is through a tree of airways, which is known to present a flow-resistive pressure drop. One could further guess that at sufficiently low frequencies, inertial effects are unimportant. Thus prior to any measurements the investigator might guess that the essential physics of flow, volume, and pressure in the lung are governed primarily by the compliance of the lung and the resistance to gas flow. This preconceived notion of the system constitutes a model. Prior to the measurements the investigator does not, of course, know the magnitudes of the compliance and resistance, nor where and how the simple model fails to account adequately for the data, but is reasonably sure that over at least some range the model is sufficient.

The series nature of the pressure drops in this simple resistance-compliance model of the lung allows some further observations. Transpulmonary pressure is divided into two components: a resistive component between airway opening and alveoli and an elastic component between alveoli and pleural space. These components sum to give transpulmonary pressure; this is equivalent to the system's "equation of motion," as defined by Mead and Milic-Emili (21), if one identifies the resistive component with flow dependence and the elastic component with volume dependence. Note further that such a description is not limited to small volume excursions or flow rates. Such a division of the pressure drop is often extremely useful in describing the gross nonlinear behavior of the lungs over wide ranges of volume and flow.

This, then, is the first step in the modeling procedure: to make a guess regarding the underlying structure of the system and the essential principles governing its behavior. One then calculates the behavior of the model with its small number of parameters left free. This is sometimes called the forward problem. The model itself determines what kind of curve should then be fitted to the data; the parameters thus determined are not simply a convenient reduction set as in pure curve fitting but rather have real implications to the system's structure and properties via their identification with the model.

Certainly no model with a reduced number of parameters can account for data collected over a sufficiently large range of the external variables (e.g., large lung volume excursions and large frequency ranges). Thus the model must fail at some point, and two remarks are in order. First, the point at which model failure occurs is itself a kind of measured value, crude as it may be. In the example above, the frequency at which the simple resistance-compliance model fails gives a hint as to the magnitude of the inertial effects, although not in a quantitative way. Second, one may try to refine the model to cover a larger range of the external variables.

Two different types of refinement of the model must be distinguished. The first type is to look for elements that had been ignored in the simplest versions of the model (e.g., inertial effects). In the expanded range of the external variables, certain features of the system may have simply been overlooked. Adding such features typically adds a corresponding number of parameters to the model, and the investigator may proceed as before but with a refined model.

For example, consider the refinement of mechanical models of the respiratory system since the original measurements of impedance by DuBois et al. (7). Between 2 and 15 Hz they were able to fit their data with a three-parameter resistance-inertance-compliance (RIC) model. Peslin et al. (25) later measured impedances from 2 to 70 Hz and found that above 20 Hz the RIC model could not fit the data but that a more complex six-parameter model did fit over the entire frequency range. Thus by extending the frequency range, Peslin found where the simple model failed and was further able to extract additional information from the data.

It is important to appreciate a few points regarding the parameter-optimization techniques common in these approaches. First, one must ensure that the optimal solution is unique. This is often difficult to prove, but one must take care that a locally optimal parameter set is the one desired. Even if mathematical uniqueness is guaranteed, however, there may be broad ranges of parameter values that yield substantially the same measure of goodness of fit. This usually implies that the model is too complex and that the system is underdetermined as modeled. Finally, the speed with which such techniques find the optimal parameters is the only characteristic of practical interest.

The other major type of refinement of a failing model appears when the underlying physics is believed to be understood (no essential elements of the system have been neglected), but the system comprises some number (perhaps large) of these elemental units. In other words, one believes that the physics is understood on a local level within the system, but the measurements are made globally on a distribution of these local phenomena. This is the general field of compartmental (finite number of units) or distributional (infinite number of units) analysis. It must be emphasized that this approach explicitly assumes that the underlying physics or dynamics of the local system components are understood.

A prototypical example is the situation of parallel compartments. The local physics is said to be described by a kernel $k(x,y)$, where x is some independent variable external to the distribution phenomenon [time or breath number in the case of washout problems, and gas solubility in the case of retention and excretion of inert gases in ventilation-perfusion ratio ($\dot{V}_A/\dot{Q}$) problems] and y is the internal variable of interest, which is presumed to be distributed throughout the system. In the above examples, y would correspond to specific ventilation or an equivalent time constant, or to $\dot{V}_A/\dot{Q}$. The distribution of y in the system is given by a distribution function $\rho(y)$. Finally, the global quantity that is measured [$g(x)$] is given by a sum or integral of the local responses [$k(x, y)$] weighted by the distribution $\rho(y)$

$$g(x) = \int_D k(x,y)\, \rho(y)\, dy$$

The domain of integration (D) or summation is taken over all possible values of y that may obtain in the system. In addition it is assumed that the distribution function has been normalized to unit area

$$\int_D \rho(y)\, dy = 1$$

(The normalization to achieve this might correspond physically either to the total ventilation or blood flow or to the total volume of dilution.) As examples, the kernels for three common types of problems are: *1*) Hilbert: $k(x,y) = 1/(x + y)$ for $\dot{V}_A/\dot{Q}$; *2*) Laplace: $k(x,y) = \exp(-xy)$ for washout and time constant; and *3*) Heaviside: $k(x,y) = H(x - y)$ for the step function and derivative estimation (e.g., $\dot{V}$ from V). Inferring $\rho(y)$ from the data $g(x)$ can be a very delicate task. Depending on the smoothness of the kernel, large variations in the distribution function may contribute little to the global measurement $g(x)$. The ill-conditioned character of the problem arises by virtue of the converse of this; small variations in the measured values of $g(x)$ (e.g., by contamination with noise) can result in unacceptably large variations in the estimate of $\rho(y)$.

There are several approaches that can be taken to improve the situation, although the ill-conditioned character of the problem remains as an essential feature. The first method might be termed pure compartmental analysis. In particular the distribution function is taken to be a sum of n delta functions, with arbitrary weights and arbitrary placements of the delta functions. [The delta function is defined as a limiting function that has unit area concentrated at a fixed point. For example, a fast space–slow space description of the lung in a washout procedure is equivalent to describing the distribution of specific ventilation as a sum of 2 delta functions. Their amplitudes (or weights) represent the lung volume fractions at the different specific ventilations, and the delta-function placements are at those specific ventilations.] A distribution function consisting of n delta functions then represents n compartments contributing to the globally measured quantity. Often a compartmental approach is the method of choice, for several reasons. First, the reduction of the number of parameters to be estimated constitutes a strong improvement on the ill-conditioned character of the original problem. (However, as the number of compartments is increased, the ill-conditioned character returns in the form of poor estimates for the large number of parameters.) Second, a two- or three-compartment model is wonderfully simple conceptually. Third, if the distribution function is relatively smooth and the kernel is not too responsive to fine detail in $\rho(y)$, such a compartmentalization may indeed be a perfectly adequate representation of the system.

A quite different and extremely powerful technique has recently emerged. Wagner et al. (33) and Evans and Wagner (8) have developed a method for estimating $\rho(y)$ itself. Although it is true that even violent filtering may not help the inverse problem of a standard ill-conditioned equation, they observed that the nonnegativity constraint on $\rho(y)$ can dramatically improve the estimate. [This constraint follows from the fact that $\rho(y)$ is a density function and can therefore never be negative. Indeed $\rho(y)\,dy$ is the nonnegative differential probability of an element of the system being in the range y to $y + dy$.] Using this constraint and simultaneously minimizing the sum of squared residuals and a smoothing functional (associating a numerical value with the lack of smoothness of the distribution), they were able to estimate the distribution of $\dot{V}A/\dot{Q}$ from inert-gas retention and excretion measurements. This technique has been used in a wide variety of circumstances but is most useful when the distribution function is rather broad, as is the case for $\dot{V}A/\dot{Q}$, and when the amount or intensity of smoothing has been carefully scrutinized. It suffers from mathematical complexity and uncertainty over the actual information content (4, 8, 23).

More recently, Wagner (32) exploited the method of linear programming. In essence, this technique estimates the maximum and minimum values of the distribution function in some $\dot{V}A/\dot{Q}$ range (sometimes called a window) that are simultaneously consistent with the observed data and the strong constraint of nonnegativity. The extent to which this approach is successful depends on the tightness of the resulting bounds. Again the ill-conditioned nature of the problem appears as follows. As the windows get narrower the bounds get farther apart, thus compromising the

estimate. Conversely, with wide windows the bounds may be tight, yielding good estimates.

NOISE

This discussion of noise distinguishes between two quite different phenomena. Referring to Figure 1, one can see that within the biological system there may be unwanted effects that contribute to the actual signal being presented by that system. This is called intrinsic noise. In addition, without the biological system there may be introduced extraneous signals contaminating the measurements. This is called extrinsic noise.

Intrinsic Noise

There are several categories of intrinsic noise and various techniques available to deal with this phenomenon. First, the unwanted contaminating signal may be temporally separated from the signal of interest. One obvious example of this type of noise is the contamination of an electromyogram signal by the electrocardiogram (ECG). That is, the Truth appears at the body surface as a potential, which contains contributions from both muscle (desired) and the heart (unwanted). The ECG is a phenomenon of intrinsic noise that contributes to the Truth. Even if the Truth could be exactly measured, the investigator is confronted with the task of extracting the desired part of the Truth from the measurement. Electronic or manual gates may be employed to physically delete the unwanted portion of the signal (see the chapter by Loring and Bruce in this *Handbook*). In the time domain this constitutes a perfectly adequate method. However, problems may arise when trying to characterize the time signal by a Fourier spectrum. That is, the very act of deletion mathematically constitutes multiplication by a rectangular gate. In the Fourier domain the measured spectrum is the convolution of the desired spectrum with the gate spectrum. The result is that although the measured spectrum is not contaminated by the ECG (it was deleted by construction), it is nonetheless contaminated by the deletion process. The narrower (in time) the deletion, the closer the gate spectrum is to a delta function and consequently the less the contamination.

Second, consider measuring only signals of relatively low frequency in the presence of whitish noise. The noise itself looks random. (More precisely this type of noise has a Fourier spectrum whose magnitude changes smoothly with frequency or not at all for pure white noise, and whose phase is random with frequency.) Because this type of noise contains little energy in a sufficiently narrow frequency range (including zero to some low frequency), analog or digital filtering (band-pass or low-pass) is a common approach to dealing with it. Often this simple method is more than adequate. The only thing to be careful of is that the desired signals do not have a significant amount of information at frequencies attenuated by the filter. How far the frequency range for usable signals can be pushed depends on the detailed characteristics of the filter. One can go to broader frequency ranges by broadening the filter, but at a cost of passing more noise.

Third, there is noise in systems that are probed with sinusoidal drives. The desired signal has some amplitude and phase relative to the drive. Intrinsic noise is most often uncorrelated with this phase. That is, a definite phase may be present in the desired output signal with perhaps large amounts of uncorrelated signal. Knowing the phase of the driver, one may average ensembles of signals, each phased to the driver. The uncorrelated portion tends to an average of zero, thus improving the extraction of the desired signal from the noise.

Extrinsic Noise

There are several types of extrinsic noise. First, there is the common whitish noise, which typically arises when devices are pushed to their limits of sensitivity. If the level of noise is unacceptably high, low-pass filtering or digital averaging can help. High-performance devices with low noise characteristics can also be used. Second, in contrast to random noise there is deterministic noise. The common 60-Hz contamination of signals is an obvious example. Methods of shielding range from simple to highly complex. Horowitz and Hill (15) offer an exhaustive account of the myriad ways in which signals may be handled. They pay careful attention to issues such as ground loops, capacitive coupling of stray signals, and where and how to shunt unwanted sources of noise. Third, there is a very low frequency type of extrinsic noise that may be called drift. Integrating circuits that estimate volumes from flow measurements are often plagued by drift. Again more sophisticated electronic devices can be used if simple reset capabilities do not suffice. Thermal drift in plethysmographs is another common example of this type of noise. In flow boxes, differences between box temperature and humidity and outside gas temperature and humidity, even if constant in time, present a true difference in inspired and expired volumes measured by the box flowmeter. This is reflected by a drifting base line in the volume signal, whose slope is related to minute ventilation. Air conditioning to equalize interior and exterior conditions is often sufficient to eliminate such drift. Fourth, the vast majority of measurements are made differentially. That is, pressure measurements are often made relative to barometric pressure, and flows are inferred from pressure drops across physical elements (screens, capillary tube arrays, and orifices). The perfect measuring device in this application only "sees" the difference between two inputs (e.g., pressures or voltages). The extent to which the device does not respond when the same signal is applied to the differential inputs is called the common-mode rejection. Careful matching of impedances both in the electronics and the transducer connections can improve the rejection characteristics. The latter is important in reducing the effect of fluctuations in barometric pressure on differential pressure transducers.

CALIBRATION

This section considers calibration principles with specific attention to the measurement of variables of common interest in respiratory mechanics: pressure, volume, and flow. Calibration is defined here as the determination of the relationship between the output signal of a transducer and a known input signal. This is done under static and dynamic conditions over the amplitude and frequency ranges of interest.

Calibration requires satisfactory reference standards. These may be primary standards based on easily measured and invariant quantities such as dimensions (spirometers), gravity (U-tube manometers), and time. However, primary standards may be bulky, slow, or otherwise unsatisfactory for routine use, in which case secondary standards such as rotameters, calibrated syringes, and reference transducers may be used.

It is useful to distinguish between the generation and the characterization of a calibration signal. In some cases they are inseparable, as when a calibrated syringe is used to make a known volume step. More often the signal is generated by one device and characterized by another.

It is relatively easy to generate and characterize volume steps, static pressures, and constant flows; thus static or steady-state calibrations are easy to perform. It is more difficult to characterize accurately the time-varying signals needed for dynamic calibration describing the frequency-response characteristics of the transducer. Two approaches may be used: 1) to generate a function whose characteristics are calculated or otherwise presumed to be known with adequate accuracy (but not measured) and to compare the transducer output with the presumed input function and 2) to generate a suitable dynamic function whose actual characteristics are measured with a reference transducer; its output is compared with that of the transducer being calibrated. These two approaches may be further complicated by use of indirect methods to estimate the variable of interest from measurement of some other variable. For example, by knowing the initial volume and pressure of the gas in a container one can estimate its change in volume by measuring its change in pressure (temperature conditions being known or assumed).

Static Calibrations

The output signal from the transducer should be related in some predictable way to the variable of interest. It is most convenient (though not essential) if the transducer's output is linearly related to that variable. This is checked by comparing the output signal to the variable over the appropriate range. Again this should exceed the range over which the transducer is to be used. If the transducer is used to measure positive and negative values, its linearity should be determined over both.

The transducer should be checked for any possible hysteresis. This is the phenomenon wherein an output value is not only dependent on the input value at a given time but also on the history of that input. One way to check for hysteresis is to examine the transducer output as the magnitude of the input variable is progressively increased and decreased. There is hysteresis if the output signal for a given input value is different depending on the direction taken to reach that value. Poor zero return is a particular example of hysteresis that is especially troublesome when the signal is to be integrated.

Dynamic Calibrations

Many of the principles described in PROBES, p. 29, apply to the forcing functions that may be used to characterize the dynamic behavior of transducer systems. This section gives examples of assumed and measured calibration probes in varying degrees of adequacy and complexity.

Approximate step changes in pressure are created by bursting balloons or by thumping home the plunger of a water-lubricated glass syringe. Magnitude and timing of the step may not be known, but the rise time of the transducer output, the magnitude and decay of any overshoot, and the frequency and duration of any oscillations can be observed.

Periodic pressure, volume, and flow signals may be created by sinusoidally driving a piston pump or loudspeaker. Flatness of flowmeter response, for example, can be approximately checked as a function of frequency even if the exact characteristics of the generated flow are unknown. When the response begins to deviate from constancy, this may be due to either the transducer or the generated signal changing characteristics. Within the flat region, however, the transducer response is probably adequate. Of course the driver and transducer may have rising and falling characteristics that happen to cancel. (See the remarks on the Sinnett cancellation technique in SIGNAL PROCESSING, p. 20.) On the other hand, such fortuitous cancellation of driver and transducer is unlikely, and one may have some confidence that the transducer is adequate in the flat region.

Direct measurement of the generated signal improves the usable frequency range over which calibration can be done and the device used. For example, a reference flowmeter can be interposed between the generator and the transducer being calibrated (e.g., a plethysmograph). Over its usable range the pneumo-

tachometer's output is a measure of the Truth (calibration input function), which can be compared with the plethysmograph output (after suitable signal processing). If it is necessary to use the device being calibrated past its flat range, it is essential to examine carefully the periodic character of the Truth. If it is a pure sinusoid, a direct measure of the device's output amplitude and phase relative to the drive suffices for calibration. If, however, despite sinusoidal driving of a loudspeaker the Truth contains substantial harmonic components, Fourier transforms must be performed on both the Truth and the output. Their ratio at each frequency is then the transfer function of the device.

Indirect techniques may be used to infer flow or volume events from pressure measurements. In the example above, changes in pressure within a container can be used to infer changes in volume. Such a strategy was used by Jackson and Vinegar (17) to develop a device and methodology for measuring the frequency response of volume and flow transducers. As shown in Figure 8, a reference chamber and a testing chamber are separated by a loudspeaker driven sinusoidally. The pressures in the two chambers are measured with high-quality pressure transducers. Changes in chamber 1 pressure provide an estimate of the change in its volume induced by movement of the loudspeaker cone. Because motion of the cone is symmetrical between chamber 1 and chamber 2, the change in chamber 1 volume is identical (but opposite in sign) to the change in chamber 2 volume. This volume change can either move gas through the port connected to the test transducer or it can go into gas compression within chamber 2. By knowing the volume of chamber 2 and the pressure changes within it, one can compute how much of the speaker motion goes into gas compression. Thus by subtraction one can compute the amount of volume change that goes through the port. Because flow is the first time derivative of volume, one can also compute the flow going through the port.

The advantages of using this device are that dynamic calibrations of both volume and flow can be performed from pressure measurements that can be reliably made with good quality transducers. Note also

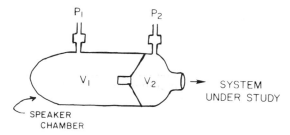

FIG. 8. Diagram of a dual-chamber system for volume and flow calibration. Sinusoidally driven loudspeaker separates the reference chamber (volume, V_1; pressure, P_1) from the testing chamber (volume, V_2; pressure, P_2). [Adapted from Jackson and Vinegar (17).]

that the dynamic calibration of a pressure transducer can be performed with this device by comparing its output to the output of one of the reference pressure transducers. The disadvantage of using this device is that complex algebraic computations that must be made are impractical without an on-line digital computer.

Additional Procedures for Specific Variables

PRESSURE. The most reliable and convenient primary standard for static calibration of pressure transducers is a U-tube manometer filled with water, mercury, or gauge oil and tall enough to cover the necessary ranges of pressure. Water manometers made with precision-bore tubing can be read with acceptable accuracy for pressure differences down to ~2 cmH$_2$O. When greater sensitivities are required, slant manometers may be used. It is essential to measure the total height of the liquid column (i.e., the vertical distance between the 2 menisci) rather than doubling the displacement of one meniscus. This is because the two menisci displacements are unequal if the bores of the two limbs are unequal. Note that if the bores are small in addition to being unequal, a static offset (error) due to capillary action is introduced.

Although U-tube manometers are excellent for static calibrations, they are not satisfactory for dynamic calibrations. This is because of their extremely slow response characteristics due to high capacitance, inertance, and associated viscous (resistive) losses.

Differential pressure transducers (i.e., transducers whose output is equal to the difference between 2 pressures) are often used. It is possible that these transducers, or the tubing connecting the different transducer parts, are not symmetrical. This should be tested for, most simply by switching the transducer around in its connection to some differential source and observing if the response is the same (but opposite in sign). In addition to symmetry, the common-mode rejection characteristics of differential transducers should be examined. Under both static and dynamic conditions, equal pressures are applied to both differential inputs. There should be no output signal under these conditions.

VOLUME. Static calibrations of volume transducers can be easily and conveniently done by measuring their output signals with volume changes of known magnitude that are generated by calibrated syringes or by water-filled spirometers. The accuracy of syringes or spirometers depends on accurate knowledge of their geometry: bell or cylinder diameter and distance traveled (manufacturers' data suffice). Even though these devices are simple, reliable, and convenient, they should be used only for static calibrations. Like U-tube manometers, their capacitive, resistive, and inertial properties make them unsuitable for dynamic calibrations.

FLOW. Flow is most often measured with a pneumotachometer. The actual variable measured is pressure, with flow inferred from a pressure drop. Most pneumotachometers are designed with the intention that their pressure-flow relationships be linear, but this is the case only for some range of flows (9, 14, 24). Thus the choice of a pneumotachometer should be based on the range of flows to be measured. It is critical to determine the linearity of such devices. The pressure-flow characteristics of pneumotachometers are also dependent on the upstream and downstream geometry (9). Thus their calibration should be done under conditions as similar as possible to those under which they are ultimately used.

Steady-state calibrations can be conveniently accomplished by using a constant-flow generator and measuring the total volume of air passing through the pneumotachometer over a given period. Such volume measurements can be made with large spirometers or dry-gas meters. In the language of linear systems, a constant-flow generator is the "dual" of a constant-pressure source. Thus although the ideal pressure source has zero impedance, the ideal flow source has infinite impedance (see Fig. 2). A useful approximation to an ideal flow source is the throttled vacuum cleaner, which can provide flows of adequate constancy over a wide range of flowmeter impedances. (But note that it should not be in the line between the flowmeter under test and the volumeter lest it change the gas temperature between the 2 devices.)

When pneumotachometers are used for measuring dynamic events, their frequency response must be known over the range of interest. This response is partly a function of the response characteristics of the pressure transducer used as well as a function of the geometry of the connectors between the pressure transducer and pneumotachometer. Thus if dynamic response is critical, the response characteristics of the entire pneumotachometer–pressure transducer plus connector system should be determined.

PROBES

Much of the discussion to this point has been restricted to general features of what might be termed passive measurements. That is, the system presents some measurable quantity that one tries to estimate. There are also active methods of measuring system properties that employ probes. This denotes any of a wide variety of means of challenging or forcing the system. The passive system may be forced by external means, or for the lungs by muscle activity. This latter sense of probe is properly the subject of pulmonary function testing; this section remarks strictly on external probes. By knowing the forcing characteristics and measuring the response of the system, certain properties of the system may be inferred.

At the outset a distinction should be made between two kinds of measurement goals in respiratory mechanics. One is the characterization of the system's amplitude and phase responses as a function of frequency. The second is the characterization of the system in maneuvers and circumstances wherein the linear theory does not apply (i.e., where low-amplitude drives and frequency dependence per se are not of interest). A wide variety of measurements falls into this latter category. Quasi-static volume-pressure relationships, maximal expiratory flow-volume curves, and isovolume pressure-flow curves are obvious examples. Although the biological relationships and interpretations that guide the choice of forcing in these examples may be complex, the actual measurement principles are straightforward and are discussed earlier in this chapter.

Consider the frequency-dependent behavior of the respiratory system when externally probed. The most widely used means of forcing in this circumstance are the impulse, random noise, step, and sine wave function. Each of these has certain features that may be exploited in determining system properties. Using the language of linear systems theory, one seeks to measure some kind of transfer function of the system, that is, to characterize the system by its amplitude and phase response as a function of frequency. Subsumed under this concept are measurements of the frequency dependence of compliance and resistance, for example. To this end it is important to appreciate the different frequency spectra of the various means of driving the system.

Impulse (delta function) (16, 30) and white noise have spectra whose amplitude is uniform with frequency. That is, the power delivered to the system in any frequency band of the same width is the same. Thus a single measurement of a linear system's response to one of these broad-spectrum forcing functions suffices, in principle, to characterize the system's response over all frequencies. Indeed, when an impulse is used as the input, the transfer function of the system is simply the Fourier transform of the temporal response.

Probing with random noise is a little more subtle (22, 26). In this case the randomness of phase as a function of frequency implies that the Fourier spectra of both the drive and the response carry poor estimates of the transfer-function phase (although the magnitude would be satisfactorily estimated). The proper approach with random noise is to exploit the autocorrelation and cross-correlation functions. These functions essentially give a measure of the relationship of one function to itself or to another function at varying time lags. They are discussed in some detail in the chapter by Loring and Bruce in this *Handbook*. The important point is that correlation functions are not unduly compromised by the randomness of phase. The system transfer function can be expressed as the ratio of the Fourier transforms of the cross-correlation and autocorrelation functions.

Step forcing is related to impulse forcing. (Step forcing is simply the integral of an impulse.) The spectrum of the forcing function falls off with frequency; the amplitude is inversely proportional to frequency. As in impulse forcing, the response of a system to step forcing contains, in principle, all of the information about its transfer function. However, less energy is delivered to the system at high frequencies. The corresponding increased attention at low frequencies means that the spectral estimates are thereby improved (at the cost of poor performance at high frequencies).

In contrast to these three methods, sinusoidal forcing has by definition a spectrum that is peaked at a single frequency. The response of the system to such a forcing function is then determined simply by its transfer function at that frequency. Such a measurement tells nothing about the characteristics of the system at frequencies other than the one used in forcing. On the other hand, because all of the energy delivered to the system is at that one frequency, the estimate of the transfer function is correspondingly good.

These considerations can be summarized by addressing the question of which type of forcing is most appropriate for a given measurement situation. In essence, the answer lies in determining the optimal power distribution in the frequency range of interest. Thus the impulse drive gives a uniform amount of power in each uniform-width frequency band. Consequently a very small fraction of the finite power that is actually used to drive the system is available to excite the system in a given small frequency range. Thus although the power is distributed over a wide range, the measured response is potentially compromised by delivery to ranges outside the one of interest. Similar considerations apply to the step, where the power falls off rapidly at high frequencies. If one is interested in a limited range of frequencies (from DC to some maximal value), the step may be a preferable mode of driving because it explicitly deemphasizes contributions from frequencies not of interest. The advantage of using broad-spectrum probes is that information over a broad range may be obtained in a relatively short period. Thus when investigating a time-varying system such as the lung, one can obtain in effect a stop-action picture (16). Furthermore the data acquisition can be triggered by other external variables such as flow or volume; this can reduce the variability of the measured parameters. Finally, sequentially driving the system with sinusoidal inputs at differing frequencies maximizes the power delivered at each frequency and hence the information content of the response at each of the frequencies driven. The cost of this method is that each run at a given frequency yields results appropriate to that frequency only, and many runs may be required to map the response of the system over the whole range of interest.

LINEAR VERSUS NONLINEAR SYSTEMS

Every physical system, when driven or challenged at sufficiently large amplitudes, exhibits nonlinear behavior. Why then, because this may be an important feature of the system under study, are most analyses restricted to linear regimes (suitably small amplitude)? The most important reason for such a restriction is that the system, when linear, may be usefully characterized by means of concepts such as the transfer function. By usefully, it is meant that a single function $T(\omega)$ suffices to describe the system's response to any type of forcing. This follows from the superposition property of linearity. Phrased differently, the properties of the system, when expressed as $T(\omega)$, are absolutely independent of the forcing function used to drive the system. These properties include the more familiar notions of time constants and resonances.

By contrast, systems that are nonlinear do not generally possess such a transfer function. That is, when superposition fails to hold, there is no convenient way to generalize from a set of measurements to the properties of the system that are forcing independent. Thus, for example, if the step response of a profoundly nonlinear system is measured, one has absolutely no idea how that system will respond to a step of half or double the size, let alone how the system will respond to an impulse or a sinusoidal drive. About all that can be said is contained in the raw data, namely, that when driven in such a fashion the system behaves in such a way. No generalized properties can thus be inferred from the data, and the usefulness of the measurements is concomitantly compromised. In particular, notions such as time constants, resonances, and decay rates fail even to exist in a manner independent of how the system is forced.

One can often make progress, however, even in the face of profound nonlinearities by considering the system to be piecewise linear. That is, although behavior at large amplitudes may not be characterizable in a linear fashion, deviations of small amplitudes about various set points may yield to linear analysis. Analysis of pressure-volume curves is a common example of this. Thus one may talk meaningfully about transfer functions about these various operating or set points (e.g., prestress conditions), although these characteristic functions surely depend strongly on the set point itself. A cautionary note is important; even if the linear behavior over a range of set points is known, it does not follow that one may necessarily be able to integrate these characteristics at small amplitudes into a full characterization of the nonlinear behavior at large amplitudes.

Finally, certain methods of nonlinear analysis are available for treating cases of elastic deformations in which the displacements are not infinitesimal. Fung (11) has proposed the use of a pseudo–strain-energy function, from which finite displacement stresses and strains may be calculated. The finite-element method is the most comprehensive of the numerical techniques and was used by West and Matthews (34) to infer the distortion of lungs in various stress fields. The finite-element method suffers from the need to know a priori the nonlinear material properties appropriate to the system. In addition, although such methods can indeed predict the displacement field in a lung when a given stress field is applied, it remains true that general characterizations of the behavior of such nonlinear deformations are problematic at best.

CONCLUSION

We have attempted to present the principles of measurement in the broadest possible context. There are myriad problems and considerations that appear when actual measurements are performed, and it has been found useful to have a structure (see Fig. 1) to aid in sorting out the implications of various questions. Such a categorization is of course not unique, nor are the lines of demarcation sharp. Nevertheless its broad applicability to virtually all measurement procedures gives a coherent framework within which common problems may be addressed.

APPENDIX

This section begins by describing the variables of interest. Intensive variables correspond essentially to stresses applied to a system, or system elements. Extensive variables correspond to the strains or strain rates that the system or element is undergoing. (This distinction is drawn by analogy to thermodynamics.) A typical stress variable might be a pressure or voltage drop. Typical strain-type variables include volumes, flows, and currents. An element is considered simple if it has one degree of freedom, which means that the state of that system, as described by one variable, is uniquely specified by only one other. Systems with more than one degree of freedom can often usefully be described (or modeled) as suitable combinations of elements with a single degree of freedom. Linearity in the element is simply the notion that a homogeneous linear relationship exists between the two variables involved in its description. More specifically, let $x(t)$ be the independent variable and $y(t)$ be the dependent variable. Let x and y be related by $y = T_{op}x$, where T_{op} is some operator (which may be time dependent); y and x are linearly related (or, equivalently, T_{op} is a linear operator) if $ay = T_{op}ax$, for any scalar a, and $y_1 + y_2 = T_{op}(x_1 + x_2)$. This is sometimes called the principle of superposition. These notions may be made more concrete by some examples drawn from electrical circuit theory. Suppose x to be a current I (analogous to flow rate $\dot{V}$) and y to be a voltage E (analogous to pressure P). The E-I relationships for the three classic elements of resistance (R), capacitance (C), and inertance (I) can be stated: 1) resistor: $E(t) = R\,I(t)$, 2) capacitor: $E(t) = (1/C)\int^t I(t')\mathrm{d}t'$, and 3) inductor: $E(t) = I\,\mathrm{d}I(t)/\mathrm{d}t$. The operators are multiplication, integration, and differentiation, respectively. These are all examples of passive elements; they generate neither voltage nor current but rather provide a link between the two. Phrased differently, they cannot generate any power. (Resistors dissipate power; inductors and capacitors are nondissipative.) By contrast, active elements do generate power. The simplest versions of active elements are voltage or current generators (analogous to pressure or flow generators). More complex active elements have their output voltage or current itself dependent on some input variable. A surprisingly wide class of problems may be treated by using the concepts from linear systems theory just enumerated.

It is apparent, however, from the form of the defining relationships between $E(t)$ and $I(t)$ for the simple elements above, that complex systems have unwieldy equations (multiple integrals and derivatives) governing their behavior. Fortunately, there is an extremely powerful technique that can be exploited to reduce the integral and differential operators seen in capacitors and inductors to simple multiplicative operators (20). This technique is the systematic use of the Fourier (or Laplace) transform; the resultant multiplicative operators correspond to the impedances of the elements. Specifically, the Fourier transform of a function $\phi(t)$ is defined to be $\hat{\phi}(\omega)$, where

$$\hat{\phi}(\omega) = \int_{-\infty}^{+\infty} \exp(-i\omega t)\,\phi(t)\mathrm{d}t$$

where ω is the angular frequency and $i = \sqrt{-1}$. [There are several forms of the defining equation for the Fourier transform; the one used here is consistent with the standard linear systems literature wherein, e.g., the imaginary part of the impedance (called the reactance) is positive (negative) for inductors (capacitors).] If the equations defining the relationships between E and I for the three basic elements are Fourier transformed, using standard techniques one

finds that all three elements have relationships of the form $\hat{E}(\omega) = Z(\omega)\,\hat{I}(\omega)$, where $\hat{E}(\omega)$ and $\hat{I}(\omega)$ are the Fourier transforms of $E(t)$ and $I(t)$, respectively, and the multiplicative factor $Z(\omega)$ is: 1) resistor: $Z(\omega) = R$, 2) capacitor: $Z(\omega) = (1/i\omega C)$, and 3) inductor: $Z(\omega) = i\omega I$. With this transform, complex systems may be reduced to essentially resistive networks where the elements have multiplicative relationships between their variables given by their respective impedances. Furthermore the complicated equations governing the system behavior are reduced to algebraic equations, which may be solved much more easily. At this point the problem is only half solved; the resultant solutions are not the desired time-dependent quantities actually measured but rather their Fourier transforms. This generalized solution $T(\omega)$ is called the system transfer function, which is simply the ratio of the transformed output to the transformed input.

Further study of the properties of this transformed solution reveals at least two highly significant features. One part of the solution describes the transient response of the system (behavior that is traceable to impulse or step-type inputs) and the other part of the solution describes the steady-state response (behavior of the system when driven periodically over a sufficiently long duration so that the output is also periodic). Furthermore if the periodic drive is sinusoidal, the output is also sinusoidal, with amplitude and phase given by $T(\omega)$. Thus given a sinusoidal driving input of current with unit amplitude and phase arbitrarily set to zero, the voltage amplitudes for resistors, capacitors, and inductors are found to be R, $1/\omega C$, and ωI, respectively. Resistors have no phase difference between current and voltage, whereas capacitors and inductors have voltages that lag and lead the current, respectively, by 90°.

Intimately linked to the Fourier transform is the Laplace transform. Its definition is identical to that of the Fourier transform, except with transform variable equal to $i\omega$, and has semi-infinite limits of integration from zero to infinity. It shares the useful properties listed above, and all essential features of the Fourier transform are equally valid for the Laplace transform. Choosing between them is largely a matter of personal preference. There is a certain generality on the theoretical side enjoyed by the Laplace transform; there is a practical advantage in reduction of actual data in the Fourier transform.

REFERENCES

1. AGOSTONI, E., AND G. MISEROCCHI. Vertical gradient of transpulmonary pressure with active and artificial lung expansion. *J. Appl. Physiol.* 29: 705–712, 1970.
2. BRACEWELL, R. *The Fourier Transform and Its Application.* New York: McGraw-Hill, 1965.
3. BROWN, R., F. G. HOPPIN, JR., R. H. INGRAM, JR., N. A. SAUNDERS, AND E. R. MCFADDEN, JR. Influence of abdominal gas on the Boyle's law determination of thoracic gas volume. *J. Appl. Physiol.: Respirat. Environ. Exercise Physiol.* 44: 469–473, 1978.
4. BUTLER, J. P., J. A. REEDS, AND S. V. DAWSON. Estimating solutions of first kind integral equations with non-negativity constraints and optimal smoothing. *SIAM J. Num. Anal.* 18: 381–397, 1981.
5. D'ANGELO, E., M. V. BONANNI, S. MICHELINI, AND E. AGOSTONI. Topography of the pleural surface pressure in rabbits and dogs. *Respir. Physiol.* 8: 204–229, 1970.
6. DUBOIS, A. B., S. Y. BOTELHO, AND J. H. COMROE, JR. A new method for measuring airway resistance in man using a body plethysmograph: values in normal subjects and in patients with

respiratory disease. *J. Clin. Invest.* 35: 327–335, 1956.

7. DuBois, A. B., A. W. Brody, D. H. Lewis, and B. F. Burgess, Jr. Oscillation mechanics of lungs and chest in man. *J. Appl. Physiol.* 8: 587–594, 1956.

8. Evans, J. W., and P. D. Wagner. Limits on $\dot{V}a/\dot{Q}$ distributions from analysis of experimental inert gas elimination. *J. Appl. Physiol.: Respirat. Environ. Exercise Physiol.* 42: 889–898, 1977.

9. Finucane, K. E., B. A. Egan, and S. V. Dawson. Linearity and frequency response of pneumotachographs. *J. Appl. Physiol.* 32: 121–126, 1972.

10. Fry, D. L. Physiologic recording by modern instruments with particular reference to pressure recording. *Physiol. Rev.* 40: 753–788, 1960.

11. Fung, Y. C. A theory of elasticity of the lung. *J. Appl. Mech.* 41: 8–14, 1974.

12. Griffin, P. M., and N. Zamel. Volume-displacement body plethysmograph using a large flowmeter without pressure compensation. *J. Appl. Physiol.: Respirat. Environ. Exercise Physiol.* 47: 1127–1130, 1979.

13. Habib, M. P., and L. A. Engel. Influence of the panting technique on the plethysmographic measurement of thoracic gas volume. *Am. Rev. Respir. Dis.* 117: 265–271, 1978.

14. Harf, A., G. Atlan, H. Lorino, S. Deshayes, C. Morin, and D. Laurent. Correction for nonlinearity of body flow plethysmograph. *J. Appl. Physiol.* 50: 658–662, 1981.

15. Horowitz, P., and W. Hill. *The Art of Electronics.* Cambridge, UK: Cambridge Univ. Press, 1980.

16. Jackson, A. C., J. P. Butler, E. J. Millet, F. G. Hoppin, Jr., and S. V. Dawson. Airway geometry by analysis of acoustic pulse response measurements. *J. Appl. Physiol.: Respirat. Environ. Exercise Physiol.* 43: 523–536, 1977.

17. Jackson, A. C., and A. Vinegar. A technique for measuring frequency response of pressure, volume, and flow transducers. *J. Appl. Physiol.: Respirat. Environ. Exercise Physiol.* 47: 462–467, 1979.

18. Leith, D. E., and J. Mead. *Principles of Body Plethysmography.* Bethesda, MD: Natl. Heart Lung Inst., Div. Lung Dis., 1974.

19. Macklem, P. T. *Procedures for Standardized Measurements of Lung Mechanics.* Bethesda, MD: Natl. Heart Lung Inst., Div. Lung Dis., 1974.

20. Mathews, J., and R. L. Walker. *Mathematical Methods of Physics.* New York: Benjamin, 1964.

21. Mead, J., and J. Milic-Emili. Theory and methodology in respiratory mechanics with glossary of symbols. In: *Handbook of Physiology. Respiration,* edited by W. O. Fenn and H. Rahn. Washington, DC: Am. Physiol. Soc., 1964, sect. 3, vol. I, chapt. 11, p. 363–376.

22. Michaelson, E. D., E. D. Grassman, and W. R. Peters. Pulmonary mechanics by spectral analysis of forced random noise. *J. Clin. Invest.* 56: 1210–1230, 1975.

23. Olszowka, A. J. Can $\dot{V}a/\dot{Q}$ distributions in the lung be recovered from inert gas retention data? *Respir. Physiol.* 25: 191–198, 1975.

24. Peslin, R., J. Morinet-Lambert, C. Duvivier. Étude de la réponse en fréquence de pneumotachographes. *Bull. Physio-Pathol. Respir.* 8: 1363–1376, 1972.

25. Peslin, R., J. Papon, C. Duvivier, and J. Richalet. Frequency response of the chest: modeling and parameter estimation. *J. Appl. Physiol.* 39: 523–534, 1975.

26. Pimmel, R. L., M. J. Tsai, D. C. Winter, and P. A. Bromberg. Estimating central and peripheral respiratory resistance. *J. Appl. Physiol.: Respirat. Environ. Exercise Physiol.* 45: 375–380, 1978.

27. Rabiner, L. R., and B. Gold. *Theory and Application of Digital Signal Processing.* Englewood Cliffs, NJ: Prentice-Hall, 1975.

28. Roth, P. R. Effective measurements using digital signal analysis. *IEEE Spectrum* 8: 62–70, 1971.

29. Shearer, J. L., A. T. Murphy, and H. H. Richardson. *Introduction to Systems Dynamics.* Reading, MA: Addison-Wesley, 1967.

30. Sidell, R. S., and J. J. Fredberg. Noninvasive inference of airway network geometry from broad band lung reflection data. *J. Biomech. Eng.* 100: 131–138, 1978.

31. Sinnett, E. E., A. C. Jackson, D. E. Leith, and J. P. Butler. Fast integrated flow plethysmograph for small mammals. *J. Appl. Physiol.: Respirat. Environ. Exercise Physiol.* 50: 1104–1110, 1981.

32. Wagner, P. D. Information content of the multibreath nitrogen washout. *J. Appl. Physiol.: Respirat. Environ. Exercise Physiol.* 46: 579–587, 1979.

33. Wagner, P. D., H. A. Saltzman, and J. B. West. Measurement of continuous distributions of ventilation-perfusion ratios: theory. *J. Appl. Physiol.* 36: 588–599, 1974.

34. West, J. B., and F. L. Matthews. Stresses, strains, and surface pressures in the lung caused by its weight. *J. Appl. Physiol.* 32: 332–345, 1972.

CHAPTER 3

Solid mechanics

THEODORE A. WILSON | *Department of Aerospace Engineering and Mechanics, University of Minnesota, Minneapolis, Minnesota*

CHAPTER CONTENTS

THE LUNG DEFORMS in response to forces acting on it. The simplest deformation is uniform expansion that occurs if uniform transpulmonary pressure is applied across the lung. However, if pleural pressure is not uniform, lung expansion is not uniform. Also, if intraparenchymal vessels or bronchi do not expand uniformly with the parenchyma, nonuniform deformations occur in the surrounding parenchyma and perivascular or peribronchial pressure is not the same as pleural pressure. Realization that details of lung deformation are physiologically significant is fairly recent. Similar questions about the relationship between force and deformation in other contexts have a much longer history. Modern methods of describing the mechanics of solids began with Galileo and have evolved continuously over the past 400 years. They provide a valuable resource that can be used to answer questions about mechanics of the lung. This brief review of solid mechanics is intended as an accessible background for later chapters in this *Handbook*.

CONTINUUM DESCRIPTION OF FORCES WITHIN THE LUNG: STRESS

A micrograph of a slice of lung tissue (Fig. 1) shows an irregular array of alveolar walls, vessels, and airways. Like all other materials, lung parenchyma is inhomogeneous and discontinuous at the microscopic scale. In the intact lung, extended elastin and collagen fibers within the tissue and surface tension at the air-liquid interface transmit forces across the plane exposed by the slice. The idea of an average force per unit area acting across a plane through the paren-

chyma is useful. If such an average is well defined it is called stress. The definition of stress needs some discussion. The small area inside square A in Figure 1, *top* does not include any force-bearing elements. As the square expands it begins to include tissue elements. The force per unit area plotted as a function of the area of the square yields a curve like that in Figure 1, *bottom*. At first the force per unit area is quite variable, but as the square becomes large enough to include several alveoli the force per unit area remains at a limiting value. For areas that are large compared to the scale of the microstructure but small compared to the size of the lung, stress is a well-defined quantity. It describes the force per unit area on a scale at which the material appears continuous.

An isolated cube of parenchyma is shown in Figure 2A. Forces are transmitted across the faces of the cube by the tissue elements and air-liquid interfaces intersecting each face. In cutting away the material outside the cube, the mechanical effect of the adjacent material can be retained by including the stresses acting on the faces of the cube. The stresses acting on each face can be resolved into the three components shown in Figure 2A: one normal component (normal stress) and two tangential components (shear stresses). The normal stress acting on the plane normal to the x-axis is denoted τ_{xx} and the shear stresses are denoted τ_{xy} and τ_{xz}. For the cube to remain stationary under the action of these stresses, the total force acting on the cube must be zero and the moment (the tendency of the forces to produce rotation) must also be zero. It can be shown that as a consequence of the requirement that the moment be zero, the shear stresses must satisfy the relationships $\tau_{xy} = \tau_{yx}$, $\tau_{xz} = \tau_{zx}$, and $\tau_{yz} = \tau_{zy}$. Therefore there are only six independent stress components. Furthermore if gravity is neglected, the total force produced by the stresses must be zero. There are many possible combinations of normal and shear stresses that satisfy this condition, but the simplest is the one in which all shear stresses are zero and all normal stresses are equal. This is the stress field that exists in a body composed of material that is homogeneous (properties independent of position) and isotropic (properties independent of direction) that is subjected to uniform normal stress and no shear stress over its surface. From experiments it appears that lung parenchyma can be modeled as a homogeneous isotropic material.

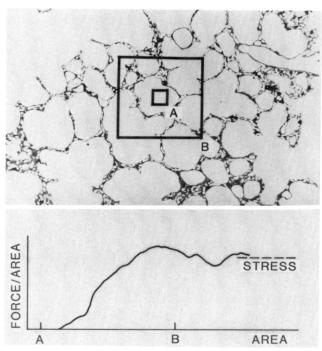

FIG. 1. *Top*: typical transmission electron micrograph of tissue from an air-filled, perfusion-fixed lung. In the intact lung, forces are transmitted across the plane of the cut by tissue elements and surface tension. Squares *A* and *B* denote expanding area in which stress is measured. (Courtesy of H. Bachofen.) *Bottom*: force per unit area plotted as a function of the area of expanding square. Limiting value of force per unit area is the stress. At the scale at which this limiting value is reached, parenchyma can be treated as a continuum.

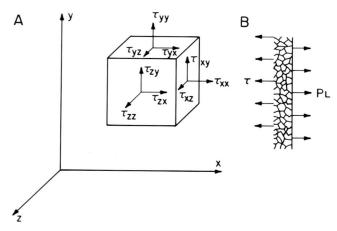

FIG. 2. *A*: stress components that act on faces of any small cube of parenchyma. *B*: thin slice of tissue at surface of lung, including pleural membrane. In the uniformly expanded lung, shear stresses equal zero and normal stresses (τ) equal transpulmonary pressure (PL).

BOUNDARY CONDITIONS

The lung is bounded by the pleural membrane. A thin slice of tissue at the surface of the lung, including the pleural membrane, is shown in Figure 2*B*. Alveolar gas pressure on the inside surface of the membrane is greater than pleural pressure on the outside. Mechanical equilibrium for the slice requires that normal stress equals transpulmonary pressure. In the uniformly expanded lung the stress distribution is quite simple—the stress transmitted by the tissue across any plane in the parenchyma is a normal stress with magnitude equal to transpulmonary pressure. This normal stress is applied to the outer boundary of bronchi and vessels within the parenchyma.

NONUNIFORM DEFORMATION: DISPLACEMENT AND STRAIN

If the lung is not uniformly inflated, the deformation must be described as a function of position of the lung. A continuum displacement field $\mathbf{V}(\mathbf{x})$ can be defined the same way that stress is defined. Vector $\mathbf{V}$ is average displacement in the neighborhood of each point $\mathbf{x}$ in the lung. Lung tissue is deformed only if displacement differs from point to point. Therefore local deformation depends on the difference of displacement between neighboring points or, in other words, on the derivatives of the displacement field. There are nine scalar derivatives of the three components of the vector displacement, but three combinations of these describe the rotation of the material. The remaining six independent combinations of these derivatives that describe the deformation are called strains.

CONSTITUTIVE EQUATIONS

Materials differ in how they deform in response to forces applied to them. Deformational properties of a material are described by relationships between stress and strain that are called constitutive equations for the material. Mathematical analysis provides guidelines for describing the relationships between stress and strain. It has isolated possible functional relationships that are internally consistent and established the number of material parameters that must be experimentally determined for each. Constitutive equations can be fairly simple or quite complicated, and a suitable choice must be made depending on the material and the problem. The simplest is a linear stress-strain relationship in which there are two material parameters. These linear stress-strain relationships are the appropriate constitutive equations to describe small deformations of an isotropic elastic material. If large deformations are considered, nonlinear stress-strain relationships are needed. If stress relaxation or creep is important, stress must be described as a function of strain rate and time. If the material exhibits hysteresis, stress must be described as a function of strain history. Lung deformations show all of these features. The modeling that is chosen depends on the effects important in the problem and on the amount of effort expended for additional accuracy.

METHODS OF PROBLEM SOLVING

The framework for describing general stress-strain relationships is well established and the physical principles that determine solid-body deformations are well known. A specific problem is set by specifying the resting or unloaded shape of a body, the constitutive equations for the material, and the boundary conditions that describe the forces or displacements imposed on the body to produce a deformation. The solution of the problem consists of nine scalar functions of position (6 components of stress and 3 components of displacement) that satisfy nine coupled scalar partial differential equations (6 scalar constitutive equations and the 3 components of the equation of static equilibrium) and match the boundary conditions on the surface. Solutions in the form of equations describing stress and displacement as functions of position can be found for a few problems for which the geometry of the body and the boundary conditions are highly symmetrical and the material properties are simple. These solutions are surprisingly useful, serving as idealized approximations for many real situations and forming our intuition about solid-body deformations. Numerical methods must be used to solve more complicated problems. Most of the lexicon of existing solutions and mathematical methods for generating solutions are limited to linear-elastic materials. Some results have been obtained for nonlinear deformation of rubber, a material for which it is appropriate to assume that volume is invariant. Development of more general nonlinear computational methods is an area of current research in solid mechanics. The art of analyzing lung deformation is in a similar state. Some general descriptions of the material properties of the lung have been proposed (e.g., ref. 3), but the linear-elasticity approximation has been used for most specific deformation problems.

LINEAR ELASTICITY

Any small deformation can be described as the superposition of two elementary deformations. The first is a uniform volume expansion. If the material is isotropic and elastic, the stress required to produce this expansion is a uniform normal stress. The ratio of normal stress to fractional volume change is called the bulk modulus. The second elementary deformation is pure shear, a change of shape with no change in volume. This is illustrated in Figure 3. Shear stresses

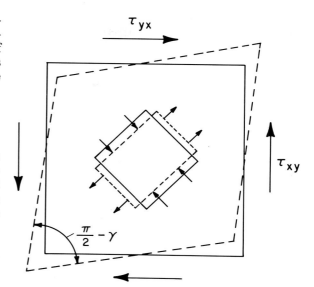

FIG. 3. Shear strain: deformation in which material changes shape with no change in volume. *Solid lines*, undeformed shapes; *dashed lines*, deformed shapes. Stresses (τ) that accompany this deformation may include shear and normal stresses, depending on the orientation of the plane on which they act. γ, Change of angle.

tangent to the plane of the faces of the cube accompany the shear strain. The ratio of the stress to the tangent of the angle γ is the shear modulus of the material. For a given deformation, the stress acting on a plane depends on the orientation of the plane. For example, the small square oriented at a 45° angle to the large square in Figure 3 changes shape by becoming longer and thinner. The stresses on the faces of this square are normal stresses, tensile in the direction of stretching and compressive in the direction of narrowing. Conversely, unequal normal stresses on orthogonal planes imply shear stresses on planes with other orientations.

In much of the engineering literature, material properties are described by values of Young's modulus and the Poisson ratio rather than bulk modulus and shear modulus. The standard test of engineering materials consists of stretching a cylindrical bar. The ratio of axial stress to the fractional change in length is Young's modulus, and the ratio of the fractional decrease in cross-sectional dimension to the fractional change in length is the Poisson ratio. This test produces both a shape change and a volume change, and there are simple equations relating Young's modulus and the Poisson ratio to bulk modulus and shear modulus. Because lung parenchyma is not available in cylindrical bar specimens, this test, Young's modulus, and the Poisson ratio are not particularly pertinent to the lung.

The lung cannot be modeled as a linear-elastic material if deformations are large or if time- or history-dependent effects are important. Nonetheless the linear-elasticity model is useful because it describes small departures from any uniformly expanded state, not just the stress-free state. Extensive literature on linear elasticity can be applied to problems that involve small nonuniform deformations from any state of uniform lung expansion. Bulk and shear moduli depend on the neighboring uniformly expanded state. Bulk modulus can be obtained from the local slope of the pressure-volume curve. It is typically several times greater than transpulmonary pressure. Shear modulus, measured by punch-indentation tests, is slightly less than transpulmonary pressure (4). Because lung parenchyma is more easily deformable in shape than volume, it responds to nonuniform forces by changing shape more than volume.

TWO ELEMENTARY DEFORMATIONS

Two examples of solutions of boundary-value problems in linear elasticity are described: radial expansion of a cylindrical hole in the parenchyma and gravitational deformation of an elastic material in a rigid container.

Figure 4 illustrates the expansion of a cylindrical hole in the parenchyma. If the parenchyma around the hole is initially in the same uniformly expanded state as the rest of the lung, the normal or radial stress in the tissue at the boundary of the hole equals transpulmonary pressure. If an airway or vessel fits per-

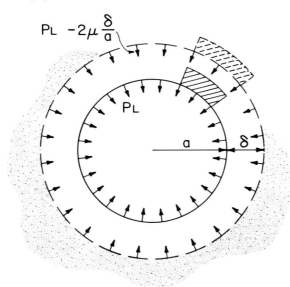

FIG. 4. Model of cylindrical hole cut in uniformly expanded lung. Normal stress equal to transpulmonary pressure (PL) has to be applied at the inner boundary of hole to prevent distortion of the surrounding parenchyma. Vessel that fits perfectly in this hole is subjected to both alveolar gas pressure and material stress equal to and opposite that shown. If hole expands, the parenchyma distorts with no change in volume and the material stress is reduced by 2μ times the fractional change in hole radius (δ/a). μ, Shear modulus; a, radius of hole in uniformly expanded lung; δ, change of hole radius.

fectly in this hole, the radial stress on its outer surface is the sum of the tissue stress pulling outward and alveolar gas pressure pushing inward. The net peribronchial or perivascular pressure equals pleural pressure.

If the normal stress at the boundary of the hole is reduced, the hole expands. The radial displacement of the parenchyma (u) is a function of the radial distance from the center of the hole (r). The displacement at the boundary of the hole ($r = a$) is denoted by δ. Within the parenchyma the displacement falls off inversely with r. The displacement field $u = \delta(a/r)$ satisfies the boundary condition at the hole boundary, and in a linear-elastic material the stress distribution corresponding to this displacement field satisfies the equilibrium equations. The segment of parenchyma shaded in Figure 4 deforms to the shape shown by the dashed line. This segment and all other segments expand in the circumferential direction and shrink in the radial direction. The deformation changes the shape of each segment without changing the volume, and the stresses that accompany the deformation depend only on the shear modulus (μ) of the parenchyma, not the bulk modulus. The decrease in normal stress at the boundary is $2\mu\delta/a$. Therefore when a vessel expands, perivascular pressure increases by 2μ times the fractional change in vessel radius.

This solution of a simple linear-elasticity boundary condition problem provides a lot of information. It describes how the deformation decreases with distance from the cylinder boundary. It shows that ventilation per unit mass of parenchyma is not affected by vessel expansion. It provides a quantitative relationship between stress and displacement at the boundary. With this solution, Lai-Fook (5) has laid to rest a long history of qualitative discussion about the behavior of intraparenchymal vessels.

The methods of solid mechanics are also necessary in answering questions about how gravity, posture, and chest wall shape affect ventilation.

Figure 5 illustrates the gravitational deformation of a solid with very simple geometry. The solid body is assumed to be a right circular cylinder, uniformly expanded in height and radius and placed inside a rigid cylindrical container of the same dimensions. In the absence of gravity, uniform negative pressure exists at the boundary between the deformable solid and the rigid container. With gravity, the body deforms to a state in which the stress distribution provides a net force per unit volume that is equal to and opposite the specific weight (w) of the solid. It is assumed that the body is free to slide but remains in contact with the container. The perturbation from the state of uniform expansion that gravity produces in a linear-elastic material with bulk modulus K, height l, and shear modulus μ is as follows. Displacements are downward and independent of radial position, and their magnitude is $[w/2(K + \tfrac{4}{3}\mu)][z(l - z)]$. Displacement is zero

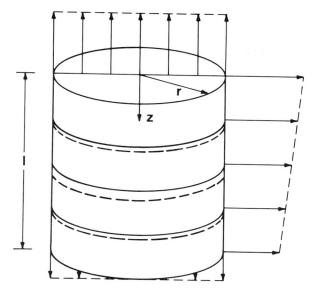

FIG. 5. Gravitational distortion of cylindrical solid in a rigid cylindrical container. This distortion produces local volume and shape changes (*dashed lines*). Because of the resistance of the solid to shear, the vertical gradient of the surface stress and the vertical gradient of the volume per unit mass are less than they would be for a liquid of the same specific weight and compressibility. l, Height; r, radius; z, vertical coordinate.

at the top ($z = 0$) and bottom ($z = l$) as required by the boundary conditions and is maximum at mid-height. Horizontal planes shown by solid circles in Figure 5 are displaced to the positions shown by dashed lines. The top half of the solid is expanded

relative to the initial state of uniform expansion and the bottom half is compressed. The stress perturbation can be described as follows. The incremental normal stress in the z-direction (τ_{zz}) is $w[(l/2) - z]$. It is positive or tensile at the top and negative or compressive at the bottom. The difference between the stress at the top and bottom of each layer of the solid balances the weight of the layer. Incremental radial normal stress (τ_{rr}) is $w[(K - \frac{2}{3}\mu)/(K + \frac{1}{3}\mu)][(l/2) - z]$. Total normal stress distribution at the surface of the cylinder is shown by dashed lines in Figure 5. Vertical gradient of surface stress is smaller by the factor $[1 - (2\mu/3K)]/[1 + (4\mu/3K)]$ than the hydrostatic gradient in a fluid with specific weight w. There are abrupt changes in surface stress across the corners at the top and bottom of the cylinder.

This example is too simple to use as a model of the lung. It does not adequately represent chest wall and lung shapes, chest wall compliance, or subdivisions of the lung. Numerical methods have been used to obtain solutions for gravitational deformation of more realistic lung shapes (6). An evolutionary development of the modeling of lung geometry and material properties guided by comparison between computer solutions and experimental data is necessary before gravitational deformation of the lung can be adequately described.

In this chapter general methods of solid mechanics have been discussed without equations, and solutions to particular boundary-value problems have been described without derivations. See Crandall et al. (1) and Fung (2) for representative textbooks at the introductory and more advanced levels.

REFERENCES

1. CRANDALL, S. H., N. C. DAHL, AND T. J. LARDNER. *An Introduction to the Mechanics of Solids.* New York: McGraw-Hill, 1972.
2. FUNG, Y. C. *Foundations of Solid Mechanics.* Englewood Cliffs, NJ: Prentice-Hall, 1965.
3. FUNG, Y. C. A theory of elasticity of the lung. *J. Appl. Mech.* 41: 8–14, 1974.
4. HAJJI, M. A., T. A. WILSON, AND S. J. LAI-FOOK. Improved measurements of shear modulus and pleural membrane tension

of the lung. *J. Appl. Physiol.: Respirat. Environ. Exercise Physiol.* 47: 175–181, 1979.
5. LAI-FOOK, S. J. A continuum mechanics analysis of pulmonary vascular interdependence in isolated dog lobes. *J. Appl. Physiol.: Respirat. Environ. Exercise Physiol.* 46: 419–429, 1979.
6. WEST, J. B., AND F. L. MATTHEWS. Stresses, strains, and surface pressures in the lung caused by its weight. *J. Appl. Physiol.* 32: 332–345, 1972.

CHAPTER 4

Aerodynamic theory

T. J. PEDLEY | *Department of Applied Mathematics and Theoretical Physics, University of Cambridge, Cambridge, England*

JEFFREY M. DRAZEN | *Department of Physiology, Harvard School of Public Health, and Department of Medicine, Brigham and Women's Hospital and Harvard Medical School, Boston, Massachusetts*

CHAPTER CONTENTS

THIS CHAPTER DESCRIBES the physical laws governing fluid flow in tubes (straight, curved, and branched) and hence airflow in the bronchi. Although written primarily for physiologists, some explanations are very concise and expressed as mathematical formulas. [For less concise discussion see refs. 5, 35; for greater depth refer to basic engineering textbooks of fluid mechanics (9, 37, 39, 40).] Our explanations of fluid flow are based on a combination of engineering theory and laboratory experiments in carefully designed conduits and specifically exclude most experiments in vivo or in casts of real bronchi. However, many details of airway aerodynamics are poorly understood, and we restrict ourselves to a qualitative discussion of the principal physiological features of airflow in the lung. We assume *1)* incompressible fluids, *2)* rigid tubes, and *3)* primarily steady flow; these assumptions are justified as follows. *1)* The compressibility of respiratory gases has a negligible effect on their flow dynamics as long as the velocities achieved are small compared with the speed of sound in air (37). Except perhaps during a cough the maximum air velocity in bronchi is not >20 m/s, whereas the speed of sound is

~350 m/s. Furthermore, although air density changes during respiratory maneuvers with a closed glottis, this is essentially a static phenomenon and the density change occurs simultaneously throughout the lung. *2)* Airway wall compliance can be neglected because, although airway caliber changes with lung volume, this is a quasi-static phenomenon because the change that occurs while an element of air traverses a given airway is negligible. Only if the airway is subjected to a substantial negative transmural pressure so that it collapses are the dynamics of flow dramatically altered. This commonly occurs when the airflow velocity in the bronchi approaches the speed of propagation of elastic waves in the bronchial walls and is most important during forced expiration (see the chapters by Wilson, Rodarte, and Butler, by Hyatt, and by Leith, Sneddon, Butler, and Brain in this *Handbook*). *3)* The pressure difference driving airflow varies with time throughout the breathing cycle. However, the flow patterns at any time are still approximately the same as if the pressure difference were held at its instantaneous value (i.e., they are quasi-steady), at least in most airways most of the time during quiet breathing. The opposite is true when the respiratory frequency is raised; i.e., the flow then is not quasi-steady except perhaps near the times when the air velocity is greatest. The available data and the criteria for deciding whether a flow is quasi-steady are discussed in UN-STEADY FLOW, p. 52.

STEADY FLOW IN A STRAIGHT TUBE

Fully Developed Laminar Flow

Consider a fluid driven at a constant flow rate through a long straight tube of circular cross section with diameter d by a constant difference in pressure applied at the two ends. Marking elements of the fluid with smoke or dye reveals that every element travels in a straight line with constant velocity when sufficiently far from the ends. This means that fluid elements experience no acceleration and are therefore acted on by zero net force (Newton's first law of motion); thus the pressure drop must be counteracted by deceleration forces of frictional, or viscous, origin. Viscosity causes the fluid in contact with the solid tube wall to adhere to it so that the fluid velocity at the wall is zero (no-slip condition); fluid velocity increases with distance from the wall, reaching a maximum in the center of the tube. As a result the distribution of velocity across the tube diameter (velocity profile) is parabolic so that

$$V(r) = 2\bar{V}(1 - 4r^2/d^2) \qquad (1)$$

where $V(r)$ is the velocity at a given radial distance r from the tube axis and $\bar{V}$ is the average velocity given by

$$\bar{V} = \frac{\dot{V}}{A} = \frac{4\dot{V}}{\pi d^2} \qquad (2)$$

where $\dot{V}$ is the volume flow rate through the tube and A is the tube cross-sectional area. In this type of flow (Poiseuille flow, ref. 36) the pressure in the fluid at any point along the tube is independent of radial position and the difference in pressure P between two points a distance l apart (neither of which is near a tube end) is given by

$$\Delta P = \frac{128\mu l\dot{V}}{\pi d^4} \qquad (3)$$

where μ is the viscosity of the fluid. Equation 3 shows that the pressure drop is proportional to l, i.e., that the pressure gradient (rate of change of P with downstream distance) is constant. Another important quantity is the wall shear stress (τ), which is the tangential force per unit area exerted by the fluid on the tube wall. Its value is given by the product of the viscosity and the velocity gradient at the wall

$$\tau = -\mu \left.\frac{\partial V}{\partial r}\right|_{r=d/2} = 8\mu \frac{\bar{V}}{d} \qquad (4)$$

All these results have been predicted theoretically and confirmed by experiment in a wide range of fluids such as water and air (37, 39, 40).

Flow in the Entrance Region

When one or both of the places where pressure is measured are near the entrance of the tube, the pressure drop observed is greater than predicted by Equation 3 because the velocity profile is not parabolic near the tube ends. Suppose that fluid enters the tube from a large still reservoir through a smoothly rounded entrance (Fig. 1); at the entrance the velocity profile is virtually flat. However, the fluid in contact with the wall must be at rest because of the no-slip condition. Therefore in a thin region adjacent to the wall the velocity rises from zero (at the wall) to $\bar{V}$, its value over most of the cross section. This region is called the boundary layer, and the central region where the velocity profile is flat is called the core. The thickness of the boundary layer (δ) is defined as the distance across which the velocity rises to a value close to its core value $\bar{V}$, usually taken to be 99% or 95% of $\bar{V}$.

In this example, viscous forces retard progressively more fluid as the flow proceeds down the tube. The initially high velocity gradient in the boundary layer is reduced, and the layer becomes thicker as more fluid is sheared. At the same time the central portion of fluid has to be accelerated to maintain a uniform volume flow rate. Thus the velocity profile changes as depicted in Figure 1 until finally the boundary layer fills the tube and Poiseuille flow is established. Once this occurs (Fig. 1, station 2) no further change takes place.

In the entrance region, fluid elements experience accelerations as they move from one point to another where the fluid velocity is different (these convective accelerations occur even in steady flow where the velocity at every point is fixed in time). Newton's second law of motion can then be used to relate the pressure-gradient force experienced by a fluid element to its acceleration. For any fluid element acted on only by pressure and viscous forces this law may be written as

mass × acceleration

= pressure-gradient force + viscous force

$$(5)$$

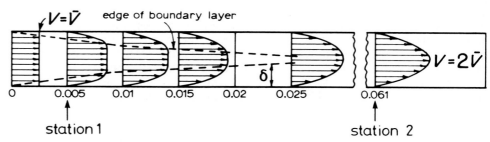

FIG. 1. Development of velocity profile with distance along a tube; thickness (δ) of boundary layer increases. Numbers are values of $x/d\mathrm{Re}$ at which corresponding profiles occur, where x is distance from entrance, d is tube diameter, V is fluid velocity, $\bar{V}$ is average fluid velocity, and Re is Reynolds number (see Eq. 8). [Adapted from Prandtl and Tietjens (37a).]

(mass × acceleration is often called inertial force). In the core the velocity is approximately uniform, viscous forces are negligible, and the small inertial force is balanced by the pressure gradient. In the boundary layer, viscous forces are important because of the steep velocity gradients, and the inertial forces must be comparable with them. This causes a growth of the boundary layer (9); its thickness is proportional to the square root of distance from the tube entrance (x) as

$$\delta = k_1(\mu x/\rho \overline{V})^{1/2} \qquad (6)$$

where μ/ρ is the kinematic viscosity ν of the fluid (~0.15 cm²/s for air) and k_1 is a numerical constant independent of the dimensional parameters of the problem. If δ is defined as before (i.e., $V = 0.95\overline{V}$ when distance from wall = δ), both experiment and theory show that $k_1 = 4.0$ (40).

When the boundary layer thickness increases to equal the tube radius, Poiseuille flow is established. This occurs at a distance l (entrance length) from the tube entrance. By substituting $d/2$ for δ and l for x in Equation 6

$$l = k_2 \frac{\rho d\overline{V}}{\mu}d = k_2\text{Re}d \qquad (7)$$

where k_2 is another numerical constant independent of the physical parameters of the problem and

$$\text{Re} = \frac{\rho d\overline{V}}{\mu} \qquad (8)$$

Re is a dimensionless quantity called the Reynolds number (38), which represents the ratio of inertial forces to viscous forces acting on a given fluid element. The number of tube diameters from the inlet at which Poiseuille flow becomes established (entrance length) equals k_2Re. Thus the higher the Re the more prominent are inertial forces and the greater is the distance required to establish Poiseuille flow. Careful experiments show that $k_2 \sim 0.03$ for Re values greater than ~50 and smaller than ~2,300. As Re decreases to ~1 or below, the idea of a thin boundary layer is not appropriate, because inertial forces become negligible everywhere and there is a balance between pressure gradient and viscous forces. In that case the ratio of the entrance length to the diameter (l/d) decreases to a constant value of ~1.5 (22). Flows in which Re > 2,300 are likely to be turbulent (see TURBULENT FLOW IN A STRAIGHT TUBE, p. 45). Note that the entrance length is also the distance it takes for Poiseuille flow to be reestablished in a tube after any disturbance of the flow, such as a curve or bifurcation, not only after entry from a tank. Following this rough rule, one can see that entrance length exceeds airway length in the trachea and larger bronchi under most respiratory conditions (Table 1). Thus Poiseuille flow is never established and calculations of pressure drop, for example, based on Poiseuille flow are inappropriate.

TABLE 1. *Lengths and Diameters of Airways in Weibel Model With Derived Airflow Data and Fluid Mechanical Parameters*

Genera-tion	Diam, cm	Length, cm	0.5 liter/s V, cm/s	Re	2 liters/s V, cm/s	Re
Trachea	1.80	12.0	197	2,325	790	9,300
1	1.22	4.76	215	1,719	859	6,876
2	0.83	1.90	235	1,281	941	5,124
3	0.56	0.76	250	921	1,002	3,684
4	0.45	1.27	202	594	809	2,376
5	0.35	1.07	161	369	643	1,476
10	0.13	0.46	38	32	151	127
15	0.066	0.20	4.4	1.9	17.8	7.6
20	0.045	0.083	0.3	0.09	1.2	0.37

V, velocity; Re, Reynolds number.

CALCULATION OF PRESSURE DROP

In the example just considered the pressure drop in the entrance length exceeds that in Poiseuille flow because the fluid elements experience acceleration and the retarding shear stress on the wall is greater when the boundary layer is thinner than it is in Poiseuille flow (Eq. 4). Thus in principle a force balance on the fluid between stations 1 and 2 in Figure 1 could be used to relate the pressure drop to the details of the flow. However, in anything except a straight tube, such a force balance would have to include contributions from the pressure forces exerted by the nonparallel walls (e.g., pressure on the flow divider in a bifurcation; see Fig. 2), and these are unknown. It is, however, possible to use an energy balance to calculate pressure drop instead (35). Basically an energy balance between stations 1 and 2 is

rate at which kinetic energy is gained at 2
− rate at which kinetic energy is lost at 1
= rate at which pressure force at 1 does work
− rate at which pressure force at 2 does work
− rate at which mechanical energy is dissipated in whole region through viscosity

This balance can be used to calculate the pressure drop if the kinetic energy and dissipation terms are known. The advantage of this approach is that in a pipe flow, where axial velocity is much larger than transverse components and where rate of change of velocity in the axial direction is much smaller than transverse velocity gradients, the rate of energy dissipation and the kinetic energy terms can be computed from fluid physical properties and measured velocity profiles at any cross section (9, 32, 35). Furthermore Poiseuille flow has a smaller dissipation rate than any other conceivable flow in the same tube, so any deviation from a parabolic profile results in greater energy dissipation.

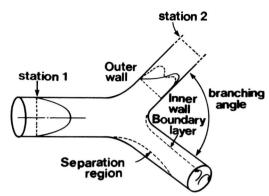

FIG. 2. Qualitative picture of flow downstream of a single symmetric bifurcation with Poiseuille flow in the parent tube. Lower branch indicates direction of secondary motions, new boundary layer, and separation region. Upper branch indicates velocity profiles in plane of the junction (*solid line*) and in normal plane (*dashed line*).

Thus in a given conduit one can determine the pressure drop either by direct pressure measurement or by prediction from measured velocity profiles. However, in many circumstances applicable to the mechanics of breathing, measuring with any degree of accuracy may be difficult or impossible. Nevertheless it may still be possible to determine the pressure drop by applying the powerful technique of dimensional analysis, which is outlined next.

DIMENSIONAL ANALYSIS—THE SIMILARITY PRINCIPLE

With dimensional analysis one combines the various physical parameters of an experiment into dimensionless groups and examines the relationships among these groups. This reduces the number of experiments required to describe the behavior of the system, and experimental results obtained in one setting can be used to predict the relationships that would hold in other settings.

For a given set of circumstances one identifies the important physical parameters based on simple knowledge of the system and experience with related systems. For example, for steady flow of fluid through a pipe the quantities of interest are overall flow rate ($\dot{V}$), fluid density (ρ), fluid viscosity (μ), pressure drop (ΔP), and the geometrical aspects of the pipe [i.e., length (l) and diameter (d)]. Thus six physical variables describe the system behavior, encompassing all three of the basic measures: length, mass, and time. These variables can be combined in various ways into dimensionless groups, but at most three such groups are independent (see appendix B in ref. 39). Three dimensionless variables are

$$\frac{\rho d \overline{V}}{\mu} = \text{Re} \qquad \frac{\Delta P}{\frac{1}{2}\rho \overline{V}^2} \qquad l/d$$

where the cross-sectionally averaged velocity $\overline{V}$ (Eq.

2) is used for convenience. Other possible dimensionless groupings are simply algebraic combinations of these three. Note that $\frac{1}{2}\rho \overline{V}^2$ is the kinetic energy per unit volume of a fluid flowing with a uniform velocity $\overline{V}$. All possible relationships between the variables can be described if the relationship among these three quantities is known. The advantage of expressing the variables in this form can be seen by extending this example. Suppose an experiment is performed in a network of tubes, such as a bifurcation, where the pressure drop across a given portion of the system is measured as a function of flow rate with a particular fluid. The data can be expressed by a simple pressure-flow curve or by a plot of the dimensionless pressure drop $\Delta P/\frac{1}{2}\rho \overline{V}^2$ versus Reynolds number (l/d is not varied for any tube). [With a system of branched tubes a different Reynolds number can be defined for each tube, but when a single Reynolds number is required it is conventional to use the one for the parent tube of the system (e.g., the trachea for the bronchial tree).] To know the pressure-flow characteristics of a geometrically similar bifurcation (i.e., with similar shape but different absolute size) it would seem necessary to perform another experiment. However, with the plot of dimensionless pressure drop versus Reynolds number obtained in the original experiment, the pressure-flow characteristics of the second tube can be calculated from the data of the first experiment. In fact the relationship between dimensionless pressure drop and Reynolds number determined for one bifurcation not only holds for geometrically similar bifurcations, but can also be used to predict pressure drops at different flow velocities or with fluids of different physical properties flowing in the bifurcation.

As discussed further in EFFECTS OF CHANGES IN GEOMETRY ON PRESSURE AND FLOW, p. 46, the pressure drop measured between two points of a system can be divided into two components: that due to changes in kinetic energy (Bernoulli effect) and that due to viscous dissipation of energy (cf. *Changes in Cross-Sectional Area—Bernoulli's Theorem*, p. 46). It is usual (21, 42) to separate the effects of changes in kinetic energy from the viscous dissipation of energy and to describe the latter in terms of a friction coefficient (C_F) as

$$C_F = \left[\text{total } \Delta P - \left(\begin{array}{c} \Delta P \text{ due to} \\ \text{changes in} \\ \text{kinetic energy} \end{array} \right) \right] \Big/ \frac{1}{2}\rho \overline{V}^2 \quad (9)$$

By the principles cited previously for a system with geometric similarity, C_F is a function of Re and this function has to be separately (usually experimentally) determined. A graph of C_F against Re for any given geometry (usually a log-log plot) is called a Moody plot; an example is given in Figure 3 that contains the measurements of pressure drop in a network of branched tubes similar to human airways (42).

Certain aspects of this diagram deserve further attention to explain its utility. For Poiseuille flow in a

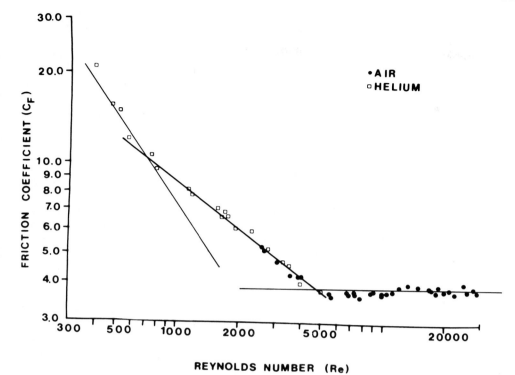

FIG. 3. Moody plot of friction factor (C_F) against tracheal Reynolds number (Re) for inspiratory flow in a cast of major airways of human bronchial tree. *Solid lines* have slopes of -1, $-\frac{1}{2}$, and 0. [Adapted from Slutsky et al. (42).]

single tube the relationship between pressure and flow rate (Eq. 3) can also be expressed as

$$C_F = 64(l/d)\mathrm{Re}^{-1} \qquad (10)$$

In a Moody plot this relationship has a slope of -1. Furthermore it has been shown on the basis of theoretical considerations that in the entrance region the contribution to the pressure drop from viscous dissipation (ΔP_v) can be expressed as $\Delta P_v = \frac{1}{8}k_3\pi(\mu\rho)^{1/2}\overline{V}^{5/2}dl^{1/2}$. In dimensionless form this equation may be written

$$C_F = k_3(l/d)^{1/2}\mathrm{Re}^{-1/2} \qquad (11)$$

where the Moody plot has a slope of $-\frac{1}{2}$ (see Fig. 3).[1] The constant $k_3 \sim 6.0$ for smooth entry to a straight circular tube.

In systems such as the lung where it is difficult to measure anything except the overall pressure drop ΔP and flow rate ($\dot{V}$), Equation 9 cannot be applied directly because the kinetic energy term is not precisely known. The results are usually represented in a dimensionless way by defining an overall pressure drop coefficient ($C_{\Delta P}$) as

$$C_{\Delta P} = \text{total } \Delta P/\tfrac{1}{2}\rho\overline{V}^2 \qquad (12)$$

where $\overline{V}$ is the average velocity in a reference airway,

usually the trachea. Then $C_{\Delta P}$ is plotted against tracheal Re. Care must be exercised in interpreting such a plot because the two contributions to total ΔP are not separated.

TURBULENT FLOW IN A STRAIGHT TUBE

When the Reynolds number of a flow in a long straight tube is increased above a critical value (Re_c) of $\sim$2,300 (e.g., by an increase in flow rate), marked fluid elements no longer travel in straight lines with constant speed and the pressure drop is no longer given by Poiseuille's law (Eq. 3). If a streak of dye is continuously injected into the fluid flow at a point in the center of the tube, it forms a straight filament in Poiseuille flow (Re less than $\sim$2,300). However, if the Reynolds number is increased somewhat above this value, the dye line becomes wavy and breaks up intermittently, whereas for sufficiently large values (Re greater than $\sim$4,000) the dye streak breaks up completely and the whole flow becomes slightly colored (38). As the dye line is broken up the velocity measured at a point is also seen to fluctuate vigorously and randomly, both in magnitude and in direction. Such a random motion is called turbulence.[2] Although

[1] If we had scaled ΔP with the Poiseuille pressure drop (Eq. 3) instead of the dynamic pressure ($\frac{1}{2}\rho\overline{V}^2$) the ratio would be $Z = (k_3/16)(d/l)^{1/2}\mathrm{Re}^{1/2}$. This was the dimensionless pressure drop defined in reference 32.

[2] Any flow without random fluctuations in velocity is called laminar; Poiseuille flow is a particular example of laminar flow, as is the flow already described near the entrance to a tube and the flow yet to be described in curved or branched tubes. The term laminar flow is not synonymous with Poiseuille flow.

the axial velocity at a point fluctuates randomly when the flow is turbulent, it has a well-defined mean value. The mean velocity profile in fully developed turbulent tube flow is slightly curved in the core and falls to zero in a boundary layer. The shape of this profile is virtually independent of Reynolds number when $Re > 10,000$. The mean centerline velocity is $\sim 1.2\,\overline{V}$, where $\overline{V}$ is the overall average velocity (cf. the value of $2\,\overline{V}$ for Poiseuille flow). The entrance length for development of the mean profile, when the incoming flow is disturbed, is ~ 40 tube diameters (40) and is approximately independent of Reynolds number. This should be compared with the value of 70 diameters predicted for laminar flow at a Reynolds number just below the transition to turbulence ($\sim 2,300$). This implies that a turbulent boundary layer grows more quickly than a laminar one at the same Reynolds number because of the greater mixing of core fluid with the fluid near the wall.

In terms of the friction factor (C_F) the pressure drop in turbulent flow can be written as

$$C_F = 0.32(l/d)Re^{-1/4} \text{ (smooth walls)} \qquad (13)$$
$$= k_4 l/d \text{ (rough walls)}$$

where the constant k_4 depends on the degree of roughness but falls in the range $0.02 < k_4 < 0.06$ if the height of the roughness element is between $0.001d$ and $0.033d$ (39). The excess dissipation over Poiseuille flow comes from two sources: the changed mean velocity profile with a higher velocity gradient at the wall and the turbulent eddying motion itself. Eddies have been calculated to contribute <4% of the total when $Re = 5,000$ and $\leq 20\%$ when $Re = 10,000$ in a smooth-walled tube (34); the percentage increases as the roughness becomes more pronounced. Thus at these moderately large Reynolds numbers the main contribution to the dissipation can be attributed to the mean velocity profile, unless the walls are extremely rough.

EFFECTS OF CHANGES IN GEOMETRY ON PRESSURE AND FLOW

Changes in Cross-Sectional Area—Bernoulli's Theorem

When the cross-sectional area (A) of a rigid tube changes, the average velocity of an incompressible fluid flowing in it must also change to maintain the same volume flow rate (Fig. 4). If the area upstream of the change in area is A_1 and that downstream is A_2, the average velocities in these regions ($\overline{V}_1$ and $\overline{V}_2$) are related by

$$\overline{V}_1 A_1 = \overline{V}_2 A_2 \qquad (14)$$

Thus in a constriction (Fig. 4, *top*) the velocity rises and in an expansion (Fig. 4, *bottom*) it falls. If the velocity of a fluid element rises, it is accelerated and hence (from Newton's law) must experience a force;

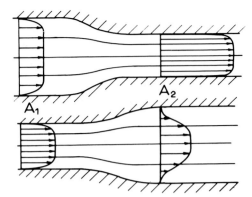

FIG. 4. Change in velocity profile shape as flow enters a region of pipe of smaller radius (*top*) and larger radius (*bottom*). A_1, A_2: cross-sectional areas at stations 1 and 2. [From Pedley et al. (35).]

the only type of force available is the pressure gradient. Thus the pressure at station 1 (Fig. 4, *top*) must exceed that at station 2, even in the absence of significant viscous forces, i.e., as the velocity rises the pressure falls and vice versa.

The extent of these pressure changes can be deduced from the energy balance equation. When the pressures and velocities are more or less uniform across the tube this may be written as

$$P_1 + \tfrac{1}{2}\rho \overline{V}_1^2 = P_2 + \tfrac{1}{2}\rho \overline{V}_2^2 + D/\dot{V} \qquad (15)$$

where D is the rate of energy dissipation in the region between stations 1 and 2. If the velocity profile at a station is not flat the corresponding kinetic energy term $\tfrac{1}{2}\rho \overline{V}^2$ has to be multiplied by a constant (β) that can be calculated from knowledge of the profile (35); $\beta = 2$ for Poiseuille flow, and usually lies between 1 and 2. Furthermore, if the energy dissipation term ($D/\dot{V}$) is small compared with the change in the kinetic energy term (i.e., C_F is small), Equation 15 leads to the prediction that the quantity $P + \tfrac{1}{2}\rho \overline{V}^2$ remains constant as the area changes. This result is known as Bernoulli's theorem and quantifies the pressure changes associated with velocity and hence with area changes.[3]

If the Reynolds number of a tube flow is large (but the flow is still laminar), C_F is small if the flow is anything like Poiseuille flow or entry flow and if the distance l between stations 1 and 2 is not large. Only if the flow is grossly distorted or becomes turbulent might the dissipation term in Equation 15 be important. In a constriction (Fig. 4, *top*) the pressure gradient tends to accelerate all fluid elements equally,

---

[3] Bernoulli's theorem has implications for pressure measurement. If the probe surface is set perpendicular to the local velocity V, the fluid is brought to rest on it. Therefore the pressure recorded (P_{rec}) equals the actual pressure plus $\tfrac{1}{2}\rho V^2$ (because Eq. 15 gives $P_{rec} + 0 = P + \tfrac{1}{2}\rho V^2$), and needs to be corrected from independent knowledge of V. On the other hand, if the pressure-sensitive surface is aligned with the local velocity and does not disturb it, no correction is required.

except for those near the wall that are prevented from responding fully because of the no-slip condition. Thus the velocity profile at station 2 is merely an elongated version of that at station 1, as indicated in Figure 4, *top*, and no dramatic increase in viscous dissipation is anticipated.

On the other hand, in an expansion (Fig. 4, *bottom*) the pressure gradient tends to decelerate all fluid elements, although again those at the wall cannot respond. The result can be a velocity profile with a point of inflection in it, which can have two important consequences. First, if the expansion is not gradual (i.e., if the angle between the wall and the axis exceeds ~5°), the flow in the boundary layer tends to reverse. This dramatically changes the character of the flow, which separates from the wall at the start of the expansion, forming a narrow jet in the center that is surrounded by slowly turning eddies (Fig. 5). The second consequence of the inflection point in the velocity profile, especially pronounced with flow separation, is that it renders the laminar flow much more liable to become turbulent than Poiseuille flow, for example, so that the flow through an expansion is often vigorously turbulent at Reynolds numbers much less than 2,300 (for an abrupt area expansion, Re_c based on the outlet's mean velocity and diameter is ~300), although of course the flow becomes laminar again far downstream. Flow separation and turbulence dramatically increase the rate of energy dissipation just downstream of an expansion, so that very little of the pressure recovery (or rise) predicted by Bernoulli's theorem actually occurs.

For example, an orifice (which is a constriction followed by an abrupt expansion in an otherwise parallel tube) has been suggested as a good model for the larynx. As shown in Figure 4, *top* the flow upstream from the expansion converges smoothly, perhaps with some flow separation against the upstream-facing wall in an abrupt narrowing. In contrast, after the expansion the inertia of the fluid forms a jet that separates from the tube wall and continues to narrow for a short distance downstream (vena contracta) before spreading again, as indicated in Figure 5. In an orifice the overall pressure drop is dominated by the energy dissipation in this jet, resulting in a friction factor that

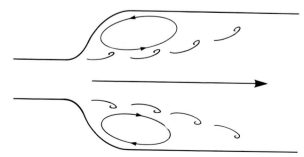

FIG. 5. Flow separation at an expansion. Note turbulence generated at edge of jet.

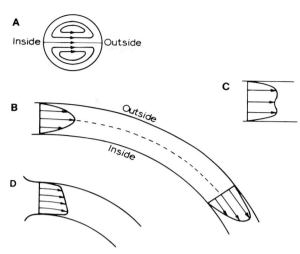

FIG. 6. *A*: secondary motions develop when fluid flows in a curved tube, with flow in center of tube directed toward outside of bend and returning near walls. *B*: axial velocity profile in plane of the bend is also distorted from Poiseuille flow (upstream) to a form having a peak near the outside wall (downstream). *C*: profile in transverse plane is distorted to an M shape. *D*: note initial skew in velocity profile when entry-flow profile is flat.

depends on the area ratio of the jet to the tube but is virtually independent of Reynolds number, as long as the Reynolds number is large enough for the jet to be turbulent.

Flow in a Curved Tube

When fluid flowing steadily and without turbulence in a long straight tube enters a bend, every element of it must change its direction of motion. That is, it must acquire a component of acceleration at right angles to its original direction and must therefore experience a force in that direction. This force is supplied by a sideways pressure gradient in the plane of the bend, directed from the outside of the bend to the inside and acting more or less uniformly over the whole cross section of the tube. Hence all fluid elements experience approximately the same sideways acceleration. However, this means that faster moving elements change their direction less rapidly than slower moving ones because of their greater inertia. Thus the faster moving fluid that originally occupied the center of the tube is swept toward the outside of the bend, being replaced by slower moving fluid from near the walls. Consequently a transverse circulation, or secondary motion, is set up (Fig. 6A) and the axial velocity profile in the plane of the bend is distorted from its symmetric shape to the form shown in Figure 6B. The profile in the perpendicular plane takes the form shown in Figure 6C, because the fluid being swept back around the side walls is still traveling faster than that pulled toward the center of the tube from the inside wall.

A similar flow pattern can be expected far from the entrance in a long continuously curved tube, whatever the initial velocity profile. This fully developed flow has attracted considerable theoretical attention. Dean (10) showed that when the radius of curvature (R) is large compared with the tube diameter (d), the flow depends on a single dimensionless parameter [now called the Dean number (De)]

$$De = 4Re(d/R)^{1/2} \qquad (16)$$

instead of on Re and (d/R) independently, as the simplest dimensional analysis would suggest. Dean presented a theory to predict the detailed flow pattern that is valid for values of De up to ~100; the flow has since been computed for values of De up to 5,000 (8, 24), confirming the picture described above and shown in Figure 6. Accurate measurements of the velocity distribution in a curved tube, both at the start of the bend and far downstream, have been made by a number of workers (1, 2, 19, 25); these both confirm our qualitative ideas and extend them into the regime of turbulent flow. The critical Reynolds number for transition to turbulence is significantly increased in a curved tube (47).

FLOW IN BRANCHED TUBES

The lung airways form a multigenerational dichotomously branching tree, with the trachea as the trunk and the alveoli as the leaves (see the chapter by Horsfield in this *Handbook*). Most of the branches of this tree are only 3 or 4 diameters long, and the Reynolds number of flow is normally small only in the most distal airways (Table 1) so that in general the entrance length is much greater than the airway length. Hence Poiseuille flow does not occur in the majority of airways, and estimates of airway resistance based on the assumption of Poiseuille flow may be grossly inaccurate. The flow and pressure drop in short branching tubes are discussed next.

Laminar Inspiratory Flow

To examine the steady flow through a single bifurcation, one must first define the geometry of a bifurcation (see DIMENSIONAL ANALYSIS—THE SIMILARITY PRINCIPLE, p. 44), which is generally asymmetric (Fig. 7). This means that branching angles must be specified as well as the ratios to parent-tube diameter of *1*) the diameters of tubes, *2*) the radii of curvature of the outer walls and of the flow divider, and *3*) the distances from the flow divider at which the tubes become straight cylinders, for example. We must also define the proportion of the incoming flow rate distributed to either daughter branch (or, equivalently, the pressure downstream of each daughter branch), and the incoming velocity profile, which in the lung is usually not parabolic because the parent tube of one bifurcation is generally the daughter tube of another. Only when all these dimensionless quantities are specified do the velocity profiles elsewhere and the pres-

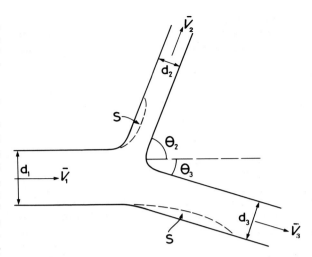

FIG. 7. Asymmetric bifurcation showing some quantities that must be specified to define flow uniquely. $\bar{V}$, average velocity; d, diameter; θ, angle size; S, possible sites of flow separation.

sure difference between two given points become functions only of the Reynolds number.

Very few bifurcation geometries have been investigated experimentally, and none has received a comprehensive theoretical treatment. Most bronchial bifurcations are to some degree asymmetric, but a "typical" human bifurcation has been represented as a symmetric one (Fig. 2), with a total branching angle of 60° or 70° (49) and a diameter ratio $d_2/d_1 = 1.1$ (area ratio = 1.2) (3, 15, 16, 20, 21, 41, 45, 48). This is the only symmetric bifurcation examined in detail. Moreover most of the flows examined have been divided symmetrically between the daughter branches (but see ref. 45), and the incoming velocity profile has been parabolic or approximately flat. The only asymmetric bifurcation to have received much attention is that of a side branch coming at right angles off a straight parent tube that remains unchanged (46), i.e., $\theta_3 = 0°$, $\theta_2 = 90°$, $d_3/d_1 = 1.0$ (Fig. 7). There have also been some measurements on scale models of the human central airways down to the lobar bronchi (6, 18, 26).

The principal features of laminar inspiratory flow through a symmetric bifurcation, with Poiseuille flow upstream at a moderately large parent-tube Reynolds number (in the range 100–1,400 that is typical of central airways of the lung during quiet breathing), can be deduced qualitatively from the preceding sections and Figure 2. First, the oncoming stream is split into two by the flow divider so that a new boundary layer is formed on the inner wall, with the maximum fluid velocity just outside it. Second, each of the two streams has to turn a bend so that secondary motions are set up, carrying faster moving fluid across the core toward the inner wall and slower moving fluid back around the walls. This tends to keep the boundary layer on the inner wall thin, with the peak axial velocity remaining just outside it. Third, the overall cross-sectional area is greater downstream than upstream so that unless the change occurs very smoothly there is a possibility of flow separation at the outer wall.

All these predictions have been verified by laboratory experiments in the range of Reynolds number consistent with laminar flow (3, 20, 25, 41, 49). Schroter and Sudlow (41) observed that secondary velocities could be as high as 50% of the average axial velocity $\bar{V}_2$ and that flow separation occurred at the outer wall of the bifurcation. Their models, however, had a rather sharp curvature there ($R = d_1/2$). In a smoother model more characteristic of the lung ($2R/d_1 = 7$), Olson (25) did not observe separation and recorded smaller secondary velocities (30% of $\bar{V}_2$). Zeller et al. (49), who also had a smooth model, observed separation only when the flow rates into the two daughter tubes were unequal (in a 3:7 ratio), and then only in the tube with the smaller flow rate. These authors also measured axial (and in Olson's case secondary) velocity profiles at various stations downstream of the bifurcation. Profiles in the plane of the junction confirmed that the boundary layer on the inner wall was very thin, and profiles in the perpendicular plane showed the characteristic M shape already seen in curved tubes (Fig. 6), indicating that the boundary layer remains thin around at least one-half the circumference of the daughter tube.

The steady flow in an asymmetric bifurcation shows features similar to those in a symmetric one but is more complicated and less easily defined. Even when one of the daughter tubes is a direct continuation of the parent its flow shows many complex features, such as reversed flow of some fluid elements near the wall back toward the side branch (Fig. 8). Also if the flow rate into the side branch is great enough (at least one-half that in the downstream daughter), there is flow separation on the smooth wall of the straight tube opposite the side branch. This arises from the change in the pressure gradient associated with deceleration

of the oncoming flow and reacceleration of it in a perpendicular direction (41). There is always a large separation eddy in the daughter tube (Fig. 8). Limited measurements of velocity profiles and wall shear stress made in asymmetric bifurcations (6, 18, 23, 26, 31, 45, 46) confirm these qualitative features of the flow. As in a symmetric bifurcation, the wall shear stress is always extremely high on or near the flow divider where a new boundary layer is generated.

There have been even fewer experiments on flow through a sequence of bifurcations than on flow through a single one. Achieving reproducible results is difficult because the incoming velocity profile is not parabolic and because secondary motions are already present. One consequence is that even when the geometry and distribution of flow rates are symmetric between the two daughters, the actual flow patterns (and hence the pressure drop) may not be, depending on the orientation of the bifurcation under study compared with the previous ones. Alternatively, for a given pressure drop, the flow rates down the daughter branches depend on the velocity distribution upstream (43). Velocity profiles in a two-generation model were measured by Schroter and Sudlow (41) and in models with three or more generations by Berger et al. (3) and by Pacome (28) with the length-to-diameter ratio of tubes in the intermediate generations of ~3.5, as in the symmetric model of the lung proposed by Weibel (48). Velocity profiles in asymmetric models have been measured by Olson et al. (26), by Chang and El Masry (6), and by Isabey and Chang (18), who measured secondary velocity components, recording values up to 40% of the mean axial velocity. The only general conclusions are that wall shear rates are always high in the new boundary layers on the flow divider and that the flow is extremely complicated and differs in detail from one branch to another. However, although it is nothing like Poiseuille flow, the flow is still laminar because the velocity remains steady everywhere and fluctuations are not observed. Therefore such laminar but disturbed flow is present almost everywhere in the lung, except in the largest airways where it is turbulent (see *Turbulent Flow in Branched Tubes*, p. 50) and in the terminal respiratory units, where although it is dominated by viscous effects it is still not Poiseuille flow because of the complex geometry there.

Laminar Expiratory Flow

Expiratory flow through a single bifurcation is quite different from inspiratory flow. Instead of a single stream being split at the flow divider where new boundary layers are generated, two streams come together so that just beyond the flow divider the velocity profile in the plane of the junction has a dip at the center. The only common feature is that each of the two streams is curved and therefore secondary motions develop. This has been confirmed by smoke-

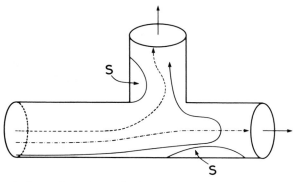

FIG. 8. Streamlines in steady flow in a T junction when flow rates in the 2 daughter tubes are comparable. *Solid line*, streamline near wall, remaining close to it; *dashed line*, streamline near center line of parent tube; *dashed-dotted line*, streamline between the two; S, sites of flow separation.

visualization measurements in the parent tube of a single bifurcation, with a more or less flat profile entering the daughters, as sketched in Figure 9 (13, 28, 41). Two of the four helices originate from each of the incoming streams.

Velocity profile measurements have also been made in two planes at various distances downstream (41). They confirm the dip in the plane of the junction just downstream of the flow divider but also demonstrate how it is very rapidly transformed into a marked velocity peak because the velocity near the walls is rapidly reduced. The profile in the perpendicular plane remains roughly flat. This can be qualitatively explained by the secondary motions, which cause the slower moving fluid along the line of the flow divider to be swept out to the walls.

Measurements have also been made on expiratory flow that has passed through several generations of junction (up to 6) and through asymmetric junctions (6, 18, 28, 35). They have revealed two interesting new facts. *1*) The peak in the velocity profile in the plane of the junction is usually absent when there are several generations, and the velocity profile either becomes virtually flat <1 diameter from the flow divider or has a shallow dip in the center with peaks near the wall (6). The secondary motions of course are very complicated in this case; they have been measured only by Isabey and Chang (18). *2*) The boundary layer surrounding the core remains very thin. There are as yet no results from which the dependence of its thickness on Reynolds number and generation number can be deduced nor any theoretical understanding of why it should remain thin, because the sites of measurement are far from the entrance to the system. Intense and convoluted secondary motions must be implicated, in the same way that in turbulent pipe flow the eddies cause a relatively thin mean velocity boundary layer to persist.

Turbulent Flow in Branched Tubes

We have discussed only laminar flow in branched tubes thus far. However, several observations suggest

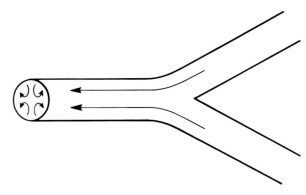

FIG. 9. Secondary motions generated in parent tube of a single bifurcation during expiratory flow. [From Schroter and Sudlow (41).]

that the critical Reynolds number for the onset of turbulence is reduced by passage through a bifurcation (7, 11, 25, 28, 44), in contrast to the effect of pure curvature. Indeed, Dekker (11) used an airway cast to obtain a tracheal Re_c as low as 500 for inspiratory flow with an open larynx (for expiratory flow it was ~1,500). In rapid deep breathing the maximum value of the tracheal Re may rise above 10,000 (Table 1), and even in quiet breathing it is of the order of 1,000. Also when the larynx is not wide open the flow enters the trachea through a constriction, which promotes turbulence; therefore turbulent flow in the trachea is normally expected.

Owen (27) has estimated the rate at which turbulence in the trachea would decay during inspiration, as it passes through subsequent generations in which the Reynolds number is below the critical value for a long straight tube. He concluded that for a tracheal Re of 3,100 the intensity of turbulence would have diminished to one-quarter of its tracheal value by generation 3 (Re = 1,230). Olson et al. (26) found random motions in the core of the trachea and major branches of a cast of the upper and central airways (from mouth to generation 4) at all flow rates above 200 ml/s (tracheal Re = 950). Thus at all but the quietest breathing rates the flow is expected to be turbulent for several generations of branching. Because most of the pressure drop is predicted to occur in the first few generations, the nature of this turbulent flow should be examined.

Douglass and Munson (12) measured inspiratory velocity and pressure profiles in a two-generation coplanar model [similar to Schroter and Sudlow's (41) but with branching angles of 60°] at parent-tube Re between 1.1×10^4 and 8.5×10^4. The flow was fully turbulent in all cases. They found mean velocity profiles that were qualitatively similar to laminar ones, except that the profile in the plane perpendicular to the junction was not markedly M shaped, resembling rather the profile in fully developed turbulent pipe flow. Similar mean velocity profiles have also been measured for intermediate (or transitional) values of Re, in the range $10^3 <$ Re $< 10^4$ (3, 23). The asymmetry of the cast used by Olson et al. (26) apparently had little effect on the mean profiles by the level of generation 2. None of the authors quoted previously has reported the strength of turbulent velocity fluctuations in branched tubes.

Pressure Drop in Branched-Tube Systems

The pressure drop for steady flow in any system of tubes can be divided into one term associated with kinetic energy changes and another associated with viscous energy dissipation (see CALCULATION OF PRESSURE DROP, p. 43). These two terms can be calculated from a knowledge of the velocity profiles in the tubes, at least in laminar flow and in turbulent flow when the fluctuating eddies do not contribute significantly to the dissipation. For example, Pedley et al. (32) noted from the measured velocity profiles of Schroter and Sudlow (41) that during laminar inspiratory flow very steep velocity gradients occurred in the new boundary layers that were formed on the flow dividers. Such layers are the sites of highest energy dissipation, so these authors proposed that the dissipation rate in branched tubes is proportional to that in the entrance region of a straight tube at the same Reynolds number, as given by the friction factor of Equation 11. Such proportionality was consistent with the dissipation rate calculated directly from their velocity profiles, and the constant of proportionality (k_3) derived from their experiments was ~21.1 (Eq. 17).

The determination of the dissipation rate is quite complex, and agreement among various groups of independent investigators is not perfect (3, 12, 21, 28, 32, 41, 42), even for symmetric bifurcations with precisely known geometry. (For a more detailed discussion see ref. 30.) Thus, with the present understanding, purely theoretical predictions of pressure drop in a complex network such as the lung probably cannot be made with great confidence and accuracy. Even so the inspiratory pressure loss in symmetrical branching networks can be reasonably estimated. One such approach follows. 1) Tabulate lengths and diameters of the tubes in each generation of the symmetric model under study. 2) For a given overall flow rate, calculate the Reynolds number in tubes of each generation assuming that the flow rate is symmetrically distributed at each bifurcation. 3) Depending on the value of the Reynolds number in a given generation, choose the appropriate value of the friction factor for that generation; if Re is in the range 180–700 (the range of daughter-tube Reynolds numbers in the experiments of Schroter and Sudlow), pressure loss can be approximated by

$$\Delta P_v = 21.1(l/d \times Re)^{1/2} \times \tfrac{1}{2}\rho \bar{V}^2 \qquad (17)$$

If Re is between 4.7×10^3 and 5.5×10^4, the dissipation is given by the fully turbulent rough pipe formula from Equation 13 with $k_4 = 0.03$ (11) so that

$$\Delta P_v = 0.03(l/d) \times \tfrac{1}{2}\rho \bar{V}^2 \qquad (18)$$

The region of greatest uncertainty is for intermediate values of Reynolds number with flow that may not be strongly turbulent. Pedley et al. (34) suggested that Equation 17 could be used, whereas Berger et al. (3) and Douglass and Munson (12) indicated that a smaller multiplicative factor should be used. 4) The overall viscous pressure drop is then computed by adding the contributions from all generations; it should be made nondimensional with respect to $\tfrac{1}{2}\rho \bar{V}_0^2$, where $\bar{V}_0$ is the average velocity in the parent tube of the system (i.e., trachea), and the result should be represented in terms of an overall C_F.

Pedley et al. (33) followed this procedure in predicting pulmonary inspiratory pressure drop at relatively low flow rates, so that Equation 17 could be used

everywhere except in the trachea (where smooth pipe turbulence was assumed) and in very small airways (where Poiseuille's law was used). Jaffrin and Kesic (21) extended the procedure to larger flow rates, so that turbulence had to be included, on the assumption that the transition to turbulence took place at a tracheal Re of 5,000. The chapter by Ingram and Pedley in this *Handbook* presents the results of these predictions. We merely note here that agreement between prediction and measurement of lower airway resistance is good.

Figure 3 shows a Moody plot (C_F against Re) of recent measurements on inspiratory flow through a cast of the principal airways of the human lung (42). The cast is asymmetric of course, beginning with the trachea and terminating in airways ~3–4 mm in internal diameter, representing five to six generations of branching. In their chapter in this *Handbook*, Ingram and Pedley discuss such measurements on casts in detail, but we may note that the first section of the plot (for tracheal Re < 700) has a slope of −1, representing dominance of the pressure drop by tubes in which there is Poiseuille flow or at least a linear pressure-flow relation, as proposed by Berger et al. (3). Then, for tracheal Re in the range 700–5,000, the plot has a slope of −½, representing dominance of the entry-flow mechanism, as proposed by Pedley et al. (32). Finally, for tracheal Re > 5,000, C_F is approximately constant, as it is for flow in a rough tube and as predicted by Douglass and Munson (12) and by Jaffrin and Kesic (21).

Finally, the pressure drop in steady expiration, which has received considerably less attention than in inspiration, must be considered. It is important to realize that expiratory pressure drop is expected to be different from inspiratory pressure drop for two reasons. 1) The velocity profiles are different so the viscous dissipation rate will be different and therefore C_F (Eq. 9) is different. 2) The air gains kinetic energy as it flows toward the trachea, whereas it loses it on inspiration, so the total $C_{\Delta P}$ (Eq. 12) exceeds C_F on expiration but is less than C_F on inspiration. Based on the previous observations of an approximately flat velocity profile with a complicated collection of secondary eddies, Pedley (30) proposed that the viscous pressure drop in a tube fed by several upstream generations should be the same as for turbulent flow in a smooth tube at the same Reynolds number. Thus in any one generation, ΔP_v would be proportional to $Re^{1.75}$ (so $C_F \sim Re^{-0.25}$) from Equation 13. Pacome (28) performed experiments for parent-tube Reynolds numbers in the range 580–4,100 and found ΔP_v to be proportional to $Re^{1.7}$, which is encouraging. Moreover Hardin et al. (13) made pressure drop measurements in a three-generation model and found the total pressure drop to be proportional to $Re^{1.6}$ for parent-tube Re in the range 1,000–4,500 (and proportional to $Re^{1.93}$ for larger values of Re). After correcting for the kinetic energy terms, these authors found that the viscous pressure drop could be represented by a friction factor of the form

$$C_F = 3.10 \ Re^{-0.4} - 0.062 \qquad (19)$$

For sufficiently small Reynolds numbers this has a slope between the -0.5 of the entry-flow model and the -0.25 of smooth pipe turbulence. Hardin et al. (13) used Equation 19 to predict expiratory pressure drop in the lung and found values below those observed. Other observations on branched-tube networks indicate that, normally, ΔP_v (or C_F) is greater on expiration than on inspiration (20, 28), but apart from those of Hardin et al. (13) such data have not been systematically translated into quantitative predictions for the lung. The experiments of Isabey and Chang (17) on a lung cast confirm that ΔP (as opposed to ΔP_v) is considerably larger on expiration than on inspiration.

UNSTEADY FLOW

In this section we examine the conditions under which the flow in a tube may be considered quasi-steady, because if it may not, predictions of time-varying pressure drop cannot yet be made accurately. A more extensive summary can be found in reference 35. The prototype of an unsteady flow is that of laminar flow in a long straight tube driven by a sinusoidally oscillating pressure gradient. The flow depends on the frequency of oscillation. If the frequency is very low, the pressure gradient changes so gradually that the velocity profile remains parabolic at all times. However, if the pressure gradient is oscillated rapidly, inertia causes changes in the velocity of fluid near the center of the tube to lag behind changes in the pressure gradient. For a given amplitude of oscillation in pressure gradient the amplitude of the core velocity falls. Fluid close to the wall, however, has a low velocity because of the no-slip condition and does not lag behind. In between there is a boundary layer in which the viscous forces, which alone would cause the fluid to respond instantaneously, are balanced by the inertial forces, which cause it to lag. The thickness of the boundary layer is proportional to the distance across which the influence of viscosity can be felt during one cycle of the oscillation, i.e., is proportional to $\sqrt{\nu/\omega}$, where $\nu \ (= \mu/\rho)$ is the kinematic viscosity of the fluid and ω is the angular frequency of the oscillation. This boundary layer is thin compared with the radius of the tube ($\frac{1}{2}d$) if the Womersley parameter

$$\alpha = \frac{1}{2}d \ \sqrt{\omega/\nu} \qquad (20)$$

is much larger than 1. In that case the motion of most of the fluid is dominated by inertia and the flow cannot be considered steady. If $\alpha < 1$, however, the boundary layer is as thick as the radius of the tube. In other words, viscous forces cause the flow everywhere to

respond almost instantaneously to changes in pressure gradient and the flow is approximately quasi-steady (40).

However, the airways are not long straight tubes. In most of them steady inspiratory flow is dominated by a boundary layer on the flow divider, whose thickness is expected to be given by Equation 6. The flow is quasi-steady as long as the oscillatory boundary layer thickness is larger than the steady boundary layer thickness, instead of the vessel radius, because then viscosity has time to cause the velocity at all points across the boundary layer to respond almost simultaneously to changes in the core velocity. This requires that the frequency parameter

$$\epsilon = \omega l/\overline{V} \qquad (21)$$

should be $\ll 1$, where l is the length of a tube and $\overline{V}$ is the cross-sectionally averaged time-varying velocity in it; ϵ roughly measures the relative importance of local acceleration to convective acceleration in a sinusoidally varying flow in an entrance region.

If the pulmonary flow rate is approximately constant during both inspiration and expiration, so is $\overline{V}$ in each airway and a characteristic value of ϵ can be defined for each. If both α and ϵ are <1, laminar flow is quasi-steady, as experiments confirm (4, 20). However, $\overline{V}$ becomes very small and passes through zero whenever the direction of flow changes, with the consequence that ϵ becomes very large and the flow cannot be quasi-steady at end inspiration and end expiration. Isabey and Chang (17) pointed out, on the basis of the theory of Pedley (29), that a more appropriate parameter is actually ϵ', where

$$\epsilon' = \frac{l(d\overline{V}/dt)}{\overline{V}^2} \qquad (22)$$

From oscillatory flow experiments in an airway cast, Isabey and Chang (17) confirmed that the total inspiratory or expiratory pressure drop is markedly greater than its quasi-steady value in those parts of the cycle for which $\epsilon > 0.4$ or $\epsilon' > 0.1$, unless in addition α is less than ~ 4.0. Because they could not separate the pressure drop into viscous and kinetic energy contributions, it is not clear from their experiments which of these terms is more severely modified by the distortions of the velocity profile that occur in unsteady flow. In a given geometry with characteristic diameter and length, a purely sinusoidal flow with

$$\overline{V} = V_0 \sin \omega t$$

can be completely specified by giving the values of the peak Reynolds numbers ($Re_0 = \rho V_0 d/\mu$) and either α or the minimum value of ϵ ($\epsilon_0 = \omega l/V_0$), because $\alpha^2 = 4(l/d)\epsilon_0 Re_0$. In a general unsteady flow, however, it may not be possible to define a unique α, and an infinite number of dimensionless parameters would be required in principle [e.g., ϵ' and $\epsilon'' = (l^2 d^2 \overline{V}/dt^2) \ \overline{V}^3$]. However, in assessing when a flow will cease to be quasi-steady, in our opinion just Re and ϵ' would provide sufficient information (see also ref. 18).

The flow in the trachea and large bronchi is normally turbulent, and there has been very little study of turbulent flows with unsteady mean velocities. The effect of unsteadiness on turbulent pipe flow can be assessed roughly by calculating a turbulent counterpart to the Womersley parameter α (Eq. 20). To do this replace ν, a property of the fluid representing the rate at which velocity gradients are reduced by the action of viscosity, by a quantity that represents the same reduction due to turbulent mixing. This quantity is called the eddy viscosity (ν^*) and depends on both the Reynolds number and the nature of the flow. Its magnitude roughly equals the square of the magnitude of the fluctuating turbulent velocities divided by a typical mean shear rate. If it is assumed that the turbulence intensity >3% (14) and that the mean shear $\mathrm{d}\bar{V}/\mathrm{d}y$ (where y is distance measured from tube wall) is roughly equal to the mean velocity divided by one-half the radius, then

$$\nu^* \approx \frac{\bar{V}^2}{\mathrm{d}\bar{V}/\mathrm{d}y} > \frac{0.03\,\bar{V}^2}{4\,\bar{V}/d} \qquad (23)$$

that is

$$\nu^* > 0.0075\,\bar{V}d$$

Thus the effective value of α is less than

$$\alpha^* = \tfrac{1}{2}d\left(\frac{\omega}{0.0075\,\bar{V}d}\right) \qquad (24)$$

Estimation of the three parameters (α, ϵ, α^*) leads to the conclusion that at breathing frequencies of up to 1 Hz the flow in all airways (except possibly the trachea) is normally quasi-steady, except near end expiration and end inspiration. Only in rapid forced-oscillation maneuvers and high-frequency ventilation may non-quasi-steady flow effects become important (see the chapter by Ingram and Pedley in this *Handbook*). Thus the relationships derived in this chapter for steady flow can be applied to normal tidal breathing.

REFERENCES

1. ADLER, M. Strömung in gekrümmten Rohren. *Z. Angew. Math. Mech.* 51: 257–275, 1934.
2. AGRAWAL, Y., L. TALBOT, AND K. GONG. Laser anemometer study of flow development in curved circular pipes. *J. Fluid Mech.* 85: 497–518, 1978.
3. BERGER, C., P. CALVET, AND C. JACQUEMIN. *Structure d'écoulements de gaz dans des systèmes tubulaires bifurqués.* Toulouse, France: Cent. Etud. Rech. Toulouse, 1972. (Report.)
4. BRECH, R., AND B. J. BELLHOUSE. Flow in branching vessels. *Cardiovasc. Res.* 7: 593–600, 1973.
5. CARO, C. G., T. J. PEDLEY, R. C. SCHROTER, AND W. A. SEED. *Mechanics of the Circulation.* Oxford, UK: Oxford Univ. Press, 1978.
6. CHANG, H. K., AND O. A. EL MASRY. A model study of flow dynamics in human central airways. Pt. I. Axial velocity profiles. *Respir. Physiol.* 49: 75–95, 1982.
7. CLARKE, S. W., J. G. JONES, AND D. R. OLIVER. Factors affecting airflow through branched tubes. *Bull. Physio-Pathol. Respir.* 8: 409–428, 1972.
8. COLLINS, W. M., AND S. C. R. DENNIS. The steady motion of a viscous fluid in a curved tube. *Q. J. Mech. Appl. Math.* 28: 133–156, 1975.
9. CURRIE, I. G. *Fundamental Mechanics of Fluids.* New York: McGraw-Hill, 1974.
10. DEAN, W. R. The streamline motion of fluid in a curved pipe. *Philos. Mag.* 7(5): 673–695, 1928.
11. DEKKER, E. Transition between laminar and turbulent flow in human trachea. *J. Appl. Physiol.* 16: 1060–1064, 1961.
12. DOUGLASS, R. W., AND B. R. MUNSON. Viscous energy dissipation in a model of the human bronchial tree. *J. Biomech.* 7: 551–557, 1974.
13. HARDIN, J. C., J. C. YU, J. L. PATTERSON, AND W. TRIBLE. The pressure/flow relation in bronchial airways on expiration. In: *Biofluid Mechanics*, edited by D. J. Schneck. New York: Plenum, 1980, vol. 2, p. 39–55.
14. HINZE, J. O. *Turbulence.* New York: McGraw-Hill, 1959.
15. HORSFIELD, K., AND G. CUMMING. Angles of branching and diameters at branches in the human bronchial tree. *Bull. Math. Biophys.* 29: 245–259, 1967.
16. HORSFIELD, K., AND G. CUMMING. Morphology of the bronchial tree in man. *J. Appl. Physiol.* 24: 373–383, 1968.
17. ISABEY, D., AND H. K. CHANG. Steady and unsteady pressure-flow relationships in central airways. *J. Appl. Physiol.: Respirat. Environ. Exercise Physiol.* 51: 1338–1348, 1981.
18. ISABEY, D., AND H. K. CHANG. A model study of flow dynamics in human central airways. Pt. II. Secondary flow velocities. *Respir. Physiol.* 49: 97–113, 1982.
19. ITO, H. Friction factors for turbulent flow in curved pipes. *Trans. ASME Ser. D* 81: 123–134, 1959.
20. JAFFRIN, M. Y., AND T. V. HENNESSEY. Pressure distribution in a model of the central airways for sinusoidal flow. *Bull. Physio-Pathol. Respir.* 8: 375–390, 1972.
21. JAFFRIN, M. Y., AND P. KESIC. Airway resistance: a fluid mechanical approach. *J. Appl. Physiol.* 36: 354–361, 1974.
22. LEW, H. S., AND Y. C. FUNG. On the low-Reynolds number entry flow into a circular cylindrical tube. *J. Biomech.* 2: 105–119, 1969.
23. LUTZ, R. J., J. N. CANNON, K. B. BISCHOFF, AND R. L. DEDRICK. Wall shear stress distribution in a model canine artery during steady flow. *Circ. Res.* 41: 391–399, 1977.
24. McCONALOGUE, D. J., AND R. S. SRIVASTAVA. Motion of fluid in a curved tube. *Proc. R. Soc. London Ser. A* 307: 37–53, 1968.
25. OLSON, D. E. Fluid Mechanics Relevant to Respiration: Flow Within Curved or Elliptical Tubes and Bifurcating Systems. London: Imperial College, 1971. Dissertation.
26. OLSON, D. E., L. D. ILIFF, AND M. F. SUDLOW. Some aspects of the physics of flow in the central airways. *Bull. Physio-Pathol. Respir.* 8: 391–408, 1972.
27. OWEN, P. R. Turbulent flow and particle deposition in the trachea. In: *Circulatory and Respiratory Mass Transport*, edited by G. E. W. Wolstenholme and J. Knight. London: Churchill, 1969, p. 236–252. (Ciba Found. Symp. 69.)
28. PACOME, J. J. Structures d'écoulement et pertes de charge calculée dans le modèle d'arbre bronchique de Weibel. Toulouse, France: Paul Sabatier Univ., 1975. Dissertation.
29. PEDLEY, T. J. Viscous boundary layers in reversing flow. *J. Fluid Mech.* 74: 59–79, 1976.
30. PEDLEY, T. J. Pulmonary fluid dynamics. *Annu. Rev. Fluid Mech.* 9: 229–274, 1977.
31. PEDLEY, T. J. *The Fluid Mechanics of Large Blood Vessels.* Cambridge, UK: Cambridge Univ. Press, 1980.
32. PEDLEY, T. J., R. C. SCHROTER, AND M. F. SUDLOW. Energy losses and pressure drop in models of human airways. *Respir. Physiol.* 9: 371–386, 1970.
33. PEDLEY, T. J., R. C. SCHROTER, AND M. F. SUDLOW. The prediction of pressure drop and variation of resistance within

the human bronchial airways. *Respir. Physiol.* 9: 387–405, 1970.

34. PEDLEY, T. J., R. C. SCHROTER, AND M. F. SUDLOW. Flow and pressure drop in systems of repeatedly branching tubes. *J. Fluid Mech.* 46: 365–383, 1971.

35. PEDLEY, T. J., R. C. SCHROTER, AND M. F. SUDLOW. Gas flow and mixing in the airways. In: *Lung Biology in Health and Disease. Bioengineering Aspects of the Lung*, edited by J. B. West. New York: Dekker, 1977, vol. 3, chapt. 3, p. 163–265.

36. POISEUILLE, J. L. M. Recherches experimentales sur le mouvement des liquides dans les tubes de très petits diamètres. *C. R. Acad. Sci.* 11: 961–967, 1041–1048, 1840.

37. PRANDTL, L. *The Essentials of Fluid Dynamics.* Glasgow: Blackie, 1952.

37a. PRANDTL, L., AND O. G. TIETJENS. *Applied Hydro- and Aeromechanics.* New York: Dover, 1957.

38. REYNOLDS, O. An experimental investigation of the circumstances which determine whether the motion of water shall be direct or sinuous, and of the law of resistance in parallel channels. *Philos. Trans. R. Soc. London* 174: 935–982, 1883.

39. ROUSE, H. (editor). *Engineering Hydraulics.* New York: Wiley, 1950.

40. SCHLICHTING, H. *Boundary Layer Theory* (6th ed.). New York: McGraw-Hill, 1968.

41. SCHROTER, R. C., AND M. F. SUDLOW. Flow patterns in models of the human bronchial airways. *Respir. Physiol.* 7: 341–355, 1969.

42. SLUTSKY, A. S., G. G. BERDINE, AND J. M. DRAZEN. Steady flow in a model of human central airways. *J. Appl. Physiol.: Respirat. Environ. Exercise Physiol.* 49: 417–423, 1980.

43. SNYDER, B., AND M. J. JAEGER. Lobar flow patterns in a hollow cast of canine central airways. *J. Appl. Physiol.: Respirat. Environ. Exercise Physiol.* 54: 749–756, 1983.

44. STEHBENS, W. E. Turbulence of blood flow. *Q. J. Exp. Physiol.* 44: 110–115, 1959.

45. TALUKDER, N. An investigation on the flow characteristics in arterial branchings. (Abstract). *Mech. Eng.* 97: 81, 1975.

46. TALUKDER, N., AND R. M. NEREM. Flow characteristics in vascular graft models. In: *Digest Int. Conf. Mech. Med. Biol., 1st, Aachen, 1978*, vol. 7, p. 281–284.

47. TAYLOR, G. I. The criterion for turbulence in curved pipes. *Proc. R. Soc. London Ser. A* 124: 243–249, 1929.

48. WEIBEL, E. R. *Morphometry of the Human Lung.* Heidelberg: Springer-Verlag, 1963.

49. ZELLER, H., N. TALUKDER, AND J. LORENZ. Model studies of pulsating flow in arterial branches and wave propagation in blood vessels. *AGARD Conf. Proc.* 65: 15–15.8, 1970.

CHAPTER 5

Wave-speed and viscous flow limitation

THEODORE A. WILSON | *Department of Aerospace Engineering and Mechanics, University of Minnesota, Minneapolis, Minnesota*

JOSEPH R. RODARTE | *Departments of Internal Medicine and of Physiology and Biophysics, Mayo Medical School and Mayo Clinic, Rochester, Minnesota*

JAMES P. BUTLER | *Department of Physiology, Harvard School of Public Health, Boston, Massachusetts*

CHAPTER CONTENTS

THE AIRWAYS OF THE LUNG are compliant; their caliber depends on transmural pressure, which is the difference between the gas pressure at the inner surface of the airway and peribronchial pressure (pressure resulting from alveolar pressure and parenchymal attachments at outer surface). To the first approximation, peribronchial pressure equals pleural pressure (see the chapters by Wilson and by Rodarte and Fung in this *Handbook*). With flow the pressure distribution inside the bronchial tree depends on lung volume, gas properties, flow, and airway caliber. Thus the mechanics of the airways and the mechanics of flow are coupled. Fry and Hyatt (2) realized quite early that this coupling might lead to expiratory flow limitation, but the concept of airway compression did not immediately lead to a quantitative model. The phenomenological description of flow limitation is simple: at a given lung volume, flow is independent of the difference between alveolar pressure and mouth pressure if that pressure difference is sufficiently large. The fact that flow limitation occurs at all lung volumes in most species and in normal and diseased lungs fostered the belief that a flow-limiting mechanism existed that acted under a wide range of conditions.

In 1977 Dawson and Elliot (1) pointed out that flow in a compliant tube could not exceed the lowest flow at which the local fluid velocity equaled the local wave speed at any point in the tube and that this mechanism had the properties needed to explain expiratory flow limitation. Griffiths (3) had proposed this mechanism of flow limitation in micturition. Methods developed to describe flow of water in an open channel and flow of a compressible gas through a nozzle were available for analyzing flows through a compliant tube. The mathematical representations of all these physical systems are identical; only the physical entities that the mathematical symbols represent are different. Expiratory flow limitation and the restriction on blood flow through pulmonary vessels had already been likened to a waterfall in which the rate of flow over the falls is independent of the level of the downstream reservoir (4). This analogy turned out to be much more than a phenomenological similarity.

Flow limitation at wave speed is a result of the coupling between convective acceleration of the gas and airway compliance. Convective acceleration occurs when a fluid moves from a region where the cross-sectional area available to the flow is large and the fluid velocity is low into a region where the cross-sectional area is small and the fluid velocity is high. A pressure drop is required to accelerate the gas as it moves from the region of low velocity to the region of high velocity. Therefore with flow from a large reservoir out through a compliant tube, pressure falls between the reservoir and the tube. The pressure drop determines transmural pressure, which in turn determines the cross-sectional area according to the area–transmural pressure relationship of the compliant tube. If the volume flow is low, the pressure drop is small, the area decrease of the tube is small, and a pressure and area mutually agreeable to the fluid and the tube are reached. However, if the volume flow is higher, the rate at which pressure decreases with decreasing area is larger. If the tube is sufficiently compliant, there is a maximum flow above which the pressure in the flow would decrease with decreasing area faster than could be accommodated by the rate of decrease of transmural pressure with decreasing area of the tube. As that limiting flow is approached, the pressure drop increases more rapidly with increasing flow and the plot of pressure drop versus flow becomes horizontal. The wave speed or speed of propagation of a small disturbance in a fluid-filled compliant tube is also determined by the coupling between tube compliance and fluid inertia. Hence the condition that limits steady flow through a compliant tube is related to the wave speed.

A limiting flow can also result from the coupling between dissipative pressure losses and tube compliance (5). A pressure drop is required to drive flow through a tube because of laminar or turbulent energy dissipation. For a given total flow, the smaller the tube area, the greater the pressure loss. A compounding of the pressure loss and area decrease can occur; if the tube area decreases fast enough with decreasing pressure, a finite flow can require an infinite pressure loss along the tube.

The wave-speed mechanism can be described without including dissipative effects, and the dissipative mechanism can be described without considering convective acceleration. In this chapter each mechanism is described separately and the relationship between the two is then discussed.

In expiratory flow from the lung, laminar and turbulent dissipation and convective acceleration all contribute to the pressure distribution that causes airway compression and limits flow. Expiratory flow limitation is described in the chapter by Hyatt in this *Handbook*. We focus on the physics of the flow-limiting mechanisms by describing simplified idealized examples.

WAVE-SPEED FLOW-LIMITING MECHANISM

Figure 1 shows a compliant tube as the exit nozzle attached to a pressurized reservoir. At each position x

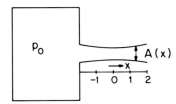

FIG. 1. A compliant tube forms the exit nozzle from a large chamber. Area-pressure behavior of tube is a function of axial position (x). Compressibility of the gas is neglected and absolute pressure is not significant. The pressure in the chamber (P_0) and the pressure at the exit of the nozzle, $P(x = 2)$, are pressures relative to the pressure applied to the outside of the tube. The pressure outside the tube is analogous to pleural pressure, chamber pressure is analogous to recoil pressure of the lung, and exit pressure is analogous to pressure at the mouth. Lowering the exit pressure and holding chamber pressure constant in this system is therefore analogous to increasing pleural pressure and holding recoil pressure constant.

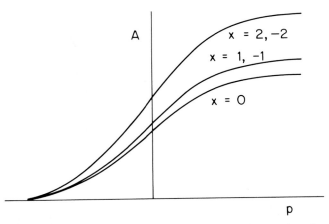

FIG. 2. Area-pressure behavior of compliant tube as a function of axial position.

along the tube the cross-sectional area (A) of the tube depends on the pressure (P) inside the tube. The dependence of area on pressure is different at different positions and hence A is a function of P and x. For convenience we choose a particularly simple form for this function, a product of a function of P and a simple function of x

$$A = [1 + (x^2/8)]f(P) \qquad (1)$$

The coordinate system is chosen so that $x = 0$ is the midpoint of the tube that extends from $x = -2$ to $x = 2$. The function of pressure [f(P)] in Equation 1 is $A(P)$ at $x = 0$ and is shown by the line marked $x = 0$ in Figure 2. We neglect dissipative effects and assume the pressure distribution is entirely the result of convective acceleration. The Bernoulli equation is then applicable

$$P = P_0 - (\tfrac{1}{2}\rho \dot{V}^2/A^2) \qquad (2)$$

where P_0 is the pressure in the reservoir, ρ is the fluid density, $\dot{V}$ is the volume flow rate, and $\dot{V}/A$ is the fluid velocity.

For a given volume flow the pressure and area at each axial position are the pair of values that are simultaneous solutions to Equations 1 and 2. These values are graphically determined by plotting Equations 1 and 2 on the same diagram (Fig. 3). The solution at each position x is given by the intersection of the $A(P)$ curve at that x and the Bernoulli equation for the given $\dot{V}$. Bernoulli equations are plotted for three values of $\dot{V}$ in Figure 3. The solutions, $P(x)$ and $A(x)$, are shown in Figure 4. As flow increases, the pressure and area at each point decrease. For flows greater than the critical flow ($\dot{V}_c$), no simultaneous solution exists for all values of x because the pressure in the flow decreases with decreasing area too rapidly to allow an intersection of the Bernoulli and $A(P)$ curves at $x = 0$. For $\dot{V}_c$ the line representing the Bernoulli equation in Figure 3 is tangent to the $A(P)$ line at $x = 0$, with both curves having the same slope

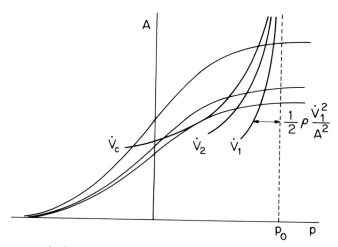

FIG. 3. Area-pressure curves of tube with curves showing area-pressure relation in the flow calculated from Bernoulli equation for 3 different volume flow rates. For each flow rate the area and pressure that occur at each position are given by the intersection of flow and tube curves.

at the point of tangency. From the differential of the Bernoulli equation [$dP = \rho(\dot{V}_c^2/A^3)dA$], the slope of that curve (dA/dP) can be found; this must equal the slope of the $A(P)$ curve of the tube. Setting these equal and solving for $\dot{V}_c$ yields

$$\dot{V}_c = A[A/\rho(dA/dP)]^{1/2} \qquad (3)$$

The quantity $[A/\rho(dA/dP)]^{1/2}$ is the speed at which a small disturbance, or wave, propagates in a compliant tube. At the point of tangency, fluid velocity ($\dot{V}_c/A$) equals wave speed. The location in the tube where this occurs is called the choke point, the critical point, or the flow-limiting site.

The Bernoulli curve for $\dot{V} = \dot{V}_c$ has two intersections with the airway $A(P)$ curves for $x > 0$, and there are two possibilities for continuing the solution for $P(x)$ and $A(x)$ downstream of the critical point. The pressure and area can return up the Bernoulli curve, producing the symmetric solution shown in Figure 4, or pressure and area can continue to decrease, following the Bernoulli curve past the point of tangency to lower values of P and A for $x > 0$. The existence of two branches of the solution curve originating from the critical point is a distinctive feature of the critical point, and there is a distinctive difference between the branches. On the branch on which airway area is larger than its value at the critical point, the slope of the $A(P)$ curves is less than the slope of the Bernoulli equation and on the branch that extends to lower values of airway area, it is greater. The ratio of the slope of the $A(P)$ curve to the slope of the Bernoulli equation is $(dA/dP)/(A^3/\rho\dot{V}_c^2)$. By rearranging this expression into the form $(\dot{V}_c^2/A^2)/[A/\rho(dA/dP)]$ it can be identified as the ratio of the square of the fluid velocity to the square of the wave speed. Therefore on the upper branch, the local fluid velocity is less than wave speed and on the lower branch it is greater. The

flow rate cannot exceed the value at which the fluid velocity equals wave speed at any point in the tube. However, additional airway compression and increased fluid velocity downstream of the critical point can produce a region in which the fluid velocity is greater than wave speed. This is called a region of supercritical flow, meaning that the local fluid velocity exceeds the local wave speed in this region, not that the total flow exceeds the critical flow.

A region of supercritical flow can end with an abrupt increase in area and pressure called a hydraulic jump in analogy with the jump in water depth occurring, for example, at the bottom of a spillway in open-channel flow. A dissipative mechanism is necessary to allow a jump off the Bernoulli curve, and this mechanism is discussed next. If the tube area decreases in the flow direction or increases very gradually, the flow fills the tube and the Bernoulli equation is applicable. However, if the tube area increases abruptly, the flow separates from the tube wall, forming a stream in the center of the expanded region surrounded by quiescent fluid filling the rest of the tube. The boundary between the flowing and stagnant fluid is unstable, and farther downstream from the area increase, turbulent mixing reestablishes flow over the entire cross section. Energy

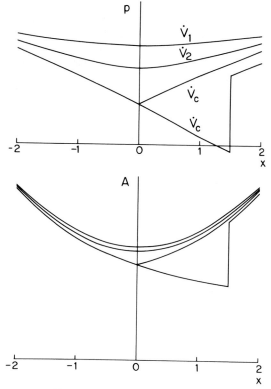

FIG. 4. Pressure (*top*) and area (*bottom*) as functions of axial position in compliant tube for each flow rate. For limiting flow ($\dot{V}_c$) 2 possible branches of the solution are shown downstream of the critical point. Along lower branch a region of supercritical flow ends with a dissipative jump.

is lost in the mixing process, but momentum is conserved.

The law of conservation of momentum can be applied to the region (Fig. 5) between the point of minimum area and the point where a uniform flow has been reestablished. This law states that the net force acting on the fluid in the region equals the rate of change of momentum of the fluid as it passes through the region. A net force in the flow direction is provided by the pressure acting on the boundaries shown by the dashed lines in Figure 5. This net force can be written as the sum of three terms: the pressure force acting over the cross section at station 1 (P_1A_1), the net force provided by the pressure distribution along the tapering side walls ($\int_{A_1}^{A_2} PdA$), and a force acting opposite to the flow direction at station 2 ($-P_2A_2$). As the fluid passes through the region, the rate of change of momentum is given by the difference between the momentum flux out of the region at station 2 and the momentum flux into the region at station 1. The mass flux is ρV, the fluid velocity is $\dot{V}/A$, and the momentum flux is the product of the two. Setting the net force equal to the rate of change of momentum yields

$$P_1A_1 + \int_{A_1}^{A_2} PdA - P_2A_2 = \rho\dot{V}^2/A_2 - \rho\dot{V}^2/A_1 \quad (4)$$

The value of A_2 and the corresponding value of P_2 that satisfy this equation can be found if tube behavior $A(P)$ and values of $\dot{V}$, A_1, and P_1 are given so that the second and third terms on the left side of Equation 4 can be evaluated as functions of A_2.

A simplified example is described. Suppose the $A(P)$ curve can be approximated by a straight line over a certain range of pressure so that

$$A - A_1 = (P - P_1)/K \quad (5)$$

where K is a constant. Then

$$\int_{A_1}^{A_2} PdA = P_1(A_2 - A_1)$$

$$+ \frac{1}{2}K(A_2^2 - A_1^2) - KA_1(A_2 - A_1)$$

and $P_2A_2 = P_1A_2 + KA_2(A_2 - A_1)$. By substituting

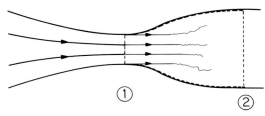

FIG. 5. Flow separation occurs downstream of an area minimum. Energy is dissipated in mixing process that reestablishes flow throughout tube cross section. Momentum balance for fluid within the control volume (*dashed lines*) determines the jump in pressure and area that occurs across mixing region.

these expressions into Equation 4 and simplifying, the following equation for A_2 is obtained

$$(A_2 - A_1)[A_2^2 + A_1A_2 - (2\rho\dot{V}^2/KA_1)] = 0 \quad (6)$$

The only positive root of this equation, apart from the trivial solution $A_2 = A_1$, is

$$A_2/A_1 = -\frac{1}{2} + \sqrt{\frac{1}{4} + (2\rho\dot{V}^2/KA_1^3)} \quad (7)$$

A solution consistent with the assumption made in deriving the equation $A_2/A_1 > 1$ is obtained only if $\rho\dot{V}^2/KA_1^3 > 1$. The wave speed at area A_1 is $\sqrt{KA_1/\rho}$ because $K = 1/(dA/dP)$. Hence the condition for an area jump to occur ($\rho\dot{V}^2/KA_1^3 > 1$) is that the square of the fluid velocity ($\dot{V}^2/A_1^2$) is greater than the square of the wave speed. A hydraulic jump can only occur if the fluid velocity is greater than wave speed, and the area ratio of the jump increases as the ratio of fluid velocity to wave speed increases. Fluid velocity decreases and wave speed increases as area increases, and it can be shown that the fluid velocity is always less than wave speed at A_2 downstream of the jump.

The flow sequence for decreasing exit pressure can now be summarized. For a particular value of P_0, as exit pressure decreases from P_0, flow increases from zero until it reaches a maximum, $\dot{V}_c$. For the exit pressure at which the volume flow first reaches this limiting value, fluid velocity equals wave speed at some point in the tube, but the local fluid velocity is less than the local wave speed elsewhere (symmetric solution for $\dot{V}_c$ in Fig. 4). As exit pressure is reduced below the value at which $\dot{V}_c$ is reached, the pressure and area distributions upstream of the critical point remain unchanged and a region of supercritical flow appears downstream of the critical point. As exit pressure is reduced further, the region of supercritical flow expands and the amplitude of the hydraulic jump and the amount of energy dissipated in the jump increase.

This sequence can be described in terms of wave propagation. If the pressure decreases at the downstream end of the compliant tube, the change in transmural pressure causes a deformation that travels upstream at the wave speed. When the deformation reaches the inlet, the information resulting from the fall in pressure at the downstream end has been transmitted to the upstream end and flow increases to a new value. However, if at a point in the tube the fluid velocity going downstream is equal to and opposite the wave speed going upstream, the deformation cannot travel past this point.

It might be thought that expiratory flow in the lung is increased by increasing alveolar pressure at the inlet rather than by decreasing the pressure at the downstream end, that the distortion initiating the wave commences at the alveoli, and that the wave therefore travels in the direction of flow. This, however, is not the case. At any given lung volume, increases in pleural pressure during expiration cause uniform increases in gas pressure in the periphery and the transmural pressure of the peripheral airways is unchanged. At the downstream end, however, the pressure within the airways does not change and transmural pressure changes as pleural pressure changes. Thus the deformation starts at the downstream end and travels upstream against the fluid velocity, and flow limitation occurs through the wave-speed mechanism.

For a tube such as the one described in Figure 2, in which the tube area at each pressure depends on x but the specific compliance does not, the choke point occurs at the point of minimum area ($x = 0$) regardless of the chamber pressure (P_0). However, the value of maximum flow and the values of pressure and area at the critical point at maximum flow depend on driving pressure; the higher the P_0, the greater $\dot{V}_c$, P, and A at the critical point. For a tube in which the area and specific compliance both depend on axial position, the location of the choke point may change with P_0. That possibility is described in the chapter by Hyatt in this *Handbook*.

VISCOUS FLOW LIMITATION

Another flow-limiting mechanism results from the coupling between dissipative pressure losses and tube compliance. Both turbulent and laminar viscous losses can produce flow limitation. Flow limitation by laminar viscous dissipation is described in this section. If viscous forces dominate, the pressure gradient in a tube is described by

$$dP/dx = -a\mu\dot{V}/A^2 \qquad (8)$$

where a is a numerical constant and μ is the fluid viscosity. Multiplying Equation 8 by A^2dx yields

$$A^2dP = -a\mu\dot{V}dx \qquad (9)$$

The analysis of this flow-limiting mechanism is simplest for a tube with uniform $A(P)$ properties along its length. Then the left side of Equation 9 is a function of P alone, and the dx coefficient on the right side is independent of x. Each side can be integrated from conditions at the tube entrance ($x = 0$, $P = P_1$) to the exit ($x = l$, $P = P_2$), where l is tube length. The resulting equation can be solved for $\dot{V}$

$$\dot{V} = \frac{1}{a\mu l} \int_{P_2}^{P_1} A^2(P)dP \qquad (10)$$

The limits of integration and sign of the right side have been changed so that the integral is positive. For a tube of given length with a given entrance pressure (P_1), Equation 10 provides the relation between flow and exit pressure (P_2). As the pressure drop along the tube becomes large, the pressure at the downstream end (P_2) becomes negative and the area at the downstream end becomes small. If $A^2(P)$, the integrand in Equation 10, approaches zero faster than $1/-P_2$ as P_2 goes to negative infinity, a finite flow is produced by

an infinite pressure drop and viscous flow limitation occurs. The viscous limit on flow is

$$\dot{V} = \frac{1}{a\mu l} \int_{-\infty}^{P_1} A^2(P)dP \qquad (11)$$

RELATION BETWEEN WAVE-SPEED AND VISCOUS FLOW-LIMITING MECHANISMS

As P_2 goes to negative infinity, the limit described by Equation 11 is not consistent with the physics of the flow. In this limit A_2 approaches zero, and for a finite volume flow the fluid velocity approaches infinity and convective acceleration cannot be ignored. If terms describing the contributions of both convective acceleration and viscous dissipation to the pressure gradient are included in Equation 8, the relation between the two flow-limiting mechanisms can be illustrated

$$(d/dx)[P + \tfrac{1}{2}\rho(\dot{V}^2/A^2)] = -a\mu\dot{V}/A^2 \qquad (12)$$

Again, multiplying by A^2dx and integrating from the upstream end of the tube ($x = 0$, $P = P_1$, and $A = A_1$) to the downstream end ($x = l$, $P = P_2$, and $A = A_2$) gives the following quadratic equation for $\dot{V}$

$$\rho\ln(A_1/A_2)\dot{V}^2 + a\mu l\dot{V} - \int_{P_2}^{P_1} A^2dP = 0 \qquad (13)$$

Given the upstream conditions and the tube law $A(P)$, the positive root of this equation describes flow as a function of downstream pressure. The objective here, however, is to use Equation 12 to demonstrate the qualitative relation between the two flow-limiting mechanisms.

Two general statements can be made about the solution to Equation 13. First, because the term that is quadratic in $\dot{V}$ is positive, the true solution must be less than the solution obtained by neglecting the quadratic term. Therefore the flow predicted by Equation 13 is less than the flow predicted by Equation 10, and the maximum flow predicted by Equation 13 is less than the maximum allowed by the viscous flow-limiting mechanism. Second, Equation 13 can be differentiated with respect to P_2 to obtain a condition on maximum flow

$$(\rho/A_2)(dA_2/dP_2)\dot{V}^2 + 2\rho\ln(A_1/A_2)\dot{V}_1(d\dot{V}/dP_2)$$
$$+ a\mu l(d\dot{V}/dP_2) - A_2^2 = 0 \qquad (14)$$

At the value of P_2 at which flow is maximum, $d\dot{V}/dP_2$ is zero and maximum flow ($\dot{V}max$) satisfies the equation

$$\dot{V}max^2 = A_2^3/\rho(dA_2/dP_2) \qquad (15)$$

This equation for $\dot{V}max$ is the wave-speed equation; maximum flow is the lowest flow for which the local fluid velocity equals the local wave speed at any point in the tube. In this case the critical point occurs at the downstream end of the tube. Equation 15 is not sufficient to predict flow because A_2 and dA_2/dP_2 depend on P_2. The relation between pressure and flow is needed to determine the pressure and the corresponding area and wave speed at which the fluid velocity equals wave speed at the end of the tube. The wave-speed limit is always reached, and in some situations the wave-speed flow-limiting mechanism dominates. In other situations it is a formal limit that is reached at a pressure at which the viscous mechanism has already effectively established a limiting flow.

These two situations are illustrated in Figure 6. An area-pressure curve (A/Amax vs. P) is shown in Figure 6A. The viscous limit on flow, given by Equation 10, scales with Amax$^2/l$. For tubes of different sizes but similar geometries, l is proportional to Amax$^{1/2}$ and the

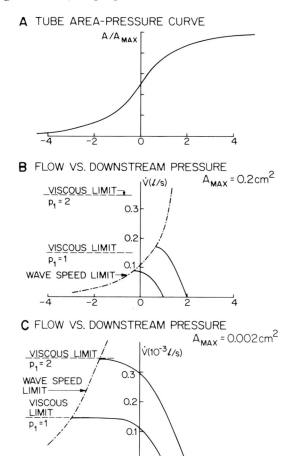

A TUBE AREA-PRESSURE CURVE

B FLOW VS. DOWNSTREAM PRESSURE

C FLOW VS. DOWNSTREAM PRESSURE

FIG. 6. Relation between wave-speed and viscous flow-limiting mechanisms. In geometrically similar tubes with the same specific compliance (A), the flow-pressure behavior in the larger tube (B) is different from the flow-pressure characteristics of the smaller tube (C). In the larger tube, wave-speed mechanism limits flow. In the smaller tube, viscous dissipation is relatively more important; for an upstream pressure of 1 cmH$_2$O, flow is limited by viscous dissipation.

viscous limit is proportional to Amax$^{3/2}$. The wave-speed limit, given by Equation 3, scales with Amax. For large tubes, the maximum flow allowed by the viscous flow-limiting mechanism is larger than that allowed by the wave-speed mechanism and the wave-speed condition effectively limits flow. For small tubes, the converse is true. In Figure 6B, the dashed lines show the viscous flow limits through a tube with Amax = 0.2 cm^2 (representative of a central airway) for the entrance pressures of 1 and 2 cmH$_2$O. The wave-speed limit, calculated from the area and slope of the A(P) curve at each pressure is shown by the interrupted line. Flow versus downstream pressure, calculated from Equation 13, for upstream pressures of 1 and 2 cmH$_2$O, is shown by the solid lines. For this relatively large tube, flow is limited by the fluid velocity reaching wave speed at a flow well below the viscous limit. Similar curves are shown for Amax = 0.002 cm^2, an area representative of a very peripheral airway, in Figure 6C. The viscous limits are smaller by a factor of 10^3, whereas the wave-speed limit is smaller by a factor of 10^2. For an upstream pressure of 2 cmH$_2$O, the viscous limit and the wave-speed condition are reached simultaneously. However, the viscous limit decreases rapidly with decreasing upstream pressure and for an upstream pressure of 1 cmH$_2$O, the wave-speed condition is reached at a downstream pressure that is lower than the pressure at which the viscous mechanism has effectively determined maximum flow.

The driving pressure in the lung at high lung volume is large, and the viscous limit for the peripheral airways is greater than the wave-speed limit for the central airways. Hence wave-speed limitation in the central airways dominates. At low lung volumes the upstream pressure is small, the viscous limit in the peripheral airways is less than the wave-speed limit in the central airways, and flow is limited by the viscous mechanism in the peripheral airways. The scaling with airway size and the gradation in total cross-sectional area and airway compliance between central and peripheral airways all play a role in the peripheral movement of the flow-limiting site and the change from wave-speed limitation to viscous flow limitation with decreasing lung volume. This transition is discussed further in the chapter by Hyatt in this *Handbook*.

COMMENTS ON MODELING

The equations used in this chapter to model the flow and airway properties are idealized representations of the real situation. They were chosen to describe the important physical phenomena, with an eye toward simplicity and transparency of analysis. Dissipative pressure losses associated with secondary flows and turbulence have not been included, nor have subtler effects such as more accurate descriptions of the fluid velocity profiles and analyses of how the velocity profile and the pressure losses depend on the shape of the tube cross section and derivatives of area with axial distance. In describing the tube behavior, it has been assumed that the area-pressure relation at each point in the tube is a local relation. In fact shear stresses within the tube wall, stresses in the surrounding parenchyma, and axial stresses in the tube wall all provide coupling between neighboring points along the airway. A more accurate description of airway mechanics would include the derivatives of area with distance. More accurate mathematical models probably require computer solutions yielding numerical results. Simplified models have been used in this chapter to expose the basic mechanisms of flow limitations. An understanding of these mechanisms should be helpful in constructing more accurate computational models and in interpreting numerical solutions.

REFERENCES

1. DAWSON, S. V., AND E. A. ELLIOT. Wave-speed limitation on expiratory flow—a unifying concept. *J. Appl. Physiol.: Respirat. Environ. Exercise Physiol.* 43: 498–515, 1977.
2. FRY, D. L., AND R. E. HYATT. Pulmonary mechanics: a unified analysis of the relationship between pressure, volume, and gas flow in the lungs of normal and diseased human subjects. *Am. J. Med.* 29: 672–689, 1960.
3. GRIFFITHS, D. J. Hydrodynamics of male micturition. I. Theory of steady flow through elastic-walled tubes. *Med. Biol. Eng.* 9: 581–588, 1971.
4. PRIDE, N. B., S. PERMUTT, R. L. RILEY, AND B. BROMBERGER-BARNEA. Determinants of maximal expiratory flow from the lungs. *J. Appl. Physiol.* 23: 646–662, 1967.
5. SHAPIRO, A. H. Steady flow in collapsible tubes. *J. Biomech. Eng.* 99: 126–147, 1977.

CHAPTER 6

Form and function of the upper airways and larynx

DONALD F. PROCTOR

Departments of Environmental Health Sciences, Otolaryngology and Head and Neck Surgery, and of Anesthesiology, The Johns Hopkins University Schools of Hygiene and Public Health and of Medicine, Baltimore, Maryland

CHAPTER CONTENTS

THE UPPER AIRWAY consists of the passages for airflow between the larynx and the ambient atmosphere (55). Ordinarily it is composed of the nasal passages (from nostrils to posterior termination of nasal septum), the nasopharynx (from end of septum to lower border of soft palate), and the pharynx (from palate to larynx) (12); but in some circumstances the mouth is also included (11). This nomenclature does not fully coincide with that of classic anatomy, but it does have functional significance. The nasal passage is a double airway with a complex shape; the nasopharynx is the region where closure can separate the nasal passage from the pharynx; the pharynx is an airway common to both nasal and oronasal breathing and, along with the larynx and trachea, is a bottleneck (Fig. 1). The larynx is part of the airway and the source of the fundamental sound for voice, but its key role physiologically is as a valve interposed between upper and lower airways.

Upper airway surfaces are the first exposed to the inspiratory tide of ambient air. Their peculiar shape and the nature of airflow over them account for the capacity of the upper respiratory surfaces to modify the condition and contents of ambient air prior to its access to the lungs. That modification consists of adjustment of air temperature toward 37°C, near saturation with water vapor, absorption of some pollutant gases (e.g., SO_2, HCHO, and O_3), and impaction of dusts. But a better understanding of the nasal passages is possible if they are viewed as a defense organ (3, 4, 13, 53). The surface area of the functional (turbinated) portion of the nasal mucosa is ~120 cm², approximately double that of the trachea. The characteristics

of the anterior nares are related to their capacity for dust impaction, whereas the nares of the main passage ensure optimal exchange of temperature and water vapor and absorption of foreign gases (54). The erectile nature of the nasal vasculature and the adjustability of the nasal secretory system are essential to maintain efficient air modification in the face of even extreme and sudden ambient change. Variations in vascular engorgement and the nature and quantity of secretions also influence the size and shape of the airway.

The olfactory sense organ lies in the upper nasal airway. It is housed in a region out of the main line of inspiratory airflow and thus is protected from the vicissitudes of the atmospheric environment. Small eddies of inspired air reach this region along the midpassage, and expiratory airflow passes freely over it. Thus the sense of smell is chiefly activated just after a sniff or at the onset of expiration.

UPPER RESPIRATORY TRACT AS A CONDUCTING AIRWAY

The nature of the upper air passages is illustrated in Figures 1 and 2. In the adult the nasal airway is 10–14 cm long, divided in two by the septum, narrow in width (1–3 mm) but large in cross section, and convoluted by the scroll-like structures of the turbinates. Its entrance consists of the funnel-shaped vestibule at the nostrils leading to the nasal valve, which has a cross section only ~30 mm² on either side. This is a far smaller total cross section than is found elsewhere in the airways. The term *nasal valve* is somewhat misleading. Under physiological circumstances it does not close but merely narrows. The portion of the airway involved in narrowing or widening of the nasal entrance extends from the nostrils through the anterior ends of the inferior turbinates (Figs. 2 and 3). Widening or stabilizing at the nostrils is accomplished through activation of the dilator naris muscles. Despite their action there may be some narrowing during high inspiratory flows, as seen in sniffing. It is possible that negative airway pressure asso-

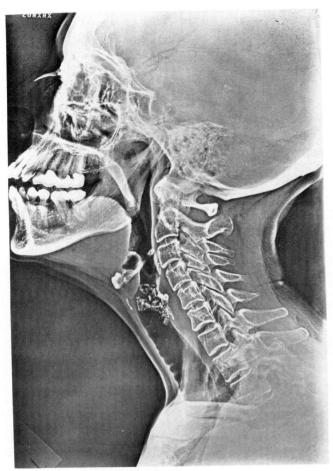

FIG. 1. Xeroradiography illustrating upper airways in contrast to surrounding structures.

but the tongue can be drawn downward and forward to provide a wide oropharyngeal passage (Fig. 5). The length of the upper airway from nostrils or lips to glottis approximates the length from glottis to alveoli.

The paranasal sinuses, eustachian tubes, and air spaces of the temporal bones are ancillary air spaces. The sinus air is normally in continual communication with the air of the nose. The eustachian tubes open only intermittently to permit equilibration of pressure in the middle ears with that in the nasopharynx. Pressure in the sinuses fluctuates in relation to the pressure changes within the nasal passages, unless the orifices are closed owing to pathological conditions.

At a flow rate of 0.4 liter/s the pressure drop from ambient air to pharynx varies between 0.3 and 1.3 cmH_2O [Fig. 6; (26)]. Nasal airflow is somewhat turbulent even in quiet breathing, more turbulent at high ventilatory rates (15, 18, 29, 32, 34, 49, 71), and limited in inspiration because of the collapsibility of the nasal valve (14). Inspiratory flow limitation occurs in the nose at ~1–2.5 liters/s with a pressure drop of ~10–12 cmH_2O [Fig. 6; (14)]. But both the pressure-flow relationship and the inspiratory flow limitation are not only highly variable among individuals but also influenced by a number of factors that affect the nasal passage. These influences include the action of the nasal muscles (42, 67), body posture [state of nasal vasculature is affected by grav-

ciated with high inspiratory flows results in filling of vascular spaces in the anterior ends of the inferior turbinates, thus contributing to airway narrowing.

In the erect posture this entrance points upward. Just beyond the nasal valve the airway direction becomes horizontal (Fig. 3) and the cross section widens to ~260 mm² (sum of the two sides), narrowing slightly again at the nasopharynx to ~200 mm². The cross section of the main passage is susceptible to change according to the state of engorgement of the erectile submucosal vasculature. Ordinarily the nasal airflow resistance accounts for about half of the total work of breathing (16).

At the nasopharynx the airway takes a 90° curve downward toward the larynx. The shape of the pharyngeal space is a flattened cylinder but is susceptible to change through action of the muscles controlling the position of the palate and tongue. During swallowing, the soft palate rises and moves backward, thus closing access between the pharynx and nose (velopharyngeal closure) (Fig. 4). When the lips are parted the mouth becomes part of the airway (11). That part is ordinarily a narrow slit between tongue and palate,

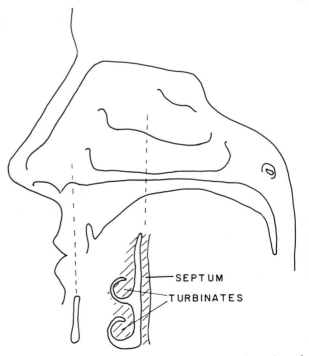

FIG. 2. Diagram of nasal airway showing sections through passage for 1 side of nasal valve (*left*) and midpassage (*right*). Nasal valve extends from nostrils through region indicated by *dashed line* at *left* and to anterior end of inferior turbinate. [From Proctor and Andersen (55).]

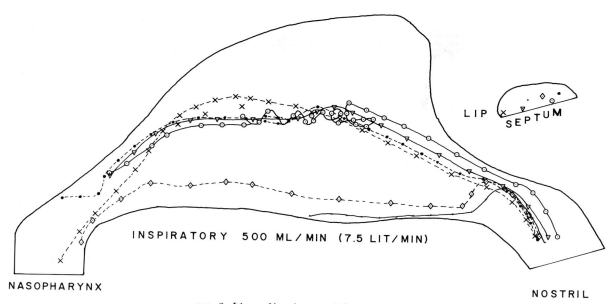

FIG. 3. Lines of inspiratory airflow determined from model studies. Most lines are between septum and meatus nasi medius. Nasal valve extends through region where bends in lines of flow begin.

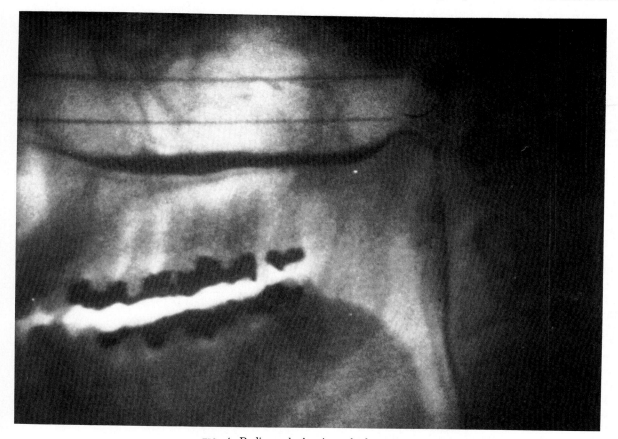

FIG. 4. Radiograph showing velopharyngeal closure (*heavy black line, upper right*) and apposition of palate to the posterior nasopharyngeal wall.

ity (57, 62)], the amount and character of the secretions (53, 55), physical exercise (20, 51, 61, 63, 64), the partial pressure of carbon dioxide (P_{CO_2}) in respired air (9, 43, 69), the temperature of ambient air (70), and the presence of certain air pollutants in ambient air (2). Appropriate studies of nasal flow limitation during exercise have not been done. Studies by K. P. Strohl (unpublished observations) show

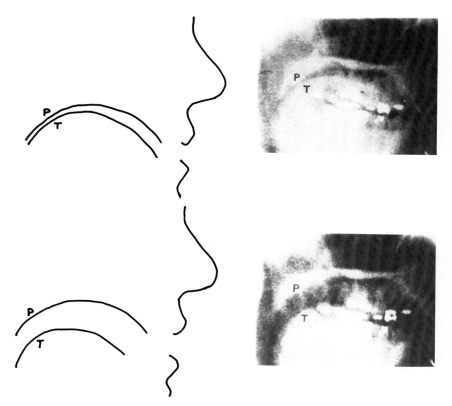

FIG. 5. Frames from cinefluorograph (*right*) and tracings (*left*) showing variable positions of palate (*P*) and tongue (*T*). *Upper pair*, position found in most instances of oronasal breathing. [From Proctor (54).]

clearly that activation of the nasal muscles decreases nasal airflow resistance and thus can increase the level of inspiratory airflow possible during exercise.

In most normal subjects during exercise, nasal airflow resistance is reduced and peak ventilation possible through the nose is increased. Nasal airflow resistance is reduced by increased P_{CO_2} in inspired air and increased by cold air (7°C–10°C) (70). At a level of 5 ppm, SO_2 increases resistance (2), whereas inert dust has no influence, even at a level of 25 mg/m³ (5); little is known of the effects of other pollutants in this regard.

The linear velocity in the airstream is an important consideration in inspired-air modification. The probability of particle impaction at bends in the airstream is directly related to high linear velocity. Conversely the slowing of the stream in the main nasal passage facilitates inspired-air modification. In quiet breathing the velocity through the nasal valve is 12–18 m/s, which is 6–12 times faster than in the trachea at the same flow. Linear velocity in the main nasal passage is slightly less than in the trachea. At the nasopharynx, linear velocity rises again and then, in the variable airway of the pharynx, ordinarily falls.

Because the nose is an important part of the airway in the removal of noxious materials from inspired air, the continual clearance of its surfaces is essential to local defense. The nasal mucociliary apparatus clears surface secretions forward from the anterior ends of

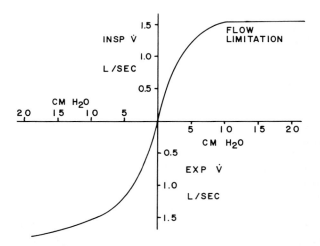

FIG. 6. Inspiratory (*upper right*) and expiratory (*lower left*) pressure-flow relationships in the nose on maximum effort. Ordinate, flow; abscissa, pressure. [From Proctor (54a).]

the turbinates and the meatus nasi medius (principal site of dust impaction). Elsewhere the mucus moves backward to the nasopharynx where the ciliated epithelium undergoes transition to squamous epithelium. Mucus is dispatched from the nasopharynx to the stomach with each swallow. The average flow rate of nasal mucus is ~6 mm/min, but even in healthy young adults it ranges from <1 to >20 mm/min (2–5, 13, 53, 55, 64).

ORONASAL BREATHING

In many mammals the epiglottis lies behind the palate, thus ensuring nasal breathing and preservation of the olfactory defense during fighting and feeding. During panting this interdigitation of the palate and epiglottis is broken. In the human infant, nasal breathing is obligatory except during crying. It is unclear why this is so. In the young infant the epiglottis approaches the palate more closely than in the adult but not sufficiently to preclude the passage of air through the oropharyngeal airway. This may be an instinctive hangover from our phylogenetic origins. In any event, nasal occlusion in the newborn may be fatal (30, 68). At ~5–6 mo the infant may begin to resort to mouth breathing during nasal obstruction (40, 52).

When the mouth is open, air usually passes through both the nose and mouth, but in one circumstance this is not the case. It is not necessary to occlude the nose when blowing up a balloon or playing a wind instrument because the palate rises and moves backward against the pharynx, closing access to the nasal space above.

Two other considerations are important in this connection, especially in studies of respiratory adjustment of inspired-air temperature or humidity or of the fate of inhaled gaseous or particulate pollutants. First, whereas the proportion of air passing through the mouth increases when nasal airflow resistance is high, some portion of the air still passes nasally. Second, whereas it is possible to create a very wide oropharyngeal airway (e.g., in yawning or achieving high flow rates), ordinarily in oronasal breathing (e.g., in exercise) the oropharyngeal airway is a narrow slit between lips, palate, and tongue (Fig. 5).

During nasal breathing a number of characteristics of breathing mechanics differ from those found in conventional pulmonary function testing in which the subject not only wears a clip to occlude the nose but also breathes through a mouthpiece between the lips. Although it might be thought that this situation simulates oronasal breathing, as in heavy exercise or partial nasal obstruction, this is not so. Breathing through a mouthpiece with the nose occluded does not simulate oronasal breathing necessary at high ventilatory volumes or when nasal airflow resistance is increased. Nasal occlusion (with Vaseline nasal packing) has been shown to increase tracheobronchial airflow resistance (75). The effect of occlusion with a simple nose clip on pulmonary mechanics has not been tested.

In one study of 30 healthy young adults (46–48), 4 were oronasal breathers at rest, whereas 5 continued nasal breathing even during fairly heavy exercise. Most of the subjects were nasal breathers at rest and began oronasal breathing at a ventilation volume of 35.3 ± 10.8 liters/min. At the start of oronasal breathing, 56% of the minute volume continued nasally, and

even at a minute volume of 90 liters/min, 39% of the volume remained nasal (17, 19). Thus a significant portion of inspired air passes through the nose even under conditions requiring marked elevation in pulmonary ventilation (47, 48).

Oronasal breathing is best understood if the mouth and nose are viewed as a pair of parallel resistors. With the lips parted the volume of air moved through nose or mouth is related to the pressure drop and relative resistance of the two passages. The nasal airway in any individual has relatively constant resistance characteristics. The oropharyngeal is the most variable portion of the whole airway. With the mouth widely opened, airflow resistance through the oropharyngeal airway is quite low (Fig. 7). Ordinarily the shape and size of the oral airway offer an airflow resistance approximately equal to that of the nasal passage. Thus parting the lips approximately doubles the volume of pulmonary ventilation at the same pressure drop. The switch from nasal to oronasal breathing generally occurs when pulmonary ventilation exceeds ~30–35 liters/min at a pressure drop of ~10–12 cmH$_2$O.

NASAL CYCLE

In many human subjects and experimental animals the airflow resistance regularly shifts from one side of

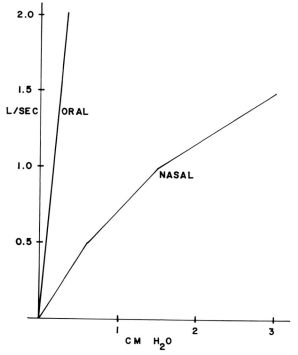

FIG. 7. Airflow resistance through the wide oral airway (oral) and nose (nasal). Ordinate, flow; abscissa, pressure. [From Proctor (54b).]

the nose to the other. As the resistance on one side increases, the resistance on the other side decreases proportionately. After a cycle of ~3–4 h this inequality reverses [Fig. 8; (21–23, 39)]. Such a cycle may allow one side of the nasal passages to recover from injury suffered as a result of ambient air effects while the other side assumes the job of air modification. There is evidence that the cycle is influenced by breathing

ambient air. Keuning (39) points out that the cycle could not be found in patients who had undergone laryngectomy.

EFFECTS OF NASAL BREATHING ON BREATHING MECHANICS

How do these characteristics of nasal airflow affect breathing? Conventional testing of pulmonary function is done with the subject breathing through a mouthpiece while the nose is occluded by a noseclip. It seems reasonable to ask how these measurements might be influenced if the subject were breathing naturally through the nose or the oronasal airway. Differences would be attributable to the added resistance of the nasal airway, but the arrival of relatively unmodified air in the trachea and even possible reflex effects of nasal occlusion (75) might also affect tracheobronchial mechanics (Fig. 9). Certainly peak flow rates will be reduced, especially in inspiration. The shape of the flow-volume curve, as well as that of the forced vital capacity spirogram and the pneumotachogram (53), will be altered. The overall work of breathing will be approximately doubled (16). Pressure drops related to flow will remain unaltered along the tracheobronchial airways, but pressure differences between the atmosphere and the pleural space and between the mediastinum and the intravascular spaces will be increased more in rapid breathing than in quiet. Transmural pressure across the extrathoracic trachea will be greater with nasal breathing.

Body posture affects nasal and oral breathing in different ways. In both types of breathing, lung volumes shift because of the effects of the weight of abdominal contents on the position of the diaphragm. But, in nasal breathing alone, airflow resistance increases in the recumbent or head down position (57, 62).

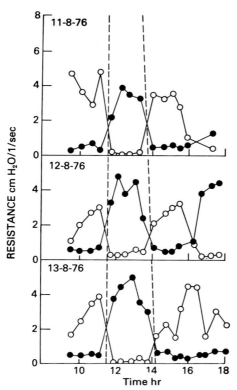

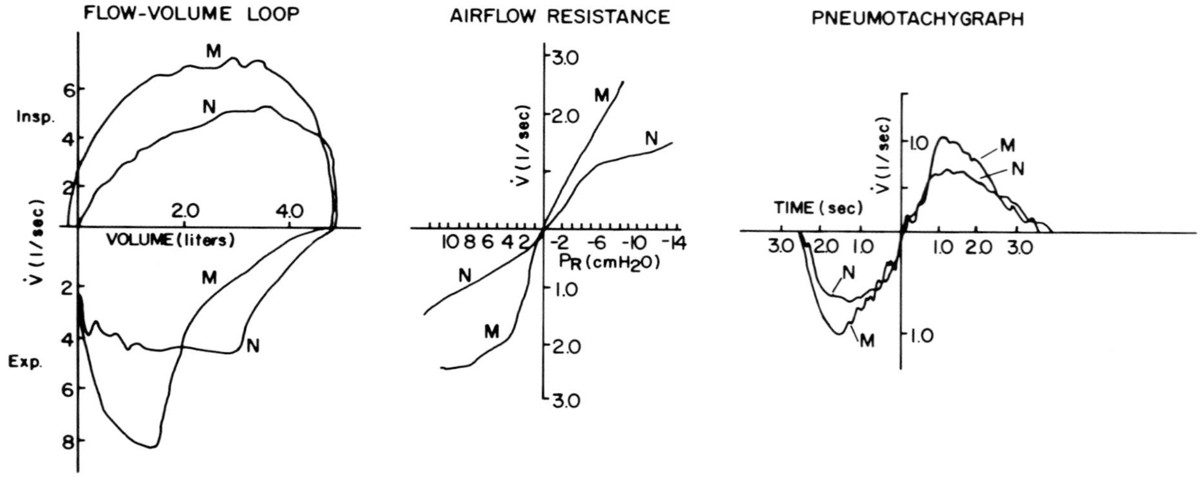

FIG. 8. Changes in nasal airflow resistance from side to side in the nasal cycle. [From Eccles (22).]

FIG. 9. Flow-volume curves, pressure-flow charts, and pneumotachograms from normal subject breathing through nose (N) and mouthpiece (M) with nose clipped. (Data from M. Sheridan, unpublished observations.)

In interpreting tests of pulmonary functions one should be aware that nasal or oronasal breathing is normal and mouthpiece and noseclip breathing is abnormal. Some thought should be paid to these facts.

LARYNX

The larynx developed phylogenetically as a valve interposed between the upper and lower airways, which closes during swallowing to prevent soiling of the lungs. It also closes to permit elevation of intra-abdominal pressure for the evacuation of abdominal contents and the increase of intrathoracic pressure prior to coughing. Its adaptation for sound production and speech development in humans is a later evolutionary development. (Breathing for phonation is discussed in my other chapter in this *Handbook*.) When the larynx acts as a valve, closure occurs through approximation of a series of folds: the aryepiglottic, the vestibular (false cords), and the vocal (true cords) (27, 28). For phonation the vocal folds alone come together and only with force sufficient to allow subglottic pressure appropriate to the desired sound intensity (54).

Tight laryngeal and velopharyngeal closure are of course essential during swallowing to prevent soiling of the lower airways and nasopharynx. Deglutition is a complex process and not in the scope of this chapter. Briefly stated, reflexes producing gagging on stimulation of the base of the tongue and pharynx are inhibited, access to the nasopharynx and intrinsic larynx is tightly closed, the larynx rises in the neck and tilts backward, the epiglottis acts as a shelf to shunt the bolus being swallowed into the pyriform sinuses, and the cricopharyngeal portion of the inferior constrictors relaxes. Table 1 lists some of the muscles involved in these processes.

Several intrinsic muscle pairs are involved in closing the glottis, whereas only one pair opens it (Figs. 10 and 11). All these muscles are innervated by the recurrent laryngeal nerve except for the cricothyroids, which are innervated by the superior laryngeal nerve. The superior laryngeal nerve carries most of the sensory fibers for this region, and there is evidence that some fibers also pass to the interarytenoid muscles. Some sensory fibers also pass along the recurrent laryngeal nerves. The intrinsic laryngeal muscles act on the cartilages and ligaments of the larynx. The cricoid cartilage is the only strongly supported complete ring in the laryngotracheal airway. Its integrity is vital to the airway, which may collapse if this cartilage is injured. It might be thought that the tracheal cartilages, through their attachments to the posterior membranous wall, would suffice to maintain a patent airway, but any clinician who has dealt with patients with cricoid trauma knows that injury is often followed by upper tracheal stenosis.

For glottic closure the interarytenoid muscles draw

TABLE 1. *Accessory Muscles in Breathing Mechanics*

Muscle	Nerve Connection
Dilator naris*	CN 7
Levator veli palatini†	CN 9 and 10
Palatopharyngeal	CN 10
Salpingopharyngeal	CN 10
Pharyngeal constrictors	CN 10
Masseter	CN 5
Pterygoideus	CN 5
Intrinsic tongue muscles	CN 12
Genioglossal	CN 10
Hyoglossal	CN 12
Styloglossal	CN 12
Anterior digastric	CN 5
Posterior digastric	CN 7
Mylohyoid	CN 5
Geniohyoid	Cerv 1 and 2
Stylohyoid	CN 7
Omohyoid	Cerv 2 and 3
Thyrohyoid	Cerv 2 and 3
Sternohyoid	Cerv 2 and 3
Sternothyroid	Cerv 2 and 3
Aryepiglottic	CN 10 (Rec)
Interarytenoid	CN 10 (Rec)
Lateral cricoarytenoid	CN 10 (Rec)
Posterior cricoarytenoid	CN 10 (Rec)
Thyroarytenoid	CN 10 (Rec)
Cricothyroid	CN 10 (Sup)

All these muscles, except for dilator naris muscle, are involved in swallowing. Innervation is indicated after each muscle: CN, cranial nerve; Cerv, cervical nerve; Rec, recurrent laryngeal nerve; Sup, superior laryngeal nerve. *Undergoes rhythmic change in tone with breathing cycle. †Active in forced inspiration and expiration.

the posterior aspects of the arytenoid cartilages together, whereas the lateral cricoarytenoid and the thyroarytenoid muscles keep the vocal processes of the arytenoid cartilages and the vocal folds themselves in the midline. The cricothyroid muscles draw the thyroid cartilage forward and approximate it to the anterior part of the cricoid, thus lengthening the vocal folds. The folds can be lengthened by ~15% of their resting length through this action, e.g., as occurs in a singer reaching the highest tones of the voice. Glottic opening is achieved through the action of the posterior cricoarytenoid muscles alone, which draw the arytenoids apart (Fig. 11).

During quiet breathing the glottic space is roughly triangular and the vocal folds are parted at the posterior commissure and approximated at their anterior ends. Exact laryngeal dimensions are difficult to measure in the living human. Studies demonstrate that the anterior-posterior distance in the glottic aperture is ~2.5 cm (2.2–3.0) in the male and ~2 cm (1.6–2.1) in the female (8, 35). At the posterior commissure the width is ~5–18 mm. Thus the cross section of the glottic space varies between 40 and 270 mm^2, smaller than the airway above and below in the adult and smaller in the female than in the male. Higenbottam [(35); unpublished observations] has found in the cadaver a correlation between both the anterior-posterior length and the posterior width of the glottis and

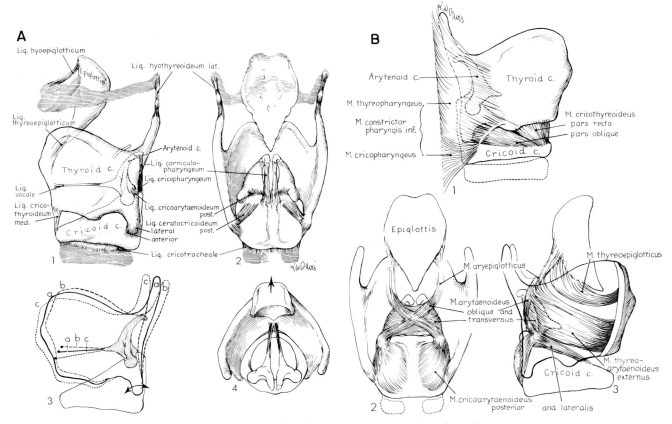

FIG. 10. *A*: laryngeal cartilages and ligaments; *3*, vocal cords lengthen when cricothyroid muscles approximate the anterior ends of thyroid and cricoid cartilages. *B*: intrinsic laryngeal musculature. [From Proctor (52a).]

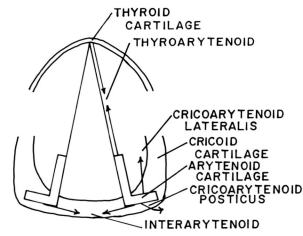

FIG. 11. Action of various intrinsic muscles on arytenoid cartilages to open and close the glottis.

body height. The vocal folds part somewhat in inspiration [especially in panting (36)] and close somewhat in expiration. The intrinsic laryngeal musculature that produces these changes is activated just prior to the onset of each respiratory phase (33). Although the posterior cricoarytenoid is activated in inspiration and the adductor muscle group is activated in expiration, the thyroarytenoid muscles remain inactive during breathing (45). Changes in glottic area are also affected by other influences including hypercapnia, hypoxia, and bronchoconstriction (9, 10, 35, 58).

In the infant the narrowest cross section in this portion of the airway is through the cricoid ring immediately below the glottis (24, 25, 44). In the adult the space through the cricoid ring is only slightly smaller than that through the trachea below but is a fixed dimension, unlike the trachea with its membranous wall (53).

The larynx accounts for only a small part of the total resistance to respiratory airflow (65, 66). Despite the shelflike projection of the vocal cords into the airway, air converges and diverges in its glottic passage in relatively clean streamlines. Small turbulent eddies develop several centimeters down the trachea; these eddies occur higher up with rapid breathing.

PATENCY AND OBSTRUCTION OF THE AIRWAYS

Stimuli in the larynx or the nose have reflex effects on bronchomotor tone (1, 7, 50, 72). Some studies have indicated that nasal stimuli result in bronchodilation and laryngeal stimuli cause bronchoconstriction, but apparently some nasal stimuli may produce bronchoconstriction also. Kaufman et al. (37, 38) have found increased bronchial airflow resistance after blowing silica dust into the nose and out of the mouth. After section of the trigeminal nerve (for tic douloureux), no bronchoconstriction occurred after exposure to dust on the denervated side.

Strohl et al. (67) have shown that in humans the muscles that dilate the nostrils are activated prior to the onset of each inspiration. This was "more apparent during sleep and during CO_2-induced hyperpnea" (67). Such an action only partly reduces the inspiratory resistance of the nasal valve, which extends somewhat further back than the region controlled by the alae nasi (14). This study (67) and others demonstrate that centrally controlled mechanisms affect the patency of the airway and are somehow timed to relate to the other factors determining the rhythm of the breathing cycle. Other investigators have shown that in exercise nasal airflow resistance is reduced (20), and this seems to be related to oxygen demands of the body (40). During both hypercapnia and hypoxia, nasal airflow resistance is also reduced and laryngeal airflow resistance is affected (9, 10, 35, 43, 58, 70). The nasal cycle ensures that as resistance on one side of the nose increases, resistance on the other side decreases proportionately (21, 33).

The mechanisms involved in the decrease or increase of nasal airflow resistance have not been clearly determined. Strohl et al. (67) conclusively show that activation of the nasal muscles can reduce it by ~20%. To what extent nasal vasoconstriction or dilation contributes to these changes is not known. Certainly the effect of body posture is attributable to vascular change, and probably the effects of cold air and irritant gases such as SO_2 are also largely influenced by vascular change. Dilation of the nostrils is characteristic of dyspneic breathing, and the effects of hypoxia and hypercapnia are probably a result of nasal muscle activity, but associated changes in nasal vasculature may also contribute.

During breathing the position of the larynx is stabilized in the neck by rhythmic action of the extralaryngeal muscles (72). The glottic aperture varies with the phases of respiration and some investigators have suggested that this is an important control of expiratory airflow (8–10, 59). In infants there is an indication that upper and lower airway resistance may vary reciprocally (40, 52). During sleep the muscles that maintain a patent pharyngeal airway normally continue to be active, and failure of this mechanism may be an important factor in so-called sleep apnea (70).

Finally, it is important to reiterate that the pharynx, larynx, and trachea compose a bottleneck in the airway. Obstruction there can be fatal. In the infant the nose must be included in this category. Nasal mucosal swelling, inspissated secretions, grossly enlarged adenoids, and choanal atresia (in view of obligatory nasal breathing in infants) all may lead to cor pulmonale or death. Similarly, serious cardiovascular problems can develop in the adult with so-called sleep apnea (8, 41, 60, 70). The exact nature of the obstruction is unclear. Recent investigations indicate the locus is in the pharynx. An increase in airflow resistance of the upper airway may set off a vicious cycle involving highly negative pressure in the pharynx with each inspiratory effort. If this is not counteracted by increased tone in the genioglossal and geniohyoid muscles, the tongue and epiglottis may fall backward, occluding the airway (see Table 1). Failure of rhythmic tethering of the laryngeal position in the neck might result in its descent with inspiratory effort and closure of its folds.

Injury to the recurrent laryngeal nerve results in vocal cord paralysis. Because of the unopposed action of the cricothyroid muscles, in that condition the cord moves toward the midline, its position of shortest length. When this action is bilateral it reduces the glottic aperture to ~25–50 mm^2. Hoarseness may be almost undetectable owing to the midline position of the cords, and this condition may well be overlooked unless the larynx is appropriately examined.

Certainly, sufficient obstruction anywhere along this path can be fatal. Obstruction in this bottleneck of the airway can result from many factors, including unconsciousness, neurological disease, foreign bodies, benign and malignant tumors, acute inflammation (especially epiglottitis), and trauma.

Significant obstruction can be readily recognized and its degree roughly measured by observation of retraction in the soft parts of the thoracic cage with each inspiratory effort. With sufficiently severe obstruction, it is necessary to promptly provide an artificial airway by tracheal intubation or tracheotomy. The conscious subject will work to maintain normal alveolar ventilation until totally exhausted. Cardiac arrest can then occur suddenly, with only a very brief period when cyanosis or other evidence of insufficient alveolar ventilation has been apparent.

REFERENCES

1. ALLISON, D. J., T. P. CLAY, J. M. B. HUGHES, H. A. JONES, AND A. SHERIS. Effects of nasal stimulation on total respiratory resistance in the rabbit (Abstract). *J. Physiol. London* 239: 23P–24P, 1974.
2. ANDERSEN, I., G. R. LUNDQVIST, P. L. JENSEN, AND D. F. PROCTOR. Human response to controlled levels of sulfur dioxide. *Arch. Environ. Health* 28: 31–39, 1974.
3. ANDERSEN, I., G. R. LUNDQVIST, P. L. JENSEN, AND D. F. PROCTOR. Human response to 78 hours exposure to dry air. *Arch. Environ. Health* 29: 319–324, 1974.
4. ANDERSEN, I., G. R. LUNDQVIST, AND D. F. PROCTOR. Human mucosal function in a controlled climate. *Arch. Environ. Health* 23: 408–420, 1971.
5. ANDERSEN, I., G. R. LUNDQVIST, D. F. PROCTOR, AND D. L.

SWIFT. Human response to controlled levels of inert dust. *Am. Rev. Respir. Dis.* 119: 619–628, 1979.

6. ANDREW, B. L. The respiratory displacement of the larynx: a study of the innervation of accessory respiratory muscles. *J. Physiol. London* 130: 474–487, 1955.

7. ANGELL-JAMES, J. E., AND M. B. DALY. Some aspects of upper respiratory tract reflexes. *Acta Oto-Laryngol.* 79: 242–252, 1975.

8. BAIER, H., A. WANNER, S. ZARZECKI, AND M. A. SACKNER. Relationships among glottis opening, respiratory flow, and upper airway resistance in humans. *J. Appl. Physiol.: Respirat. Environ. Exercise Physiol.* 43: 603–611, 1977.

9. BARTLETT, D., JR. Effects of hypercapnia and hypoxia on laryngeal resistance to airflow. *Respir. Physiol.* 37: 293–302, 1979.

10. BARTLETT, D., JR., J. E. REMMERS, AND H. GAUTIER. Laryngeal regulation of respiratory airflow. *Respir. Physiol.* 18: 194–204, 1973.

11. BOSMA, J. F. Physiology of the mouth. In: *Otolaryngology: Basic Sciences and Related Disciplines*, edited by M. A. Paparella and D. A. Shumrick. Philadelphia, PA: Saunders, 1980, vol. 1, p. 319–331.

12. BOSMA, J. F., AND M. W. DONNER. Physiology of the pharynx. In: *Otolaryngology: Basic Sciences and Related Disciplines*, edited by M. A. Paparella and D. A. Shumrick. Philadelphia, PA: Saunders, 1980, vol. 1, p. 332–345.

13. BRAIN, J. D., D. F. PROCTOR, AND L. M. REID (editors). *Lung Biology in Health and Disease. Respiratory Defense Mechanisms.* New York: Dekker, 1977, vol. 5, pt. I.

14. BRIDGER, G. P., AND D. F. PROCTOR. Maximum nasal inspiratory flow and nasal resistance. *Ann. Otol. Rhinol. Laryngol.* 79: 481–489, 1970.

15. BRODY, A. W., R. R. STOUGHTON, T. L. CONNOLLY, J. J. SHEHAN, J. J. NAVIN, AND E. E. KOBALD. Experimental value of the Reynolds critical flow in the human airway. *J. Lab. Clin. Med.* 67: 43–57, 1966.

16. BUTLER, J. The work of breathing through the nose. *Clin. Sci.* 19: 55–62, 1960.

17. CAMNER, P., AND B. BAKKE. Nose or mouth breathing. *Environ. Res.* 21: 394–398, 1980.

18. COCKCROFT, D. W., D. W. MacCORMACK, S. M. TARIO, F. E. HARGREAVE, AND L. D. PENGALLY. Nasal airway inspiratory resistance. *Am. Rev. Respir. Dis.* 119: 921–926, 1979.

19. COLE, P., S. MINTZ, V. NIINIMAA, AND F. SILVERMAN. Nasal aerodynamics. *J. Otolaryngol.* 8: 191–195, 1979.

20. DALLIMORE, N. S., AND R. ECCLES. Changes in human nasal resistance associated with exercise, hyperventilation and rebreathing. *Acta Oto-Laryngol.* 84: 416–421, 1977.

21. ECCLES, R. Proceedings: cyclic changes in human nasal resistance to air flow (Abstract). *J. Physiol. London* 272: 75P–76P, 1977.

22. ECCLES, R. The central rhythm of the nasal cycle. *Acta Oto-Laryngol.* 86: 464–468, 1978.

23. ECCLES, R., AND R. L. MAYNARD. Proceedings: studies on the nasal cycle in the immobilized pig (Abstract). *J. Physiol. London* 247: 1P, 1975.

24. ECKENHOFF, J. E. Some anatomic considerations of the infant larynx influencing endotracheal anesthesia. *Anesthesiology* 12: 401–410, 1951.

25. ENGEL, S. *Lung Structure.* Springfield, IL: Thomas, 1962.

26. FERRIS, B. G., JR., J. MEAD, AND L. H. OPIE. Partitioning of respiratory flow resistance in man. *J. Appl. Physiol.* 19: 653–658, 1964.

27. FINK, B. R. *The Human Larynx: A Functional Study.* New York: Raven, 1975.

28. FINK, B. R., AND R. J. DEMAREST. Respiratory folding. In: *Laryngeal Biomechanics.* Cambridge, MA: Harvard Univ. Press, 1978.

29. FISCHER, R. Das Strömungsprofil der Respirationsluft in der Nase bei physiologischer Atmung. *Arch. Klin. Exp. Ohren Nasen Kehlkopfheilkd.* 188: 404–408, 1967.

30. FRANTZ, I. D., III, S. M. ADLER, I. F. ABROMS, AND B. T. THACH. Respiratory response to airway occlusion in infants: sleep state and maturation. *J. Appl. Physiol.* 41: 634–638, 1976.

31. GAUTIER, H., J. E. REMMERS, AND D. BARTLETT, JR. Control of the duration of expiration. *Respir. Physiol.* 18: 205–221, 1973.

32. GRAAMANS, K. *Neus en lachtweg. Plethysmografischi meting van luchtwegweerstanden bij klachten over neusobstructie.* Rotterdam, The Netherlands: Wyt & Zoner, 1980.

33. GREEN, J. H., AND E. NEIL. The respiratory function of the laryngeal muscles. *J. Physiol. London* 129: 134–141, 1955.

34. HAMILTON, L. H. Nasal airway resistance: its measurement and regulation. *Physiologist* 22(3): 43–49, 1979.

35. HIGENBOTTAM, T. Narrowing of glottis opening in humans associated with experimentally induced bronchoconstriction. *J. Appl. Physiol.: Respirat. Environ. Exercise Physiol.* 49: 403–407, 1980.

36. JACKSON, A. C., P. J. GULESIAN, JR., AND J. MEAD. Glottal aperture during panting with voluntary limitation of tidal volume. *J. Appl. Physiol.* 39: 834–836, 1975.

37. KAUFMAN, J., J. C. CHEN, AND G. W. WRIGHT. The effect of trigeminal resection on reflex bronchoconstriction after nasal and nasopharyngeal irritation in man. *Am. Rev. Respir. Dis.* 101: 768–769, 1970.

38. KAUFMAN, J., AND G. W. WRIGHT. The effect of nasal and nasopharyngeal irritation on airway resistance in man. *Am. Rev. Respir. Dis.* 100: 626–630, 1969.

39. KEUNING, J. On the nasal cycle. *Rhinology Rhin.* 6: 99–136, 1968.

40. LACOURT, G., AND G. POLGAR. Interaction between nasal and pulmonary resistance in newborn infants. *J. Appl. Physiol.* 30: 870–873, 1971.

41. LUGARESI, E., G. COCCAGNA, AND F. CIVIGNOTTA. Polygraphic and cineradiographic aspects of obstructive apneas occurring during sleep: physiological implications. In: *Central Nervous Control Mechanisms in Breathing*, edited by C. von Euler and H. Lagercrantz. Oxford, UK: Pergamon, 1979, vol. 32, p. 495–501. (Wenner-Gren Ctr. Int. Symp. Ser.)

42. MANN, D. G., C. T. SASAKI, M. SUZUKI, H. FUKUDA, AND J. R. HERNANDEZ. Dilator naris muscle. *Ann. Otol. Rhinol. Laryngol.* 86: 362–372, 1977.

43. McCAFFREY, T. V., AND E. B. KERN. Response of nasal airway resistance to hypercapnia and hypoxia in man. *Ann. Otol. Rhinol. Laryngol.* 88: 247–252, 1979.

44. MOSTAFA, S. M. Variation in subglottic size in children. *Proc. R. Soc. Med.* 69: 793–795, 1976.

45. NAKAMURA, F., Y. OYEDA, AND Y. SONODA. Electromyographic study of respiratory movements of the intrinsic laryngeal muscles. *Laryngoscope* 68: 109–119, 1958.

46. NIINIMAA, V., P. COLE, S. MINTZ, AND R. J. SHEPHARD. A head-out exercise body plethysmograph. *J. Appl. Physiol.: Respirat. Environ. Exercise Physiol.* 47: 1336–1339, 1979.

47. NIINIMAA, V., P. COLE, S. MINTZ, AND R. J. SHEPHARD. The switching point from nasal to oronasal breathing. *Respir. Physiol.* 42: 61–71, 1980.

48. NIINAMAA, V., P. COLE, S. MINTZ, AND R. J. SHEPHARD. Oronasal distribution of respiratory airflow. *Respir. Physiol.* 43: 69–75, 1981.

49. NOLTE, D., AND I. LUDER-LÜHR. Comparing measurements of nasal resistance by body plethysmograph and by rhinomanometer. *Respiration* 30: 31–38, 1973.

50. OGURA, J. H. Physiologic relationships of the upper and lower airways. *Ann. Otol. Rhinol. Laryngol.* 79: 495–498, 1970.

51. PATRICK, G. A., AND G. R. SHARP. Oronasal distribution of inspiratory flow during various activities (Abstract). *J. Physiol. London* 206: 22P–23P, 1970.

52. POLGAR, G., AND T. R. WENG. The functional development of the respiratory system. *Am. Rev. Respir. Dis.* 120: 625–695, 1979.

52a. PROCTOR, D. F. Physiology of the upper airway. In: *Handbook of Physiology. Respiration*, edited by W. O. Fenn and H. Rahn. Washington, DC: Am. Physiol. Soc., 1964, sect. 3, vol. I, chapt. 8, p. 309–345.

53. PROCTOR, D. F. The upper airways. I. Nasal physiology and the defense of the lungs. *Am. Rev. Respir. Dis.* 115: 97–130, 1977.

54. PROCTOR, D. F. The upper airways. II. The larynx and trachea. *Am. Rev. Respir. Dis.* 115: 315–342, 1977.
54a. PROCTOR, D. F. The upper respiratory tract. In: *Pulmonary Diseases and Disorders*, edited by A. P. Fishman. New York: McGraw-Hill, 1979, p. 3–17.
54b. PROCTOR, D. F. *Breathing, Speech, and Song.* New York: Springer-Verlag, 1980.
55. PROCTOR, D. F., AND I. ANDERSEN (editors). *The Nose, Upper Airway Physiology and the Atmospheric Environment.* Amsterdam: Elsevier/North-Holland, 1982.
56. PROCTOR, D. F., AND J. B. HARDY. Studies of respiratory air flow. I. Significance of the normal pneumotachogram. *Bull. Johns Hopkins Hosp.* 85: 253–280, 1949.
57. RAO, S., AND A. POTDAR. Nasal airflow with body in various positions. *J. Appl. Physiol.* 28: 162–165, 1970.
58. RATTENBURG, C. Laryngeal regulation of respiration. *Acta Anaesthesiol. Scand.* 5: 129–140, 1961.
59. REMMERS, J. E., AND D. BARTLETT, JR. Reflex control of expiratory airflow and duration. *J. Appl. Physiol.: Respirat. Environ. Exercise Physiol.* 42: 80–87, 1977.
60. REMMERS, J. E., W. J. deGROOT, E. K. SAUERLAND, AND A. M. ANCH. Pathogenesis of upper airway occlusion during sleep. *J. Appl. Physiol.: Respirat. Environ. Exercise Physiol.* 44: 931–938, 1978.
61. RICHERSON, H. B., AND P. M. SEEBOHM. Nasal airway response to exercise. *J. Allergy* 41: 269–284, 1968.
62. RUNDCRANTZ, H. Postural variations of nasal patency. *Acta Oto-Laryngol.* 68: 435–443, 1969.
63. SAIBENE, F., P. MOGNONI, C. L. LAFORTUNA, AND R. HOSTARD. Oronasal breathing during exercise. *Pfluegers Arch.* 378: 64–69, 1978.
64. SAKETKHOO, K., I. KAPLAN, AND M. A. SACKNER. Effect of exercise on nasal mucous velocity and nasal airflow resistance in normal subjects. *J. Appl. Physiol.: Respirat. Environ. Exercise Physiol.* 46: 369–371, 1979.
65. SCHIRATZKI, H. The oral and laryngeal components of the upper airway resistance during mouth breathing. *Acta Oto-Laryngol.* 60: 71–82, 1965.
66. SPANN, R. W., AND R. E. HYATT. Factors affecting upper airway resistance in conscious man. *J. Appl. Physiol.* 31: 708–712, 1971.
67. STROHL, K. P., M. J. HENSLEY, M. HALLETT, N. A. SAUNDERS, AND R. H. INGRAM, JR. Activation of upper airway muscles before onset of inspiration in normal humans. *J. Appl. Physiol.: Respirat. Environ. Exercise Physiol.* 49: 638–642, 1980.
68. SWIFT, P. G. F., AND J. L. EMERY. Clinical observations on response to nasal occlusion in infancy. *Arch. Dis. Child.* 48: 947–951, 1973.
69. TAKAGI, Y., D. F. PROCTOR, S. SALMAN, AND S. EVERING. Effects of cold air and carbon dioxide on nasal air flow resistance. *Ann. Otol. Rhinol. Laryngol.* 78: 40–49, 1969.
70. THACH, B. T., AND R. T. BROUILLETTE. The respiratory function of pharyngeal musculature: relevance to clinical obstructive apnea. In: *Central Nervous Control Mechanisms in Breathing*, edited by C. von Euler and H. Lagercrantz. Oxford, UK: Pergamon, vol. 32, p. 483–494. (Wenner-Gren Ctr. Int. Symp. Ser.)
71. UDDSTROMER, M. Nasal respiration: critical survey of some of the current physiological and clinical aspects on respiratory mechanism with description of new method of diagnosis. *Acta Oto-Laryngol. Suppl.* 42: 3–146, 1940.
72. WIDDICOMBE, J. G. Proceedings: reflex control of the larynx (Abstract). *Bull. Physio-Pathol. Respir.* 11: 102P–103P, 1975.
73. WYKE, B. D. (editor). *Ventilatory and Phonatory Control Systems: An International Symposium.* London: Oxford Univ. Press, 1974.
74. WYKE, B. D., AND J. A. KIRCHNER. Neurology of the larynx. In: *Scientific Foundation of Otolaryngology.* London: Heinemann, 1976, p. 546–574.
75. WYLLIE, J. W., E. B. KERN, P. C. O'BRIEN, AND R. E. HYATT. Alteration of pulmonary function associated with artificial nasal obstruction. *Surg. Forum* 27: 535–537, 1976.

CHAPTER 7

Morphometry of airways

KEITH HORSFIELD | *The Midhurst Medical Research Institute, Midhurst, England*

MANY TREELIKE STRUCTURES are found in nature, including such diverse examples as arteries, veins, bronchi, biliary ducts, neurons, botanical trees, rivers, and electrical discharges. All share the function of transport, whether of gases, liquids, or energy. Some also have a physical support function, most obvious in trees. It is therefore not surprising that they have physical and mathematical properties in common, properties that are probably related to the way in which structures have evolved to work efficiently. This chapter is concerned primarily with the pulmonary airways, particularly those aspects of structure that can be analyzed in mathematical terms and related to their function. References to "trees" imply branching treelike structures in general, such as those just listed. Krahl (43) dealt with the detailed anatomy of the mammalian lung in the 1964 edition of the *Handbook* section on respiration. This chapter in no way supersedes Krahl's superb account of the subject; rather it should be considered as complementary to it.

DEFINITIONS AND PROPERTIES OF TREES

A simple tree is shown in Figure 1*A*; it is composed of three links, a, b, and c, meeting at a node n. Link a is the stem and b and c are the terminals. Botanical trees are normally represented this way up, but it is easier for lung physiologists to think about them inverted, and this is done in subsequent figures. A larger tree is shown in Figure 1*B*, in which d, e, f, and g are the terminals and b and c are intermediate links. The number of links (N_e) is given by $2N_n + 1$, where N_n is the number of nodes. This is obvious in Figure 1*A*, *B*, but it is true of all trees where three links meet at a node, whether symmetrical or asymmetrical (Fig. 1*C*). The number of terminals (N_t) is given by $N_n + 1$, and furthermore $N_e = 2N_t - 1$. At any node the link nearest the stem is commonly called the parent and the other two links are called the daughters, although other appropriate family relations have been used by various authors. Thus in Figure 1*C*, link e is the parent of f and g but the daughter of b. Such descriptions are useful for trees that grow by division of the end of a terminal into two new branches; this method of growth constitutes dichotomy. Division into three such daughter branches is trichotomy, and more than this is polychotomy; different numerical laws apply to trees branching in these ways, which are not dealt with in this chapter. In monopodial branching, which is found particularly in plants, growth of a single stem continues at the apex while a succession of lateral branches arises lower down (Fig. 1*D*). The result of this growth pattern gives rise to a differently shaped tree compared with dichotomous branching (Fig. 1*B*, *D*). Both patterns can be found in mammalian bronchial trees; the monopodial pattern is more marked in many quadrupeds such as the sheep, whereas the dichotomous pattern is more marked in humans. Whether these patterns reflect different modes of airway growth is not clear. The historical development of this topic has been reviewed by Miller (45).

To study the properties of branching systems, some method of classification of their branches is required. Although several methods have been described (13), only three are commonly used for analyzing the bronchial tree.

1. Generations as used by Weibel (78). With this

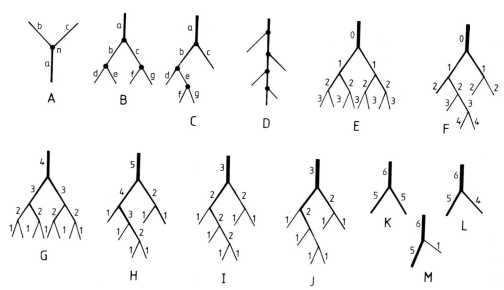

FIG. 1. Terminology in branching trees. *A*, *B*, *C*: nodes and links in dichotomous branching. *D*: monopodial branching. *E*: generations in a symmetrical tree. *F*: generations in an asymmetrical tree. *G*: Horsfield orders in a symmetrical tree. *H*: Horsfield orders in an asymmetrical tree. *I*: Strahler orders, stage 1. *J*: Strahler orders, stage 2. *K*: symmetrical branching, delta = 0. *L*: asymmetrical branching, delta = 1. *M*: asymmetrical branching, delta = 4.

method counting starts at the stem branch, which is usually called generation 0, and proceeds toward the terminals, increasing by one at each dichotomy. The procedure can be applied to both symmetrical and asymmetrical trees (Fig. 1*E*, *F*).

2. Orders as described by Horsfield (24, 33). Terminal links are defined as order 1, two of which meet at a node to give a parent link of order 2. At each subsequent node the parent link is one order higher than the higher-ordered daughter link (Fig. 1*G*, *H*).

3. Orders as described by Strahler (69, 70). There are two stages in this method of ordering. In stage 1, terminal links are defined as order 1 and at each node the parent link increases by one if both daughter links are of the same order. If they are different the parent takes the same order as the higher-ordered daughter link (Fig. 1*I*). In stage 2, contiguous links of the same order are considered to represent just one branch, which may have one or more lateral daughter branches arising from it (Fig. 1*J*). With symmetrical trees, Horsfield's and Strahler's methods give the same results (Fig. 1*G*). With asymmetrical trees, Strahler's method gives fewer branches and fewer orders than Horsfield's method (Fig. 1*H*, *J*).

Generations are useful for locating a branch in relation to the trachea and may therefore be appropriate in relation to bronchoscopic or bronchographic investigations. Orders are impossible to use in these circumstances. Some anatomical studies have utilized generations down an axial bronchial pathway (20, 22) to locate a branch. The axial pathway is normally the longest in a lobe and thus includes branches of every order. In this case generations and orders correspond, the numbering of one being the reverse of the num-

bering of the other. When used for classifying branches in the asymmetrical bronchial tree, one generation may include large branches on longer paths and small branches on shorter paths. Thus unlike branches are classified together, which is unsatisfactory. Either method of ordering is better at grouping together similar branches in asymmetrical trees, but complete or nearly complete data are needed to do this. Orders are especially helpful when describing, classifying, or comparing branching systems within and between species. They are also useful for comparing different kinds of branching systems, for example, arteries and bronchi. Both generations and orders can be used to express asymmetry in dichotomously branching trees. Regarding generations, in symmetrical trees there is an equal number of links or dichotomous divisions from the stem to the terminals (Fig. 1*E*), but in asymmetrical trees there are short and long pathways from stem to terminal. This can be expressed as a frequency distribution of generations of terminal branches; thus in Figure 1*F* there are three generation 2, one generation 3, and two generation 4 terminals. The greater the asymmetry, the wider the distribution. Horsfield orders can be used to express asymmetry at a bifurcation by using delta, the difference between the orders of the two daughter branches. Thus in the symmetrical dichotomy shown in Figure 1*K* both daughters are order 5, so delta = 0. The least degree of asymmetry is when delta = 1 (Fig. 1*L*), whereas there is greater asymmetry when delta = 4 (Fig. 1*M*). Although daughter branches may be of the same order, asymmetry with respect to diameter or length may nevertheless exist.

When the number of branches in each order is

plotted logarithmically versus order, relatively straight lines are obtained (Fig. 2). Thus the number of branches in successive orders increases by a constant factor. This is called the branching ratio (R_b) and is defined as the absolute value of the antilog of the slope of the regression line of log number versus order. Although this is true for both methods of ordering, Strahler orders generally give straighter lines (Figs. 2 and 3). Thus the factor by which the number of branches increases in successive Strahler orders is more consistent throughout the tree. In symmetrical trees such as in Figure 1G, Horsfield and Strahler orders give the same result, namely $R_b = 2.0$. With increasing asymmetry the value of R_b diverges from 2.0; with Strahler orders it becomes greater with a limit at infinity, and with Horsfield orders it becomes smaller with a limit of 1.0. With Horsfield orders every link (the section between successive bifurcations) is separately ordered, making possible a more complete description with greater detail and the reconstruction of the branching pattern. In contrast, with Strahler orders not every link is separately ordered. This makes for a simpler description, but with loss of detail and difficulty in reconstructing the branching pattern. Strahler's method is particularly good for dealing with highly asymmetric systems. In real branching systems the mean diameter and mean length of branches in each order can be determined; these give similar linear plots when plotted logarithmically versus order. Thus mean diameter and mean length increases with order by constant factors, the diameter ratio (R_d) and the length ratio (R_l), respectively. These equal the antilog of the slopes of the regression lines of log mean dimension versus order.

The number of terminals supplied by a branch is similarly related to order. Thus in Figure 1G the number of terminals doubles with successful orders, giving a terminal ratio (R_t) of 2.0. In larger trees in

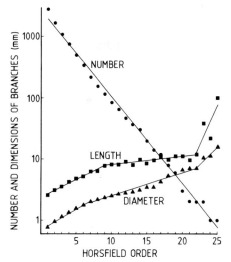

FIG. 3. Number, mean diameter, and mean length of branches in each Horsfield order of a cast of the human bronchial tree (same cast as in Fig. 2). Straight lines represent the regression equations.

which local irregularities are averaged out, it is found that $R_t = R_b$, an equality to be expected. For example, using Strahler orders where $R_b = 3.0$, the average number of terminals supplied by each branch in successive orders increases threefold as the number of branches supplying them decreases to one-third, the total number of terminals being constant. Further details of the mathematical properties of trees, with special reference to the bronchial tree, are available (25, 26, 30, 37, 38).

TECHNIQUES OF AIRWAY CASTING

Much of the data on airway morphometry has been obtained from bronchial casts. In general, their preparation utilizes some method of maintaining the lung in an expanded state while the casting material is run into the airways and allowed to set. The lung tissues are then macerated in an acid or alkaline bath. Methods of achieving and maintaining inflation include blowing air (60) or formaldehyde gas (78) through the lung and instillation of liquid formaldehyde or alcohol (76). Casting materials include Wood's metal (9), latex (57), wax (74), polyester resin (76), and silicone rubber (55).

Inflation

Dimensions of the airways vary with the degree of inflation (39), and this must be reflected in the cast. However, I know of no published studies relating dimensions of airway casts to the degree of lung inflation. Most present-day workers use one of two approaches. Either the lung is retained within the thoracic cavity during casting in an attempt to give dimensions similar to those pertaining during life (55) or the lung is inflated to a standard pressure, usually

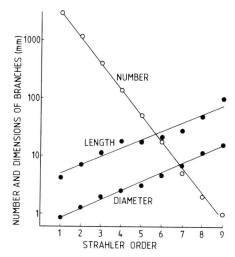

FIG. 2. Number, mean diameter, and mean length of branches in each Strahler order of a cast of the human bronchial tree. Straight lines represent the regression equations.

25 cmH$_2$O (36). For excised lungs the latter approach facilitates comparison of data obtained by different workers. The problem of comparability was encountered by lung pathologists using random-sampling techniques for quantitative studies. They have settled on a standard inflation pressure of 25 cmH$_2$O (1), which gives a fully inflated lung on the flat part of its pressure-volume curve, at which small changes in pressure make little difference to the volume. Airway dimensions obtained from resin casts inflated in this way are therefore close to a maximum, with a small shrinkage due to fixation. To compare such data with those obtained from lungs inflated to a lesser degree, the best estimate is that linear dimensions are proportional to the cube root of lung volume (14, 39). Thus for comparison with data obtained from a lung 75% inflated, for example, a correction factor of $0.75^{1/3} = 0.9$ can be applied to the larger lung.

Fixation

Most methods of fixing cause some shrinkage of the tissues, as much as 18% linear in the case of formaldehyde gas (78), and this too must be allowed for when comparing cast data with the living lung. According to Heard (18), 20% formaldehyde saline causes no shrinkage if it is pumped into the lung at a constant pressure. The method of casting with the lungs in situ described by Phalen et al. (55) avoids this problem because fixation is not required.

Filling Pressure

With polyester resins a pressure 5–10 cmH$_2$O greater than inflation pressure is adequate to obtain a well-filled cast. This small extra pressure in an already fully inflated and fixed lung makes little difference to airway dimensions. Silicone rubber requires a greater pressure for injection, which most workers do not actually measure. Raabe et al. (59) estimate that this produces an 18% increase in airway dimensions, corresponding to those existing in the lungs at end inspiration. Wood's metal is very dense and may therefore cause some distortion of the airways. However, this can be minimized by using an air-dried lung in which the tissues are relatively inelastic.

Casting Material

Wood's metal has the disadvantage of being heavy and having to be poured at ~80°C. It expands ~2% on setting and is reusable. Wax shrinks and produces very delicate casts of the smaller branches, so is not very satisfactory. Latex is flexible and is useful for casting small structures, including blood vessels. Modern resins and silicone rubber shrink very little and give high-quality casts. Resin casts are rigid, being easy to prune but liable to accidental breakage. Rubber casts are flexible, almost unbreakable, difficult to prune, yet rigid enough to maintain their shape. Both materials are satisfactory, and the choice depends on the desired method of preparing the lung and on whether a rigid or flexible cast is required.

HUMAN AIRWAY MORPHOMETRY

Definitions

The conducting airways include all airways that do not bear alveoli. The most peripheral one on each pathway is a terminal bronchiole, and each supplies a portion of lung termed an acinus. Within the acinus the terminal bronchiole gives rise to respiratory bronchioles. These bear a variable number of alveoli, but none is found on the wall that runs adjacent to the accompanying branch of the pulmonary artery. At least part of the respiratory bronchiole is lined with cuboidal bronchial epithelium. Alveolar ducts arise from the respiratory bronchioles. They are completely surrounded by openings into other ducts, alveolar sacs, or alveoli, so that their walls consist of the thin ridges of tissue surrounding these openings. Their structure may be likened to a rolled-up piece of chicken wire. There is no bronchial epithelium, only flattened respiratory epithelium. Alveolar sacs give rise only to alveoli. Their structure is similar to that of the alveolar ducts, from which they originate, and they constitute the most peripheral airway.

Conducting Airways

Several authors have studied the major airways with reference to the bronchopulmonary segments (3, 5). Weibel (78) measured diameter and length of branches of an airway cast down to generation 10. The data were complete down to generation 4, then increasingly incomplete until at generation 10 only 10% of branches were measured. The mean values for diameter and length are given by Weibel (ref. 78, Figs. 93 and 94).

Horsfield and Cumming (24, 33) measured a resin cast down to branches 0.7 mm in diameter, about two or three generations proximal to the terminal bronchioles. Their data are complete down to airways 2.2 mm in diameter and 90% complete at airways 0.7 mm in diameter. Each branch was given an identification number so that by recording the parent-branch number with each branch, the way in which all the branches join together, termed the *connectivity*, was defined. The connectivity permits the branching pattern of the original tree to be reconstructed from the data, which are available on magnetic tape. Branching angles were measured on a sample of 116 dichotomies (32).

Raabe et al. (59) made silicone rubber casts of two human lungs, as well as lungs from two dogs, a rat, and a hamster. They measured diameter, length, branching angle, and the angle the branch made with the direction of gravity. They also recorded the connectivity. One cast of a human lung was measured completely down to 3 mm, the other down to various distances; in three lobes 10% of the data are complete to terminal bronchioles. The detailed data are given in their publication and are also available on magnetic tape.

The total cross-sectional area of the airways at any level, defined by generation, order, or distance down, can be determined from cast data by summing all the individual bronchial areas at that level. Some interesting techniques for estimating this in intact lungs and during life have been developed. Jackson et al. (41) used high-frequency acoustic oscillations to determine the area-distance function in the airways and to quantify changes in cross-sectional area caused by changes in lung volume and bronchial muscle tone. Scherer and Pack (64) derived cross-sectional area as a function of cumulative airway volume from a single-breath washout of nitrogen. Palmes (52) used the deposition rate of inhaled aerosols to gain information about the size of airways, particularly in normal subjects but also in patients with emphysema.

Number of Conducting Airways

Because each terminal bronchiole supplies one acinus by definition, the number of terminal bronchioles (N_{tb}) and the number of acini are equal. If N_{tb} is known, the total number of conducting airways (N_c) can be calculated. Assuming dichotomous branching, $N_c = 2N_{tb} - 1$. Rohrer (62) estimated 14,944 terminal bronchioles, Findeisen (10) estimated 54,000, and Weibel (78) estimated 65,536. More recent studies put the number between these two extremes. Horsfield and Cumming (33) estimated 27,992 from their study of an airway cast. Thurlbeck and Wang (73) gave estimates varying from 16,000 to 26,000, and Hansen and Ampaya (16) estimated 23,000. Thus in round numbers there are on average ~25,000 terminal bronchioles and acini and ~50,000 conducting airways.

Variability of Airway Dimensions

Although data obtained from measurements of bronchial casts have proved useful in physiological calculations, it is important to remember that airway dimensions change in various circumstances. Hughes et al. (39) and Hahn et al. (14), using the technique of tantalum bronchography (49), have shown that length and diameter vary as the cube root of lung volume (although diameter shows much greater variability) because of the presence of variable bronchomotor tone. Tantalum bronchography has also been used to demonstrate the effects of expiratory flow (40), vagal tone (14), and transpulmonary pressure (75) on airway dimensions. There are few data available on bronchial dimensions in adult subjects or animal species in relation to body weight. One such study suggested that dimensions are in proportion to cube root of body weight (81), but the relation is not very precise.

Morphometric Parameters

The linear relations between log mean diameter and log mean length versus generation were first demonstrated by Weibel (78). He found $R_d = 2^{1/3}$ for generations 2–10, $R_l = 2.509$ for generations 0–3, and $R_l = 1.185$ for generations 4–10. By definition with generations, $R_b = 2.0$. The linear relations between order versus log number of branches, log number of terminals, log mean diameter, and log mean length were demonstrated by Horsfield and Cumming (24, 33). Figures 2 and 3 illustrate some of these plots, and Table 1 shows the ratios obtained from 15 Strahler-ordered lungs of five species.

Intra-acinar Airways

Most authors agree that there are usually three generations of dichotomously branching respiratory bronchioles, typically labeled RB_1, RB_2, and RB_3. These give rise to a variable number of generations of alveolar ducts, so that some pathways are longer than others (Fig. 4). Older descriptions of the anatomy of the acinus, for example, that of Miller (45), are often difficult to understand because of differences in terminology. Furthermore the degree of lung inflation was often poorly controlled so that dimensions varied between studies.

Ogawa (50) described 2–9 generations of alveolar ducts from RB_1 to alveolar sacs, the terminal structures of the duct system, but examination of his diagram (Fig. 4B) suggests 11 generations altogether. Willson (79) found fewer generations, namely 5–7 from terminal bronchiole to alveolar sac.

Pump (57, 58) studied the human acini by using a latex-injection technique and found up to 10 generations from terminal bronchiole to alveolar sac (Fig. 4E). Alveolar numbers, alveolar surface area, and mean acinar volume work out at ~25% of currently accepted values; the number of ducts and sacs was

TABLE 1. *Morphometric Parameters From Measurements of Airway Casts*

	Branching Ratio	Diameter Ratio	Length Ratio
Sheep	3.533	1.666	1.508
	3.565	1.712	1.387
Dog	3.609	1.692	1.675
	3.468	1.562	1.662
	3.445	1.480	1.560
	3.261	1.495	1.596
	3.379	1.558	1.624
	3.057	1.516	1.704
	3.583*	1.530*	1.692*
	3.040*	1.509*	1.528*
Human	2.805	1.427	1.402
	2.508*	1.351*	1.333*
	2.735*	1.452*	1.464*
Rat	3.314*	1.532*	1.820*
Hamster	3.258*	1.502*	1.915*

* Calculated from data of Raabe et al. (59). [Adapted from Horsfield and Thurlbeck (37).]

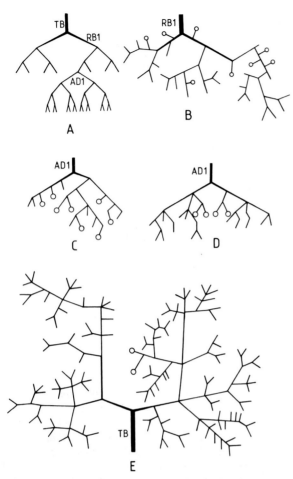

FIG. 4. Branching patterns in human pulmonary acini. *A*: Weibel's (78) models. For simplicity only 1 alveolar duct system is shown. *B*: model from Ogawa (50). *C*: model from Parker, Horsfield, and Cumming (53). *D*: model from Hansen et al. (17). *E*: model from Pump (57). TB, terminal bronchiole; RB1, first-generation respiratory bronchiole; AD1, first-generation alveolar duct; ○, incomplete structure.

much less than 25% of currently accepted values. This is partly because of the difficulty in identifying branch points in negative casts when branching is profuse. Boyden (4) used positive and negative reconstructions of an acinus of a 6-yr-old child and found up to five generations of alveolar ducts. He, too, remarked on the degree of asymmetry that was evident.

With the use of random-sampling techniques, Weibel (78) studied five pairs of lungs and estimated the mean number of alveolar ducts to be 13.8×10^6. Respiratory bronchiole and duct diameters were measured on histological sections and duct lengths were estimated from the length-diameter ratio obtained by viewing whole-lung sections stereoscopically. The data are given by Weibel (ref. 78, p. 128–131) and shown in the branching pattern in Figure 4*A*.

Parker, Horsfield, and Cumming (53) gave the number, order, and length of branches between an airway 0.7 mm in diameter and RB₃. Some rather sketchy

data on numbers of ducts and their branching patterns are also given, based on a three-dimensional reconstruction. They found 3–8 generations of ducts (Fig. 4*C*).

By far the most complete study of the human acinus to date is that of Hansen and co-workers (16, 17), who reconstructed part of an acinus from serial sections. They described three generations of respiratory bronchioles and up to nine generations of alveolar ducts and sacs. Respiratory bronchioles usually divide by dichotomy, but trichotomy is frequent in the ducts. Alveolar sacs are hemispherical or saucer-shaped structures, each of which gives rise to 2–8 alveoli. They are the most peripheral structures in the acinus, constituting the final division of the distal ducts, but are also situated laterally on respiratory bronchioles and ducts. Over half of the alveolar sacs arise in this latter manner, averaging three or four sacs per duct. Alveoli also arise directly from respiratory bronchioles and ducts, without the interposition of a sac. Alveolar ducts are thus surrounded by the openings of both sacs and alveoli. Sacs are shallow structures that in turn give rise to alveoli, and these alveoli are therefore situated close to the parent duct. Numbers of alveoli per structure arising without the interposition of a sac are greatest on the respiratory bronchioles, averaging about nine, and decrease peripherally to three or four per distal duct. Their estimates of acinar numbers and volume and alveolar numbers are compatible with accepted values. Table 2 gives the data of Hansen and co-workers (16, 17), slightly simplified, with the number of ducts about double that in Weibel's model and the number of duct generations from four to eight (Fig. 4*D*). The three-dimensional reconstruction enables a more accurate definition of a branching point than two-dimensional sections. It shows more frequent branching, more generations, and more, but shorter, ducts than Weibel's data. The authors suggest that the length-diameter ratio is nearer to 1.5 than the 2.0 used by Weibel, and this explains the different numbers obtained (15). The technique of three-dimensional reconstruction from serial sections used by Parker, Horsfield, and Cumming (53) and by Hansen and co-workers (16, 17) is extremely difficult. Alveolar septae, being thin, are particularly troublesome to represent on the correct scale and in continuity. The definition of the boundaries of a structure is fraught with difficulty and often arbitrary. It is this point above all that results in the larger numbers of ducts and sacs in the data of Hansen et al. (17) compared with the data of Weibel (78). Thus the data from serial sections in the above two studies must be treated with some reserve until confirmatory evidence becomes available. No single complete acinus has been studied by reconstruction from serial sections, so information of this region of the lung is still scanty and none of it is really satisfactory. This is an area where further research would be most helpful to facilitate analysis

TABLE 2. *Numbers and Dimensions of Structures in an Acinus*

Generation	Structure	Number in Acinus	Diameter, mm	Length, mm	Sacs on Respiratory Bronchioles and Alveolar Ducts	Alveoli on Respiratory Bronchioles, Alveolar Ducts, and Sacs	Mean Number of Alveoli	
							Per sac	Per respiratory bronchiole or alveolar duct
1	Terminal bronchiole	1	0.55	1.20	0	5		5.0
2	Respiratory bronchiole 1	2	0.47	0.97	4	32	3.5	9.0
3	Respiratory bronchiole 2	4	0.47	0.97	16	96	3.5	10.0
4	Respiratory bronchiole 3	8	0.49	0.88	24	119	2.4	7.7
5	Alveolar duct 1	19	0.50	0.66	74	373	3.0	8.2
6	Alveolar duct 2	45	0.49	0.51	186	678	2.6	4.3
7	Alveolar duct 3	108	0.51	0.58	405	1,542	2.6	4.6
8	Alveolar duct 4	254	0.40	0.43	627	2,812	2.9	3.8
9	Alveolar duct 5	374	0.38	0.41	1,020	4,516	3.4	2.9
10	Alveolar duct 6	366	0.30	0.30	1,135	6,420	4.0	4.0
11	Alveolar duct 7	146	0.27	0.28	498	2,191	3.7	2.3
12	Alveolar duct 8	58	0.24	0.22	274	973	2.8	3.7

Sacs are not considered to constitute a separate generation. [Data from Hansen et al. (16, 17).]

of such problems as convective flow and diffusive mixing within the acinus (2).

Bifurcations

The points of branching in the airways are of considerable functional importance. Pertubations occur at junctions (65), which impart secondary rotatory flows to the air. As a result the loss of energy downstream from a junction on inspiration is ~1.85 times that due to Poiseuille dissipation alone (54). Thus the sum of the effects of the junctions contributes significantly to airway resistance. The structure at a branch point affects the patterns of secondary flow and the resulting energy losses (54) and is therefore of interest to physiologists working in the field of fluid mechanics. Snyder et al. (68) demonstrated how distribution of flow can be asymmetrical even in symmetrical branching tubes because of the effect of pertubations at the bifurcations. Slutsky et al. (67), using a hollow cast of human airways, also showed asymmetry of flow distribution that varied with branching angle and tracheal flow. Some details of airway shape at bifurcations are available (35).

Branching Angle

Most, but not all, dichotomous branchings of the conducting airways are asymmetrical with respect to diameter, that is, the daughter branches have different diameters. The larger one is called the major branch and the smaller one the minor branch. The angle that the major branch makes with the projected line of the parent (the major-branch angle) is usually smaller than that made by the minor branch (the minor-branch angle). The more asymmetrical the branching in terms of order or diameter, the greater the minor-branch angle and the smaller the major-branch angle. Toward the periphery of the tree the branching angles

increase. Branching-angle data have been published by various authors (32, 35, 56, 59, 72, 81).

Diameter Ratios

Because the three branches forming a dichotomous branching are usually of different diameter, it is of interest to observe their relative proportions. Let the diameter of the parent be d_1, that of the major daughter be d_2, and that of the minor daughter be d_3. Although d_2 and d_3 are each usually less than d_1, the summed cross-sectional area of the two daughters usually exceeds that of the parent. The distributions of the ratios d_2/d_1, d_3/d_1, d_3/d_2, and $d_1^2/(d_2^2 + d_3^2)$ have been studied (32) and their mean values related to parent-branch diameter (56).

DETERMINANTS OF AIRWAY SIZE AND SHAPE

Diameter Ratios, Length Ratios, and Branching Ratios

The airways of the lungs serve a function vital to the whole organism. Performance of this function requires the expenditure of energy, not just for the movement of air in and out of the lung but for the maintenance of the lung itself. This dual requirement necessitates certain compromises in the "design" of the lungs, a design that has evolved because it presumably represents an efficient solution for these compromises. To take a simple example: the greater the diameter of the airways, the less work expended against frictional resistance, but the greater the mass of airway tissue requiring energy for its maintenance. The earlier work on this topic was with reference to blood flow in the arterial system, but the principles are the same for gas flow in the airways. In 1808 Young (85) forecast that an appropriate value for the parent-daughter diameter ratio is 1.26 (actually $2^{1/3}$ = 1.2599). Unfortunately he did not enlarge on how he came to this conclusion. Hess (19) investigated the relation between resistance to blood flow and vessel volume but failed to bring out the importance of energy. Murray (48) believed that minimum power dissipation, including that used to maintain the tissues, was the basic determinant. He showed that, assuming laminar flow and minimum energy dissipation in an ideal system, $F = kr^3$, where F is flow, r is the radius of a vessel, and k is a constant for all branches in the system. The analysis can equally well be applied to airways, which will have a different value of k. This concept was extended by Uylings (77) to include turbulent and transitional flow regimes; he showed that $F = kr^{(j+2)/(j-2)}$. The value of the constant j depends on Reynolds number and the relative roughness of the vessel wall; it is 4 for laminar flow, 5 for turbulent flow, and between 4 and 5 for transitional flow regimes. Substituting these values into the equation gives $F = kr^3$ for laminar flow and $F = kr^{2.333}$ for turbulent flow. A method for calculating the average exponent in this equation from morphometric data for the conducting airways has been developed (38). Its value is given by log R_b/log R_d. Thus in a human lung using Strahler orders, R_b = 2.805, R_d = 1.427, and the exponent = log 2.805/log 1.427 = 2.9, a value nearer to that expected for laminar flow than for turbulent flow.

Other authors have calculated the value of R_d that gives minimum volume (42), minimum resistance (6, 32, 61, 71, 78), and minimum entropy production (80). It is not known which, if any, of these approaches is correct, but all come to the same conclusion, namely $R_d = 2^{1/3}$. In each of these studies symmetrical dichotomy was assumed with R_b = 2.0. If instead asymmetry is assumed and a different value of R_b used, a more general result can be obtained, namely $R_d = R_b^{1/3}$ for either method of ordering. It has been shown for rivers that the fall in pressure (height) should be equal in each order for minimal entropy production (44), and this concept has been extended to flow in the bronchial tree (27). When the fall in pressure in each order is equal, and assuming laminar flow, then $R_b R_l / R_d^4 = 1$, and given $R_d^3 = R_b$, then $R_l = R_d$. These are the equations that apply for minimal resistance and minimal entropy production with laminar flow (29). In one human lung, values for the ratios using Strahler orders were R_b = 2.805, R_d = 1.427, and R_l = 1.402, which are close to the relations predicted by these equations.

If airway branching and dimensions are optimized in some way, it is interesting to speculate which physiological conditions are important in determining the optimization. Because the lungs have evolved, any such optimization must represent a biological advantage that would be unlikely to operate while the animal is resting. Much more probably the advantage would operate during times of maximum stress, such as hunting, fighting, or fleeing from enemies. Thus the airways should be optimized for maximum flow conditions.

Geometric factors must play a part in determining R_b and R_l. Long thin lungs are likely to have a higher Strahler-order R_b than round ones, given that the acini are of similar size. Some evidence in favor of this shape dependence is given by the lower values for R_b found in humans (2.5–2.8) than in dogs (3.0–3.6), the latter having the longer thinner lungs.

Trees on a surface (e.g., rivers) have length ratios that approximate to $R_b^{0.5}$, although the exponent is often a little greater than 0.5. This stems from the fact that order 1 branches drain unit areas (drainage basins), and areas drained by successive orders increase by R_b, whereas length increases by square root of area. In three-dimensional trees (e.g., the airways) volumes supplied by successive orders increase by R_b while length increases by the cube root of volume and hence tends toward $R_b^{1/3}$.

Genetic factors have been shown to influence the branching pattern of the larger branches of the pulmonary artery. Members of families who have died from accidental carbon monoxide poisoning have similar pulmonary angiograms that can be distinguished from those of other families (21). Whether the same applies to the airways is not known.

Several studies of randomly generated mathematical branching trees have given average Strahler-order branching ratios of 3.0, 3.5, or 4.0, depending on the rules employed to generate them (13a, 25). Thus it is an inherent property of random trees that they tend toward a given value of R_b, and insofar as the airways develop randomly the same must be true of them. In humans the conducting airways are all present in the fetus at 20 weeks of gestation, so the branching ratio must also be determined at that stage. It is not known whether R_d and R_l have already reached adult values in the fetus or whether they change as the airways grow. In dogs, adult values are present one week postpartum (28).

Branching Angles

Honda (23), using computer simulations, demonstrated that branching angles are important determinants of the form of trees. Angles must also affect the volume of tissue in the tree, path lengths, resistances, and hence power dissipated by the system. Murray (47) considered the case of a simple bifurcation of a branch to supply points A and B, with branching angles x and y, respectively. He showed that for minimum power dissipation

$$\cos x = (r_0^4 + r_1^4 - r_2^4)/2r_0^2 r_1^2$$

and

$$\cos y = (r_0^4 + r_2^4 - r_1^4)/2r_0^2 r_2^2$$

where r_0 is the radius of the parent branch and r_1 and

r_2 are the radii of the daughter branches going to points A and B, respectively. Other authors have undertaken similar analyses based on different optimization principles, including minimum volume (32, 42, 86), minimum power (77, 86), minimum drag (86), and minimum internal surface area (86), but none has proved to be very satisfactory when tested against data. If either $F = kr^3$ for minimal power dissipation or $R_d = 2^{1/3}$ for minimal resistance is considered along with Murray's equation, an "ideal" branching angle can be calculated that is 37°28′ (32, 47). The above analyses are all based on the assumption of laminar flow, but Uylings (77) extended the concept to include all flow regimes from laminar to turbulent and calculated the branching angles for minimal power dissipation. It must be admitted that it is not known which functional variables are optimized by the branching angles.

MODELS OF AIRWAYS

Physiologists are often interested in making calculations based on airway anatomy. Gas mixing by diffusion, flow regimes in different generations of airway, the site and nature of airway resistance, and the behavior of gases of differing molecular weights are examples of physiological problems that have been studied with the aid of anatomical knowledge. It is only relatively recently that nearly complete sets of data for conducting airways have become available (33, 59). Although they are on magnetic tapes suitable for computer use, the magnitude of the information makes them difficult to use. Most workers have instead used simplified dimensional models that express airway anatomy in some kind of average way. Although many models differing in detail can be found in the literature, they can be divided into four main groups: symmetrical with and without connectivity and asymmetrical with and without connectivity. Connectivity is the way in which the branches of the model join together. When it is defined, the branching pattern of the entire model can be reconstructed. Models that treat the airways as a "black box" or use electrical analogues are not included in this account.

Symmetrical Model With Connectivity

Weibel's (78) symmetrical model A, or some variant of it, is the most widely used model for physiological calculations. It is based on the assumption of symmetrical dichotomous branching with each pathway consisting of an equal number of generations. Three of these generations are taken by respiratory bronchioles and four by alveolar ducts. The number of alveolar ducts was counted in each of five lungs and a mean value of 13.8×10^6 found, on which the number in the model was based. Thus for four successive dichotomous generations to give approximately this total number, they need to be generations 20, 21, 22,

and 23 because $2^{20} + 2^{21} + 2^{22} + 2^{23} = 15.7 \times 10^6$. It follows that respiratory bronchioles constitute generations 17, 18, and 19, and terminal bronchioles generation 16, numbering $2^{16} = 65,536$, the number of acini in the model. Dimensions were determined by interpolation between data on the first 10 generations of conducting airways and data on the alveolar ducts. Because every branch (except the trachea) has a parent one generation number lower, the connectivity of the model is defined. All branches of a given generation are identical, as are all the pathways from the trachea to distal alveolar ducts.

Symmetrical Model Without Connectivity

A model of the rat lung of this type was described by Yeh et al. (84) and is shown in Table 3. It is based on very complete data for the conducting airways obtained by Raabe et al. (59). The number of terminal bronchioles was counted and the median number of generations (n) down all the pathways to terminal bronchioles was calculated. By using the equation $N_{tb} = x^{n-1}$, a value of x was obtained that represents a kind of branching ratio with respect to generations, such that a tree branching symmetrically would have N_{tb} terminal bronchioles in the nth generation. It must be understood that x is a noninteger, so that it would be impossible to actually draw the model as can be done when x has an integer value (in Weibel's model $x = 2$). Thus the connectivity is undefined. Dimen-

TABLE 3. *Typical-Path Model of Airways of the Rat Lung*

Genera-tion	Number	Length, mm	Diameter, mm	Branching Angle, °	Angle to Gravity, °
1	1	26.80	3.40	0	86
2	2	7.15	2.90	15	90
3	3	4.00	2.63	43	86
4	5	1.76	2.03	36	71
5	8	2.08	1.63	32	59
6	14	1.17	1.34	22	58
7	23	1.14	1.23	16	61
8	38	1.30	1.12	17	58
9	65	0.99	0.95	20	55
10	109	0.91	0.87	15	58
11	184	0.96	0.78	16	61
12	309	0.73	0.70	17	56
13	521	0.75	0.58	17	58
14	877	0.60	0.49	22	58
15	1,477	0.55	0.36	24	57
16	2,487	0.35	0.20	44	58
17	4,974	0.29	0.17	45	60
18	9,948	0.25	0.16	45	60
19	19,896	0.22	0.15	45	60
20	39,792	0.20	0.14	45	60
21	79,584	0.19	0.14	45	60
22	159,168	0.18	0.14	45	60
23	318,336	0.17	0.14	45	60
24	636,672	0.17	0.14	45	60
25	3×10^7	0.072	0.086	45	60

Generation 1 is trachea; generation 16 is terminal bronchioles; generation 25 is alveoli. [Data from Yeh et al. (84).]

sions and branching angles are the mean values obtained from the various pathways that, in their data, actually had *n* generations. Distal to the terminal bronchioles a symmetrical model of the acinus was constructed. Yeh et al. (84) call this a "typical path" lung model, a slight misnomer because there is no pathway having the characteristics of the model; a better name might be "average path" lung model. The method of modeling was also applied to the human lung (83).

Asymmetrical Models With Connectivity

The first model of this kind was described by Horsfield et al. (35). They solved the problem of how to define both asymmetry and connectivity by the use of an average value of delta. This approach requires the branches to be classified by order instead of by generation. Given a dichotomously branching tree with a known fixed value of delta, the branching ratio of the tree can be calculated (26, 35). Some examples are shown in Table 4. Conversely, given a tree with a known branching ratio, the nearest corresponding value of delta can be found and this value used for a model of the tree. Such a model represents some kind of average of the asymmetry found in the original tree, which has values of delta above and below that used in the model. Horsfield et al. (35) used bronchial tree data to make their model, which has three zones. Zone 1, down to the lobar branches, was used unchanged. Zone 2, from lobar branches to bronchioles, has delta = 3, except for the lower four orders in which delta decreases to 0. Zone 3, the bronchioles, has delta = 0. Dimensions were taken from the mean values for each order in the data. This method of modeling was also applied to the bronchopulmonary segments individually.

Fredberg and Hoenig (12) extended the principle to include the central branches. In their model of the human airways all branches of a given order divide with the same value of delta, and the connectivity is defined (Table 5). A similar model of the dog lung (Table 6) has also been described (36). Weibel's symmetrical model A can be considered to be a special

TABLE 4. *Delta Values and Resulting Branching Ratios in Dichotomously Branching Trees*

Delta	Branching Ratio
0	2.0000
1	1.6180
2	1.4656
3	1.3803
4	1.3247
5	1.2852
6	1.2554

Delta is difference in order between 2 daughter branches. If delta is the same at all bifurcations, the tree has a defined branching ratio.

TABLE 5. *Model of Airways of the Human Lung Based on Delta*

Order (*n*)	Delta	Diameter, mm	Length, mm	Number of Endings
35	1	16.00	100.0	6.81×10^6
34	2	12.00	50.0	4.11×10^6
33	3	11.00	22.0	2.69×10^6
32	3	8.00	11.0	1.95×10^6
31	3	7.30	10.5	1.41×10^6
30	3	5.90	11.3	1.02×10^6
29	3	5.90	11.3	7.43×10^5
28	3	5.40	9.7	5.38×10^5
27	3	4.30	10.8	3.90×10^5
26	3	3.50	9.5	2.82×10^5
25	3	3.50	8.6	2.04×10^5
24	3	3.10	9.9	1.48×10^5
23	3	2.90	8.0	1.07×10^5
22	3	2.80	9.2	7.78×10^4
21	3	2.70	8.2	5.63×10^4
20	3	2.50	8.1	4.09×10^4
19	3	2.40	7.7	2.96×10^4
18	3	2.18	6.4	2.15×10^4
17	3	2.00	6.3	1.53×10^4
16	3	1.80	5.17	1.12×10^4
15	3	1.60	4.80	8.19×10^3
14	2	1.40	4.20	6.14×10^3
13	2	1.10	3.60	4.09×10^3
12	1	0.95	3.10	3.07×10^3
11	0	0.76	2.50	2.04×10^3
10	0	0.63	1.10	1.02×10^3
9	0	0.53	1.31	5.12×10^2
8	0	0.48	1.05	2.56×10^2
7	0	0.43	0.75	1.28×10^2
6	0	0.80	0.59	6.40×10
5	0	0.80	0.48	3.20×10
4	0	0.80	0.48	1.60×10
3	0	0.80	0.48	8.00
2	0	0.80	0.48	4.00
1	0	0.80	0.48	2.00
0		0.80	0.48	1.00

Order 35 is trachea; order 8 is terminal bronchioles; order 0 is alveolar sacs. Delta is difference in order between the 2 daughter branches arising from a parent of order *n*; number of endings is number of order 1 branches supplied by a branch of order *n*. Orders are defined by Horsfield's method. [Data from Fredberg and Hoenig (12).]

case of this type of model, with delta = 0 throughout. Because in these models all the patterns of branching are defined and are identical for all branches of a given order, it follows that the segments of tree distal to each and every branch of a given order are also identical. Thus it is only necessary to define delta at each order to be able to reconstruct the whole tree. This property facilitates the use of these models in computer analyses, especially of asymmetrical trees, because the calculations for branches of a given order need be done for only one such branch and then applied to all the other similar branches (12).

Asymmetrical Models Without Connectivity

The study of the dog lung by Ross (63) was the first attempt to describe the asymmetry of the conducting airways as a whole. Horsfield and Cumming (33) used

TABLE 6. *Model of Airways of the Dog Lung Based on Delta*

Order (*n*)	Delta	Diameter, mm	Length, mm	Number of Endings
47	2	21.0	200.0	150,077
46	2	21.0	7.5	108,292
45	2	20.3	18.0	72,530
44	10	11.5	10.1	41,785
43	10	10.8	9.61	35,762
42	10	10.1	9.11	30,745
41	10	9.39	8.63	26,486
40	10	8.76	8.18	22,801
39	10	8.18	7.75	19,553
38	10	7.64	7.34	16,636
37	10	7.14	6.96	13,967
36	10	6.66	6.60	11,482
35	10	6.22	6.25	9,134
34	10	5.81	5.92	7,360
33	10	5.43	5.61	6,023
32	10	5.07	5.32	5,017
31	10	4.73	5.04	4,259
30	10	4.42	4.78	3,685
29	10	4.13	4.53	3,248
28	10	3.85	4.29	2,917
27	10	3.60	4.07	2,669
26	10	3.36	3.85	2,485
25	4	3.14	3.65	2,348
24	4	2.93	3.46	1,774
23	4	2.74	3.28	1,337
22	4	2.55	3.11	1,006
21	4	2.38	2.94	758
20	4	2.23	2.79	574
19	4	2.08	2.64	437
18	4	1.94	2.51	331
17	4	1.81	2.37	248
16	4	1.69	2.25	184
15	4	1.58	2.13	137
14	4	1.48	2.02	106
13	4	1.39	1.91	83
12	4	1.24	1.81	64
11	4	1.10	1.72	47
10	4	0.983	1.63	31
9	4	0.876	1.54	23
8	4	0.781	1.46	19
7	4	0.697	1.39	17
6	0	0.621	1.31	16
5	0	0.554	1.25	8
4	0	0.494	1.18	4
3	0	0.440	1.12	2
2	0	0.393	1.06	1
1				

Order 47 is trachea; order 5 is terminal bronchiole; orders 2, 3, and 4 are respiratory bronchioles; order 1 is alveolar ducts. Delta is difference in order between the 2 daughter branches arising from a parent of order *n*; number of endings is number of order 2 branches supplied by a branch of order *n*. Orders are defined by Horsfield's method. [Data from Horsfield et al. (36).]

orders (originally called divisions up) for describing the asymmetry of the airways and based their model on this concept. Similar models based on Strahler orders have been constructed for the dog lung (34) and the human lung (31).

Merits and Demerits of the Models

Weibel's symmetrical model has proved to be particularly attractive to lung physiologists. Because all the pathways are identical and in parallel, the calculations need only be made for one pathway, or alternatively all the pathways can be combined and the calculations done for the whole lung. Connectivity is simple, easily visualized and understood, and readily used in calculations. Its main defect is that it is based on the assumption of symmetrical dichotomy and therefore cannot be used to investigate phenomena that are caused by or dependent on asymmetry. Another defect is the assumption of four generations of alveolar ducts. Several authors have clearly demonstrated that the acinus is often highly asymmetrical, with up to nine generations of ducts (4, 16, 17, 50, 53, 57, 58, 79). Furthermore the average number of acini is probably ~25,000, as already described, so that calculations of flow in a terminal bronchiole based on Weibel's model may be underestimated by a factor of ~25,000/65,000 or 0.38. The problems of counting alveolar ducts by Weibel's method have been alluded to in *Intra-acinar Airways*, p. 79, and probably result in an underestimate. Any worker using Weibel's model must be clear about its limitations and satisfy himself that ignoring asymmetry will not negate his conclusions.

The model of Yeh and Schum (83) is designed especially for use in calculating particle deposition. Because it models numbers of branches and their dimensions in an average way and is the only model to include all the branching angles, it can be used to calculate average particle deposition at various levels in the lungs. Again the information on asymmetry is lost, which may sometimes be important in this topic.

Asymmetrical airway models without connectivity have proved more difficult to use. When calculations such as pressure drop down a pathway in the model are made, these will usually include a branch of every order. In fact it is only the longest pathways that include a branch of every order. Short pathways miss some orders altogether. Thus the calculations may be for a very unrepresentative pathway at one extreme of the range. As long as this is understood, it does at least set one limit on the possible range of values.

With symmetrical models it is usual to assume that all the branches of a given generation carry an equal flow. The same assumption can be made for the order 1 branches in asymmetrical models, hence flow in any branch is proportional to the number of order 1 branches supplied by it. Thus in the case of lung models in which the number of order 1 branches supplied by each branch is defined (12, 33, 35, 36), flow can be calculated. In those in which it is not defined (31, 34), calculation of flow is dubious. Models based on delta (the difference in order between daughter branches) have taken some of the difficulty out of working with asymmetry. They are easy to handle in a computer and have reduced the computing time required for calculations based on the total data sets. Several groups have used asymmetrical models successfully (8, 12, 35, 46, 66, 82).

CONCLUSION

The internal lung of the mammal and its ventilation by reciprocal flow impose certain constraints on function. Perhaps the most important of these is that convective flow cannot continue up to the alveolar-capillary membrane, and therefore the movement of gas molecules at this level must be mediated by diffusion. There are thus two mechanisms in series for the movement of gas down the airways, namely convective flow and molecular diffusion. Diffusion is less efficient in moving gases over large distances than convective flow. Thus, in order to cope with the requirements of gas exchange, diffusion distance must be minimized and cross-sectional area maximized. It is just these requirements that are provided by the very rapid increase in cross-sectional area with respect to distance down the intracinar airways. Looked at in evolutionary terms, the centrifugal development of the intrapulmonary bronchial tree, from amphibians through reptiles to mammals, can be interpreted as a means of minimizing diffusion distance. A penalty to be paid for this is that gas in the conducting airways does not take part in gas exchange and thus constitutes a dead space that has to be ventilated. If the lungs were to empty completely and refill during each respiratory cycle there would be large swings in alveolar and arterial partial pressures of O_2 and CO_2. Such changes are minimized by the volume of resident gas in the peripheral airways and alveoli that smoothes out the phasic changes in gas composition over the respiratory cycle. Finally, the increasing cross-sectional area of the airways distally results in a diminution of gas transport per unit area by convective flow, coupled with a simultaneous increase in gas transport per unit area by molecular diffusion. At some point (usually in the respiratory bronchioles) the two processes become equal, resulting, during inspiration, in a stationary interface of concentration between inspired gas and resident gas (7, 51). In fact the stationary interface extends over several generations of airways, with the concentration of resident gas increasing distally. It is usual to refer to the inflexion point of the plot of concentration versus distance down the airways as being "the" position of the interface, and it is this that defines the distal end of the "anatomical" dead space as measured by Fowler's (11) method and makes a functional division between conducting and respiratory airways. This important concept is discussed in greater detail elsewhere in this *Handbook*.

REFERENCES

1. BEREND, N., C. SKOOG, L. WASZKIEWICZ, AND W. M. THURLBECK. Maximum volumes in excised human lungs: effects of age, emphysema and formalin inflation. *Thorax* 35: 859–864, 1980.
2. BOWES, C., G. CUMMING, K. HORSFIELD, J. LOUGHHEAD, AND S. PRESTON. Gas mixing in a model of the pulmonary acinus with asymmetrical alveolar ducts. *J. Appl. Physiol.: Respirat. Environ. Exercise Physiol.* 52: 624–633, 1982.
3. BOYDEN, E. A. *Segmental Anatomy of the Lungs.* New York: McGraw-Hill, 1955.
4. BOYDEN, E. A. The structure of the pulmonary acinus in a child of six years and eight months. *Am. J. Anat.* 132: 275–300, 1971.
5. BROCK, R. C. *The Anatomy of the Bronchial Tree With Special Reference to Lung Abscess.* Oxford, UK: Oxford Univ. Press, 1946.
6. COHN, D. L. Optimal systems. II. The vascular system. *Bull. Math. Biophys.* 17: 219–227, 1955.
7. CUMMING, G., K. HORSFIELD, AND S. B. PRESTON. Diffusion equilibrium in the lungs examined by nodal analysis. *Respir. Physiol.* 12: 329–345, 1971.
8. DAWSON, S. V., AND K. E. FINUCANE. A prediction of the distribution of oscillatory flow in human airways. *Bull. Physio-Pathol. Respir.* 8: 293–304, 1972.
9. EISMAN, M. M. Lung models: hollow, flexible reproductions. *J. Appl. Physiol.* 29: 531–533, 1970.
10. FINDEISEN, V. Uber das Absetzen kleiner, in der Luft suspendierter Teilchen in der menschlichen Lunge bei der Atmung. *Pfluegers Arch. Gesamte Physiol. Menschen Tiere* 236: 367–379, 1935.
11. FOWLER, W. S. Lung function studies. III. Uneven pulmonary ventilation in normal subjects and in patients with pulmonary disease. *J. Appl. Physiol.* 2: 283–299, 1949.
12. FREDBERG, J. J., AND A. HOENIG. Mechanical response of the lungs at high frequencies. *J. Biomech. Eng.* 100: 57–66, 1978.
13. HAGGETT, P., AND R. J. CHORLEY. *Network Analysis in Geography.* London: Arnold, 1969, p. 10–17.

13a. HAGGETT, P., AND R. J. CHORLEY. *Network Analysis in Geography.* London: Arnold, 1969, p. 285–293.
14. HAHN, H. L., P. D. GRAF, AND J. A. NADEL. Effect of vagal and tone on airway diameters and on lung volume in anesthetized dogs. *J. Appl. Physiol.* 41: 581–589, 1976.
15. HANSEN, J. E., AND E. P. AMPAYA. Lung morphometry: a fallacy in the use of the counting principle. *J. Appl. Physiol.* 37: 951–954, 1974.
16. HANSEN, J. E., AND E. P. AMPAYA. Human air space shapes, sizes, areas, and volumes., *J. Appl. Physiol.* 38: 990–995, 1975.
17. HANSEN, J. E., E. P. AMPAYA, G. H. BRYANT, AND J. J. NAVIN. Branching pattern of airways and air spaces of a single human terminal bronchiole. *J. Appl. Physiol.* 38: 983–989, 1975.
18. HEARD, B. E. A pathological study of emphysema of the lungs with chronic bronchitis. *Thorax* 13: 136–149, 1958.
19. HESS, W. R. Über die periphere Regulierung der Blutzirkulation. *Pfluegers Arch. Gesamte Physiol. Menschen Tiere* 168: 439–490, 1971.
20. HISLOP, A., D. C. F. MUIR, M. JACOBSEN, G. SIMON, AND L. REID. Postnatal growth and function of the pre-acinar airways. *Thorax* 27: 265–274, 1972.
21. HISLOP, A., AND L. REID. The similarity of the pulmonary artery branching system in siblings. *Forensic Sci.* 2: 37–52, 1973.
22. HOGG, J. C., J. WILLIAMS, J. B. RICHARDSON, P. T. MACKLEM, AND W. M. THURLBECK. Age as a factor in the distribution of lower-airway conductance and in the pathologic anatomy of obstructive lung disease. *N. Engl. J. Med.* 282: 1283–1287, 1970.
23. HONDA, H. Description of the form of trees by the parameters of the tree-like body: effect of branching angle and the branch length on the shape of the tree-like body. *J. Theor. Biol.* 31: 331–338, 1971.
24. HORSFIELD, K. *Morphology of the Human Bronchial Tree.* Birmingham, UK: Univ. of Birmingham, 1967. MD thesis.
25. HORSFIELD, K. *Analysis and Modelling of Branching Systems.* Birmingham, UK: Univ. of Birmingham, 1972. PhD thesis.

26. HORSFIELD, K. Some mathematical properties of branching trees with application to the respiratory system. *Bull. Math. Biol.* 38: 305–315, 1976.

27. HORSFIELD, K. Morphology of branching trees related to entropy. *Respir. Physiol.* 29: 179–184, 1977.

28. HORSFIELD, K. Postnatal growth of the dog's bronchial tree. *Respir. Physiol.* 29: 185–191, 1977.

29. HORSFIELD, K. Are diameter, length and branching ratios meaningful in the lung? *J. Theor. Biol.* 87: 773–784, 1980.

30. HORSFIELD, K. The science of branching systems. In: *Scientific Foundations of Respiratory Medicine*, edited by J. G. Scadding and G. Cumming. London: Heinemann, 1981, chapt. 5, p. 45–54.

31. HORSFIELD, K. The structure of the tracheobronchial tree. In: *Scientific Foundations of Respiratory Medicine*, edited by J. G. Scadding and G. Cumming. London: Heinemann, 1981, chapt. 6, p. 54–70.

32. HORSFIELD, K., AND G. CUMMING. Angles of branching and diameters of branches in the human bronchial tree. *Bull. Math. Biophys.* 29: 245–259, 1967.

33. HORSFIELD, K., AND G. CUMMING. Morphology of the bronchial tree in man. *J. Appl. Physiol.* 24: 373–383, 1968.

34. HORSFIELD, K., AND G. CUMMING. Morphology of the bronchial tree in the dog. *Respir. Physiol.* 26: 173–182, 1976.

35. HORSFIELD, K., G. DART, D. E. OLSON, G. F. FILLEY, AND G. CUMMING. Models of the human bronchial tree. *J. Appl. Physiol.* 31: 207–217, 1971.

36. HORSFIELD, K., W. KEMP, AND S. PHILLIPS. An asymmetrical model of the airways of the dog lung. *J. Appl. Physiol.: Respirat. Environ. Exercise Physiol.* 52: 21–26, 1982.

37. HORSFIELD, K., AND A. THURLBECK. Volume of the conducting airways calculated from morphometric parameters. *Bull. Math. Biol.* 43: 101–109, 1981.

38. HORSFIELD, K., AND A. THURLBECK. The relation between diameter and flow in branches of the bronchial tree. *Bull. Math. Biol.* 43: 681–691, 1981.

39. HUGHES, J. M. B., F. G. HOPPIN, JR., AND J. MEAD. Effect of lung inflation on bronchial length and diameter in excised lungs. *J. Appl. Physiol.* 32: 25–35, 1972.

40. HUGHES, J. M. B., H. A. JONES, A. G. WILSON, B. J. B. GRANT, AND N. B. PRIDE. Stability of intrapulmonary bronchial dimensions during expiratory flow in excised lungs. *J. Appl. Physiol.* 37: 684–694, 1974.

41. JACKSON, A. C., J. P. BUTLER, E. J. MILLET, F. G. HOPPIN, JR., AND S. V. DAWSON. Airway geometry by analysis of acoustic pulse response measurements. *J. Appl. Physiol.: Respirat. Environ. Exercise Physiol.* 43: 523–536, 1977.

42. KAMIYA, A., AND T. TOGAWA. Optimal branching structure of the vascular tree. *Bull. Math. Biophys.* 34: 431–438, 1972.

43. KRAHL, V. E. Anatomy of the mammalian lung. In: *Handbook of Physiology. Respiration*, edited by W. O. Fenn and H. Rahn. Washington, DC: Am. Physiol. Soc., 1964, sect. 3, vol. I, chapt. 6, p. 213–284.

44. LEOPOLD, L. B., AND W. B. LANGBEIN. *The Concept of Entropy in Landscape Evolution*. Washington, DC: US Dept. Interior, 1962, p. A1–A20. (Geological Survey Professional Paper 500-A.)

45. MILLER, W. S. *The Lung* (2nd ed.). Springfield, IL: Thomas, 1947.

46. MON, E., AND J. S. ULTMAN. Monte Carlo simulation of simultaneous gas flow and diffusion in an asymmetric distal pulmonary airway model. *Bull. Math. Biol.* 38: 161–192, 1976.

47. MURRAY, C. D. The physiological principle of minimum work applied to the angle of branching of arteries. *J. Gen. Physiol.* 9: 835–841, 1926.

48. MURRAY, C. D. The physiological principle of minimum work. I. The vascular system and the cost of blood volume. *Proc. Natl. Acad. Sci. USA* 12: 207–214, 1926.

49. NADEL, J. A., W. G. WOOLFE, AND P. D. GRAF. Powdered tantalum as a medium for bronchography in canine and human lungs. *Invest. Radiol.* 3: 229–238, 1968.

50. OGAWA, C. The finer ramifications of the human lung. *Am. J. Anat.* 27: 315–332, 1920.

51. PAIVA, M. Gas transport in the human lung. *J. Appl. Physiol.* 35: 401–410, 1973.

52. PALMES, E. D. Measurement of pulmonary air spaces using aerosols. *Arch. Intern. Med.* 131: 76–79, 1973.

53. PARKER, H., K. HORSFIELD, AND G. CUMMING. Morphology of distal airways in the human lung. *J. Appl. Physiol.* 31: 386–391, 1971.

54. PEDLEY, T. J., R. C. SCHROTER, AND M. F. SUDLOW. Energy losses and pressure drop in models of the human airways. *Respir. Physiol.* 9: 371–386, 1970.

55. PHALEN, R. F., H. C. YEH, O. G. RAABE, AND D. J. VELASQUEZ. Casting the lungs in-situ. *Anat. Rec.* 177: 255–263, 1973.

56. PHALEN, R. F., H. C. YEH, G. M. SCHUM, AND O. G. RAABE. Application of an idealized model to morphometry of the mammalian tracheobronchial tree. *Anat. Rec.* 190: 167–176, 1978.

57. PUMP, K. K. The morphology of the finer branches of the bronchial tree of the human lung. *Dis. Chest* 46: 379–398, 1964.

58. PUMP, K. K. Morphology of the acinus of the human lung. *Dis. Chest* 56: 126–134, 1969.

59. RAABE, O. G., H. C. YEH, G. M. SCHUM, AND R. F. PHALEN. *Tracheobronchial Geometry: Human, Dog, Rat, Hamster.* Albuquerque, NM: Lovelace Found. Med. Educ. Res., 1976.

60. RAHN, H., AND B. B. ROSS. Bronchial tree casts, lobe weights and anatomical dead space measurements in the dog's lung. *J. Appl. Physiol.* 10: 154–157, 1957.

61. RASHEVSKY, N. The principle of adequate design. In: *Foundations of Mathematical Biology*, edited by R. Rosen. New York: Academic, 1973, vol. 3, p. 143–175.

62. ROHRER, F. Der Strömungwiderstand in den menschlichen Atemwegen und der Einfluss der unregelmässigen Verzweigung des Bronchialsystems auf den Atmungsverlauf in verschiedenen Lungenbezirken. *Pfluegers Arch. Gesamte Physiol. Menschen Tiere* 162: 225–259, 1915.

63. ROSS, B. B. Influence of bronchial tree structure on ventilation of the dog's lung as inferred from measurements of a plastic cast. *J. Appl. Physiol.* 10: 1–14, 1957.

64. SCHERER, P. W., AND A. I. PACK. Bronchial cross-section from lung gas washout. *J. Bioeng.* 1: 347–356, 1977.

65. SCHROTER, R. C., AND M. F. SUDLOW. Flow patterns in models of the human bronchial airways. *Respir. Physiol.* 7: 341–355, 1969.

66. SIDELL, R. S., AND J. J. FREDBERG. Non-invasive inference of airway network geometry from broadband lung reflection data. *J. Biomech. Eng.* 100: 131–138, 1978.

67. SLUTSKY, A. S., G. G. BERDINE, AND J. M. DRAZEN. Steady flow in a model of human central airways. *J. Appl. Physiol.: Respirat. Environ. Exercise Physiol.* 49: 417–423, 1980.

68. SNYDER, B., D. R. DANTZKER, AND M. J. JAEGER. Flow partitioning in symmetric cascades of branches. *J. Appl. Physiol.: Respirat. Environ. Exercise Physiol.* 51: 598–606, 1981.

69. STRAHLER, A. N. Revision of Horton's quantitative factors in erosional terrain. *Trans. Am. Geophys. Union* 34: 345, 1953.

70. STRAHLER, A. N. Quantitative analysis of watershed geomorphology. *Trans. Am. Geophys. Union* 38: 913–920, 1957.

71. THOMPSON, D. *On Growth and Form* (2nd ed.). Cambridge, UK: Cambridge Univ. Press, 1952.

72. THURLBECK, A., AND K. HORSFIELD. Branching angles in the bronchial tree related to order of branching. *Respir. Physiol.* 41: 173–181, 1980.

73. THURLBECK, W. M., AND N.-S. WANG. The structure of the lungs. In: *Respiratory Physiology I*, edited by J. G. Widdicombe. London: Butterworths, 1974, ser. 1, vol. 2, chapt. 1, p. 1–30. (Int. Rev. Physiol. Ser.)

74. TIMBRELL, V., N. E. BEVAN, A. S. DAVIES, AND D. E. MUNDAY. Hollow casts of lungs for experimental purposes. *Nature London* 255: 97–98, 1970.

75. TISI, G. M., V. D. MINH, AND P. J. FRIEDMAN. In vivo dimensional response of airways of different size to transpulmonary pressure. *J. Appl. Physiol.* 39: 23–29, 1975.

76. TOMPSETT, D. H. *Anatomical Techniques*. London: Livingstone, 1956.
77. UYLINGS, H. B. M. Optimization of diameters and bifurcation angles in lung and vascular tree structures. *Bull. Math. Biol.* 39: 509–520, 1977.
78. WEIBEL, E. R. *Morphometry of the Human Lung*. Berlin: Springer-Verlag, 1963.
79. WILLSON H. G. The terminals of the human bronchiole. *Am. J. Anat.* 30: 267–295, 1922.
80. WILSON, T. A. Design of the bronchial tree. *Nature London* 213: 668–669, 1967.
81. WOLDEHIWOT, Z., AND K. HORSFIELD. Diameter, length and branching angles of the upper airways in the dog lung. *Respir. Physiol.* 33: 213–218, 1978.
82. YEATS, D. B., AND N. ASPIN. A mathematical description of the airways of the human lungs. *Respir. Physiol.* 32: 91–104, 1978.
83. YEH, H. C., AND G. M. SCHUM. Models of human lung airways and their application to inhaled particle deposition. *Bull. Math. Biol.* 42: 461–480, 1980.
84. YEH, H. C., G. M. SCHUM, AND M. J. DUGGAN. Anatomic models of the tracheobronchial and pulmonary regions of the rat. *Anat. Rec.* 195: 483–492, 1979.
85. YOUNG, T. On the functions of the heart and arteries. *Philos. Trans. R. Soc. London* 99: 1–31, 1808.
86. ZAMIR, M. Optimality principles in arterial branching. *J. Theor. Biol.* 62: 227–251, 1976.

CHAPTER 8

Functional morphology of lung parenchyma

EWALD R. WEIBEL | *Department of Anatomy, University of Berne, Berne, Switzerland*

CHAPTER CONTENTS

THE LUNG'S STRUCTURAL DESIGN permits air and blood to be maintained in intense contact over a very large surface and across a very thin yet highly organized tissue barrier.

The mechanical properties of lung parenchyma are determined to a large extent—though not exclusively—by a tension skeleton made of connective tissue fibers that pervade the lung according to a strictly hierarchical design pattern. In the preceding chapter in this *Handbook*, Horsfield shows that the airway tree branches systematically until the final branches form acini, the gas-exchange units of the lung, which expand to fill the available space with alveoli. These conducting airways are enwrapped by a sheath of connective tissue that penetrates deep into the acini along the alveolar duct. On the other hand, the visceral pleura bounds the lung's lobes and thus forms a set of fiber bags from which fibrous septa penetrate deep into lung parenchyma. The alveolar walls with their network of fine fibers are extended between alveolar ducts and pleural septa. A tension skeleton is thus established that consists of *1*) *axial* fibers that fan out centrifugally from the hilum along the branching airway tree, *2*) *peripheral* fibers that emanate from the pleura and penetrate centripetally into the lung, and *3*) alveolar *septal* fibers that join the two. Thus the tension that is indirectly exerted on the visceral pleura by chest wall and diaphragm is transmitted to the entire fiber skeleton.

Several additional factors affect the lung's mechanical properties. To maintain a large air-fluid interface within a comparatively small volume calls for stabilizing factors; a surfactant lining that regulates surface tension to very low values plays the foremost role, together with the deformability of the underlying tissue that allows the surface to be smoothed to some extent as a result of balancing the interactive forces of surface tension, tissue tension, and vascular distending pressure.

ELEMENTS OF LUNG STRUCTURE

Histologically the lung is organized into three basic tissue layers interposed between air and blood: the airway epithelium and the vascular endothelium, which are bound together by the interstitial connective tissue. Epithelium and endothelium form two uninterrupted and more or less tight cell layers that govern the movement of solutes and water between three fluid spaces: the blood, the interstitial fluid, and the surface lining layer of air spaces. Grossly, the lung can be divided into two major functional parts: lung parenchyma that contains the delicate gas-exchange tissue of the respiratory zone and nonparenchyma that comprises all conducting structures, airways, and blood vessels, as well as the coarser connective tissue components. Because of the different functions subserved, the tissue layers are structured differently depending on their location in the respiratory or conducting zone of the lung. Table 1 presents an overview of the volume fractions of lung tissue ascribed to the major components of lung structure (25).

Epithelium

Epithelium predominantly consists of two basic cell types: lining cells and secretory cells. In the conducting airways the lining cells are ciliated cells whose cilia move the mucous blanket centripetally; the lining

TABLE 1. *Composition of the Lung*

A. Cells*		
Structure	Cells	% of Total Lung Cells
Parenchyma	Total	86
	Alveolar type I	4
	Alveolar type II	6
	Endothelial	33
	Mesenchymal	43
Nonparenchyma	Total	14
Airways		5
	Ciliated	2–3
	Glandular	<1
Blood vessels		9

B. Connective Tissue†		
Structure	Component	% of Total Lung Connective Tissue
Parenchyma	Total	62
	Collagen	46
	Elastin	16
Nonparenchyma	Total	38
	Collagen	28
	Elastin	10

*74% of mass of lung.   †26% of mass of lung.   [From Fulmer and Crystal (25), by courtesy of Marcel Dekker, Inc.]

cells of alveoli (Fig. 1) consist of the type I alveolar cells (type I pneumonocyte), a very large and complex cell type—in spite of its "small" appearance on sections—characterized by very thin cytoplasmic leaflets that spread over an area of several thousand square micrometers (19, 20, 43, 104). Secretory cells of major conducting airways are mostly mucus-secreting cells that occur either as goblet cells intercalated between ciliated cells or as small glands located in the submucosal layer; Clara cells replace goblet cells in the bronchioles. In the alveolar epithelium the secretory cells are type II pneumonocytes, small cuboidal cells (Fig. 1) whose function is to synthesize and secrete the surfactant phospholipids (3, 10, 35, 53, 77, 120) that are needed to reduce surface tension at the air-fluid interface in the respiratory air spaces. At all levels several additional, though rarer, cell types occur scattered in the epithelium. Although they need not concern us in this chapter, they are discussed in the first volume of this *Handbook* section on the respiratory system (110).

One of the important features of the air-space epithelium relevant for considerations of fluid mechanics in the lung is the fact that the epithelial lining is sealed by tight intercellular junctions (89, 90, 92) that do not allow any significant fluid exchange through intercellular pathways (91, 102). This is particularly well established for the alveolar epithelium; any fluid or solute exchange between the interstitial space and the alveolar (air-space) lining layer must therefore involve a transcellular movement and is consequently subject to active intervention on the part of the epithelial lining (91, 102).

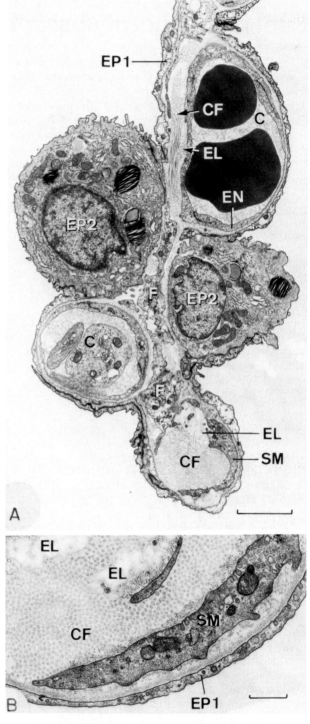

FIG. 1. *A*: alveolar septum of dog lung showing delicate fiber bundle in septum and strong bundle at free edge forming the alveolar entrance ring as boundary of alveolar duct. Note collagen (*CF*) and elastic (*EL*) fibers, fibroblasts (*F*), and smooth muscle cell (*SM*). Capillaries (*C*) lined by endothelial cells (*EN*), alveolar surface lined by epithelium made of cuboidal type II (*EP2*) and squamous type I (*EP1*) cells. Scale, 2 μm. *B*: entrance ring at higher power. Scale, 0.5 μm.

Surface Lining of Air Spaces

According to the different functions to be served, the surface lining of lung epithelia differs between conducting and respiratory air spaces. In the conducting airways a highly viscous mucous blanket lies on top of a hypophase of low viscosity within which the cilia beat (96). The mucous layer catches and conveys outward inhaled particles that become deposited in these airways, as well as macrophages (e.g., dust cells) that carry such materials from deeper lung regions. In the most peripheral bronchioles the lining is similar to that found in alveoli (37). In the respiratory zone the very thin surface lining of alveoli and alveolar ducts is again made of two layers: an aqueous hypophase and a surface film of phospholipids or lipoproteins that reduces surface tension.

Endothelium

The vascular endothelium is made of a simple squamous epithelium. In the alveolar capillaries the endothelial cells are lining cells that are very thinned out (see Fig. 1) whose intercellular junctions appear to be relatively leaky so that extensive pathways exist for fluid and solute exchange between the blood space and the interstitium (89–91, 102). The leakiness of the endothelium of larger pulmonary vessels is not as well established, although it has been claimed but not proven that lung lymph is predominantly formed from smaller pulmonary or bronchial veins (80, 97–99).

Interstitial Space and Structures

In the broadest sense the pulmonary interstitium is the space bounded by the basement membranes of the air-space epithelium, the vascular endothelium, and the pleural mesothelium. Its structural constituents are those of connective tissue in general: a fiber system, a set of various interstitial cells, and some free extracellular fluid related to lymph (21, 24, 81).

The pulmonary interstitium appears to form a fluid continuum along the fiber system, from the alveolar walls to spaces enwrapping major airways and blood vessels and to the visceral pleura and septa emanating from it. This concept of a fluid continuum is important in view of the fact that the major drainage pathway for interstitial fluid is via the lymphatics that originate in the connective tissue masses associated with larger vessels and airways and interlobular septa (58, 59). Because lymphatics are missing in alveolar septa, one tends to conclude that interstitial fluid formed from alveolar capillaries needs to be drained to "juxtaalveolar" regions where it can be collected by lymphatic capillaries (97, 99, 111). However, this concept has recently been challenged because fibroblasts were found to span across the insertion of alveolar septa on perivascular sheaths (34); the effect of this feature as a potential limit to fluid flow still needs to be demonstrated.

Fibroblasts are ubiquitous, occurring in major connective tissue structures and in the delicate alveolar walls (see Fig. 1A). Typically they are associated with fibers along which they course with very long and irregular cytoplasmic extensions that are often very thin and poor in organelles. The fibroblasts are responsible for manufacturing the materials (e.g., proteins) from which fibers are assembled, both during fibrogenesis and during maintenance of established fibers.

In recent years it has been shown that some or all fibroblasts have contractile properties (29, 51, 52, 63), due to the presence of bundles of cytoplasmic microfilaments 6 nm thick that are anchored in the cell membrane. With immunocytochemical techniques it has been demonstrated that these bundles of microfilaments contain actin and myosin of the smooth muscle type, thus they are called myofibroblasts (29, 63, 87). The distribution and arrangement of such myofibroblasts in the lung have not been fully worked out. They are particularly conspicuous in the alveolar septa where their microfilaments appear to extend crosswise, joining the basement membranes bounding the septal interstitium (51, 52, 111); they have been ascribed a hypothetical function as regulators of either capillary blood flow (51, 52) in the framework of the sheet-flow model (27, 28) or compliance of the interstitial space for fluid accumulation (111). One could also imagine that they may play a role in regulating tissue elasticity, introducing a component of the elastic modulus that can be regulated by modifying the tone of the actomyosin fibers. Such an effect may occur particularly in association with the prominent fiber bundles around the alveolar duct where one finds such myofibroblasts in larger quantity and in all stages of differentiation toward actual smooth muscle cells (see Fig. 1B). There is no evidence to show the arrangement of such actomyosin fibrils along the fiber system of the alveolar septa, although physiological evidence obtained by pharmacological stimulation appears to indicate that such elements can cause parenchymal tissue strips (presumably a sequence of connected septa) to contract (51). In relation to the blood vessels one must note the presence of pericytes on alveolar capillaries (106) that contain the same type of microfilaments and may be seen to be, at least in part, continuous with septal myofibroblasts; whether they are a separate cell type or merely a special differentiation of some general myofibroblast remains to be shown.

Smooth muscle cells are prominent elements in the walls of all conducting channels, airways as well as blood vessels. In smaller bronchi and bronchioles, immediately beneath the mucosa they form a sleeve of helical bundles of low pitch arranged in a crisscross pattern. At the transition to the respiratory zone these bundles extend into the helical strands of connective tissue forming the major framework of central alveolar ducts (see GEOMETRY AND MECHANICS OF THE ACI-

NUS, p. 105), where they finally become reduced to myofibroblasts in the more peripheral elements.

ELEMENTS OF THE FIBER SYSTEM

There are three types of extracellular fibers of connective tissue: collagen, reticulin, and elastic fibers, which differ by structural, biochemical, and functional properties. Although the overall mechanical properties of the lung depend to a lesser degree on them, two additional and closely related elements of the interstitial space must be mentioned: the proteoglycans of the interstitial ground substance and the basement membranes of epithelium, endothelium, and smooth muscle cells.

Collagen and Reticulin Fibers

By their chemical nature four different types of collagen can be distinguished (44), but only type I collagen appears to be responsible for the formation of collagen fibers. The structural unit of collagen fibers are cylindrical fibrils 40–200 nm thick and as long as the fiber itself (Fig. 2). These fibrils show a characteristic banding of 64-nm periodicity, which is due to a typical staggered arrangement of the building block tropocollagen (a triple helix of 2 different collagen molecules) that is manufactured and secreted by fibroblasts (44, 84). Fibrils are assembled extracellularly and given their high tensile strength by multiple crosslinks within and between tropocollagen units. The collagen fiber is formed by assembling a bundle of these fibrils, which are usually rather homogeneous in thickness, and binding them together with some proteoglycans. In the lung, collagen fibers show an entire spectrum of sizes, from a few fibrils to bundles of several hundred fibrils 1–4 μm or more in thickness. Collagen fibers have a very high elastic modulus and tensile strength; they are practically inextensible (<2%) and rupture at loads of 50–70 $\times$ 10^6 dyn·cm^{-2} (47, 100).

Reticulin fibers, also called argyrophilic fibers because they stain intensely with silver salts, are built predominantly of collagen with some additional material; they are composed of smaller fibrils only 20–30 nm thick (44, 60, 61). These fibrils are also bundled to make reticulin fibers and are often—if not regularly—associated with actual collagen fibrils either singly or in small bundles (50).

Several other small fibrils have been described, particularly as anchoring fibrils for epithelia (44, 60); they appear to be made of a different type of collagen (type III?) and seem related to basement membranes that contain type IV collagen. Yet these questions need further clarification, particularly because the conditions may vary from tissue to tissue; little or nothing is known about it for the lung.

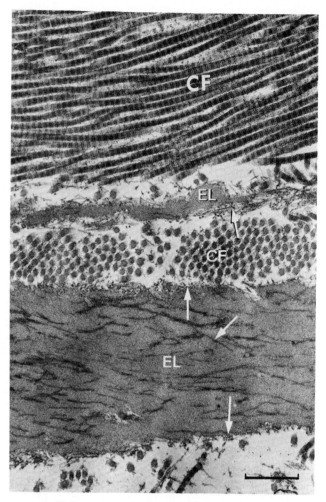

FIG. 2. Fine structure of collagen (*CF*) and elastic (*EL*) fibers in perivascular sheath. Collagen fibers are bundles of banded fibrils seen in longitudinal and transverse section. Elastic fibers are made of amorphous core surrounded by microfibrils (*arrows*) that are partly embedded in core in thicker fibers. Scale, 0.5 μm.

Elastic Fibers

The biochemical nature of elastic fibers is poorly understood, particularly because of the extreme insolubility of elastin (5, 49). Electron microscopy reveals that elastic fibers are made of two structural components: an amorphous core surrounded by microfibrils in the form of fine tubules 11 nm thick (Fig. 2). During fiber formation the microfibrils develop first, then the amorphous component is added to them (2). The microfibrils are found at the periphery of the fiber but in larger fibers also occur as fine bundles in the interior of the amorphous core. It is believed that the amorphous core represents the actual elastin (41, 85) and thus has the elastic properties typical of elastic fibers, namely a relatively high extensibility (to ~130% relaxed length) and a low tensile strength when compared with collagen fibers (14).

In contrast to collagen fibers, elastic fibers do not have a fibrillar substructure in spite of the associated microfibrils (see Figs. 1*B* and 2); they enlarge by thickening the amorphous core. The smallest elastic fibers that can be recognized as such by electron microscopy are ~100 nm thick, slightly larger than a collagen fibril, but larger fibers may be several micrometers thick.

Integral Fiber Strand

In terms of tissue mechanics it is actually incorrect to consider collagen and elastic fibers as separate entities; jointly they constitute integral fiber strands. There is barely any connective tissue in the body where there is only one fiber type, perhaps with the exception of such highly specialized organs as the cornea. The same is true for the lung where collagen and elastic fibers occur in tandem anywhere (see Figs. 1 and 2); for the human lung, Pierce and Ebert (79) have found that the ratio of collagen to elastin is ~2.5 for lung parenchyma but >10 for the pleura in young adults.

In a relaxed state one finds that the elastic fibers form a network of more or less straight fibers, whereas the collagen fibers appear wavy (Fig. 3). If such a tissue is stretched, the elastic fibers become extended until the collagen fibers are straight. The integral fiber strand of connective tissue is hence not to be compared with a rubber band but rather with an elastic band of interwoven rubber and cotton threads, which is extensible only to a certain limit determined by the length of the inextensible fibers. The extension capacity of connective tissue is accordingly determined by the length of the collagen fibers, whereas the elastic fibers keep the integral fiber network under a certain tension at lower levels of expansion.

Collagen and elastic fibers form networks of interwoven fibers, providing the tissue with what has been called a "nylon-stocking" extensibility (11, 44, 67): stretching in one direction leads to temporary rearrangement of the fibers. It is the interweaving of such a sheet with elastic fibers that restores the original arrangement upon relaxation and, to some extent, distributes the forces evenly to all fibers of the sheet. It is not fully understood to what extent the proteoglycans, which form a gel-like matrix around these connective tissue fibers, contribute to the mechanical properties of this integral fiber network.

FIBER CONTINUUM OF THE LUNG

Formation of a fiber continuum that pervades the entire lung from hilum to visceral pleura has its origin in the integral mesenchymal bed into which the airway tubes branch systematically during lung morphogenesis (13, 22, 62).

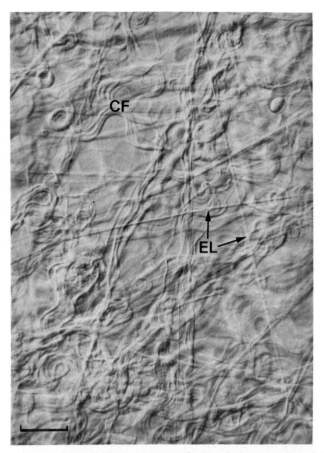

FIG. 3. Integral fiber system seen by interference-contrast microscopy of subcutaneous tissue of rat. Elastic fibers (*EL*) form network of straight fibers associated with wavy collagen fibers (*CF*). Scale, 50 μm.

The original lung anlage consists of an epithelial bronchial bud and a mesenchymal mass, the latter derived from the splanchnopleura that bounds it toward the chest cavity (13). The lung becomes progressively structured by the growth and sequential dichotomous branching of the bronchial buds. This is accompanied by a number of changes in the mesenchymal bed, which enlarges as the bronchial tree grows. The airway tubes become enwrapped by a sheath of mesenchyme that is closely apposed to the epithelium. On the other hand, the branching airway tree forms glandlike lobules that remain separated by broader septa that are continuous with the visceral pleura (Fig. 4). These two distinct parts of pulmonary mesenchyme form the anlage for the two major connective tissue tracts of the mature lung: the axial fiber system, which follows the airway tree, and the peripheral fiber system, which is connected to the pleura and separates—incompletely—the airway units. However, these two systems are never separated completely. Within the lobules the mesenchyme appears condensed and contains the vascular network that gives rise to the alveolar capillaries; out of this intralobular

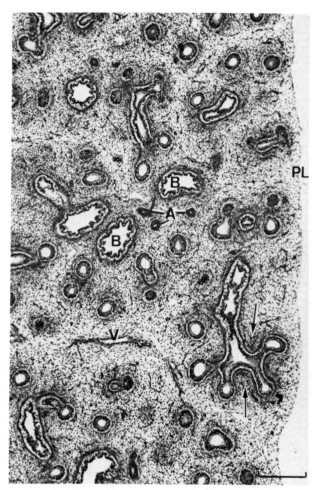

FIG. 4. Section of fetal human lung showing continuity of loose peripheral mesenchymal bed from pleura (*PL*) to deeper parts of lung, and condensed mesenchyme (*arrows*) around bronchi (*B*) and within lobules as anlage of axial fiber system. Note location of pulmonary veins (*V*) and arteries (*A*) in loose mesenchyme. Scale, 200 μm.

part the septal fibers eventually form during late fetal and early postnatal development (12, 13). On larger airways one finds the condensed axial mesenchymal sheath directly in contact with loose peripheral mesenchyme (see Fig. 4). It is noteworthy that all major blood vessels (pulmonary arteries and veins) develop into the loose mesenchyme and are hence also related to the peripheral fiber system; in spite of the fact that arteries develop in close association with bronchi, their sheath is not directly related to the axial fiber system. Peribronchial and perivascular sheaths are hence parts of the peripheral fiber system.

Axial Fiber System

As one progresses from bronchi through bronchioles to alveolar ducts, the structural design of the axial fiber system shows a different pattern. In the bronchial wall strong connective tissue fibers are found predominantly in two locations. Immediately beneath the epithelial lining one finds a substantial amount of heavy fibers with a dominance of elastic fibers that course mostly longitudinally (72). This mucosal fiber sheath continues without interruption into the bronchioles but becomes thinner as the airways become smaller. At branch points it appears reinforced by fiber loops to brace the saddle-shaped spur formed where the two daughter branches separate. In the bronchi a second external fiber sheath is formed that incorporates the cartilaginous plates characteristic of bronchi. In this so-called fibrocartilaginous sheath collagen fibers dominate; elastic fibers become more prominent in smaller bronchi where the plates are made of elastic cartilage. This external sheath continues into the bronchioles as a simple fiber sheath without cartilage but gradually becomes finer. Internal and external fiber sheaths are separated by the layer of smooth muscle, but there are multiple connections between the two sheaths.

The geometry and topology of the axial fiber system drastically change at the transition from bronchioles to alveolar ducts, with respiratory bronchioles forming an intermediate (Fig. 5). It has been shown repeatedly that the fibers of the bronchiolar wall continue into the wall of the alveolar duct conducting pathway in the form of a spiral (78, 79, 119, 125). This forms the main scaffold on which a network of finer but still strong fibers is anchored that encircles the mouths of alveoli and thus forms the actual outline of the duct's conducting pathway (Fig. 6). At branch points of the alveolar ducts the main fiber strand passes through the spur of duct branching and then continues into both branches. This arrangement of a main fiber tract is noteworthy because it clearly demonstrates, on one hand, the continuity of the axial fiber system from bronchioles into the alveolar ducts and, on the other hand, provides a mechanism for extensibility of the duct system of lung parenchyma by allowing this spiral fiber scaffold to "unfold" as the lung expands (79). The existence of such strong spiral fibers has been demonstrated in the human lung for the first orders of alveolar ducts (125); toward the periphery it is less conspicuous as the fibers forming the network of alveolar entrance rings become finer, in general (Fig. 6).

The general conclusion from this description is that the axial fiber system extends without interruption from the bronchi and bronchioles into the alveolar ducts, which form the axial structure of the pulmonary acinus to which all alveolar walls are connected.

Peripheral Fiber System

The visceral pleura, the main supporting structure for the peripheral fiber system, consists of three basic fiber layers (Fig. 7): *1*) an outer fiber bag that sheathes an entire lobe, *2*) an inner fiber layer that is intimately related to adjoining alveolar walls, and *3*) a variable

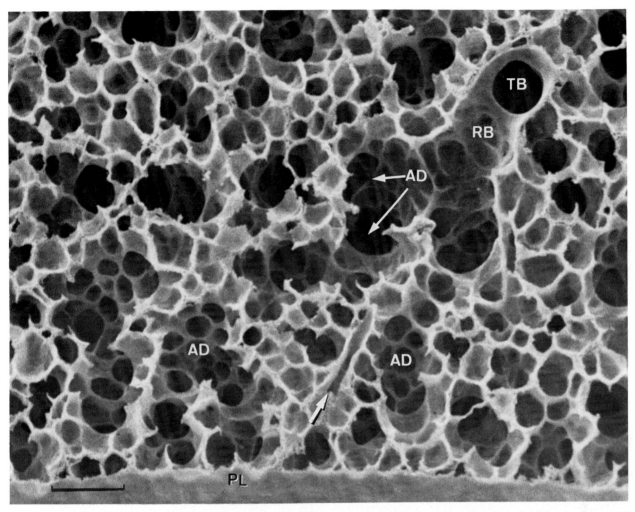

FIG. 5. Acinar airways of perfusion-fixed rabbit lung. Note that the wall of alveolar ducts (*AD*) is formed by network of coarse fiber bundles around alveolar mouths that represent the acinar extension of the axial fiber system from terminal (*TB*) and respiratory (*RB*) bronchioles. Peripheral fiber system is represented by pleura (*PL*) and a small septum with a branch of the pulmonary vein (*arrow*). Scale, 200 μm. [From Weibel (109).]

layer of loose connective tissue with some blood vessels and lymphatics separating—or joining—the two main fiber sheets (46, 71).

The outer fiber bag is directly apposed to the pleural mesothelium. It is made of rather strong collagen and elastic fibers that take a more or less orderly course following geodesic lines over the curved surface (1, 46, 71). This layer is thus rather similar to the capsule of many organs.

The inner fiber layer is made of somewhat more delicate fibers. It is of particular interest in the present context because it is directly connected to the most distal elements of lung parenchyma and thus constitutes the actual structure on which the septal fibers are anchored.

Interlobular septa are formed where this inner layer bends inward to penetrate between parenchymal units (Figs. 7 and 8). In general we call interlobular septa

any connective tissue sheet that lies between parenchymal units irrespective of their order, be they acini, primary or secondary lobules, or even higher-order units such as subsegments or segments.[1] From the point of view of the fiber continuum and lung me-

[1] Of the various lung units described only two are naturally and unambiguously definable (109). *1*) The acinus from within the lung, as that part of the airway tree supplied by a first order respiratory bronchiole, i.e., the parenchymal unit beyond anatomical dead space in which all airways participate in gas exchange. *2*) The lobe from without the lung, as that part enwrapped more or less completely by visceral pleura. All other units are defined by arbitrary criteria because they result from grouping smaller units that share higher-order conducting airways; accordingly there is a continuum of units from acini to lobes. Two units are commonly used, though: secondary lobules, which correspond in the human lung to those units of ~1 cm³ that are visible on the lung surface due to prominent septa (they comprise about a dozen acini); and segments, which are the first subdivisions of the lobes.

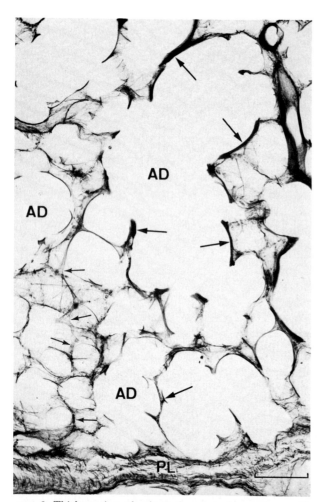

FIG. 6. Thick section of acinar airways in human lung with elastic fiber stain. Fiber strands in wall of alveolar ducts (*AD, heavy arrows*) decrease in thickness toward periphery. *Light arrows* outline peripheral fiber strands that extend from pleura (*PL*). Scale, 200 μm. [From Weibel (109a).]

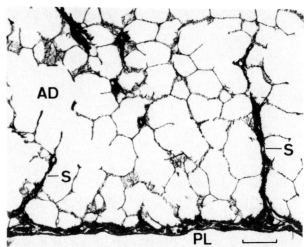

FIG. 7. Subpleural region of human lung with 2 interlobular septa (*S*) extending from pleura (*PL*). Gomori fiber stain. *AD*, alveolar duct. Scale, 200 μm.

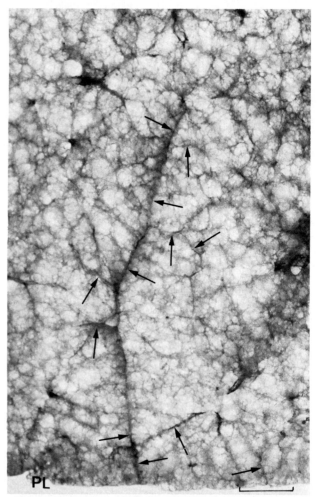

FIG. 8. Thick slice of dried human lung showing hierarchy of interlobular septa (*arrows*). *PL*, pleura. Scale, 1 mm.

chanics such distinctions do not play a major role because the septa of all orders serve the same basic function: to provide a peripheral anchoring point for the alveolar septal fibers, which always emanate from acini. Yet the hierarchy of septa does matter in one respect, namely that the higher-order septa transmit the pleural stress deeper into the lung. In fact, a higher-order septum can be conceived as a "stem" for many septa of lower order. It is not easy to visualize the general construction principle of this system of partitions that forms a large number of densely packed spatial "chambers." This chamber system is the result of the development processes described in the previous section in which the airway tree branches into an originally compact mesenchymal bed (see Fig. 4). Perhaps it helps to consider a simple two-dimensional model such as a fractal tree (64) that, by systematic reduction of the airway dimensions at each branching, allows the space to be filled homogeneously with distal branches of any generation (Fig. 9). If the branching is stopped at a given generation and the terminal generation is allowed to expand into a "bubble," mimicking the alveolation of alveolar ducts in the acinus, a model not unlike the lung results. In this model the

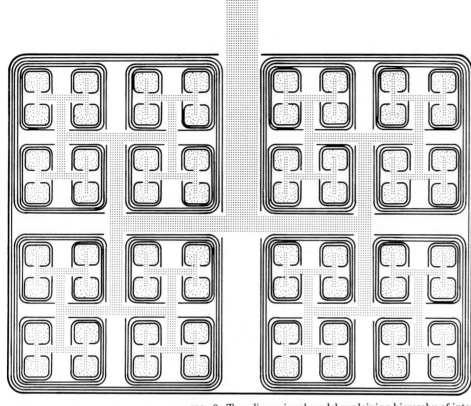

FIG. 9. Two-dimensional model explaining hierarchy of interlobular septa as a sequence of shells around the branchings of a fractal airway tree.

peripheral fiber system is represented by the hull of the fractal tree, which enwraps the units of different order with a sequence of "shells" of different size and gives rise to a hierarchy of interlobular septa all connected directly or indirectly to the outermost hull, the equivalent of the visceral pleura (Fig. 9).

In the real lung this hull structure is complete only during fetal lung development (see Fig. 4). As the lung matures, some of the septa are reduced to slim strands of connective tissue only slightly coarser than those within the acini. This is true for most mammalian lungs with a few exceptions: in the pig and the calf, for example, the interlobular septa remain very prominent so that lobules are clearly separated (46, 71). In the human lung some incomplete septa are visible on thick slices down to about the order of secondary lobules, structures ~1 cm in diameter (see Fig. 8). The mechanical consequences of these different designs are not known.

Interlobular septa of all orders contain the branches of the pulmonary veins. In higher-order septa these are enwrapped in a sheath of loose connective tissue that may also contain lymphatics.

The peripheral fiber system extends centrally toward the hilum. To further complicate matters it also reaches the bronchial walls where it forms the peribronchium, a sheath of loose connective tissue outside the fibrocartilaginous layer, on which acini abut. This layer is not present in peripheral bronchioles. The loose connective tissue sleeves of the branches of the pulmonary arteries also must be assigned to the peripheral fiber system; these sleeves are not truly related to the axial fiber system, although the pulmonary arteries course along the bronchi and bronchioles. This classification of peribronchial and periarterial sleeves as part of the peripheral fiber system may seem surprising. However, it is understood immediately by referring to the model of Figure 9. The peripheral fiber system by definition enwraps the outer surface of acini and has to form the contact surface between lung parenchyma and larger airways or blood vessels where deep acini abut on them. This is the result of the space-filling branching pattern of the airway tubes, as becomes evident by considering lung development (see Fig. 4).

Alveolar Septal Fiber System

In the lung of the newborn the airways of the gas-exchange region consist of simple wide saccules corresponding approximately to the conducting channels of the alveolar ducts and sacs of the mature lung; alveoli form mostly during the early postnatal period by a process that is not fully understood (12). The first step appears to be the reinforcement of the fiber net around the saccule, at which time the spiral course of the main alveolar duct fibers (78, 125) is probably established. Subsequently the regions between the fiber strands allow pouches to be formed that gradually enlarge to become alveoli; the ridges that separate the original pouches and lengthen as these enlarge contain capillaries, fibroblasts, and some finer fibers. When this process has been completed alveolar septa have been formed that separate, on one hand, adjoining alveoli of the same alveolar duct (lateral wall septa) and, on the other hand, alveoli of adjacent alveolar ducts (roof septa) (Fig. 10A). The structure resulting is similar to that of a foam with the various septa meeting along triple lines, and triple lines making quadruple points where they meet, the typical picture of packed polyhedral chambers. It is essential to note that all the alveolar septa thus formed are continuous with each other and that each chamber is open to an alveolar duct. The connective tissue fibers of these septa, integral strands of elastic, collagen, and reticular fibers of various thicknesses, spread out in the form of a "flat" network within each wall (Fig. 10B) but are seen to extend across the triple lines to join the network of the next septa. The fiber system of the entire complex of septa is hence a continuum, at least within one acinus.

Yet now it must be noted that the lateral wall septa are directly attached to the fiber net of the alveolar duct (see Figs. 1, 6, and 10B) and their fibers are thus connected to the distal extensions of the axial fiber system. The roof septa have been formed in the region where the peripheral connective tissue had penetrated with some fine extensions between the primitive saccules so that the fibers in these septa are connected to the peripheral fiber system. By this a fiber continuum is established throughout the lung as has been described repeatedly (15, 55, 56, 78, 109, 113, 124) but for the first time authoritatively by Orsós (74, 75).

DESIGN OF THE ALVEOLAR SEPTUM

The structural elements of pulmonary gas exchange are concentrated in alveolar septa and are thus directly related to the septal fiber system (105, 109, 111, 113). The alveolar capillaries form a dense network within the septum that is interwoven with the fiber net of the septal fiber system (Fig. 11). Each septum commonly contains a single network of capillaries with occasional duplications (42a). If lungs are fixed at high inflation levels by conventional fluid instillation into the airways (30, 105), the septal fibers appear taut and the capillaries weave back and forth from one side of the wall to the other (Fig. 11B), alternately bulging into one then the other of the two alveoli separated by the septum.

The design of the gas-exchange unit is best seen on a section (Fig. 12). The tissue barrier separating air

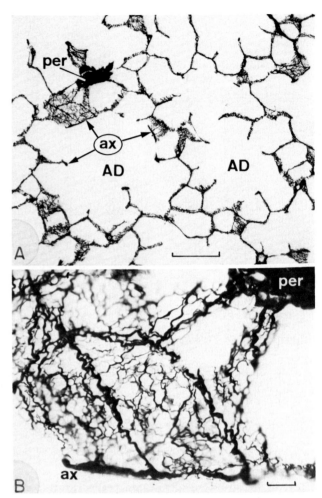

FIG. 10. Septal fiber network of human lung. A: alveolar septa are extended between alveolar ducts (AD) marked by axial fibers (ax). per, Peripheral fibers. Scale, 200 μm. B: flat view at higher power of septal fibers extended between axial and peripheral fibers. Scale, 20 μm.

and blood shows two distinct regions: a thin part where the basement membranes of epithelium and endothelium are fused thus excluding an actual interstitial space from this minimal barrier, and a thick part where the interstitial space contains fibers and fibroblasts as well as some free fluid. Because the capillary network is interwoven with a single fiber meshwork (Fig. 11B), one finds the thin and thick parts on alternate sides with each covering about half the gas-exchange surface (109, 111).

Another structural property of alveolar septa needs to be mentioned: the occurrence of alveolar pores that extend from one alveolus to the other (see Fig. 11A). These pores, called the pores of Kohn, are located in loops of the capillary meshwork and are delimited by alveolar epithelium. The frequency of such pores is apparently species dependent; in lungs of humans, rats, and rabbits there are only a few pores of various sizes, whereas in lungs of dogs and shrews nearly every capillary mesh is perforated by a pore (105). Their

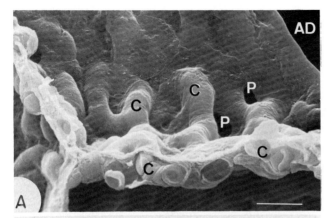

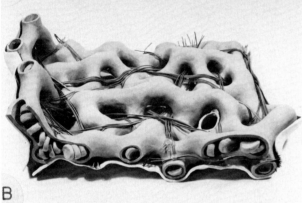

FIG. 11. Structure of human alveolar septum. A: scanning electron micrograph showing capillaries (C) in cross-sectional and surface view; note free edge of septum toward alveolar duct (AD) and alveolar pores (P). Scale, 10 µm. B: model reconstruction of interweaving between capillaries and septal fiber meshwork. [From Weibel (109).]

material (16, 17, 76, 77) originally called antiatelectatic factor and later surfactant (see the chapter by Goerke and Clements in this *Handbook*). It is now well established that this material is predominantly a disaturated phospholipid dipalmitoyl lecithin (16, 35, 77). Some debate persisted about how this material was related to lung structure because electron micrographs of lung tissue, such as those shown in Figures 1 and 12, did not reveal any traces of such material

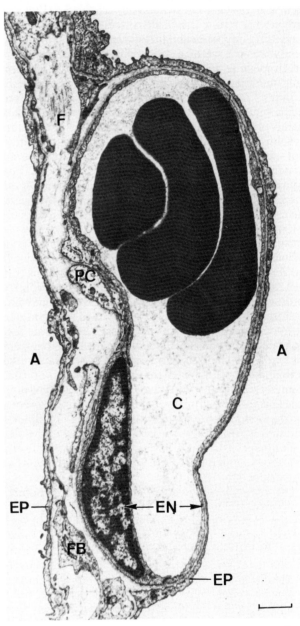

FIG. 12. Alveolar septum of human lung in thin section. Capillary (C) bounded toward alveoli (A) by tissue barrier made of endothelium (EN) and type I epithelium (EP). On the left side the interstitium contains fibers (F) and fibroblast processes (FB); on the right side it is reduced to the fused basement membranes (minimal barrier). Note pericytes (PC). Scale, 1 µm. [From Weibel (109).]

function is not clear; they have been thought to be the major pathways for collateral ventilation, but it must be noted that in the air-filled lung most, if not all, of them are closed by surface lining layer (33, 36). It is therefore just as possible that they constitute the route for redistribution of surface lining layer and macrophages from one alveolus to the other. Some interalveolar pores may be considerably enlarged, however, particularly in the aging lung. It is conceivable that such larger openings in alveolar walls may constitute pathways for collateral ventilation.

ALVEOLAR SURFACE LINING LAYER

The alveolar surface lining layer plays a major role in lung mechanics because it regulates the mechanical forces that arise at the air-liquid interface. One of the major breakthroughs in lung physiology was the recognition that surface forces play a dominant role in lung mechanics (67, 70, 73) and that the maze of tiny curved air spaces, all open to ambient air through the bronchial tubes, can only maintain a large surface area because the air spaces are lined by a surface-active

(30, 57, 103, 105). It is now known that this was due to the conventional preparation procedures by which this film was removed before it could be fixed. These procedures consist of either instilling the aqueous fixative solutions through the airways or of immersing small pieces of tissue in the solution; this causes the hydrophilic surface film to break up and the surface lining to be washed away. In order to fix this lining in situ another strategy had to be employed: the fixative had to be applied to this lining "from behind," i.e., from the tissue side. This was achieved either by perfusion through the blood vessels (36, 112) or by immersing unopened lung tissue from the pleura (23). Similar results were later also obtained by fixing frozen tissue, e.g., by freeze-fracturing (86, 101, 120) or, with moderate success, by freeze-substitution (66, 115).

The picture that evolved from these studies is that the alveolar epithelial surface is provided with a duplex lining layer (Fig. 13), where a fine osmiophilic film is apposed to the surface of a hypophase of variable thickness and composition (33, 36, 88). The hypophase is apparently fluid and hence distributes primarily into the many depressions in the epithelial surface, pits and crevasses formed between capillaries, and in the folds of the air-blood barrier. The result is a rather smooth air-liquid interface whose surface area is significantly smaller than that of the epithelial cell membranes (33, 116). It should be mentioned that this fluid hypophase is not an artifact of preparation by perfusion fixation, such as the result of fluid leakage, because it is also found in unfixed frozen preparations (101) and after perfusion with highly hypertonic fixative solutions that are shown to extract water from the lung tissue (102). On electron micrographs the hypophase appears mostly as an amorphous fluid that probably contains proteins, proteoglycans [possibly attached to the cell membranes (4, 82)], lipoproteins, and lipid micelles (8, 9, 18, 42). Yet the hypophase contains its own cell population as well: the alveolar macrophages that are totally immersed in this lining and partly contribute to the smoothing of the epithelial surface (36, 109, 113).

The hypophase contains, however, one structural component that is directly related to the surfactant system: tubular myelin, a lipoprotein structure of high surface activity (35, 45, 114, 120). Figure 13 shows some of this material in relation to the surface film. Its characteristic structure is made of parallel sheets of osmiophilic lamellae that intersect at right angles to make a system of packed square tubules (Fig. 13A). The lamellae are double leaflets, suggesting that they consist of paired monolayers of phospholipids with the hydrophobic surfaces facing each other. It has been shown that the phospholipid of tubular myelin is predominantly the highly surface active dipalmitoyl lecithin (35), the major component of pulmonary surfactant. The interior of the tubules shows some faint structure that appears as ordered filaments on cross

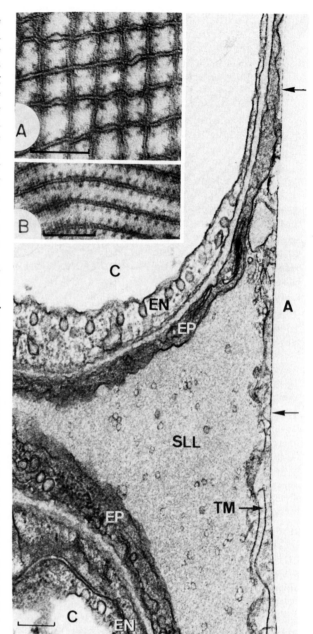

FIG. 13. Surface lining layer (*SLL*) from perfusion-fixed rat lung filling crevice in epithelial lining (*EP*) between 2 capillaries (*C*). Note osmiophilic surface film, presumably surfactant phospholipids, associated with some tubular myelin (*TM*). *EN*, endothelium; *A*, alveolus. Scale, 0.2 μm. *Insets*: fine structure of tubular myelin in transverse (*A*) and longitudinal (*B*) section. Scale, 0.1 μm. [Insets from Hassett et al. (45).]

sections (Fig. 13A) and exhibits a periodicity on longitudinal sections [Fig. 13B; (45, 120)], suggesting that this material might represent some of the apoproteins of surfactant (18, 54). Tubular myelin is a characteristic structure of the lungs of mammals, amphibians, and reptiles but not of birds or lungfishes; it is observed not only in perfusion-fixed or freeze-fractured preparations (36, 45, 120) but has been repeatedly observed as "fingerprint structures" in air spaces of lungs fixed by conventional methods (105, 114). The functional role of tubular myelin remains unclear. Because it apparently represents a spatial condensation of the actual surface film, one could speculate that it constitutes a reserve of surfactant lipoprotein assembled and arranged in a lattice that allows easy unraveling when the surface must be enlarged.

The exact structure of the surface film itself is still a matter of debate. Considering the exceedingly low surface tensions that are seemingly maintained at the air-fluid interface, one would have to postulate that the film of surfactant phospholipids is confluent, at least at low lung volumes. This is the picture one observes in freeze-fractured preparations (57, 86, 101, 120); in perfusion-fixed lungs the film very often appears fragmented, disposed in patches (33, 36). It is not known whether this is a faithful representation because it cannot be excluded that the exchange of solutes between the perfusate and the surface lining layer, as well as the postfixation procedures, causes sufficient perturbations to disrupt an originally intact monomolecular layer. This is likely, so a conclusive statement about the true structure of the surface film must await further improvements in the methods. There is no evidence now that clearly demonstrates real discontinuities in the surface film, at least at low volumes.

All evidence available suggests that the surface lining layer (surfactant film and hypophase) covers the entire alveolar surface. Larger pools of hypophase, including macrophages and tubular myelin masses, occur mostly in concavities of the epithelial surface and also fill all or most of the alveolar pores (33, 36). Over convexities, such as over the bulging aspect of capillaries or over alveolar entrance rings, the lining is reduced to the surface film with a minimal layer of hypophase interposed between film and cell membrane. The thickness of this minimal layer is perhaps no more than that of the glycocalyx of the apical cell membrane of the epithelium (4). It is of particular importance to note that such a minimal film extends over the free edge of the lateral wall septa so that the alveolar ducts are also lined by surfactant. The importance of this finding is discussed in GEOMETRY AND MECHANICS OF THE ACINUS, p. 105. In the center of the acinus one finds that the alveolar surface lining also extends over the cuboidal epithelium of the respiratory bronchiole and even to smaller bronchioles (37). It is not known whether this plays a major functional role in stabilizing the surface of these small flaccid airways or whether it merely reflects the process of removing surface lining by outflow up the airway surface.

The pathways for formation and turnover of surfactant and surface lining material are not discussed extensively in this chapter. Suffice to say that it is now well established that the surfactant phospholipids are manufactured by the type II alveolar epithelial cell (see Fig. 1) and stored in its characteristic lamellar bodies prior to secretion (3, 10, 18, 53, 86, 120). The origin of surfactant apoproteins and other components of the hypophase is incompletely understood (18, 54); some of this material may again be secreted by the type II cell and some may come directly from the blood plasma through the air-blood barrier. Even less clear is the role of various pathways for the removal and breakdown of surfactant. Part of it is doubtless phagocytosed by macrophages and degraded in their well-developed lysosomal system; another part leaves the lung through the airways and is transported up the "escalator" by ciliary movements. Yet it is not clear how much, if any, of this material is resorbed locally into either the interstitium or the capillaries.

DEFORMATION OF THE ALVEOLAR SEPTUM UNDER THE EFFECT OF INTERACTING FORCES

Three major mechanical forces are active in molding the alveolar septal structure in the lung during breathing (Fig. 14).

1. Tissue tension. The fiber net of the alveolar septum extends from the axial to the peripheral fiber system. The fiber continuum is under a certain tension due to pleural traction, whose magnitude depends on the level of lung inflation. This tends to straighten the septal fibers and to unfold the capillary network that is interwoven with this fiber net (see Fig. 11B), shifting the capillaries to one side of the septum or the other. The tension on the fibers exerts a pressure normal to the fiber axis.

2. Capillary distending pressure. The capillary walls are exposed to luminal pressure, which is the result of the prevailing perfusion pressures in pulmonary artery and vein; capillary distending pressure is also influenced by gravitation resulting in different capillary width from top to bottom of the lung (40, 65, 66). If this distending pressure acts homogeneously over the circumference of a capillary segment, its result will be to shift the capillary away from the fiber tension skeleton of the septum (Fig. 14), thus exacerbating the bulging of the capillaries toward the alveolar space.

3. Surface forces. These forces are generated at any air-liquid interface if the surface-tension coefficient of the fluid is positive. If the surface is curved, a

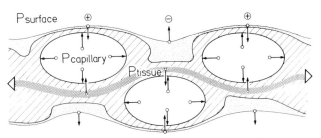

FIG. 14. Forces interacting in molding structure of alveolar septum. [From Weibel (109a).]

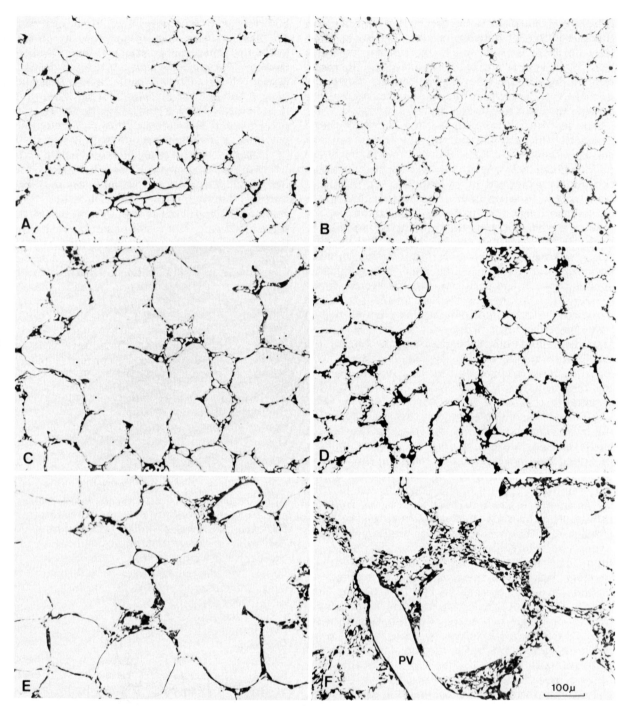

FIG. 15. Arrangement of alveolar septa in perfusion-fixed rabbit lungs at 80% TLC (*A, C, E*) and 40% TLC (*B, D, F*). *A, B*: saline-filled; *C, D*: normal air-filled; *E, F*: detergent-rinsed, air-filled lungs. *PV*, pulmonary venule. Scale, 100 μm. [*A, B* from Gil et al. (33); *C–F* from Bachofen et al. (6).]

pressure normal to the surface is generated, which is directed toward the air space over negative curvatures and toward the tissue over positive curvatures (Fig. 14). The surface forces will tend to minimize the free surface energy by reducing the surface areas; thus any local curvatures will be reduced to the minimum that can be supported by any counteracting forces, i.e., the alveolar septal surface must be smoothed as much as possible.

A fourth force can be considered: interstitial pressure. To a large extent this pressure is, however, the resultant of the three major forces imposed on the septum from without. Consequently interstitial pressure may vary from point to point over the septum

(Fig. 14); much of the tissue deformation discussed in this section tends to minimize such inhomogeneities. It is possible, however, that interstitial pressure is lower in alveolar corners (i.e., where three septa meet) than in the flat part of the alveolar walls. This may establish a slight gradient in interstitial pressure large enough to drain fluid away from the alveolar walls toward the fluid sumps in those parts of the peripheral connective tissue that contain lymphatics, such as perivascular sheaths (111).

The effect of the three major forces on septal structure can be examined on preparations fixed by vascular perfusion with careful monitoring during the entire experiment (i.e., to the end of fixation) of the flow rate, perfusion pressures, and other variables to be within the physiological range (33, 102). The effect of tissue tension can be investigated by varying the lung volume from low inflation levels to total lung capacity (TLC); consistent results are obtained by considering the range of 100% to 40% TLC on the deflation limb of the pressure-volume curve (6, 33). The effect of surface forces can be studied by comparing normal air-filled lungs with saline-filled specimens in which surface tension is eliminated (33) and with air-filled lungs rinsed with a detergent to remove surfactant and thus increase the surface-tension coefficient at the air-liquid interface (6). There was some hope that rapid freezing followed by freeze-substitution fixation might allow control of all these physiological factors simultaneously (66). Unfortunately this procedure does not result in sufficiently homogeneous and reproducible preparations to be useful for that purpose (115).

Figure 15 compares normal air-filled with saline-filled and detergent-rinsed rabbit lungs fixed by vascular perfusion at two different inflation levels on deflation from TLC (6, 33). In the saline-filled lungs the septa are completely unfolded and the capillaries are seen to bulge toward the alveoli; this is similar for all lung volumes, except that at levels ≤60% TLC the septa appear undulated, indicating that major parts of the fiber system may be relaxed or unstretched. This is interesting because as noted in *Elastic Fibers*, p. 92, elastic fibers can be stretched to ~130% of their resting length, about the span required to allow the lung to expand comfortably from 60% to 100% TLC. The picture presented by detergent-rinsed lungs is entirely different (6). At high lung volumes some of the septa appear highly stretched with no capillaries visible; they are evidently collapsed. Capillaries appear open in those regions where a group of septa has been pushed together due to the collapse of entire air spaces; accordingly the patent alveoli are much larger than in the air- or saline-filled specimens. At low lung volumes (Fig. 15F) the areas of air-space collapse are drastically increased; paradoxically the patent air spaces are enlarged and correspond to widened alveolar ducts, whereas virtually all alveoli are collapsed into the microatelectatic regions, where the capillaries are,

however, open. The normal air-filled lung (Fig. 15C, D) takes an intermediate position. At all inflation levels the septa appear straight, with the length of their profiles about proportional to the degree of expansion; however, at all levels one finds small areas of septal folding in the region of triple lines, i.e., where three septa join (32, 33). The capillaries are generally patent, but at high inflation levels those found in the stretched part of the septa are slitlike, whereas those in the corners of the triple lines are wide (32, 33).

These results allow the following conclusions on the interaction of surface forces and tissue tension in the air-filled lung (Fig. 16). At moderate to low lung volumes the length of the fiber system is such that the septa are flaccid; as a result of surface tension part of the septal fibers becomes folded into the region of triple lines so that in the free part of the septum the fibers come to lie under tension adequate to evenly spread the capillary network beneath the alveolar surface. However, this requires only a moderate surface force that acts as well on the septal surfaces as on the free edge of lateral wall septa; if surface tension is too high, as in detergent-rinsed lungs, most or all of the septa are pushed into the corners leaving only a

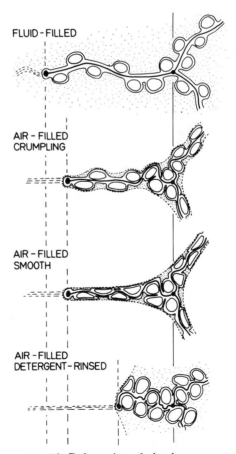

FIG. 16. Deformation of alveolar septum under the effect of surface forces counteracted by tissue force and capillary distending pressure. [From Weibel (109a).]

very small gas-exchange surface. In the air-filled lung the septal surface is generally smaller than the tissue surface marked by the alveolar epithelium (116). This requires the sheetlike septal structures to become pleated beneath the surface lining layer. In addition to the pleats involving the entire septum with the fiber system (as discussed in relation to Fig. 16), smaller folds appear in the thin parts of the air-blood barrier (Fig. 17) and thus reduce the surface area of that part of the capillary that bulges in saline-filled lungs (33).

The interaction between surface force and capillary distending pressure becomes evident at higher powers in the same specimens. For example, on the surface of a capillary network in detergent-rinsed lungs fixed at a low inflation level (Fig. 18) the capillaries appear squashed, particularly in the central parts of the air-space face, by the spherical meniscus of the air-fluid interface (6). In normal air-filled lungs fixed at higher inflation levels the alveolar surface looks smooth; this is due partly to a similar but less-marked squashing of the capillary walls and partly to a distribution of lining layer into residual clefts or crevices at the epithelial surface, both because of positive surface tension at this inflation level. At low inflation levels, however, the surface is no longer smooth but rather shows marked crumpling (33) because the capillaries are now allowed to bulge toward the alveolar space (Fig. 19). This results in high local curvatures so the surface tension must be very low, perhaps approaching zero (33); this is also evidenced by the fact that very

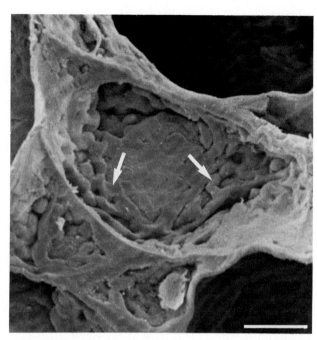

FIG. 18. Perfusion-fixed air-filled rabbit lung at 80% TLC after detergent rinsing. Capillaries are squashed by high surface tension (*arrows*). Scale, 20 μm. [From Bachofen et al. (6).]

fine films of lining layer can be seen to span alveolar pores (Fig. 19).

A stable configuration of the alveolar septum is achieved by the balance between these three interacting forces (see Fig. 14). This is best seen at moderate inflation levels, where tissue tension is comparatively low (Fig. 20). The combination of surface and vascular distending pressure pushes the capillary segments toward the interior of the septum; they become aligned in a plane, appearing like a capillary "sheet" (27, 28, 83), and one finds that the septal fibers weave from one side to the other. As tissue tension increases at higher lung volumes the capillaries tend to retain this position, but they become flattened in the free part of the septum as the surface force, which is also increased at higher inflation levels (47, 94), pushes the capillary against the tight fiber net (see Fig. 15C). The capillary distending pressure is now smaller than the combined counteracting forces of tissue and surface pressure (see Fig. 14).

In view of the principal role of this mechanical system it is noteworthy that the structural design of alveolar septal tissue is such that the major part of the thin minimal air-blood barrier—that made exclusively of the squamous extensions of epithelium and endothelium together with their fused basement membranes (see Fig. 12)—remains at the free alveolar surface, whereas thicker portions containing fiber strands and cell bodies are pushed into the interior of the septum (105, 109, 116). As a consequence the effective barrier thickness for gas exchange, i.e., its harmonic mean (105), is smaller in air-filled lungs

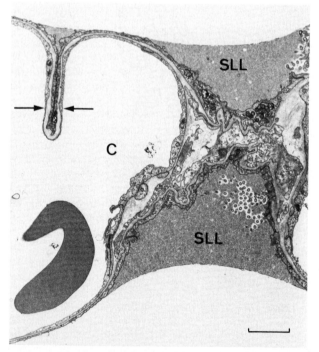

FIG. 17. Smoothing of alveolar surface by pools of surface lining layer (*SLL*) and folding of barrier (*arrows*) in perfusion-fixed human lung. C, capillary. Scale, 2 μm. [From Weibel (108).]

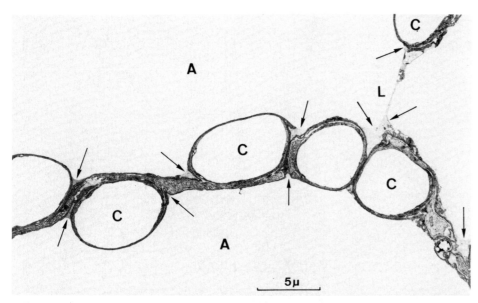

FIG. 19. Crumpling of alveolar surface in perfusion-fixed air-filled rabbit lung at 40% TLC. High local curvatures (*arrows*) are sustained and a thin lamella of lining layer (*L*) spans across an alveolar pore (*A*). *C*, capillaries. Scale, 5 μm. [From Gil et al. (33).]

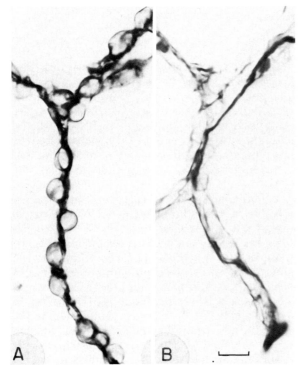

FIG. 20. Deformation of alveolar septum under the effect of surface forces. *A*: fluid-filled lung; capillaries weave around a fiber sheet. *B*: air-filled lung; capillaries appear arranged as a sheet and fibers weave across the septum. Scale, 10 μm.

than that measured in fully expanded septa, despite the apparent compaction of structures onto a smaller surface (116).

GEOMETRY AND MECHANICS OF THE ACINUS

The mechanics of lung parenchyma is not fully described in terms of the events that occur in the alveolar septa, although adequate expansion of the septa must be the target of well-designed lung mechanics for it is one of the prime determinants of gas exchange. However, septal expansion depends essentially on the arrangement of the two main force-bearing elements of lung structure with respect to the acinus, the basic structural unit of lung parenchyma: the acinar extensions of the axial and peripheral fiber systems on which the septal fibers are anchored and on which the other forces, particularly the surface force, also act (121–123).

An idealized and greatly reduced structural model of this interrelation of fiber system and surface forces in the acinus is shown in Figure 21. The separation of axial and peripheral fiber systems depends on the level of lung inflation because the pleural pull is transmitted to the acinar periphery through the hierarchy of connective tissue elements of the peripheral fiber hull (see Figs. 8 and 9). This volume-dependent peripheral traction is evenly distributed throughout the lung; in perfusion-fixed lungs one can note a remarkably homogeneous expansion of the acini whether they are near the pleura or deep in the lung, with recognizable differences due to gravitational effects occurring only between upper and lower regions in large lungs (39, 117, 118). Wilson and Bachofen (123) noted that all septal and axial fibers appear to hang loose in saline-filled lungs even at moderately high lung volumes between 60% and 80% TLC; they become stretched only when approaching TLC. This is particularly the

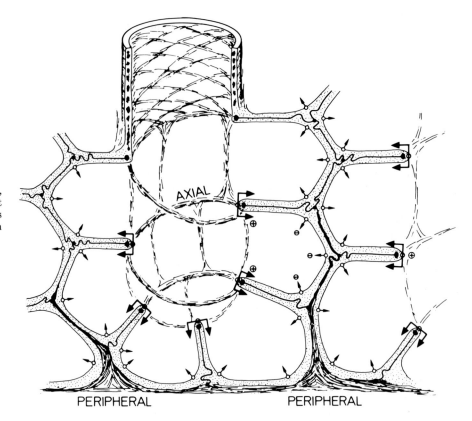

FIG. 21. Model, reduced in length, of acinar fiber system under the effect of surface forces (*arrows*). Septal fibers become folded into corners. [From Weibel (109a).]

case for the septal fibers that appear to be longer than the distance between their supports. This changes when surface tension is added in the air-filled lung: the acinar extensions of the axial fiber system form smooth (helical) loops around the alveolar duct and the more or less smooth alveolar walls are formed about a flat mid-plane, as shown in Figures 15, 16, and 20. There is one additional remarkable feature, namely that alveolar ducts are wider in air-filled lungs than in saline-filled lungs expanded to the same volume (33) and extremely dilated if surface tension is abnormally high (6), as shown in Figure 15E, F.

This change in acinar structure is essentially the result of surface tension balanced by counteracting fiber tensions. As shown in the idealized model (Fig. 21), the acinar surface forms alternating positive and negative curvatures. The positive curvatures are over the axial fibers and have a small radius of curvature; the resulting surface force (surface tension times curvature) is relatively large and acts outward but is supported by comparatively thick fibers combined with some smooth muscle (see Figs. 1 and 10). The negative curvatures are largest in the region of the triple lines related to the region where peripheral fibers are intercalated between two adjacent alveolar duct systems; the curvatures and the resulting surface forces are smaller but directed inward. As a result, the excess fiber length of the septa becomes crumpled into the regions around the triple lines (see Fig. 16); because the regions of the triple lines are exposed to the

action of three negative surface curvatures the capillaries compacted in these corners are relatively wide. The phenomenon of septal pleating, which leads to a reduction of the free alveolar surface compared with that measured in fully unfolded fluid-filled lungs (116), is hence the result of this mechanism of disposing of excess septal fiber length in relation to the main stress-bearing axial and peripheral fiber systems (123).

This mechanism of balancing interacting forces is valid in principle at all levels of lung expansion except at high lung volumes (>80% TLC), where the fiber system is stretched to its limit. Even at TLC, however, surface forces appear to exert their molding effect, because it has been shown that lungs can be expanded by fluid to a volume 10%–20% in excess of TLC measured in air-filled lungs (7). As the lung is deflated from TLC to lower volumes some changes occur in the structure and disposition of acinar structures (see Fig. 15) that are the results of changing tissue and surface tensions, which both decrease as the degree of lung inflation is reduced (38, 47, 94).

This description should not be ended without mentioning that the mechanical properties of lung parenchyma are related to some measurable morphometric quantities characterizing its structure, although little work has been done in this direction. The local surface force is related to the surface-tension coefficient (γ) (dyn/cm) of the lining layer and the local mean curvature (K) [the symbol H has been used in some previous publications (6, 38, 105, 113)]. By the formula of Gibbs the overall pressure differential due to surface forces (P_γ) is related to the average mean curvature ($\bar{K}$) by

$$P_\gamma = \gamma \cdot \bar{K} \qquad (1)$$

assuming that γ is homogeneous throughout the lung. The $\bar{K}$ value (cm^{-1}) can be estimated on sections (107) by obtaining an intersection and a tangent count in relation to a stereological test system, because $\bar{K}$ is the mean curvature density in space averaged over the alveolar surface density, which are both related to lung volume (107). The average mean air-space curvature has been shown to decrease with increasing lung inflation in air-filled rat (38) and rabbit lungs (6). In detergent-rinsed rabbit lungs, $\bar{K}$ measured at TLC was similar to that in normal air-filled lungs but decreased as inflation was reduced (6), in keeping with the formation of larger air spaces (see Fig. 16). It is, however, difficult to estimate the prevailing surface force from such measurements because the contribution of tissue tension to total recoil pressure is not easy to appreciate.

It has also been shown (47, 122) that P_γ can be expressed as a function of the surface-to-volume ratio of the air spaces, $(S/V)_A$, by

$$P_\gamma = \tfrac{2}{3} \cdot \gamma \cdot (S/V)_A \qquad (2)$$

The surface-to-volume ratio can be measured on sections by stereological methods (107): using a test lattice made of lines and points, $(S/V)_A$ is directly proportional to the ratio of line intersections with the alveolar surface trace to point hits on the profiles of the acinar air spaces, alveoli, and ducts taken together. Such measurements have been obtained on rat and rabbit lungs fixed by vascular perfusion (6, 33, 38). The data set on rabbit lungs (8, 33) is of particular interest because it includes measurements on air-filled normal, air-filled detergent-rinsed, and saline-filled lungs in relation to well-controlled lung volumes (Fig. 22). Compared with that in normal air-filled lungs, $(S/V)_A$ is ~40% higher in saline-filled and 35% lower in detergent-rinsed lungs; with increasing lung volume this parameter remains unchanged in the detergent-rinsed lungs, whereas it decreases in air-filled and saline-filled lungs. Wilson and Bachofen (123) recently exploited these data in an attempt to establish a relation between structure and mechanics of lung parenchyma on the basis of a new model that accounts as well for the surface forces as for the contribution of the alveolar duct fibers to total lung recoil. They estimate that the contribution of "tissue line elements"—a physical equivalent to some unit fiber—must be proportional to the length density (J_{Vf}) of such unit fibers in the unit volume of parenchyma. With T as the tension of the line element, the contribution of this fiber system to recoil pressure (P_T) is

$$P_T = \tfrac{1}{3} T \cdot J_{Vf} \qquad (3)$$

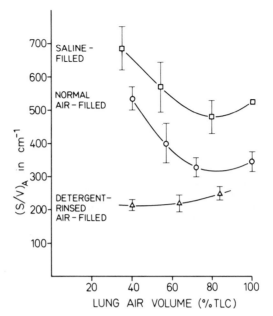

FIG. 22. Surface-to-volume ratio of parenchymal air spaces in rabbit lungs as a function of lung volume. [Data from Bachofen et al. (6) and Gil et al. (33).]

J_{Vf} could actually again be estimated on sections by simply counting the number of transections of these fiber elements on the unit section area (107). No such measurements have been performed; although the stereological method as such is very simple, the complexity of the integral fiber strands, made of three different fiber types of various thicknesses, does not permit a simple measurement before the theoretical term "line element" is translated into histological terms.

Despite this lack of information, Wilson and Bachofen (123) were able to draw some conclusions on the interaction of forces and structure in a stable lung by using the physiological and morphometric data set obtained on perfusion-fixed rabbit lungs. They were able to show that their model, based on the combination of Equations 2 and 3, was able to describe the relation between measured alveolar surface area and the recoil pressure difference between air-filled lungs and saline-filled lungs inflated at 40%–80% TLC. They also estimated the surface tension prevailing in the air-filled lungs, obtaining values of 2, 6, and 16 dyn/cm at 40%, 60%, and 80% TLC, respectively, in very close agreement with those measured in rat lungs by Schürch et al. (93, 94). In detergent-rinsed lungs surface tension was estimated at 28–35 dyn/cm at 40%–60% TLC, but the method failed to give realistic values at higher inflation levels.

The morphological approach from which these data were derived clearly has some limitations, mainly because the specimen reflects a more or less static condition of the lung. Thus it is difficult to fully appreciate the role of surfactant for stabilizing alveoli; its

TABLE 2. *Estimated Values of Surface-to-Volume Ratio of Air Spaces for Various Mammalian Species*

| | Body Weight, kg | Lung Volume, ml | Air Space | | $(S/V)_A$, cm^{-1} | $(S/V)_A$,* cm^{-1} (corrected) |
			Volume, ml	Surface, m²		
Human	74	4,341	3,386	143	431	280
Sheep	22	1,705	1,108	67	605	394
Dog	23	1,501	822	90	1,091	709
	11	736	406	41	1,002	650
Rabbit	2.88	81.9	54.8	4.9	881	573
Saline-filled at 60% TLC	3.05	88.8	66	3.7		569
Guinea pig	0.43	13.0	9.44	0.91	964	627
Rat	0.14	6.34	4.14	0.39	937	609
Mouse	0.042	1.45	0.94	0.125	1,330	864

Data obtained by electron microscopy on lungs fixed by instillation at ∼⅔ TLC. $(S/V)_A$, surface-to-volume ratio of air spaces.   *Values made comparable to those obtained by light microscopy on perfusion-fixed lungs by correcting by a factor of 0.65 to account for differences in resolution and preparation (see Fig. 22 and refs. 6, 38).   [Data from Weibel et al. (13, 30, 31, 113).]

most important property, namely that surface tension falls when the film is compressed, can be assessed only indirectly. It is interesting, however, that the surface tensions estimated when the lung was fixed at certain lung volumes obtained on deflation from TLC agreed closely with those measured directly (93, 94). And the fact that these surface tensions fell as the volume was reduced indicates that the method reflects not only the static but also the dynamic properties of surfactant.

A considerable amount of morphometric data has been obtained on the lungs of 33 mammalian species ranging from shrews of 2 g body wt to horses and cattle weighing up to 700 kg (31). Although these data have been obtained with the purpose of estimating the gas-exchange characteristics of the lung, they should allow some estimates of the mechanical properties of these lungs as well. Table 2 lists estimates of $(S/V)_A$ for some selected species including humans. The conditions of measurement were different, however, from those in the studies of lung mechanics, so an appropriate correction was necessary based on the results obtained on rabbit lungs, where both approaches were followed in a closely correlated study. It is evident from Table 2 that $(S/V)_A$ differs greatly between species, from the lowest value of 280 cm^{-1} in the human lung with comparatively large alveoli to 864 cm^{-1} in the mouse lung, the dog lung having a comparatively high $(S/V)_A$. In relation to the data on the morphometric basis of lung mechanics (see Fig. 22), these data are about comparable to those found in saline-filled lungs fixed at 60% TLC because by instillation the lung is fixed at ∼⅔ TLC. Clearly these data are tentative but should reflect the relative properties of mammalian lungs of different species.

CONCLUSIONS

An understanding of the mechanics of lung parenchyma requires an integral view of the structural arrangement of a variety of elements that interact to form a stable system of patent air spaces with the blood capillaries exposed to the air over an adequate surface and across a thin tissue barrier. The lung is structured according to a systematic plan so that the supporting fiber system associated with the airways and the pleura also becomes the scaffold on which the gas-exchange units are mounted; this assures an interdependence of all units (26, 47, 67–69, 113). Yet it is now known that this fiber skeleton is greatly affected by the surface forces generated at the air-liquid interface due to the surface texture of acinar air spaces, both in the alveoli and the alveolar ducts, and regulated by surfactant (18, 47, 68, 70, 77, 113). Less well known is the effect of the blood pressure that distends the capillaries and also interacts with the tissue and surface forces to form a stable gas-exchange system (28, 65).

A deeper understanding of the interplay between structures and forces in this delicate part of the lung and of its role in the development of lung disease will require concerted research combining physiological and morphological measurements. Most of the methods required are worked out; they need only be exploited in well-designed experiments.

Work has been supported by grants from the Swiss National Science Foundation (3.332.78). The contributions by Dr. H. Bachofen, G. Reber, and K. Babl in preparing this chapter are gratefully acknowledged.

REFERENCES

1. AGOSTONI, E. Mechanics of the pleural space. *Physiol. Rev.* 52: 57–128, 1972.
2. ALBERT, E. N. Developing elastic tissue. An electron microscopic study. *Am. J. Pathol.* 69: 89–102, 1972.
3. ASKIN, F. B., AND C. KUHN. The cellular origin of pulmonary surfactant. *Lab. Invest.* 25: 260–268, 1971.
4. ATWAL, O. S., AND L. M. BROWN. Membrane-bound glycoprotein in the alveolar cells of the caprine lung. *Am. J. Anat.* 159:

275–283, 1980.

5. AYER, J. P. Elastic tissue. *Int. Rev. Connect. Tissue Res.* 2: 33–100, 1964.

6. BACHOFEN, H., P. GEHR, AND E. R. WEIBEL. Alterations of mechanical properties and morphology in excised rabbit lungs rinsed with a detergent. *J. Appl. Physiol.: Respirat. Environ. Exercise Physiol.* 47: 1002–1010, 1979.

7. BACHOFEN, H., J. HILDEBRANDT, AND M. BACHOFEN. Pressure-volume curves of air- and liquid-filled excised lungs—surface tension in situ. *J. Appl. Physiol.* 29: 422–431, 1970.

8. BERNSTEIN, J., S. S. YANG, H. S. HAHN, AND Y. KIKKAWA. Mucopolysaccharide in the pulmonary alveolus. I. Histochemical observations on the development of the alveolar lining layer. *Lab. Invest.* 21: 420–425, 1969.

9. BIGNON, J., M. C. JAURAND, M. C. PINCHON, C. SAPIN, AND J. M. WARNET. Immunoelectron microscopic and immunochemical demonstrations of serum proteins in the alveolar lining material of the rat lung. *Am. Rev. Respir. Dis.* 113: 109–120, 1976.

10. BUCKINGHAM, S., H. O. HEINEMANN, S. C. SOMMERS, AND W. F. MCNARY. Phospholipid synthesis in the large pulmonary alveolar cells. *Am. J. Pathol.* 48: 1027–1041, 1966.

11. BULL, H. B. Protein structure and elasticity. In: *Tissue Elasticity*, edited by J. W. Remington. Washington, DC: Am. Physiol. Soc., 1957, p. 33–42.

12. BURRI, P. H. The postnatal growth of the rat lung. III. Morphology. *Anat. Rec.* 180: 77–98, 1974.

13. BURRI, P. H., AND E. R. WEIBEL. Ultrastructure and morphometry of the developing lung. In: *Lung Biology in Health and Disease. Development of the Lung*, edited by W. A. Hodson. New York: Dekker, 1977, vol. 6, p. 215–268.

14. CARTON, R. W., J. DAINAUSKAS, AND J. W. CLARK. Elastic properties of single elastic fibers. *J. Appl. Physiol.* 17: 547–551, 1962.

15. CARTON, R. W., J. DAINAUSKAS, B. TEWS, AND C. M. HASS. Isolation and study of the elastic tissue network of the lung in three dimensions. *Am. Rev. Respir. Dis.* 82: 186–194, 1960.

16. CLEMENTS, J. A. Pulmonary surfactant. *Am. Rev. Respir. Dis.* 101: 984–990, 1970.

17. CLEMENTS, J. A., R. F. HUSTEAD, R. P. JOHNSON, AND I. GRIBETZ. Pulmonary surface tension and alveolar stability. *J. Appl. Physiol.* 16: 444–450, 1961.

18. CLEMENTS, J. A., AND R. KING. Composition of surface active material. In: *Lung Biology in Health and Disease. The Biochemical Basis of Pulmonary Function*, edited by R. G. Crystal. New York: Dekker, 1976, vol. 2, p. 363–387.

19. CRAPO, J. D., B. E. BARRY, H. A. FOSCUE, AND J. SHELBURNE. Structural and biochemical changes in rat lungs occurring during exposures to lethal and adaptive doses of oxygen. *Am. Rev. Respir. Dis.* 122: 123–143, 1980.

20. CRAPO, J. D., J. MARSH-SALIN, P. INGRAM, AND P. C. PRATT. Tolerance and cross-tolerance using NO_2 and O_2. II. Pulmonary morphology and morphometry. *J. Appl. Physiol.: Respirat. Environ. Exercise Physiol.* 44: 370–379, 1978.

21. CRYSTAL, R. G. (editor). *Lung Biology in Health and Disease. The Biochemical Basis of Pulmonary Function.* New York: Dekker, 1976, vol. 2.

22. EMERY, J. Connective tissue and lymphatics. In: *The Anatomy of the Developing Lung*, edited by J. Emery. Lavenham, UK: Heinemann, 1969, p. 49–73.

23. FINLEY, T. N., S. A. PRATT, A. J. LADMAN, L. BREVER, AND M. B. MCKAY. Morphological and lipid analysis of the alveolar lining material in dog lung. *J. Lipid Res.* 9: 357–365, 1968.

24. FISHMAN, A. P., AND E. M. RENKIN (editors). *Pulmonary Edema.* Bethesda, MD: Am. Physiol. Soc., 1979.

25. FULMER, J. D., AND R. G. CRYSTAL. The biochemical basis of pulmonary function. In: *Lung Biology in Health and Disease. The Biochemical Basis of Pulmonary Function*, edited by R. G. Crystal. New York: Dekker, 1976, vol. 2, p. 419–466.

26. FUNG, Y. C. Stress, deformation, and atelectasis in the lung. *Circ. Res.* 37: 481–496, 1975.

27. FUNG, Y. C., AND S. S. SOBIN. Theory of sheet flow in lung alveoli. *J. Appl. Physiol.* 26: 472–488, 1969.

28. FUNG, Y. C., AND S. S. SOBIN. Elasticity of the pulmonary alveolar sheet. *Circ. Res.* 30: 451–469, 1972.

29. GABBIANI, G., B. J. HIRSCHEL, G. B. RYAN, P. R. STATKOV, AND G. MAJNO. Granulation tissue as a contractile organ. A study of structure and function. *J. Exp. Med.* 135: 719–734, 1972.

30. GEHR, P., M. BACHOFEN, AND E. R. WEIBEL. The normal human lung ultrastructure and morphometric estimation of diffusion capacity. *Respir. Physiol.* 32: 121–140, 1978.

31. GEHR, P., D. K. MWANGI, A. AMMANN, G. M. MALOIY, C. R. TAYLOR, AND E. R. WEIBEL. Design of the mammalian respiratory system. V. Scaling morphometric pulmonary diffusing capacity to body mass: wild and domestic mammals. *Respir. Physiol.* 44: 61–86, 1981.

32. GIL, J. Influence of surface forces on pulmonary circulation. In: *Pulmonary Edema*, edited by A. P. Fishman and E. M. Renkin. Bethesda, MD: Am. Physiol. Soc., 1979, chapt. 4, p. 53–64.

33. GIL, J., H. BACHOFEN, P. GEHR, AND E. R. WEIBEL. Alveolar volume-surface area relation in air- and saline-filled lungs fixed by vascular perfusion. *J. Appl. Physiol.: Respirat. Environ. Exercise Physiol.* 47: 990–1001, 1979.

34. GIL, J., AND J. M. MCNIFF. Interstitial cells at the boundary between alveolar and extraalveolar connective tissue in the lung. *J. Ultrastruct. Res.* 76: 149–157, 1981.

35. GIL, J., AND O. K. REISS. Isolation and characterization of lamellar bodies and tubular myelin from rat lung homogenates. *J. Cell Biol.* 58: 152–171, 1973.

36. GIL, J., AND E. R. WEIBEL. Improvements in demonstration of lining layer of lung alveoli by electron microscopy. *Respir. Physiol.* 8: 13–36, 1969.

37. GIL, J., AND E. R. WEIBEL. Extracellular lining of bronchioles after perfusion-fixation of rat lungs for electron microscopy. *Anat. Rec.* 169: 185–199, 1971.

38. GIL, J., AND E. R. WEIBEL. Morphological study of pressure-volume hysteresis in rat lungs fixed by vascular perfusion. *Respir. Physiol.* 15: 190–213, 1972.

39. GLAZIER, J. B., J. M. B. HUGHES, J. E. MALONEY, AND J. B. WEST. Vertical gradient of alveolar size in lungs of dogs frozen intact. *J. Appl. Physiol.* 23: 694–705, 1967.

40. GLAZIER, J. B., J. M. B. HUGHES, J. E. MALONEY, AND J. B. WEST. Measurements of capillary dimensions and blood volume in rapidly frozen lungs. *J. Appl. Physiol.* 26: 65–76, 1969.

41. GREENLEE, T. K., JR., R. ROSS, AND J. L. HARTMAN. The fine structure of elastin fibers. *J. Cell Biol.* 30: 59–71, 1966.

42. GRONIOWSKI, J., AND W. BICZYSKOWA. Structure of the alveolar lining film of the lungs. *Nature London* 204: 745–747, 1964.

42a. GUNTHEROTH, W. G., D. L. LUCHTEL, AND I. KAWABORI. Pulmonary microcirculation: tubules rather than sheet and post. *J. Appl. Physiol.: Respirat. Environ. Exercise Physiol.* 53: 510–515, 1982.

43. HAIES, D., J. GIL, AND E. R. WEIBEL. Morphometric study of rat lung cells. I. Numerical and dimensional characteristics of parenchymal cell population. *Am. Rev. Respir. Dis.* 123: 533–541, 1981.

44. HANCE, A. J., AND R. G. CRYSTAL. Collagen. In: *Lung Biology in Health and Disease. The Biochemical Basis of Pulmonary Function*, edited by R. G. Crystal. New York: Dekker, 1976, vol. 2, p. 215–271.

45. HASSETT, R. J., W. ENGELMAN, AND C. KUHN. Extramembranous particles in tubular myelin from rat lung. *J. Ultrastruct. Res.* 71: 60–67, 1980.

46. HAYEK, H. VON. *Die menschliche Lunge* (2nd ed.). Berlin: Springer-Verlag, 1970.

47. HOPPIN, F. G., AND J. HILDEBRANDT. Mechanical properties of the lung. In: *Lung Biology in Health and Disease. Bioengineering Aspects of the Lung*, edited by J. B. West. New York: Dekker, 1977, vol. 3, p. 83–162.

48. HORSFIELD, K., G. DART, D. E. OLSON, G. F. FILLEY, AND G. CUMMING. Models of the human bronchial tree. *J. Appl.*

Physiol. 31: 207–217, 1971.

49. HORWITZ, A. L., N. A. ELSON, AND R. G. CRYSTAL. Proteoglycans and elastic fibers. In: *Lung Biology in Health and Disease. The Biochemical Basis of Pulmonary Function*, edited by R. G. Crystal. New York: Dekker, 1976, vol. 2, p. 273–311.

50. HUGHES, G. M., AND E. R. WEIBEL. Similarity of supporting tissues in fish gills and mammalian reticuloendothelium. *J. Ultrastruct. Res.* 39: 106–114, 1972.

51. KAPANCI, Y., A. ASSIMACOPOULOS, C. IRLE, A. ZWAHLEN, AND G. GABBIANI. "Contractile interstitial cells" in pulmonary alveolar septa: a possible regulator of ventilation-perfusion ratio? Ultrastructural, immunofluorescence, and in vitro studies. *J. Cell Biol.* 60: 375–392, 1974.

52. KAPANCI, Y., Y. P. M. COSTABELLA, AND G. GABBIANI. Location and function of contractile interstitial cells of the lungs. In: *Lung Cells in Disease*, edited by A. Bouhuys. Amsterdam: North-Holland, 1976, p. 69–82.

53. KIKKAWA, Y., K. YONEDA, F. SMITH, B. PACKARD, AND K. SUZUKI. The type II epithelial cells of the lung. II. Chemical composition and phospholipid synthesis. *Lab. Invest.* 32: 295–302, 1975.

54. KING, R. J., H. MARTIN, D. MITTS, AND F. M. HOLMSTROM. Metabolism of the apoproteins in pulmonary surfactant. *J. Appl. Physiol.: Respirat. Environ. Exercise Physiol.* 42: 483–491, 1977.

55. KRAHL, V. E. Microscopic anatomy of the lungs. *Am. Rev. Respir. Dis.* 80: 23–44, 1959.

56. KRAHL, V. E. Anatomy of the mammalian lung. In: *Handbook of Physiology. Respiration*, edited by W. O. Fenn and H. Rahn. Washington, DC: Am. Physiol. Soc., 1964, sect. 3, vol. I, chapt. 6, p. 213–284.

57. KUHN, C. A comparison of freeze-substitution with other methods for preservation of the pulmonary alveolar lining layer. *Am. J. Anat.* 133: 495–508, 1972.

58. LAUWERYNS, J. M. The juxta-alveolar lymphatics in the human adult lung. *Am. Rev. Respir. Dis.* 102: 877–885, 1970.

59. LAUWERYNS, J. M., AND J. H. BAERT. Alveolar clearance and the role of pulmonary lymphatics. *Am. Rev. Respir. Dis.* 115: 625–683, 1977.

60. LOW, F. N. Microfibrils: fine filamentous components of the tissue space. *Anat. Rec.* 142: 131–137, 1962.

61. LOW, F. N. Extracellular components of the pulmonary alveolar wall. *Arch. Intern. Med.* 127: 847–852, 1971.

62. LOW, F. N. Lung interstitium. Development, morphology, fluid content. In: *Lung Biology in Health and Disease. Lung Water and Solute Exchange*, edited by N. C. Staub. New York: Dekker, 1978, vol. 7, p. 17–48.

63. MAJNO, G., G. GABBIANI, B. J. HIRSCHEL, G. B. RYAN, AND P. R. STATKOV. Contraction of granulation tissue in vitro: similarity to smooth muscle. *Science* 173: 548–550, 1971.

64. MANDELBROT, B. B. *Fractals: Form, Chance and Dimension.* San Francisco, CA: Freeman, 1977.

65. MAZZONE, R. W. Influence of vascular and transpulmonary pressures on the functional morphology of the pulmonary microcirculation. *Microvasc. Res.* 20: 295–306, 1980.

66. MAZZONE, R. W., C. M. DURAND, AND J. B. WEST. Electron microscopy of lung rapidly frozen under controlled physiological conditions. *J. Appl. Physiol.: Respirat. Environ. Exercise Physiol.* 45: 325–333, 1978.

67. MEAD, J. Mechanical properties of lungs. *Physiol. Rev.* 41: 281–330, 1961.

68. MEAD, J. Mechanics of respiratory structures. In: *Pulmonary Structure and Function*, edited by A. V. S. de Reuck and M. O. O'Connor. London: Churchill, 1962, p. 111–138. (Ciba Found. Symp.)

69. MEAD, J., T. TAKISHIMA, AND D. LEITH. Stress distribution in lungs: a model of pulmonary elasticity. *J. Appl. Physiol.* 28: 596–608, 1970.

70. MEAD, J., J. L. WHITTENBERGER, AND E. P. RADFORD, JR. Surface tension as a factor in pulmonary volume-pressure hysteresis. *J. Appl. Physiol.* 10: 191–196, 1957.

71. MILLER, W. S. *The Lung* (2nd ed.). Springfield, IL: Thomas, 1947.

72. MONKHOUSE, W. S., AND W. F. WHIMSTER. An account of the longitudinal mucosal corrugations of the human tracheobronchial tree, with observations on those of some animals. *J. Anat.* 122: 681–695, 1976.

73. NEERGAARD, K. VON. Neue Auffassungen über einen Grundbegriff der Atemmechanik. Die Retraktionskraft der Lunge, abhängig von der Oberflächenspannung in den Alveolen. *Z. Gesamte Exp. Med.* 66: 373–394, 1929.

74. ORSÓS, F. Ueber das elastische Gerüst der normalen und der emphysematösen Lunge. *Beitr. Pathol. Anat. Allg. Pathol.* 41: 95–121, 1907.

75. ORSÓS, F. Die Gerüstsysteme der Lunge und deren physiologische und pathologische Bedeutung. I. Normal-anatomische Verhältnisse. *Beitr. Klin. Tuberk.* 87: 568–609, 1936.

76. PATTLE, R. E. Properties, function and origin of the alveolar lining layer. *Nature London* 175: 1125–1126, 1955.

77. PATTLE, R. E. Surface lining of lung alveoli. *Physiol. Rev.* 45: 48–79, 1965.

78. PIERCE, J. A. The elastic tissue of the lung. In: *The Lung*, edited by A. A. Liebow and D. E. Smith. Baltimore, MD: Williams & Wilkins, 1968, p. 41–47.

79. PIERCE, J. A., AND R. V. EBERT. Fibrous network of the lung and its change with age. *Thorax* 20: 469–476, 1965.

80. PIETRA, G. G., M. MAGNO, L. JOHNS, AND A. P. FISHMAN. Bronchial veins and pulmonary edema. In: *Pulmonary Edema*, edited by A. P. Fishman and E. M. Renkin. Bethesda, MD: Am. Physiol. Soc., 1979, chapt. 14, p. 195–206.

81. PROCKOP, D. J. Collagen, elastin, and proteoglycans: matrix for fluid accumulation in the lung. In: *Pulmonary Edema*, edited by A. P. Fishman and E. M. Renkin. Bethesda, MD: Am. Physiol. Soc., 1979, chapt. 9, p. 125–135.

82. RAMBOURG, A., AND C. P. LEBLOND. Electron microscope observations on the carbohydrate-rich cell coat present at the surface of cells in the rat. *J. Cell Biol.* 32: 27–53, 1967.

83. ROSENQUIST, T. H., S. BERNICK, S. S. SOBIN, AND Y. C. FUNG. The structure of the pulmonary interalveolar sheet. *Microvasc. Res.* 5: 199–212, 1973.

84. ROSS, R., AND E. P. BENDITT. Wound healing and collagen formation. V. Quantitative electron microscope radioautographic observations of proline-H^3 utilization by fibroblasts. *J. Cell Biol.* 27: 83–106, 1965.

85. ROSS, R., AND P. BORNSTEIN. The elastic fiber. I. The separation and partial characterization of its macromolecular components. *J. Cell Biol.* 40: 366–381, 1969.

86. ROTH, J., H. WINKELMANN, AND H. W. MEYER. Electron microscopic studies in mammalian lungs by freeze-etching. IV. Formation of the superficial layer of the surfactant system by lamellar bodies. *Exp. Pathol.* 8: 354–362, 1973.

87. RYAN, G. B., W. J. CLIFF, G. GABBIANI, C. IRLE, P. R. STATKOV, AND G. MAJNO. Myofibroblasts in an avascular fibrous tissue. *Lab. Invest.* 29: 197–206, 1973.

88. SANDERSON, R. J., G. W. PAUL, A. E. VATTER, AND G. F. FILLEY. Morphological and physical basis for lung surfactant action. *Respir. Physiol.* 27: 379–392, 1976.

89. SCHNEEBERGER, E. E. Barrier function of intercellular junctions in adult and fetal lungs. In: *Pulmonary Edema*, edited by A. P. Fishman and E. M. Renkin. Bethesda, MD: Am. Physiol. Soc., 1979, chapt. 2, p. 21–37.

90. SCHNEEBERGER, E. E., AND M. J. KARNOVSKY. The ultrastructural basis of alveolar-capillary membrane permeability to peroxidase used as a tracer. *J. Cell Biol.* 37: 781–793, 1968.

91. SCHNEEBERGER, E. E., AND M. J. KARNOVSKY. The influence of intravascular fluid volume on the permeability of newborn and adult mouse lungs to ultrastructural protein tracers. *J. Cell Biol.* 49: 319–334, 1971.

92. SCHNEEBERGER, E. E., AND M. J. KARNOVSKY. Substructure of intercellular junctions in freeze-fractured alveolar-capillary membranes of mouse lung. *Circ. Res.* 38: 404–411, 1976.

93. SCHÜRCH, S., J. GOERKE, AND J. A. CLEMENTS. Direct deter-

mination of surface tension in the lung. *Proc. Natl. Acad. Sci. USA* 73: 4693–4702, 1976.

94. SCHÜRCH, S., J. GOERKE, AND J. A. CLEMENTS. Direct determination of volume and time dependence of alveolar surface tension in excised lungs. *Proc. Natl. Acad. Sci. USA* 75: 3417–3421, 1978.

95. SIEGWART, B., P. GEHR, J. GIL, AND E. R. WEIBEL. Morphometric estimation of pulmonary diffusion capacity. IV. The normal dog lung. *Respir. Physiol.* 13: 141–159, 1971.

96. SLEIGH, M. A. The nature and action of respiratory tract cilia. In: *Lung Biology in Health and Disease. Respiratory Defense Mechanisms*, edited by J. D. Brain, D. F. Proctor, and L. M. Reid. New York: Dekker, 1977, vol. 5, pt. 1, p. 247–288.

97. STAUB, N. C. Pulmonary edema. *Physiol. Rev.* 54: 678–811, 1974.

98. STAUB, N. C. Extravascular forces in lung affecting fluid and protein exchange. *Am. Rev. Respir. Dis.* 115: 159–163, 1977.

99. STAUB, N. C. Pathways for fluid and solute fluxes in pulmonary edema. In: *Pulmonary Edema*, edited by A. P. Fishman and E. M. Renkin. Bethesda, MD: Am. Physiol. Soc., 1979, chapt. 8, p. 113–124.

100. STROMBERG, D. D., AND C. A. WIEDERHIELM. Viscoelastic description of a collagenous tissue in simple elongation. *J. Appl. Physiol.* 26: 857–862, 1969.

101. UNTERSEE, P., J. GIL, AND E. R. WEIBEL. Visualization of extracellular lining layer of lung alveoli by freeze-etching. *Respir. Physiol.* 13: 171–185, 1971.

102. WANGENSTEEN, D., H. BACHOFEN, AND E. R. WEIBEL. Lung tissue volume changes induced by hypertonic NaCl: morphometric evaluation. *J. Appl. Physiol.: Respirat. Environ. Exercise Physiol.* 51: 1443–1450, 1981.

103. WEIBEL, E. R. *Morphometry of the Human Lung.* Heidelberg: Springer-Verlag, 1963.

104. WEIBEL, E. R. The mystery of "non-nucleated plates" in the alveolar epithelium of the lung explained. *Acta Anat.* 78: 425–443, 1971.

105. WEIBEL, E. R. Morphological basis of alveolar-capillary gas exchange. *Physiol. Rev.* 53: 419–495, 1973.

106. WEIBEL, E. R. On pericytes, particularly their existence on lung capillaries. *Microvasc. Res.* 8: 218–235, 1974.

107. WEIBEL, E. R. *Stereological Methods. Practical Methods for Biological Morphometry.* London: Academic, 1979, vol. 1.

108. WEIBEL, E. R. Looking into the lung: what can it tell us? *Am. J. Roentgenol.* 133: 1021–1031, 1979.

109. WEIBEL, E. R. Design and structure of the human lung. In: *Pulmonary Diseases and Disorders*, edited by A. P. Fishman. New York: McGraw-Hill, 1980, p. 224–271.

109a. WEIBEL, E. R. *The Pathway for Oxygen.* Cambridge, MA: Harvard Univ. Press, 1984.

110. WEIBEL, E. R. Lung cell biology. In: *Handbook of Physiology. The Respiratory System. Circulation and Nonrespiratory Functions*, edited by A. P. Fishman and A. B. Fisher. Bethesda, MD: Am. Physiol. Soc., 1985, sect. 3, vol. I, chapt. 2, p. 47–91.

111. WEIBEL, E. R., AND H. BACHOFEN. Structural design of the alveolar septum and fluid exchange. In: *Pulmonary Edema*, edited by A. P. Fishman and E. M. Renkin. Bethesda, MD: Am. Physiol. Soc., 1979, chapt. 1, p. 1–20.

112. WEIBEL, E. R., AND J. GIL. Electron microscopic demonstration of an extracellular duplex lining layer of alveoli. *Respir. Physiol.* 4: 42–57, 1968.

113. WEIBEL, E. R., AND J. GIL. Structure-function relationships at the alveolar level. In: *Lung Biology in Health and Disease. Bioengineering Aspects of the Lung*, edited by J. B. West. New York: Dekker, 1977, vol. 3, p. 1–81.

114. WEIBEL, E. R., G. S. KISTLER, AND G. TÖNDURY. A stereologic electron microscope study of "tubular myelin figures" in alveolar fluids of rat lungs. *Z. Zellforsch. Mikrosk. Anat.* 69: 418–427, 1966.

115. WEIBEL, E. R., W. LIMACHER, AND H. BACHOFEN. Electron microscopy of rapidly frozen lungs: evaluation on the basis of standard criteria. *J. Appl. Physiol.: Respirat. Environ. Exercise Physiol.* 53: 516–527, 1982.

116. WEIBEL, E. R., P. UNTERSEE, J. GIL, AND M. ZULAUF. Morphometric estimation of pulmonary diffusion capacity. VI. Effect of varying positive pressure inflation of air spaces. *Respir. Physiol.* 18: 285–308, 1973.

117. WEST, J. B. Stresses. In: *Regional Differences in the Lung*, edited by J. B. West. New York: Academic, 1977, p. 281–322.

118. WEST, J. B., AND F. L. MATTHEWS. Stress, strains, and surface pressures in the lung caused by its weight. *J. Appl. Physiol.* 32: 332–345, 1972.

119. WHIMSTER, W. F. The microanatomy of the alveolar duct system. *Thorax* 25: 141–149, 1975.

120. WILLIAMS, M. C. Freeze-fracture studies of tubular myelin and lamellar bodies in fetal and adult rat lungs. *J. Ultrastruct. Res.* 64: 352–361, 1978.

121. WILSON, T. A. Parenchymal mechanics at the alveolar level. *Federation Proc.* 38: 7–10, 1979.

122. WILSON, T. A. Relations among recoil pressure, surface area, and surface tension in the lung. *J. Appl. Physiol.: Respirat. Environ. Exercise Physiol.* 50: 921–926, 1981.

123. WILSON, T. A., AND H. BACHOFEN. A model for mechanical structure of the alveolar duct. *J. Appl. Physiol.: Respirat. Environ. Exercise Physiol.* 52: 1064–1070, 1982.

124. WRIGHT, R. R. Elastic tissue of normal and emphysematous lungs. A tridimensional histologic study. *Am. J. Pathol.* 39: 355–367, 1961.

125. YOUNG, C. D., G. W. MOORE, AND G. M. HUTCHINS. Connective tissue arrangement in respiratory airways. *Anat. Rec.* 198: 245–254, 1980.

CHAPTER 9

Static behavior of the respiratory system

EMILIO AGOSTONI | *Istituto di Fisiologia Umana I, Università di Milano, Milano, Italy*

ROBERT E. HYATT | *Mayo Medical School and Mayo Clinic, Rochester, Minnesota*

CHAPTER CONTENTS

THE STATIC BEHAVIOR of the respiratory system is studied by determining and analyzing its volume-pressure relations. It is useful to define volumes relative to the classic pulmonary subdivisions at the outset and then to develop the mechanical basis of these subdivisions as the volume-pressure relations are analyzed.

This chapter stems partly from the basic research by Rohrer (127) but mainly from that by Fenn and his co-workers, who first pointed out the analytical value of the volume-pressure diagram of the respiratory system. Some of the figures in this chapter are patterned after those by Rahn et al. (116) and by Fenn (49, 50).

LUNG VOLUMES

Figure 1 illustrates the subdivisions of the gas volume contained in the lungs during various breathing maneuvers. Tidal volume (VT) is the volume of a particular breath or the average volume of a series of breaths. Inspiratory reserve volume (IRV) is the maximum volume that can be inspired from an end-tidal inspiratory level. Expiratory reserve volume (ERV) is the maximum volume that can be expired from the end-expiratory level. Residual volume (RV) is the volume of gas in the lungs and airways after as much gas as possible has been exhaled. Total lung capacity (TLC) is the volume of gas in the lungs and airways after as much gas as possible has been inhaled. Vital capacity (VC) is the volume of the deepest possible breath (i.e., TLC − RV). Functional residual capacity (FRC) is the volume of gas in the lungs and airways either at the end of a spontaneous expiration or at the resting volume of the respiratory system. Inspiratory capacity (IC) is the maximum volume that can be inspired from the end-expiratory level.

In resting individuals, breathing can be defined as a volume variation initiated from a somewhat relaxed state at end expiration, i.e., from the FRC. Because TLC, RV, and VC require voluntary maximum efforts, they apply only to awake humans. Other definitions for these volumes are needed for animals and anesthetized humans.

A young adult man 1.75 m tall has a TLC of ~6.5 liters and an RV of ~1.5 liters. Because his lungs would weigh ~700 g and have a tissue volume of nearly 0.7 liters, even after the deepest possible expiration his lungs would contain a volume of gas about twice the tissue volume, and after the deepest possible inspiration his lungs would expand ~10-fold.

Individual differences in lung volumes relate mainly to body size (35, 45, 75, 80, 84). Over a small range of body size, e.g., in humans, VC, RV, and TLC vary approximately as the cube of a linear dimension such as body height (20, 70, 80) or arm span, which is a useful predictor in subjects with spinal deformity (69). For example, the average coefficients (20, 68, 70) that, when multiplied by height (in meters) cubed, yield the VC and TLC (in liters) for men 5–44 yr old and 1.2–2 m tall are 0.89 ± 0.11 (SD) and 1.17 ± 0.14, respectively. Table 1 presents data from a large European study (80). The lower values found in the United States (45) may reflect population and sampling differences.

The greatest change with age is in RV, which increases ~50% from ages 20 to 60. Changes are quite erratic beyond the age of 60, which reflects the increasing difficulty of defining normal subjects among the elderly. Volumes for women average 10% lower than for men of the same age and size (45, 80). The postural

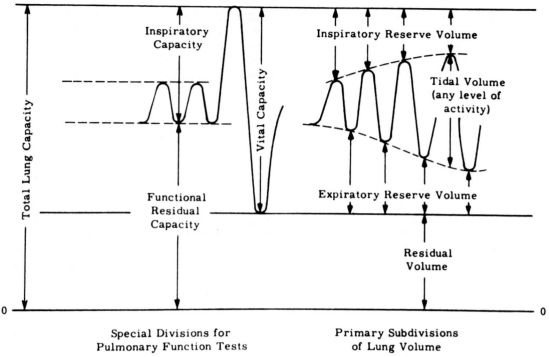

FIG. 1. Subdivisions of lung volume. [From Pappenheimer et al. (109).]

TABLE 1. *Ratios of VC, RV, and TLC to Cube of Height for Men in Upright Posture*

Age	VC/ht³	RV/ht³	TLC/ht³
18–19	0.990	0.240	1.230
20–29	1.025	0.275	1.300
30–34	1.020	0.300	1.300
35–39	1.010	0.310	1.320
40–44	1.000	0.320	1.320
45–49	0.990	0.330	1.320
50–54	0.970	0.350	1.320
55–59	0.950	0.370	1.320
60–65	0.930	0.390	1.320
Normal limits	±17%	±31%	±22%
No. of subjects	3,153	1,098	1,098

Values are ratios for lung volumes (liters) to cube of height (m³). Vital capacity (VC), residual volume (RV), and total lung capacity (TLC) expressed at body temperature, ambient pressure, saturated with water vapor (BTPS). [Adapted from Jouasset (80).]

changes of lung volumes are discussed in *Effects of Gravity and Posture*, p. 118.

Most volumes in the remainder of this chapter are expressed in percent of VC. This is done for two reasons. First, it is a convenient reference for a given subject: after a little practice, VC, RV, and TLC are highly reproducible; for VC measurements taken on the same individual over monthly periods, SD = 2%–3% (59, 115, 144). Second, in normal subjects of similar age, differences in VC probably reflect mainly differences in lung and chest wall size, and expressions of volumes relative to VC allow differences in size to be taken into account. It is apparent that when differ-

ences in VC have other bases, e.g., diseases, and when the ratios of RV to TLC are outside the normal range, this representation of volumes loses much of its usefulness.

VOLUME-PRESSURE RELATIONS OF RESPIRATORY SYSTEM DURING RELAXATION

Total Respiratory System

During relaxation of the respiratory muscles under static conditions the pressure exerted by the respiratory system depends on various elastic, surface, and accelerative (e.g., gravitational) forces operating on the lung and the chest wall (rib cage and diaphragm-abdomen). The static pressure exerted by the respiratory system is equal to the difference between alveolar pressure and body surface pressure; in static conditions with the glottis open, alveolar pressure equals the pressure at the airway opening, and therefore it can be measured at the mouth or in a nostril. To determine the relation between lung volume and relaxation pressure of the respiratory system (116, 127), the subject inspires or expires a volume of gas and then relaxes against an obstructed airway, and the pressure across the obstruction is measured. Then the subject breathes in or out maximally from a spirometer so that the volume at which the pressure was measured can be related to an extreme of VC. This volume must be corrected for the compression or expansion of the gas in the respiratory system due to the change of pressure during relaxation. These measurements are made at several volumes to obtain the volume-pressure curve during relaxation. Reproducible results cannot be obtained in all subjects and some training is necessary. Approximately one out of three subjects learns to be a good relaxer; "good relaxer" means only that the data are consistent. It is interesting that total respiratory system compliance is the same in subjects studied awake and then under hypnosis (138).

The volume-pressure curve of the relaxed respiratory system with the trunk erect is shown in Figure 2 along with the spirogram illustrating the pulmonary subdivisions. The volume at an airway pressure of zero is the resting volume of the respiratory system; it usually corresponds to the end of a spontaneous expiration during quiet breathing. In the middle volume range the relation is almost straight; the volume change per 1 cmH$_2$O is ~2% of VC. The slope of the static volume-pressure curve, the compliance (C), is expressed in liters or milliliters per centimeter of water. The horizontal distance from the curve to the ordinate at zero pressure indicates the pressure exerted by the passive structure of the system at a given volume. Conversely, this distance indicates the pressure that the respiratory muscles must exert to maintain that lung volume with open airways. This is true, however, only if the shape of the chest wall is the same when the respiratory muscles are relaxed as when they are active at the same lung volume. In fact the energy of the passive structures of the system is minimum for the configuration occurring during relaxation; at the same lung volume, whenever this configuration is changed the energy of the passive structure is increased (8). The pressure exerted by the

muscles is larger than that indicated by the volume-pressure diagram to the extent that contraction of the respiratory muscles deforms the respiratory system relative to its relaxed configuration at a given volume. The extra pressure exerted by the muscles is difficult to assess. One other fact may confound the measurement of the static relaxation characteristic of the chest wall. It was recently shown that submaximal neuromuscular blockade reduced FRC in seated humans (44). The outward recoil of the chest wall decreased, whereas lung recoil did not change. It was concluded that involuntary respiratory muscle activity was present in addition to the elastic properties of the chest wall. Recent evidence also has been presented suggesting the existence of tonic diaphragmatic muscle activity at end expiration in supine humans (103).

Another method of estimating the volume-pressure relation of the relaxed respiratory system in the tidal volume range was proposed by Heaf and Prime (66) to overcome the difficulty of voluntary relaxation. With the subject breathing spontaneously, the pressure at the airway opening is raised above that acting on the body surface [positive-pressure breathing (PPB)]; if the subject is relaxed at the end of expiration, the relation is obtained by measuring the change in end-expiration lung volume and the applied pressure. The relation obtained by this method over the tidal volume range is usually similar to that obtained during voluntary relaxation (32, 66, 78, 99, 104). On the other hand the volume-pressure curve obtained by Rahn et al. (116) from the end-expiratory values during PPB and negative-pressure breathing (NPB) was different from that obtained during voluntary relaxa-

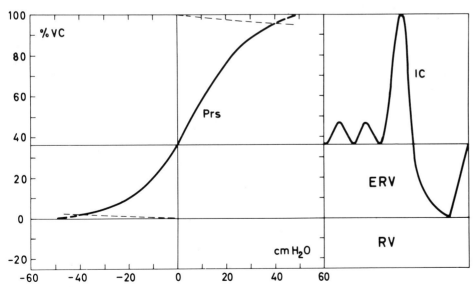

FIG. 2. Static volume-pressure curve of total respiratory system (Prs) during relaxation in sitting posture, with spirogram showing subdivisions of lung volume. Curve was extended to include full vital capacity (VC) range by means of externally applied pressures. IC, inspiratory capacity; ERV, expiratory reserve volume; RV, residual volume. *Broken lines*, volume change during relaxation against an obstruction due to gas compression at TLC and expansion at RV. [Adapted from Rohrer (127) by Agostoni and Mead (6).]

tion. This difference may relate to the fact that in their experiments during PPB and NPB the head and neck were not exposed to the same pressure as the rest of the body surface (78, 116). However, because the volume-pressure curve obtained during voluntary relaxation with closed glottis is equal to that with open glottis, the pressure across the cheeks and the neck does not seem to influence the results (99). For some subjects the volume-pressure curve determined from the end-expiratory values during PPB and NPB was different from that obtained during voluntary relaxation even if during both PPB and NPB the head and neck were exposed to the same pressure as the rest of the body (2, 99). The different results may partly relate to the period of PPB because the activity of the expiratory muscles seems to appear only after some minutes of PPB (3).

General anesthesia, muscular paralysis, and their combination have been studied for their effects on the mechanics, especially the volume-pressure characteristics, of the respiratory system [(28, 44, 56, 73, 106, 118, 139, 143); see the chapter by Rehder and Marsh in this *Handbook*].

Chest Wall and Lung

The chest wall and the lung are mechanically in series; thus the algebraic sum of the pressure exerted by the wall (Pw) and by the lung (PL) equals the pressure of the respiratory system (Pw + PL = Prs), whereas the change of volume (ΔV) of each part must be equal (except for shifts of blood volume) and equal to that of the respiratory system ($\Delta Vw = \Delta VL = \Delta Vrs$). Static Prs is the difference between alveolar pressure (PA) and body surface pressure (Pbs), thus when the latter is atmospheric, PA = Pw + PL. Be-

cause Pw generally indicates pressure exerted by the relaxed chest wall, when the respiratory muscles are active, PA = Pw + PL + Pmus.

Under static conditions the pressure exerted by the lung is the difference between alveolar pressure and pleural surface pressure (Ppl), PL = PA − Ppl. The pressure exerted by the chest wall is the difference between pleural surface pressure and body surface pressure (Pbs), Pw = Ppl − Pbs. The chest wall pressure may be obtained either indirectly by subtracting the pressure exerted by the lung from that exerted by the respiratory system, or directly from Ppl measurements. In fact when the subject is relaxed (with closed airways to keep a static condition), because PA = PL + Pw and PL = PA − Ppl, substitution gives Pw = Ppl. Moreover Ppl = PA − PL and Ppl = Pmus + Pw when the muscles are active. When the subject actively holds a given lung volume with open airways, PA may be made equal to zero; then Ppl = −PL. When the muscles are relaxed with the airways closed, Pmus may be made equal to zero; then Ppl = Pw. In humans Ppl is usually estimated from esophageal pressure measurements.

Figure 3 shows static volume-pressure curves of the relaxed chest wall and of the lung, with trunk erect. At the resting volume of the respiratory system the chest wall recoils outward with a pressure equal to that by which the lung recoils inward. The resting volume of the lung is below 0% VC, i.e., less than RV. That of the chest wall is ~55% VC (6). Above this volume both the chest wall and the lung recoil inward, whereas below this volume the chest wall recoils outward; thus the lung and the chest wall behave like two opposing springs. According to Turner et al. (136) the compliance of the chest wall (Cw) decreases slightly above 80%–90% VC; if so the resting volume of the

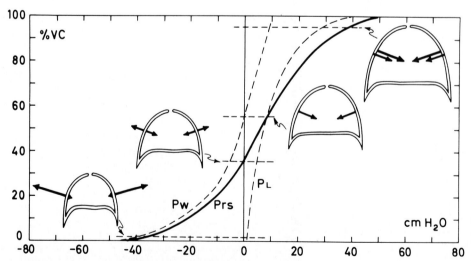

FIG. 3. Static volume-pressure curves of lung (PL), chest wall (Pw), and total respiratory system (Prs) during relaxation in sitting posture. *Large arrows*, static forces of lung and chest wall (dimensions of *arrows* are not to scale). *Horizontal broken lines*, volume for each drawing. [Adapted from Rahn et al. (116) by Agostoni and Mead (6).]

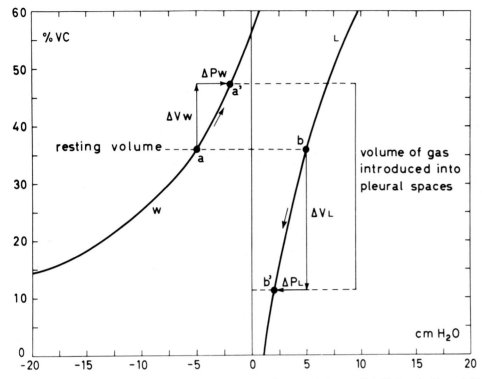

FIG. 4. Volume changes of chest wall (ΔVw) and of lung (ΔVL) when volume of gas is introduced into both pleural spaces so that pleural pressure changes from −5 to −2 cmH₂O. Position of chest wall (w) moves from *point a to a'* and that of lung (L) moves from *b to b'* as indicated by *arrows*. ΔPw, change in pressure across chest wall; ΔPL, change in transpulmonary pressure. [Adapted from Fenn (50) by Agostoni and Mead (6).]

chest wall is slightly higher than indicated above. In the tidal volume range Cw and the compliance of the lung (CL) are about the same. Because the chest wall and the lung are placed in series, their reciprocals are additive $(1/\text{CL} + 1/\text{Cw} = 1/\text{Crs})$.

If in a relaxed subject both pleural spaces were opened to the ambient air, the lungs would collapse and the chest wall would expand to the corresponding resting volumes; a volume of air of ~60% VC would then be sucked into the pleural spaces. The static effects of a smaller pneumothorax are illustrated in Figure 4. If a volume of gas is introduced into the pleural spaces so that Ppl changes from −5 to −2 cmH₂O, the position of the chest wall will move from a to a′ and that of the lung from b to b′; Pw will change from −5 to −2 cmH₂O, and PL from 5 to 2 cmH₂O. The volume of gas required to produce such changes (ΔVw + ΔVL) corresponds to ~35% VC. The partitioning of this volume between the chest wall and the lungs depends on the compliance of the two structures. Note that the volume of gas introduced into the pleural space is greater than the volume of gas that leaves the lung.

For analytical purposes, pleural surface pressure is expressed in the volume-pressure diagrams as a single value, i.e., as if it were uniformly distributed. Under physiological conditions, however, pleural surface pressure varies at different sites because of the effects of gravity on the lung and the chest wall and because of the different natural shapes of these two structures (see the chapter by Agostoni in this *Handbook*). Therefore it is important to keep in mind that the actual balance between the lung and the chest wall under physiological conditions results from a wide distribution of pressures (see the next section) and that esophageal pressure must not be considered as an average of pleural surface pressure in different places.

Static volume-pressure relations have previously been represented as single lines, suggesting that static pressures depend only on volume. These pressures actually differ depending on the volume history of the respiratory system. For example, static pressures tend to be lower after deep inspirations and higher after deep expirations. Consequently static curves obtained as volume is changed in progressive steps from minimum (RV) to maximum (TLC) levels and back again are loops rather than single lines (Fig. 5). When volume changes are initiated from resting levels, the pressures are intermediate (see Figs. 6, 9–12).

Loops such as those shown in Figure 5 are called hysteresis loops. Hysteresis is the failure of a system to follow identical paths of response upon application and withdrawal of a forcing agent (85). Static or quasi-

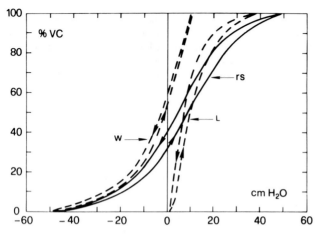

FIG. 5. Static volume-pressure hysteresis of total respiratory system (rs), lung (L), and chest wall (w). Volume shifts (*arrowheads*) were produced by gradually changing pressure at the mouth relative to that at body surface; a complete cycle took ~1 min during which the subject attempted to relax respiratory muscles as completely as possible. Volume changes were measured with body plethysmograph. Pleural pressure was estimated from esophageal pressure measurements. [Adapted from Agostoni and Mead (6).]

static (i.e., long-term) elastic hysteresis is a common phenomenon exhibited by various structural tissues of the body (119) and by nonbiological materials such as rigid metals and rubber. Hysteresis in the respiratory system depends on viscoelasticity, such as stress adaptation, i.e., a rate-dependent phenomenon, and on plasticity, i.e., a rate-independent phenomenon. Hysteresis occurs both in the lung and in the chest wall (27, 130, 137). In the lung it is mainly due to surface properties and alveolar recruitment-derecruitment (58), whereas in the chest wall it seems mainly related to muscles and ligaments because both skeletal muscles (25) and elastic fibers (120) exhibit hysteresis. Hysteresis is negligible for volume changes such as those occurring during quiet breathing. This is functionally desirable because the area of the hysteresis loop represents energy lost from the system. Volume-pressure loops observed during breathing, i.e., the dynamic hysteresis of the respiratory system, are based on the flow resistance of gas and tissues. One consequence of the static hysteresis of the respiratory system is that its resting volume [Prs = 0; (see Fig. 5)] will be higher when reached after deflation from TLC than after inflation from RV.

Effects of Gravity and Posture

The volume-pressure curves considered so far refer to the erect trunk. They change with posture mainly because of the effect of gravity on the abdomen. The abdomen is mechanically like a container filled with liquid (48). When humans are in the upright posture and the respiratory muscles are relaxed, the abdomen behaves like a container in which part of its wall is distensible. The pressure in the upper part of this container is negative (83). Experimental evidence for

this behavior of the abdomen in humans was provided by Duomarco and Rimini (48). Because the top of this container (the diaphragm) is also distensible, it would be pulled downward by the gravitational effect of the abdomen contents were it not for the pleural pressure, which provides a lifting force in the opposite direction.

The level at which the abdominal pressure is equal to ambient pressure, the zero level, depends on the equilibrium among the elastic forces of the abdominal wall, diaphragm, rib cage, and lung and the gravitational force exerted by the abdominal contents. From the data of Duomarco and Rimini (48) it can be estimated that in the erect posture the zero level at the end of a normal expiration, i.e., at the resting volume of the respiratory system, is ~3–4 cm beneath the diaphragmatic dome. The pressure just beneath the dome of the diaphragm is approximately the same as that found at the surface of the lungs above the diaphgram. This suggests that the diaphragm is nearly, if not completely, relaxed; furthermore it apparently is not under any appreciable passive stretch. The elastic recoil of the lung thus is counterbalanced, at least at the dome of the diaphragm, by the hydrostatic pressure of the abdominal contents.

In supine subjects the zero level corresponds to the ventral wall of the abdomen (48). The diaphragm is then distended by the pressure of the abdominal contents. It is generally held that there is no electrical activity of the diaphragm either in humans (134) or in anesthetized animals (51, 128) during the last part of expiration, although tonic diaphragmatic activity has been reported recently in supine humans (103). If one assumes no activity, it seems probable that in the supine position the diaphragm balances with its own elasticity the pressure exerted by the abdominal contents. The zero level in the prone position corresponds to the dorsal wall of the abdomen, and when the subject is lying on one side, it is midway between the two sides (48). The zero level is expected to shift with lung volume and to a different degree in the upright and supine postures.

Because the volume of gas in the human abdomen is normally negligible compared with the lung volume, the volume of the abdomen is considered constant when its pressure is changed. Therefore the values of abdominal pressure at different lung volumes can be represented in the volume-pressure diagram of the respiratory system (10). The pressure on the abdominal side of the diaphragm (Pab) can be estimated from gastric pressure (10). Because the abdomen (wall and contents) and the diaphragm are placed in series relative to the lungs, the pressure of the abdomen-diaphragm is equal to the sum of the pressures exerted by its component parts.

In the upright posture during relaxation the transdiaphragmatic pressure (Pdi) is nil above the resting volume of the respiratory system, whereas it becomes progressively negative below the resting volume (Fig. 6, *top left*). In the upright posture the hydrostatic

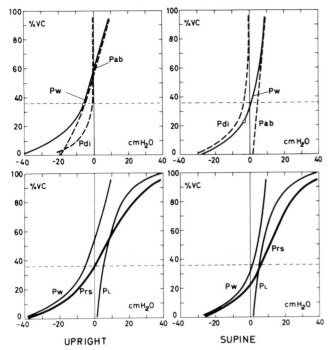

FIG. 6. Pressures contributed by various parts of respiratory system in sitting and supine postures. *Top*: volume-pressure relations of chest wall (Pw), diaphragm (Pdi), and abdomen (Pab); *open circles*, resting volume of respiratory system. *Bottom*: volume-pressure relations of chest wall, lung (PL), and total respiratory system (Prs). [Adapted from Agostoni and Mead (6).]

pressure applied on the abdominal surface of the diaphragm changes markedly with lung volume (Fig. 6, *top left*). At RV the zero level is ~20 cm below the diaphragmatic dome. At ~55% VC, which is the resting volume of the chest wall, the zero level is at the top of the abdominal cavity. At higher volume the zero level is above the top of the abdomen; i.e., the pressure on the abdominal surface of the diaphragm is above atmospheric.

In the upright posture gravity acts in the inspiratory direction on the abdomen-diaphragm and in the expiratory direction on the rib cage. The hydrostatic effect of the abdomen is greater at small than at large volumes, because at large volumes the height of the abdomen is less and its wall is stiffer. When a subject at FRC moves from the sitting to the standing position, the weight of the abdominal contents acting via the abdominal wall pulls the ribs down and in. Therefore gravity, acting through the abdomen, enhances its small direct expiratory effect on the rib cage. When a subject moves to the standing position the lung volume is slightly increased or unchanged, whereas the cross-sectional area of the rib cage at the xiphoid level is reduced to approximately the same extent as in the seated relaxed subject whose lung volume is reduced from FRC to ~16% VC (9). The decrease in cross section becomes insignificant at the angle of Louis (E. Agostoni and E. D'Angelo, unpublished observations).

In the supine posture (Fig. 6, *top right*) changes of Pab over the VC are nearly 50% of those occurring in the upright posture; shift of the zero level with lung volume is accordingly smaller. In the supine posture at TLC, the height of the abdomen is ~18 cm and the zero level of Pab is close to the ventral abdominal wall; hence the average hydrostatic pressure of the supine abdomen should be ~9 cmH$_2$O. This value is similar to that of the pressure acting on the thoracic side of the diaphragm during relaxation against an obstructed airway at full VC; at this lung volume therefore the pressure across the central part of the diaphragm should be approximately nil.

In the supine posture, gravity has a marked expiratory action on the abdomen-diaphragm, and a small, complex action on the rib cage. When a subject moves from the sitting to the supine posture, the cross-sectional area of the rib cage increases at the xiphisternal level (40, 140) but decreases at the angle of Louis (40). As a consequence of gravity the compliance of the chest wall, and thus that of the total respiratory system, in the middle volume range increases as a subject changes from the upright to the supine position (Fig. 6, *bottom*). When a subatmospheric pressure of 55 cmH$_2$O is applied to the abdominal wall caudal to the iliac crest of a supine subject, the volume-pressure curve of the respiratory system during relaxation becomes almost equal to that in the sitting posture (146). The mechanisms underlying this change have not been elucidated.

In the lateral posture the action of gravity on the abdomen-diaphragm is expiratory in the dependent region and inspiratory in the nondependent region. When anesthetized paralyzed subjects were moved from the supine to the lateral posture, FRC increased by 0.63 liters (117). When anesthetized paralyzed subjects in a more recent study were moved from the supine to the left or right lateral posture, FRC increased by 0.79 liters (15% VC) and 0.93 liters (17% VC), respectively (67). In the left lateral posture, FRC of the right (upper) lung was 2.20 liters and that of the left lung 0.85 liters. In the right lateral posture, FRC of the left (upper) lung was 2.09 liters and that of the right lung 1.12 liters (67).

In this analysis of the effect of gravity and posture in terms of volume-pressure diagrams, pleural surface pressure is considered uniform. Figure 7 illustrates the probable distribution of the pressure on the pleural surface at the resting volume of the respiratory system in the upright and lateral postures, taking into account the effect of gravity on the lung and the chest wall. In the upright posture the lung facing the diaphragmatic dome recoils inward with a pressure of probably 3–4 cmH$_2$O, i.e., nearly equal to the pull of the abdominal weight (10, 48). The nondependent part of the lung recoils inward with a pressure of ~10 cmH$_2$O; the superior part of the rib cage balances the lung recoil with an equal outward recoil. In the lateral position the lung recoil in the lowermost part is probably nil

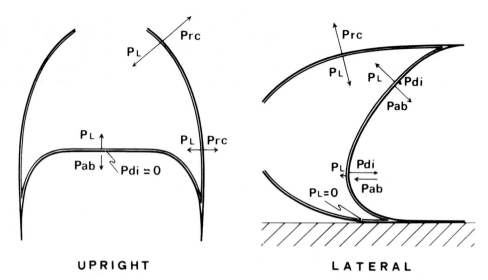

FIG. 7. Probable distribution of pressures in rib cage (Prc), lung (PL), abdomen (Pab), and diaphragm (Pdi) at the end of spontaneous expiration in upright and lateral postures. Figure takes into account effect of gravity on chest wall and lung and is based on data for humans and animals. Transdiaphragmatic pressure (Pdi) = Pab − PL. [From Agostoni (3).]

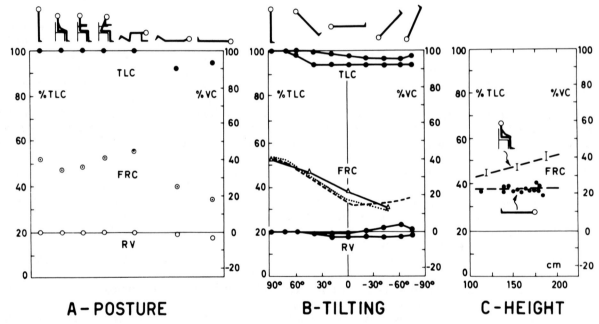

FIG. 8. Pulmonary subdivisions in various postures (A), during tilting (B), and as function of body height (C). In instances where residual volume (RV) was not determined it was assumed to be 20% of total lung capacity (TLC) in upright posture. A: standing (141; J. Mead, unpublished observations); seated erect (38, 74, 144); seated erect, arms supported (38); seated leaning forward, arms supported (38); on hands and knees (38); prone (100); supine (38, 45, 74, 100, 144). B: *triangles* (141); all remaining points (J. Mead, unpublished observations). *Dotted* (supported at shoulders) and *broken lines* (supported by ankles) are average values for 5 subjects. Values of TLC and RV are for individual subjects. C: seated (35); ranges are SE for groups of 10 subjects; *broken line* is fit by eye; supine (101, 124). [From Agostoni and Mead (6).]

and the lowermost part of the chest wall under this condition behaves like a rigid structure. The upper part of the lung recoils inward with a pressure of ~6 cmH$_2$O; this recoil is balanced by an opposite recoil of the superior part of the rib cage. The relaxed dia-

phragm in the upper part is pulled cranially by the lung recoil and caudally by the abdominal pressure, which is subatmospheric. In the lower part the lung and the abdominal contents distend the diaphragm cranially, the latter progressively more so than the former (3). Transdiaphragmatic pressure is Pab − PL and is given by the length of the Pdi line in Figure 7.

Figure 8A shows average values from a number of sources for the major pulmonary subdivisions in various postures; most of the effect of posture depends on the influence of gravity. The largest variation is in the resting end-expiratory volume (FRC). The increase of FRC for the subject in the sitting position with the arms supported reflects the influence of the weight and position of the shoulder girdle (38). As the subject leans forward the zero level of the abdomen moves downward, because the lower part of the abdomen becomes flexible. This effect is further increased in the elbows-and-knees position, when the zero level is presumably a little above the ventral wall of a relaxed abdomen. Similarly, if in the prone posture the weight of the abdomen is supported by the upper thorax and pelvis (46), FRC increases. On the other hand, in the usual prone posture with the ventral abdominal wall supported from the outside, the zero level is near the dorsal wall of the abdomen and the FRC decreases. The FRC is even smaller in the supine posture, and it is further decreased when the head is tilted downward (Fig. 8B).

During gradual tilting from standing to supine, the changes of FRC are about linearly related to the sine of the angle of tilt from the vertical to the horizontal. Beyond the horizontal, the volume change may be reduced (34). Indeed, in subjects suspended on a smooth flat surface by their ankles, beyond about −10° the FRC increases (Fig. 8B). Two events are involved here. 1) The hydrostatic pressure of the abdomen, which continues to increase as the head is tilted downward, is increasingly opposed by the elastic recoil of the diaphragm (see Fig. 6). 2) At the same time the action of gravity on the rib cage, shoulder girdle, and associated structures, which is expiratory in the upright posture, becomes inspiratory in the head-down positions, countering the abdominal hydrostatic pressure; as the latter comes increasingly under diaphragmatic restraint, gravity finally supersedes hydrostatic pressure.

Figure 8C shows that tall individuals have relatively larger values for FRC than short individuals in the upright posture but similar values in recumbency because of hydrostatic pressure.

The only significant changes in TLC and RV occur between the upright posture and recumbency. These changes are small; even in the head-down position the two subjects illustrated in Figure 8B had reductions of <10% in TLC and VC. The changes in lung volumes considered here are those occurring within minutes; they relate mainly to shifts in blood between the thoracic cavity and the rest of the body (134a). 1) The differences between upright and supine VC are smaller after applications of tourniquets to the extremities (16, 47, 64, 94, 132) or immersion in water (63), i.e., in conditions that minimize the differences of thoracic blood volume between the two positions. 2) The VC

changes with ambient temperature, according to the expected shifts of blood from the thorax to the extremities and vice versa (60, 115). 3) The VC in the supine posture increases 5.6% if the PA is maintained at 55 cmH₂O for 5 s by a Valsalva maneuver near maximal inspiration immediately before a VC measurement; the same maneuver in the upright posture produces only 50% of this increase (18, 53). These results are due to the shifts of blood out of the thorax and support the view that the intrathoracic blood volume is larger in the supine than in the upright posture.

Although these shifts are commonly thought to occur between the lungs and the rest of the body, other shifts in and out of the intrathoracic, extrapulmonary structures such as the great veins, atria, and ventricles are also clearly involved; this implies a change in the chest wall volume. The mechanical effects of changes in the blood volume outside the lungs are the easiest to understand (65). At middle lung volume an increase in intrathoracic, extrapulmonary blood volume causes a decrease in lung volume and an increase in chest wall volume (88). As far as the volume extremes are concerned, an increase in intrathoracic, extrapulmonary blood volume would be expected to reduce both TLC and RV, which are the changes observed in passing from the upright to the supine posture. The intrathoracic, extrapulmonary blood volume would change with pleural pressure, increasing as pleural pressure becomes more subatmospheric. Accordingly the VC of the chest wall should exceed that of the lungs by an amount equal to this blood volume change. This discrepancy can be reduced by maneuvers that displace blood out of the chest wall, as previously mentioned.

The mechanical effects of changes in intrapulmonary blood volume are more complicated. An increase in pulmonary blood volume increases the recoil of the lungs at high lung volumes and decreases the recoil at low lung volumes. These changes tend to lower TLC and increase RV, but the effects are small in magnitude; it is probable that the observed changes chiefly reflect the influence of changes in extrapulmonary blood volume. Finally, blood shifts into the abdomen on assuming the supine posture may cause cephalad displacement of the diaphragm and contribute to the reduction in FRC.

Figure 9 shows the displacement of the volume-pressure curve of the relaxed chest wall that occurs when a sitting subject is submerged up to the xiphoid or to the shoulders (5, 39, 71). The changes occurring during submersion to the xiphoid reflect the lack of downward pull produced by the gravitational field on the abdomen. Thus the broken curve of Figure 9 approximates the volume-pressure curve of the relaxed chest wall when gravity free; it is displaced ~1 cmH₂O to the left because of the lack of shoulder weight (38). Accordingly the ERV when gravity free decreases by ~8% of the VC (5).

During submersion to the shoulders the end-expi-

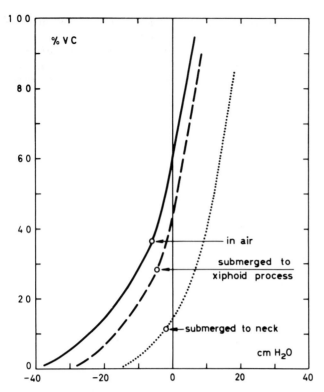

FIG. 9. Volume-pressure curves of relaxed chest wall with subject sitting in air (*solid line*), submerged to the xiphoid process (*broken line*), and submerged to neck (*dotted line*). *Open circles*, end of spontaneous expirations. Volume-pressure curve of lung is not appreciably changed during submersion, and therefore volume-pressure curve of relaxed respiratory system during submersion undergoes same shift as that of chest wall. Volume differences at upper end of curves are due partly to larger compression of gas and partly to a decreased upper limit of VC occurring during submersion. [From Agostoni et al. (5).]

ratory volume is reduced to ~11% of the VC (Fig. 9). The volume decrease produced by this submersion is almost entirely (⅚) due to the displacement of the abdomen-diaphragm, partly because of the higher hydrostatic pressure acting on the abdomen and partly because of diaphragm–rib cage interaction. The diaphragm at the end of expiration is displaced craniad nearly as far as it is at full expiration under normal conditions and it is essentially relaxed. Only part of the ambient pressure is transmitted through the abdominal wall, which is stretched toward the abdominal cavity and recoils outward. The average hydrostatic pressure acting on the submerged rib cage is ~17 cmH$_2$O. The average hydrostatic pressure acting on the chest wall is ~20 cmH$_2$O (5, 76). However, a subject completely immersed in the head-up posture chooses to breathe at a pressure lower than the average pressure acting on the chest wall to avoid the discomfort produced by stretching the pharynx and the cheeks (135). In the supine subject submerged to the ventral wall the average hydrostatic pressure acting on the chest wall is 6–7 cmH$_2$O (39, 72, 76). In the upright subject submerged to the shoulders the VC is

reduced by ~9% (Fig. 9), with 6% probably accounted for by a decrease of the upper volume extreme caused by the hydrostatic pressure counteracting that exerted by the inspiratory muscles (see *Upper Volume Extreme*, p. 126) and 3% by the shift of the blood into the chest cavity (3, 5). However, Hong et al. (72) suggested that as much as 60% of the reduction in VC could be due to increased intrathoracic blood volume. Note that the reduction in lung volumes varies somewhat among studies and may partly reflect the method used to measure absolute volume (123).

Changes Throughout Life Span

The static behavior of the respiratory system changes throughout life. In the mature fetus the resting volume of the chest wall corresponds to that of the nonaerated lung, and therefore the pressure on the pleural surface is not subatmospheric (1, 12, 17, 21). This condition is functionally significant; in fact if the chest recoiled outward, as in extrauterine life, one of two situations should occur. *1*) If the lung followed the expansion of the chest, an equilibrium would be reached at a volume close to the resting volume of the chest because the lung recoil would be relatively small as a result of the lack of surface tension provided by the air-liquid interface in the alveoli (see the chapter by Goerke and Clements in this *Handbook*). Consequently the lung at birth would contain a considerable amount of liquid, which would presumably compromise breathing. *2*) If the lung did not follow the expansion of the chest, liquid would fill the pleural space; the critical factor here is that in the fetus the pulmonary capillaries, and therefore the visceral pleura, do not absorb protein-free liquid against the recoil of the lung as they do in extrauterine life (see the chapter by Agostoni in this *Handbook*). The amount of liquid in the resting lung of the fetus is small but not negligible; from specific-gravity measurements and lung weights, Avery and Cook (17) found that the volume of the liquid is one to two times that of the lung tissue. Recent measurements have shown that a considerable fraction of this liquid resides in perivascular and peribronchial cuffs (23).

Above resting volume the chest wall of the fetus is so compliant that no significant recoil is found over a considerable volume range. Below resting volume, however, the chest wall resists further compression (17).

After birth, breathing produces a decrease of pressure in the pulmonary capillary and an increase of pulmonary lymph flow; the lung liquid is removed by blood capillaries and lymphatics (23, 73a). The mere substitution of air for liquid in part of the alveoli provides some recoil to the lung because of the surface tension of the air-liquid interface that was not present before at the same volume (1). This recoil of the aerated lung tends to pull in the chest wall, which otherwise opposes it. This opposition increases progessively, because the end-expiratory volume of the chest wall increases during the first breaths, probably because of a plasticlike phenomenon similar to that shown for the fetal tissue in the lung (1, 12) and the development of inspiratory muscle tone (103). These events initiate the opposing recoil of the lung and chest wall and thus the negative pressure on the pleural surface. Then the resorptive pressure of the visceral pleura prevents a collection of liquid in the pleural space, which keeps the lung expanded in the chest.

The changes of the volume-pressure relations of the chest wall and of the lung during growth are usefully expressed and interpreted only if referred to a reliable unit. Because all lung volume subdivisions depend on mechanical properties as well as on size (89), the weight of the lung, measured or predicted from body size, is preferred as a reference unit (17). For the chest wall, it is not feasible to distinguish between size and elastic properties.

At the resting volume of the respiratory system the recoil pressure of the lung in a 1-wk-old newborn is ~50% of that in an adult (1, 52). In this connection the end-expiratory volume in newborns is generally greater than the resting volume of the respiratory system because of airway closure, an insufficiently long expiratory duration (108, 114), or tonic activity of inspiratory muscles (103). The resting volume of the respiratory system expressed per unit TLC in the 1-wk-old newborn animal is smaller than that in adult dogs (1, 52), equal in rabbits, and larger in rats and cats (52); if expressed per unit lung weight it is smaller in newborns; if expressed per unit body weight it is smaller in dogs, equal in pigs, and larger in rats, guinea pigs, rabbits, and cats (52).

Wide-range volume-pressure measurements in newborn dogs (1), goats (17), and humans (114, 121) have shown that the compliance of the chest wall, expressed per unit either of lung volume or of estimated lung weight, is higher than that of the adult. Chest wall compliance then markedly decreases with growth. However, Fisher and Mortola (52) found that Cw per unit body weight in newborn rats, rabbits, and cats is higher than in adults, whereas in newborn dogs it is equal; Cw per unit lung weight in newborn rabbits, cats, and dogs is similar in adults, whereas in newborn rats it is smaller. The compliance of the lung is lower in the newborn than in the adult if expressed per unit of lung weight (17, 37, 52), whereas it is similar, or slightly lower, if expressed per unit of lung volume (1, 37, 114). Sharp et al. (130) measured total respiratory compliance during anesthesia and paralysis in normal subjects 1–69 yr of age and found Cw (ml/cmH$_2$O) = $3.95 \times ht^{2.38}$ (cm) $\times 10^{-4}$ for the group. No striking changes in the volume-pressure curve of the total respiratory system were seen with growth from 1 to 18 yr although anesthesia and paralysis alter Cw and CL (118, 143). The main static change of the respiratory system during growth is the increasing outward recoil of the chest wall. It is not clear how much of this is due to changes in the mechanical properties of the chest wall and how much to a disproportionate growth of the chest wall relative to that of the lung (see the chapter by Bryan and Wohl in this *Handbook*).

From young adulthood VC decreases almost linearly with age; at 70 yr it is ~75% of that at 30 yr (19, 24, 105, 110, 124, 144). This decrease is due to an increase of the RV (24, 62, 81, 105, 107, 113, 136). In fact the TLC does not decrease (107, 113, 136); a small decrease was found in some studies (97, 105, 112), probably because the older subjects were smaller, as pointed out by Turner et al. (136). The recoil of the lung decreases with age, particularly at high lung volume (33, 54, 97, 112, 113, 136). In the region of spontaneous breathing, the compliance of the lung increases with age, whereas that of the chest wall decreases. In a 20-yr-old normal erect subject the lungs are less compliant than the chest wall, whereas in a 60-yr-old subject the reverse is true and the overall compliance is somewhat less (136). At low lung volume the outward recoil of the chest wall increases with age. On the other hand the resting volume of the chest wall seems to decrease in old subjects, hence the volume-pressure curve of the chest wall becomes less steep with age, pivoting at about middle lung volume, where its recoil remains the same (136). The increase of FRC with age found by most investigators (54, 62, 81, 105, 107, 113) therefore is mainly due to the decrease of lung recoil and is less marked than the increase of RV (136). Pulmonary changes with aging are discussed in the chapter by Brody and Thurlbeck in this *Handbook*.

There are relatively few studies of respiratory mechanics during pregnancy (96, 142). Although TLC and VC do not change significantly, late in pregnancy there are 25% and 40% reductions in FRC and ERV, respectively (57). In the same study no change in CL was found. However, a more recent study also of subjects in the sitting posture (14) found a 22% decrease in RV and a 6% decrease in TLC; both changes were statistically significant.

VOLUME-PRESSURE RELATIONS OF RESPIRATORY SYSTEM DURING STATIC MUSCULAR EFFORTS

Alveolar Pressure

The alveolar pressures during maximum static inspiratory and expiratory efforts exerted for 1–2 s at different lung volumes in the upright posture are shown in Figure 10. The horizontal distance between these curves and the relaxation pressure curve (Prs) gives the net pressure exerted by the contraction of the respiratory muscles (broken lines). Similar curves are obtained if, instead of performing the effort against the obstructed airways, the subject starting from full inspiration or expiration breathes into or out of containers of different capacities (36).

The expiratory pressures are larger when the chest is inflated, whereas the inspiratory pressures are larger when it is deflated. This behavior depends on the force-length relation of the muscles, besides being influenced by the mechanical features of the passive structures involved, by the action of the antagonist muscles (see the next section), and by a hypothetical inhibition of the efforts. The length of the expiratory muscles increases with the lung volume and the op-

posite occurs for the inspiratory muscles. There are few data comparing maximal pressures for upright and supine postures. In 10 normal males no difference was found in the maximal expiratory pressures at TLC (225 cmH₂O standing, 226 cmH₂O supine) or maximal inspiratory pressures at RV (118 cmH₂O both standing and supine) when posture and lung volumes were carefully controlled (R. E. Hyatt, unpublished observations). It would be interesting to make these comparisons at FRC because changes in rib cage cross section in various postures suggest that the length of rib cage muscles at FRC should be different at similar lung volumes (standing and sitting) or almost the same at different lung volumes (sitting and supine).

The volume-pressure relations of the respiratory system during maximum efforts in groups of upright males of different ages are shown in Figure 11. The pressures exerted by children are nearly the same as those of adults. This is probably related to the smaller radius of curvature of the rib cage, of the diaphragm, and of the abdominal wall in children (6, 36). In fact, according to Laplace's law, if the radius of curvature of the wall is small, thin muscles with a small force may exert pressures as great as those exerted by thick muscles of a wall with a greater radius. A human newborn can lower the intrathoracic pressure to −70 cmH₂O to overcome the high resistance to the first breath (82). The main difference between children and adults is during expiratory efforts at large lung

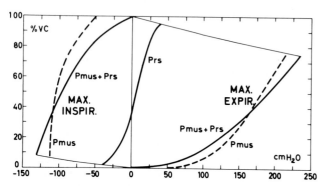

FIG. 10. Lung volume vs. alveolar pressure during maximum static inspiratory and expiratory efforts and during relaxation in upright posture (*solid lines*). *Broken lines*, pressure contributed by muscles (Pmus). Prs, total respiratory system pressure. [Adapted from Rohrer (127) by Agostoni and Mead (6).]

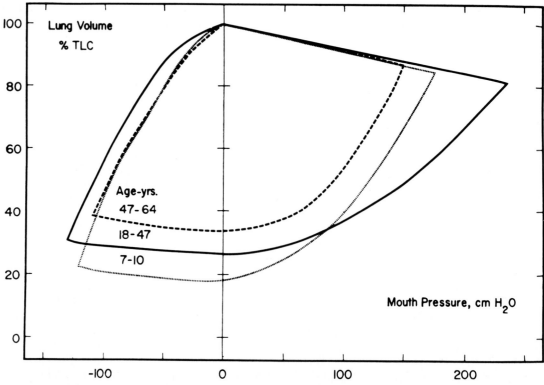

FIG. 11. Volume-pressure relations of respiratory system during maximum static inspiratory and expiratory efforts made by upright males of different ages. [From Cook et al. (36).]

volumes. This is due to the greater contribution of accessory expiratory muscles in adults, to antagonistic muscle activity, or to reflex inhibition (see the next section).

Young adult women do not develop maximum pressures as high as those of men of similar age (36). Some of this difference may be due to the difference in strength of the accessory muscles (122). Maximum inspiratory pressures in the Korean diving women were significantly greater than those in a control group, whereas the maximum expiratory pressures were about the same. The greater development of inspiratory muscles is possibly related to negative-pressure breathing that these women underwent daily while in water between dives (133).

Leith and Bradley (86) showed that ventilatory muscle strength and endurance can be increased by appropriate training programs. For static efforts, they found that after 5 wk of strength training (~30 min/day for 5 days/wk) maximum pressure increased by 55% and TLC by 4%. The decrease of the maximum respiratory pressures with age, the difference in maximum pressures between sexes, and the variation in these pressures among subjects parallel observations for the maximum strength of other groups of muscles in the body (122).

The values in Figures 10 and 11 do not necessarily represent the maximum that the inspiratory and expiratory muscles can exert because antagonist muscles may be active, particularly in the expiratory efforts (see the next section). In this case the pressure exerted by the agonists could be higher than that recorded in terms of alveolar pressure. Moreover pressure measurements do not give information about the muscle forces deforming the chest wall. Values of maximum pressure are obtained by voluntary efforts in the laboratory and they do not necessarily represent the effect of a maximum contraction of the muscles involved. The time course of the pressure change during the quickest and maximum effort suggests that the degree of excitation can be maximum, as it is during tetanic stimulation (98).

The maximum values of pressure found in recent years (4, 10, 22, 29, 36, 93, 122) are generally higher than most of those given in the older literature [for a survey of data on maximum respiratory pressure see Ringqvist (122)]. These differences are probably related to *1*) the type of mouthpiece used (36), *2*) the inhibition elicited by pain at the tympanic membrane (4) when measurements are made through the nostrils, and *3*) the inhibition possibly elicited by interference with circulation when the subject maintains the pressure for more than 1–2 s (93, 102).

When the pressure in the lung is changed, the lung volume changes owing to the compression or expansion of the gas; consequently the pressure attained is smaller than it would have been if the system had been filled with liquid. This effect may increase substantially if the same efforts are performed at low

ambient pressure. Therefore at high altitude the whole volume-pressure diagram is greatly curtailed, although of course the actual mechanics of the chest are not changed (116).

During slight neuromuscular blockade with either *d*-tubocurarine (77) or decamethonium (79), maximum inspiratory and expiratory pressures are reduced comparatively less than the maximum force of other muscles such as those involved in handgrip and head lift. Expiratory muscle force is reduced more than inspiratory force, and decreases in VC are greater than predicted (129). With partial paralysis, changes in lung volume may partly reflect unequal distribution of muscle weakness and a decreased ability to change rib cage dimensions (129). The effects of neuromuscular blockade, particularly in connection with anesthesia, are discussed in the chapter by Rehder and Marsh in this *Handbook*.

Abdominal and Thoracic Pressures

Transthoracic pressure measurements express only the results of agonist and antagonist groups of muscles acting simultaneously. The contributions by inspiratory and expiratory muscles can be separated only at the abdominal boundary of the respiratory system through transdiaphragmatic and transabdominal pressure measurements (see *Effects of Gravity and Posture*, p. 118).

Figure 12 shows the pressures on the thoracic and abdominal side of the diaphragm at different lung volumes during static inspiratory, expiratory, and expulsive efforts. During maximum inspiratory efforts the abdominal pressure in the majority of trained subjects remains roughly the same as during relaxation (see Fig. 6). Up to ~60% VC, the Pdi remains about the same or decreases slightly as the volume increases; above this volume the Pdi decreases progressively. Therefore up to ~60% VC the maximum Pdi (horizontal distance between solid and broken lines) is similar to the maximum transthoracic pressure (horizontal distance between solid line and ordinate at zero pressure). Mainly in untrained subjects (44a) the abdominal pressure frequently increases at large volumes. This is because of contraction of the muscles of the abdominal wall (30, 31, 42, 95). In these subjects the transdiaphragmatic pressure is roughly the same at all lung volumes; thus at large lung volumes it becomes progressively higher than the transthoracic pressure. The different behavior of Pdi at large lung volumes suggests that, at such volumes, the diaphragm may exert more pressure if the lower ribs are fixed by the contraction of the abdominal muscles. This explanation is supported by the high value of Pdi that can be reached during expulsive efforts at large lung volumes.

During a moderate expiratory effort (Valsalva maneuver) above resting volume Pdi is nil (10), but during maximum effort a pressure difference develops

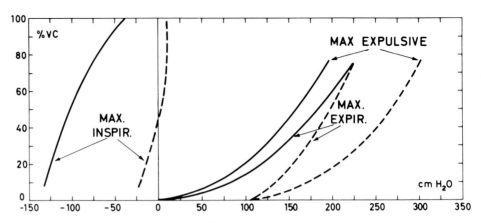

FIG. 12. Lung volume vs. pressure above (*solid lines*) and below (*broken lines*) diaphragmatic dome during maximum static inspiratory, expiratory, and expulsive efforts. [Adapted from Agostoni and Rahn (10) by Agostoni (3).]

(Fig. 12). Because at these volumes the diaphragm is not expected to be passively distended, this pressure should be the result of diaphragmatic contraction, as was confirmed by electromyographic findings (11). With decreasing lung volumes the pressure contributed by diaphragm contraction increases progressively (13).

During expulsive efforts the muscles of the abdominal wall contract more vigorously than during maximum expiratory efforts and the diaphragm also increases its activity. The Pab reaches its maximum and Ppl becomes somewhat smaller than during maximum expiratory efforts, suggesting that during expulsive efforts the action of the muscles of the abdominal wall on the rib cage is more than balanced by diaphragmatic contraction. The differences between maximum expulsive and expiratory efforts decrease with the decrease of lung volume, becoming nil at RV. At low lung volume the diaphragm can develop a greater pressure than the abdominal muscles; it is strongly but not maximally contracted (93). At large and middle lung volumes the values of Pdi are generally somewhat higher during expulsive efforts than during inspiratory ones, suggesting that diaphragmatic contraction yields the largest abdominal-thoracic pressure difference when the lower ribs are fixed by the contraction of the muscles of the abdominal wall. The lateral diameter of the rib cage at the xiphoid level, relative to its lung isovolume value during relaxation, is reduced by the activity of the expiratory muscles (7, 91a) and increased by that of the inspiratory muscles (7). The reduction of the radius of curvature of the diaphragm along the lateral diameter could explain why Pdi is greater during expulsive efforts.

The maximum static value of Pab during 2-s expulsive efforts is ~400 cmH$_2$O, the maximum value of Pdi is ~200 cmH$_2$O, and the maximum value of Ppl is ~300 cmH$_2$O and is reached during expiratory efforts (6).

FACTORS LIMITING VOLUME EXTREMES

Upper Volume Extreme

Mills (95) proposed that glottis closure is the main factor limiting the expansion of the lung. However, Mead et al. (91) found that only one in six normal subjects closed the upper airways at the end of maximum inspiration.

A balance between the passive opposing force, which increases markedly at both volume extremes (see Fig. 3), and the driving force of the agonist muscles, which decreases at both extremes, is the factor setting the upper volume limit for those subjects whose abdominal muscles do not contract at the end of maximum inspiration (91). Some subjects, however, contract the abdominal muscles at full inspiration, as shown by their marked electrical activity (30, 31, 42, 95). This contraction partly antagonizes the action of inspiratory muscles but partly improves the action of the diaphragm. It is difficult to assess whether the decrease of the force of the agonist muscles at large volume depends only on mechanical disadvantage related to their length-tension behavior or also on a reflex inhibition of the effort (3). Marked increases of TLC have occurred during acute asthmatic attacks (15, 55, 61, 111, 145), although some of the increase may be due to measurement artifact. These increases were accompanied by a loss of lung recoil, and an increase of strength of the inspiratory muscles was found in one subject (111). Finally, small but significant increases in TLC were found in normal subjects breathing 6% CO$_2$; the mechanism was unclear, but because lung recoil was unaltered, changes in the chest wall were most likely responsible (126).

Lower Volume Extreme

In young normal humans RV is determined by a static balance between the pressure exerted by the expiratory muscles and that exerted by the passive structures of the chest wall plus the contraction of antagonist muscles. The patency of most airways at RV is shown by the following findings: *1)* at full expiration esophageal pressure was 1–2 cmH$_2$O below atmospheric (90), *2)* a positive expiratory pressure suddenly applied to the respiratory system at or near RV produces a sudden expiration of a volume of air greater than that which could be squeezed from the intrathoracic airways (87), and *3)* maximum expiratory flow near RV was dependent on effort (87). Thus maximum expiration is performed quickly, and at full expiration a condition of no flow can be kept for several seconds (87). In the dependent part of the lung at RV, pleural pressure is positive and therefore airways are likely closed in this part even in the upright posture (26, 92, 125). The closure of the airways in the dependent part may elicit inhibition of the expiratory motoneurons and excitation of the inspiratory ones, thus preventing a further collapse of the lung, but no experimental evidence supports this hypothesis (3). As shown both by the electrical activity of the diaphragm (13, 43) and by Pdi being higher than at relaxation [Fig. 12; (10)], this muscle is contracted at RV. The mechanism leading to the marked contraction of the diaphragm may relate to the simultaneous activity of the abdominal muscles rather than to a reflex, because this contraction is negligible when the same lung volume is reached by an external force, such as during submersion or breathing from a tank in which the pressure is kept subatmospheric (5).

The static balance just described does not occur in older humans because expiration at low lung volume proceeds so slowly that it is ended by an abrupt inspiration before expiratory flow has ceased and therefore before a static balance is achieved (87). In older subjects the airway flow resistance is high and a positive pressure applied suddenly to the respiratory system at or near RV does not appreciably affect expiratory flow at the mouth. Expiratory flow is independent of effort because of dynamic compression of the airways; hence alveolar pressure may be markedly positive and dependent on effort (87). Airway closure occurs over a much greater portion of the lung in older subjects than in younger subjects (41). Airway closure, however, affects only indirectly the setting of RV. When airway closure involves a large fraction of the lung, the units still open have to be at a lower volume by the same amount that the closed units are at a higher volume. Thus the open units still reach a flow-limiting condition. Therefore the transition from the static RV of young subjects to the flow-time–limited RV of old subjects occurs by decreasing whole-lung maximum flow (no closure) and by trapping a larger and larger volume of gas in closed units, thus forcing the remaining open units to operate at correspondingly lower regional volumes and maximum flows.

REFERENCES

1. AGOSTONI, E. Volume-pressure relationships of the thorax and lung in the newborn. *J. Appl. Physiol.* 14: 909–913, 1959.
2. AGOSTONI, E. Diaphragm activity and thoracoabdominal mechanics during positive pressure breathing. *J. Appl. Physiol.* 17: 215–220, 1962.
3. AGOSTONI, E. Statics. In: *The Respiratory Muscles: Mechanics and Neural Control,* edited by E. J. M. Campbell, E. Agostoni, and J. Newsom Davis. London: Lloyd-Luke, 1970, p. 48–79.
4. AGOSTONI, E., AND W. O. FENN. Velocity of muscle shortening as a limiting factor in respiratory air flow. *J. Appl. Physiol.* 15: 349–353, 1960.
5. AGOSTONI, E., G. GURTNER, G. TORRI, AND H. RAHN. Respiratory mechanics during submersion and negative-pressure breathing. *J. Appl. Physiol.* 21: 251–258, 1966.
6. AGOSTONI, E., AND J. MEAD. Statics of the respiratory system. In: *Handbook of Physiology. Respiration,* edited by W. O. Fenn and H. Rahn. Washington, DC: Am. Physiol. Soc., 1964, sect. 3, vol. I, chapt. 13, p. 387–409.
7. AGOSTONI, E., AND P. MOGNONI. Deformation of the chest wall during breathing efforts. *J. Appl. Physiol.* 21: 1827–1832, 1966.
8. AGOSTONI, E., P. MOGNONI, G. TORRI, AND A. FERRARIO-AGOSTONI. Static features of the passive rib cage and abdomen-diaphragm. *J. Appl. Physiol.* 20: 1187–1193, 1965.
9. AGOSTONI, E., P. MOGNONI, G. TORRI, AND G. MISEROCCHI. Forces deforming the rib cage. *Respir. Physiol.* 2: 105–117, 1966.
10. AGOSTONI, E., AND H. RAHN. Abdominal and thoracic pressures at different lung volumes. *J. Appl. Physiol.* 15: 1087–1092, 1960.
11. AGOSTONI, E., G. SANT'AMBROGIO, AND H. DEL PORTILLO CARRASCO. Electromyography of the diaphragm in man and transdiaphragmatic pressure. *J. Appl. Physiol.* 15: 1093–1097, 1960.
12. AGOSTONI, E., A. TAGLIETTI, A. FERRARIO-AGOSTONI, AND I. SETNIKAR. Mechanical aspects of the first breath. *J. Appl. Physiol.* 13: 344–348, 1958.
13. AGOSTONI, E., AND G. TORRI. Diaphragm contraction as a limiting factor to maximum expiration. *J. Appl. Physiol.* 17: 427–428, 1962.
14. ALARLY, A. B., AND K. B. CARROL. Pulmonary ventilation in pregnancy. *Br. J. Obstet. Gynaecol.* 85: 518–524, 1978.
15. ANDERSON, S. D., J. D. S. McEVOY, AND S. BIANCO. Changes in lung volumes and airway resistance after exercise in asthmatic subjects. *Am. Rev. Respir. Dis.* 106: 30–37, 1972.
16. ASMUSSEN, E., E. H. CHRISTENSEN, AND T. SJÖSTRAND. Über die Abhängigkeit der Lungenvolumen von der Blutverteilung. *Skand. Arch. Physiol.* 82: 193–200, 1939.
17. AVERY, M. E., AND C. D. COOK. Volume-pressure relationships of lungs and thorax in fetal, newborn, and adult goats. *J. Appl. Physiol.* 16: 1034–1038, 1961.
18. BAHNSON, H. T. *The Effect of a Valsalva Maneuver Upon Changes in the Vital Capacity Volume of the Lung.* Dayton, OH: Wright-Patterson AFB, 1951, p. 518. (Tech. Rep. 6528.)
19. BALDWIN, E. DE F., A. COURNAND, AND D. W. RICHARDS, JR. Pulmonary insufficiency. I. Physiological classification, clinical methods of analysis, standard values in normal subjects. *Medicine Baltimore* 27: 243–278, 1948.
20. BATEMAN, J. B. Studies of lung capacities and intrapulmonary mixing: normal lung capacities. *J. Appl. Physiol.* 3: 133–142, 1950.
21. BERNSTEIN, J. Zur Entstehung der Aspiration der Thorax bei

der Geburt. *Pfluegers Arch. Gesamte Physiol. Menschen Tiere* 28: 229–242, 1882.

22. BLACK, L. F., AND R. E. HYATT. Maximal respiratory pressures: normal values and relationship to age and sex. *Am. Rev. Respir. Dis.* 99: 696–702, 1969.

23. BLAND, R. D., D. D. McMILLAN, M. A. BRESSACK, AND L. DONG. Clearance of liquid from lungs of newborn rabbits. *J. Appl. Physiol.: Respirat. Environ. Exercise Physiol.* 49: 171–177, 1980.

24. BRISCOE, W. A. Lung volumes. In: *Handbook of Physiology. Respiration*, edited by W. O. Fenn and H. Rahn. Washington, DC: Am. Physiol. Soc., 1965, sect. 3, vol. II, chapt. 53, p. 1345–1379.

25. BUCHTHAL, F., AND P. ROSENFALCK. Elastic properties of striated muscle. In: *Tissue Elasticity*, edited by J. W. Remington. Washington, DC: Am. Physiol. Soc., 1957, p. 73–93.

26. BURGER, E. J., JR., AND P. MACKLEM. Airway closure: demonstration by breathing 100% O_2 at low lung volumes and by N_2 washout. *J. Appl. Physiol.* 25: 139–148, 1968.

27. BUTLER, J. The adaptation of the relaxed lungs and chest wall to changes in volume. *Clin. Sci.* 16: 421–433, 1957.

28. BUTLER, J., AND B. H. SMITH. Pressure-volume relationships of the chest in the completely relaxed anesthetized patient. *Clin. Sci.* 16: 125–146, 1957.

29. BYRD, R. B., AND R. E. HYATT. Maximal respiratory pressures in chronic obstructive lung disease. *Am. Rev. Respir. Dis.* 98: 848–856, 1968.

30. CAMPBELL, E. J. M. An electromyographic study of the role of the abdominal muscles in breathing. *J. Physiol. London* 117: 222–233, 1952.

31. CAMPBELL, E. J. M., AND J. H. GREEN. The variations in intra-abdominal pressure and the activity of the abdominal muscles during breathing; a study in man. *J. Physiol. London* 122: 282–290, 1953.

32. CHERNIACK, R. M., AND E. BROWN. A simple method for measuring total respiratory compliance: normal values for males. *J. Appl. Physiol.* 20: 87–91, 1965.

33. COHN, J. E., AND H. D. DONOSO. Mechanical properties of lung in normal men over 60 years old. *J. Clin. Invest.* 42: 1406–1410, 1963.

34. COLVILLE, P., C. SHUGG, AND B. G. FERRIS, JR. Effects of body tilting on respiratory mechanics. *J. Appl. Physiol.* 9: 19–24, 1956.

35. COOK, C. D., AND J. F. HAMANN. Relation of lung volumes to height in healthy persons between the ages of 5 and 38 years. *J. Pediatr.* 59: 710–714, 1961.

36. COOK, C. D., J. MEAD, AND M. M. ORZALESI. Static volume-pressure characteristics of the respiratory system during maximal efforts. *J. Appl. Physiol.* 19: 1016–1022, 1964.

37. COOK, C. D., J. M. SUTHERLAND, S. SEGAL, R. B. CHERRY, J. MEAD, M. B. McILROY, AND C. A. SMITH. Studies of the respiratory physiology in the newborn infant. III. Measurements of mechanics of respiration. *J. Clin. Invest.* 36: 440–448, 1957.

38. CRAIG, A. B., JR. Effects of position on the expiratory reserve volume of the lungs. *J. Appl. Physiol.* 15: 59–61, 1960.

39. CRAIG, A. B., JR., AND M. DVORAK. Expiratory reserve volume and vital capacity of the lungs during immersion in water. *J. Appl. Physiol.* 38: 5–9, 1975.

40. D'ANGELO, E. Cranio-caudal rib cage distortion with increasing inspiratory airflow in man. *Respir. Physiol.* 44: 215–237, 1981.

41. DAVIS, C., E. J. M. CAMPBELL, P. OPENSHAW, N. B. PRIDE, AND G. WOODROOF. Importance of airway closure in limiting maximal expiration in normal man. *J. Appl. Physiol.: Respirat. Environ. Exercise Physiol.* 48: 695–701, 1980.

42. DELHEZ, L., J.-M. PETIT, AND G. MILIC-EMILI. Influence des muscles expiratures dans la limitation de l'inspiration. (Etude electromyographique chez l'homme.) *Rev. Franc. Etud. Clin. Biol.* 4: 815–818, 1959.

43. DELHEZ, L., J. TROQUET, J. DAMOISEAU, F. PIRNAY, R. DE-ROANNE, AND J.-M. PETIT. Influence des modalités d'exécu-tion des maneuvres d'expiration forcée et d'hyperpression thoraco-abdominale sur l'activité électrique du diaphragme. *Arch. Int. Physiol. Biochem.* 72: 76–94, 1964.

44. DE TROYER, A., AND J. BASTENIER-GEENS. Effects of neuromuscular blockade on respiratory mechanics in conscious man. *J. Appl. Physiol.: Respirat. Environ. Exercise Physiol.* 47: 1162–1168, 1979.

44a. DE TROYER, A., AND M. ESTENNE. Limitations of measurement of transdiaphragmatic pressure in detecting diaphragmatic weakness. *Thorax* 36: 169–174, 1981.

45. DITTMER, D. S., AND R. M. GREBE (editors). *Handbook of Respiration.* Philadelphia, PA: Saunders, 1958, p. 28–40.

46. DOUGLAS, W. W., K. REHDER, F. M. BEYNEN, A. D. SESSLER, AND H. M. MARSH. Improved oxygenation in patients with acute respiratory failure: the prone position. *Am. Rev. Respir. Dis.* 115: 559–566, 1977.

47. DOW, P. The venous return as a factor affecting the vital capacity. *Am. J. Physiol.* 127: 793–795, 1939.

48. DUOMARCO, J. L., AND R. RIMINI. *La presion intra-abdominal en el hombre.* Buenos Aires: El Ateneo, 1947.

49. FENN, W. O. Mechanics of respiration. *Am. J. Med.* 10: 77–91, 1951.

50. FENN, W. O. The pressure-volume diagram of the breathing mechanism. In: *Handbook of Respiratory Physiology*, edited by W. M. Boothby. Randolph AFB, TX: USAF School of Aviation Medicine, 1954, p. 19–27.

51. FINK, B. R., S. NGAI, AND D. A. HOLADAY. Effect of air flow resistance on ventilation and respiratory muscle activity. *J. Am. Med. Assoc.* 168: 2245–2249, 1958.

52. FISHER, J. T., AND J. P. MORTOLA. Statics of the respiratory system in newborn mammals. *Respir. Physiol.* 41: 155–172, 1980.

53. FOWLER, R. C., M. GUILLET, AND H. RAHN. *Lung Volume Changes With Positive and Negative Pulmonary Pressures.* Wright-Patterson AFB, OH: 1951, p. 522–528. (Tech. Rep. 6528.)

54. FRANK, N. R., J. MEAD, AND B. G. FERRIS, JR. The mechanical behaviour of the lungs in healthy elderly persons. *J. Clin. Invest.* 36: 1680–1687, 1957.

55. FREEDMAN, S., A. E. TATTERSFIELD, AND N. B. PRIDE. Changes in lung mechanics during asthma induced by exercise. *J. Appl. Physiol.* 38: 974–982, 1975.

56. FROESE, A. B., AND A. C. BRYAN. Effects of anesthesia and paralysis on diaphragmatic mechanics in man. *Anesthesiology* 41: 242–255, 1974.

57. GEE, J. B. L., B. S. PACKER, J. E. MILLEN, AND E. D. ROBIN. Pulmonary mechanics during pregnancy. *J. Clin. Invest.* 46: 945–952, 1967.

58. GIL, J., AND E. R. WEIBEL. Morphological study of pressure-volume hysteresis in rat lungs fixed by vascular perfusion. *Respir. Physiol.* 15: 190–213, 1972.

59. GILSON, J. C., AND P. HUGH-JONES. The measurement of total lung volume and breathing capacity. *Clin. Sci.* 7: 185–216, 1949.

60. GLASER, E. M. The effect of cooling and warming on the vital capacity, forearm and hand volume, and skin temperature of man. *J. Physiol. London* 109: 421–429, 1949.

61. GOLD, W. M., H. S. KAUFMAN, AND J. A. NADEL. Elastic recoil of the lungs in chronic asthmatic patients before and after therapy. *J. Appl. Physiol.* 23: 433–438, 1967.

62. GREIFENSTEIN, F. E., R. M. KING, S. S. LATCH, AND J. H. COMROE, JR. Pulmonary function studies in healthy men and women 50 years and older. *J. Appl. Physiol.* 4: 641–648, 1952.

63. HAMILTON, W. F., AND J. P. MAYO. Changes in the vital capacity when the body is immersed in water. *Am. J. Physiol.* 141: 51–53, 1944.

64. HAMILTON, W. F., AND A. B. MORGAN. Mechanism of the postural reduction in vital capacity in relation to orthopnea and storage of blood in the lungs. *Am. J. Physiol.* 99: 526–533, 1932.

65. HEAF, P. J. D., AND F. J. PRIME. The mechanical aspects of artificial pneumothorax. *Lancet* 2: 468–470, 1954.

66. HEAF, P. J. D., AND F. J. PRIME. The compliance of the thorax in normal human subjects. *Clin. Sci.* 15: 319–327, 1956.

67. HEDENSTIERNA, G., L. BINDSLEV, J. SANTESSON, AND O. P. NORLANDER. Airway closure in each lung of anesthetized human subjects. *J. Appl. Physiol.: Respir. Environ. Exercise Physiol.* 50: 55–64, 1981.

68. HELLIESEN, P. J., C. D. COOK, L. FRIEDLANDER, AND S. AGATHON. Studies of respiratory physiology in children. I. Mechanics of respiration and lung volume in 85 normal children 5 to 17 years of age. *Pediatrics* 22: 80–93, 1958.

69. HEPPER, N. G. G., L. F. BLACK, AND W. S. FOWLER. Relationships of lung volume to height and arm span in normal subjects and in patients with spinal deformity. *Am. Rev. Respir. Dis.* 91: 356–362, 1965.

70. HEPPER, N. G. G., W. S. FOWLER, AND H. F. HELMHOLZ, JR. Relationship of height to lung volume in healthy men. *Dis. Chest* 37: 314–320, 1960.

71. HONG, S. K., P. CERRETELLI, J. C. CRUZ, AND H. RAHN. Mechanics of respiration during submersion in water. *J. Appl. Physiol.* 27: 535–538, 1969.

72. HONG, S. K., E. Y. TING, AND H. RAHN. Lung volumes at different depths of submersion. *J. Appl. Physiol.* 15: 550–553, 1960.

73. HOWELL, J. B. L., AND B. W. PECKETT. Studies of the elastic properties of the thorax of supine anesthetized paralyzed human subjects. *J. Physiol. London* 136: 1–19, 1957.

73a. HUMPHREYS, P. W., I. C. S. NORMAND, E. O. R. REYNOLDS, AND L. B. STRANG. Pulmonary lymph flow and the uptake of liquid from the lungs of the lamb at the start of breathing. *J. Physiol. London* 193: 1–29, 1967.

74. HURTADO, A., AND W. W. FRAY. Studies of total pulmonary capacity and its subdivisions. III. Changes with body posture. *J. Clin. Invest.* 12: 825–832, 1933.

75. HUTCHINSON, J. On the capacity of the lungs and on the respiratory functions, with a view of establishing a precise and easy method of detecting disease by the spirometer. *Med. Chir. Trans. London* 29: 137–252, 1846.

76. JARRETT, A. S. Effect of immersion on intrapulmonary pressure. *J. Appl. Physiol.* 20: 1261–1266, 1965.

77. JOHANSEN, S. H., M. JØRGENSEN, AND S. MOLBECH. Effect of tubocurarine on respiratory and nonrespiratory muscle power in man. *J. Appl. Physiol.* 19: 990–994, 1964.

78. JOHNSON, L. F., JR., AND J. MEAD. Volume-pressure relationships during pressure breathing and voluntary relaxation. *J. Appl. Physiol.* 18: 505–508, 1963.

79. JØRGENSEN, M., S. MOLBECH, AND S. H. JOHANSEN. Effect of decamethonium on head lift, hand grip, and respiratory muscle power in man. *J. Appl. Physiol.* 21: 509–512, 1966.

80. JOUASSET, D. Normalisation des épreuves fonctionnelles respiratoires dans les pays de la Communauté Européenne du Charbon et de l'Acier. *Poumon Coeur* 10: 1145–1159, 1960.

81. KALTREIDER, N. L., W. W. FRAY, AND H. VAN HYDE. The effect of age on the total pulmonary capacity and its subdivisions. *Am. Rev. Tuberc.* 37: 662–689, 1938.

82. KARLBERG, P. Breathing and its control in premature infants. In: *Physiology of Prematurity*, edited by J. T. Lanman. New York: Macy, 1957, p. 77–150.

83. KELLING, G. Untersuchungen über die Spannungszustände der Bauchwand, der Magen und der Darmwand. *Z. Biol.* 44: 161–258, 1903.

84. KORY, R. C., R. COLLAHAN, AND H. G. BOREN. The Veterans Administration–Army cooperative study of pulmonary function. *Am. J. Med.* 30: 243–258, 1961.

85. LANDOWNE, M., AND R. W. STACY. Glossary of terms. In: *Tissue Elasticity*, edited by J. W. Remington. Washington, DC: Am. Physiol. Soc., 1957, p. 191–201.

86. LEITH, D. E., AND M. BRADLEY. Ventilatory muscle strength and endurance training. *J. Appl. Physiol.* 41: 508–516, 1976.

87. LEITH, D. E., AND J. MEAD. Mechanisms determining residual volume of the lungs in normal subjects. *J. Appl. Physiol.* 23: 221–227, 1967.

88. MAINS, R. C., F. W. ZECHMAN, AND F. S. MUSGRAVE. Pulmonary mechanics with a simulated postural blood redistribution. *Respir. Physiol.* 5: 288–301, 1968.

89. MEAD, J. Mechanical properties of lungs. *Physiol. Rev.* 41: 281–330, 1961.

90. MEAD, J., AND J. MILIC-EMILI. Theory and methodology in respiratory mechanics with glossary of symbols. In: *Handbook of Physiology. Respiration*, edited by W. O. Fenn and H. Rahn. Washington, DC: Am. Physiol. Soc., 1964, sect. 3, vol. I, chapt. 11, p. 363–376.

91. MEAD, J., J. MILIC-EMILI, AND J. M. TURNER. Factors limiting depth of a maximal inspiration in human subjects. *J. Appl. Physiol.* 18: 295–296, 1963.

91a. MELISSINOS, C. G., M. GOLDMAN, E. BRUCE, E. ELLIOT, AND J. MEAD. Chest wall shape during forced expiratory maneuvers. *J. Appl. Physiol.: Respirat. Environ. Exercise Physiol.* 50: 84–93, 1981.

92. MILIC-EMILI, J., J. A. M. HENDERSON, M. B. DOLOVICH, D. TROP, AND K. KANEKO. Regional distribution of inspired gas in the lung. *J. Appl. Physiol.* 21: 749–759, 1966.

93. MILIC-EMILI, J., M. M. ORZALESI, C. D. COOK, AND J. M. TURNER. Respiratory thoraco-abdominal mechanics in man. *J. Appl. Physiol.* 19: 217–223, 1964.

94. MILLS, J. N. The influence upon the vital capacity of procedures calculated to alter the volume of blood in the lungs. *J. Physiol. London* 110: 207–216, 1949.

95. MILLS, J. N. The nature of the limitation of maximal inspiratory and expiratory efforts. *J. Physiol. London* 111: 376–381, 1950.

96. MILNE, J. A. The respiratory response to pregnancy. *Postgrad. Med. J.* 55: 318–324, 1979.

97. MITTMAN, C., N. H. EDELMAN, A. H. NORRIS, AND N. W. SHOCK. Relationship between chest wall and pulmonary compliance and age. *J. Appl. Physiol.* 20: 1211–1216, 1965.

98. MOGNONI, P., F. SAIBENE, G. SANT'AMBROGIO, AND E. AGOSTONI. Dynamics of the maximal contraction of the respiratory muscles. *Respir. Physiol.* 4: 193–202, 1968.

99. MOGNONI, P., G. TORRI, AND E. AGOSTONI. Confronto della relazione volume-pressione del sistema respiratorio ottenuta con diversi procedimenti. *Atti Accad. Naz. Lincei.* 38: 925–928, 1965.

100. MORENO, F., AND H. A. LYONS. Effect of body posture on lung volumes. *J. Appl. Physiol.* 16: 27–29, 1961.

101. MORSE, M., F. W. SCHULTZ, AND D. E. CASSELS. The lung volume and its subdivisions in normal boys 10–17 years of age. *J. Clin. Invest.* 31: 380–391, 1952.

102. MOSLER, E., AND S. BALSAMOFF. Über den Valsalva-versuch. *Klin. Wochenschr.* 3: 491–495, 1924.

103. MULLER, N., G. VOLGYESI, L. BECKER, M. H. BRYAN, AND A. C. BRYAN. Diaphragmatic muscle tone. *J. Appl. Physiol.: Respirat. Environ. Exercise Physiol.* 47: 279–284, 1979.

104. NAIMARK, A., AND R. M. CHERNIACK. Compliance of the respiratory system and its components in health and obesity. *J. Appl. Physiol.* 15: 377–382, 1960.

105. NEEDHAM, C. D., M. C. ROGAN, AND I. McDONALD. Normal standards for lung volumes, intrapulmonary gas-mixing, and maximum breathing capacity. *Thorax* 9: 313–325, 1954.

106. NIMS, R. G., E. H. CONNER, AND J. H. COMROE, JR. The compliance of the human thorax in anesthetized patients. *J. Clin. Invest.* 34: 744–750, 1955.

107. NORRIS, A. H., N. W. SHOCK, M. LANDOWNE, AND J. A. FALZONE. Pulmonary function studies: age differences in lung volumes and bellows functions. *Gerontologia* 11: 379–387, 1956.

108. OLINSKY, A., M. H. BRYAN, AND A. C. BRYAN. Influence of lung inflation on respiratory control in neonates. *J. Appl. Physiol.* 36: 426–429, 1974.

109. PAPPENHEIMER, J. R., J. H. COMROE, JR., A. COURNAND, J. K. W. FERGUSON, G. F. FILLEY, W. S. FOWLER, J. S. GRAY, H. F. HELMHOLZ, JR., A. B. OTIS, H. RAHN, AND R. L. RILEY. Standardization of definitions and symbols in respiratory physiology. *Federation Proc.* 9: 602–615, 1950.

110. PEMBERTON, J., AND E. G. FLANAGAN. Vital capacity and timed vital capacity in normal men over forty. *J. Appl. Physiol.*

9: 291–296, 1956.

111. PERESS, L., G. SYBRECHT, AND P. T. MACKLEM. The mechanism of increase in total lung capacity during acute asthma. *Am. J. Med.* 61: 165–169, 1976.

112. PERMUTT, S., AND H. B. MARTIN. Static pressure-volume characteristics of lungs in normal males. *J. Appl. Physiol.* 15: 819–825, 1960.

113. PIERCE, J. A., AND R. V. EBERT. The elastic properties of the lungs in the aged. *J. Lab. Clin. Med.* 51: 63–71, 1958.

114. POLGAR, G., AND T. R. WENG. The functional development of the respiratory system from the period of gestation to adulthood. *Am. Rev. Respir. Dis.* 120: 625–695, 1979.

115. RAHN, H., W. O. FENN, AND A. B. OTIS. Daily variations of vital capacity, residual air and expiratory reserve including a study of the residual air method. *J. Appl. Physiol.* 1: 725–736, 1949.

116. RAHN, H., A. B. OTIS, L. E. CHADWICK, AND W. O. FENN. The pressure-volume diagram of the thorax and lung. *Am. J. Physiol.* 146: 161–178, 1946.

117. REHDER, K., D. J. HATCH, A. D. SESSLER, H. M. MARSH, AND W. S. FOWLER. Effects of general anesthesia, muscle paralysis, and mechanical ventilation on pulmonary nitrogen clearance. *Anesthesiology* 35: 591–601, 1971.

118. REHDER, K., A. D. SESSLER, AND H. M. MARSH. General anesthesia and the lung. *Am. Rev. Respir. Dis.* 112: 541–563, 1975.

119. REMINGTON, J. W. Hysteresis loop behavior of the aorta and other extensible tissues. *Am. J. Physiol.* 180: 83–95, 1955.

120. REMINGTON, J. W. (editor). *Tissue Elasticity.* Washington, DC: Am. Physiol. Soc., 1957.

121. RICHARDS, C. C., AND L. BACHMAN. Lung and chest wall compliance of apneic paralyzed infants. *J. Clin. Invest.* 40: 273–278, 1961.

122. RINGQVIST, T. The ventilatory capacity in healthy subjects. An analysis of causal factors with special reference to the respiratory forces. *Scand. J. Clin Lab. Invest. Suppl.* 88: 5–179, 1966.

123. ROBERTSON, C. H., JR., C. M. ENGLE, AND M. E. BRADLEY. Lung volumes in man immersed to the neck: dilution and plethysmographic techniques. *J. Appl. Physiol.: Respirat. Environ. Exercise Physiol.* 44: 679–682, 1978.

124. ROBINSON, S. Experimental studies of physical fitness in relation to age. *Arbeitsphysiologie* 10: 251–323, 1938.

125. RODARTE, J. R., L. W. BURGHER, R. E. HYATT, AND K. REHDER. Lung recoil and gas trapping during oxygen breathing at low lung volumes. *J. Appl. Physiol.* 43: 138–143, 1977.

126. RODARTE, J. R., AND R. E. HYATT. Effect of acute exposure to CO_2 on lung mechanics in normal man. *Respir. Physiol.* 17: 135–145, 1973.

127. ROHRER, F. Der Zusammenhang der Atemkräfte und ihre Abhängigkeit vom Dehnungszustand der Atmungsorgane. *Pfluegers Arch. Gesamte Physiol. Menschen Tiere* 165: 419–444, 1916.

128. SANT'AMBROGIO, G., D. T. FRAZIER, M. F. WILSON, AND E. AGOSTONI. Motor innervation and pattern of activity of cat diaphragm. *J. Appl. Physiol.* 18: 43–46, 1963.

129. SAUNDERS, N. A., J. R. A. RIGG, L. D. PENGELLY, AND E. J. M. CAMPBELL. Effect of curare on maximum static PV relationships of the respiratory system. *J. Appl. Physiol.: Respirat.*

Environ. Exercise Physiol. 44: 589–595, 1978.

130. SHARP, J. T., W. S. DRUZ, R. C. BALAGOT, V. R. BANDELIN, AND J. DANON. Total respiratory compliance in infants and children. *J. Appl. Physiol.* 29: 775–779, 1970.

131. SHARP, J. T., F. N. JOHNSON, N. B. GOLDBERG, AND P. VAN LITH. Hysteresis and stress adaptation in the human respiratory system. *J. Appl. Physiol.* 23: 487–497, 1967.

132. SJÖSTRAND, T. Über die Bedeutung der Lungen als Blutdepot beim Menschen. *Acta Physiol. Scand.* 2: 231–248, 1941.

133. SONG, S. H., D. H. KANG, B. S. KANG, AND S. K. HONG. Lung volumes and ventilatory responses to high CO_2 and low O_2 in the ama. *J. Appl. Physiol.* 18: 466–470, 1963.

134. TAYLOR, A. The contribution of the intercostal muscles to the effort of respiration in man. *J. Physiol. London* 151: 390–402, 1960.

134a. TENNEY, S. M. Fluid volume redistribution and thoracic volume changes during recumbency. *J. Appl. Physiol.* 14: 129–132, 1959.

135. THOMPSON, L. J., AND M. MCCALLY. Role of transpharyngeal pressure gradients in determining intrapulmonary pressure during immersion. *Aerosp. Med.* 38: 931–935, 1967.

136. TURNER, J. M., J. MEAD, AND M. E. WOHL. Elasticity of human lungs in relation to age. *J. Appl. Physiol.* 25: 664–671, 1968.

137. VAN DE WOESTIJNE, K. P. Influence of forced inflations on the creep of lungs and thorax in the dog. *Respir. Physiol.* 3: 78–89, 1967.

138. VAN LITH, P., M. BARROCAS, R. A. NELSON, AND J. T. SHARP. Effect of hypnosis on total respiratory compliance. *J. Appl. Physiol.* 27: 804–806, 1969.

139. VAN LITH, P., F. N. JOHNSON, AND J. T. SHARP. Respiratory elastances in relaxed and paralyzed states in normal and abnormal men. *J. Appl. Physiol.* 23: 475–486, 1967.

140. VELLODY, V. P., M. NASSERY, W. S. DRUZ, AND J. T. SHARP. Effects of body position change on thoracoabdominal motion. *J. Appl. Physiol.: Respirat. Environ. Exercise Physiol.* 45: 581–589, 1978.

141. WADE, O. L., AND J. C. GILSON. The effect of posture on diaphragmatic movement and vital capacity in normal subjects with a note on spirometry as an aid in determining radiological chest volumes. *Thorax* 6: 103–126, 1951.

142. WEINBERGER, S. E., S. T. WEISS, W. R. COHEN, J. W. WEISS, AND T. S. JOHNSON. Pregnancy and the lung. *Am. Rev. Respir. Dis.* 121: 559–581, 1980.

143. WESTBROOK, P. R., S. E. STUBBS, A. D. SESSLER, K. REHDER, AND R. E. HYATT. Effects of anesthesia and muscle paralysis on respiratory mechanics in normal man. *J. Appl. Physiol.* 34: 81–86, 1973.

144. WHITFIELD, A. G. W., J. A. H. WATERHOUSE, AND W. M. ARNOTT. The total lung volume and its subdivisions. A study in physiological norms. I. Basic data. *Br. J. Soc. Med.* 4: 1–25, 1950.

145. WOOLCOCK, A. J., AND J. READ. Lung volumes in exacerbations of asthma. *Am. J. Med.* 41: 259–273, 1966.

146. ZECHMAN, F. W., F. S. MUSGRAVE, R. C. MAINS, AND J. E. COHN. Respiratory mechanics and pulmonary diffusing capacity with lower body negative pressure. *J. Appl. Physiol.* 22: 247–250, 1967.

CHAPTER 10

Dynamics of respiration

JOSEPH R. RODARTE | *Departments of Internal Medicine and of Physiology and Biophysics, Mayo Medical School and Mayo Clinic, Rochester, Minnesota*

KAI REHDER | *Departments of Anesthesiology and of Physiology and Biophysics, Mayo Medical School and Mayo Clinic, Rochester, Minnesota*

CHAPTER CONTENTS

VENTILATION OF THE LUNGS involves motion of the respiratory system, which is produced by forces required to overcome the flow-resistive, inertial, and elastic properties of the lungs and chest wall. Except during mechanical ventilation, these forces are produced by the respiratory muscles. This chapter provides an overview of how the forces generated by the muscles act on the respiratory system and how the static and dynamic forces generated by the respiratory system oppose them. This chapter is based on the chapter by Mead and Agostoni (24) in the 1964 edition of the *Handbook* section on respiration.

EQUATION OF MOTION

To analyze the dynamic forces operating on a mechanical system, most introductory physics courses consider a system that has motion in one direction (Fig. 1*A*). The respiratory system can be considered as a three-dimensional analogue (Fig. 1*B*) in which the spring shown in Figure 1*A* is replaced by an elastic bellows, the sliding friction is replaced by the resistance to gas flow in a tube, and the mass to be accelerated is replaced by the mass of the gas and bellows.

The equation of motion describes the balance of forces acting on such systems

$$F = Kx + R(dx/dt) + M(d^2x/dt^2) \qquad (1a)$$

$$P = (1/C)V + R\dot{V} + I\ddot{V} \qquad (1b)$$

Equation 1a refers to the one-dimensional system (Fig. 1*A*) with motion along the coordinate x in time t. If a force (F) is applied, this system will respond with a displacement (x), a linear velocity (dx/dt), and an acceleration (d^2x/dt^2). The force necessary to achieve a given response is determined by the spring constant (K), which relates force to displacement; by the frictional resistance (R), which relates force to velocity; and by the mass (M), which determines the force required to produce acceleration. The equation of motion for a three-dimensional system (Fig. 1*B*) is given by Equation 1b in which the perturbation is caused by pressure (P) and the analogue of displacement is volume (V). The reciprocal of compliance (1/C) relates pressure to volume; resistance relates pressure to flow ($\dot{V} = dV/dt$); and inertance (I) relates pressure to acceleration ($\ddot{V} = d^2V/dt^2$). The reciprocal of compliance rather than elastance is used to preserve the similarity between Equation 1b and the equations for electromotive force in which a capacitance is analogous to compliance. Electrical analogues are useful because many problems in respiratory mechanics can be approached by analogy to electronic circuits, utilizing solutions from electronics to predict mechanical responses.

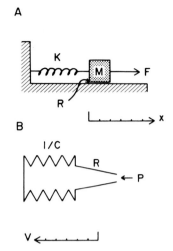

FIG. 1. Equation of motion with mechanical analogues. *A*: mechanical system that has motion in 1 direction. Force (F) is applied to mass (M), causing it to be displaced along the coordinate *x*, sliding along a surface with a coefficient of friction (R) and distending the spring with a spring constant (*K*). *B*: three-dimensional mechanical system. Pressure (P) causes gas to flow through a tube with resistance (R) into elastic bellows with compliance (C). Volume (V) is analogue of displacement.

Application of Equation of Motion to a Model

An application of the equation of motion is illustrated in Figure 2, in which for simplicity we consider a system that oscillates around a mean volume and a pressure of zero. This example (Fig. 2*A*) shows a volume-time record for a sinusoidal volume change with a peak-to-peak amplitude of 1 liter and a frequency of 10 cycles/min; thus a complete cycle requires 6 s. The first and second time derivatives of volume, flow ($\dot{V}$) and acceleration ($\ddot{V}$), are also shown. Because the derivative of sine is cosine and the derivative of cosine is negative sine, flow and acceleration are also sine wave functions. The flow is one-quarter of a cycle (90°) ahead of the volume and is maximal at the midpoints of the volume (a and b in Fig. 2*A*). Zero flow occurs at the extremes of the volume (c and d) where the slope of the volume-time relationship is zero. Acceleration is one-half of a cycle (180°) out of phase with the volume; i.e., the zero crossings coincide but the sign of the slope is reversed.

An alternative approach to the relationships among the variables under consideration is to display one against the other, eliminating the display of time. In the relationship between flow and volume (Fig. 2*B*), if the volume was not a sine wave function, peak flows would not necessarily be equal or occur at the midpoint of volume, as in this example.

Because V, $\dot{V}$, and $\ddot{V}$ are known mathematical functions, the functions can be substituted into Equation 1b. To use the form of the equation commonly employed in texts, we let the flow be sinusoidal with an amplitude *a*

$$P = -\left(\frac{a}{C\omega}\right) \cos \omega t + Ra \sin \omega t + Ia\omega \cos \omega t \quad (2a)$$

or recast

$$P = Ra \sin \omega t + \left(Ia\omega - \frac{a}{C\omega}\right) \cos \omega t \quad (2b)$$

where the angular velocity in radians per unit time (ω) = $\pi 2f$ (where f is frequency), and sine and cosine waves go full cycle between zero and 2π. Given values of R = 2 cmH$_2$O·liter^{-1}·s, C = 0.2 liter·cmH$_2$O^{-1}, and I = 0.01 cmH$_2$O·liter·s^2, the pressure may be computed from Equation 2b. Each term in Equations 1b and 2a, b has the units of pressure; the terms represent the pressure required to overcome elastic [(1/C)V], flow-resistive (R$\dot{V}$), and inertial (I$\ddot{V}$) forces, respectively. Because the pressure due to inertial forces in this example is negligibly small, only the total, elastic, and flow-resistive pressures are shown as a function of time (Fig. 2*A*) and as a function of volume and flow (Fig. 2*B*). The pressures required to overcome the elastic and flow-resistive properties are sinusoidal and are in phase with the volume and flow, respectively. If the same volume oscillation occurred at a higher frequency (i.e., at a shorter cycle length), the amplitude of the flow and acceleration and the amplitude of the pressures produced by resistance and inertance would be increased; the phase relationships between these variables, however, would be unchanged.

The total pressure, which is the sum of the two component pressures, is not in phase with either volume or flow. The phase of the total pressure depends on the relative amplitudes of the component waves. If the pressure required to overcome elastic forces is much larger than the flow-resistive pressure (Fig. 2), the total pressure will be nearly in phase with the pressure necessary to overcome the elastic forces and thus in phase with the volume. Conversely, if resistance were increased by a factor of 10, the amplitude of the R$\dot{V}$ component would be increased 10-fold, and if compliance were constant, the total pressure would be nearly in phase with the flow-resistive pressure.

Determination of Resistance and Compliance

In Figure 2 the pressure was computed from the volume and flow using values of resistance and compliance. When resistance and compliance are not known, they can be computed from the total pressure, flow, and volume. At the midpoints of volume (a and b in Fig. 2*A*, *B*) elastic pressure is zero. Therefore total pressure equals flow-resistive pressure at this volume. Thus resistance can be computed by dividing the difference in total pressure at these instants by the difference in flow. It is not necessary to select the midpoint of the volume excursion. It can be seen that at any constant volume (Eq. 1; Fig. 2*A*, *B*), the term (1/C)V will have the same value. Therefore the difference in the total pressure at the same volume during inspiration and expiration will give the flow-resistive component. (This is more apparent in Fig. 2*B* than in Fig. 2*A*.) The ratio of the difference in pressure at

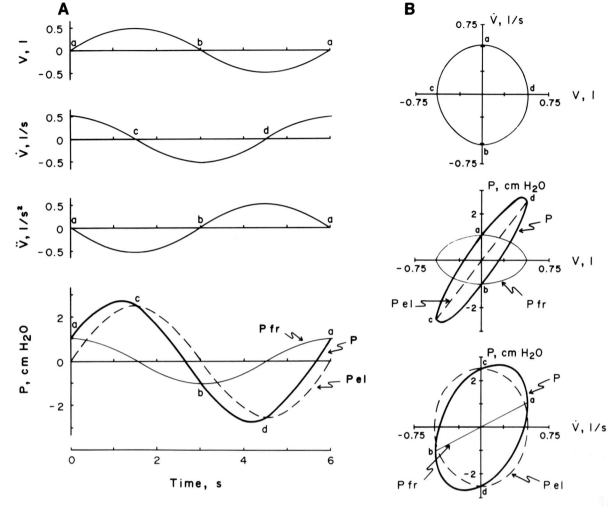

FIG. 2. Equation of motion was used to compute pressure from volume (V), flow ($\dot{V}$), and acceleration ($\ddot{V}$) during sinusoidal oscillation for a sinusoidal volume change of 1 liter at a frequency of 10 cycles/min. Elastic pressure (Pel), flow-resistive pressure (Pfr), and total pressure (P) have been computed assuming resistance = 2 $cmH_2O \cdot liter^{-1} \cdot s$, compliance = 0.2 $liter \cdot cmH_2O^{-1}$, and inertance = 0.01 $cmH_2O \cdot liter \cdot s^2$. *Points a and b*, midpoints of volume; *points c and d*, extremes of volume where flow = 0. *A*: all variables shown as function of time. *B*: *top*, flow vs. volume. *Middle*, pressure vs. volume. Because elastic pressure is directly determined by volume, relationship is represented by *straight line* (slope = 1/C). Flow-resistive pressure-volume relationship (Pfr) represented by loop similar to flow-volume loop in *top*, because resistive pressure is the product RV. *Bottom*, pressure vs. flow. Because resistive pressure is directly proportional to flow, the relationship is represented by *straight line* (slope = R). Elastic pressure is directly proportional to volume and is represented by an ellipse similar to flow-volume curve in *top*, except that flow is plotted on a horizontal rather than vertical axis and amplitude of pressure is 1/C times amplitude of volume.

isovolume points to the difference in flow is the resistance (13).

When flow is zero (c and d in Fig. 2A, B), total pressure equals elastic pressure because flow-resistive pressure is zero. Thus the compliance can be computed from the amplitude of the volume divided by the difference in total pressure at instances of zero flow.

Inertance and Reactance

Inertance (I) is analogous to inductance (L) in an electrical circuit. The pressure required to produce acceleration is in phase with acceleration. When inertial pressures are not negligible, compliance cannot

be determined (as indicated in Fig. 2A, B at instants of zero flow) because the total pressure is the sum of elastic and inertial pressures (term in parentheses in Eq. 2b). This sum is reactance (X). If a system is oscillated with a constant volume at increasing frequencies, the elastic pressure will remain constant but the inertial losses will increase progressively and the reactance will decrease. At the frequency at which $Ia\omega = a/(C\omega)$, elastic and inertial pressures cancel and reactance becomes zero. The frequency at which reactance is zero is the resonant or natural frequency. At the resonant frequency, the total pressure equals the resistive pressure throughout the cycle.

Impedance

Another concept from electronics that is used increasingly in respiratory dynamics is impedance (Z). Impedance in a sinusoidally oscillating system is the ratio of the amplitude of the total pressure to the amplitude of the flow. Thus impedance is a measure of the pressure required to achieve a given flow pattern. A system is characterized by its impedance and the phase angle (θ). The phase angle is the fraction of the total cycle by which pressure leads or lags the flow multiplied by 360°. Figure 3 illustrates that impedance and the phase angle are the vector sum of pressure losses due to resistance and reactance.

Time Constant

As noted in the preceding section, reactance is zero at the resonant frequency (i.e., when $Z = R$ and $\theta = 0$). Systems in which inertance is not negligible are characterized as *LRC systems* by an analogy to electronics. When inertance is negligible, the systems are characterized by resistance and compliance, or more specifically by the time constants, the product of resistance and compliance. The units of resistance times compliance are $P/\dot{V}/t \times V/P = t$.

As an example of how the time constant controls the behavior of a mechanical system, consider the response of an RC system to a sudden change in pressure. Assume a bellows with compliance C is held inflated to a volume V by a pressure P; then $P = (1/C)V$. If the gas from the bellows is allowed to flow through a tube with resistance R, flow ($\dot{V}$) will be determined by the relationship $\dot{V} = P/R$. Eliminating P from these equations yields $\dot{V} = (1/RC)V$; that is, the emptying rate is directly proportional to the volume. The constant of proportionality is the reciprocal of RC or the reciprocal of the time constant of the system. This equation is a first-order linear differential equation that can be integrated to obtain an expression of volume as a function of time, $V = V_0 e^{-t/RC}$, in which V_0 is the initial volume and e is the base of the natural logarithm. Thus the volume-time relationship is a single exponential function, and volume would be linear if the logarithm of volume were plotted versus time. If $t = RC$, then $V = V_0/e = 0.37 V_0$. An RC system also could be characterized by a half time, as is done by convention in other disciplines in which the rate of change of a quantity is proportional to the quantity (e.g., half-life of a radioisotope).

Nonlinear Resistance and Hysteresis

To this point, resistance and compliance have been considered constants that are independent of flow direction. If resistance were different between inspiration and expiration, the resistive-pressure wave would be asymmetric. Inspiratory and expiratory resistances can be computed separately if the elastic pressure at that volume is known. The elastic properties of all elastic bodies also are dependent on the direction of change. This phenomenon is called hysteresis. If the system shown in Figure 2A, B is repetitively cycled, the elastic pressures at the extremes of volume (c and d in Fig. 2A, B) would be constant, but the elastic pressures at all intermediate volumes would be dependent on the direction of volume change; the elastic pressures would be larger when volume was increasing than when volume was decreasing. In Figure 2B, the elastic pressure would form an open loop rather than a straight line. Therefore in computing resistance by the isovolume method, a component of the total pressure difference will be a result of hysteresis of the pressure-volume relationship (see PULMONARY FLOW RESISTANCE, p. 138).

Application of Equation of Motion to the Respiratory System

The respiratory system is not a linear system; resistance and compliance are not constants. They are dependent on volume, volume history, and flow. Values of resistance and compliance are assigned for a certain volume, volume history, and flow. Even this is a gross oversimplification of the mechanical behavior of the respiratory system. The respiratory system consists of a complex system of branching airways so that resistances in series and in parallel connect to the elastic elements of the lung parenchyma, which are in turn connected in series with the chest wall, which is composed of the different structures of the rib cage and diaphragm of the abdomen. In spite of its inexactness, this simple model provides a useful framework for examining the dynamic behavior of the normal respiratory system and is used as the conceptual framework for this chapter.

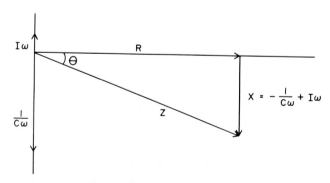

FIG. 3. Impedance and phase. Length of vector Z represents the magnitude of impedance and θ represents the phase angle between pressure and flow. Horizontal component of impedance vector is magnitude of resistance (R). Vertical component is magnitude of reactance (X), which is vector sum of a component due to compliance (C) and a component due to inertance (I). ω, Angular velocity.

APPLIED PRESSURES

Relationship to Lung Volume

The primary muscles of inspiration are the diaphragm, parasternal intercostals, and scalene muscles, with the sternocleidomastoids, external intercostals, and other accessory muscles assuming more importance at high ventilatory rates or at the extremes of lung volume (3, 30). The abductors of the vocal cords and the muscles of the hypopharynx also are important inspiratory muscles because of their roles in maintaining the airway patent [(33); also see the chapter by Proctor on the upper airways and larynx in this *Handbook*].

The relationships among length, tension, and contraction velocity of the respiratory muscles and volume, pressure, and flow of the respiratory system are complex. For example, the maximal force that can be generated by muscles decreases as the muscle shortens below an optimal length. Also, at a given length, muscle force diminishes as velocity of contraction increases (see Fig. 9 in the chapter by Sharp and Hyatt in this *Handbook*). Thus maximal pressures that can be generated by the respiratory muscles are determined by both lung volume and gas flow.

Figure 4 shows the maximal static pressures that can be generated by the inspiratory and expiratory muscles as a function of lung volume. The maximal pressure developed by the respiratory system is the sum of the pressures resulting from contraction of the respiratory muscles (Pmus) and from the elastic recoil of the respiratory system (Pel,rs). The maximal pressure generated by the respiratory muscles can thus be obtained by subtraction (Pmus curves). After a complete inspiration, maximal inspiratory Pmus is equal in magnitude but opposite in sign to Pel,rs. Therefore no residual pressure is available at this lung volume to produce further inspiratory flow. Conversely after complete exhalation in young persons, maximal expiratory Pmus is balanced by the outward recoil of the respiratory system. In older persons and in patients with obstructive lung disease, complete exhalation to residual volume (RV) is determined by the high airway flow resistance (20). Flow limitation or even closure of airways occurs at very low flows, so that RV is determined by how long the subject can maintain the expiratory effort. The curve for expiratory Pmus does not begin at 100% vital capacity (VC) because lung volume is reduced by gas compression during maximal static expiratory effort. Similarly the curve for inspiratory Pmus begins above RV because of gas expansion.

To understand the dynamics of the respiratory system, it is useful to consider separately the pressures applied to the lung and to the chest wall. A plot suited for this type of analysis is shown in Figure 4B (4, 16). The static pressure-volume relationship of the lung

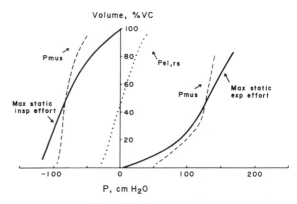

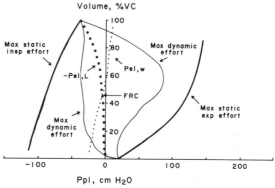

FIG. 4. Pressure (P)-volume relationships. *A*: airway opening pressure during relaxation (Pel,rs) and during maximal static expiratory and inspiratory efforts shown as a function of lung volume (VC, vital capacity). Pressures generated by respiratory muscles (Pmus) during maximal efforts are computed from total pressure and passive pressure-volume characteristics. Pel,rs represents static pressure-volume relationship of respiratory system. *B*: pleural pressure (Ppl) plotted as function of lung volume during maximal static and dynamic inspiratory and expiratory efforts. Relationship between lung volume and Ppl when lung volume is increased voluntarily (−Pel,L) or by passive inflation (Pel,w) also shown. Functional residual capacity (FRC) is that lung volume at which inward recoil of lung (−Pel,L) is equal in magnitude and opposite in sign to outward recoil of the chest wall (Pel,w) and corresponds to volume at which passive recoil of respiratory system in Fig. 2*A* is zero. Horizontal separation between curves −Pel,L and Pel,w is the passive pressure-volume relationship of respiratory system (Pel,rs), shown in Fig. 2*A*.

can be obtained by determining pleural pressure during breath holding while the glottis is open, so that alveolar pressure is atmospheric [elastic recoil pressure of the lung (−Pel,L) curve]. With this maneuver, lung volume is maintained by the action of the respiratory muscles. Elastic recoil pressure of the chest wall (Pel,w) curve depicts the static pressure-volume relationship of the chest wall that can be obtained when the respiratory muscles are relaxed against a closed airway. In this circumstance, alveolar pressure is not atmospheric, except at that lung volume where the two curves intercept; this lung volume is the functional residual capacity (FRC). The horizontal distance between Pel,w and −Pel,L curves is equal to the increase in airway opening pressure that occurs when the subject relaxes the respiratory muscles while the airway is closed. This pressure difference is equal to the transrespiratory pressure.

The pleural pressure-volume relationships during maximal static and dynamic inspiratory and expiratory efforts are shown in Figure 4B. For a given lung volume, pleural pressures are lower during a maximal dynamic expiratory effort than during a maximal static expiratory effort for three reasons. 1) A finite time is necessary for skeletal muscles to achieve maximal tension. For example, it takes ~0.2 s after the initiation of an expiratory dynamic effort from 100% VC to achieve maximal pleural pressure (26). Assuming a mean expiratory flow of ~1 VC/s over this period, ~20% of the VC will have been expired before maximal muscle tension is achieved. 2) The respiratory muscles have a significant rate of shortening during high flows, which reduces the Pmus that can be generated at a given lung volume. 3) Some portion of Pmus is utilized to overcome the opposing forces of the chest wall, thus reducing pleural pressure during expiration and increasing it during inspiration. As RV or total lung capacity (TLC) is approached, maximal flows diminish greatly and hence the maximal dynamic and static curves converge.

The total pressure applied to the respiratory system during a maximal static inspiratory effort consists of three components: Pmus, Pel,w and −Pel,L. The Pmus applied to the lung during maximal static inspiratory or expiratory maneuvers is indicated by the horizontal distance between the outer envelope and the Pel,w curve. The pressure available to produce changes in lung volume is shown by the horizontal distance between the −Pel,L curve and the outer envelope, assuming that the elastic properties of the respiratory system are not influenced by configurational changes associated with forceful muscular effort and that these properties are independent of flow. Thus at 100% VC, a maximal inspiratory effort is required to overcome the elastic recoil of the respiratory system so that no net force remains to produce inspiratory flow. Conversely the net pressure available to produce expiratory flow is the sum of the difference between the −Pel,L and Pel,w curves at maximal lung volume and Pmus. Again, the expiratory curve does not include 100% VC and the inspiratory curve does not include 0% VC because of gas compression or expansion as alveolar pressure is increased or decreased, respectively.

Tidal Breathing

The dynamic relationship between pleural pressure and lung volume during quiet breathing is illustrated in Figure 5. Because inertial forces are negligible during quiet breathing (23), they are not considered. Figure 5A shows the pleural pressure-volume relationships of the lung and chest wall during a quiet inspiration. In this example, FRC is at 45% VC and pleural

pressure at FRC is −6.5 cmH$_2$O. The static pleural pressure-volume relationship of the lung (−Pel,L curve) is the mirror image of the more familiar static transpulmonary pressure-volume curve. During a spontaneous inspiration (from 45% to 55% VC) pleural pressure is less than it would be under static conditions. The difference in pleural pressure between the static and dynamic curves is the additional pressure required to overcome the flow resistance of the lung tissue and the resistance to gas flow in the airways. The work of inspiration (area between ordinate and heavy solid line) has two components: the work performed by the outward recoil of the chest wall (area between thin solid line and ordinate) and the work performed by the muscles (area between solid lines). If during inspiration the configurations of the rib cage and abdomen are different from their passive configurations, the chest wall pressure-volume curve will be altered and elastic work of inspiration will be greater than predicted from the relaxation curve illustrated in this figure.

Figure 5B shows the pleural pressure-volume relationship during quiet expiration. Pleural pressure must be more positive than −Pel,L to overcome the flow resistance of the lung tissue and airways (heavy solid line to right of −Pel,L curve). Pleural pressure must be less than predicted from the static pressure-volume curve of the chest wall (thin solid line to left of Pel,w curve). This pressure difference is necessary to overcome the flow resistance of the chest wall. Normally, expiration is not truly passive but is retarded by the inspiratory muscles (15). The magnitude of the inspiratory Pmus applied to the respiratory system during a quiet expiration is the pressure difference between the two dynamic curves.

In contrast, Figure 5C shows the pleural pressure-volume relationship during a passive expiration, that is, without retardation by inspiratory muscles (e.g., during muscular relaxation or drug-induced paralysis). During passive expiration no Pmus is applied to the respiratory system; therefore the dynamic curves for lung and chest wall are identical after an initial accelerative phase. Because the rates of volume change of lung and chest wall are the same, the position of the pleural pressure between the two static curves −Pel,L and Pel,w is determined by the relative magnitude of the resistances of the lung and chest wall. During passive expiration the flow-resistive work performed on the lung and chest wall is produced entirely by the elastic recoil of the lung.

When expiratory flow is greater than flow during passive expiration, the dynamic pleural pressure curve for the lung is displaced to the right of the passive case and the curve for the chest wall is displaced to the left (Fig. 5D). The pressure difference between the two curves reflects the expiratory Pmus that is required to generate the increased expiratory flow, and the area represents the work performed by the

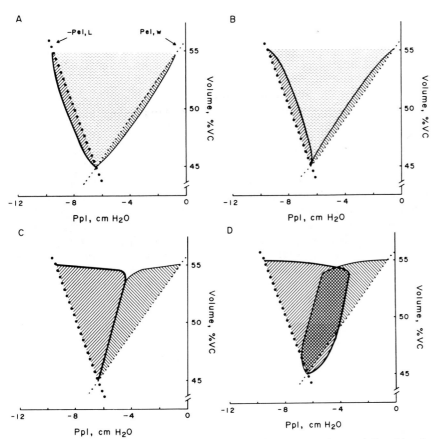

FIG. 5. Dynamic pressure-volume relationship of respiratory system. Static pressure-volume relationships of lung (−Pel,L) and of chest wall (Pel,w) plotted as in Fig. 4B. *A: quiet inspiration. Heavy solid line* to left of −Pel,L depicts dynamic pleural pressure-volume relationship during spontaneous inspiration. *Diagonally hatched area* to left of −Pel,L, which has units of pressure × volume or work ($\int PdV$), equals flow-resistive work done on lung during inspiration. *Thin solid line* to right of Pel,w depicts pleural pressure-volume relationship that would occur if an identical inspiration had been produced by positive pressure applied at the airway opening. *Diagonally hatched areas* to right of Pel,w equals work done on chest wall to overcome its flow resistance. *Horizontally hatched area* between the 2 static curves is pressure required to overcome elastic recoil of lung and chest wall. *B: quiet expiration. Heavy solid line* to right of −Pel,L depicts dynamic pleural pressure-volume relationship during a quiet expiration; *thin solid line* to left of Pel,w depicts pleural pressure-volume relationship that would occur if an identical expiration were produced passively by reducing positive pressure at airway opening. *Diagonally hatched areas* between these dynamic and static curves represent the pressures required to overcome flow resistance of lung and chest wall, respectively. *Horizontally hatched area* between these 2 dynamic curves represents the pressure generated by inspiratory muscles required to retard expiratory flow rate. *C: passive expiration.* Curves for dynamic pressure-volume relationship of lung and chest wall now coincide, indicating that there is no pressure produced by respiratory muscles. *Diagonally hatched area* between static and dynamic curves represents the pressure required to overcome flow resistances of lung and chest wall, and the sum of these resistances is equal to elastic recoil of respiratory system. *D: active expiration.* Pleural pressure-volume relationships occurring during a modest expiratory effort. *Cross-hatched area* between the 2 dynamic curves represents the pressure generated by expiratory muscle that is required to produce increased expiratory flow over that which would occur with a truly passive expiration.

expiratory muscles. This condition may occur without the pleural pressure exceeding atmospheric pressure.

OPPOSING PRESSURES

The forces that drive the respiratory system are opposed by forces due to elastic, flow-resistive, and inertial properties of the respiratory system (Eqs. 1 and 2). Although the mass of the lung tissue and chest wall is much greater than that of the gas in the lung, the linear acceleration of these tissues is small compared with that of the gas—that is, inertial opposing forces are primarily a result of acceleration of the gas. Inertial forces are negligibly small during quiet breathing, but they may become important during fast breathing, as may occur during exercise or physiological testing. Inertial effects also are important in species that utilize the respiratory system for thermal regulation, for example, panting dogs. Static elastic properties of the lung and chest wall of the respiratory system are discussed in the chapter by Agostoni and Hyatt in this *Handbook* and are not discussed further in this chapter. Flow-resistive pressures are covered in detail in the chapters by Pedley and Drazen and by Ingram and Pedley in this *Handbook*.

Flow Resistance

RESPIRATORY SYSTEM RESISTANCE. Various strategies for measuring resistance of the respiratory system and its chest wall and pulmonary components can be understood in terms of the equation of motion (Eq. 1b). Resistance can be determined by establishing conditions in which all other terms in the equation are known (see Fig. 2). Because Pmus cannot be determined during spontaneous breathing, resistance of the respiratory system must be measured either during muscular relaxation or during quiet breathing by determining the changes in flow produced by superimposing known changes in pressure. Compliance can be calculated over a linear portion of the pressure-volume curve. A passive expiration over that lung volume requires no muscular effort so that Pmus = 0. After an initial transient, pressure losses from volume acceleration are negligibly small so that Equation 1b becomes $(1/C)V + R\dot{V} = 0$ (6, 22). If compliance, volume, and flow have been determined, Equation 1b can be solved for resistance.

Alternatively a sinusoidal flow may be superimposed on the normal breathing pattern and the pressure drop across the respiratory system can be measured (9, 12). Equation 2b is the equation of motion for sinusoidal flow. Because flow and reactance are 90° out of phase, reactance is zero when the imposed flow is maximal or minimal, and at these instants the total and flow-resistive pressures are identical. Thus resistance is the ratio of the pressure at peak flow to the flow amplitude. Alternatively oscillation frequency may be varied so that the pressure is in phase with the flow, that is, at the resonant frequency, which is ~5–10 Hz in normal humans (9). Also, impedance and phase may be measured, and the resistance and reactance components can then be determined (Fig. 3).

CHEST WALL RESISTANCE. If pleural pressure is known, then the two components of the flow resistance of the respiratory system, that is, the resistances of the chest wall and lung, can be determined individually. Chest wall flow resistance at middle lung volume and at moderate flow is about one-third that of the pulmonary flow resistance during mouth breathing (10). There is little information about the flow dependence of chest wall flow resistance. Chest wall flow resistance decreases slightly with increasing lung volume, presumably because at a constant flow the velocities of the tissues of the chest wall decrease with increasing volume.

PULMONARY FLOW RESISTANCE. The pulmonary flow resistance is the sum of airway resistance and lung tissue resistance. In *Application of Equation of Motion to a Model*, p. 132, it is noted that when pulmonary flow resistance is computed from the isovolume method (13), hysteresis of the elastic tissue is included in the dynamic total transpulmonary pressure difference between the inspiratory and the expiratory flow. The hysteresis of the lung contributes the major component of lung tissue resistance.

Lung tissue resistance has been studied extensively in excised cat lungs in which lung volume was changed by compressing and expanding a fixed amount of air in the lung (i.e., while the airway was occluded). Hence there was no flow of gas, that is, alveolar and airway opening pressures were nearly equal, thereby eliminating airway flow resistance. Lung tissue resistance was determined by relating the difference between airway and lung surface pressures to the rate of change of lung volume (17). Lung tissue resistance determined by this method was found not to be Newtonian, that is, the pressure drop varied with tidal volume, not flow. Lung tissue resistance is small compared with airway resistance, except at very high lung volumes (see the chapter by Hoppin et al. in this *Handbook*).

Airway resistance is the pressure drop between the alveoli and the airway opening divided by the flow. The magnitude of this pressure difference is dependent on the airway geometry. Flow and airway opening pressure are easily measured, but alveolar pressure cannot be directly determined. It must be computed from the rarefaction and compression of alveolar gas estimated by body plethysmography (8).

DETERMINANTS OF FLOW RESISTANCE. Airways lengthen and increase their diameters with lung inflation. These two changes in the dimensions of the airways have opposite effects on the airway resistance. As a first approximation, airway resistance (Raw) is inversely proportional to lung volume, Raw = K/V, where K is a constant. The shape of this relationship is such that resistance increases relatively little over most of the VC but increases sharply at lung volumes close to RV. It follows that the reciprocal of airway resistance, airway conductance (Gaw), is nearly linearly related to lung volume [Gaw = $(1/K)V$] (2). The observed relationship between conductance and volume is consistent with predictions from a simple model. In long, straight, circular tubes, laminar flow resistance is proportional to the length of the tube and inversely proportional to the fourth power of the radius. If, with a change of lung volume, all linear dimensions of both the lung and airways change by a similar fraction a, the increase in volume would be proportional to a^3. In this case, airway conductance would increase by $a^4/a = a^3$. Therefore conductance would be directly proportional to volume.

At low gas flow, the pressure-flow relationship is nearly linear; thus the resistance can be characterized by its slope. As flow increases, the pressure-flow relationship is better described either by a quadratic equation, as suggested by Rohrer [Eq. 3a; (32)], or by an exponential function, as described by Ainsworth and Eveleigh [Eq. 3b; (1)]

$$P = K_1\dot{V} + K_2\dot{V}^2 \qquad (3a)$$

$$P = a V^b \qquad (3b)$$

in which K_1, K_2, a, and b are constants. For a given pressure-flow curve, best-fit values of these constants can be determined by standard statistical methods. For a system of tubes with constant geometry, b must have a value between 1 and 2. These constants depend on the nature of the flow regimes, which range from laminar flow ($b = 1$) to fully developed turbulent flow ($b = 2$). There are no a priori constraints on the values of the other constants. Different parts of the airway have different pressure-flow relationships and different dependence of pressure losses on gas density and viscosity. Therefore originally it was believed that the constants K_1 and K_2 might have physical significance, but they do not.

In the periphery of the lung, airway diameters are small but the total cross-sectional area of all the airways in the periphery is large. Hence gas velocities become progressively slower toward the periphery. Pressure loss in the periphery is predominantly a result of the viscous shear forces in the gas, that is, pressure loss is proportional to flow and depends on gas viscosity. In the more central airways, even though individual airway diameters are relatively large, the total cross-sectional area of the airways is smaller than in the periphery. Gas flow in the central region becomes turbulent. The pressure loss due to turbulent gas flow across an orifice such as the glottis is proportional to the kinetic energy of the flow, that is, to the square of flow and to gas density. During expiration additional pressure losses are required to accelerate the gas coming from the large cross-sectional area of the lung periphery where linear velocities are small and moving to the smaller cross-sectional area of the central airways where linear velocities are much greater. This is convective acceleration or acceleration in space rather than in time because it occurs in steady flow. The pressure losses due to convective acceleration are directly proportional to the gas density and the square of gas velocity and are inversely proportional to the square of the cross-sectional area.

At a flow of <1 liter·s^{-1}, the pressure-flow curve is relatively linear. At high flow, however, the effects of turbulence and convective acceleration dominate and the relationship between pressure and flow becomes nonlinear. Furthermore as pressure along the airways decreases in the direction of flow, the cross-sectional areas of the elastic airways become progressively smaller than if the pressure did not decrease. During expiratory flow the intrathoracic airways that are exposed to pleural pressure on their outer surfaces

have transmural pressures that decrease progressively from the terminal bronchioles to the thoracic outlet. During inspiratory flow the airway transmural pressures also decrease progressively in the direction of flow. Most of the flow resistance of intrathoracic airways occurs in the more proximal generations because total cross-sectional area of the more peripheral generations is large (21).

UPPER AIRWAY RESISTANCE. The mouth, nose, pharynx, and larynx contribute significantly to flow resistance. During mouth breathing at low flow the mouth and larynx may contribute as much as 40% of the total respiratory resistance, with large intrasubject and intersubject variabilities (10, 18). The glottic aperture is greater during inspiration than expiration because of inspiratory activation of the laryngeal muscles (11). Therefore inspiratory laryngeal resistance is somewhat less than expiratory resistance. The nose is also a prominent site of loss of pressure due to flow resistance (34). The resistance can change greatly with flow. During expiration through the nose, intranasal pressure is greater than atmospheric pressure and the nasal airway is expanded. Conversely, during inspiration, negative intranasal pressure reduces the size of the nasal airway, thereby greatly increasing its resistance. During exercise, nasal breathing is facilitated by a potent sympathetic nerve discharge that shrinks the nasal mucosa and decreases nasal resistance (31). Nevertheless most normal adults switch from nasal to oronasal breathing during exercise at a ventilatory rate somewhat less than half that achieved with maximal exercise (27). Some animals (e.g., horses) are obligatory nasal breathers even during extreme exercise. In these animals, inspiratory activation of the alae nasi muscles prevents the collapse of the nasal airways. A reduction of the cyclic variation of glottic aperture during exercise also facilitates expiration.

MAXIMAL EXPIRATORY FLOW

Having discussed the opposing forces and having defined the pressure-generating capacity of the respiratory muscles, we examine next how these forces interact during various patterns of breathing. Because the mechanical efficiency of the respiratory muscles, lung elasticity, and airway resistance depends on lung volume, lung volume rather than time is the most appropriate independent variable for the analysis of dynamic pressure and flow. The reader is referred to the classic article of Fry and Hyatt (14) in which these variables are depicted in three-dimensional plots.

Figure 6 shows the flow-volume and the pleural pressure-volume relationships during a series of VC maneuvers of graded muscular efforts. Except at the extremes of lung volume, each inspiratory and expiratory effort shows a progressively greater departure from the static pleural pressure-volume relationship of the lung (Fig. 6B). Note that progressive increases

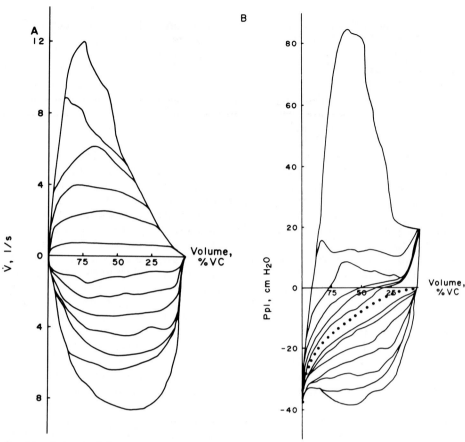

FIG. 6. Flow-volume-pressure relationships during graded vital capacity (VC) maneuvers. *A:* flow (V̇)-volume relationships during a series of inspiratory and expiratory VC maneuvers with progressively increasing efforts. Expiratory flow plotted above and inspiratory flow below volume axis. *B:* pleural pressure (Ppl)-volume relationships during the same maneuvers shown in Fig. 6A. *Dotted lines,* static pressure-volume relationship of the lung. Over lower half of VC, large increases in expiratory effort, indicated by increasing pleural pressure, are not associated with increases in expiratory flow.

in inspiratory effort produce a corresponding progressive increase in inspiratory flow. In contrast, during expiration progressive increases in effort do not all produce increases in flow. This effort independence of maximal expiratory flow occurs with more modest efforts at low than at high lung volumes.

To demonstrate the relationship between pleural pressure and flow, data measured at 75%, 50%, and 25% VC from each effort in Figure 6 have been plotted in Figure 7. Each isovolume pressure-flow curve represents the pleural pressure-flow relationship at the indicated lung volume. The pressure at which maximal expiratory flow is achieved (P*) is a rather weak function of lung volume. During maximal expiratory efforts begun with an open airway, the respiratory muscles cannot contract rapidly enough to reach P* at volumes higher than ~70% VC; therefore no P* is shown for 75% VC. At 50% VC the muscles can generate pressure greatly in excess of that required to achieve maximal flow, and at 25% VC the maximal pressure is less than at 50% VC because of the length-tension effect of the respiratory muscles.

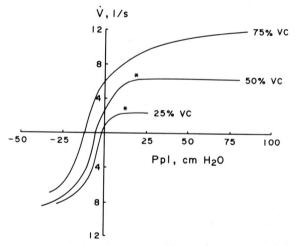

FIG. 7. Isovolume pressure-flow curves. Flow (V) shown as a function of pleural pressure (Ppl). Expiratory flow plotted above horizontal axis and inspiratory flow below. Data obtained at 75%, 50%, and 25% vital capacity (VC) from graded VC efforts shown in Fig. 6 were used to construct these curves. Below 75% VC, there is a point (*asterisk*) beyond which further increases in Ppl are not associated with increases in V̇.

All mammalian lungs exhibit expiratory flow limitation. Once a threshold value of applied pressure is achieved, further increases in effort do not produce further increases in expiratory flow (14). The mechanism by which expiratory flow limitation occurs is complex, but the understanding of it has increased significantly in recent years (see the chapters by Wilson, Rodarte, and Butler and by Hyatt in this *Handbook*). For the purposes of this chapter, it is sufficient to say that there are critical points in the airway (choke points) (7) that determine maximal flow. With increasing expiratory effort, the airways downstream from these points are increasingly compressed so that additional pressure is dissipated to produce extremely high linear gas velocities. The maximal possible velocity of the gas in an airway is the speed at which a pressure wave is propagated along the airway. The speed of a pressure wave is determined by the elasticity of the airway and the density of the gas in the airway.

Lowering the pressure downstream from the choke point cannot increase flow because the effect of the lowered pressure cannot travel upstream through this region where local gas velocity equals the wave speed. Thus the analogy of a waterfall in which flow is independent of events at the downstream region is appropriate (29). It might seem that forced expiration would be different from lowering the pressure at the airway opening, but this is not true. Because flow limitation occurs in intrathoracic airways, the increase of pleural pressure that increases alveolar pressure also increases the pressure surrounding the airways by an equal amount. Therefore lowering intraluminal pressure at the downstream end of the intrathoracic airway is equivalent to increasing pleural pressure (25).

With decreasing lung volume, the choke points migrate to more peripheral locations in the airway. At a given lung volume, both the locations of the choke points and the value of maximal expiratory flow are determined by the static elastic recoil of the lung and the magnitude and distribution of airway resistance. Thus once a threshold value of effort has been reached, maximal expiratory flow is determined by the mechanical properties of the lung parenchyma and airways and hence is a relatively sensitive, although somewhat nonspecific, measure of the overall mechanical properties of the lung. As such, it is a useful diagnostic test used in clinical medicine.

Gas Compression and Measurement of
Flow-Volume Curves

Maximal expiratory flow at a given lung volume may vary slightly because of differences in volume and flow histories and posture. The primary determinant of maximal expiratory flow, however, is the recoil pressure of the lung. Thus it is absolute lung volume and not the expired gas volume that determines measured flow. This distinction is important in evaluating

flow-volume curves. Two flow-volume curves obtained simultaneously from a single forced VC are shown in Figure 8. Flow was measured at the mouth. However, in one curve the volume signal was obtained from the expired gas volume (Vexp), whereas in the other curve it was obtained from the absolute lung volume determined plethysmographically (Vpleth). During maximal exhalation the absolute lung volume is reduced by two mechanisms, namely, by the gas volume expired and by gas compression within the lung. Because the two flow-volume curves were obtained simultaneously, the horizontal distance (from c to b in Fig. 8) represents the reduction of absolute lung volume due to gas compression. If a subject makes an expiratory effort just sufficient to achieve maximal flow, there will be minimal gas compression, and flow-volume curves using Vpleth and Vexp will be nearly identical. However, with more forceful efforts Vexp curves will show progressive diminution of flow for a given lung volume (e.g., from a to c in Fig. 8). There will appear to be a negative effort dependence.

The magnitude of this error can be substantial. Assume a barometric pressure of 1,000 cmH₂O. Increasing alveolar pressure by 100 cmH₂O would compress the alveolar gas by 10%. The absolute lung volume of a normal adult male at 50% VC is ~4 liters. Therefore gas compression will reduce the absolute lung volume by 0.4 liter during maximal efforts. If the slope of the flow-volume curve is ~2 liters·s⁻¹·liter⁻¹, this would produce a difference of ~0.8 liters·s⁻¹ in maximal flow at 50% VC expired between a threshold and a maximal effort. Given a typical normal flow of 4 liters·s⁻¹, this amounts to a variability of ~20% due to this artifact. Nearly all clinical and many research

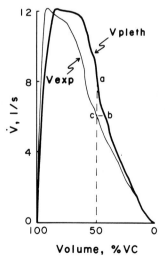

FIG. 8. Flow-volume curves of a maximal forced expiratory vital capacity (VC) maneuver. Flow (V̇) measured at mouth plotted as function of simultaneously determined expired gas volume (Vexp) and plethysmographically determined lung volume (Vpleth). At same flow, the 2 volume signals differ by amount equal to reduction of absolute lung volume due to gas compression; absolute lung volume can be detected only by plethysmograph.

laboratories use expired gas volume for the determination of flow-volume curves. The compression artifact is an important and vexing source of variability.

DYNAMICS OF BREATHING

Breathing at Rest and During Exercise

Flow-volume and pressure-volume relationships during quiet breathing at rest are shown in Figure 9, which also shows the maximal dynamic pressure and flow-volume relationships. The static pressure-volume relationship of the lung (−Pel,L curve) and the minimal pressure required to achieve maximal flow (P*) are also shown. Note the large reserve of flow and pressure that is available to the normal person to meet increased demands for ventilation.

With exercise, ventilation increases in a characteristic pattern. Tidal volume increases more than respiratory frequency. During moderate exercise the subject breathes through the mouth (Fig. 9). At low levels of exercise humans normally breathe through the

nose, but as exercise increases they switch to oronasal breathing. At higher levels of exercise, end-expiratory lung volume is reduced below resting FRC. At maximal exercise, maximal expiratory flow may be achieved near end expiration. During maximal exercise there can be a large negative pleural pressure during inspiration, but during expiration normal persons rarely, if ever, produce pleural pressures in excess of those that are required for maximal expiratory flow (28). This avoids the waste of muscular effort that would occur if expiratory flow became flow limited. The maximal ventilation occurring during exercise is only about two-thirds of the maximal ventilation that can be achieved for brief periods by voluntary effort (28). Thus in normal persons the ability to exercise is not considered to be limited by the ability to ventilate. This is probably true in sedentary persons but may not be true for world-class endurance athletes. The ventilatory response to exercise is discussed in detail in the chapter by Whipp and Pardy in this *Handbook*.

When subjects achieve the maximal voluntary ventilation (MVV) the pattern of ventilation is different

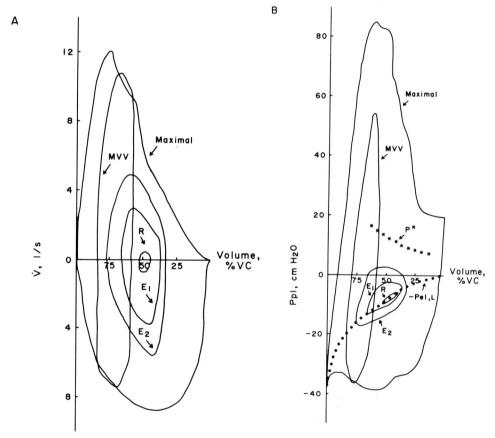

FIG. 9. Flow-volume-pressure relationships during quiet and augmented breathing. *A*: flow ($\dot{V}$)-volume relationships during quiet breathing (R), during progressive levels of exercise (E₁ and E₂), during maximal voluntary ventilation (MVV), and during maximal forced inspiratory and expiratory vital capacity (VC) efforts. *B*: pleural pressure (Ppl)-volume relationships corresponding to flow-volume curves in Fig. 9*A*. Curve −Pel,L is static pressure-volume relationship of lung. Minimal pressure required to achieve maximal flow at a given lung volume (P*) is exceeded only during the MVV and maximal forced expiratory maneuvers but not during progressive levels of exercise.

from that achieved during exercise. Tidal volume is smaller, frequency is higher, and end-expiratory volume is greater than at resting FRC (Fig. 9). However, the most striking difference is that during MVV most subjects, unless specifically instructed, generate pleural pressures far in excess of the pressure required to achieve maximal expiratory flow.

Factors Affecting Respiratory Dynamics

So far we have considered the respiratory system as if it changed volume with a single degree of freedom and was independent of posture. In fact, the respiratory system operates with multiple degrees of freedom: volume changes of the respiratory system may occur from many combinations of shape changes of rib cage and abdominal compartments. The partitioning of volume change between rib cage and abdomen is a function of body position, spinal column attitude, and the level of ventilation. Thoracoabdominal partitioning of ventilation can be studied by detecting linear displacements of the rib cage and abdominal wall with magnetometers (19) or by detecting changes in cross-sectional area with inductance coils (5). The interactions of the respiratory muscles and thoracoabdominal partitioning are discussed in the chapters by Loring and Bruce and by De Troyer and Loring in this *Handbook*. The respiratory system also has other functions that alter the patterns of ventilation discussed above. For example, during phonation the ventilatory pattern is altered to meet simultaneously the need for ventilation and for the subglottic pressures and respiratory flows necessary to produce sound (see the chapter by Proctor on breathing for phonation in this *Handbook*).

From the teleologic standpoint, what might be the "purpose" of expiratory flow limitation? Normal subjects do not perform forced VC or MVV maneuvers outside the laboratory, and during normal ventilation they do not produce pleural pressures greater than the minimum required to produce maximal expiratory flow (Fig. 9). During a cough the glottis is initially closed and subjects generate near-maximal pleural pressures. When the glottis is opened, flow rapidly accelerates to the maximal value defined by the flow-volume envelope and pressures remain far in excess of that required to achieve maximal flow. This extra pressure is dissipated by frictional losses in the compressed airway segment downstream from the flow-limiting site. The extremely high linear velocities in this compressed segment produce high levels of shear at the wall, which strip the mucous blanket and aid in clearance of mucus and particulate material from the central airways. In a series of coughs to progressively lower lung volumes, the flow-limiting site moves peripherally, progressively clearing more distal regions of the airway (see the chapter by Leith et al. in this *Handbook*).

In this discussion we have considered the respiratory muscles as if their sole functions were respiration and related events such as phonation or cough. Yet respiratory muscles also have other functions. Muscles attached to the rib cage may in one circumstance be considered as having an inspiratory or expiratory effect, yet the rib cage serves as the origin of these muscles in their function of supporting the head and shoulder girdle. The glottis is closed and the abdomen-diaphragm utilized for expulsive maneuvers, such as defecation and parturition, and for maximal exertion of the trunk muscles, for example, during weight lifting. At a given metabolic demand for increased ventilation, the respiratory pattern may depend on the type of activity. During certain types of activity, for example, swimming or rowing, respiration must be entrained by the physical activity. The dynamics of respiration for a subject engaged in such activities must be different, and ventilation may have a significant role in determining maximal performance.

We are grateful to Dr. Kenneth C. Beck, who served as a 34-yr-old normal subject for Figures 4–9 in this chapter.

REFERENCES

1. AINSWORTH, M., AND J. W. EVELEIGH. *A Method of Estimating Lung Airway Resistance in Humans.* Ministry of Supply, Chem. Defence Exp. Estab., 1952. (Porton Tech. Paper 320.)
2. BRISCOE, W. A., AND A. B. DuBois. The relationship between airway resistance, airway conductance and lung volume in subjects of different age and body size. *J. Clin. Invest.* 37: 1279–1285, 1958.
3. CAMPBELL, E. J. M. The role of the scalene and sternomastoid muscles in breathing in normal subjects. An electromyographic study. *J. Anat.* 89: 378–386, 1955.
4. CAMPBELL, E. J. M. *The Respiratory Muscles and the Mechanics of Breathing.* London: Lloyd-Luke, 1958.
5. COHN, M. A., H. WATSON, R. WEISSHAUT, F. STOTT, AND M. A. SACKNER. A transducer for non-invasive monitoring of respiration. In: *Proc. 2nd Int. Symp. on Ambulatory Monitoring,* edited by F. D. Stott, E. B. Raferty, P. Sleigh, and L. Gouldring. London: Academic, 1975, p. 119–128.
6. COMROE, J. H., JR., O. I. NISELL, AND R. G. NIMS. A simple method for concurrent measurement of compliance and resistance to breathing in anesthetized animals and man. *J. Appl. Physiol.* 7: 225–228, 1954.
7. DAWSON, S. V., AND E. A. ELLIOTT. Wave-speed limitation on expiratory flow—a unifying concept. *J. Appl. Physiol.: Respirat. Environ. Exercise Physiol.* 43: 498–515, 1977.
8. DuBois, A. B., S. Y. BOTELHO, AND J. H. COMROE, JR. A new method for measuring airway resistance in man using a body plethysmograph: values in normal subjects and in patients with respiratory disease. *J. Clin. Invest.* 35: 327–335, 1956.
9. DuBois, A. B., A. W. BRODY, D. H. LEWIS, AND B. F. BURGESS, JR. Oscillation mechanics of lungs and chest in man. *J. Appl. Physiol.* 8: 587–594, 1956.
10. FERRIS, B. G., JR., J. MEAD, AND L. H. OPIE. Partitioning of respiratory flow resistance in man. *J. Appl. Physiol.* 19: 653–658, 1964.
11. FINK, B. R. *The Human Larynx: A Functional Study.* New York: Raven, 1975.
12. FISHER, A. B., A. B. DuBois, AND R. W. HYDE. Evaluation of the forced oscillation technique for the determination of resist-

ance to breathing. *J. Clin. Invest.* 47: 2045–2057, 1968.

13. FRANK, N. R., J. MEAD, AND B. G. FERRIS, JR. The mechanical behavior of the lungs in healthy elderly persons. *J. Clin. Invest.* 36: 1680–1687, 1957.

14. FRY, D. L., AND R. E. HYATT. Pulmonary mechanics. A unified analysis of the relationship between pressure, volume and gas flow in the lungs of normal and diseased human subjects. *Am. J. Med.* 29: 672–689, 1960.

15. GREEN, J. H., AND J. B. L. HOWELL. The correlation of intercostal muscle activity with respiratory air flow in conscious human subjects. *J. Physiol. London* 149: 471–476, 1959.

16. HEAF, P. J. D., AND F. J. PRIME. The mechanical aspects of artificial pneumothorax. *Lancet* 2: 468–470, 1954.

17. HILDEBRANDT, J. Dynamic properties of air-filled excised cat lung determined by liquid plethysmograph. *J. Appl. Physiol.* 27: 246–250, 1969.

18. HYATT, R. E., AND R. E. WILCOX. Extrathoracic airway resistance in man. *J. Appl. Physiol.* 16: 326–330, 1961.

19. KONNO, K., AND J. MEAD. Measurement of the separate volume changes of rib cage and abdomen during breathing. *J. Appl. Physiol.* 22: 407–422, 1967.

20. LEITH, D. E., AND J. MEAD. Mechanisms determining residual volume of the lungs in normal subjects. *J. Appl. Physiol.* 23: 221–227, 1967.

21. MACKLEM, P. T., AND J. MEAD. Resistance of central and peripheral airways measured by a retrograde catheter. *J. Appl. Physiol.* 22: 395–401, 1967.

22. MCILROY, M. B., D. F. TIERNEY, AND J. A. NADEL. A new method for measurement of compliance and resistance of lungs and thorax. *J. Appl. Physiol.* 18: 424–427, 1963.

23. MEAD, J. Measurement of inertia of the lungs at increased ambient pressure. *J. Appl. Physiol.* 9: 208–212, 1956.

24. MEAD, J., AND E. AGOSTONI. Dynamics of breathing. In: *Handbook of Physiology. Respiration,* edited by W. O. Fenn and H. Rahn. Washington, DC: Am. Physiol. Soc., 1964, sect. 3, vol. I, chapt. 14, p. 411–427.

25. MEAD, J., J. M. TURNER, P. T. MACKLEM, AND J. B. LITTLE. Significance of the relationship between lung recoil and maximum expiratory flow. *J. Appl. Physiol.* 22: 95–108, 1967.

26. MOGNONI, P., F. SAIBENE, G. SANT'AMBROGIO, AND E. AGOSTONI. Dynamics of the maximal contraction of the respiratory muscles. *Respir. Physiol.* 4: 193–202, 1968.

27. NIINIMAA, V., P. COLE, S. MINTZ, AND R. J. SHEPHARD. Oronasal distribution of respiratory airflow. *Respir. Physiol.* 43: 69–75, 1981.

28. OLAFSSON, S., AND R. E. HYATT. Ventilatory mechanisms and expiratory flow limitation during exercise in normal subjects. *J. Clin. Invest.* 48: 564–573, 1969.

29. PRIDE, N. B., S. PERMUTT, R. L. RILEY, AND B. BROMBERGER-BARNEA. Determinants of maximal expiratory flow from the lungs. *J. Appl. Physiol.* 23: 646–662, 1967.

30. RAPER, A. J., W. T. THOMPSON, JR., W. SHAPIRO, AND J. L. PATTERSON, JR. Scalene and sternomastoid muscle function. *J. Appl. Physiol.* 21: 497–502, 1966.

31. RICHERSON, H. B., AND P. M. SEEBOHM. Nasal airway response to exercise. *J. Allergy* 41: 269–284, 1968.

32. ROHRER, F. Der Strömungswiderstand in den menschlichen Atemwegen und der Einfluss der unregelmässigen Verzweigung des Bronchialsystems auf den Atmungsverlauf in verschiedenen Lungenbezirken. *Pfluegers Arch. Gesamte Physiol. Menschen Tiere* 162: 225–299, 1915.

33. SAUERLAND, E. K., AND S. P. MITCHELL. Electromyographic activity of intrinsic and extrinsic muscles of the human tongue. *Tex. Rep. Biol. Med.* 33: 444–455, 1975.

34. SPEIZER, F. E., AND N. R. FRANK. A technique for measuring nasal and pulmonary flow resistance simultaneously. *J. Appl. Physiol.* 19: 176–178, 1964.

CHAPTER 11

Oscillation mechanics of the respiratory system

RENÉ PESLIN | *Institut National de la Santé et de la Recherche Médicale,*
Vandoeuvre-les-Nancy, France

JEFFREY J. FREDBERG | *The Biomechanics Institute, Boston, Massachusetts*

CHAPTER CONTENTS

OSCILLATION MECHANICS is the study of structural and mechanical properties of the respiratory system as deduced from its mechanical responses to small time-varying forces. The forces can be generated internally by respiratory system muscles or vocal cords or externally by loudspeakers or pumps coupled at the mouth or the chest wall. The time histories of the forces may be periodic, steplike, impulsive, or random, and the characteristic frequencies may be smaller than that of spontaneous breathing or up to several orders of magnitude greater. The mechanical properties in question include overall properties, e.g., respiratory system compliance and resistance, and local properties, e.g., tracheal dimensions and tracheal compliance. In this chapter our attention is limited to external forcing of the respiratory system at frequencies larger than those occurring naturally.

The method most often used in oscillation mechanics is the construction of computational models of the respiratory system that reflect as closely as possible the oscillatory data. These models are usually linear and their parameters are the physical properties in question or some combination of them.

MODELING THE RESPIRATORY SYSTEM AS A LINEAR SYSTEM

Models

DYNAMIC SYSTEMS. To study oscillation mechanics and frequency-response characteristics of the respiratory system, a definition of a mechanical system is required. Accordingly a mechanical system is a collection of matter and components defined by a real or imaginary boundary. This boundary might include only a single airway, a whole lung, or even the entire respiratory system including accessory muscles of respiration and equipment for measurement and system forcing (e.g., plethysmographs, loudspeakers, and pneumotachographs). The system boundary is chosen to provide a convenient conceptual separation of the system from its environment. An input variable of a system is an external influence prescribed by the environment, whereas an output variable is a response of the system to an external influence. It is important to select system boundaries for which outputs of interest are observable and inputs are controllable or at least observable. The lungs, for example, may be the system in question with the system boundaries defined by the pleural surface and the airway opening. Transpulmonary pressure [airway opening pressure (Pao) minus pleural pressure (Ppl)] may be thought of as an input and lung volume as an output.

PASSIVE MECHANICAL ELEMENTS. Although the respiratory system is a complex interconnection of solid and fluid components, it is useful to consider it as an assemblage of three simpler types of primitive passive elements called elastances, inertances, and resistances, with each element corresponding to a unique mode of energy handling. These three modes are: *1*) storage by means of potential energy (most often elastic and less frequently gravitational); *2*) storage by means of kinetic energy (inertial); and *3*) dissipation by means of friction (viscous). These ideas apply equally well to solid systems, in which we deal with springs, masses, and dashpots, and to fluid systems, in which we deal with fluid elastances, fluid inertances, and flow resistances.

In respiration mechanics it is a convention to characterize these elements in terms of pressure differences (ΔP) across the element and associated volumetric flow rates ($\dot{V}$) passing through the element. The relationship of pressure differences to volume flow for each primitive element depends on only the physical material and geometry of the system. For this reason it is called the constitutive relation, in the symbolic form

$$\Delta P = P_2 - P_1 = P_{21} = f(\dot{V}) \qquad (1)$$

where $f(\dot{V})$ is a function of the volumetric flow rate and P is gas pressure. Rohrer's (162) equation for flow resistance

$$P_{21} = k_1\dot{V} + k_2\dot{V}|\dot{V}| \qquad (2)$$

is an example of a well-known constitutive relation, where k is a constant (Fig. 1). Because the pressure difference is a nonlinear function of the flow rate, Equation 2 is an example of a nonlinear constitutive relation.

LINEARIZATION. Constitutive relations for elastances, inertances, and resistances are all nonlinear to greater or lesser degrees. To avoid the complexities of dealing with nonlinear systems, we limit attention to very small departures of the system from a prescribed reference state. In this case the curvilinear constitutive relations may be replaced by a linear approximation and entail only small errors. This greatly simplifies analysis but is valid only in the immediate neighborhood of the reference state defined by a prescribed volume history, lung volume, and volumetric flow rate.

The linearized relationship of pressure difference to

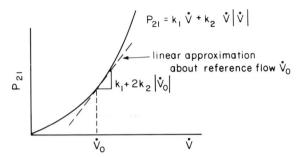

FIG. 1. Rohrer relation (Eq. 2) taken as an example of nonlinear pressure-flow relations linearized for small departures about any given bias flow rate ($\dot{V}_o$). Oscillatory resistance for slow oscillations is the local tangent slope of the pressure-flow curve. For long straight tubes, slope at $\dot{V}_o = 0$ is the Poiseuille flow resistance.

volume flow is called an ideal elemental equation. For resistive pressure differences specified by Rohrer's equation, the ideal elemental equation is

$$P_{21} = R\dot{V} \qquad (3)$$

where the constant of proportionality between pressure and flow is the resistance (R), the slope of the tangent line of Equation 2 evaluated at bias flow $\dot{V}_o$ (Fig. 1). The slope is the derivative of Equation 2 with respect to $\dot{V}$, so

$$R = k_1 + 2k_2|\dot{V}_o| \qquad (4)$$

which may be regarded as a constant for small oscillatory flows about the steady DC $\dot{V}_o$. This is referred to as the oscillatory or incremental resistance (116). Similar linearizations may be done to determine incremental elastances and inertances.

In contrast to the tangent slope (Eq. 4), the chord slope ($k_1 + k_2|\dot{V}_o|$) is also an estimate, though not a good one, of the oscillatory flow resistance. The chord slope is more often used when flow excursions are large enough to reveal marked nonlinearities in the pressure-flow relation.

Elemental Equations

The elemental relations of common fluid and mechanical elements and the elemental relations for three common electrical components often used to simulate and model the respiratory system are presented in this section and summarized in Table 1.

INERTANCES. In the absence of viscosity, the pressure difference applied across a fluid column of length l and cross-sectional area A is balanced by fluid acceleration in accordance with Newton's law that force (F) equals mass (ρlA) times acceleration (du/dt). Because force is pressure difference times area, Newton's law becomes

$$F = A(P_2 - P_1) = AP_{21} = n\rho lA(du/dt) \qquad (5)$$

where u is velocity, ρ is the fluid density, and d/dt denotes rate of change with respect to time t. The

TABLE 1. *Elemental Relations for Active and Passive Primitive Elements*

Physical Element	Electrical Analogue	Elemental Equation	Impedance $Z(\omega) = P_{21}/\dot{V}$
fluid $P_2(A)\ \rho\ P_1$; L / M mass (A)	inductor $P_2 \ooo\ P_1$, I	$P_{21} = I\dfrac{d}{dt}\dot{V}$	$Z = j\omega I$ $\begin{cases} I_f = n\rho L/A \\ \\ I_s = M/A^2 \end{cases}$
Chamber w/ rigid walls $P_2\ \boxed{P_0 V_0\ \text{gas}}\ P_1$; Chamber w/ elastic walls $P_2\ \bigcirc\ P_1$	capacitor $P_2 \dashv\vdash P_1$, $C, 1/E$	$\dfrac{d}{dt}P_{21} = E\dot{V}$	$Z = -j\dfrac{E}{\omega}$ $\begin{cases} E_f = \beta P_0/V_0 \\ \\ E_s = f(\text{geometry, elastic moduli}) \end{cases}$
fluid $P_2(A)\ \mu, f\ P_1$; L / Chamber w/ viscous walls $P_2'\ \bigcirc\ P_1$	resistor $P_2 \diagdown\diagup P_1$, R	$P_{21} = R\dot{V}$	$Z = R$ $\begin{cases} R_f = f(\text{geometry, }\dot{V}_0, \omega, \rho, \mu,) \\ \\ R_s = f(\text{geometry, visco-elastic moduli}) \end{cases}$
Flow Source	$2\ \dot{V}s(t)\ 1$ $\bigcirc$	$\dot{V} = \dot{V}s(t)$	$\dot{V}s(t)$ prescribed indep of P_{21}
Pressure Source	$2\ Ps(t)\ 1$ $\bigcirc$	$P = Ps(t)$	$Ps(t)$ prescribed indep of $\dot{V}$

factor n is 1 if the velocity profile is blunt and $4/3$ if parabolic. Faster oscillations in larger ducts tend toward the blunted velocity profile (9, 20, 44, 55, 59, 205). The volumetric flow rate ($\dot{V}$) is the cross-sectional area times the average particle velocity (u); thus the ideal elemental equation becomes

$$P_{21}(t) = I(d/dt)\dot{V}(t) \qquad (6)$$

where

$$I = n\rho l/A \qquad (7)$$

Note that the fluid inertance (I) increases proportionately with tube length and gas density but decreases in inverse proportion with tube cross section. This latter fact is somewhat counterintuitive but occurs because area enters in three ways: *1)* force is pressure times area, *2)* mass is density times length times area, and *3)* volume flow rate is velocity times area. Equation 6 demonstrates that the pressure drop P_{21} across an inertance is largest when flow rate changes rapidly, and is zero when flow is steady. Energy stored in inertial elements by virtue of their motion is called kinetic energy.

In the case of a solid mass (M) exposed to a pressure difference across an area (A), a solid inertance can be defined by Equation 6

$$I = M/A^2 \qquad (8)$$

The $\dot{V}$ in Equation 6 then represents the rate of volume swept by the mass surface, as in the motions of the chest wall or dilations of an airway wall.

If electrical voltage (v) and current (i) are taken as analogues of pressure and flow, respectively, electrical inductance (I) and mechanical inertance are analogues of one another ($v = Idi/dt$; cf. Eq. 6).

ELASTANCES (COMPLIANCES). An ideal fluid elastance (E) has pressure differences in direct proportion to volume, $P_{21} = EV$. Rate of volume change (dV/dt) is the volumetric flow rate, so this relation may be expressed

$$(d/dt)P_{21}(t) = E\dot{V}(t) \qquad (9)$$

where

$$E = 1/C \qquad (10)$$

The elastance (E) is the reciprocal of the compliance (C). In the respiratory system, gas compressibility is the most important source of fluid elastance. For an ideal gas volume (V_o) at absolute mean pressure (P_o), the elastance is a nonlinear function of the pressure variations but may be linearized to yield

$$E = \beta P_o/V_o \qquad (11)$$

where β is unity if the compression is isothermal and is the ratio of specific heats if it is adiabatic. Faster changes in larger containers tend toward the adiabatic condition (9, 55, 58). Equation 9 demonstrates that the volumetric flow through a fluid capacitance is largest when pressure rapidly changes and zero when the pressure is steady. Energy stored in elastic elements by virtue of compression of gas or distension of elastic walls is called elastic potential energy.

In the case of an elastic cavity exposed to distending pressures, a solid elastance can be defined by Equation 9. Solid elastances encountered in respiration mechanics tend to be dependent on volume history and profoundly nonlinear. Lung parenchyma, airway walls, and chest wall are specific examples. Linearization of solid elastances about the proper reference volume becomes an important factor. The tangent slope at a point on the pressure-volume curve is the elastance and is called the incremental modulus (116).

Again, if electrical voltage and current are taken as analogues of pressure and flow, respectively, then electrical capacitance (C) and mechanical capacitance are analogues of one another [$i = C(dv/dt)$; cf. Eq. 9].

RESISTANCES. An ideal fluid resistance exhibits a pressure drop proportional to flow rate according to the elemental relation

$$P_{21}(t) = R\dot{V}(t) \qquad (12)$$

For steady fully developed laminar flow at low Reynolds number (parabolic velocity profile) in a long straight pipe of length l and cross section A containing fluid viscosity μ

$$R = 8\pi\mu l/A^2 \qquad (13a)$$

which is the Poiseuille formula for flow resistance. This result also applies to slower oscillatory flows, but fails at higher frequencies, at higher oscillatory Reynolds numbers, and in the presence of bias flows. In these cases the oscillatory resistance may become dependent on frequency, density, and/or flow rate (9, 20, 44, 55, 205).

A useful approximation that takes into account unsteadiness and the superposition of steady bias flows is (37, 119)

$$R \approx R_{DC} + \frac{\sqrt{2}\mu}{\pi r^4}\left(\frac{r^2\omega}{\nu}\right)^{1/2} l \qquad (13b)$$

where circular frequency (ω) is 2π times the frequency (f) in cycles per second (Hz). The steady DC incre-

mental flow resistance (R_{DC}) is measured or calculated from the tangent of the steady-state pressure-flow curve (see Fig. 1) and is frequency invariant. The kinematic viscosity (ν) is μ/ρ and tube radius is r. The frequency-dependent second term arises as oscillations become more rapid and fluid inertia changes the velocity profile from its steady-state shape. Fluid inertia makes the velocity profile more blunt, which increases the velocity gradient and viscous shear stress at the walls. Thus for small-amplitude but rapid oscillations, the oscillatory flow resistance is always greater than or equal to the tangent resistance of Figure 1. Furthermore the oscillatory flow resistance approaches a single high-frequency asymptote regardless of whether the bias flow is laminar or turbulent. This occurs because the thickness of the unsteady viscosity-dominated boundary layer near the wall becomes smaller than tube radius in the case of laminar flow and smaller than the thickness of the laminar sublayer in the case of turbulent flow.

The pressure-flow relationship through an orifice such as the glottis or an orifice flowmeter is markedly nonlinear. In this case pressure drop is proportional to the square of the flow rate, and the resistance is given by

$$R = \frac{\rho}{2C_d^2 A_o^2}|\dot{V}| \qquad (14)$$

where C_d is a discharge coefficient ($\sim$0.6) and A_o is orifice area. This implies a nonlinear relation of pressure to flow, dependence on fluid density, but remarkable independence from fluid viscosity.

Energy dissipated in resistive elements by virtue of friction is lost irreversibly to heat. In contrast with inertial and elastic elements, which store mechanical energy, resistors dissipate mechanical energy.

In the case of a distensible cavity with viscous walls a solid or viscous resistance can be defined by Equation 12, where R is the solid resistance, usually determined empirically. The electrical analogue of mechanical resistance is electrical resistance (R), for which $v = iR$, which is Ohm's law for electrical resistances (cf. Eq. 12).

ACTIVE MECHANICAL ELEMENTS. There are active elements capable of delivering energy to the system over an extended period that account for sustained respiratory system motions; they may be respiratory system muscles or external loudspeakers and pumps. Two useful idealized sources are the volume flow source (current source) and the pressure source (voltage source). The ideal flow source maintains a prescribed volumetric flow rate as a function of time through its terminals independent of the pressure drop required to achieve that flow. The ideal pressure source maintains a prescribed pressure rise as a function of time across its terminals independent of the flow required to maintain that pressure.

Table 1 summarizes the elemental relations for all the active and passive primitive elements described.

Sinusoidal Forcing and Complex Impedance

If the active elements in a system generate sinusoidal time histories, the equations may be written more simply and manipulated more easily. Physicists and engineers use an exponential shorthand to represent sinusoidal waves. There are advantages that make this notation worth the effort of mastering it; for example, instead of writing cos (ωt), they write $e^{j\omega t}$, both of which represent the same sinusoidal wave. Historically the quantity j is called the unit imaginary number.[1]

A geometric interpretation of this relationship is given in Figure 2A. It represents the so-called complex plane where real numbers are plotted on the x-axis and imaginary numbers plotted on the y-axis. Readers unfamiliar with the arithmetic of complex numbers may consider this to be an operational definition of $e^{j\omega t}$, and in attempting to understand Figure 2A may be assured that a little more background in complex arithmetic is necessary. It is seen from this figure that $e^{j\omega t}$ represents a ray of unit length rotating in the complex plane at an angular velocity of ω radians per second. Its projection onto the x-axis (real axis) is cos ωt, which gives rise to the laboratory strip-chart recording.

Accordingly a variation of flow at the airway opening of amplitude $\dot{V}ao(\omega)$ at a frequency ω can be written

$$\dot{V}ao(t) = \dot{V}ao(\omega) \cos \omega t = \dot{V}ao(\omega) \, \text{real}[e^{j\omega t}] \quad (15)$$

where "real" denotes the real part of the term within the brackets. Boldface type is used to distinguish complex quantities (vectors). Analogously "imag" denotes the imaginary part of the term within the brackets, where imag$[e^{j\omega t}]$ is sin ωt. It is a matter of convention that "real part of" is implied by

$$\dot{V}ao(t) = \dot{\mathbf{V}}ao(\omega)e^{j\omega t} \quad (16)$$

Similarly a variation of pressure at the airway opening (Fig. 2b) of amplitude Pao(ω) at the frequency ω can be written

$$\text{Pao}(t) = \mathbf{P}ao(\omega) \cos(\omega t + \Phi rs)$$
$$= \mathbf{P}ao(\omega)e^{j(\omega t + \Phi rs)} \quad (17)$$

where Φrs accounts for any phase shift of the pressure wave relative to flow. Here and in the remainder of this chapter pressures are defined relative to atmospheric pressure (PB), which is taken to be zero, thus the pressure difference across the respiratory sys-

[1] Although j is the "imaginary" number, it has real physical significance and utility. It allows us to deal with resistances, elastances, and inertances on an equal footing using only algebra. Suppose $x^2 + 1 = 0$, then $x = \pm\sqrt{-1}$. In "complex numbers," $\pm\sqrt{-1}$ is denoted by the symbol i or j. We use the latter.

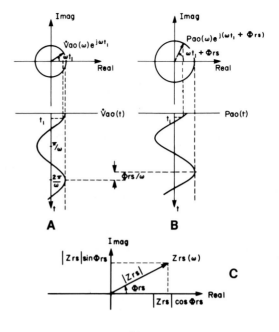

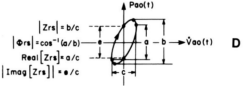

FIG. 2. A: sinusoidal strip-chart recording of flow (bottom) imagined to be the projection of a rotating ray of length $\mathbf{V}ao(\omega)$ (top). B: as in the case of flow, pressure may be thought of as the projection of a rotating ray of length $\mathbf{P}ao(\omega)$. Phase angle between pressure and flow is Φrs. C: impedance may be decomposed into real and imaginary parts or into magnitude and phase. D: Pao(t) vs. $\dot{V}ao(t)$ yields a Lissajous ellipse, from which impedance components may be deduced.

tem (Prs) in this example is Prs = Pao − Pbs = Pao − PB = Pao, where Pbs is body surface pressure.

COMPLEX IMPEDANCE. The ratio of the pressure $\mathbf{P}ao$ to the flow $\dot{\mathbf{V}}ao$ at a frequency ω is called the respiratory system impedance, $\mathbf{Z}rs(\omega)$. It is readily calculated from the ratio of Equations 16 and 17 that

$$\mathbf{Z}rs(\omega) = \frac{\mathbf{P}ao(\omega)e^{j(\omega t + \Phi rs)}}{\dot{\mathbf{V}}ao(\omega)e^{j\omega t}} = \frac{\mathbf{P}ao(\omega)}{\dot{\mathbf{V}}ao(\omega)} e^{j\Phi rs} \quad (18)$$

or simply

$$\mathbf{Z}rs = |\mathbf{Z}rs| e^{j\Phi rs} \quad (19)$$

That is, the impedance is composed of two parts: a magnitude $|\mathbf{Z}rs|$ indicating the amplitude of the pressure difference relative to the flow and a phase angle Φrs indicating the phase angle of pressure difference relative to flow. The impedance at a given frequency may be represented as a vector in the complex plane because of its magnitude and angle (Fig. 2C). The time-dependent parts of the pressure and flow ($e^{j\omega t}$) cancel when the ratio is computed, thus the impedance vector remains stationary. By simple geometrical relations suggested by Figure 2C the impedance may be separated into its real and imaginary parts.

In the laboratory the impedance may be deduced by comparing the relative amplitudes and phases of strip-chart recordings of pressure and flow as in Figure 2A, B. Another common method is to use an oscilloscope to plot pressure (on the x-axis) versus flow (on the y-axis). Because both are sinusoidal functions an ellipse (called a Lissajous figure) is traced from which the impedance may be deduced (Fig. 2D). When the ellipse is traced clockwise the phase angle and imaginary part are both positive.

Using sinusoidal exponential notation, many operations now become simple, notably

$$(d/dt)e^{j\omega t} = j\omega e^{j\omega t} \qquad (20)$$

Restricting our attention to such sinusoidal variations, the ideal elemental relations given above (Eqs. 6, 9, and 12) now may be rewritten. Dividing by $\dot{V}$ to take the ratio of pressure difference to volume flow together with Equation 20 yields the impedances for elastance (Z_E), inertance (Z_I), and resistance (Z_R)

$$(P_{21}/\dot{V})_E = Z_E = -jE/\omega \qquad (21a)$$

$$(P_{21}/\dot{V})_I = Z_I = j\omega I \qquad (21b)$$

$$(P_{21}/\dot{V})_R = Z_R = R \qquad (21c)$$

(Note that $j \cdot j = -1$, so $1/j = -j$.) In general, the elemental equation for any element may be written in a form analogous to Ohm's law for resistances

$$P_{21} = Z\dot{V} \qquad (22)$$

Hence the calculus suggested by the elemental Equations 6 and 9 is reduced to linear algebra in the form of Ohm's law (Eq. 12) when restricted to sinusoidal variations. Therefore impedance may be thought of as a generalization of the concept of resistance, but whereas resistance describes only resistive (frictional) induced pressure differences, impedance describes pressure differences across resistive, elastic, or inertial elements.

Impedance is an index of the impediment the element presents to oscillatory flow. The larger the impedance magnitude, the larger the oscillatory pressure difference needed to maintain a given oscillatory flow, or conversely, the smaller the oscillatory flow for a fixed amplitude of the oscillatory pressure difference. The explicit frequency dependence and sign of each impedance are its primary characteristics. Recalling the description of the complex plane (Fig. 2C), elastic and inertive impedances are pure imaginary numbers. Elastic impedance is a negative imaginary number whose magnitude is inversely proportional to frequency and whose phase is $-90°$. Inertive impedance is a positive imaginary number whose magnitude is directly proportional to frequency and whose phase is $+90°$. Resistive impedance is a positive real number without explicit frequency dependence and whose

phase is $0°$. In addition to the explicit frequency dependencies above (Eq. 20), the inertance, elastance, and resistance may also be implicitly frequency dependent [(9, 20, 44, 55, 58, 205); see also *Elemental Equations*, p. 146].

Continuity and Compatibility Conditions

A linear respiratory system model is formulated by assembling resistive, inertial, and elastic elements into a network or circuit. The junctions between elements are called nodes. To this network we apply two physical principles: mass must be conserved (continuity) and Newton's laws must be obeyed (compatibility).

The principle of continuity applies to the flows in the system and guarantees conservation of mass. To conserve mass at a node the sum of all flows into the node must be zero. In electrical circuits the analogous statement is Kirchoff's current law, which states that the net current flowing into a node is zero. The principle of continuity is demonstrated in the system of Figure 3A. The resistance, capacitance, and inertance must experience identical flows.

The principle of compatibility applies to pressure drops in the system and guarantees that the net pressure drop taken in a specified direction around any closed path in the system circuit be zero. In other words, a pressure walk around the system must come back to the same pressure if the walk begins and ends at the same place. Equivalently, compatibility requires that pressure drops add for elements in series and are equal for elements in parallel. In electrical circuits the equivalent statement is Kirchoff's voltage law, requiring the sum of all voltage drops around any closed circuit to be zero. The principle of compatibility is also demonstrated in Figure 3A. The pressure rise across the source (Pao − Pbs) is equal to the sum of the pressure drops across the passive elements.

By defining specific system nodes and assigning corresponding pressures, it is assumed implicitly that a single number may represent these pressures and that these pressures are spatially uniform in the system being modeled. Often spatial gradients may exist in the case of alveolar pressure, pleural pressure, and body surface pressure. Further discussions of such regional inhomogeneity are discussed later in this chapter.

Because the flows through the series elements are equal (continuity) they must be the same as flow at the airway opening (Fig. 3A). Summing the pressure drops around the closed loop (compatibility)

$$\begin{aligned} Prs &= Pao - Pbs \\ &= \dot{V}ao(Rrs) + \dot{V}ao(1/j\omega Crs) + \dot{V}ao(j\omega Irs) \end{aligned} \qquad (23)$$

It would be correct to write $e^{j\omega t}$ after each of the terms in this equation to indicate the temporal nature of each. As it multiplies each term, $e^{j\omega t}$ may be cancelled throughout, leading to Equation 23. Dividing by $\dot{V}$ao

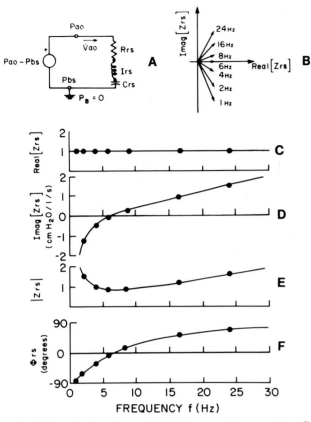

FIG. 3. *A:* simple series model of the respiratory system. *B:* impedance vector at several frequencies. Components of impedance vector: real (resistive) component (*C*); imaginary (reactive) component (*D*); magnitude (*E*); phase angle (*F*).

yields the respiratory system impedance for this model

$$\mathbf{Zrs} = \mathbf{Pao}/\dot{\mathbf{V}}ao = Rrs + j\left[\omega Irs - \frac{1}{\omega Crs}\right] \quad (24)$$

where the relation that $j \cdot j = -1$ is used. The imaginary part of the impedance is called the reactance, imag[$\mathbf{Zrs}$], or $\mathbf{Xrs}(\omega)$. The real part is called the resistance, real[$\mathbf{Zrs}$], or Rrs.

Finally, referring to Figure 2*C*

$$|\mathbf{Zrs}| = \left\{Rrs^2 + \left(\omega Irs - \frac{1}{\omega Crs}\right)^2\right\}^{1/2} \quad (25)$$

and

$$\Phi rs = \tan^{-1}\left[\left(\omega Irs - \frac{1}{\omega Crs}\right)\Big/ Rrs\right] \quad (26)$$

The corresponding frequency-response curves are shown in Figure 3*B–D*. At low frequencies, because $1/\omega Crs$ is much larger than ωIrs, the system behaves like a compliance in that the impedance magnitude decreases with frequency, Φrs is negative (pressure lags flow), and the imaginary part Xrs is negative. At higher frequencies the effect of inertance predomi-

nates (because ωIrs is larger than $1/\omega Crs$), so that Zrs increases, Φrs is positive (pressure leads flow), and the imaginary part Xrs is positive. Finally, at some intermediate frequency called resonant frequency (f_o), the effects of compliance and inertance, which are opposite in sign, completely cancel each other so that the system behaves like a pure resistance: $|\mathbf{Zrs}| = Rrs$ and $\Phi rs = 0$ (pressure in phase with flow). This is achieved at $f_o = \frac{1}{2}\pi(IrsCrs)^{1/2}$.

SERIES AND PARALLEL ADDITION OF IMPEDANCE. When elements are arranged in series, and thereby share the same flow, the impedance of the circuit is the sum of the impedances of the individual elements as suggested in Equation 24

$$Z = Z_1 + Z_2 \quad (27)$$

On the other hand, when the two elements Z_1 and Z_2 are in parallel, and thereby divide the flow but share the same pressure drop, the equivalent impedance is

$$1/Z = 1/Z_1 + 1/Z_2 \quad (28)$$

General Formulation of System Models

The model depicted in Figure 4 is widely used in oscillation mechanics of the respiratory system and can account for forcing at the mouth and/or at the body surface. This system is used to exemplify the general method for formulation of system equations. If Raw and Iaw represent resistance and inertance of central airway gas, Cg represents alveolar gas compressibility, and Rt, It, and Ct represent lung tissue and chest wall properties, then this model is equivalent to that first put forward by DuBois et al. (40) in 1956 and used by Peslin et al. (151) in 1972. Atmospheric reference pressure (Pв) is taken to be zero. An external source at the mouth (loudspeaker or pump) generates a pressure difference between airway opening and atmosphere. An external source at the body surface (body box) generates a pressure difference

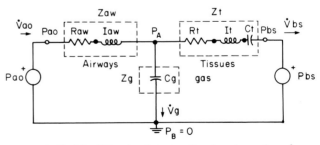

FIG. 4. Model of T network accounting for airway impedance (Zaw), tissue impedance (Zt), and gas compression (Zg). Forcing may be at mouth, body surface, or both. Either generator may be short-circuited (no pressure difference) or open-circuited (no flow) to deal with the case of a single input. Note the sign convention for flows: continuity applied at node Pa (alveolar pressure) requires $\dot{V}$ao $-\dot{V}$bs $-\dot{V}$g $= 0$. Raw, airway resistance; Iaw, airway inertance; Rt, tissue resistance; It, tissue inertance; Ct, tissue compliance; Cg, gas compressibility; Pв, barometric pressure; $\dot{V}$g, alveolar gas flow.

between body surface and atmosphere. The pressure difference between alveolar gas and atmosphere is $\mathbf{P}_A$. Clearly, if alveolar gas compressibility is small [Cg $\simeq$ 0, $\dot{V}$g (alveolar gas flow) $\simeq$ 0], then this model reduces to the series resistance-inertance-compliance model (Fig. 3A), where Rrs = Raw + Rt, Irs = Iaw + It, and Crs = Ct.

In this example, the number of elements (b) is 8, the number of sources (s) is 2, and the number of nodes (n) is 7. The complete set of system equations is formulated by writing elemental equations for each of the 6 passive elements (generally b − s), continuity equations for each of 6 nodes (generally n − 1), and compatibility equations for each of the 2 closed loops (generally b − n + 1) (171).

The compatibility, continuity, and elemental equations form a complete set for solving 2b − s equations in the same number of unknowns.[2] Out of these 2b − s = 14 equations in this example, four will contain time derivatives or, if exponential notation is used, algebraic factors of jω (Eq. 20). This is required because there are four energy storage elements in the circuit (Iaw, Cg, It, Ct), each containing a differential (or factor of jω) in its elemental relation (Eqs. 6, 9, and 21a, b). By manipulation the 2b − s equations may always be reduced to no more than m simultaneous first-order differential equations (in this case 4) or a single differential equation of order less than or equal to m. If exponential notation is used, these become m simultaneous first-order algebraic equa-

---

[2] For any output $y(t)$ and any single input $x(t)$, the elemental, compatibility, and continuity equations lead to

$$[a_m \frac{d^m}{dt^m} + a_{m-1} \frac{d^{m-1}}{dt^{m-1}} \ldots + a_0]y(t)$$

$$= [b_l \frac{d^l}{dt^l} + b_{l-1} \frac{d^{l-1}}{dt^{l-1}} \ldots + b_0]x(t)$$

where m and l are integers, and $y(t)$ might be Vao(t) and $x(t)$ might be Pao(t), for example. If the input of a linear system is sinusoidal, the output will also be sinusoidal. From Euler's formula, $e^{j\omega t} = \cos \omega t + j \sin \omega t$, so the real part of $e^{j\omega t}$ may be thought of as representing the sinusoidal time history. The sinusoidal input $x(t)$ and output $y(t)$ may then be written

$$y(t) = \mathbf{Y}(\omega)e^{j\omega t}$$

$$x(t) = \mathbf{X}(\omega)e^{j\omega t}$$

with amplitudes $\mathbf{Y}(\omega)$ and $\mathbf{X}(\omega)$, respectively. Recalling that d/dt becomes jω, the differential equation becomes an mth order polynominal in ω

$$[a_m(j\omega)^m + a_{m-1}(j\omega)^{m-1} + \ldots + a_0]\mathbf{Y}(\omega)$$

$$= [b_l(j\omega)^l + b_{l-1}(j\omega)^{l-1} + \ldots + b_0]\mathbf{X}(\omega)$$

Forming the ratio of polynomials, $\mathbf{H}(\omega)$, this may be expressed by the linear relation $\mathbf{Y}(\omega) = \mathbf{H}(\omega) \mathbf{X}(\omega)$. The system depicted by Figure 4 has two inputs, but either can be set to zero in favor of the other. Figure 3A is an example of a second-order system. Its system equation (Eq. 23) is seen to be of a second-order polynomial in jω by grouping terms [IrsCrs$(j\omega)^2$ + RrsCrs$(j\omega)^1$ + 1]Vao(ω) = [Crs$(j\omega)^1$]Pao(ω).

tions or a single algebraic equation with powers of jω less than or equal to m.

This integer m is called the system order and is less than or equal to the number of energy storage elements (i.e., the number of inertances and compliances). The number of variables necessary to specify the state of the system at any instant is also equal to the system order m. Furthermore m is the number of initial conditions necessary to predict the state of a system in the future (assuming the forcing to be specified).

The system order concept is useful for at least three reasons. 1) The behaviors of systems of any given order are very well characterized and documented, particularly in the cases of m = 0, 1, and 2 (171). Hence, if the system order is known, the response data of the system may be anticipated qualitatively and to some degree quantitatively. 2) If the data are in hand but a model to interpret the data is sought, the order of the model (i.e., the number of elastic and inertial elements) often can be identified by cursory inspection of the data. 3) The order is a simple way to classify systems according to their simplicity, and as such is commonly used in the physiological literature.

System Functions

The ratio of an output variable $\mathbf{Y}(\omega)$ (a pressure difference or a flow) to an input variable $\mathbf{X}(\omega)$ (a pressure difference or a flow) is called a system function $\mathbf{H}(\omega)$

$$\mathbf{H}(\omega) = \mathbf{Y}(\omega)/\mathbf{X}(\omega) \tag{29}$$

Thus the respiratory system is characterized by the ratio of the output to an input, H(ω), indicative of the relative magnitude and phase of $\mathbf{X}$ and $\mathbf{Y}$.

There are many different types of system functions. If the input $\mathbf{X}(\omega)$ is a flow and the output $\mathbf{Y}(\omega)$ is a pressure difference, the ratio is called an impedance $Z(\omega)$. If the input $\mathbf{X}(\omega)$ is a pressure difference and the output $\mathbf{Y}(\omega)$ is a flow, then H(ω) is called an admittance G(ω). If the input and output are both pressure differences or both flows, the ratio is called a transfer function $\mathbf{T}(\omega)$.

If a pressure difference and flow are measured at the same terminals and the flow is defined as positive into the port, the impedance (admittance) is called an input or drive-point impedance (input admittance). If a pressure difference and flow are measured at different terminals, the impedance (admittance) is called a transfer impedance (transfer admittance). Examples from Figure 4 are

input admittances: $\dot{V}ao(\omega)/\mathbf{P}ao(\omega),$

$$-\dot{V}bs(\omega)/\mathbf{P}bs(\omega) \tag{30a}$$

input impedances: $\mathbf{P}ao(\omega)/\dot{V}ao(\omega),$

$$\mathbf{P}bs(\omega)/-\dot{V}bs(\omega) \tag{30b}$$

transfer impedances: $\mathbf{Pao}(\omega)/\dot{\mathbf{V}}\text{bs}(\omega),$

$$\mathbf{Pbs}(\omega)/-\dot{\mathbf{V}}\text{ao}(\omega) \tag{30c}$$

transfer functions: $\dot{\mathbf{V}}\text{bs}(\omega)/\dot{\mathbf{V}}\text{ao}(\omega),$

$$\mathbf{Pbs}(\omega)/\mathbf{Pao}(\omega) \tag{30d}$$

As stated in *Sinusoidal Forcing and Complex Imped-ance*, p. 149, in writing pressure rather than pressure difference it is implied that the reference pressure is atmospheric (PB), which is zero. Also note that $\dot{\mathbf{V}}$bs has been defined as positive in the inspiratory direction (Figs. 4 and 5B), and accordingly the flow into the port at the body surface is $-\dot{\mathbf{V}}$bs.

Each of these system functions indicates relative amplitude and phase, which vary with frequency. The frequency dependence of any of these system functions is called a frequency-response characteristic of the respiratory system.

Equivalent Circuits

ONE-PORT SYSTEMS. If pressure (relative to atmos-phere) and flow variations are applied and measured only at the mouth, the respiratory system can be represented schematically as a black box with a single set of terminals as in Figure 5A. By definition a set of terminals across which pressure may be varied and through which flow may pass is called a port. The system of Figure 5A possesses only one port, and accordingly is called a one-port system. The only system functions relevant to a one-port system be-come input admittance and its reciprocal, input impedance

$$\mathbf{Zrs} = (\mathbf{Pao} - \mathbf{Pbs})/\dot{\mathbf{V}}\text{ao} \tag{31}$$

or equivalently, $[\mathbf{Pao}/\dot{\mathbf{V}}\text{ao}]_{\text{Pbs}=0}$. This reduction to a single equivalent impedance can be accomplished for any passive linear one-port system, no matter how complex the actual circuit may be. The impedance measured at the airway opening, called respiratory system impedance, can be divided into its real (resis-tive) and imaginary (reactive) components

$$\mathbf{Zrs} = \text{Rrs} + j\text{Xrs} \tag{32}$$

In general, Rrs and Xrs can be frequency dependent,

but Rrs must be positive, therefore $\mathbf{Zrs}$ must fall in the right half of the complex plane (see Figs. 2C and 3B) with phase angle Φrs between $-90°$ and $+90°$.

Similarly if attention is restricted to the lung, then one deals with pulmonary impedance

$$\mathbf{Z_L} = \mathbf{P_L}/\dot{\mathbf{V}}\text{ao} \tag{33}$$

where $\mathbf{P_L}$ is transpulmonary pressure $\mathbf{Pao} - \mathbf{Ppl}$.

Although the single equivalent impedance of Figure 5A and Equation 31 may be applied to any linear one-port system regardless of complexity, the components of the impedance $\mathbf{Zrs}$ may take on special physical meaning when the system in question actually com-prises a serial distribution of elements. The system of Figure 3A is a specific example of a one-port system composed of elements in series. In this system the real part of $\mathbf{Zrs}$ is the same Rrs, and the imaginary part of $\mathbf{Zrs}$, the reactance, is the sum of inertive ($j\omega$Irs) and capacitive ($1/j\omega$Crs) contributions. An example of a system containing elements both in series and parallel (Fig. 4) also may be treated as a one-port system by restricting our attention to forcing and measurements at the airway opening during exposure of the body surface to atmosphere ($\mathbf{Pbs} = \mathbf{PB} = 0$). However, as shown in the next section, the correspondence of the real part of $\mathbf{Zrs}$ (i.e., Rrs) to the system elements then will be more complicated (see Eqs. 36–39).

TWO-PORT SYSTEMS. If the mouth is viewed as one port and the body surface as a second port, then during measurement of pressure (relative to atmosphere) and flow at each port the respiratory system may be viewed as a black box with two sets of terminals, or a gener-alized two-port system (Fig. 5B). The system of Figure 4 is one specific example falling within this general classification. In such a system (Eq. 30) the input impedances, transfer impedances, and transfer func-tions are relevant. Even if alveolar pressure and/or body surface motions are spatially nonuniform, one may regard the body surface as a single port by sum-ming displacements as in a body plethysmograph. Although we are using the entire respiratory system as an example, two-port analysis could be applied individually to airways, lung, lung tissue, and/or chest wall.

Any passive linear two-port system, no matter how complex, may be represented by an equivalent T cir-cuit as in Figure 5B. It is important to realize that if the actual circuit is not in the form of a T network, it can still be represented as an equivalent T network without loss of generality. This implies that of all the system functions that can be imagined for a general-ized two-port system, only three impedances are nec-essary and sufficient to generate all of them and to describe everything that can be known about the two-port system. All other system functions are redundant. The system impedances corresponding to the equiva-lent T network of Figure 5B are given algebraically in terms of the pressure differences and flows at the

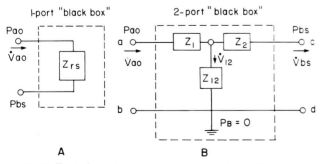

FIG. 5. Equivalent circuits for one-port systems (A) and two-port systems (B).

system ports

$$\mathbf{P}ao = (\mathbf{Z}_1 + \mathbf{Z}_{12})\dot{V}ao - \mathbf{Z}_{12}\dot{V}bs \qquad (34a)$$

$$\mathbf{P}bs = \mathbf{Z}_{12}\dot{V}ao - (\mathbf{Z}_2 + \mathbf{Z}_{12})\dot{V}bs \qquad (34b)$$

where the pressures are defined relative to atmospheric pressure. By continuity

$$\dot{V}ao - \dot{V}bs - \dot{V}_{12} = 0 \qquad (34c)$$

The sign convention for positive direction of flows is arbitrary, but once defined it must be maintained. The meaning of the impedance coefficients is given by example. Applying Figure 5B and Equation 34 to the respiratory system forced at the chest wall we find

$$[\mathbf{P}bs/-\dot{V}bs]_{\dot{V}ao=0} = \mathbf{Z}_2 + \mathbf{Z}_{12} \qquad (35)$$

which is the ratio of pressure at the chest ($\mathbf{P}bs$) to flow forced at the chest ($\dot{V}bs$) when mouth flow is zero, i.e., airway opening blocked or terminals a to b open-circuited. (The negative signs arise because $\dot{V}bs$ is taken to be positive during inspiratory motions.)

On the other hand, when forcing at the mouth with the body surface free, $\mathbf{P}bs$ is zero and gas is free to flow without impediment from the body surface to atmosphere (terminals c to d short-circuited). Equation 34 then yields

$$[\mathbf{P}ao/\dot{V}ao]_{\mathbf{P}bs=0} = \mathbf{Z}rs = \mathbf{Z}_1 + \mathbf{Z}_{12}\mathbf{Z}_2/(\mathbf{Z}_2 + \mathbf{Z}_{12}) \qquad (36)$$

which is respiratory system impedance, but here interpreted in terms of a model more sophisticated than represented by Figure 3A and Equation 24. Nonetheless Rrs and Xrs as given by Equation 32 are the real and imaginary parts in the expression above.

In a similar manner every imaginable system function can be generated from Equation 34 and knowledge of the equivalent T-circuit impedances $\mathbf{Z}_1$, $\mathbf{Z}_2$, and $\mathbf{Z}_{12}$.

Although the equivalent T network of Figure 5B may be applied to any linear two-port system regardless of complexity, the network impedances ($\mathbf{Z}_1$, $\mathbf{Z}_2$, and $\mathbf{Z}_{12}$ of Eq. 34a, b) may take on special physical meaning when the circuit is actually in the form of a T. One such case (Fig. 4) represents a reasonable respiratory system model if the parallel pathways of the tracheobronchial tree, lung tissue and chest properties, and alveolar pressure are homogeneous. Comparison of Figures 4 and 5B reveals that $\mathbf{Z}aw = \mathbf{Z}_1$, $\mathbf{Z}t = \mathbf{Z}_2$, $\mathbf{Z}g = \mathbf{Z}_{12}$, and $\dot{V}g = \dot{V}_{12}$. For the specific circuit of Figure 4, Equation 34a, b may be rewritten

$$\mathbf{P}ao = \left(j\omega\text{Iaw} + \text{Raw} + \frac{1}{j\omega\text{Cg}}\right)\dot{V}ao$$
$$- \left(\frac{1}{j\omega\text{Cg}}\right)\dot{V}bs \qquad (37)$$

$$\mathbf{P}bs = \left(\frac{1}{j\omega\text{Cg}}\right)\dot{V}ao$$
$$- \left(j\omega\text{It} + \text{Rt} + \frac{1}{j\omega\text{Ct}} + \frac{1}{j\omega\text{Cg}}\right)\dot{V}bs \qquad (38)$$

and from continuity

$$\dot{V}ao = \dot{V}g + \dot{V}bs \qquad (39)$$

$\mathbf{Z}_1$, $\mathbf{Z}_2$, and $\mathbf{Z}_{12}$ are obtained by comparison of Equation 34a, b with Equations 37 and 38. Every system function for that model is now readily generated by algebraic manipulation. However, the special idealization leading to Figure 4 and Equations 37–39 may not be applicable in processes leading to parallel inhomogeneities. Figure 5B and Equation 34a, b have no such restrictions.

RECIPROCITY RELATIONS. If only three out of the numerous system functions of a passive linear two-port system are necessary for a complete description, interrelations must exist between the rest. They are called reciprocity relations. In particular, applied to the generalized two-port representation of the total respiratory system (Fig. 5B)

$$[\mathbf{P}ao/\dot{V}bs]_{\mathbf{P}bs=0} = -[\mathbf{P}bs/\dot{V}ao]_{\mathbf{P}ao=0} \qquad (40a)$$

$$[\mathbf{P}bs/\dot{V}ao]_{\dot{V}bs=0} = -[\mathbf{P}ao/\dot{V}bs]_{\dot{V}ao=0} \qquad (40b)$$

$$[\dot{V}bs/\dot{V}ao]_{\mathbf{P}bs=0} = [\mathbf{P}ao/\mathbf{P}bs]_{\dot{V}ao=0} \qquad (40c)$$

$$[\mathbf{P}ao/\mathbf{P}bs]_{\dot{V}bs=0} = [\dot{V}bs/\dot{V}ao]_{\mathbf{P}ao=0} \qquad (40d)$$

Again pressures are defined relative to atmospheric pressure, which is zero.

These reciprocity relations between system functions can often provide simple solutions to difficult experimental problems or can provide a check on measurement validity. For example, apply Equation 40c to the respiratory system: the transfer function of flow at the body surface ($\dot{V}bs$) caused by a flow imposed at the mouth ($\dot{V}ao$) [when the body surface is free ($\mathbf{P}bs = 0$; terminals c to d short-circuited; see Fig. 5B)] is equal to the transfer function of pressure at the mouth ($\mathbf{P}ao$) caused by pressure oscillations imposed at the body surface ($\mathbf{P}bs$) when the airway is closed ($\dot{V}ao = 0$). If reciprocal experiments are executed correctly, they are obligated to lead to the same transfer function if the system is truly linear and passive. One contains no more or less information than the other and either could be chosen according to equipment availability and ease of use. Both could be chosen to validate the measurements and/or assess measurement errors (see *Pressure and Flow Transfer Functions*, p. 165). In particular because flows are generally more difficult to measure and calibrate than pressures, the pressure transfer function, $[\mathbf{P}ao/\mathbf{P}bs]_{\dot{V}ao=0}$, might be a preferable choice to the reciprocal flow transfer function.

A more extreme example is suggested by the left

sides of Equation 40b, d, which require $\dot{V}bs = 0$. To achieve the zero flow boundary condition at the body surface one could either conceive fiendish preparations or opt to execute more tractable reciprocal experiments suggested by the right sides.

Distributed-Parameter Models

The models discussed above deal with pressures and flows at specific system boundaries or nodes such as the airway opening, alveolar spaces, and body surface. In these models the morphological characteristics of airways are bypassed a priori by assignment of extensive dynamic variables. These variables include airway inertance and resistance, which lump together the entire spatial extent of the upper airway and tracheobronchial tree. Lumped-parameter modeling methods such as this become awkward in at least three circumstances when: *1)* spatial distribution of oscillatory pressures and flows within the upper and lower airways are to be investigated, *2)* specific physical properties of the airway tree (airway sizes, wall properties, and branching) are to be taken into account, and *3)* oscillatory frequencies become high enough that wavelike phenomena occur in the airways, similar to standing waves in an organ pipe. In these circumstances spatially distributed models become preferable to lumped-parameter models.

A spatially distributed model is one in which spatial dimensions, coordinates, and branching topology are dealt with explicitly. Pressures and flows are computed not only at convenient nodes such as P_A or P_{ao} but also at every position in every airway in between. Even parenchyma itself is no longer described by a single alveolar pressure but rather by pressure that could be different from point to point throughout.

For example, consider an airway segment with its associated pressures and flows. The equivalent circuit for an infinitesimal element of airway of length dx is given in Figure 6 (19, 60, 94, 108). The airway's series impedance per unit length associated with viscous resistance and gas inertia is

$$\mathbf{Z} = Raw + j\omega Iaw \qquad (41)$$

The shunt admittance per unit length (Y) associated with the parallel combination of gas compression, gas thermal conductance (Gt), and airway wall distensions is

$$\mathbf{Y} = j\omega Cg + Gt \qquad (42)$$
$$+ \frac{1}{j\omega Iaww + (j\omega)^{-1}Eaww + Raww}$$

where aww refers to airway wall properties and includes the mechanical support of surrounding tissues (58, 93).

For a parent airway and its two daughters, compatibility conditions require the pressures at the bound-

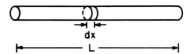

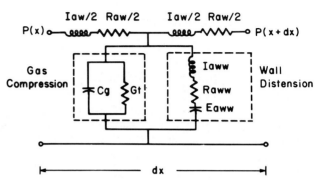

FIG. 6. An airway of length L may be divided into infinitesimal segments of length dx. The equivalent circuit for such a segment incorporates airway inertance (Iaw) and viscous resistance (Raw) as series elements. Shunt elements can be subdivided into the gas compressibility pathway, consisting of gas compressibility (Cg) and gas thermal conductance (Gt), and the wall distension pathway, consisting of airway wall elastance (Eaww), inertance (Iaww), and resistance (Raww).

ary between the airways to be equal. Pressure changes associated with convective acceleration ($\frac{1}{2}\rho u^2$) are negligible if oscillatory flow amplitudes are small. Continuity requires that the net flow into the bifurcation must be zero. The angle of the bifurcation plays no role in the case of small-amplitude flow oscillations to a first approximation (186).

RECURSION RELATIONS. The impedances, pressures, and flows of these small segments referred to above must be marched along airways between bifurcations and combined among airways at bifurcations. This procedure sometimes becomes computationally infeasible when dealing with a tree of millions of airways. In this case extremely efficient computational schemes may be employed to execute the repeated application of these equations for a relatively general class of asymmetrically branching models of the tracheobronchial tree (58, 60).

OTHER MOTIONS. The model of airway mechanics in Figure 6 describes the pressure waves and corresponding distensional motions in the airways. Other types of motion are possible but have not been investigated in the airways. These include the longitudinal (axial) mode consisting of axial compressional waves in the airway wall, the torsional mode consisting of torsional waves in the wall, and the flexural mode consisting of lateral motions of the wall as a whole as influenced by bending stiffness and axial tension. In the case of the cardiovascular system all of these motions have been addressed (116).

HISTORY

The first series of studies employing small-amplitude external oscillations at high frequencies was made by DuBois and co-workers in the early 1950s (39–41). They obtained frequency-response curves from 1 to 15–20 Hz in healthy humans by applying sinusoidal pressure variations both at the chest and at the mouth while measuring flow at the mouth. They also measured chest and abdomen surface displacements and observed that the chest wall did not behave homogeneously at high frequencies. Using simple modeling they derived values from their measurements for total respiratory resistance and the first estimates of respiratory inertance.

At the same time and following this pioneer work, a number of animal studies were done by DuBois and his associates, in particular Brody et al. (16–18) and Nisell (146), and a few years later by Hull and Long (87–89) and Long et al. (115).

Respiration physiologists were not the only people to be interested in lung impedance at high frequencies. As early as 1958 an acoustician, Van den Berg, obtained input impedance data from 3 to 2,000 Hz from dog and human cadavers (193). In order to interpret his data he also built a sophisticated electrical analogue of the airways and of the tissues (194).

Clinical applications of the method required the development of pressure generators that were easier to handle than those that physiologists previously used. This was achieved by Mead and associates, who described loudspeaker-based systems that permitted application of pressure variations at the chest (126) and mouth (43). The first clinical studies concerned obese subjects (49, 168–170), patients with chronic obstructive lung disease (22, 49, 69, 181), patients with various lung or cardiac disorders (49, 181), and children (204). At the same period Allen et al. (2) obtained frequency-response curves in normal subjects from 5 to 90 Hz, Coermann et al. (25) and Zechman et al. (208) studied the response of respiratory flow to sinusoidal vibrations applied to the entire body, and Hildebrandt (78, 79) started his series of studies on excised cat lungs.

The 1970s were marked by various technical and methodological improvements that permitted further applications. Up to that time it had been difficult to obtain amplitude ratios and phase angles from the original recordings. Goldman et al. (66) proposed a method that could more easily obtain the real component of the impedance. The same year Hyatt et al. (90) presented an analog device to directly record the real part of the impedance. Later, special-purpose signal analyzers and analog and digital computers made the data immediately available. They also permitted processing a greater amount of information and improved the quality of the measurements. On the other hand, computers made it possible to analyze the response to nonsinusoidal signals and pulses (61, 75, 97), random noise (132), and regularly recurring impulses (113) that could substantially reduce the time necessary to explore a given frequency range.

During that period, measurements of impedance at one or at a few frequencies progressively became a routine tool to estimate total respiratory resistance. The method requires very little cooperation and appeared particularly useful in children. Also more information was gained on the frequency response of the total respiratory system driven at the chest (6, 155) and at the airway opening (94, 132), of the lung (97, 143) and chest wall (143), and of the airways (44). In addition to experimental work, several theoretical studies led to better understanding of how frequency responses were influenced by various factors, including gas velocity profiles, airway geometry and branching, and airway wall properties (33, 58, 59).

Finally new applications of external forcing were found in the late 1970s. Studies of sound transmission across the lung (34) and the inference of airway geometry from sound reflection (62, 96) appear promising. Artificial ventilation at high frequencies (2–40 Hz), another application of external forcing, is not considered in this chapter.

EXPERIMENTAL METHODS

Equipment

GENERATORS. The central piece of equipment in frequency-response studies is the external source used to impose motion on the respiratory system or one of its parts. Flow or pressure sources are most commonly used in the form of reciprocating pumps and loudspeakers (Fig. 7), although forced oscillations of the

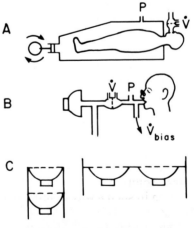

FIG. 7. Pressure and flow generators: reciprocating pump to apply pressure variations at the chest (A); loudspeaker to apply pressure variations at the mouth (B); loudspeakers arranged in series and in parallel to obtain larger pressures and volume changes (C).

human thoracoabdominal system have been obtained by submitting the whole body to longitudinal vibrations (25, 208). Reciprocating pistons usually behave like powerful high internal impedance sources (flow generators) and are able to impose preset volume or flow variations almost independent of the load. They behave like ideal flow sources and permit work from very low frequencies up to 20 Hz or more. Loudspeakers supplied with some input signal from a power amplifier have a comparatively low internal mechanical impedance so that the motion of the cone mostly depends on the mechanical load and behave almost like ideal pressure sources. Large powerful (100 W or more) loudspeakers are now available and relatively inexpensive. When large pressure variations or volume displacements are required, various arrangements of two or more speakers may be used (Fig. 7C). In contrast to pumps, loudspeakers permit imposition of signals of any shape and permit work at high frequencies but behave poorly at low frequencies (<1 Hz).

When pressure is to be applied around the chest, the loudspeaker or pump is connected to a box enclosing the body (Fig. 7A). For this purpose a Drinker respirator was used by DuBois and Ross (41), whereas Mead (126) modified a body plethysmograph. The subject may be enclosed either completely inside the box and breathe outside through a tube (6) or be enclosed up to the neck (41, 126). In the latter case various means may be used to make the system relatively leak free: wooden diaphragm and cloth scarf around the neck (126) or rubber bag filled with small beads and connected to a vacuum line (129). Care should be taken that the neck seal does not compress the upper airways. A difference between the two conditions is that when the subject is enclosed completely within the box the walls of extrathoracic airways, in particular the cheeks, are submitted to the same pressure swings as the respiratory system. These body chambers usually contain a few hundred liters of gas, the compliance of which lowers the effective internal impedance of the generator, particularly at high frequencies. Consequently the volume displacement of the chest is a very small fraction of that of the driver (~1% at 20 Hz for 200 liters of gas). On the other hand, this gas compliance, together with the leaks, permits the subject to breathe spontaneously without developing too-large low-frequency pressure swings that could influence the generator. At frequencies greater than 15–20 Hz it is difficult to maintain spatial homogeneity of the pressure field over the body surface (155). An empirical solution is to use several sources and distribute them in such a way to minimize spatial pressure differences. A different method to impose motion to the chest was proposed by Gropper et al. (70), who devised a hydraulically driven mechanical vest permitting application of sinusoidal forcing up to 40 Hz. The advantage of the device is that, unlike the systems just described, it does not preclude measuring flow at the chest with a body plethysmograph.

When the pressure is to be applied at the mouth, the pump or loudspeaker may be connected simply to the subject's mouthpiece by tubing, as originally done by DuBois et al. (40). However, to permit spontaneous breathing the generator is more commonly open to the atmosphere through another tube that behaves like an inertance. That is, it offers little impedance for low-frequency events in order to shunt the subject's breathing to atmosphere, but offers a larger impedance for higher frequencies in order to contain the forced oscillations. To avoid rebreathing of expired air, a flow of fresh air is usually drawn through the system via a side tap. Such a setup, as first used by Ferris et al. (43) and Schwaber et al. (166) and described in detail by Grimby et al. (69), is shown schematically in Figure 7B. Interruption of airway flow represents a different type of generator (128, 150, 165, 199); rather than using an external pressure or flow source, small pressure disturbances are generated at the mouth by obstructing the airway for short periods during spontaneous breathing. Finally, for making impedance measurements at higher frequencies (up to 10,000 Hz), Jackson et al. (97) and Fredberg et al. (61) used a high-voltage electrical discharge across two electrodes to generate short pressure pulses.

Albright and Bondurant (1) applied pressure swings as large as 20–40 cmH$_2$O at the chests of their subjects, whereas most authors tried to minimize the influence of nonlinearities by using comparatively small flow inputs. In most studies on humans the pressure applied to the respiratory system did not exceed ± 1 cmH$_2$O, corresponding to flow values below ± 0.5 liter·s^{-1}. For larger pressure or flow amplitudes, nonlinear behavior has been evidenced (6, 44).

PRESSURE AND FLOW MEASUREMENTS. Frequency responses of the respiratory system are usually derived from pressure and/or flow measurements except for a few studies in which linear displacements or deformations of the chest wall and/or of the abdomen were also measured (25, 40, 208). The dynamic characteristics of the equipment are important in most mechanical studies and are especially critical when investigating frequency responses. The responses of all measuring devices should be either perfectly matched or compensated. It is not particularly important that equipment responses be flat, provided the signals do not become too small to be accurately recorded and calibrated. When equipment frequency response is not flat, in some instances it is possible to match the responses of two channels using mechanical, electrical, or digital filtering.

When dealing with two pressures measured either with conventional pressure transducers or microphones, it is easiest to test the equipment by applying the same sinusoidal input to the two channels and measuring at various frequencies their amplitude ratio and phase difference. When identical pressure transducers (and amplifiers) with similar connecting tubes and pressure taps or identical microphones are used, the responses are usually evenly matched. If some discrepancy is observed it may often be reduced by slightly changing the length or diameter of one of the tubes. When a differential pressure transducer is used, it is also important to verify that the sensitivity and frequency response are the same for the two sides of the transducer. This may be assessed by simultaneously applying the same sinusoidal pressure variations to both sides and relating the observed signal to that obtained when this pressure is applied to only one side. The ratio of the former pressure swing to the latter pressure swing is the common-mode rejection ratio. The requirements in terms of common-mode rejection ratio depend on the magnitude of the pressure difference to be measured compared with that of the pressure swings in the two places. If the pressure difference to be measured is only 10% of the local pressure swing and if the required accuracy of the measurement is 1%, the common-mode rejection ratio should be lower than 0.1% over all the frequency range.

When two flows are measured, it is easiest to test the equipment by placing the two flowmeters in series in such a way that they are submitted to the same flow input. Usually flow determinations necessitate the measurement of a pressure difference across a resistive element, in which case the common-mode rejection ratio of the transducer may be critically important. Such is the case when the flowmeter is placed between the pressure source and the subject and if the latter presents a large impedance compared with that of the flowmeter itself. The frequency response of a flow channel depends not only to a large extent on the pressure transducer and its connections (64, 101) but also on the type of resistive element. Fleisch-type pneumotachographs (50) of all sizes exemplify behavior of first-order systems (equivalent to a series resistance-inertance circuit) having a time constant of a little more than 2 ms (45, 122, 154, 206). Screen-type flowmeters (114, 175) behave similarly but may have smaller time constants provided the pressure taps are very close to the screen (122, 154). Finally, when a substantial amount of compressible gas is interposed between the subject and the flowmeter (body plethysmograph, face mask), it may dominate the response.

The most difficult and most frequent case is when a pressure or pressure difference is to be related to a flow. An indirect method is to measure the frequency response of some simple known physical system, for instance, a "pure" resistance or compliance, and to compare those data with the expected response (35). When the frequency response of the flowmeter itself is known, such as for Fleisch pneumotachographs, a reasonable approach is to match the two pressure transducers and then correct the data for the flowmeter response. A low-pass filter has been described that compensates for the phase lead introduced by Fleisch pneumotachographs (206). Finally, some authors have preferred to replace direct flow measurement by that of the pressure in or the pressure drop across some reference mechanical element submitted to the same flow as the subject (2, 55, 94, 95, 101, 123); here again the value of the method entirely depends on how well the reference system is known. A slightly different approach was used by Franetzki et al. (53), who measured only mouth pressure and imposed a known flow input to the subject and to a reference impedance placed in parallel with him.

Inputs and Data Processing

SINE WAVES. The main practical advantage of sine waves is that the frequency response is directly obtained by reading the amplitude ratio of the variables and their relative phase angle. Although a signal analyzer or a computer may be very helpful and save a great deal of time, it is a convenience rather than a necessity. In almost all pre-1970 studies and in several subsequent ones, amplitude ratios and phase angles were derived by hand either from recordings obtained with direct-writing oscillographs or from Lissajous figures obtained by playing back on a storage oscilloscope the variables previously recorded on magnetic tape (see Fig. 2).

For a number of physiological or clinical applications, it is of value to measure at one or at a few frequencies the in-phase component, real[Z_{rs}], of respiratory impedance. Several methods have been proposed to simplify its determination. The simplest one consists of making the measurement at a frequency where the reactance is zero (39, 126). At that particular frequency (resonant frequency), pressure and flow are in phase and real[Z_{rs}] is equal to their amplitude ratio. Because it is not always possible to find a resonant frequency (181) or to measure at several frequencies, Grimby et al. (69) proposed a method to simulate resonance. They subtracted from the pressure signal a signal 90° out of phase with flow (i.e., proportional to volume or volume acceleration), adjusting the amplitude and sign of this signal in such a way as to cancel any phase difference between the resulting corrected pressure and flow as judged on an oscilloscope. This is equivalent to subtracting from the pressure that part of it related to the reactance. The method assumes linearity but does not imply that the respiratory system is a second-order system, governed by Equation 24. Landau and Phelan (110) observed some difference between the real[Z_{rs}] values obtained by that method and from direct reading of the records that may reflect the influence of nonlinearities. An alternative to using actual or simulated resonance is to electronically detect that part of the pressure signal corresponding to the in-phase component of the impedance. Two methods have been proposed that make use of the fact that it is equal to the pressure difference between the extremes of the oscillatory flow (see Fig. 2D). Goldman et al. (66) presented an electronic circuit that superimposed on the pressure signal short pulses synchronous to the maxima and minima of the flow signal. Hyatt et al. (90) in 1970 and later Sharp et al. (167) proposed a more sophisticated system by which that pressure difference was automatically measured cycle by cycle and divided by the flow amplitude, thus providing direct writeout of real[Zrs]. A different approach was used by Ross et al. (163), who described a system where real[Zrs] was derived from its relationship to the average power (pressure-flow product) and also computed the phase angle.

Special-purpose circuits, signal analyzers, lock-in amplifiers, and computers offer a more rapid but more expensive method for processing impedance data. Allen et al. (2) used the resolved components indicator to electronically determine the amplitude and phase of the variables with respect to a reference sine wave. Pimmel et al. (158) described an impedance analyzer that obtains the same information at 20 preselected frequencies in the range of 1–16 Hz and also provides the sinusoidal signal to be applied to a loudspeaker-type generator. Finally, use of digital computers is increasing because they also permit extensive manipulation of the data (e.g., correction for the response of the transducers, averaging, and grouping of the data according to the value of some variable).

Although DuBois and co-workers (40) made their measurements in subjects who voluntarily relaxed their respiratory muscles at the end of a normal expiration, most of the subsequent human studies were performed in subjects who breathed spontaneously. To be able to recognize and analyze easily the superimposed forced oscillations, their frequency should be at least one order of magnitude higher than the breathing frequency. Even so, spontaneous breathing is a cause of variability because mechanical properties may change during the respiratory cycle. Another source of error arises if breathing itself generates pressure of flow signals with substantial energy in the same frequency range as the forced oscillations (90, 112, 183). Because there is no direct way to eliminate these signals, several techniques have been used to minimize their influence based on the fact that they are coherent with the respiratory cycle but incoherent with the external forcing. Stănescu et al. (183) used filters with a narrow bandwidth (0.4 Hz) that removed the low frequencies and provided weighted ensemble averages of the signals. Aronsson et al. (4) divided the forced-oscillation cycle into a large number of time intervals and obtained for each of them average values of the variables from a large number of cycles.

NONSINUSOIDAL INPUTS. A disadvantage of sine waves is that a number of measurements at different frequencies are required to characterize the response. Although the frequency range may be swept automatically, it takes more time than would be necessary if all the frequencies were explored simultaneously. This is made possible by using as an input to the system a signal containing all the frequencies of interest. This approach was first applied to physiological studies by Taylor (189), who used random-noise excitation of the heart to investigate the cardiovascular system. It was introduced in respiratory mechanics by Michaelson et al. (132), who used a random-noise pressure wave, and by Lándsér et al. (113), who applied regularly recurring impulses containing all harmonics of 2 Hz up to 30 Hz.

To process such input and output signals, which represent the superposition of a number of sine waves, it is necessary to perform spectral analysis, i.e., decomposition of these signals into their individual frequency components. This is achieved using a specific mathematical tool called the Fourier transform. The frequency response is obtained by combining the spectra of the input and the output variables. In practice, a fast Fourier transform (FFT) is employed using Fourier analyzers or general-purpose digital computers. An additional advantage of this method is that at each frequency the correlation coefficient of the input and the output (called the coherence) may be computed. The coherence is that fraction of the output power that is linearly related to the input. Hence decreased coherence (<1) indicates the degree to which the results are influenced by system nonlinearities and extraneous noise. Confidence limits for the data may be derived from the coherence. A number of references concerning the mathematical, numerical, and statistical aspects of the method may be found in the paper by Michaelson et al. (132). Lándsér et al. (113) observed a good agreement between impedance values obtained at 6 Hz using a sinusoidal and a nonsinusoidal input (impulses) in healthy humans and in patients with obstructive lung disease. An alternative for obtaining impedance data from forced random noise measurements is to begin the analysis in the time domain using adaptive digital filters (31). Finally, using a nonsinusoidal input does not eliminate the errors occurring when the subject breathes spontaneously (36, 113). To minimize this factor Michaelson et al. (132) averaged a large number of spectra, each obtained over a short period, whereas Daróczy and Hantos (30) introduced into the analysis the spectrum of the voltage applied to the loudspeaker.

Upper Airway Variability and Shunt

In addition to the problems related to the equipment and to data analysis, a difficulty in assessing frequency responses in humans is that the impedance of the upper airways may vary considerably with time. Glottis closure, when complete and sudden, is easily recognized by the drastic change in the pressure-flow relationship. Fisher et al. (49) recommended that the subject be encouraged to relax the upper airways. Because the glottis is more open after panting maneuvers (98, 185), Goldstein and Mead (67) made the measurements immediately after such maneuvers and showed that it decreased variability.

Another major problem is the so-called shunt impedance constituted by the extrathoracic airway walls, in particular the cheeks, and the compliance of the gas in the oral cavity. The problem was recognized by DuBois et al. (40) who reported "visible motion in the soft tissues between the chin and neck" at 15–20 Hz. Mechanical properties of extrathoracic airway walls have been investigated by various methods, including forced oscillations (132). This pathway behaves approximately like a series resistance-inertance-compliance system (132). When the cheeks are not supported, the compliance ranges from 1 to 3 × 10^{-3} liters·cmH_2O^{-1} (24, 132, 172), the resistance from 3 to 15 cmH_2O·$liter^{-1}$·s (24; R. Peslin, unpublished observations), and the inertance from 2 to 4 × 10^{-2} cmH_2O·$liter^{-1}$·s^2 (R. Peslin, unpublished observations); the resulting impedance increases from 20–40 cmH_2O·$liter^{-1}$·s at 5 Hz to 5–15 cmH_2O·$liter^{-1}$·s at 20–40 Hz and increases thereafter.

The influence of this shunt pathway depends largely on what is measured and how it is measured. When the pressure is applied at the mouth and flow is measured at the mouth, upper airway walls are submitted approximately to the same pressure difference as the total respiratory system and therefore are in parallel with it. Because flow is distributed between parallel pathways in proportion to their admittance (the reciprocal of impedance) and because the admittance of the cheeks may be at some frequency of the same order of magnitude as that of the respiratory system, the effect may be extremely important (131, 173). The situation is quite different when the pressure is applied at the chest and flow measured at the mouth with the face exposed to ambient pressure. In this case the cheeks are in parallel with a low-impedance pathway (flowmeter) and interfere little with the measurements. The usual way to minimize the influence of extrathoracic airway walls is to add support by compressing them with the palms (40), which roughly doubles their impedance (132). The alternative is to assess their frequency response, which may be done by observing the pressure-flow relationship at the mouth during Valsalva maneuvers and using it to correct the data (132).

FREQUENCY RESPONSES BELOW 100 HZ

Total Respiratory System

Transrespiratory pressure may be varied by applying pressure changes either at the chest or at the airway opening. Were the respiratory system made of elements arranged in series and subjected to the same flow, there would be no difference between the two conditions as in Figure 3A. Such is not the case for a slightly more elaborate model originally proposed by DuBois et al. (40). In this specific two-port or T-network model (see Fig. 4): 1) the lung and chest wall tissues are characterized by their impedance Zt and are submitted to the difference between alveolar (P_A) and perithoracic pressures (Pbs); 2) the alveolar gas (impedance Zg), which is compressible, is submitted to the difference between alveolar and atmospheric reference pressure; and 3) the gas in the airways (or airway compartment, impedance Zaw) is submitted to the difference between airway opening and alveolar pressure. The important feature of this model is that it incorporates a shunt pathway corresponding to alveolar gas compressibility. As a consequence, flow at the mouth will differ from chest flow by an amount equal to the rate of alveolar gas compression (Eq. 39). Moreover the functional arrangement of the compartments depends on where the pressure is applied. When it is varied at the airway opening (Fig. 8A), with perithoracic pressure equal to barometric pressure, the tissue and gas compartments are submitted to the same pressure difference ($P_A - P_B$) and therefore arranged in parallel; both are in series with the airways. Similarly, when the pressure is varied at the chest (Figure 8B) with mouth open ($Pao = P_B$), the gas compartment is in parallel with the airways and both are in series with the tissues. Finally, when pressure swings are applied to the entire body (Fig. 8C), i.e., both at the mouth and at the chest ($Pao = Pbs$), tissues and airways are in parallel and both are in series with the gas compartment.

Why study the numerous relationships between these various pressure differences and flows? The ultimate objective is to deduce some specific mechanical property of the respiratory system from oscillatory data. However, in most cases the specific pressure difference and flow relevant to that property is not directly available in the laboratory. This unavailability may occur either because it would be too invasive to place catheters or flowmeters inside the body at the critical positions or because the relevant pressures or flows are inherently unobservable. As an example of the latter, one cannot measure directly the resistive pressure drop across lung tissue because there is no physical separation between the resistive, elastic, and inertial constituents of the tissue. Rather, one can measure the total pressure drop (resistive plus elastic and inertial) and then infer the resistive component.

Thus the strategy is necessarily more subtle. One considers the variety of measurable variables, preferably in a noninvasive fashion, and then chooses from them those measures that are most sensitive to the property of interest and with the fewest confounding, obscuring, or unknown factors. Although the measures

A – Pressure varied at the mouth : Pbs = P_B

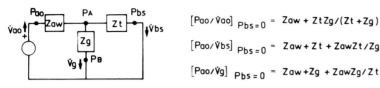

$$[Pao/\dot{V}ao]_{Pbs=0} = Zaw + ZtZg/(Zt+Zg)$$

$$[Pao/\dot{V}bs]_{Pbs=0} = Zaw + Zt + ZawZt/Zg$$

$$[Pao/\dot{V}g]_{Pbs=0} = Zaw + Zg + ZawZg/Zt$$

B – Pressure varied at the chest : Pao = P_B

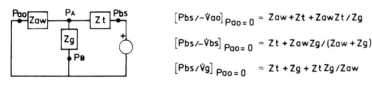

$$[Pbs/-\dot{V}ao]_{Pao=0} = Zaw + Zt + ZawZt/Zg$$

$$[Pbs/-\dot{V}bs]_{Pao=0} = Zt + ZawZg/(Zaw+Zg)$$

$$[Pbs/\dot{V}g]_{Pao=0} = Zt + Zg + ZtZg/Zaw$$

C – Pressure varied at the mouth and at the chest : Pbs = Pao

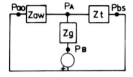

$$[Pao/\dot{V}ao]_{Pao=Pbs} = Zaw + Zg + ZawZg/Zt$$

$$[Pao/\dot{V}bs]_{Pao=Pbs} = Zt + Zg + ZtZg/Zaw$$

$$[Pao/\dot{V}g]_{Pao=Pbs} = Zg + ZtZaw/(Zt+Zaw)$$

FIG. 8. Model of T network including the airways (complex impedance Zaw), tissues (lung plus chest wall, complex impedance Zt), and compressible alveolar gas (complex impedance Zg). Functional arrangement of the compartments depends on where the pressure variations are applied. Equations on right express relationships between measured impedance and that of the compartments when the output variable is airway opening (A), body surface (B), and gas compression flow (C). [Adapted from Peslin et al. (155).]

described in Figure 8 include all the elements, other measures tend to be more specific. As shown in *Pressure and Flow Transfer Functions*, p. 165, the quantity $[\dot{V}bs/\dot{V}ao]_{Pao=0}$ depends on Zaw and Zg but is independent of lung and chest tissue (Zt) and hence would be a preferred measure for studies of airways. Conversely $[\dot{V}ao/\dot{V}bs]_{Pbs=0}$ depends on tissues and gas (Zt, Zg) but is independent of airways properties and accordingly would be a preferred measure for studies of lung and chest tissues.

As a final factor, often we trade off measurement specificity for measurement ease. For example, input impedance measured at the airway opening $[\mathbf{P}ao/\dot{V}ao]_{Pbs=0}$ depends on all the factors (airways, gas, and tissues) but is relatively easy to measure and this has garnered most of the attention in this field. On the other hand, such nonspecific measures can be preferable to more specific ones if one is clever enough to infer from the data the values of all the parameters of the system in one fell swoop. The drawbacks are that this usually requires data over ranges of frequency wide enough that system response is not dominated by only one or a few parameters; it requires sophisticated computational procedures to estimate parameters, and these estimates tend to become model or method sensitive (42, 151, 155, 190).

Input Impedance Forcing at the Airway Opening

In most studies devoted to the relationship between transrespiratory pressure and airway flow, pressure is varied at the mouth, $[\mathbf{P}ao/\dot{V}ao]_{Pbs=0}$. The experimental setup is typically similar to that shown in Figure 7B and the external forcing is superimposed on quiet breathing. Representative data in healthy humans, taken from the study by Michaelson et al. (132), are shown in Figure 9A (data corrected for the parallel shunt impedance of the mouth). As noted by most authors, the total respiratory system in healthy individuals behaves roughly like a second-order linear system with constant coefficients (see Fig. 3A): the magnitude of the impedance first decreases then increases with frequency, and the phase angle is always between $-90°$ and $+90°$; it is negative at low frequencies, increases with increasing frequency, and tends asymptotically toward $+90°$. On the other hand, the data depart in several respects from those to be expected for a second-order system: the minimum impedance does not coincide precisely with the zero of the phase angle but is observed at a slightly higher frequency (132), and the real part of the impedance, $real[\mathbf{Z}rs] = |\mathbf{Z}rs|\cos\Phi rs$, which would be constant according to the model of Figure 3, has been found to decrease (76, 109, 132, 152) or to increase (2, 84, 113, 143) with increasing frequency in healthy subjects.

Frequency dependence of resistance of either sign is thought to reflect frequency-dependent alteration in the distribution of gas flow within the system, i.e., both spatial and temporal inhomogeneity. Because the model depicted in Figure 3A has but a single pathway, the distribution of flow is frequency invariant and all flows must distend lung tissues uniformly. In the real respiratory system and in more sophisticated models,

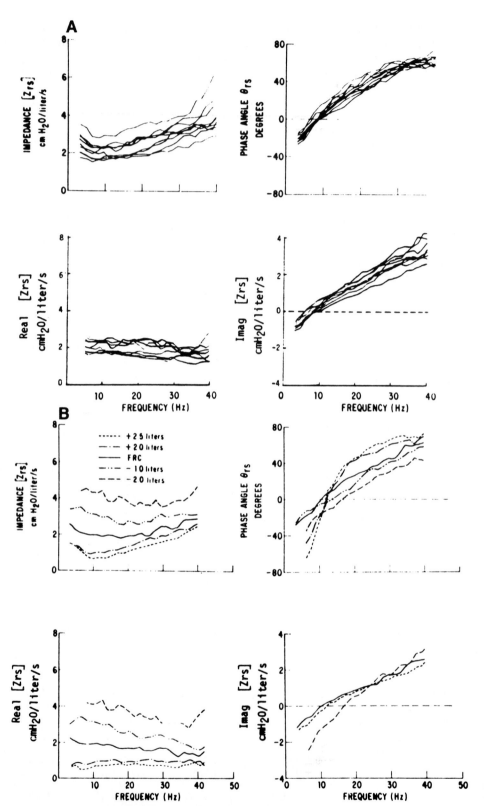

FIG. 9. *A*: modulus ($|\mathbf{Z}\mathrm{rs}|$), phase angle (θrs), and real (real [$\mathbf{Z}$rs] or equivalent resistance) and imaginary (imag[$\mathbf{Z}$rs] or equivalent reactance) parts of the relationship between transrespiratory pressure and flow when pressure is varied at the mouth, $[\mathbf{P}\mathrm{ao}/\dot{\mathrm{V}}\mathrm{ao}]_{\mathrm{Pbs=0}}$. Data from 9 healthy humans. [*Upper part* from Michaelson et al. (132); *lower part* from E. D. Michaelson, unpublished observations.] *B*: modulus ($|\mathbf{Z}\mathrm{rs}|$), phase angle (θrs), and real (real [$\mathbf{Z}$rs]) and imaginary (imag[$\mathbf{Z}$rs]) parts of the total respiratory input impedance observed at 5 lung volumes in a healthy human. [Adapted from Michaelson et al. (132).]

flow entering the airway opening may be apportioned among alveolar gas compression, upper airway distension, central airway distention, and lung tissue distension. Furthermore lung distension may be nonuniform as a result of nonuniformity of lung tissue impedance coupled with parallel nonuniformity of airway impedance serving the lung tissues. Gas distributes itself dynamically according to the relative values of impedance presented by the various pathways that are mechanically in parallel (i.e., exposed to the same pressure difference), and insofar as all of these impedances may be frequency dependent [caused by inertial (ωI) and compliant ($1/\omega C$) behaviors], the distribution of flows among the pathways also may be frequency dependent.

To explain the role of gas compressibility, DuBois et al. (40) proposed the T-network model of Figure 4. Although gas compressibility is conceptually very important, its influence on $\mathbf{Z}$rs, when pressure is varied at the mouth, is negligible at low frequencies (<20 Hz) because alveolar gas is in parallel with the tissues (see Fig. 8) that have a substantially larger compliance and a small inertance.

This model was modified by Shephard (173) to account for distensions of the upper airway (shunt impedance of the upper airway). Unless it is taken into account, this shunt pathway may have a substantial influence on $\mathbf{Z}$rs and may induce frequency-dependent variations of real[$\mathbf{Z}$rs] in either direction (131, 132). Therefore it is a factor to consider for explaining the discrepancies among published data.

Another model used by Michaelson et al. (132) neglects gas compressibility but incorporates extra-thoracic airway walls and two resistance-inertance-compliance compartments arranged in parallel beyond the shared airway inertance and impedance (Fig. 10). One of the compartments (R_1, I_1, C_1) represents more peripheral airways and lung parenchyma, but the other (R_2, I_2, C_2) may be assigned different anatomical counterparts and interpretations: 1) a second lung compartment, as originally proposed by Otis et al. (149) to explain frequency-dependent compliance as a result of nonuniform peripheral resistance-compliance time constants, 2) a collaterally ventilated compartment (82), or 3) intrathoracic airway walls (127). Considering the values of the coefficients necessary to simulate his data in normal subjects, Michaelson et al. (132) concluded that the data were best explained by the third possibility, a conclusion supported by Müller and Vogel (138). There exist several variants of that model that assume purely compliant intrathoracic airways ($R_2 = I_2 = 0$) and negligible peripheral airway inertance ($I_1 = 0$). One that neglected shunt impedance of the upper airway but incorporated gas compliance was found to fit experimental data in both normal subjects and patients with airway obstruction (164). Another forms the basis for the method proposed by Pimmel et al. (159) to partition central and peripheral airway resistance [a method subsequently improved on by Slutsky and Drazen (177) (cf. CLINICAL APPLICATIONS, p. 170)]. Finally, in addition to these factors, departure from second-order behavior may reflect implicit frequency dependence of airways or tissue properties themselves. The problem is further discussed in *Airway Impedance*, p. 167.

Although all of the findings are not explained, the second-order model (see Fig. 3A) has been used as a convenient tool to describe the data in terms of total respiratory resistance, inertance, and compliance. Values found in healthy adults are shown in Table 2 together with the resonant frequencies. These resistances are larger than those measured by body ple-

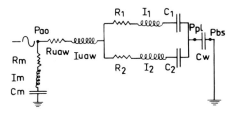

FIG. 10. Model proposed by Michaelson et al. (132) to interpret input impedance measurements. The lung, distal to central airways [upper airway resistance (Ruaw) and inertance (Iuaw)], is represented by 2 resistance-inertance-compliance pathways arranged in parallel; also featured are the properties of extrathoracic airway walls [mouth resistance (Rm), inertance (Im), and compliance (Cm)] and chest wall compliance (Cw). [From Michaelson et al. (132), by copyright permission of The American Society for Clinical Investigation.]

TABLE 2. *Coefficients Derived From Input Impedance Measurements in Healthy Adults*

Number of Subjects	Sex	Rrs, cmH₂O·liter⁻¹·s	f_o, Hz	Crs, liter·cmH₂O⁻¹	Irs, cmH₂O·liter⁻¹·s²	Comment	Ref.
10	Male	2.08 ± 0.41	8.04 ± 0.96	0.029 ± 0.017	0.0146 ± 0.0107		132
12	Male	2.09 ± 0.44	9.30 ± 2.35	0.053 ± 0.031	0.0074 ± 0.0024		76
15	Male	2.47 ± 0.19	7.70 ± 2.20	0.054 ± 0.017	0.0100 ± 0.0010	40% VC	143*
15	Male	1.70 ± 0.14	8.10 ± 1.90	0.043 ± 0.009	0.0120 ± 0.0010	70% VC	143*
15	Male	3.68 ± 0.35	13.30 ± 9.90	0.034 ± 0.008	0.0050 ± 0.001	25% VC	143*
28	Male	2.36 ± 0.83	9.61 ± 1.75	0.030 ± 0.008	0.0101 ± 0.0027		152
19	Female	3.24 ± 0.79	10.50 ± 1.88	0.021 ± 0.005	0.0119 ± 0.0037		152

Coefficients derived from total respiratory input impedance (pressure input at the mouth) using second-order linear model. Rrs, total respiratory resistance; Crs, total respiratory compliance; Irs, total respiratory inertance; f_o, resonant frequency. Definition of Rrs differs among studies: Zrs observed at f_o (132); Rrs observed at 4 Hz (143) and 5 Hz (152); value obtained by analyzing the data from 5 to 30 Hz using a parameter-estimation technique (76).   * Some data from Nagels et al., unpublished observations.

thysmography because the former include tissue viscous resistances. Good correlations with other resistance measurements have been found in several studies (10, 69, 113, 143, 157, 181).

Remarkably inertance values measured forcing at the mouth are generally lower than those found by other methods for the total respiratory system (12) and even for the inertance of the airways alone (104, 196). Similarly total respiratory compliance is low, compared with the values obtained with other techniques (77, 135, 144, 168, 195). These observations could reflect an inhomogeneous behavior of the chest wall (40). If the rib cage is a low-inertance pathway in parallel with the abdomen, a high-inertance pathway (above a few hertz) that is the ratio of their impedances may be such that the abdomen contributes very little to the motion (40). Thus the measured compliance would correspond to that of the lung in series with the rib cage alone.

Several other factors influence Zrs. Larger values are found when the subject breathes through the nose, the pressure being applied with a face mask, than when breathing through the mouth (2, 124). As might be expected, Zrs is also a function of lung volume, which changes gas compliance, airway dimensions and compliance, and tissue elasticity. Many studies have shown that the real part of Zrs was substantially lower above functional residual capacity (FRC) and larger below FRC [Fig. 9B; (49, 105, 132, 143, 156)]. The resonant frequency was increased at low lung volume because of decreased compliance (143). In addition, breathing close to residual volume tended to promote (143) or exaggerate (132) the decrease of real[Zrs] with increasing frequency. Variations during the respiratory cycle have also been made for the transfer impedance $[Pbs/\dot{V}ao]_{Pao=0}$, i.e., when pressure is varied at the chest (6, 68, 133, 153, 181). Respiratory system resistance usually increases with increasing spontaneous flow during inspiration and expiration and is minimum at end inspiration (153). Also Michaelson et al. (132) obtained larger impedance values and lower resonant frequencies when sampling the signals at FRC than when sampling them continuously during quiet breathing or during early inspiration. These seemingly flow-related and/or volume-related variations may in part be due to changes in glottal aperture. Goldstein and Mead (67) have shown that glottis artifacts may be minimized by measuring immediately after panting. Finally, larger impedance values were obtained when spontaneous ventilation increased (2, 124).

Frequency variations of Zrs were also studied in several animal species and interpreted using the second-order model (72, 102, 103, 158, 160, 190). Tsai et al. (190) used a parameter-estimation technique to analyze impedance data obtained in anesthetized intubated dogs. The real part of the impedance in dogs decreased with increasing frequency, as observed in several human studies. Jackson et al. (103) measured the real part of the impedance in anesthetized intubated monkeys and observed a decrease as frequency went from 2 to 10 Hz, followed by an increase with frequency above 10 Hz. Partitioning lung and chest wall impedances in two animals, they showed that the decrease was entirely caused by the chest wall and the increase to the lung and airways.

Transfer Impedance Forcing at the Chest

There are fewer studies concerning the relationship between transrespiratory pressure and resulting airway flow when pressure is varied at the chest, $[Pbs/-\dot{V}ao]_{Pao=0}$ (Fig. 11). Recalling that $-\dot{V}ao$ is the flow out of the mouth: 1) the real part of $[Pbs/-\dot{V}ao]_{Pao=0}$ decreases progressively with increasing frequency so that it becomes negative between 30 and 50 Hz, which is possible for a transfer impedance but impossible for an input impedance; 2) the imaginary part reaches a maximum at 60–70 Hz and then decreases abruptly to take negative values; and 3) as a consequence the phase angle does not plateau at or below 90°, as seen for input impedances, but reaches or even exceeds 180° at 60–70 Hz (151). The resonant frequency seems to be lower when oscillating at the chest (4–6 Hz) than when oscillating at the mouth (7–10 Hz) (6, 38, 151, 168). Unfortunately there is little information available concerning the input and transfer impedances in the same subjects (5, 38).

Such frequency-response curves have been interpreted successfully up to 50 Hz using the T-network model shown in Figure 4 (155). The value of airway resistance inferred from these data (Table 3) is similar to that obtained by body plethysmography (3, 134). Gas inertance in the airways is larger than total inertance derived from $[Pao/\dot{V}ao]_{Pbs=0}$ using a second-order model (Table 2) and is also a little larger than the values obtained by body plethysmography (104, 196). Tissue compliance appears very low, as was the case for the values derived from $[Pao/\dot{V}ao]_{Pbs=0}$, presumably for the same reason. Tissue inertance represents but a small fraction of total inertance, which is in agreement with the observations of Sharp et al. (168), who partitioned the inertance by measuring resonant frequency while the subject breathed gases of different densities. Tissue resistance is similar to the values found using other techniques, as reviewed by Varène et al. (197). At up to 30 Hz, tissue inertance could be neglected and the data analyzed using a simpler third-order model (155).

Other observations of $[Pbs/-\dot{V}ao]_{Pao=0}$ have been made in a variety of species and the data interpreted using a second-order model (27, 28, 87, 89, 115, 146).

Transfer Impedance Forcing at the Mouth

Except for a few observations by Brody et al. (18) in cats, the relationship between transrespiratory

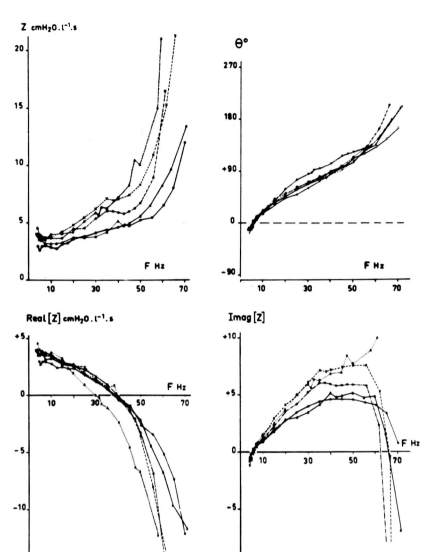

FIG. 11. Transfer impedance forcing at the chest, $[\mathbf{P}bs/(-\dot{\mathbf{V}}ao)]_{\mathbf{Pao=0}}$. Modulus ($|\mathbf{Z}|$), phase angle ($\theta$), and real (real[$\mathbf{Z}$]) and imaginary (imag[$\mathbf{Z}$]) parts of the relationship between transrespiratory pressure and flow when pressure is varied around the chest. Data from 5 healthy humans. Note that $-\dot{\mathbf{V}}ao$ is the flow out of the mouth according to sign convention of Figs. 4 and 5. [*Upper part* adapted from Peslin et al. (151).]

TABLE 3. *Coefficients Derived From Transfer Impedance Measurements*

	Ct, liter· cmH$_2$O^{-1}	Rt, cmH$_2$O· liter^{-1}·s	It, cmH$_2$O· liter^{-1}·s^2	Raw, cmH$_2$O· liter^{-1}·s	Iaw, cmH$_2$O· liter^{-1}·s^2
Mean	0.0208	1.099	0.0021	1.353	0.0255
±SD	0.0059	0.346	0.0007	0.625	0.0067

Values derived from total respiratory transfer impedance (pressure input at the chest) in 15 normal adults using the model in Fig. 4 corrected for pneumotachograph resistance and inertance. Ct, tissue (lung plus chest wall) compliance; Rt, tissue resistance; It, tissue inertance; Raw, airway resistance; Iaw, airway inertance. [From Peslin et al. (155).]

pressure and chest flow in response to mouth pressure variations, $[\mathbf{P}ao/\dot{\mathbf{V}}bs]_{\mathbf{Pbs=0}}$, has not been investigated. Such data would be interesting because they would permit verification of the prediction on the basis of the generalized T-network model that $[\mathbf{P}ao/$

$\dot{\mathbf{V}}bs]_{\mathbf{Pbs=0}}$ is equal to $-[\mathbf{P}bs/\dot{\mathbf{V}}ao]_{\mathbf{Pao=0}}$ (Eq. 40). The only information available in humans is from studies in which rib cage and abdominal surface displacements have been measured. With a constant-amplitude volume excursion at the mouth, DuBois et al. (40) observed that rib cage displacement was maximum at 10–12 Hz, whereas abdominal displacement was maximum at only 6 Hz. This demonstrated that the chest wall does not behave as a single unit but rather as a two-compartment system as hypothesized to interpret low compliance values. They also observed, as Brody et al. (16) did in cats, phase differences between various parts of the wall and, accordingly, transverse surface waves.

Pressure and Flow Transfer Functions

On the basis of the T-network model (see Figs. 4 and 8), when pressure variations are applied at the mouth, the flow transfer function is given by

$$[\dot{V}ao/\dot{V}bs]_{Pbs=0} = 1 + Zt/Zg \qquad (43)$$

suggesting independence from airway properties. Finucane et al. (44, 46) measured $\dot{V}ao$ and $\dot{V}bs$ when pressure was varied at the mouth but did not report the corresponding flow transfer function. Rather they used the measurements to compute alveolar pressure and from it airway and tissue impedances.

By reciprocity (Eq. 40) the flow transfer function of Equation 43 is equivalent to the pressure transfer function $[Pbs/Pao]_{\dot{V}ao=0}$, with forcing at the chest with the airway closed. In the latter condition the changes in lung volume are obtained by compressing alveolar gas without flow in the airways. This method was proposed initially by Brody et al. (18), who studied the phase relationship between perithoracic and tracheal pressures in cats and found that tissue resistance (lung plus chest wall) represented 24% of total respiratory resistance.

Alternatively, when pressure is varied at the chest with the airway open, the model of Figures 4 and 8 yields

$$[\dot{V}bs/\dot{V}ao]_{Pao=0} = 1 + Zaw/Zg \qquad (44)$$

suggesting independence from tissue impedance and more direct information concerning the airways. The difficulty of the experiment consists in measuring chest flow when the external input is also applied at the chest. To solve the problem, the Harvard group devised a mechanical generator directly coupled to the thorax in such a way that chest flow could be measured by body plethysmography (71).

Lung Impedance

In a few studies, lung and chest wall properties were partitioned by measuring intrathoracic pressure with an esophageal balloon. To test the validity of the technique at high frequencies, Nagels et al. (143) compared esophageal and pleural pressures in anesthetized dogs and found that from 2 to 20 Hz the differences of amplitude and phase did not exceed 10% and 7°, respectively. Thus measuring transpulmonary pressure does not eliminate completely the influence of the chest wall when pressure is varied at the mouth. Indeed the chest wall influences the distribution of flow between gas compression and the tissue displacement.

Nagels et al. (143) applied a pressure signal and measured flow at the mouth to obtain lung, $[PL/\dot{V}ao]_{Pbs=0}$, and chest wall, $[Pw/\dot{V}ao]_{Pbs=0}$, impedances at 25%, 40%, and 70% of the vital capacity (VC) in 15 healthy subjects (Fig. 12). For the lung (including the airways), the real part of the impedance increased with frequency as observed above 10 Hz by Jackson et al. (103) in two bonnet monkeys. The resonant frequency was lower than that of the total respiratory system (3 Hz compared with 7 Hz at 40% VC). Lung

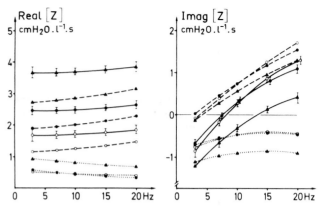

FIG. 12. Real (real[Z]) and imaginary (imag[Z]) parts of total respiratory input impedance (*continuous lines*), lung impedance (*dashed line*), and an approximation to chest wall impedance [Pw/$\dot{V}ao$] (*dotted lines*) at 3 levels of vital capacity: 70% (*open circles*), 40% (*closed circles*), and 25% (*triangles*). Average values in 15 healthy subjects ±1 SD. [From Nagels et al. (143).]

elastance, computed with a second-order model, was minimum at middle lung volume where it represented 24% of total elastance. Lung inertance did not vary with lung volume and was similar to that found for the entire system. Finally, the real part of the impedance at 4 Hz represented 70%–80% of the value obtained for the total respiratory system in all lung volumes, a result similar to that found by Wohl et al. (204) in humans (including newborns) and by Hull and Long (87) in anesthetized dogs with a pressure input at the chest. Atlan et al. (5) used a model similar to that shown in Figure 4 to analyze lung impedance data, $[PL/\dot{V}ao]_{Pao=0}$. They varied pressure at the chest and partitioned lung tissue and airway properties. They found that the tissues had a negligible inertance, as already suggested by Mead (125), and a resistance a little below 0.5 $cmH_2O \cdot liter^{-1} \cdot s$.

In several lung impedance studies an airway catheter or a retrograde catheter (117) was used to partition the impedance into a central portion corresponding to large airways and a peripheral portion corresponding to small airways and lung tissue (65, 92, 107, 192, 198). Irvin et al. (92) found in anesthetized dogs that the real part of total lung impedance increased with increasing frequency from 0.5 to 14 Hz, whereas Van Brabandt et al. (192) observed a decrease from 2 to 32 Hz in excised human lungs and Kappos et al. (107) observed a decrease from 2 to 10–15 Hz followed by an increase from 20 to 30 Hz in open-chest dogs. In the three studies, however, when present the decrease with increasing frequency was mostly caused by the peripheral segment, and the increase entirely caused by the central airways. Frequency dependence and its distribution were also seen to be altered by changing gas density (92), by histamine infusion (92, 107), and by vagal stimulation (107).

Measurements on the lung were also performed with closed airways. Hildebrandt (78, 79) used a specially designed pressure generator (80) to study the relationship between transpulmonary pressure and lung volume, $[P_L/\dot{V}bs]_{\dot{V}ao=0}$, in excised cat lungs. Hildebrandt observed that up to 2 Hz, dynamic elastance (i.e., the product of the reactance and of the circular frequency) increased almost linearly with the logarithm of frequency, whereas the area of the pressure-volume loop (related to the in-phase component of the impedance) was virtually frequency independent. The first finding indicates that the lung behaves like a viscoelastic material, whereas the second may be explained by the existence of several viscoelastic elements with different time constants. Above 2 Hz the areas of the loops increased with increasing frequency (as expected for a viscous resistance). Model simulation (79) indicates that some of the observed energy loss cannot be explained by the factors mentioned above and could be accounted for by dry friction. Smith et al. (180) used a very similar method to investigate dog lobes from 1 to 40 Hz and also observed a slight increase of dynamic elastance with increasing frequency.

Chest Wall Impedance

Little information has been obtained concerning the frequency response of the chest wall. Indeed chest wall impedance, $Zw = [Pw/\dot{V}bs]$, has never been measured. The only study in humans over a substantial frequency range is that of Nagels et al. (143), who studied at three lung volumes the relationship between the pressure drop across the chest and mouth flow when pressure was varied at the mouth, $[Pw/\dot{V}ao]_{Pbs=0}$. Considering the T-network model (see Figs. 4 and 8), one should point out that mouth flow may differ substantially from chest flow if the impedance of the tissues (lung plus chest wall) is not small compared with that of the compressible alveolar gas. Thus more reliable information on chest wall impedance could be derived from chest flow measurements, $[Pw/\dot{V}bs]_{Pbs=0}$. Nagels et al. (143) observed that the real part of this approximation to chest wall impedance tended to decrease from 2 to 20 Hz, in contrast to what they observed for lung and total impedance in the same subjects (see Fig. 12). A similar frequency dependence of the real part of chest impedance was seen by Jackson et al. (103) from 2 to 10 Hz in two monkeys. In Nagels' study, the chest wall represented 20%–30% of total respiratory resistance, which is between the values found in dogs [19% (87)], in humans [25%–40% (4, 204)], and in intubated bonnet monkeys [50%–80% (103)].

Nagels et al. (143) also observed that chest wall reactance was negative and did not increase much with frequency. In part this may be due to the fact that mouth flow rather than chest flow was measured, and this also may reflect mechanical inhomogeneity of the chest wall, as suggested and evidenced by DuBois et al. (40). Chest wall compliance was low compared with that found with other methods (135,

144, 195), which is also an indication of inhomogeneous behavior. Another possible explanation for low chest wall compliance is that the subjects were not relaxed. Finucane and Mead (46) have shown that both the real and imaginary parts of total tissue impedance (lung plus chest wall) are a function of respiratory muscle activity.

Airway Impedance

The airways have been shown to be responsible for most lung resistance (43) and inertance (5, 125). Thus the real part of lung impedance and its imaginary part at high frequencies (when elastic impedance is small) may be expected to approximate airway impedance closely. Combining sinusoidal forcing at the mouth and body plethysmography, Finucane et al. (44) devised a method to estimate alveolar pressure swings during forced-oscillation measurements. Using that method and measuring lateral tracheal pressure, the same group investigated lower airway impedance, $(Paw - P_A)/\dot{V}ao$, from 1.4 to 10 Hz in three healthy subjects (44). The real part of the impedance was, as expected, larger at low lung volume and increased with increasing frequency as observed for lung impedance (143). The changes with frequency between 1.4 and 10 Hz ranged from 40% to 150% and were relatively more important at high lung volume. Airway resistance was also seen to increase with flow amplitude. The problem was reexamined by Fredberg and Mead (59), who used a spatially distributed model of the lung (58, 60) based on anatomical data (86, 201) in which the following factors could be controlled: gas compressibility within the airways, distortion of velocity profile in relation to gas inertia, parallel inhomogeneity, and airway wall impedance. With that model Fredberg and Mead (59) predicted a closely similar resistance and the frequency dependence of resistance. The latter could be explained mainly by parallel imhomogeneities (47%), distortion of velocity profiles (35%), and to a smaller extent by gas compliance (11%) and airway wall distensibility (7%).

FREQUENCY RESPONSES ABOVE 100 HZ

Wave Propagation in the Airways

The ideas of waves in the airway and wave speeds are familiar to investigators of flow limitation during forced expiration (32). The flow-limiting wave speed in the airways is much smaller than the speed of sound waves in free space. Surprisingly both of these wave speeds are relevant to the propagation of pressure and flow oscillations in the airways as studied in oscillation mechanics.

If the airway is modeled as in Figure 6, wave speeds are readily derived from the physical properties of the working gas and airway walls (e.g., ref. 28). Guelke and Bunn (71) have measured the speed at which

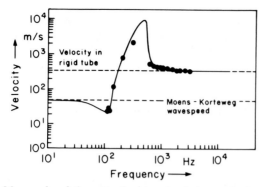

FIG. 13. Measured and theoretically determined phase velocity for an excised canine trachea with static distending pressure of zero. [From Guelke and Bunn (71).]

energy and information waves advance along the trachea (Fig. 13). Although the details of this picture likely depend on airway size and airway wall properties, some general principles may be deduced.

There are at least three distinct frequency ranges of physiological interest. At low frequencies (<20 Hz) the wave speed is very nearly frequency invariant. In this low-frequency range, airway wall inertance and airway wall resistance play no role (see Fig. 6); gas compressibility, being far smaller than airway distensibility, is also of little consequence. As a result, waves in this frequency range propagate by virtue of inertia in the gas coupled to compliance of the airway walls (Eaww^{-1}). In this case the waves are called Moens-Korteweg waves and the propagation wave speed becomes the Moens-Korteweg wave speed (116)

$$c_{MK} = \sqrt{A \; Eaww/\rho} \tag{45}$$

where Eaww is the combined elastance ($\partial \rho / \partial A$) of the wall and supporting structures, ρ is gas density, and A is tube cross-sectional area.

Moens-Korteweg waves are precisely the type that arises in blood flow in the great blood vessels. Of greater significance to respiration physiologists, Moens-Korteweg waves are also relevant to the wave speed concept of maximal expiratory flow limitation (32), wherein maximal expiration flow ($\dot{V}$max) is the product of airway area and wave speed

$$\dot{V}max = A \; c_{MK} \tag{46}$$

Because c_{MK} is given by Equation 45, and the specific wall elastance Eaww is $A(\partial P/\partial A)$, which yields the familiar formula given by Dawson and Elliott (32)

$$\dot{V}max = \sqrt{(A^3/\rho)(\partial P/\partial A)} \tag{47}$$

Flow limitation occurs when information of downstream pressure variations cannot propagate upstream; information propagating upstream at wave speed is brought to a standstill by equal and opposite downstream convectional flow speed. If flow is independent of downstream pressure, flow limitation is said to have occurred.

Proceeding to higher frequencies the wave speed increases by nearly an order of magnitude over the next two frequency decades (20–2,000 Hz). In this range, airway wall resistance (Raww) and airway wall inertance (Iaww) impede the shunt pathway accommodating airway wall distensions (see Fig. 6). The wall elastance, in comparison, begins to play less of a role. The dynamics in this range become relatively complicated and include resonance of the airway walls. The smoothness of the curve is attributable in large part to the dominant influence of airway wall resistance. The wave speed in this range has been inferred also by a variety of indirect means (58, 94, 194), by independent measures of Eaww (e.g., ref. 120) and Raww (15), and by estimates of Iaww.

At frequencies above 1–2 kHz the wave speed attains another frequency-invariant plateau. At these frequencies the dominant effect of airway wall inertance virtually freezes all wall motions. Because airway walls are unable to distend as a result of their inertia, waves in the airway propagate by virtue of gas inertia coupled to gas compliance, which is precisely the nature of sound waves in free space. Rice (161) has confirmed that high-frequency disturbances in the airway do propagate at the speed of sound in free space.

Input Impedance Forcing at the Airway Opening

The effect of subglottic impedance on vocal cord vibration during speech motivated the earliest studies of respiratory system impedance at high frequencies (100–10,000 Hz). Van den Berg (193, 194) had expected that the lung, because it was highly dissipative and constructed of numerous small airways, would absorb all sound waves incident at the trachea in a fashion analogous to an anechoic chamber. To his surprise he found in measurements of human and dog cadavers that pronounced reflections occurred with corresponding well-defined peaks (antiresonances) and dips (resonances) in respiratory system impedance. He modeled the airways and the very small shunt impedance accorded by alveolar gas compressibility at high frequencies as a uniform tube open to atmosphere at an alveolar end, much like an organ pipe.

The impedance over the range of frequencies between 100 and 10,000 Hz has been measured in humans and in dogs by a variety of methods (61, 94, 97, 193) with generally similar results. A series of impedance peaks and dips is observed corresponding to standing waves in the airways, much like organ pipe resonances and overtones (Fig. 14).

Based on a variety of distributed-parameter modeling methods in symmetrical and asymmetrical airway branching morphologies (58, 94, 194), it is generally concluded that the resonant frequencies do not correspond well to a rigid-walled airway model, but rather that the resonant frequencies are shifted upward by airway wall dynamic responses. The magni-

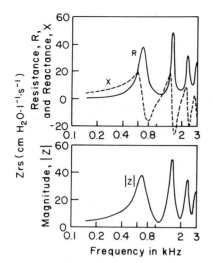

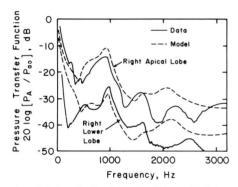

FIG. 14. Measured input impedance components of human at tracheostomy opening. [From Ishizaka et al. (94).]

FIG. 15. Measured and theoretically determined transfer functions of alveolar pressure to airway opening pressure in excised canine lung. [From Fredberg (56).]

tudes of the impedance peaks also are controlled by dynamic distensions of the central airway walls over much of this frequency range (<2,000 Hz). Impedance measured at the airway opening becomes increasingly insensitive to chest wall and lung tissue properties with increasing frequency because the shunt pathway through alveolar gas compression uncouples central airway gas motions from chest wall motions.

Pressure Transfer Functions

The earliest studies of sound transmission through lung and chest wall were carried out by investigators of lung and heart sounds to deduce the influence of transmission processes. Martini (121), Hannon and Lyman (74), Butler and Dornhorst (21), Van den Berg (193), and Forgacs (51) have reported that the lung acts as a low-pass filter that greatly suppresses the passage of high-frequency energy compared with passage of low-frequency energy. Miyakawa et al. (136) and Zalter et al. (207) reported resonant behavior of the chest wall transmission near 200 Hz. The relation-

ship of this resonance to a percussion note and the mechanical impedance of the chest wall is unclear (7, 51, 142). Van den Berg (194) modeled sound transmission from airway opening to chest wall and also found a resonance in this range.

More recent quantitative measurements and models at higher frequencies reveal a strong frequency-dependent transmission loss, approaching 40 dB at 500 Hz, interrupted by resonant peaks (Fig. 15) and strongly dependent on chest or pleural measurement site (51, 56, 60).

Few other data exist concerning the distribution of pressures and flows within the airways at high frequencies. Models of the distribution of the standing pressure waves along the airway reveal that most of the pressure drop occurs in the peripheral air spaces [Fig. 16; (60)]. As frequency is increased the pressure minima move toward the alveoli. The frequencies at which the pressure minima are located at the airway opening ($x = 0$) correspond to the resonant frequencies of the system (i.e., input impedance minima). It is noteworthy that at frequencies below 20 Hz, model predictions of the pressure distribution (amplitude and phase) within the airways are nearly uniform, with small differences associated with viscous pressure drops. In contrast, above 30 Hz well-defined standing-wave patterns are evident and strong spatial gradients in pressure arise.

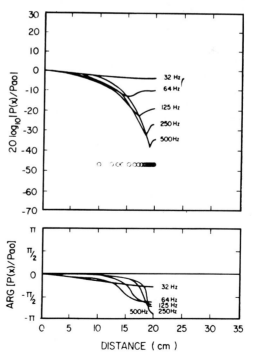

FIG. 16. Pressure distribution along the tracheobronchial tree varying with oscillatory frequency. Glottis corresponds to $x = 0$; *open circles* correspond to locations of successive bifurcations. As a result of standing waves, the pressure does not fall monotonically from glottis to alveolus except at low frequencies [From Fredberg and Moore (60).]

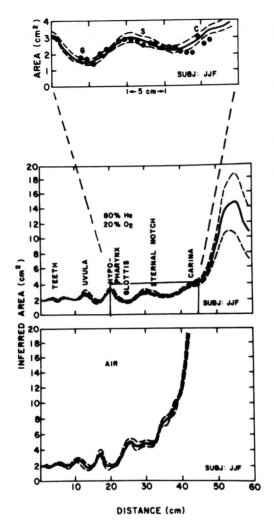

FIG. 17. Airway area by acoustic reflection (*solid lines*) yields good agreement with radiographic determinations (*filled circles*) of tracheal area (*top*). G, glottis; S, sternal notch; C, carina. Result is accurate with light gases (HeO₂, *top* and *middle*) but erroneous when air is employed (*bottom*). *Dashed lines* indicate ±1 SD. [From Fredberg et al. (62).]

Airway Area by Acoustic Reflections

Sondhi and Gopinath (182) developed theoretical arguments suggesting that the reflection of a pulse from the airway opening could be used to infer the cross-sectional area of the supraglottal cavity as a function of distance from the lips. This idea was applied to the subglottal airways of excised canine lungs by Jackson and co-workers (96) and to the airways of human subjects by Fredberg and co-workers [Fig. 17; (62)].

The theoretical formalisms permitting inference of airway dimensions from acoustic reflection data require a number of idealized assumptions, most notably rigid airway walls, one-dimensional wave propagation, symmetrical airway branching, and inviscid working gas (174). The first and second of these prevent accurate determinations of airway area when air is used

as a working gas but can be overcome to yield accurate inferences of airway area in humans at least as far as the carina when lighter gases are employed [Fig. 17; (62)]. Lighter gases boost the working range of frequencies above 1–2 kHz, in which the airway walls are effectively rigid (see Fig. 13). Beyond the carina, asymmetrical airway branching affects the area inference in a manner that makes it difficult to relate inferred airway area to well-defined anatomic correlates. Nonetheless simulation studies (174) and experimental studies of airway casts (100) suggest that the area inference is accurate up to 5–10 cm beyond the carina. Although anatomic correlates and accuracy of the inferred area for small airways are speculative, empirical evidence of small airway area responses has been detected by airway area acoustic reflections (99).

CLINICAL APPLICATIONS

The forced-oscillation technique is a potentially powerful method for exploring the respiratory system. Together with modeling and parameter estimation it should prove valuable in detecting and interpreting abnormalities in disease. However, little has been done in that direction. Indeed in most clinical studies measurements have been made at a single frequency, the method being used as little more than a convenient tool to estimate total respiratory resistance.

Pulmonary Function in Children

In contrast with most pulmonary function tests, forced-oscillation measurements do not require cooperation on the part of the patient and therefore are applicable to young children. The method was first applied to newborns and infants by Wohl et al. (204), who devised a body chamber to apply pressure variations around the chest and a face mask to measure resulting flow at the airway opening.

In all subsequent studies in children, total respiratory resistance was derived from input impedance measurements, i.e., from the relationship between transrespiratory pressure and mouth flow when pressure was varied at the mouth. In most cases the equipment was similar to that shown in Figure 7B. The only studies in which both the real and imaginary parts of the impedance were obtained at a number of frequencies are those of Williams et al. (202, 203), who examined children 3–5 yr old and interpreted the data with the second-order model. Total respiratory resistance averaged 5.61 ± 0.49 cmH₂O·liter⁻¹·s, total compliance averaged 4.03 ± 1.04 ml·cmH₂O⁻¹, and total inertance averaged 0.012 ± 0.0024 cmH₂O·liter⁻¹·s²; the three coefficients were significantly correlated to both body height and forced vital capacity. Correlations between respiratory system resistance and height have also been found by others (10, 26, 118, 184, 204). In Williams' study the real part of the impedance was seen to decrease with increasing frequency; this was also observed in children 3–14 yr old by Stănescu et al. (184). These investigators found that the frequency dependence was negatively correlated to body height and suggested that it could be explained on the basis of the model proposed by Mead (127). This model showed a large peripheral airway resistance in parallel with central airway compliance. Williams et al. (203) used a method explicitly based on that model (159) to compute from their data a ratio of peripheral resistance to total resistance and found a value of 0.53 ± 0.07. Though it was originally proposed and used by Williams, the method is based on a number of assumptions (177).

Total respiratory resistance was found to be fairly reproducible in healthy children with coefficients of variation of repeated measurements between 7% and 15% (4, 26, 203). This makes the method particularly suitable to detect changes in airway patency during bronchomotor challenge in asthmatics (4, 130, 200). Another advantage of the method for such studies is that it permits continuous measurements with an extremely good time resolution. Wanner et al. (200) were able to detect changes in the bronchomotor tone within seconds after the administration of isoproterenol in asthmatic children. A device for directly recording dose-response curves of the total respiratory system has been described (187). Total respiratory resistance was also measured and found to be occasionally abnormal in cystic fibrosis (26, 110) and in a variety of other respiratory disorders (11, 81, 110, 204).

Obstructive Lung Diseases

Total respiratory resistance determinations by forced oscillations have been shown to be as sensitive as other resistance measurements to detect induced airway obstruction in healthy subjects (13, 54, 157). The method has been applied to patients with asthma (8, 22, 63, 69, 83–85, 145, 147, 148, 181, 187) and patients with chronic obstructive lung diseases (42, 48, 49, 52, 69, 76, 84, 85, 90, 106, 109, 111, 113, 132, 139, 143, 145, 179, 181, 183, 187). In these patients the real part of impedance has been found to be abnormally high and to decrease abnormally with increasing frequency, the variations being particularly large at low frequencies (42, 69, 76, 84, 109, 111, 132, 139, 143, 183). The frequency dependence has been shown to be more pronounced at low lung volume (143) and in patients with more severe airway obstruction (69, 84, 113) and to diminish or even disappear after bronchodilation (113, 132). This has been demonstrated to be entirely caused by the lung and airways with resistance of the chest wall being normal and almost independent of frequency (69, 143). It is commonly interpreted as reflecting mechanical inhomogeneity of the lung, i.e., the presence of unequal time constants, either between parenchymal compartments (149) or between the parenchyma and the airways

(127). The existence of a correlation between the frequency dependence of respiratory system resistance and that of lung compliance (109, 141) and computer simulation (178) supports this interpretation. However, other factors may be involved, such as shunt impedance of the upper airway (see *Upper Airway Variability and Shunt*, p. 159). Another common finding in obstructive patients is an increased resonant frequency with phase angles lower than normal (42, 76, 84, 111, 113, 132, 139, 143, 176, 181), usually interpreted as related to mechanical inhomogeneity.

The value of this method in recognizing the early stages of airway obstruction has been investigated. Results of studies comparing smokers and nonsmokers (76, 109, 111, 132, 152) indicate that total resistance tends to be higher and more frequency dependent in smokers and that the resonant frequency is slightly increased. The differences, however, are small and not always significant. There is some indication that the sensitivity of the method to peripheral airway abnormalities may be improved by having the subject breathe a low-density gas mixture to decrease the contribution of density-dependent resistances in the vicinity of the glottis [Eq. 14; (14, 191)].

Restrictive Lung Diseases

Forced-oscillation measurements have been performed in patients with various kinds of restrictive lung diseases (49, 84, 85, 139, 176, 181). In most studies total respiratory resistance or impedance was found to be increased, but less than in chronic obstructive lung disease. Fisher et al. (49), however, in nine patients with diffuse lung disease observed that specific total respiratory resistance (respiratory system resistance times absolute lung volume) was normal and pointed out the necessity to take into account lung volume to discriminate between obstructive and restrictive disorders. Although to a lesser extent than in chronic obstructive lung disease, the real part of impedance was also seen to decrease with increasing frequency (139, 140), which was attributed to mechanical inhomogeneity. Both Sinha et al. (176) and Holle et al. (85) observed that the phase angle between pressure and flow in these patients was substantially more negative at end inspiration than during tidal breathing, whereas the opposite was true in obstructive patients.

Miscellaneous Lung Diseases

A few observations have been made on obese subjects. Sharp et al. (169) found total respiratory resistance was significantly increased and was almost entirely caused by an increased pulmonary resistance, whereas Fisher et al. (49) found that specific resistance was abnormal in only one out of five subjects. Sharp et al. (168, 170) observed a lower resonant frequency, from which they computed an inertance value that was more than twice the normal. In these subjects tissue inertance would represent 68% of total respiratory inertance, compared with 16% in normal subjects.

Finally, a few studies have been performed in subjects with various acute respiratory or cardiac conditions. Total respiratory resistance was found to be initially increased (73, 91, 137), abnormally frequency dependent (73, 91), and to come back to normal values within a few weeks.

We thank Dr. Jere Mead for his assistance in preparing this manuscript. This chapter was made possible in part by support from The Biomechanics Institute and the Institut National de la Santé et de la Recherche Médicale.

REFERENCES

1. ALBRIGHT, C. D., AND S. BONDURANT. Some effects of respiratory frequency on pulmonary mechanics. *J. Clin. Invest.* 44: 1362–1370, 1965.
2. ALLEN, G. R., K. R. MASLEN, AND G. F. ROWLANDS. Some aspects of the dynamic behavior of aircrew breathing equipment. *Aerosp. Med.* 36: 1047–1053, 1965.
3. AMREIN, R., R. KELLER, H. JOOS, AND H. HERZOG. Valeurs théoriques nouvelles de l'exploration de la fonction ventilatoire du poumon. *Bull. Physio-Pathol. Respir.* 6: 317–349, 1970.
4. ARONSSON, H., L. SOLYMAR, J. DEMPSEY, J. BJURE, T. OLSSON, AND B. BAKE. A modified forced oscillation technique for measurements of respiratory resistance. *J. Appl. Physiol.: Respirat. Environ. Exercise Physiol.* 42: 650–655, 1977.
5. ATLAN, G., G. CANNET, C. JACQUEMIN, P. VARÈNE, R. POULIQUEN, L. DAMS, AND J. RICHALET. Un modèle synthétique du système mécanique ventilatoire. II. Validation. *Bull. Physio-Pathol. Respir.* 8: 237–249, 1972.
6. ATLAN, G., P. VARÈNE, C. JACQUEMIN, R. POULIQUEN, J. F. BOISVIEUX, AND J. RICHALET. Étude critique des méthodes d'oscillations forcées en mécanique ventilatoire. *Bull. Physio-Pathol. Respir.* 7: 63–78, 1971.
7. AUENBRUGGER, L. *Invention nobum ex percussione thoracic humaniet signo abstrusos interni pectoris morbos delegendi.* London: Dawson, 1966. [Reprint of Forbes' English translation (1824).]
8. BAUR, X., H. BERGSTERMANN, G. FRUHMANN, H. POLKE, AND G. PRAML. Oszillatorische und ganzkorperplethysmographische Messung des Atemwiderstands bei allergeninduzierten Bronchial-obstruktionen. *Atemwegs-Lungenkr.* 4: 262–264, 1978.
9. BENADE, A. H. On the propagation of sound waves in a cylindrical conduit. *J. Acoust. Soc. Am.* 44: 616–623, 1968.
10. BERDEL, D., H. MAGNUSSEN, J. P. HOLLE, AND V. HARTMANN. Measurement of resistance by an oscillation technique and by body plethysmography: a comparative study in children (Abstract). *Lung* 155: 156, 1978.
11. BERDEL, D., H. MAGNUSSEN, J. P. HOLLE, AND V. HARTMANN. Vergleich der oszillatorischen Atemwiderstandsmessung mit der Plethysmographie und der Spirometrie im Kindesalter. *Schweiz. Med. Wochenschr.* 109: 92–94, 1979.
12. BERGMAN, N. A. Measurements of respiratory inertance in anesthetized subjects. *Respir. Physiol.* 9: 65–73, 1970.
13. BERGMAN, N. A., AND C. L. WALTEMATH. A comparison of some methods for measuring total respiratory resistance. *J. Appl. Physiol.* 36: 131–134, 1974.
14. BHANSALI, P. V., C. G. IRVIN, J. A. DEMPSEY, R. BUSH, AND J. G. WEBSTER. Human pulmonary resistance: effect of frequency and gas physical properties. *J. Appl. Physiol.: Respirat. Environ. Exercise Physiol.* 47: 161–168, 1979.
15. BOBBAERS, H., J. CLÉMENT, AND K. P. VAN DE WOESTIJNE. Dynamic viscoelastic properties of the canine trachea. *J. Appl. Physiol.: Respirat. Environ. Exercise Physiol.* 44: 137–143, 1978.
16. BRODY, A. W., J. J. CONNOLLY, JR., AND H. J. WANDER. Influence of abdominal muscles, mesenteric viscera and liver on respiratory mechanics. *J. Appl. Physiol.* 14: 121–128, 1959.
17. BRODY, A. W., AND A. B. DUBOIS. Determination of tissue, airway and total resistance to respiration in cats. *J. Appl. Physiol.* 9: 213–218, 1956.
18. BRODY, A. W., A. B. DUBOIS, O. I. NISELL, AND J. ENGELBERG. Natural frequency, damping factor and inertance of the chest-lung system in cats. *Am. J. Physiol.* 186: 142–148, 1956.
19. BROWN, F. T. A unified approach to the analysis of uniform one-dimensional distributed systems. *J. Basic Eng.* 89: 423–432, 1967.
20. BROWN, F. T., D. L. MARGOLIS, AND R. P. SHAH. Small amplitude frequency behavior of fluid lines with turbulent flow. *J. Basic Eng.* 91: 678–693, 1969.
21. BUTLER, A. J., AND A. C. DORNHORST. The physics of some pulmonary signs. *Lancet* 2: 649, 1956.
22. CASS, L. J. Measurement of total respiratory and nasal airflow resistance. *J. Am. Med. Assoc.* 199: 396–398, 1967.
23. CHONG, C. C., AND H. B. ATABEK. The inlet length for oscillatory flow and its effects on the determination of the rate of flow in arteries. *Phys. Med. Biol.* 6: 303–317, 1961.
24. CLEMENTS, J. A., J. T. SHARP, R. P. JOHNSON, AND J. O. ELAM. Estimation of pulmonary resistance by repetitive interruption of air flow. *J. Clin. Invest.* 38: 1262–1270, 1959.
25. COERMANN, R. R., G. H. ZIEGENTRUECKER, A. L. WITTWER, AND H. E. VON GIERKE. The passive dynamic properties of the human thorax-abdomen system and the whole body system. *Aerosp. Med.* 31: 443–445, 1960.
26. COGSWELL, J. J. Forced oscillation technique for determination of resistance to breathing in children. *Arch. Dis. Child.* 48: 259–266, 1973.
27. CRAWFORD, E. C., JR. Mechanical aspects of panting in dogs. *J. Appl. Physiol.* 17: 249–251, 1962.
28. CRAWFORD, E. C., JR., AND G. KAMPE. Oscillation mechanics of the respiratory system as related to panting in pigeons (Abstract). *Federation Proc.* 30: 556, 1971.
29. CRAWFORD, F. S., JR. *Waves.* New York: McGraw-Hill, 1968.
30. DARÓCZY, B., AND Z. HANTOS. An improved forced oscillation estimation of respiratory impedance. *Int. J. Biomed. Comput.* 13: 221–235, 1982.
31. DARÓCZY, B., Z. HANTOS, AND J. KLEBNICZKI. An adaptive filtering technique for the determination of forced oscillatory impedance (Abstract). *Bull. Eur. Physiopathol. Respir.* 16: 187P–188P, 1980.
32. DAWSON, S. V., AND E. A. ELLIOTT. Wave-speed limitation on expiratory flow—a unifying concept. *J. Appl. Physiol.: Respirat. Environ. Exercise Physiol.* 43: 498–515, 1977.
33. DAWSON, S. V., AND K. E. FINUCANE. A prediction of the distribution of oscillatory flow in human airways. *Bull. Physio-Pathol. Respir.* 8: 293–304, 1972.
34. DEJONG, R. G., AND J. J. FREDBERG. Transpulmonary pressure transmissibility in excised and in situ canine lungs. In: *Pulmonary Function Testing in Infants and Children,* edited by J. J. Fredberg and M. E. B. Wohl. Bethesda, MD: Natl. Inst. Health, 1977, HR-6-2901-2A, p. 133–156.
35. DELAVAULT, E., G. SAUMON, AND R. GEORGES. Identification of transducer defect in respiratory impedance measurements by forced random noise. Correction of experimental data. *Respir. Physiol.* 40: 107–117, 1980.
36. DELAVAULT, E., G. SAUMON, AND R. GEORGES. Characterization and validation of forced input method for respiratory impedance measurement. *Respir. Physiol.* 40: 119–136, 1980.
37. DORKIN, H. L., A. C. JACKSON, D. J. STRIEDER, AND S. V. DAWSON. Interaction of oscillatory and unidirectional flows

in straight tubes and an airway cast. *J. Appl. Physiol.: Respirat. Environ. Exercise Physiol.* 52: 1097–1105, 1982.

38. DRUZ, W. S., H. B. VANIA, AND J. T. SHARP. Comparison of driving point and transfer impedances of the respiratory system (Abstract). *Federation Proc.* 37: 367, 1978.
39. DuBois, A. B. Resistance to breathing measured by driving the chest at 6 cps. *Federation Proc.* 12: 35–36, 1953.
40. DuBois, A. B., A. W. BRODY, D. H. LEWIS, AND B. F. BURGESS, JR. Oscillation mechanics of lungs and chest in man. *J. Appl. Physiol.* 8: 587–594, 1956.
41. DuBois, A. B., AND B. B. ROSS. A new method for studying mechanics of breathing using cathode ray oscillograph. *Proc. Soc. Exp. Biol. Med.* 78: 546–549, 1951.
42. EYLES, J. G., AND R. L. PIMMEL. Estimating respiratory mechanical parameters in parallel compartment models. *IEEE Trans. Biomed. Eng.* 28: 313–317, 1981.
43. FERRIS, B. G., JR., J. MEAD, AND L. H. OPIE. Partitioning of respiratory flow resistance in man. *J. Appl. Physiol.* 19: 653–658, 1964.
44. FINUCANE, K. E., S. V. DAWSON, P. D. PHELAN, AND J. MEAD. Resistance of intrathoracic airways of healthy subjects during periodic flow. *J. Appl. Physiol.* 38: 517–530, 1975.
45. FINUCANE, K. E., B. A. EGAN, AND S. V. DAWSON. Linearity and frequency response of pneumotachographs. *J. Appl. Physiol.* 32: 121–126, 1972.
46. FINUCANE, K. E., AND J. MEAD. Impedance of the respiratory tissues as a function of respiratory muscle activity (Abstract). *Federation Proc.* 30: 555, 1971.
47. FINUCANE, K. E., AND J. MEAD. Estimation of alveolar pressure during forced oscillation of the respiratory system. *J. Appl. Physiol.* 38: 531–537, 1975.
48. FISCHER, J., H. MATTHYS, K. H. RÜHLE, AND G. KLEIN. Oscillatory resistance and forced expiratory measurements for screening of lung disorders. In: *Progress in Respiration Research. Biomedical Engineering and Data Processing in Pneumonology*, edited by H. Matthys. Basel: Karger, 1979, vol. 11, p. 202–214.
49. FISHER, A. B., A. B. DuBois, AND R. W. HYDE. Evaluations of the forced oscillation technique for the determination of resistance to breathing. *J. Clin. Invest.* 47: 2045–2057, 1968.
50. FLEISCH, A. Le pneumotachographe. *Helv. Physiol. Pharmacol. Acta* 14: 363–368, 1956.
51. FORGACS, P. *Lung Sounds.* London: Baillière, Tindal, & Cox, 1978, p. 11–12.
52. FÖRSTER, E., D. BERGER, AND D. NOLTE. Vergleichmessungen des Atemwiderstandes mit der Oszillationsmethode und mit der Bodyplethysmographie. *Verh. Dtsch. Ges. Inn. Med.* 84: 392–395, 1978.
53. FRANETZKI, M., K. PRESTELE, AND V. KORN. A direct-display oscillation method for measurement of respiratory impedance. *J. Appl. Physiol.: Respirat. Environ. Exercise Physiol.* 46: 956–965, 1979.
54. FRANK, N. R., J. MEAD, AND J. L. WHITTENBERGER. Comparative sensitivity of four methods for measuring changes in respiratory flow resistance in man. *J. Appl. Physiol.* 31: 934–938, 1971.
55. FRANKEN, H., J. CLEMENT, M. CAUBERGHS, AND K. P. van DE WOESTIJNE. Oscillating flow of a viscous compressible fluid through a rigid tube: a theoretical model. *IEEE Trans. Biomed. Eng.* 28: 416–420, 1981.
56. FREDBERG, J. J. Spatial considerations in oscillation mechanics of the lungs. *Federation Proc.* 39: 2747–2754, 1980.
57. FREDBERG, J. J., AND R. G. DeJONG. Measurements of sound transmission in the lung. *Am. Conf. Eng. Med. Biol. 15th*, 1979.
58. FREDBERG, J. J., AND A. HOENIG. Mechanical response of the lungs at high frequencies. *J. Biomech. Eng.* 100: 57–66, 1978.
59. FREDBERG, J. J., AND J. MEAD. Impedance of intrathoracic airway models during low-frequency periodic flow. *J. Appl. Physiol.: Respirat. Environ. Exercise Physiol.* 47: 347–351, 1979.
60. FREDBERG, J. J., AND J. J. MOORE. The distributed response

of complex branching duct networks. *J. Acoust. Soc. Am.* 63: 954–961, 1978.
61. FREDBERG, J. J., R. S. SIDELL, M. E. WOHL, AND R. G. DeJONG. Canine pulmonary input impedance measured by transient forced oscillations. *J. Biomech. Eng.* 100: 67–71, 1978.
62. FREDBERG, J. J., M. E. B. WOHL, G. M. GLASS, AND H. L. DORKIN. Airway area by acoustic reflections measured at the mouth. *J. Appl. Physiol.: Respirat. Environ. Exercise Physiol.* 48: 749–758, 1980.
63. FRIEDMAN, M., P. G. CANADAY, J. M. FULTON, R. L. PIMMEL, AND P. A. BROMBERG. Fractionation of airways resistance using forced random noise technique (FRN) in asthmatic subjects (Abstract). *Am. Rev. Respir. Dis.* 125, Suppl.: 223, 1982.
64. FRY, D. L., R. E. HYATT, C. B. McCALL, AND A. J. MALLOS. Evaluation of three types of respiratory flowmeters. *J. Appl. Physiol.* 10: 210–214, 1957.
65. FULLTON, J. M., D. A. HAYES, AND R. L. PIMMEL. Pulmonary impedance in dogs measured by forced random noise with a retrograde catheter. *J. Appl. Physiol.: Respirat. Environ. Exercise Physiol.* 52: 725–733, 1982.
66. GOLDMAN, M., R. J. KNUDSON, J. MEAD, N. PETERSON, J. R. SCHWABER, AND M. E. WOHL. A simplified measurement of respiratory resistance by forced oscillation. *J. Appl. Physiol.* 28: 113–116, 1970.
67. GOLDSTEIN, D., AND J. MEAD. Total respiratory impedance immediately after panting. *J. Appl. Physiol.: Respirat. Environ. Exercise Physiol.* 48: 1024–1028, 1980.
68. GRIMBY, G. Measurement of respiratory resistance with forced oscillations. *Scand. J. Clin. Lab. Invest.* 24, Suppl. 110: 37–39, 1969.
69. GRIMBY, G., T. TAKASHIMA, W. GRAHAM, P. MACKLEM, AND J. MEAD. Frequency dependence of flow resistance in patients with obstructive lung disease. *J. Clin. Invest.* 47: 1455–1465, 1968.
70. GROPPER, A., A. C. JACKSON, AND J. P. BUTLER. Measurement of the flow properties of the airways during forced oscillations from 2 to 30 Hz (Abstract). *Federation Proc.* 35: 231, 1976.
71. GUELKE, R. W., AND A. E. BUNN. Transmission line theory applied to sound wave propagation in tubes with compliant walls. *Acustica* 48: 101–106, 1981.
72. HADDAD, A. G., R. L. PIMMEL, D. D. SCAPEROTH, AND P. A. BROMBERG. Forced oscillatory respiratory parameters following papain exposure in dogs. *J. Appl. Physiol.: Respirat. Environ. Exercise Physiol.* 46: 61–66, 1979.
73. HALL, W. J., R. G. DOUGLAS, R. W. HYDE, F. K. ROTH, A. S. CROSS, AND D. M. SPEERS. Pulmonary mechanics after uncomplicated influenza A infection. *Am. Rev. Respir. Dis.* 113: 141–147, 1976.
74. HANNON, R. R., AND R. S. LYMAN. Studies on pulmonary acoustics. II. The transmission of tracheal sounds through freshly exenterated sheep's lungs. *Am. Rev. Tuberc.* 19: 360–375, 1929.
75. HARRY, R. R., H. S. HSIAO, AND H. J. PROCTOR. A pulse technique for measuring the mechanical properties of the lung. *Proc. Biomed. Symp., 12th, San Diego, 1973*, p. 85–90.
76. HAYES, D. A., R. L. PIMMEL, J. M. FULLTON, AND P. A. BROMBERG. Detection of respiratory mechanical dysfunction by forced random noise impedance parameters. *Am. Rev. Respir. Dis.* 120: 1095–1100, 1979.
77. HEAF, P. J. D., AND F. J. PRIME. The compliance of the thorax in normal human subjects. *Clin. Sci.* 15: 319–327, 1956.
78. HILDEBRANDT, J. Dynamic properties of air-filled excised cat lung determined by liquid plethysmograph. *J. Appl. Physiol.* 27: 246–250, 1969.
79. HILDEBRANDT, J. Pressure-volume data of cat lung interpreted by a plastoelastic, linear viscoelastic model. *J. Appl. Physiol.* 28: 365–372, 1970.
80. HILDEBRANDT, J., AND A. C. YOUNG. Fluid plethysmographic

method for obtaining dynamic pressure-volume data. *J. Appl. Physiol.* 27: 286–290, 1969.

81. HOFMANN, D., M. PFLUG, AND R. WONNE. Oscillatorische Impedanz-Messung bei Kindern und ihre Bedeutung für die pneumologische Diagnostik. *Atemwegs-Lungenkr.* 5: 124–128, 1979.

82. HOGG, J. C., P. T. MACKLEM, AND W. M. THURLBECK. The resistance of collateral channels in excised human lungs. *J. Clin. Invest.* 48: 421–431, 1969.

83. HOLLE, J. P., V. HARTMANN, G. HEER, AND H. MAGNUSSEN. Die Kontinuierliche Messung des oszillatorischen Atemwiderstandes unter Salbutamol-Aminophyllin und Ipratropiumbromid-Gabe. *Atemwegs-Lungenkr.* 4: 418–420, 1978.

84. HOLLE, J. P., F. LÁNDSÉR, B. SCHULLER, V. HARTMANN, AND H. MAGNUSSEN. Measurement of respiratory mechanics with forced oscillations. Comparison of two methods (Siregnost FD 5 versus a pseudo-random noise technique). *Respiration* 41: 119–127, 1981.

85. HOLLE, J. P., H. MAGNUSSEN, AND V. HARTMANN. Measurement of oscillatory impedance during air and helium breathing. In: *Progress in Respiration Research. Biomedical Engineering and Data Processing in Pneumonology*, edited by H. Matthys. Basel: Karger, 1979, vol. 11, p. 162–171.

86. HORSFIELD, K., AND G. CUMMING. Morphology of the bronchial tree in man. *J. Appl. Physiol.* 24: 373–383, 1968.

87. HULL, W. E., AND E. C. LONG. Respiratory impedance and volume flow at high frequency in dogs. *J. Appl. Physiol.* 16: 439–443, 1961.

88. HULL, W. E., AND E. C. LONG. Right atrial and esophageal pressures during forced high frequency respiration in dogs (Abstract). *Physiologist* 4(3): 50, 1961.

89. HULL, W. E., AND E. C. LONG. Change of thoraco-abdominal resonant frequency with driving pressure (Abstract). *Physiologist* 6: 205, 1963.

90. HYATT, R. E., I. R. ZIMMERMAN, G. M. PETERS, AND W. J. SULLIVAN. Direct writeout of total respiratory resistance. *J. Appl. Physiol.* 28: 675–678, 1970.

91. INTERIANO, B., R. HYDE, M. HODGES, AND P. N. YU. Interrelation between alterations in pulmonary mechanics and hemodynamics in acute myocardial infarction. *J. Clin. Invest.* 52: 1994–2006, 1973.

92. IRVIN, C., P. BHANSALI, AND J. DEMPSEY. Characterization of airways constriction with frequency dependence of resistance and gas density (Abstract). *Federation Proc.* 38: 1445, 1979.

93. ISHIZAKA, K., J. C. FRENCH, AND J. L. FLANAGAN. Direct determination of vocal tract wall impedance. *IEEE Trans. Acoust. Speech Signal Process.* 23: 370–373, 1975.

94. ISHIZAKA, K., M. MATOUDAIRA, AND T. KANEKO. Input acoustic impedance measurements of the subglottal system. *J. Acoust. Soc. Am.* 60: 190–197, 1976.

95. JACKSON, A. C. Lung impedance determinations by a discrete frequency technique without flow measurements. In: *Pulmonary Function Testing in Infants and Children*, edited by J. J. Fredberg and M. E. B. Wohl. Bethesda, MD: Natl. Inst. Health, 1977, HR-6-2901-2A.

96. JACKSON, A. C., J. P. BUTLER, E. J. MILLET, F. G. HOPPIN, JR., AND S. V. DAWSON. Airway geometry by analysis of acoustic pulse response measurements. *J. Appl. Physiol.: Respirat. Environ. Exercise Physiol.* 43: 523–536, 1977.

97. JACKSON, A. C., J. P. BUTLER, AND R. W. PYLE. Acoustic input impedance of excised dog lungs. *J. Acoust. Soc. Am.* 64: 1020–1026, 1978.

98. JACKSON, A. C., P. J. GULESIAN, JR., AND J. MEAD. Glottal aperture during panting with voluntary limitation of tidal volume. *J. Appl. Physiol.* 39: 834–836, 1975.

99. JACKSON, A. C., S. H. LORING, AND J. M. DRAZEN. Serial distribution of bronchoconstriction induced by vagal stimulation or histamine. *J. Appl. Physiol.: Respirat. Environ. Exercise Physiol.* 50: 1286–1292, 1981.

100. JACKSON, A. C., AND D. E. OLSON. Comparison of direct and acoustical area measurements in physical models of human central airways. *J. Appl. Physiol.: Respirat. Environ. Exercise Physiol.* 48: 896–902, 1980.

101. JACKSON, A. C., AND A. VINEGAR. A technique for measuring frequency response of pressure, volume, and flow transducers. *J. Appl. Physiol.: Respirat. Environ. Exercise Physiol.* 47: 462–467, 1979.

102. JACKSON, A. C., AND J. W. WATSON. Oscillatory mechanics of the respiratory system in normal rats. *Respir. Physiol.* 48: 309–322, 1982.

103. JACKSON, A. C., C. D. WEGNER, J. D. BERRY, AND J. R. GILLESPIE. Frequency dependence of respiratory resistances between 2 and 32 Hz in normal bonnet monkeys (Abstract). *Federation Proc.* 39: 835, 1980.

104. JAEGER, M. J., AND A. B. OTIS. Measurement of airway resistance with a volume displacement body plethysmograph. *J. Appl. Physiol.* 19: 813–820, 1964.

105. JORDAN, C., J. R. LEHANE, J. G. JONES, D. G. ALTMAN, AND J. P. ROYSTON. Specific conductance using forced airflow oscillation in mechanically ventilated human subjects. *J. Appl. Physiol.: Respirat. Environ. Exercise Physiol.* 51: 715–724, 1981.

106. KABIRAJ, M. U., C. ROLF, AND B. G. SIMONSSON. Drug-induced changes in airways obstruction reflected by forced expiratory flows and airway resistance measured with an oscillometric method using quiet breathing. *Respiration* 41: 90–95, 1981.

107. KAPPOS, A. D., J. R. RODARTE, AND S. J. LAI-FOOK. Frequency dependence and partitioning of respiratory impedance in dogs. *J. Appl. Physiol.: Respirat. Environ. Exercise Physiol.* 51: 621–629, 1981.

108. KAZANSKY, B. G. Outline of the theory of non-uniform transmission lines. *Proc. Inst. Electr. Eng. Part C* 105: 126–138, 1958.

109. KJELDGAARD, J. M., R. W. HYDE, D. M. SPEERS, AND W. W. REICHERT. Frequency dependence of total respiratory resistance in early airway disease. *Am. Rev. Respir. Dis.* 114: 501–508, 1976.

110. LANDAU, L. L., AND P. O. PHELAN. Evaluation of two techniques for the measurement of respiratory resistance by forced oscillation. *Thorax* 28: 136–141, 1973.

111. LÁNDSÉR, F. J., J. CLÉMENT, AND K. P. VAN DE WOESTIJNE. Normal values of total respiratory resistance and reactance determined by forced oscillations. Influence of smoking. *Chest* 81: 586–591, 1982.

112. LÁNDSÉR, F. J., J. NAGELS, J. CLÉMENT, AND K. P. VAN DE WOESTIJNE. Errors in the measurement of total respiratory resistance and reactance by forced oscillations. *Respir. Physiol.* 28: 289–301, 1976.

113. LÁNDSÉR, F. J., J. NAGELS, M. DEMEDTS, L. BILLIET, AND K. P. VAN DE WOESTIJNE. A new method to determine frequency characteristics of the respiratory system. *J. Appl. Physiol.* 41: 101–106, 1976.

114. LILLY, J. C. Flowmeter for recording respiratory flow of human subjects. In: *Methods in Medical Research*, edited by J. H. Comroe. Chicago, IL: Year Book, 1950, vol. 2, p. 113–121.

115. LONG, E. C., W. E. HULL, AND E. L. GEBEL. Respiratory dynamic resistance. *J. Appl. Physiol.* 17: 609–612, 1962.

116. MACDONALD, D. *Blood Flow in Arteries*. Baltimore, MD: Williams & Wilkins, 1974.

117. MACKLEM, P. T., AND J. MEAD. Resistance of central and peripheral airways measured by a retrograde catheter. *J. Appl. Physiol.* 22: 395–401, 1967.

118. MANSELL, A., H. LEVISON, K. KRUGER, AND T. L. TRIPP. Measurement of respiratory resistance in children by forced oscillations. *Am. Rev. Respir. Dis.* 106: 710–714, 1972.

119. MARGOLIS, D. L. An Experimental Investigation of Acoustic Waves in Turbulent Fluid Transmission Lines. Cambridge, MA: MIT, 1972, p. 97–101. PhD thesis.

120. MARTIN, H. B., AND D. F. PROCTOR. Pressure-volume measurements on dog bronchi. *J. Appl. Physiol.* 13: 337–343, 1958.

121. MARTINI, P. Studien aber Percussion und Auskultation, Deutsches. *Arch. Klin. Med.* 139: 257–285, 1922.
122. MASLEN, K. R. *Dynamic Calibration of Gas Flowmeters.* Teddington, UK: Aeronaut. Res. Counc., 1971. (Curr. Pap. 1224.)
123. MASLEN, K. R., AND G. F. ROWLANDS. *A New Method of Measuring the Impedance of the Human Respiratory System at Moderate Frequencies.* Farnborough, UK: Royal Aircraft Establishment, 1966. (Tech. Rep. 66296.)
124. MASLEN, K. R., AND G. F. ROWLANDS. Simulation of the impedance of the human respiratory system in dynamic testing of aircraft breathing equipment. *Aerosp. Med.* 39: 458–462, 1968.
125. MEAD, J. Measurement of inertia of the lungs at increased ambient pressure. *J. Appl. Physiol.* 9: 208–212, 1956.
126. MEAD, J. Control of respiratory frequency. *J. Appl. Physiol.* 15: 325–336, 1960.
127. MEAD, J. Contribution of compliance of airways to frequency-dependent behavior of lungs. *J. Appl. Physiol.* 26: 670–673, 1969.
128. MEAD, J., AND J. L. WHITTENBERGER. Evaluation of airway interruption technique as a method for measuring pulmonary air-flow resistance. *J. Appl. Physiol.* 6: 408–416, 1954.
129. MEAD, W. J., AND V. P. COLLINS. The principles of dilatancy applied to techniques of radiotherapy. *Am. J. Roentgenol. Radium Ther. Nucl. Med.* 71: 864–866, 1954.
130. MENENDEZ, R., H. W. KELLY, AND W. TUTTLE. A comparison of total respiratory conductance by forced oscillations with spirometry in evaluating the response of asthmatic children to inhaled isoproterenol (Abstract). *Am. Rev. Respir. Dis.* 123, Suppl.: 162, 1981.
131. MICHAELSON, E. D. Effects of the mouth shunt impedance on the frequency response of the respiratory system (Abstract). *Proc. Int. Congr. Physiol. Sci., 27th, Paris, 1977,* vol. 13, p. 505.
132. MICHAELSON, E. D., E. D. GRASSMAN, AND W. R. PETERS. Pulmonary mechanics by spectral analysis of forced random noise. *J. Clin. Invest.* 56: 1210–1230, 1975.
133. MILLER, T. K., AND R. L. PIMMEL. Forced noise mechanical parameters during inspiration and expiration. *J. Appl. Physiol.: Respirat. Environ. Exercise Physiol.* 52: 1530–1534, 1982.
134. MITCHELL, M., S. WATANABE, AND A. D. RENZETTI. Evaluation of airway conductance measurements in normal subjects and patients with chronic obstructive pulmonary disease. *Am. Rev. Respir. Dis.* 96: 685–691, 1967.
135. MITTMAN, C., N. H. EDELMAN, A. H. NORRIS, AND N. W. SHOCK. Relationship between chest wall and pulmonary compliance and age. *J. Appl. Physiol.* 20: 1211–1216, 1965.
136. MIYAKAWA, M., K. YAMAMOTO, AND T. MIKAMI. Acoustic measurement of the respiratory system—an acoustic pneumograph. *Med. Biol. Eng.* 14: 653–659, 1976.
137. MLCZOCH, J. Impedance of the lung in acute pulmonary infarction. In: *Progress in Respiration Research. Pulmonary Embolism,* edited by J. Widimsky. Basel: Karger, 1980, vol. 13, p. 82–87.
138. MÜLLER, E., AND J. VOGEL. Modeling and parameter estimation of the respiratory system using oscillatory impedance curves (Abstract). *Bull. Eur. Physiopathol. Respir.* 17: 10P–11P, 1981.
139. MÜLLER, E., H. WUTHE, AND J. VOGEL. Estimation of respiratory parameters using oscillatory impedance data and results of modeling (Abstract). *Bull. Eur. Physiopathol. Respir.* 16: 189P–190P, 1980.
140. MURPHY, D. M. F., L. F. METZGER, D. A. SILAGE, AND L. M. HOLLMANN. Frequency dependent resistance in simple coal workers' pneumoconiosis (Abstract). *Am. Rev. Respir. Dis.* 123, Suppl.: 143, 1981.
141. MURPHY, D. M. F., D. A. SILAGE, L. F. METZGER, AND G. R. OWENS. Forced oscillation measurements of total respiratory resistance (Abstract). *Am. Rev. Respir. Dis.* 121, Suppl.: 171, 1980.
142. MURRAY, A., AND J. M. M. NEILSON. Diagnostic percussion sounds. I. A qualitative analysis. *Med. Biol. Eng.* 13: 19–28, 1975.
143. NAGELS, J., F. J. LÁNDSÉR, L. VAN DER LINDEN, J. CLÉMENT, AND K. P. VAN DE WOESTIJNE. Mechanical properties of lungs and chest wall during spontaneous breathing. *J. Appl. Physiol.: Respirat. Environ. Exercise Physiol.* 49: 408–416, 1980.
144. NAIMARK, A., AND R. M. CHERNIACK. Compliance of the respiratory system and its components in health and obesity. *J. Appl. Physiol.* 15: 377–382, 1960.
145. NIEDING, G. VON, AND U. SMIDT. Pharmacokinetics of different bronchodilators as measured continuously with the oscillation method (Abstract). *Bull. Eur. Physiopathol. Respir.* 13: 126P–127P, 1977.
146. NISELL, O. I., AND A. B. DUBOIS. Relationship between compliance and FRC of the lungs in cats, and measurement of resistance to breathing. *Am. J. Physiol.* 178: 206–210, 1954.
147. NOLTE, D., D. BERGER, AND E. FORSTER. Theoretical and clinical aspects of impedance measurements of the respiratory system. In: *Progress in Respiration Research. Biomedical Engineering and Data Processing in Pneumonology,* edited by H. Matthys. Basel: Karger, 1979, vol. 11, p. 172–178.
148. OLIVE, J. T., AND R. E. HYATT. Maximal expiratory flow and total respiratory resistance during induced bronchoconstriction in asthmatic subjects. *Am. Rev. Respir. Dis.* 106: 366–376, 1972.
149. OTIS, A. B., C. B. MCKERROW, R. A. BARTLETT, J. MEAD, M. B. MCILROY, N. J. SELVERSTONE, AND E. P. RADFORD, JR. Mechanical factors in distribution of pulmonary ventilation. *J. Appl. Physiol.* 8: 427–443, 1956.
150. OTIS, A. B., AND D. F. PROCTOR. Measurement of alveolar pressure in human subjects. *Am. J. Physiol.* 152: 106–112, 1948.
151. PESLIN, R., C. DUVIVIER, AND J. MORINET-LAMBERT. Réponse en fréquence du système mécanique ventilatoire total de 3 à 70 Hz. *Bull. Physio-Pathol. Respir.* 8: 267–279, 1972.
152. PESLIN, R., B. HANNHART, AND J. PINO. Impédance mécanique thoraco-pulmonaire chez des sujets fumeurs et non-fumeurs. *Bull. Eur. Physiopathol. Respir.* 17: 93–105, 1981.
153. PESLIN, R., T. HIXON, AND J. MEAD. Variations des résistances thoraco-pulmonaires au cours du cycle ventilatoire étudiées par méthode d'oscillation. *Bull. Physio-Pathol. Respir.* 7: 173–188, 1971.
154. PESLIN, R., J. MORINET-LAMBERT, AND C. DUVIVIER. Étude de la réponse en fréquence de pneumotachographes. *Bull. Physio-Pathol. Respir.* 8: 1363–1376, 1972.
155. PESLIN, R., J. PAPON, C. DUVIVIER, AND J. RICHALET. Frequency response of the chest: modeling and parameter estimation. *J. Appl. Physiol.* 39: 523–534, 1975.
156. PETRO, W., G. VON NIEDING, W. BOLL, AND U. SMIDT. Determination of respiratory resistance by an oscillation method. Studies of long-term and short-term variability and dependence upon lung volume and compliance. *Respiration* 42: 243–251, 1981.
157. PIMMEL, R. L., J. M. FULLTON, J. F. GINSBERG, M. J. HAZUCHA, E. D. HAAK, W. F. MCDONNELL, AND P. A. BROMBERG. Correlation of airway resistance with forced random noise resistance parameters. *J. Appl. Physiol.: Respirat. Environ. Exercise Physiol.* 51: 33–39, 1981.
158. PIMMEL, R. L., R. A. SUNDERLAND, D. J. ROBINSON, H. B. WILLIAMS, R. L. HAMLIN, AND P. A. BROMBERG. Instrumentation for measuring respiratory impedance by forced oscillations. *IEEE Trans. Biomed. Eng.* 24: 89–93, 1977.
159. PIMMEL, R. L., M. J. TSAI, D. C. WINTER, AND P. A. BROMBERG. Estimating central and peripheral respiratory resistance. *J. Appl. Physiol.: Respirat. Environ. Exercise Physiol.* 45: 375–380, 1978.
160. PIMMEL, R. L., D. C. WINTER, AND P. A. BROMBERG. Forced oscillatory parameters of the canine respiratory system with altered vagal tone. *IEEE Trans. Biomed. Eng.* 27: 146–149, 1980.
161. RICE, D. A. Sound speed in the upper airways. *J. Appl. Physiol.: Respirat. Environ. Exercise Physiol.* 49: 326–336, 1980.

162. ROHRER, R. Der Strömungswiderstand in den menschlichen Atemwegen und der Einfluss der unregelmassigen Verzweigung des bronchial Systems auf den Atmungsverlauf in verschiedenen Lungenbezirken. *Pfluegers Arch. Gesamte Physiol. Menschen Tiere* 162: 225–299, 1915.

163. ROSS, A. J., M. B. RABER, B. W. KIRK, AND D. H. GOLDSTEIN. Direct readout of respiratory impedance. *Med. Biol. Eng.* 14: 558–564, 1976.

164. SAUMON, G., E. DELAVAULT, AND R. GEORGES. Modeling of the frequency response of the respiratory system from mouth input (Abstract). *Bull. Eur. Physiopathol. Respir.* 17: 14P–16P, 1981.

165. SCHMID-SCHOENBEIN, G. W., AND Y. C. FUNG. Forced perturbation of respiratory system. A. The traditional model. *Ann. Biomed. Eng.* 6: 194–211, 1978.

166. SCHWABER, J. R., M. KHAN, G. TANABE, AND M. STEIN. Determination of total respiratory flow resistance by forced oscillations (Abstract). *Clin. Res.* 13: 352, 1965.

167. SHARP, J. T., J. DANON, AND W. S. DRUZ. The continuous direct reading measurement of respiratory resistance at multiple frequencies (Abstract). *Am. Rev. Respir. Dis.* 105: 1016, 1972.

168. SHARP, J. T., J. P. HENRY, S. K. SWEANY, W. R. MEADOWS, AND R. J. PIETRAS. Total respiratory inertance and its gas and tissue components in normal and obese men. *J. Clin. Invest.* 43: 503–509, 1964.

169. SHARP, J. T., J. P. HENRY, S. K. SWEANY, W. R. MEADOWS, AND R. J. PIETRAS. The total work of breathing in normal and obese men. *J. Clin. Invest.* 43: 728–739, 1964.

170. SHARP, J. T., S. K. SWEANY, J. P. HENRY, R. J. PIETRAS, AND W. R. MEADOWS. Total respiratory inertance in normal and obese persons (Abstract). *Physiologist* 5: 212, 1962.

171. SHEARER, J. L., A. T. MURPHY, AND H. H. RICHARDSON. *Introduction to System Dynamics.* Reading, MA: Addison-Wesley, 1967.

172. SHEPHARD, R. J. Mechanical characteristics of the human airway in relation to use of the interrupter valve. *Clin. Sci.* 25: 263–280, 1963.

173. SHEPHARD, R. J. Dynamic characteristics of the human airways and the behavior of unstable breathing systems. *Aerosp. Med.* 37: 1014–1021, 1966.

174. SIDELL, R. S., AND J. J. FREDBERG. Non-invasive inference of airway network geometry from broadband lung reflection data. *J. Biomech. Eng.* 100: 131–138, 1978.

175. SILVERMAN, L., AND J. L. WHITTENBERGER. Clinical pneumotachograph. In: *Methods in Medical Research*, edited by J. H. Comroe. Chicago, IL: Year Book, 1950, vol. 2, p. 104–112.

176. SINHA, R., A. ELIRAZ, AND P. KIMBEL. Correlation of forced oscillation technique with spirometry in evaluation of pulmonary function (Abstract). *Am. Rev. Respir. Dis.* 119, Suppl.: 170, 1979.

177. SLUTSKY, A. S., AND J. M. DRAZEN. Estimating central and peripheral respiratory resistance: an alternative analysis. *J. Appl. Physiol.: Respirat. Environ. Exercise Physiol.* 47: 1325–1331, 1979.

178. SLUTSKY, A. S., AND J. J. FREDBERG. Analysis of frequency dependence of respiratory system resistance using a computer simulation model (Abstract). *Am. Rev. Respir. Dis.* 121, Suppl.: 405, 1980.

179. SMIDT, U., H. LÖLLGEN, G. VON NIEDING, M. FRANEZTKI, V. KORN, AND K. PRESTELE. A new oscillation method for determining resistance to breathing. *Verh. Ges. Lungen-Atmungsforsch.* 6: 211–225, 1976.

180. SMITH, J. C., J. P. BUTLER, AND F. G. HOPPIN, JR. Dynamic mechanical properties of lung parenchyma (Abstract). *Physiologist* 23(4): 45, 1980.

181. SOBOL, B. J. Tests of ventilatory function not requiring maximal subject effort. II. The measurement of total respiratory impedance. *Am. Rev. Respir. Dis.* 97: 868–879, 1968.

182. SONDHI, M. M., AND B. GOPINATH. Determination of vocal tract shape from impulse response at the lips. *J. Acoust. Soc. Am.* 49: 1867–1873, 1971.

183. STĂNESCU, D. C., R. FESLER, C. VERITER, A. FRANS, AND L. BRASSEUR. A modified measurement of respiratory resistance by forced oscillation during normal breathing. *J. Appl. Physiol.* 39: 305–311, 1975.

184. STĂNESCU, D., N. E. MOAVERO, C. VERITER, AND L. BRASSEUR. Frequency dependence of respiratory resistance in healthy children. *J. Appl. Physiol.: Respirat. Environ. Exercise Physiol.* 47: 268–272, 1979.

185. STĂNESCU, D. C., J. PATTIJN, J. CLÉMENT, AND K. P. VAN DE WOESTIJNE. Glottis opening and airway resistance. *J. Appl. Physiol.* 32: 460–466, 1972.

186. STRUTT, J. W., AND BARON RAYLEIGH. *The Theory of Sound.* New York: Dover, 1945, vol. 2, p. 62–66.

187. TAKASHIMA, T., W. HIDA, M. SASAKI, S. SUZUKI, T. SASAKI. Direct-writing recorder of the dose-response curves of airway to methacoline clinical applications. *Chest* 80: 600–606, 1981.

188. TAYLOR, M. G. Input impedance of an assembly of randomly branching elastic tubes. *Biophys. J.* 5: 29–51, 1966.

189. TAYLOR, M. G. Use of random excitations and spectral analysis in the study of frequency-dependent parameters of the cardiovascular system. *Circ. Res.* 18: 585–595, 1966.

190. TSAI, M. J., R. L. PIMMEL, E. J. STIFF, P. A. BROMBERG, AND R. L. HAMLIN. Respiratory parameter estimation using forced oscillatory impedance data. *J. Appl. Physiol.: Respirat. Environ. Exercise Physiol.* 43: 322–330, 1977.

191. TUTTLE, W. C., J. A. LOEPPKY, AND U. C. LUFT. Effect of gas density on total respiratory conductance measured by forced oscillations (Abstract). *Federation Proc.* 36: 614, 1977.

192. VAN BRABANDT, H., M. CAUBERGHS, P. MOERMAN, AND K. P. VAN DE WOESTIJNE. Partitioning of pulmonary impedance in excised human lungs (Abstract). *Am. Rev. Respir. Dis.* 123, Suppl.: 194, 1981.

193. VAN DEN BERG, J. W. Myoelastic-aerodynamic theory of voice production. *J. Speech Hear. Res.* 1: 227–244, 1958.

194. VAN DEN BERG, J. W. An electrical analogue of the trachea, lungs and tissues. *Acta Physiol. Pharmacol. Neerl.* 9: 361–385, 1960.

195. VAN LITH, P., F. N. JOHNSON, AND J. T. SHARP. Respiratory elastances in relaxed and paralyzed states in normal and abnormal men. *J. Appl. Physiol.* 23: 475–486, 1967.

196. VARÈNE, P., AND C. JACQUEMIN. Plethysmographic measurement of the impedance of the gaseous ventilatory system. In: *Progress in Respiration Research. Body Plethysmography*, edited by A. B. DuBois and K. P. van de Woestijne. Basel: Karger, 1969, vol. 4, p. 88–101.

197. VARÈNE, P., J. TIMBAL, AND C. JACQUEMIN. Étude comparative des résistances respiratoires tissulaires et gazeuses de l'homme. *Arch. Sci. Physiol.* 20: 303–341, 1966.

198. VINCENT, N. J., R. KNUDSON, D. E. LEITH, P. T. MACKLEM, AND J. MEAD. Factors influencing pulmonary resistance. *J. Appl. Physiol.* 29: 236–243, 1970.

199. VON NEERGAARD, K., AND K. WIRZ. Die Messung der Strömungswiderstande in den Atemwegen des Menschen insbesondere bei Asthma und Emphysem. *Z. Klin. Med.* 105: 51–82, 1927.

200. WANNER, A., S. ZARZECKI, AND M. B. MARKS. Continuous measurement of respiratory resistance in asthmatic children. *Respiration* 34: 61–68, 1977.

201. WEIBEL, E. R. Morphometrics of the lung. In: *Handbook of Physiology. Respiration*, edited by W. O. Fenn and H. Rahn. Washington, DC: Am. Physiol. Soc., 1964, sect. 3, vol. I, chapt. 7, p. 285–307.

202. WILLIAMS, S. P., J. M. FULLTON, M. J. TSAI, R. L. PIMMEL, AND A. M. COLLIER. Respiratory impedance and derived parameters in young children by forced random noise. *J. Appl. Physiol.: Respirat. Environ. Exercise Physiol.* 47: 169–174, 1979.

203. WILLIAMS, S. P., R. L. PIMMEL, J. M. FULLTON, M. J. TSAI, AND A. M. COLLIER. Fractionating respiratory resistance in young children. *J. Appl. Physiol.: Respirat. Environ. Exercise*

Physiol. 47: 551–555, 1979.
204. WOHL, M. E., L. C. STIGOL, AND J. MEAD. Resistance of the total respiratory system in healthy infants and infants with bronchiolitis. *Pediatrics* 43: 495–509, 1969.
205. WOMERSLEY, J. R. Method for calculation of velocity rate of flow, and viscous drag in arteries when the pressure gradient is known. *J. Physiol. London* 127: 553–563, 1955.
206. YAMASHIRO, S. M., S. K. KARUZA, AND J. D. HACKNEY. Phase compensation of Fleisch pneumotachographs. *J. Appl. Physiol.* 36: 493–495, 1974.
207. ZALTER, R., H. C. HARDY, AND A. A. LUISADA. Acoustic transmission characteristics of the thorax. *J. Appl. Physiol.* 18: 428–436, 1963.
208. ZECHMAN, F. W., JR., D. PECK, AND E. LUCE. Effect of vertical vibration on respiratory airflow and transpulmonary pressure. *J. Appl. Physiol.* 20: 849–854, 1965.

CHAPTER 12

Respiratory mechanics in children

A. CHARLES BRYAN | *The Hospital for Sick Children, Toronto, Ontario, Canada*
MARY ELLEN B. WOHL | *Children's Hospital, Boston, Massachusetts*

CHAPTER CONTENTS

IN THE 1964 EDITION of the *Handbook* section on respiration, Agostoni and Mead (4) stated that

> the main static change of the respiratory system during growth is the increasing outward recoil of the chest wall. It is not clear how much of this is due to changes in the mechanical properties of the chest wall and how much to a disproportionate growth of the chest wall relative to that of the lungs.

The questions implicit in this statement have still not been answered, but a number of factors may play a part.

MECHANICAL PROPERTIES OF CHEST WALL

Structural Changes in Rib Cage

During development the shape of the thorax changes significantly. At birth the ribs extend horizontally from the vertebral column, and the cross section of the thorax is more circular than it is in the adult (112). As a result the diaphragm is also much more horizontal than it is in the adult. This mechan-ical arrangement seems inefficient. In the adult the volume of the rib cage is increased by raising the ribs, which enlarges the volume by both a "bucket handle" and a "pump handle" effect (54).

With growth the thoracic cavity not only enlarges but changes in shape and texture. There is a progressive mineralization of the ribs and an increase in the ratio of bone to cartilage. Assumption of the upright posture alters the forces acting on the rib cage (63). In addition to gravitational forces, the ribs are subjected to an increasingly vigorous pull from the sacrospinal and abdominal muscles. The ribs develop a distinct caudal inclination. In addition, dorsal inclination of the ribs at their vertebral ends is more marked, bringing the thoracic cavity alongside and dorsal to the vertebral column. These changes lead to a relative decrease in the anteroposterior diameter of the rib cage. In addition, in front view the thorax assumes the shape of a Gothic arch compared with a Roman arch in the infant.

The gravitational effects of the abdominal contents also have a major effect on the compliance of the chest wall (28). In the upright position gravity acts in an expiratory direction on the rib cage, but this is offset by the inspiratory action on the diaphragm, the net effect being to decrease the compliance of the chest wall and increase its outward recoil (54). The magnitude of this effect depends on the height of the abdominal hydrostatic column; thus the effect is probably trivial in babies but increasingly important with changes in height. This point stresses a general impression that the stiffening of the chest wall appears to occur faster than the mineralization of the ribs, presumably because of changes in the shape and forces applied to the chest wall.

Changes in Respiratory Muscles

With growth there is a progressive increase in the bulk of the muscles attached to the rib cage. There is also an increase, which is essentially complete by the end of the first year, in the number of type I fibers (slow-twitch, high-oxidative fibers) in the diaphragm and intercostal muscles (58). Several investigators have shown an increase in maximum inspiratory and expiratory pressures with a substantial difference between the sexes at all age groups (17, 35) coinciding with the increases in muscle bulk. There are minor differences between different investigators, but typical values are shown in Table 1.

The maximum pressures exerted by children compared with those exerted by adults are surprisingly high compared with other indices of muscle strength. However, this is probably related to the small radius of curvature of the rib cage, diaphragm, and abdomen, which by the Laplace relationship can convert small tensions into large pressures. Newborn infants have been reported to generate very large (-70 cmH$_2$O) pressures during the first breath (56). Furthermore during the first year of life pressures in excess of -60 cmH$_2$O have been reported in anesthetized children just prior to extubation (73).

The increasing bulk of respiratory muscle with growth may also play a part in the stiffening of the chest wall. Furthermore the decrease in rapid-eye-movement (REM) sleep with growth decreases the amount of time during which there is tonic inhibition of the respiratory muscles.

Compliance of Chest Wall

In the newborn dog (3), goat (5), and human (36, 89, 98, 99), the compliance of the chest wall above functional residual capacity (FRC) is very high, whether it is expressed per unit lung volume or per unit lung weight. In preterm infants (<32 wk) the compliance is ~6.4 ml$\cdot$cmH$_2$O$^{-1}\cdot$kg^{-1}, decreasing to ~4.2 ml$\cdot$cmH$_2$O$^{-1}\cdot$kg^{-1} by term (36). This compliance is high because the ratio of cartilage to rib is high, the cartilage is thinner, and the bone is softer due to incomplete mineralization. During growth there is a progressive decrease in the compliance of the chest wall, but data on this important development are scanty. In animals the stiffening appears to occur rapidly (3, 5); however, this does not appear to be the case in humans (99). In paralyzed infants there appear to be no major changes in compliance over the first 6 mo of life. However, paralysis by eliminating the thoracic muscle tone may produce an artificially high compliance. Total respiratory system compliance continues to decrease from age 5 to 16 yr; most of this change is attributable to changes in the chest wall (83, 102).

Although lack of recoil is advantageous because it minimizes the amount of pulmonary liquid contained in the lung at birth, it poses a number of mechanical problems to the maintenance of both lung volume and ventilation.

Functional Residual Capacity

In the adult the FRC is defined as the static passive balance of forces between the lung and chest wall. This establishes an FRC of $\sim50\%$ of total lung capacity (TLC) in the upright position and $\sim40\%$ in the supine position (Fig. 1). In the infant the outward recoil of the chest wall is exceedingly small (3, 5) and the inward recoil of the lung is slightly lower than that in the adult (31). Consequently the static balance of forces would dictate an FRC of $\sim10\%$ of TLC. Such a small FRC seems incompatible with stability of the terminal airways or adequate gas exchange. From the measured FRC (87) and the anatomic estimate of TLC (31), the dynamic FRC/TLC value appears to be $\sim40\%$ (similar to the supine adult). Thus there are compelling reasons to believe that the dynamic end-expiratory volume is substantially above the passively determined FRC. The most obvious evidence for this is that during apnea the end-expiratory volume generally falls to a substantially lower volume, which is presumably the passive FRC. Thach et al. (114) showed that in one paraplegic infant (in whom expiration was entirely passive) the end-expiratory relaxation pressure was consistently positive, indicating that the end-expiratory volume was not passively determined. Kosch and Stark (62) have shown that in the infant, in contrast to the adult, expiration is terminated at substantial flow rates. This suggests an active interruption of a relaxed expiration. However, the nature of this active braking is not fully understood. Olinsky et al. (90) suggested that because the infant has a relatively long pulmonary time constant with respect to expiratory time, there might not be time to expire passively to FRC (except during apnea). Harding et al. (45) have shown that, in the lamb, adductor muscles of the larynx act as an expiratory brake in awake and non-rapid-eye-movement (NREM) sleep but not in REM sleep. Fisher et al. (32) have shown that glottic closure is a very important mechanism for establishing a lung volume in the immediate postnatal period. Respiration at this time is quite irregular; it is interrupted abruptly during expiration at elevated lung volumes. This striking pattern is not seen after the first few hours of life; however, laryngeal braking may still be present. Muller et al. (85) have suggested that tonic activity in both the diaphragm and intercostals effectively stiffens the chest wall and establishes a higher active end-expiratory volume. The end-expiratory volume is certainly related to sleep. Henderson-Smart and Read

TABLE 1. *Maximum Inspiratory Pressure at Functional Residual Capacity*

Age, yr	Pressure, cmH$_2$O	
	Male	Female
7–8	70	59
9–10	97	77
11–12	105	98
18–47	107	
18–32		82

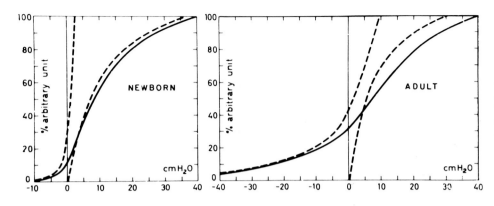

FIG. 1. Static pressure-volume curve of lung (*right dashed line*), chest wall (*left dashed line*), and total respiratory system (*solid line*) in newborn and adult. [From Agostoni (3).]

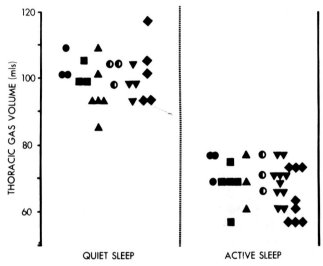

FIG. 2. Changes in thoracic gas volume at end expiration in 6 normal human newborn infants (indicated by different symbols) from quiet (NREM) sleep to active (REM) sleep. [From Henderson-Smart and Read (49).]

[Fig. 2; (49)] have shown an ~30% fall in the thoracic gas volume in infants going from NREM to REM sleep. This very large fall results from either loss of tonic activity of the respiratory muscles (85), loss of laryngeal braking (45), or both. Lopes et al. (70) have shown that there is a substantial fall in end-expiratory volume during apnea in NREM sleep. In contrast the fall in volume is smaller and very variable in REM sleep; this variability is related to the variability of tonic diaphragmatic electromyogram (EMG) in REM sleep. One of the consequences of the fall in the end-expiratory volume in REM sleep is the concomitant fall in the transcutaneous partial pressure of O_2 (P_{O_2}) (78), presumably because of dependent airway closure. Also because the FRC is the major O_2 store, a smaller FRC must lead to a more rapid fall of arterial P_{O_2} during apnea in REM sleep.

It is not known at what age the FRC is no longer determined dynamically but by the static passive balance of forces between the lung and the chest wall.

Ventilation

In the adult roughly half of the total impedance of the respiratory system resides in the chest wall; thus about half of the force generated by the respiratory muscles is dissipated in moving the chest wall rather than effecting volume exchange. From this point of view the highly compliant chest wall of the infant appears advantageous. But there is a price to be paid. The chest wall is not a single generator but basically two (39, 42). The caudal surface of the lung is driven by the diaphragm and the remaining surface by the rib cage; the problem is that these two generators oppose one another. Inspiratory action of either one lowers pleural pressure; this has an expiratory action on the other, thus wasting some of its displacement. The magnitude of this paradoxical motion depends on the relative compliances of the lung and chest wall, because the diaphragm acts on these in parallel and divides its displacement accordingly. Herein lies the major dynamic problem for the baby. The ratio of the passive compliance of the chest wall to the passive compliance of the lung in the preterm infant is ~6.7:1 (36), which would be an impossible division for adequate ventilation. However, passive properties imply total relaxation of any muscle (or structure) that might influence pressure development. But active muscles may be thought of as having passive properties in the sense that they also respond passively to externally applied forces. The intercostals will have force-length characteristics that reduce the compliance of the rib cage progressively as their force of contraction increases.

A further stabilizing factor follows from the fact that the lower rib cage and that portion of the diaphragm apposed to it form part of the abdominal wall. The diaphragm acts on the rib cage directly through its insertion and indirectly by increasing abdominal pressure. The forces tend to elevate and evert the lower rib cage. However, this mechanical coupling is much more effective in the upright position than in the supine position, and babies (in civilized societies) are usually kept in a prone or supine position. Furthermore for the diaphragmatic action on the rib cage to be effective in changing lung volume, actions applied to the lower rib cage must be transmitted to the upper rib cage. This transmission also depends on the compliance of the rib cage. If the rib cage is very compliant, motion of the lower ribs is not transmitted and there is paradoxical breathing, that is, splaying of the lower rib cage and sternal retraction. In the very premature infant, in whom it is difficult to identify NREM sleep (26) and who has very compliant ribs, paradoxical breathing is almost constant (21). As the infant matures, paradoxical breathing is more clearly confined to episodes of REM sleep, but even in NREM sleep there is little outward motion of the rib cage during inspiration (59). Outward motion of the rib cage during NREM sleep is only seen in mature infants. Distortion of the rib cage from its relaxation line during REM sleep is still quite marked in older children (111) and present in the adult (116). It should be noted that distortion of the ribs is another way of stiffening the system and is probably the major factor that increases the active compliance of the very premature infant.

Several attempts have been made to measure the active compliance of infants (1, 11, 37), and although there are substantial differences in the actual numbers there is general agreement that it is lower than the passive compliance. Furthermore these estimates must be regarded as maximum values for active compliance. They assume that the respiratory system will expand along its relaxation line. Any distortion away from the relaxation line will further stiffen the chest wall.

Cost of Rib Cage Distortion

When there is rib cage distortion the diaphragm is in effect sucking in ribs rather than fresh air. Therefore to maintain the tidal volume the diaphragm has to increase its force of contraction. To the extent that during REM sleep the FRC falls, the diaphragm is longer and hence a more efficient pressure generator (42). However, this is clearly inadequate. The diaphragm has to shorten more, and this is reflected by a considerable increase in the abdominal motion (59). During distortion there is a very substantial increase in the diaphragmatic EMG, measured either from moving time average or from total power (84). This increase is characteristically variable—the increase is anywhere from 50% to 450% and correlates with the magnitude of the distortion. Heldt et al. (46) attempted to partition the work done on the lung and chest wall using abdominal and thoracic motion and transdiaphragmatic pressure. There are only approximations (40), but the results are quite striking. The work done on the chest wall varied from 90% to 396% of the work done on the lung (46), the variation being roughly proportional to the degree of distortion.

Respiratory Muscle Fatigue

It is clear that a substantial amount of the work of the diaphragm is dissipated in distorting the rib cage. In addition, in preterm infants with respiratory distress syndrome (lungs are small and stiff) or in infants with superimposed lung disease, the work that must be done on the lung is high. It is now well established in adults that the inspiratory muscles can fatigue; that is, fail as force generators in much the same way and for many of the same reasons that the heart can fail (72, 100). The preterm infant appears to be more vulnerable than the adult. The paucity of type I fibers in their respiratory muscles (58) may make them poorly equipped to sustain high work rates and the substrate supply for muscle contractions is tenuous (118). Respiratory muscle fatigue is dealt with elsewhere in this *Handbook*, and only studies relevant to infants are discussed here. The only method of diagnosing respiratory muscle fatigue in infants is to use the spectral frequency analysis of the diaphragmatic EMG developed by Kogi and Hakamada (61) and Kaiser and Petersen (55). They showed that with a fatiguing load there was a decrease in the high-frequency power and an increase in the low-frequency power of the EMG *before* the muscle failed as a force generator. Muller et al. (84) showed identical changes in the frequency spectrum of surface diaphragmatic EMG in preterm infants going from no distortion to gross distortion. When the infants showed these signs of impending failure, there was a variety of responses: *1*) an overt change in sleep state, which reduced the distortion; *2*) recruitment of the intercostals, which also reduced the distortion; and *3*) apnea. In a subsequent study on sick infants being weaned from ventilators, weaning failure was heralded by marked changes in the EMG spectrum followed by frequent apneas and a rising end-tidal CO_2 (85). A return to the ventilator led to prompt normalization of the EMG spectrum. Lopes et al. (69) have shown that when the EMG shows signs of impending fatigue, if there is intercostal recruitment, breathing continues. However, if the intercostals fail to recruit or cannot sustain the recruitment, apnea ensues. Also, in impending fatigue infants shorten their ratio of inspiratory time to total respiratory cycle duration (T_I/T_T) to shorten the "duty cycle" of the diaphragm. These strategies are also used by adults breathing against fatiguing loads (41).

Thus it appears that respiratory muscle fatigue in the preterm infant can lead to both hypoventilation and apnea. Clinically this makes sense. Carbon dioxide retention and apnea are common in infants with respiratory distress syndrome, whereas CO_2 retention is often absent in the adult respiratory distress syndrome. Apnea is closely linked to load; if the load is acutely relieved (i.e., after ligation of a patent ductus), the apnea usually remits. Apnea is also common when substrate for muscle contraction is low (e.g., hypoglycemia, hypoxia, and hypocalcemia).

Pleural Pressure and Distortion

In dogs electrophrenic stimulation produces greater negative pressure over the lower lobes than over the upper lobes (20). Conversely after section of the phrenic nerves, the pleural pressure swings during spontaneous breathing are greater over the upper lobes. In adult humans, selective activation of the diaphragm or intercostals can similarly alter the distribution of pleural surface pressure (25). Therefore in the infant, who frequently exhibits paradoxical respiration, it is probable that there will be a nonuniform distribution of pleural surface pressure. This leads to both methodological and physiological problems.

The methodological problem is how to measure average pleural surface pressure. Beardsmore et al. (8) have paid great attention to the design of the esophageal balloon. They point out that the ratio of esophageal pressure (Pes) to mouth pressure (Pm) should be close to unity during airway occlusion when pressure changes should equilibrate through a closed system, and they use this to check their balloon. However, they note that when in patients with neuromuscular disease "the respiratory muscles and thoracic cage do not move in their usual synchronous fashion," it is sometimes impossible to get a satisfactory Pes/Pm. Unfortunately many preterm babies are breathing asynchronously most of the time, and generally the greater the distortion, the lower the Pes/Pm (68). Thus it is probable that Pes does not equal average pleural surface pressure when there is distortion, and great caution should be used in interpreting pleural pressures particularly in preterm infants.

The physiological problem is that nonuniform pleural pressure changes probably imply nonuniform distribution of ventilation. This probably has little importance in the normal infant's lung but may be a significant factor in infants with lung disease.

MECHANICAL PROPERTIES OF THE LUNG

General Considerations

During early gestation, the full complement of airways is laid down (13). In contrast, most of the 300 million alveoli develop in the early postnatal years (27). Substantial changes in lung tissue occur with development of collagen, elastin, and muscle. The details of these changes are discussed in the chapter by Brody and Thurlbeck in this *Handbook*. This section is concerned with the main features of the mechanical properties of the lung and airways in humans during this postnatal period of remarkable growth; its purpose is to trace the general pattern of development of the mechanical properties of the respiratory system.

One of the main problems in expressing these properties is standardization according to lung size. One might like to describe the elastic properties of the lung as the volume per unit mass at a specified distending pressure. Alternatively one might express volume at a specified distending pressure as it relates to the volume of the lung in the unstressed state. Even in the excised lung, where these might be possible, difficulties exist. A gram of lung from an infant probably represents more airway tissue and less parenchymal (alveolar and interstitial) tissue than a gram of lung from an adult. Although volume can be measured, the volume of the unstressed lung may be influenced by material in the airways. However, a major advantage of measurements made on excised lungs is the ability to specify the distending pressure accurately. Most investigators have chosen to refer not to the volume in the unstressed state but to the volume in the fully distended state, usually a distending pressure of 20 or 30 cmH$_2$O in the excised lung. Measurements obtained in vivo are even more complicated to assess. A standard stress cannot be specified. With increasing muscle strength children may distend the lung to variable degrees (76). However, this influence appears to be small.

Measurements of distending pressures are also difficult in vivo. Esophageal balloons of different sizes and elasticity have been used at different volumes for estimating esophageal pressures (22, 76, 123). The mechanical characteristics of the esophageal balloon and the esophagus influence the results (123). Gradients of pleural pressure exist within the chest and may change with growth. The location of the sampling site for pressure can vary with the size of the child, thus influencing the estimate of mean pleural or esophageal pressures. Finally, descriptions of the changes in elastic recoil over the full period of growth require comparing measurements made on excised lungs with those made in vivo. Systematic differences in lung volume between excised and in vivo lungs exist (9) but should not influence the shape of the volume-pressure relationship.

Comparing and contrasting the flow-resistive properties of the airways during growth is also difficult. Ideally but impractically one would like to measure airway size or resistance at the same distending pressure and be able to relate it to some measure of lung or body size. When comparing the measurements of airway resistance across age groups one must take into account the conditions of measurements, which vary from infant to adult. Measurements of airway resistance are carried out in sleeping, sometimes sedated, supine infants breathing spontaneously through their noses and in awake, sitting, older children panting on a mouthpiece.

Despite these limitations, some inferences about the relative rates of growth of airways and lung parenchyma can be made from measurements of lung mechanics. The inverse of airway resistance, airway conductance (Gaw), corrected for differences in upper airway resistances and for the degree of turbulence, is sensitive to airway size. Lung volume is an index of lung size and compliance. Specific airway conductance (sGaw), the conductance divided by the lung volume at which it is measured, can then be considered as an index of the relative size of the airways and parenchyma. This ratio has the additional merit of reflecting airway and lung size at the same distending pressure.

Elastic Properties of the Lung

Measurements of the volume-pressure relationship of the lung have been obtained from excised lungs of infants and some children (30, 31, 106) and in older children in vivo using esophageal balloons to measure transpulmonary pressure. Virtually no measurements of static volume-pressure curves of in vivo lungs have been made in children under 6 yr. In excised preparations, lungs have been taken to a pressure of 30 cmH$_2$O, and in vivo TLC is taken to represent full inflation. Comparisons of shape of the volume-pressure relationship can be made by considering the fraction of the volume at full inflation (Vmax) at various distending pressures. Most evidence indicates a shape change in the volume-pressure relationships of the lung as it matures. This may be related to changes in the amount, distribution, and structure of collagen, elastin, and smooth muscle and possibly to changes in the contribution of surface forces as alveoli increase in volume during growth. The details of these biochemical and structural changes are covered in the chapter by Brody and Thurlbeck in this *Handbook*.

Stigol et al. (106) and Fagan (30, 31) obtained quasi-static volume-pressure curves on excised lungs from infants and young children. Stigol et al. (106) showed that during the period of rapid alveolar growth in early childhood, lung volume expressed as milliliters per gram lung weight at a distending pressure of 20 cmH$_2$O increased linearly with body weight. At birth with a body length of 50 cm, the volume was 3.3 ml/g lung weight; at ~16 mo with a body length of 75 cm, the volume was 4.7 ml/g lung weight. Measurements of lung volumes made by Fagan (30) when related to lung weight (29) are similar. Fagan (30, 31) took particular care to exclude abnormal lungs, and the lungs were distended to a fixed pressure of 30 cmH$_2$O. When lung volume is expressed as a fraction of the lung volume at 30 cmH$_2$O (Vmax) there is a marked change in the overall shape of the volume-pressure curve in the age range examined (a gestational age of 33 wk to a postnatal age of 2 yr). The younger lung holds a greater fraction of Vmax at 1, 2.5, and 5 cmH$_2$O than the older lung. Volume at zero distending pressure remains constant (Fig. 3).

When similar information has been expressed as the transpulmonary pressure at a specified lung volume, a similar trend emerges (Fig. 4A). However, the

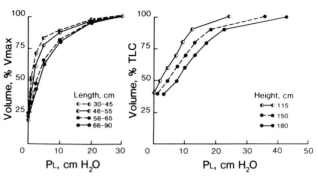

FIG. 3. *Left*: volume-pressure curves obtained from excised lungs. Curves are grouped by body length. Lengths of 30–45, 46–55, 56–65, and 66–90 cm correspond to premature infants, 1 mo, 4.4 mo, and 16 mo, respectively. [From Fagan (30, 31).] *Right*: volume-pressure curves obtained from children. Heights of 115, 150, and 180 cm correspond to ~6, 12–13, and 17 yr as estimated from growth charts. Vmax, maximum volume; TLC, total lung capacity; P$_L$, elastic recoil pressure of lung. [From Zapletal et al. (124).]

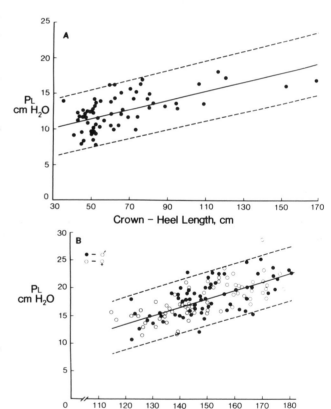

FIG. 4. *A*: elastic recoil pressure of lung at 90% of Vmax, volume at distending pressure of 30 cmH$_2$O, vs. body length in cm. [Adapted from Fagan (31).] *B*: elastic recoil pressure of lung at 90% TLC vs. height in cm. ●, Males; ○, females. [Adapted from Zapletal et al. (124).]

number of in vitro observations in presumably normal lungs from individuals between 2 and 20 yr is limited.

Despite the difficulties with the measurements, increasing lung recoil measured by quasi-static volume-pressure curves during deflation has been observed in vivo in children 6–18 yr (22, 77, 124). A variety of indices of growth has been used, including height, age, and lung volume. In general the changes in lung recoil are best observed at high lung volumes (Fig. 4*B*), which is different from the data obtained in vitro in younger children by Fagan (31) in which the best correlations were obtained at low lung volumes. Nonetheless Figure 4*A*, *B* shows that transpulmonary pressure increases with growth. The variability in measurements is considerable and even greater at low lung volumes.

Despite the variability in lung recoil and the difficulties of measurements, different investigators have observed, in vivo, comparable changes with age, namely an increase in lung recoil at a specified fraction of TLC with increasing age (Table 2). The shift in the shape of the volume-pressure relationship during childhood is shown in Figure 3, taken from the in vitro data of Fagan (30, 31) and the in vivo data of Zapletal et al. (124). The increase in lung recoil in children 6–18 yr is consistent with the observed fall in residual volume/TLC with increasing age (77).

Flow-Resistive Properties of the Lung

An infant's airways are formed by ~16 wk of gestational age (13). Unlike alveoli, new airways are not formed in postnatal life. Airway growth results in increased radius and length and changes in the mechanical properties of airway walls.

AIRWAY WALL COMPLIANCE. The airway walls of infants and young children are more compliant than those of adults. Radiographic studies in normal infants show variations of 20%–50% in anteroposterior dimensions, particularly in intrathoracic tracheal segments during exertion (121). When volume is ex-

pressed as a percent change from volume at zero transmural pressure, the excised trachea of the newborn is twice as compliant as the excised adult trachea (19). Similar measurements show the trachea of the premature to be even more compliant than that of the newborn (14). These data are limited, but they suggest that major changes occur in the first weeks and months of postnatal life. The increase in the amount of cartilage in airways may be responsible (103).

RESISTANCE AND CONDUCTANCE. Measurements of airway (7, 12, 16, 23, 24, 38, 47, 82, 94, 97, 107, 108, 117, 125), pulmonary (14, 18, 53, 57, 64, 91, 92, 94, 110), and total respiratory resistance (15, 16, 77, 105, 120, 122) have been made in the newborn (14, 18, 24, 57, 92, 94, 107, 108, 122) and children 5 yr and older. A limited number of measurements have been made in older infants and young children (23, 53, 64, 91, 107, 108, 122). Any comparison of measurements made in infants with those made in older children and adults must take into account the influence of differences in posture, state of wakefulness, pharyngeal configuration on the measurement, and varying contribution of the glottis. Nonetheless measurement of resistance of airways, lung, and respiratory system remains one of the few measurements in the mechanics of the respiratory system that can be made over the entire age span.

Airway resistance falls from values ranging from 19 to 28 $cmH_2O \cdot liter^{-1} \cdot s$ in the term newborn to values <2 $cmH_2O \cdot liter^{-1} \cdot s$ in the adolescent and adult. The meticulous measurements of Stocks et al. (107, 109) in infants show that airway resistance is higher in preterm than in term infants, suggesting growth of airways in late gestational age. The sGaw falls rapidly as an infant approaches 40 wk postconceptional age, whether or not the child was born prematurely, and continues to fall during the first year of life. This fall in sGaw is an example of the use of a ratio to express relative growth of structures and relative change in mechanical properties. The fall in sGaw suggests a greater increase in lung volume and/or compliance for Gaw during late gestation and early postnatal life. A similar trend is observed in data from 35 normal infants and children 1–60 mo in whom sGaw decreases with increasing height and therefore presumably age (23).

From ~5 yr through adolescence, values for sGaw remain fairly constant; they do not vary with age, height, or lung size. Mean values range from 0.193 to 0.199 $s^{-1} \cdot cmH_2O^{-1}$ (7, 82, 117, 125) except those reported by Godfrey et al. (38), which for unclear reasons are much higher, 0.457 $s^{-1} \cdot cmH_2O^{-1}$.

Stocks and Godfrey (107, 108) have analyzed the changing relationship of airway growth and lung size (Fig. 5). Their analysis is consistent with a high sGaw during infancy, which gradually falls during childhood and then may increase in adolescence. This is consistent with a greater increase in alveolar volume than in

TABLE 2. *Elastic Recoil Pressure of the Lung at 60% and 90% Total Lung Capacity*

Age, yr	90%	60%	Ref.
7	15.4	4.8	22*
	13.6	5.0	124†
	17.1		77
10	17.4	6.2	22*
	16.4	6.5	124†
	18.9		77
13	19.5	7.6	22*
	18.1	7.5	124†
	20.7		77
16	21.6	9.0	22*
	21.0	9.2	124†
	22.4		77

* Average elastic recoil pressure of lung (Pel,L) at each lung volume calculated from published regression equations.   † Pel,L at specified age calculated from regression equations for Pel,L vs. height, assuming height to be 120 cm at age 7, 138 cm at age 10, 150 cm at age 13, and 170 cm at age 16.

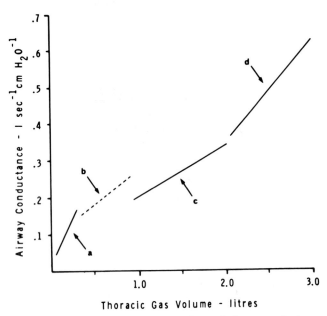

FIG. 5. Comparison of regression lines of airway conductance during mouth breathing from infancy to adulthood. Regression lines were obtained from the following studies: *line a*, data on infants from Stocks and Godfrey (108); *line b*, data on children 1–5 yr from Doershuk et al. (23), calculated by assuming that 49% of airway resistance obtained during nose breathing was due to nasal resistance; *line c*, data on children and adolescents from Zapletal et al. (123); *line d*, data on adult males from Briscoe and DuBois (12). [From Stocks and Godfrey (108).]

Gaw during early life and possibly some increase in airway size during adolescence and adult life. The details of these later changes are not worked out.

Mean values of pulmonary resistance in newborns range from 25 to 38 $cmH_2O \cdot liter^{-1} \cdot s$ (14, 18, 57, 94, 110) and in infants from 21 to 27 $cmH_2O \cdot liter^{-1} \cdot s$ (53, 64, 91). Part of the variability in measurements includes artifacts introduced in the measurement of Pes by the heart. A few efforts to measure the resistance of lung tissue in infants and children have been made (6, 94). However, estimates of changing relative contributions from infancy to adulthood are complicated not only because measurements are made in the infant during nose breathing and in the older child during mouth breathing but also by the possible effect of frequency on the measurement of tissue resistance and the role of lung tissue hysteresis on the measurement (6).

Total respiratory system resistance (Rrs) measured by forced oscillations applied at the airway (15, 16, 76) or the body surface (122) includes resistance of the airway, lung tissue, and chest wall. The magnitude of the contribution of chest wall resistance to total Rrs has not been well defined in children. In a very limited number of measurements, chest wall resistance in infants was estimated (assuming nasal resistance to be 25% of pulmonary resistance) to be 28% of total Rrs during inspiration and 36% during expiration compared with 35% and 39%, respectively, in adult

subjects (122). Cogswell et al. (16) measured Rrs and airway resistance in boys ranging from 115 to 173 cm in height. If the assumption is made that the contribution of the glottis to airway resistance was the same during the two measurements, the contribution of the resistance of lung tissue and chest wall as a fraction of total Rrs can be calculated to range from 22% to 35%.

Frequency dependence of Rrs has not been observed in infants (122) over a very limited range of frequencies (4.5–7.5 Hz) but has been observed in older children examined at 4 and 9 Hz (105, 120). Stănescu et al. (105) found a decrease in frequency-dependent behavior as children grew from 3 to 14 yr. They interpreted frequency dependence of resistance in young children to reflect asynchronous distribution of volume between central airways and peripheral units as the result of high peripheral resistance in young children.

DISTRIBUTION OF RESISTANCE. Studies investigating the distribution of resistance along the tracheobronchial tree are limited in children. Recent measurements of nasal resistance (108) on 30 white and 13 black infants avoid manipulation of the nose or airway present in earlier studies (65, 92) and show that nasal resistance comprises 49% of airway resistance in white infants and significantly less (31%) in black infants. In older children, resistance can be measured during mouth breathing, and the contribution of nasal resistance to airway resistance has not been described.

Hogg et al. (52), using the retrograde-catheter technique (51, 71), partitioned central (trachea to 12th–15th generation) and peripheral (12th–15th generation to alveoli) resistance in excised lungs of infants, children, and adults. They found central Gaw per gram of lung weight, predicted from body length, to be constant from the newborn to the adult. The peripheral Gaw per gram predicted lung weight increased markedly with increasing age, particularly in children over 5 yr (Fig. 6). They interpreted this to indicate that airways distal to the catheter were disproportionately small in the child under 5 yr. Their anatomic measurements in young children are limited and not consistent with those of Hislop et al. (50). It is difficult to translate the measurements made by Hogg et al. (52) to measurements made in vivo. If central Gaw per gram lung weight is constant with growth it can be anticipated that sGaw would be relatively constant. However, a gram of lung in the infant may represent more central airway and less parenchymal tissue than in the older child and adult. Thus a constant central Gaw per gram lung weight need not imply a constant sGaw. Furthermore the very young infant's lung contains more air volume at 5 cmH_2O than older lungs when volume is expressed as percent Vmax (Fig. 3). Thus dividing Gaw by volume does not ensure that the airways are distended to the same degree during measurements made in younger and older children. If

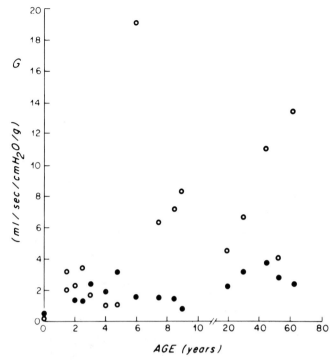

FIG. 6. Retrograde-catheter data showing change in conductance (G) of central (●) and peripheral (○) airways per gram of predicted lung weight with age. [From Hogg et al. (52).]

peripheral Gaw is disproportionately low in infants compared with older children, then one would anticipate relatively low maximum expiratory flows at low lung volumes. Relatively high flows at 25% of the vital capacity (VC) were observed in studies carried out in healthy infants and children undergoing anesthesia (83). However, the low peripheral Gaw relative to central Gaw in infants is an attractive observation to partially explain the severity of abnormalities of gas exchange in infants but not in older children with bronchiolitis. It is also consistent with the frequency dependence of resistance (105, 120) and higher closing volumes observed in children in contrast to young adults (75), although the latter is partly explained by the lower elastic recoil in younger children.

MAXIMUM EXPIRATORY FLOW. Children are able to perform forced expiratory maneuvers with reliability at ~8 yr, and considerable data have been accumulated in normal children (60a, 67, 82, 101, 104, 119, 123, 125). Despite technical differences between studies most investigators have found that maximum expiratory flow in children correlates with height, that the variability in flow at a given lung volume is large, and that, as in adults (43, 60a), standardizing flow by correcting it for lung volume does not substantially reduce the variability.

The relationship between maximum expiratory flow expressed as TLC or VC per second and age or height has been investigated to discern patterns of relative growth of airways and lung parenchyma. In studies in which the number of subjects was small (22, 123), the relationship between expiratory flow and lung volume appears constant from ~6 to 18 yr. In other studies (67, 82, 104) flows expressed as VC or TLC per second decrease with increasing age and height through childhood.

The relative constancy of expiratory flow divided by lung volume throughout childhood has been taken by some to be evidence in favor of isotropic growth through childhood (123). However, a decrease in expiratory flow/lung volume with growth is predictable if flow is turbulent [(80); see the next section].

In young infants, forcing the respiratory system at the body surface can produce maximum expiratory flow over a lung volume probably equivalent to the lower 25% of the VC in older children (2). From these curves one can draw a slope of flow/volume. This has the units of $1/t$, where t is time, and is a constant describing how fast the lung empties. Rate constants for infants, children, and adults (Table 3) show that the infant lung empties some fourfold faster than the adult lung.

Two additional analyses of the forced expiratory maneuver reveal differences between younger and older children and adults (79, 88). The shape of the flow-volume relationship changes with increasing age. In early childhood, flow tends to be convex to the volume axis. With increasing age through early adult life it becomes progressively more concave to the volume axis, and with aging again becomes convex (79). This is compatible with the lower elastic recoil observed in younger children and with nonhomogeneous emptying of the lung in the young and elderly. In some youngsters there is an abrupt fall in expiratory flow to zero at low lung volumes, which is usually attributed to the stiffness of the chest wall. The spirogram can be analyzed so that volume is divided into segments to which a transit time is assigned. The mean transit time, like the slope of the flow-volume relationship, represents the average rate at which the lung empties. The coefficient of variance of transit times indicates the spread of transit times and, like

TABLE 3. *Rate Constants From Maximum Expiratory Flow-Volume Curves From Newborns to Adults*

Age	Rate Constant
Newborn	7.8 ± 2.1 SD*
3–5 yr	3.9, 2.7†
6–8 yr	2.5 ± 0.8 SD‡
9–11 yr	2.0 ± 0.5 SD‡
25–33 yr	1.7 ± 0.6 SD§

* Data from Adler and Wohl (2).   † Assuming functional residual capacity (FRC) = 40% total lung capacity (TLC) and residual volume (RV) = 20% TLC and alternatively FRC = 40% TLC and RV = 15% TLC. [Data from Taussig (113).]   ‡ Data from M. E. B. Wohl, unpublished observations.   §Data from Knudson et al. (60a).

the shape of the flow-volume curve, is an index of nonhomogeneity; the skewness of this spread indicates whether the spread occurs primarily at high or low lung volumes. This analysis, carried out in children, shows a decrease in transit time with increasing age from 9 to 22 yr (88); this is attributed to decreased elastic recoil and higher resistance of the peripheral airways in the young child. Higher coefficients of variance, like greater convexity of the flow-volume curve in young compared with older children, is compatible with nonhomogeneous emptying in young children, and the higher index of skewness of the distribution of transit time is compatible with events occurring in small airways.

Density dependence of maximum expiratory flow has been investigated in small numbers of children (33, 66, 119). The mean ratios of maximum expiratory flow at 50% VC while breathing He-O_2 ($\dot{V}max_{50,HeO_2}$) to that while breathing air ($\dot{V}max_{50,air}$) range from 1.30 ± 0.25 (SD) to 1.47 ± 0.24 (SD). If there is a change in the relative contribution of peripheral and central airways to pressure losses along the airways during maximum expiratory flow, as suggested by the data of Hogg et al. (52), increasing density dependence of maximum expiratory flow with growth might be expected. Sufficient data are not yet available to explore this relationship.

MAXIMUM FLOW–STATIC RECOIL RELATIONSHIPS. With ideas originally developed by Mead et al. (81) and Pride et al. (96), the relationships between maximum expiratory flow and static lung recoil (MFSR curves) have been examined in children and adolescents from 7 to 18 yr (22, 77, 123). De Troyer et al. (22) found a significant increase in upstream conductance (Gus), which they calculated from the slope of the MFSR curve between 50% and 80% of TLC, with increasing age and height. However, when this Gus was divided by TLC and expressed as $TLC \cdot s^{-1} \cdot cmH_2O^{-1}$ there was a significant decrease with increasing age and height. A similar decrease in Gus/TLC was observed by Mansell et al. (76). Both groups interpreted these findings as being consistent with disproportionate growth of lung parenchyma relative to airways.

By applying ideas developed by Mead (80) to predict the relationship between conductance/lung volume and lung volume during growth, one would anticipate that the relationship between Gus/TLC and TLC would be constant when flow is laminar and airways and lung grow isotropically. However, if flow is turbulent, which is more likely during maximal expiratory flow in the middle range of VC, Gus/TLC will be proportional to volume to the $-2/7$ power. Therefore as growth produces increasing lung volume, Gus/TLC might be expected to decrease even if growth is isotropic. The values of Gus observed by De Troyer et al. (22) and Mansell et al. (76) for children 6–8 yr are

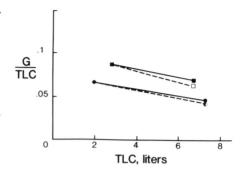

FIG. 7. *Solid line* connecting *squares* represents predicted upstream conductance (Gus)/TLC vs. TLC if Gus/TLC changes proportionally to TLC to $-2/7$ power during growth. The Gus/TLC and TLC for 8-yr-old child are used to develop the prediction. *Dashed line,* observed relationship. [Data from Mansell (77).] *Solid line* connecting *circles* represents similar predictions developed from Gus/TLC vs. TLC for a 120-cm (6–8 yr) child. *Dashed line,* observed relationship. [From De Troyer et al. (22).]

used to develop predictions (Fig. 7) for adolescents 16–18 yr. Their observed values are in close agreement with these predictions suggesting that their findings may be compatible with isotropic growth.

Influences of Sex, Race, and Genetic Factors on Lung Mechanics

Recently attention has been focused on possible differences in the mechanical properties of the lung related to sexual, racial, or genetic factors (74). Polgar et al. (93, 95) have gathered most of the values for lung volumes in growing children. Their summarized data show that TLC and VC are higher in male than in female children of the same height. These differences are small and not significant in each individual study. The lower maximum inspiratory and expiratory pressures observed in girls compared with those in boys (34) probably do not account for these differences, particularly because of the recent work of Thurlbeck (115), who observed higher lung volumes in excised lungs obtained from boys compared with lungs obtained from girls.

Although most studies of maximum expiratory flow in children have not shown significant differences between boys and girls, a few have shown maximum expiratory flow to be higher in prepubertal girls (67, 113). This is in contrast to data obtained from adults (60a) in which expiratory flows are lower in women than in men.

Lung volumes as indicated by VC are substantially smaller in blacks compared with whites (10, 101). This difference is explained, at least partly, by differences in ratios of sitting height to standing height in blacks compared with whites. Although Stocks and Godfrey (108) observed lower nasal resistances in black compared with white infants, differences in maximum expiratory flow have not been observed (101).

REFERENCES

1. ADLER, S. M., B. T. THACH, AND I. D. FRANTZ III. Maturational changes of effective elastance in the first 10 days of life. *J. Appl. Physiol.* 40: 539–542, 1976.
2. ADLER, S. M., AND M. E. B. WOHL. Flow-volume relationship at low lung volumes in healthy term newborn infants. *Pediatrics* 61: 636–640, 1978.
3. AGOSTONI, E. Volume-pressure relationships of the thorax and lung in the newborn. *J. Appl. Physiol.* 14: 909–913, 1959.
4. AGOSTONI, E., AND J. MEAD. Statics of the respiratory system. In: *Handbook of Physiology. Respiration,* edited by W. O. Fenn and H. Rahn. Washington, DC: Am. Physiol. Soc., 1964, sect. 3, vol. I, chapt. 13, p. 387–409.
5. AVERY, M. E., AND C. D. COOK. Volume-pressure relationships of lungs and thorax in fetal, newborn, and adult goats. *J. Appl. Physiol.* 16: 1034–1038, 1961.
6. BACHOFEN, H., AND G. DUC. Lung tissue resistance in healthy children. *Pediatr. Res.* 2: 119–124, 1968.
7. BARAN, D., AND M. ENGLERT, La conductance des voies aériennes chez l'enfant et l'adolescent normaux. *Bull. Physio-Pathol. Respir.* 7: 125–135, 1971.
8. BEARDSMORE, C. S., P. HELMS, J. STOCKS, D. J. HATCH, AND M. SILVERMAN. Improved esophageal balloon technique for use in infants. *J. Appl. Physiol.: Respirat. Environ. Exercise Physiol.* 49: 735–742, 1980.
9. BEREND, N., C. SKOOG, AND W. M. THURLBECK. Pressure-volume characteristics of excised human lungs: effects of sex, age, and emphysema. *J. Appl. Physiol.: Respirat. Environ. Exercise Physiol.* 49: 558–565, 1980.
10. BINDER, R. E., C. A. MITCHELL, J. B. SCHOENBERG, AND A. BOUHUYS. Lung function among black and white children. *Am. Rev. Respir. Dis.* 114: 955–959, 1976.
11. BOYCHUK, R. B., M. M. K. SESHIA, AND H. RIGATTO. The effect of gestational age on the effective elastance of the respiratory system in neonates. *Pediatr. Res.* 11: 791–793, 1977.
12. BRISCOE, W. A., AND A. B. DUBOIS. The relationship between airway resistance, airway conductance and lung volume in subjects of different age and body size. *J. Clin. Invest.* 37: 1279–1285, 1958.
13. BUCHER, U., AND L. REID. Development of the intrasegmental bronchial tree: the pattern of branching and development of cartilage at various stages of intrauterine life. *Thorax* 16: 207–218, 1961.
14. BURNARD, E. D., P. GRATTAN-SMITH, C. G. PICTON-WARLOW, AND A. GRAUAUG. Pulmonary insufficiency in prematurity. *Aust. Paediatr. J.* 1: 12–38, 1965.
15. COGSWELL, J. J. Forced oscillation technique for determination of resistance to breathing in children. *Arch. Dis. Child.* 48: 259–266, 1973.
16. COGSWELL, J. J., D. HULL, A. D. MILNER, A. P. NORMAN, AND B. TAYLOR. Lung function in childhood. III. Measurement of airflow resistance in healthy children. *Br. J. Dis. Chest* 69: 177–187, 1975.
17. COOK, C. D., J. MEAD, AND M. M. ORZALESI. Static volume-pressure characteristics of the respiratory system during maximal efforts. *J. Appl. Physiol.* 19: 1016–1022, 1964.
18. COOK, C. D., J. M. SUTHERLAND, S. SEGAL, R. B. CHERRY, J. MEAD, M. B. McILROY, AND C. A. SMITH. Studies of respiratory physiology in the newborn infant. III. Measurements of mechanics of respiration. *J. Clin. Invest.* 36: 440–448, 1957.
19. CROTEAU, J. R., AND C. D. COOK. Volume-pressure and length-tension measurements in human tracheal and bronchial segments. *J. Appl. Physiol.* 16: 170–172, 1961.
20. D'ANGELO, E., G. SANT'AMBROGIO, AND E. AGOSTONI. Effect of diaphragm activity or paralysis on distribution of pleural pressure. *J. Appl. Physiol.* 37: 311–315, 1974.
21. DAVI, M., K. SANKARAN, M. MACCALLUM, D. CATES, AND H. RIGATTO. Effect of sleep state on chest distortion and on the ventilatory response to CO_2 in neonates. *Pediatr. Res.* 13: 982–986, 1979.

22. DE TROYER, A., J.-C. YERNAULT, M. ENGLERT, D. BARAN, AND M. PAIVA. Evolution of intrathoracic airway mechanics during lung growth. *J. Appl. Physiol.: Respirat. Environ. Exercise Physiol.* 44: 521–527, 1978.
23. DOERSHUK, C. F., T. D. DOWNS, L. W. MATTHEWS, AND M. D. LOUGH. A method for ventilatory measurements in subjects 1 month–5 years of age: normal results and observations in disease. *Pediatr. Res.* 4: 165–174, 1970.
24. DOERSHUK, C. F., AND L. W. MATTHEWS. Airway resistance and lung volume in the newborn infant. *Pediatr. Res.* 3: 128–134, 1969.
25. DOSMAN, J., A. GRASSINO, P. T. MACKLEM, AND L. A. ENGEL. Factors influencing the esophageal pressure gradient in upright man (Abstract). *Physiologist* 18: 194, 1975.
26. DREYFUS-BRISAC, C. Sleep ontogenesis in early human prematurity from 24 to 27 weeks of conceptional age. *Dev. Psychobiol.* 1: 162–169, 1968.
27. DUNNILL, M. S. Postnatal growth of the lung. *Thorax* 17: 329–333, 1962.
28. DUOMARCO, J. L., AND R. RIMINI. *La presion intra-abdominal en el hombre.* Buenos Aires: El Ateneo, 1947.
29. EMERY, J., AND A. MITHAL. The weight of the lungs. In: *The Anatomy of the Developing Lung,* edited by J. Emery. London: Heineman, 1969, p. 203–209.
30. FAGAN, D. G. Post-mortem studies of the semistatic volume-pressure characteristics of infants' lungs. *Thorax* 31: 534–543, 1976.
31. FAGAN, D. G. Shape changes in static V-P loops for children's lungs related to growth. *Thorax* 32: 198–202, 1977.
32. FISHER, J. T., J. P. MORTOLA, J. B. SMITH, G. S. FOX, AND S. WEEKS. Respiration in newborns: development of the control of breathing. *Am. Rev. Respir. Dis.* 125: 650–657, 1982.
33. FOX, W. W., M. A. BUREAU, L. A. TAUSSIG, R. R. MARTIN, AND P. H. BEAUDRY. Helium flow-volume curves in the detection of early small airway disease. *Pediatrics* 54: 293–299, 1974.
34. GAULTIER, C., L. PERRET, M. BOULE, A. BUVRY, AND F. GIRARD. Occlusion pressure and breathing pattern in healthy children. *Respir. Physiol.* 46: 71–80, 1981.
35. GAULTIER, C., AND R. ZINMAN. Maximal static pressures in healthy children. *Respir. Physiol.* 51: 45–61, 1983.
36. GERHARDT, T., AND E. BANCALARI. Chest wall compliance in full term and premature infants. *Acta Paediatr. Scand.* 69: 359–364, 1980.
37. GERHARDT, T., AND E. BANCALARI. Components of effective elastance and their maturational changes in human newborns. *J. Appl. Physiol.: Respirat. Environ. Exercise Physiol.* 53: 766–769, 1982.
38. GODFREY, S., P. L. KAMBUROFF, AND J. R. NAIRN. Spirometry, lung volumes and airway resistance in normal children aged 5 to 18 years. *Br. J. Dis. Chest* 64: 15–24, 1970.
39. GOLDMAN, M. D., A. GRASSINO, J. MEAD, AND T. A. SEARS. Mechanics of the human diaphragm during voluntary contraction: dynamics. *J. Appl. Physiol.: Respirat. Environ. Exercise Physiol.* 44: 840–848, 1978.
40. GOLDMAN, M. D., G. GRIMBY, AND J. MEAD. Mechanical work of breathing derived from rib cage and abdominal V-P partitioning. *J. Appl. Physiol.* 41: 752–763, 1976.
41. GRASSINO, A., AND F. BELLEMARE. Respiratory muscle fatigue and its effects on the breathing cycle. In: *Central Nervous Control Mechanisms in Breathing,* edited by C. von Euler and H. Lagercrantz. Oxford, UK: Pergamon, 1979, p. 465–472.
42. GRASSINO, A., M. D. GOLDMAN, J. MEAD, AND T. A. SEARS. Mechanics of the human diaphragm during voluntary contraction: statics. *J. Appl. Physiol.: Respirat. Environ. Exercise Physiol.* 44: 829–839, 1978.
43. GREEN, M., J. MEAD, AND J. M. TURNER. Variability of maximum expiratory flow-volume curves. *J. Appl. Physiol.* 37: 67–74, 1974.
44. GRIBETZ, I., N. R. FRANK, AND M. E. AVERY. Static volume-

pressure relations of excised lung of infants with hyaline membrane disease, newborn and stillborn infants. *J. Clin. Invest.* 38: 2168–2175, 1959.

45. HARDING, R., P. JOHNSON, AND M. E. MCCLELLAND. The expiratory role in the larynx during development and the influence of behavioral state. In: *Central Nervous Control Mechanisms in Breathing*, edited by C. von Euler and H. Lagercrantz. Oxford, UK: Pergamon, 1979, p. 357–358.

46. HELDT, G. P., P. D. GOODRICH, AND M. B. MCILROY. Diaphragmatic ventilation, work, and chest wall distortion in premature infants (Abstract). *Pediatr. Res.* 15: 721, 1981.

47. HELLIESEN, P. J., C. D. COOK, L. FRIEDLANDER, AND S. AGATHON. Studies of respiratory physiology in children. I. Mechanics of respiration and lung volumes in 85 normal children 5 to 17 years of age. *Pediatrics* 22: 80–93, 1958.

48. HELMS, P., C. S. BEARDSMORE, AND J. STOCKS. Absolute intraesophageal pressure at functional residual capacity in infancy. *J. Appl. Physiol.: Respirat. Environ. Exercise Physiol.* 51: 270–275, 1981.

49. HENDERSON-SMART, D. J., AND D. J. C. READ. Reduced lung volume during behavior active sleep in the newborn. *J. Appl. Physiol.: Respirat. Environ. Exercise Physiol.* 46: 1081–1085, 1979.

50. HISLOP, A., D. C. F. MUIR, M. JACOBSEN, G. SIMON, AND L. REID. Postnatal growth and function of the pre-acinar airways. *Thorax* 27: 265–274, 1972.

51. HOGG, J. C., P. T. MACKLEM, AND W. M. THURLBECK. Site and nature of airway obstruction in chronic obstructive lung disease. *N. Engl. J. Med.* 278: 1355–1360, 1968.

52. HOGG, J. C., J. WILLIAMS, J. B. RICHARDSON, P. T. MACLEM, AND W. M. THURLBECK. Age as a factor in the distribution of lower-airway conductance and in the pathologic anatomy of obstructive lung disease. *N. Engl. J. Med.* 282: 1283–1287, 1970.

53. HOWLETT, G. Lung mechanics in normal infants and infants with congenital heart disease. *Arch. Dis. Child.* 47: 707–715, 1972.

54. JORDANOGLOU, J. Vector analysis of rib movement. *Respir. Physiol.* 10: 109–120, 1970.

55. KAISER, E., AND I. PETERSEN. Frequency analysis of muscle action potentials during tetanic contraction. *Electromyogr. Clin. Neurophysiol.* 3: 5–17, 1963.

56. KARLBERG, P., R. B. CHERRY, F. E. ESCARDO, AND G. KOCH. Respiratory studies in newborn infants. II. Pulmonary ventilation and mechanics of breathing in the first minutes of life, including the onset of respiration. *Acta Paediatr.* 51: 121–136, 1962.

57. KARLBERG, P., AND G. KOCH. Respiratory studies in newborn infants. III. Development of mechanics of breathing during the first week of life: a longitudinal study. *Acta Paediatr. Scand. Suppl.* 135: 121–129, 1962.

58. KEENS, T. G., A. C. BRYAN, H. LEVISON, AND C. D. IANUZZO. Developmental pattern of muscle fiber types in human ventilatory muscles. *J. Appl. Physiol.: Respirat. Environ. Exercise Physiol.* 44: 909–913, 1978.

59. KNILL, R., W. ANDREWS, A. C. BRYAN, AND M. H. BRYAN. Respiratory load compensation in infants. *J. Appl. Physiol.* 40: 357–361, 1976.

60. KNUDSON, R. J., D. F. CLARK, T. C. KENNEDY, AND D. E. KNUDSON. Effect of aging alone on mechanical properties of the normal adult human lung. *J. Appl. Physiol.: Respirat. Environ. Exercise Physiol.* 43: 1054–1062, 1977.

60a. KNUDSON, R. J., R. C. SLATIN, M. D. LEBOWITZ, AND B. BURROWS. The maximal expiratory flow-volume curve. *Am. Rev. Respir. Dis.* 113: 587–600, 1976.

61. KOGI, K., AND T. HAKAMADA. Slowing of surface electromyogram and muscle strength in muscle fatigue. *Rep. Inst. Sci. Labour Tokyo* 60: 27–41, 1962.

62. KOSCH, P. C., AND A. R. STARK. Determination and homeostasis of functional residual capacity (FRC) in infants (Abstract). *Physiologist* 22(4): 71, 1979.

63. KRAHL, V. E. Anatomy of the mammalian lung. In: *Handbook of Physiology. Respiration*, edited by W. O. Fenn and H. Rahn. Washington, DC: Am. Physiol. Soc., 1964, sect. 3, vol. I. chapt. 6, p. 213–284.

64. KRIEGER, I. Studies on mechanics of respiration in infancy. *Am. J. Dis. Child.* 105: 51–60, 1963.

65. LACOURT, G., AND G. POLGAR. Interaction between nasal and pulmonary resistance in newborn infants. *J. Appl. Physiol.* 30: 870–873, 1971.

66. LANDAU, L. I., C. M. MELLIS, P. D. PHELAN, B. BRISTOWE, AND L. MCLENNAN. "Small airways disease" in children: no test is best. *Thorax* 34: 217–223, 1979.

67. LEEDER, S. R., A. V. SWAN, J. K. PEAT, A. J. WOOLCOCK, AND C. R. B. BLACKBURN. Maximum expiratory flow-volume curves in children: changes with growth and individual variability. *Bull. Eur. Physiopathol. Respir.* 13: 249–260, 1977.

68. LESOUËF, P. N., J. M. LOPES, N. MULLER, AND A. C. BRYAN. Effect of chest wall distortion on esophageal pressure (Abstract). *Physiologist* 24(4): 95, 1981.

69. LOPES, J. M., N. L. MULLER, M. H. BRYAN, AND A. C. BRYAN. Synergistic behavior of inspiratory muscles after diaphragmatic fatigue in the newborn. *J. Appl. Physiol.: Respirat. Environ. Exercise Physiol.* 51: 547–551, 1981.

70. LOPES, J., N. L. MULLER, M. H. BRYAN, AND A. C. BRYAN. Importance of inspiratory muscle tone in maintenance of FRC in the newborn. *J. Appl. Physiol.: Respirat. Environ. Exercise Physiol.* 51: 830–834, 1981.

71. MACLEM, P. T., AND J. MEAD. Resistance of central and peripheral airways measured by a retrograde catheter. *J. Appl. Physiol.* 22: 395–401, 1967.

72. MACKLEM, P. T., AND C. S. ROUSSOS. Respiratory muscle fatigue: a cause of respiratory failure? *Clin. Sci. Mol. Med.* 53: 419–422, 1977.

73. MALSCH, E. Maximal inspiratory force in infants and children. *South. Med. J.* 71: 428–429, 1978.

74. MAN, S. F. P., AND N. ZAMEL. Genetic influence on normal variability of maximum expiratory flow-volume curves. *J. Appl. Physiol.* 41: 874–877, 1976.

75. MANSELL, A., C. BRYAN, AND H. LEVISON. Airway closure in children. *J. Appl. Physiol.* 33: 711–714, 1972.

76. MANSELL, A. L., A. C. BRYAN, AND H. LEVISON. Relationship of lung recoil to lung volume and maximum expiratory flow in normal children. *J. Appl. Physiol.: Respirat. Environ. Exercise Physiol.* 42: 817–823, 1977.

77. MANSELL, A., H. LEVISON, K. KRUGER, AND T. L. TRIPP. Measurement of respiratory resistance in children by forced oscillations. *Am. Rev. Respir. Dis.* 106: 710–714, 1972.

78. MARTIN, R. J., A. OKKEN, AND D. RUBIN. Arterial oxygen tension during active and quiet sleep in the normal neonate. *J. Pediatr.* 94: 271–274, 1979.

79. MEAD, J. Analysis of the configuration of maximum expiratory flow-volume curves. *J. Appl. Physiol.: Respirat. Environ. Exercise Physiol.* 44: 156–165, 1978.

80. MEAD, J. Dysanapsis in normal lungs assessed by the relationship between maximal flow, static recoil, and vital capacity. *Am. Rev. Respir. Dis.* 121: 339–342, 1980.

81. MEAD, J., J. M. TURNER, P. T. MACKLEM, AND J. B. LITTLE. Significance of the relationship between lung recoil and maximum expiratory flow. *J. Appl. Physiol.* 22: 95–108, 1967.

82. MICHAELSON, E. D., H. WATSON, G. SILVA, A. ZAPATA, S. M. SERAFINI-MICHAELSON, AND M. A. SACKNER. Pulmonary function in normal children. *Bull. Eur. Physiopathol. Respir.* 14: 525–550, 1978.

83. MOTOYAMA, E. K. Pulmonary mechanics during early postnatal years. *Pediatr. Res.* 11: 220–223, 1977.

84. MULLER, N., G. GULSTON, D. CADE, J. WHITTON, A. B. FROESE, M. H. BRYAN, AND A. C. BRYAN. Diaphragmatic muscle fatigue in the newborn. *J. Appl. Physiol.: Respirat. Environ. Exercise Physiol.* 46: 688–695, 1979.

85. MULLER, N., G. VOLGYESI, L. BECKER, M. H. BRYAN, AND A. C. BRYAN. Diaphragmatic muscle tone. *J. Appl. Physiol.: Res-*

pirat. Environ. Exercise Physiol. 47: 279–284, 1979.

86. MULLER, N., G. VOLGYESI, M. H. BRYAN, AND A. C. BRYAN. The consequence of diaphragmatic muscle fatigue in the newborn infant. *J. Pediatr.* 95: 793–797, 1979.

87. NELSON, N. M., L. S. PROD'HOM, R. B. CHERRY, P. J. LIPSITZ, AND C. A. SMITH. Pulmonary function in the newborn infant. V. Trapped gas in the normal infant's lung. *J. Clin. Invest.* 42: 1850–1857, 1963.

88. NEUBURGER, N., H. LEVISON, A. C. BRYAN, AND K. KRUGER. Transit time analysis of the forced expiratory spirogram in growth. *J. Appl. Physiol.* 40: 329–332, 1976.

89. NIGHTINGALE, D. A., AND C. C. RICHARDS. Volume pressure relations of the respiratory system of curarized infants. *Anesthesiology* 26: 710–714, 1965.

90. OLINSKY, A., M. H. BRYAN, AND A. C. BRYAN. Influence of lung inflation on respiratory control in neonates. *J. Appl. Physiol.* 36: 426–429, 1974.

91. PHELAN, P. D., AND H. E. WILLIAMS. Ventilatory studies in healthy infants. *Pediatr. Res.* 3: 425–432, 1969.

92. POLGAR, G., AND G. P. KONG. The nasal resistance of newborn infants. *J. Pediatr.* 67: 557–567, 1965.

93. POLGAR, G., AND V. PROMADHAT. *Pulmonary Function Testing in Children: Techniques and Standards.* Philadelphia, PA: Saunders, 1971.

94. POLGAR, G., AND S. T. STRING. The viscous resistance of the lung tissues in newborn infants. *J. Pediatr.* 69: 787–792, 1966.

95. POLGAR, G., AND T. R. WENG. The functional development of the respiratory system. *Am. Rev. Respir. Dis.* 120: 625–695, 1979.

96. PRIDE, N. B., S. PERMUTT, R. L. RILEY, AND B. BROMBERGER-BARNEA. Determinants of maximal expiratory flow from the lungs. *J. Appl. Physiol.* 23: 646–662, 1967.

97. RADFORD, M. Measurement of airway resistance and thoracic gas volume in infancy. *Arch. Dis. Child.* 49: 611–615, 1974.

98. REYNOLDS, R. N., AND B. E. ETSTEN. Mechanics of respiration in apneic anesthetized infants. *Anesthesiology* 27: 13–19, 1966.

99. RICHARD, C. C., AND L. BACHMAN. Lung and chest wall compliance in apneic paralyzed infants. *J. Clin. Invest.* 40: 273–278, 1961.

100. ROUSSOS, C. S., AND P. T. MACKLEM. Diaphragmatic fatigue in man. *J. Appl. Physiol.: Respirat. Environ. Exercise Physiol.* 43: 189–197, 1977.

101. SCHOENBERG, J. B., G. J. BECK, AND A. BOUHUYS. Growth and decay of pulmonary function in healthy blacks and whites. *Respir. Physiol.* 33: 367–393, 1978.

102. SHARP, J. T., W. S. DRUZ, R. C. BALAGOT, V. R. BANDELIN, AND J. DANON. Total respiratory compliance in infants and children. *J. Appl. Physiol.* 29: 775–779, 1970.

103. SINCLAIR-SMITH, C. C., J. L. EMERY, D. GADSDON, F. DINSDALE, AND J. BADDELEY. Cartilage in children's lungs: a quantitative assessment using the right middle lobe. *Thorax* 31: 40–43, 1976.

104. SOLYMAR, L., P. H. ARONSSON, B. BAKE, AND J. BJURE. Nitrogen single breath test, flow-volume curves and spirometry in healthy children, 7–18 years of age. *Eur. J. Respir. Dis.* 61: 275–286, 1980.

105. STĂNESCU, D., N. E. MOAVERO, C. VERITER, AND L. BRASSEUR. Frequency dependence of respiratory resistance in healthy children. *J. Appl. Physiol.: Respirat. Environ. Exercise Physiol.* 47: 268–272, 1979.

106. STIGOL, L. C., G. F. VAWTER, AND J. MEAD. Studies on elastic recoil of the lung in a pediatric population. *Am. Rev. Respir.*

Dis. 105: 552–563, 1972.

107. STOCKS, J., AND S. GODFREY. Specific airway conductance in relation to postconceptional age during infancy. *J. Appl. Physiol.: Respirat. Environ. Exercise Physiol.* 43: 144–154, 1977.

108. STOCKS, J., AND S. GODFREY. Nasal resistance during infancy. *Respir. Physiol.* 34: 233–246, 1978.

109. STOCKS, J., N. M. LEVY, AND S. GODFREY. A new apparatus for the accurate measurement of airway resistance in infancy. *J. Appl. Physiol.: Respirat. Environ. Exercise Physiol.* 43: 155–159, 1977.

110. SWYER, P. R., R. C. REIMAN, AND J. J. WRIGHT. Ventilation and ventilatory mechanics in the newborn. *J. Pediatr.* 56: 612–622, 1960.

111. TABACHNIK, E., N. L. MULLER, A. C. BRYAN, AND H. LEVISON. Changes in ventilation and chest wall mechanics during sleep in normal adolescents. *J. Appl. Physiol.: Respirat. Environ. Exercise Physiol.* 51: 557–564, 1981.

112. TAKAHASHI, E., AND H. ATSUMI. Age differences in thoracic form as indicated by thoracic index. *Hum. Biol.* 27: 65–74, 1955.

113. TAUSSIG, L. M. Maximal expiratory flows at functional residual capacity: a test of lung function for young children. *Am. Rev. Respir. Dis.* 116: 1031–1038, 1977.

114. THACH, B. T., I. F. ABROMS, I. D. FRANTZ III, A. SOTREL, E. N. BRUCE, AND M. D. GOLDMAN. Intercostal muscle reflexes and sleep breathing patterns in the human infant. *J. Appl. Physiol.: Respirat. Environ. Exercise Physiol.* 48: 139–146, 1980.

115. THURLBECK, W. M. Postnatal human lung growth. *Thorax* 37: 564–571, 1982.

116. TUSIEWICZ, K., H. MOLDOFSKY, A. C. BRYAN, AND M. H. BRYAN. Mechanics of the rib cage and diaphragm during sleep. *J. Appl. Physiol.: Respirat. Environ. Exercise Physiol.* 43: 600–602, 1977.

117. WENG, T. R., AND H. LEVISON. Standards of pulmonary function in children. *Am. Rev. Respir. Dis.* 99: 879–894, 1969.

118. WIDDOWSON, E. M. Growth and composition of the fetus and newborn. In: *Biology of Gestation. The Fetus and Neonate,* edited by N. S. Assali. New York: Academic, 1968, vol. 2, p. 1–44.

119. WIESEMANN, H., AND H. VON DER HARDT. Reliability of flow-volume measurements in children. *Respiration* 41: 181–187, 1981.

120. WILLIAMS, S. P., R. L. PIMMEL, J. M. FULLTON, M. J. TSAI, AND A. M. COLLIER. Fractionating respiratory resistance in young children. *J. Appl. Physiol.: Respirat. Environ. Exercise Physiol.* 47: 551–555, 1979.

121. WITTENBORG, M. H., M. T. GYEPES, AND D. CROCKER. Tracheal dynamics in infants with respiratory distress, stridor, and collapsing trachea. *Radiology* 88: 653–662, 1967.

122. WOHL, M. E. B., L. C. STIGOL, AND J. MEAD. Resistance of the total respiratory system in healthy infants and infants with bronchiolitis. *Pediatrics* 43: 495–509, 1969.

123. ZAPLETAL, A., E. K. MOTOYAMA, K. P. VAN DE WOESTIJNE, V. R. HUNT, AND A. BOUHUYS. Maximum expiratory flow-volume curves and airway conductance in children and adolescents. *J. Appl. Physiol.* 26: 308–316, 1969.

124. ZAPLETAL, A., T. PAUL, AND M. ŠAMÁNEK. Pulmonary elasticity in children and adolescents. *J. Appl. Physiol.* 40: 953–961, 1976.

125. ZAPLETAL, A., M. ŠAMÁNEK, AND T. PAUL. Upstream and total airway conductance in children and adolescents. *Bull. Eur. Physiopathol. Respir.* 18: 31–37, 1982.

Lung mechanics

More is known about lung mechanics than the mechanics of the chest wall, and this is reflected in the somewhat greater emphasis of this volume on the gas-exchanging part of the respiratory system rather than the pump. This emphasis does not reflect our personal preference (indeed most of our recent research has been in the field of chest wall mechanics) but rather reflects the greater knowledge and interest in lung mechanics in the past.

Here too is the area in which engineering, physics, and mathematics have made their most important contribution. These disciplines have given great insight into lung elasticity, stress distribution within lungs, pressure-flow relationships within airways, and the nature of expiratory flow limitation. The discovery of surfactant and its role in promoting alveolar stability has resulted in an explosion of new knowledge. This subject was in its infancy when the first *Handbook* on respiration was published. Indeed it was thought premature to publish a chapter on surfactant in the first volume, although the topic appeared in the second. In the intervening years research into surfactant has been the jewel of lung mechanics. It is the major contribution of lung mechanics to the field of biochemistry. This area has now become so large that the metabolic nonrespiratory functions of the lung are the subject of half of another volume in this *Handbook* section.

A relatively new area is developing very rapidly, namely, growth and development of the lung. This field alone will keep physiologists interested in lung mechanics busy for many years.

PETER T. MACKLEM
JERE MEAD

CHAPTER 13

Lung recoil: elastic and rheological properties

FREDERIC G. HOPPIN, JR. | *The Memorial Hospital, Brown University, Pawtucket, Rhode Island*

JOSEPH C. STOTHERT, JR. | *St. Louis University Medical Center, St. Louis, Missouri*

IAN A. GREAVES | *Harvard School of Public Health, Boston, Massachusetts*

YIH-LOONG LAI | *University of Kentucky, Lexington, Kentucky*

JACOB HILDEBRANDT | *Virginia Mason Research Center, University of Washington, Seattle, Washington*

CHAPTER CONTENTS

MAMMALIAN LUNGS NORMALLY REMAIN INFLATED above their resting volume throughout life; in other words they are always under some tension. The ten-sions in the fibrous structures of the lungs and in the interface between alveolar gas and the alveolar lining liquid exert a deflating force that is referred to as the lung's "elastic recoil." This elastic recoil force main-tains the configuration of the internal structures of the lung much as the tensions in its stays support a tent. Thus elastic recoil forces are directly responsible for the distribution of alveolar gas volume and venti-lation within the lung and have an important influence (because of their tethering the airways, blood vessels, and interstitial spaces) on airflow, blood flow, and interstitial fluid dynamics. This chapter presents a current perspective on elastic recoil: how it varies with lung volume, with the filling medium, and with tem-perature, and how it reflects the contributions of the various force-bearing structures of the lung. The chap-ter by Greaves, Hildebrandt, and Hoppin in this *Handbook* deals with configurational aspects, the in-teractions of fibrous and interfacial tensions, and the complexities of opening, closing, and air-space stabil-ity.

HISTORICAL BACKGROUND

In 1820 Carson (14) addressed the question of why the lungs collapsed when the chest was opened. He had observed that "if a piece of the substance of the lungs be cut out and stretched, it will recover its former dimensions when released from the extending power." Carson proposed that this elastic retraction force was responsible for collapse of the lungs, and he proved this by measuring an increase in the air pres-sure within a bullock's trachea when its chest was opened and the lungs were allowed to collapse. By reinflating the lungs until they were evenly reexpanded, he showed that the elastic retraction force varied with lung volume from a pressure of ~13 cmH$_2$O in the collapsed state to 30–45 cmH$_2$O in the expanded state. He obtained similar results in a calf, dog, and cat.

Carson's observations mark the start of the modern phase of respiratory mechanics. Working independently some years later, Donders (33) and almost simultaneously Hutchinson (68) suggested that an approximately linear relationship existed between distending pressure and lung volume during inflation of whole excised lungs. Heynsius (53) in 1882 repeated these experiments and found a markedly variable inflation pressure-volume relationship. Subsequently, in 1900 van der Brugh (131) found deflation pressure-volume curves to be distinctly curvilinear. However, Cloetta (21) in 1913 again reinforced the concept of a constant slope (compliance) for pressure-volume curves; this simple view of the elastic behavior of the lung was widely held until the 1950s (108), and in fact it is still useful in medical teaching and clinical discussion, although more accurate descriptions of the pressure-volume curve now exist.

Hutchinson (68) summarized his views of the origins of lung recoil as follows: "The longitudinal fibers which enter into the structure of the air tubes throughout their entire extent are very elastic, like the coat of arteries, and these are justly supposed to possess the power of contracting each minute ramification of the lungs." He was also aware of the importance of airway closure in preventing complete emptying of the lungs. "When this elastic power is at rest, and the lungs are collapsed to their minimum, no external pressure can discharge the remaining volume of air, because the very pressure, to accomplish this, compresses the exit tube in some part of its course."

Opening phenomena were recognized by Heynsius (53) in 1882. When he measured the retractive pressures at different lung volumes, he found poor repeatability of his measurements at low volumes; reexpansion from the collapsed state often occurred unevenly, and pressures were greater or smaller according to the proportion of air spaces open at a given lung volume. Liebermeister (78) measured inflation pressure-volume curves of excised human and cat lungs and first noted the sigmoid shape of the inflation curve. At low volumes a marked increase in pressure accompanied a small change in volume; this was attributed to the reopening of collapsed air passages that, once opened, permitted inflation of the lungs more freely.

At about the same time Keith (75) set down his views on how the lungs inflated. From his observations of excised lungs he concluded that collapsed lungs reinflated unevenly because they contained areas with different degrees of elasticity. He considered the infundibula (comprising the respiratory bronchioles and alveolar ducts) to be the most distensible elements in the lungs. To support this notion he constructed a working model of the terminal bronchiole, infundibulum, and alveoli from a rubber balloon and showed that inflation of this model produced the greatest volume change in the infundibular space; the alveoli, which were implanted on the walls of the infundibulum, widened during inflation but at the same time became more shallow so that their volume remained constant as the total volume changed. A critical uncertainty in such a model is the elastic characteristic of the alveolar mouth, that is, the spiral fibers around the duct. Keith's conclusions could readily be reversed by other choices of this characteristic and indeed would seem not to be justified.

In 1929 Macklin (82) expanded on Keith's model and emphasized the central role played by changes in airway caliber. Drawing mainly from observations of the major bronchi made directly through a bronchoscope, as well as bronchographic evidence of changes in airway caliber during the ventilatory cycle, Macklin argued that changes in lung volume were accommodated largely, if not exclusively, by changes in the size of airways and also that alveolar volume changed very little. The major change in airway volume was thought to be peripherally in the alveolar ducts. This concept, though probably incorrect, was not functionally unreasonable, because diffusion of gases between alveolar ducts and alveoli could have accounted for gas exchange.

Macklin assigned an important role to airway muscle in this scheme: during inspiration, airway muscle relaxed and permitted a large volume of gas to reach the widely dilated alveolar ducts; the muscle then contracted vigorously during expiration, reducing the dead space to a minimum. To further facilitate emptying of gas from the airways, bronchial muscle was thought to contract in a peristaltic fashion—a feature referred to as "tracheal vomiting" by Reinberg (109).

In the same year that Macklin published his detailed review of airway muscle, von Neergaard (136) described a new feature of the mechanical properties of the lung—surface tension. Von Neergaard measured the deflation pressure-volume curve of an air-filled lung, then degassed the lung, filled it with an isotonic solution of gum arabic, and remeasured the pressure-volume curve. Pressures were substantially lower after liquid filling, and he reasoned that the differences in pressure between the air- and liquid-filled states represented the effects of surface tension arising at air-tissue interfaces. By subtraction he calculated the force exerted by surface tension and concluded that, at all volumes, surface tension contributed a greater proportion of the total elastic recoil force than did tensions in the solid tissues. To account for the marked effects of surface tension and the fact that these effects increased with lung volume, von Neergaard attributed the major changes in lung volume to changes in alveolar configuration. He envisioned the alveolus inflating as a soap film does on the end of a tube from a flat configuration [infinite radius of curvature (r)] to a hemispherical one (with a radius equal to that of the tube). Thus, even for a fixed surface tension (as he erroneously assumed), the decreasing r would cause recoil to rise with inflation.

Von Neergaard's concept of how configuration changes with inflation and deflation clearly differed from that of Macklin but, for various reasons discussed by Comroe (28), von Neergaard's ideas went unrecognized for 25 years. The theory of Macklin therefore prevailed and can be found in standard physiology texts until the 1960s. Not until the rediscovery of alveolar surface forces in the late 1950s (16, 100) and the development of quantitative morphometry (34, 124) were the alveoli again recognized as important sites of volume change in the lungs.

PRESSURE-VOLUME RELATIONSHIPS

Because of lung recoil force, alveolar gas pressure is greater than the pressure on the pleural surface. In practice this pressure difference can be readily measured when the airways are open and gas flow is either interrupted ("static" conditions) or kept so low ("quasi-static" conditions) that the pressure difference along the airways between the alveoli and the airway opening can be neglected. In these circumstances lung recoil forces can be evaluated directly from the pressure difference between the airway opening and the pleural surface, that is, transpulmonary pressure. When plotted against lung volume, this pressure difference behaves similarly whether the lung is in situ or excised (139), despite the nonhomogeneities of pleural pressure and regional volume that are present in situ.

Excised Lungs

Pressure-volume relationships vary somewhat among species and are dependent on experimental parameters such as temperature and prior volume history. They also depend on the filling medium, such as gas, saline, or oil. When these sources of variability are held constant, however, pressure-volume relationships are almost precisely reproducible. Typical pressure-volume behavior is illustrated in Figure 1.

In this example a rabbit lung was first degassed. Degassing the lungs can be accomplished by one of two methods. The first requires perfusion with blood to absorb all alveolar gas (after a period of O_2 breathing) until complete alveolar collapse (atelectasis) has occurred (30). The second method, applicable to nonperfused lungs, requires placing the lung in a vacuum chamber containing some water or saline and reducing the pressure in and around the lung to the vapor pressure of the liquid. With only water vapor left in the alveolar spaces, the lung collapses gas free when atmospheric pressure is restored to the chamber (136).

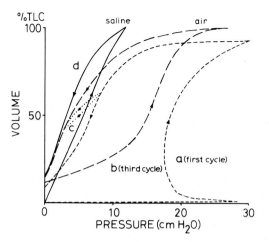

FIG. 1. Four inflation-deflation maneuvers in excised rabbit lung generating characteristic volume-pressure loops. *a*: Inflation from degassed state shows transpulmonary pressures in excess of 20 cmH_2O required before there is substantial opening. On deflation to 0 cmH_2O emptying is incomplete, with substantial air trapped in lung. *b*: Repeated cycles between 0 and 30 cmH_2O show stable loops. Lung is now much more easily opened than in *a*, but still becomes relatively stiff near 30 cmH_2O. *c*: Small volume cycles (such as in tidal breaths in vivo) run between ~3 and 8 cmH_2O. *d*: With air removed and saline introduced, lung shows much less recoil over same volume range.

Either method appears satisfactory, although evidence has been presented that alveolar gas is more completely removed by absorption (123).

When starting from the completely degassed (atelectatic) state, an initially high pressure is needed to begin inflation (Fig. 1, curve a). This peak represents the existence of critical pressures for opening atelectatic units in the range of 20–30 cmH_2O. With repeated cycling between 0 and 30 cmH_2O distending pressure, the pressure-volume loops become consistent (curve b), undergoing about a fivefold volume change between minimal (V_0) and maximal (V_{30}) inflation. This volume range is approximately that which a subject would achieve between a maximal expiratory effort [residual volume (RV)] and a maximal inspiratory effort [total lung capacity (TLC)]. At the low end of this range the lung cannot be deflated much below V_0 by making transpulmonary pressure negative. This is probably because of airway closure (see the chapter by Greaves, Hildebrandt, and Hoppin in this *Handbook*). At the high end the lung stiffens, presumably due to both connective tissue stiffness and increasing surface tension. With inflation to pressures >30 cmH_2O, volume will continue to increase, although at a relatively low but constant rate (an additional 20%, with inflation from 30 to 60 cmH_2O), until the lung ruptures and leaks develop. A choice of an upper pressure limit <25 cmH_2O could significantly underestimate maximum physiological lung volume. This would be particularly likely in studying lungs after collapse or degassing, because opening of collapsed or folded alveoli might still be incomplete.

Liquid Filling

Several other media in addition to air have been employed to obtain pressure-volume data. Each medium may provide additional information about the mechanical and structural properties of lungs. Von Neergaard (136) originally correctly surmised that the liquid would effectively eliminate the air-liquid interface. Figure 1 (curve d) and Figure 2 show the decrease in recoil for saline filling compared with air filling because of the absence of interfacial forces.

Peak recoil with saline, at the same volume as with air inflation to 30 cmH$_2$O (V$_{30}$), may be only 12–15 cmH$_2$O in the first cycle and 10–12 cmH$_2$O in the second, decreasing even further in later cycles. Whereas the pressure-volume curve of the air-filled lung bends over (becoming less compliant) near V$_{30}$, the saline-filled lung does not bend over until it reaches volumes that are 15% or 20% greater than V$_{30}$. The decreased compliance in the air-filled lung near V$_{30}$ thus is in some manner related to surface forces, either directly through a sharp increase in surface tension at high lung volume (4) or more likely indirectly, through the effects of surface tension on the configuration of the connective tissue network (see INTERFACIAL TENSION, p. 205).

Like air-filled lungs, saline-filled lungs retain ∼15% of the total inflating volume at V$_0$, and this amount may increase in later cycles. In part, V$_0$ may represent some sequestration of saline in interstitial spaces, but because the fluid permeability of alveolar epithelium is low, the relatively rapid appearance of V$_0$ must largely represent saline trapping in the alveolar air spaces.

Pressure-volume curves have also been obtained after filling the lungs with liquids other than saline (2, 4, 7, 130). Lungs filled with aqueous solutions of detergents, such as Tween 20 (4, 136) or Triton X-100 (2), exhibit pressure-volume curves similar to those obtained after saline filling of the lung. If these detergents are drained from the lung and it is then re-inflated with air, the resulting pressure-volume curves are grossly abnormal: normal inflating pressures are observed near maximal lung volume, but at lower volumes the curves are displaced markedly to the right of the normal curve for the air-filled lung (Fig. 2). Rinsing the lung with detergents presumably replaces surfactant with a surface layer of detergent, thereby producing a constant surface tension of a magnitude that would normally be present only near maximum lung volume. The fact that such a high surface tension is present throughout deflation after detergent rinsing of the lung accounts for the marked shift of pressure-volume curve to high recoil pressures in the middle- and low-volume ranges. This is presumably the model of lung mechanics alteration in the respiratory distress syndromes.

Temperature

The effects of temperature on pressure-volume curves appear to be subtle in the range of 20°C–37°C, and consequently these effects have not received much attention. Those studies made in air-filled lungs have produced discrepant findings (18, 20, 63, 64, 77). There is general agreement, however, that temperature has little effect on the pressure-volume relationship in liquid-filled lungs except at high volumes (71).

The lack of agreement for air-filled lungs may have been caused by several differences among studies: temperature ranges were not always the same, different animal species were used, and different methods for comparing volumes and pressures may have influenced the findings. Inoue et al. (71) recently attempted to resolve some of these discrepancies by comparing pressure-volume curves at the same lung volumes over a wide temperature range, from 4°C to 52°C (Fig. 3A). Generally a diminishing elastic recoil pressure was seen with warming from 4°C, particularly near TLC. Above 42°C a slight increase occurred at middle and low volumes, probably reflecting the transition zone where pure dipalmitoyl phosphatidylcholine (DPPC) melts and can no longer sustain near-zero surface tension (18). When fluid-filled lungs were examined, similar trends (Fig. 3B) were seen, although not to as great a degree, and no transition zone was seen. Little effect of temperature is noted on lung mechanics in the 32°C–42°C range, suggesting that few physiological changes due to body temperature fluctuations would normally be expected in mammals in vivo.

Quantification

It would be attractive to describe a pressure-volume curve with a single parameter. The simplest approach is the slope of a quasi-linear segment of the curve. Thus lung compliance (C$_L$) may be defined as the tangent slope, C$_L$ = dV/dP at a given volume, where V is lung volume and P is elastic recoil pressure. Because the pressure ranges for lungs in vivo vary

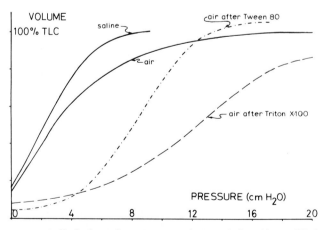

FIG. 2. Deflation volume-pressure characteristics of lungs filled with different substances.

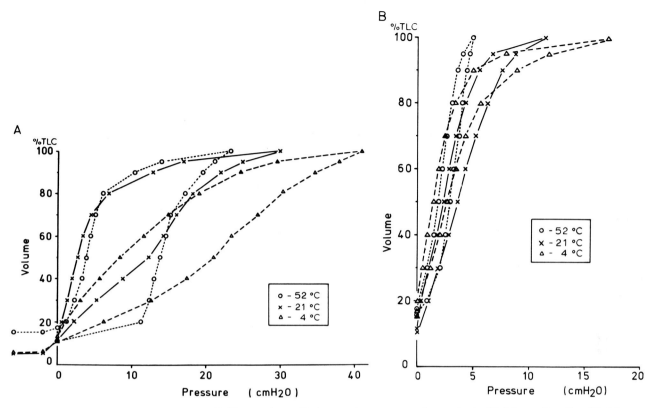

FIG. 3. Temperature effects on volume-pressure loops. *A*: air-filled lungs; *B*: saline-filled lungs. [Adapted from Inoue et al. (71).]

little within or among species despite a wide range of lung sizes and because the shapes of pressure-volume curves tend to be similar when the volume is normalized to some characteristic volume such as the volume at 30 cmH₂O (V_{30}), compliance is often normalized as specific compliance: $sC_L = (dV/dP)(1/V_{30})$, or the fractional volume change per unit pressure change. Other normalizing techniques have used lung volume at the point of interest rather than V_{30}, the animal's body weight, or the dry weight of the lung. The reciprocal of the normalized compliance (VdP/dV) is equivalent to the bulk modulus, familiar from solid mechanics. An alternative to the slope compliance is the chord compliance, that is, the slope from a given point on the pressure-volume curve to the origin. Chord compliance can be reported as a normalized volume at a single pressure. For example, V_{10} is the percent of V_{30} at 10 cmH₂O pressure, and P_{80} (the pressure at a volume of 80% V_{30}) is a variation of the same approach.

These conventional parameters of pulmonary elastic behavior are limited, because they do not express the nonlinearity of the pressure-volume relationship. The problem essentially is describing the shape of the curve. A number of investigators have approached this problem by fitting various mathematical expressions (usually exponential) to pressure-volume data (27, 42, 44, 46, 76, 91, 95, 104, 112). Salazar and Knowles (111)

introduced a singular order exponential function. More recently the application of iterative, computerized methods of curve fitting has facilitated more accurate mathematical solutions for the exponent (27, 44, 46, 104). It is now clear that a monoexponent still accurately describes the deflation pressure-volume curves of normal lungs only over the upper half of lung volume.

In its most general form, the exponential expression is given as: $V = A - Be^{-KP}$, where A, B, and K are constants; the constant A is the volume asymptote (above TLC), B is the volume decrement below A at which P is zero, and the exponent K uniquely describes the shape of the pressure-volume curve. Large values for K are associated with sharply curved deflation curves (high V_{10}, low P_{10}) and small values for K with stiffer lungs. K has the units of reciprocal pressure and is independent of maximum lung volume and the overall position of the curve with respect to the pressure axis. Differentiating, we obtain

$$dV/dP = K(Be^{-KP}) = K(A - V)$$

The slope (compliance) of the curve at any point is therefore determined by K and by the volume below the asymptote. That K is analogous to specific compliance (sC_L) may be seen from the above equation. At low lung volume, $dV/dP \simeq KA$ or $K \simeq (1/A)(dV/dP)$. Because A is related to lung size, then $K \simeq sC_L$.

Exponential analysis has been used to assess the age-related changes of pulmonary elasticity in humans (23, 44, 47, 76) and to determine the alterations in elasticity that accompany diseases such as asthma (24), pulmonary emphysema (24, 44, 47), interstitial fibrosis (44), and intermediate α_1-antitrypsin deficiency (76, 128). An intriguing finding in human lungs (47) and other mammalian species (49) has been a close correlation between the constant K measured in the air-filled state and the maximum mean alveolar size in the same lung, although no correlation existed in the same lungs filled with saline.

The monoexponential function does not consistently describe pressure-volume data below 50% of maximum lung volume. A number of other mathematical expressions have therefore been used to describe the whole curve, including hyperbolic-sigmoid (42), polynomial (23, 26), and exponential-sigmoid (98) functions. These other functions yield constants that have not yet been found to have direct, readily interpretable physiological significance, and the constants derived for different lungs have not been compared meaningfully.

RHEOLOGICAL PROPERTIES

Hysteresis, Stress Adaptation, and Creep

It has been consistently observed that recoil pressures at the same lung volume are always less during deflation than inflation (hysteresis), forming counterclockwise loops both in air- and liquid-filled lungs, although more prominently in the air-filled state (Fig. 1). The presence of looping means that the mechanical energy (work) expended during inflation is greater than that recovered during deflation; expressed mathematically this means that

$$\int_{V_{min}}^{V_{max}} P\,dV > \int_{V_{max}}^{V_{min}} P\,dV$$

With repeated cycling, loops enclose an area (A) representing the energy lost per cycle. Measurements have consistently shown A to be a nearly constant fraction (k) of the product of the tidal volume (V_T) and pressure excursions (ΔP), that is, of the area of a rectangle drawn to bound the loop

$$A = kV_T\Delta P \qquad (1)$$

The looping can also be characterized as a resistance (Rti), which can easily be shown from Equation 1 to be inversely related to compliance and cycling frequency (f) and therefore is clearly not a Newtonian viscous resistance.

In sharp contrast to airway resistance, which is generally a function of flow rate, tissue resistance is inversely related to compliance and cycling frequency (f), as is shown by the following. From consideration of a pressure-volume loop, $A = 4\int_0^{\pi/2\omega} Pres\,\dot{V}\,dt$, where

Pres is the resistive pressure drop, t is time, and $\dot{V}$ is the instantaneous flow rate; Pres equals Rti $\dot{V}$. To find Rti during sinusoidal forcing ($\dot{V} = a\sin\omega t$), we get $A = 4Rti\int_0^{\pi/2\omega} a^2\sin^2\omega t\,dt = 4Rti\,a^2\,(\pi/4\omega)$. Integrating $\dot{V}$ we get $V_T = 2a/\omega$, whence $A = RtiV_T^2\omega(\pi/4)$. Yet from Equation 1 and the definition $C_L = V_T/\Delta P$, we have $A = k\,V_T^2C_L$. Combining and solving for Rti we get

$$Rti = (2/\pi^2)k/(C_L\,f) \qquad (2)$$

The fraction k is ~0.12 for air, is slightly lower for saline (3, 56, 66, 93), and is nearly independent of lung volume, tidal volume, and cycling frequency over the range 0.01–2 Hz (5, 54). In retrospect, the wide range of results reported earlier for the "viscous tissue resistance" (6, 72, 83, 86) is probably attributable to the range of frequencies employed by various workers. These two relationships are tantalizingly simple, yet they remain unexplained in terms of mechanism (see *Rheological Models*, p. 202).

Closely related to the hysteresis seen during volume cycling of the lung are the phenomena of stress adaptation and creep. Stress adaptation is the transient change of pressure seen when the lung is held at a given volume after inflation or deflation to that volume; pressure falls after inflation (stress relaxation) and rises after deflation (stress recovery) in quasiexponential fashion, the major changes occurring in the first few seconds [Fig. 4; (13, 84, 119)]. Creep is the equivalent phenomenon seen when the lung is held at constant pressure; volume increases after inflation and decreases after deflation.

Saline-filled lungs show stress adaptation (64, 65) that appears almost as a linear function when plotted against the logarithm of time. After 20 min at a fixed volume of saline, pressure decreases ~1 cmH$_2$O at TLC (stress relaxation) but increases <0.1 cmH$_2$O when returned to lower volumes (stress recovery). Immersed in a saline bath, small parenchymal strips (43) show stress relaxation after being lengthened and stress recovery after being shortened. The sequence, magnitude, and rate of change of length can influence the degree of stress adaptation. At the beginning of a series of stretches, the larger the stress and the faster the extension, the greater the peak stress and also the stress adaptation. Tension decay relative to maximum tension is similar after stretching to different levels of extension. Qualitatively the parenchymal strip and the saline-filled lung show similar behavior, although the parenchymal strip is uniaxially distorted, in contrast to the three-dimensional expansion of the saline-filled lung, and has cut edges that may interrupt the normal fibrous network of the lung connective tissue. The importance of such differences has not been examined.

In the air-filled lung during cyclic, repeated small volume excursions (V_T), stress relaxation and recovery become almost symmetrical, their magnitude is linearly related to V_T, and stress changes linearly with

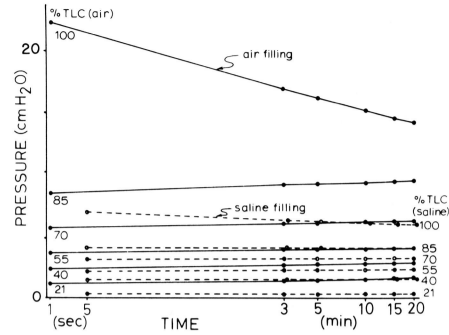

FIG. 4. Stress adaptation in normal lung showing time course of transpulmonary pressure in air-filled (*solid line*) and saline-filled (*dashed line*) cat lungs. *Top curve*, behavior after inflation to total lung capacity (TLC); *lower curves*, after deflation from TLC to 85%, 70%, 55%, 40%, and 21% TLC.

the logarithm of time (54). The stress adaptation amounts to about eight times that observed in the saline-filled lung (64, 65), implying that the presence of the air-liquid interface contributes by far the greatest proportion to the stress adaptation seen during air breathing.

Structural Basis

What structures account for these dynamic phenomena? With large volume excursions, particularly to low end-expiratory lung volumes, much of the hysteresis of the air-filled lung can be related to opening and closing of airways and alveoli (recruitment and derecruitment); once closed, such structures tend to remain stuck shut due to surface tension, and work must be done to reopen them (see the chapter by Greaves, Hildebrandt, and Hoppin in this *Handbook*). However, hysteresis is still seen even with small volume excursions, at high lung volumes when closure is unlikely, and in the saline-filled lung where surface forces are absent. This hysteresis in the saline-filled lung probably represents energy losses in the solid connective tissue elements and in the semisolid or fluid intracellular and interstitial matrices (43). Smooth muscle and blood vessels show considerable stress adaptation, decreasing their tension by one-third within 5 s after being rapidly stretched ~20% over their initial length (110). On the other hand, single collagen (125) and elastin fibers (15) show little stress adaptation. Similarly, tendon (collagen bundle)

does not demonstrate measurable hysteresis loops (110) and should not contribute to stress adaptation. However, unlike the tendon, ligamentum nuchae (primarily elastic fibrous tissue) shows considerable stress relaxation after stretching (110). This reaction is in contrast to the single elastic fiber, possibly due to network phenomena produced by the much less "organized" fibers inside the unstretched elastic bundle (125). These fibers may become aligned during stretching and tend to slide back into a more random array with time, rearrangements that require energy and thus may contribute to the dynamic phenomena.

At high lung volumes in the air-filled state, opening and closing phenomena are unlikely, but the hysteresis in the air-filled state is much greater than in the saline-filled state. The primary source of hysteresis in the air-filled lung at higher volumes, then, is the air-liquid interface. Presumably it is caused by the surface tension–surface area hysteresis, such as can readily be seen in surfactant films in vitro (18, 19). Very rapid and large adaptation can also be demonstrated in extracted surface-active material (17, 129). In these in vitro preparations, after the surface film is compressed and held at minimal area, surface tension increases from <5 dyn·cm^{-1} to 24–29 dyn·cm^{-1}, the rate of change depending strongly on temperature (minutes at body temperature, hours at room temperature). On the other hand, following film expansion to a larger area, the surface tension then decreases from ~40–50 dyn·cm^{-1} to the same equilibrium range, 24–30 dyn·cm^{-1} (129). It is not clear whether a unique equilibrium surface tension also exists in the intact lung, because rising and falling pressure transients up to 20 min in duration at the same volume show almost no tendency to converge (64, 65). Schürch et al. (116), however, have extended similar studies to 150 min and have shown that slow changes continue throughout this period such that surface tension rises to at least 20 dyn·cm^{-1}. If this equilibrium surface tension is present in situ, its value may appear at a recoil pressure of ~10 cmH$_2$O (93). Mechanisms for the stress adaptation of the surface component may relate to molecular rearrangements within the surface film, exchanges between the air-liquid interface and the subphase, and/or viscous sliding of surfactant on alveolar surfaces (93).

Hysteresis, stress adaptation, and creep thus have complex causes, including opening and closing phenomena and energy losses in the solid tissues and in the air-liquid interface.

Stress relaxation of the total respiratory system has been evaluated in humans (13, 84, 121) and can be divided into components from the lungs and the chest wall by using the esophageal balloon technique. Stress adaptation is usually larger in magnitude and faster in the lungs than in the chest wall (119), and in both structures it can be related to lung volume in a nonlinear fashion. In the chest wall, stress adaptation arises mainly from the viscoelastic properties of respiratory muscles and connective tissue.

Rheological Models

Pulmonary stress adaptation and a substantial portion of pulmonary hysteresis may be thought of as closely related viscoelastic processes in which elastic and viscous elements are arrayed so that there is a delayed or transient stress response to a rapid strain (stress adaptation) or a phase lag of recoil pressure in the response to volume cycling (hysteresis) (127). Because the whole pressure-volume curve within the vital capacity range is quite nonlinear, one would generally need to postulate the existence of nonlinear elastic elements. However, to test whether or not viscoelas-

ticity can in principle account for loop hysteresis, data can be used from the relatively linear part of the pressure-volume curve near functional residual capacity and tidal volumes can be restricted to no more than 10% or 15% of TLC during dynamic ventilation. By comparing these small loops obtained over a wide range of cycling frequencies (3 or more decades) with data from stress-relaxation curves, a mathematical model can be developed comprising a distribution of Maxwell elements in series, each including a spring (elastic element) in parallel with a dashpot (viscous element) (Fig. 5). The adequacy of the model for explaining observed rheological phenomena has been examined by using the pressure response to a step volume change to find the transfer function relating pressure and volume, calculating from this function the pressure expected for sinusoidal volume changes, and comparing the predictions with experimental results for hysteresis loop areas and elastances as functions of frequency (55). Such a model predicts dynamic elastance and its frequency dependence quite well, but it cannot account for about one-third of the energy loss (hysteresis area). This analysis then leads to the conclusion that additions of nonviscous plastoelastic elements are required that do not impart time dependence and frequency dependence (stress relaxation and dynamic elastance) but do consume energy. In the latter model the viscous dashpots may be replaced by dry-friction (coulomb) elements (Fig. 5) generating static hysteresis. It is possible to choose a suitable distribution of thresholds (yield stresses) to adequately make up the missing energy loss. Thus the plastoelastic, linear viscoelastic model can incorporate the major rheological features of tidal breathing. The structural equivalents of the mechanical elements of the model have not been identified.

FORCE-BEARING STRUCTURES

From the time of Hutchinson (68) there has been interest in identifying the structures responsible for the recoil properties of the lung. In the chapter by

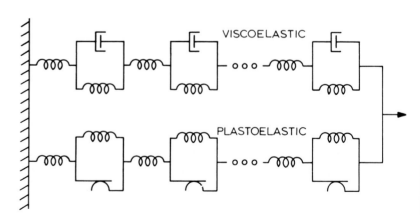

FIG. 5. Schematic description of viscoelastic, plastoelastic mechanism constructed of springs, dashpots, and dry-friction elements.

Weibel in this *Handbook*, the question is considered from the anatomist's standpoint. Emphasis here is on functional aspects.

Airways and Vasculature

The airways radiate from the hilum throughout the lung, where they are fixed to the parenchyma by direct fibrous continuity. Macklin (82) postulated that these structures, if sufficiently tense, could affect the distensibility of the lung. Indeed vagal stimulation and histamine aerosol (79) or isoproterenol (69), which increase or decrease airway smooth muscle tone, respectively, also to some extent increase or decrease lung recoil. On the other hand, two pieces of circumstantial evidence argue against the large airways playing the dominant role in lung distensibility. *1*) The diameters of bronchi increase similarly on inflation whether in situ or excised, suggesting that the radial properties of airways are reasonably similar to the properties of the surrounding parenchyma. *2*) When removed from the lung, airways are much more readily lengthened by traction than they are in situ (62), suggesting that properties of the parenchyma dominate the axial properties of the individual airway and not vice versa. The disposition of the pulmonary vasculature is radial like that of the airways and, like the airways, has peripheral fibrous connections to the parenchyma. By analogy the vasculature might also contribute to lung recoil and account for the changes in recoil with smooth muscle active agents. Only modest effects on recoil, however, are seen when the walls of the vessels are tensed by high vascular pressures (8, 41, 133).

Pleura and Interlobular Septa

Pleura and interlobular septa also contribute to lung recoil. The pleura has a laminated structure (51): the outer mesothelial layer rests on a thick elastic fiber net, and underneath it is a dense mixed layer of elastic and collagen fibers. The latter layer lies parallel to the lung surface. There is great variability among species regarding interlobular septa, the dog having very little, the pig a great deal, and the human an intermediate amount. Interlobular septa, when present, are sheets of connective tissue continuous with those in the pleura on the one hand and possibly joining the fibers of the bronchovascular network on the other. Although the connective tissue in the pleura is massive and dense relative to that in a given alveolar septum, the greater total mass of septa means that by far the greater part of the connective tissue of the lung is in the septa. With point-counting morphometric techniques on light and electron micrographs of dog lobes, it can be seen that there is ~20% as much total collagen in the pleura as there is in the network of alveolar septa (95a). This supports the conclusions of Hajji et al. (50), who estimated, from measurements

in dog lobes of the tension of stripped pieces of pleura stretched to match in situ dimensions and from the behavior of the lung surface when indented by rods of different sizes, that ~20% of the work done by the lung during deflation was contributed by the pleura.

Alveolar Septa

A random section of the lung parenchyma is so dominated by the network of alveolar septa (Fig. 6) that it has generally been assumed that this network bears the greatest part of the tensions of the lung, transmitting the inflating stresses from the pleura throughout the parenchyma and supporting the internal structures against the pull of gravity.

The septa themselves are polygonal, generally planar structures. On most of its edges a septum joins with two other septa so that in cross section the alveolar network shows an irregular, vaguely hexagonal pattern. The fibrous networks of collagen and elastin run in the plane of the septum and are continuous with those in contiguous septa and other structures. Both alveolar surfaces of a septum are covered by epithelium and have an alveolar lining layer of surface-active material (surfactant) interfacing with alveolar gas. Thus the major stress-bearing components of the lung (the fibrous network and the surface lining layer) are present in the alveolar septum.

The septum itself, however, is not a simple structure. In particular a septum may have a free edge that forms part of the alveolar entrance ring and contains a stout band of fibrous tissue as well as smooth muscle fibers. A substantial proportion of the mechanical properties of parenchyma may reside in these fibromuscular bands, and during inflation the distortion of septa with free edges may differ from that of septa without free edges.

The mechanical properties of the septum cannot be considered in isolation because of the anatomical arrangement of septa within the respiratory unit. The alveolar gas spaces, as defined by their septa, are typically polyhedra with about 14 sides, one face being open to the alveolar duct. The alveolar duct is the space bounded by the surrounding alveolar mouths and the "chicken wire" net of alveolar entrance rings. The duct then is anatomically distinct from the alveoli that surround it, and there is functional evidence that they have different mechanical properties (as reviewed in the chapter by Greaves, Hildebrandt, and Hoppin in this *Handbook*). The basic mechanical unit must comprise at least the alveolar duct and its associated alveoli. Such units vary in size and configuration (52), but they are repeated throughout the parenchyma. They are probably smaller than the basic unit of gas exchange (143).

The recoil properties of the air-filled lung are therefore probably determined by those of alveolar walls and alveolar entrance rings, with lesser contributions

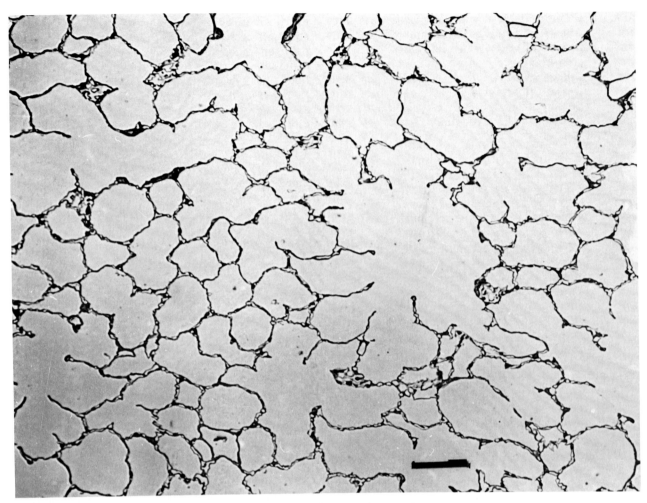

FIG. 6. Light micrograph of dog lung showing network of alveolar septa that constitutes parenchyma. Air inflated to 55% total lung capacity, fixed with intravascular osmium tetroxide and tannin. *Bar*, 100 μm; × 156.

from the airways, vasculature, pleura, and interlobular septa.

CONNECTIVE TISSUE

Components

The principal stress-bearing elements of septal tissues have been commonly assumed to be the connective tissue fibers. Collagen, elastin, and proteoglycans are major components of pulmonary connective tissue (51). Lung collagen, the most abundant component in the parenchyma by dry weight, can be further divided into distinct chemical types. Type I is probably the primary fiber forming collagen in the lung. Type IV collagen is found in basement membranes. Tracheal and bronchial cartilage contain type II collagen in the form of fine fibrils associated with a proteoglycan matrix. Collagen fibers, primarily type I, have great tensile strength but low compliance, that is, they can be extended by only 2% (125).

Elastin fibers, comprising 30%–35% by weight of parenchymal connective tissue, are composed of amorphous elastin and a microfibrillar component. Compared with collagen, elastin fibers have a lower tensile strength but a higher compliance, extending as much as 130% beyond their resting length.

Proteoglycans consist of a protein core with large polysaccharide side chains called glycosaminoglycans. In most species, total glycosaminoglycans represent 0.4%–1.0% of the dry parenchymal weight in adults. Glycosaminoglycans interact with collagen, elastin, and cells and may have a modulating role in the formation or remodeling of connective tissue (67). Their mechanical role is totally unknown.

Collagen-Elastin Interactions

It would be important to know in what way each of these two closely associated tissues, with such different physical characteristics, affects lung properties. The notion that elastin and collagen fibers function as parallel, independent networks was proposed by Setnikar and Meschia (118). They assumed that the dimensions of the elastic networks changed symmetrically with volume, and from pressure-volume curves for whole lungs they calculated length-tension relationships for the fiber networks. These relationships were compared with known length-tension curves for individual collagen and elastic fibers. They postulated that collagen fibers were stressed only at very high lung volumes and that these fibers served to limit maximum lung expansion. At lower volumes elastic fibers were considered the major stress-bearing elements, whereas the collagen fibers were curled and unstressed. In other words, elastin may act like rubber and be stressed most of the time, whereas collagen may behave passively like an accordion at low volumes, becoming straight and tense at high volumes.

The pattern of the fibrous network in the lung parenchyma is similar for collagen bundles and for elastic fibers (105). Carton et al. (15) examined the three-dimensional arrangement of elastic fibers throughout the lung and found that the elastic network was complete, that is, the elastic fibers of the alveolar septa were continuous with those of the blood vessels, airways, and pleura, and no free ends were seen. Collagen fibers also appeared to constitute a complete network.

Several lines of functional evidence also favor a degree of independence of the two networks. *1*) In liquid-filled excised lungs (74) preferential destruction of the elastin fibers with the enzyme elastase increases compliance in the low- and middle-volume ranges, but neither volume nor compliance is altered at high inflation pressures. On the other hand, destruction of collagen with collagenase increases compliance at high volumes, but behavior at lower volumes is unchanged. *2*) DL-Penicillamine interferes with the cross-linking of elastin (59) and results in decreased lung tissue recoil at low and middle lung volumes in the growing rat (60). *3*) Semicarbazide reduces cross-linking of collagen, and lung rupture occurs at recoil pressures lower than normal (122).

These findings support the concepts of Setnikar and Meschia by showing that the elastin network dominates behavior at low- and middle-volume ranges and collagen at high-volume ranges and that neither network requires the integrity of the other for its function.

Nonetheless, the volume ranges over which the two networks operate are not sharply defined. The pressure-volume curve of the saline-filled lung is smooth, unlike the biphasic curve that might be predicted from the Setnikar and Meschia hypothesis. Most likely this smoothness represents the complexity of connective tissue structure at the levels of fiber bundles, fiber networks, and gross anatomical structures rather than an error in the basic hypothesis. Stromberg and Wiederhielm (125) observed the nonlinearity and relative

inextensibility of the single collagen fiber, and by comparison with previous studies of collagen bundles they generalized that the less organized the fiber network, the larger the extensibility. When a collagen bundle is stressed, it extends by deformation rather than extension of the fibers themselves, becoming more aligned and more organized as it extends. They proposed that such network phenomena also pertained at a microscopic level, involving changes of angle between adjacent primary elements and recruitment within the composite structure and that this was responsible for the greater extensibility of fibrous bundles in comparison with single fibers. Similarly, Carton et al. (15) found that single elastic fibers were less stretchable than the ligaments from which they were taken. Because fibrous bundles are present even in the alveolar wall (137), network behavior should occur in the smallest functional unit of the lung. In addition, the bundles themselves form a larger scale network that permits even greater extensibility than, and different mechanical properties from, the individual fiber bundles.

Orsos (96) and von Hayek (135) have emphasized that bundles of elastin and collagen fibers exist in close proximity throughout the lungs, raising the possibility of direct connections. Examination of the lung parenchyma with the electron microscope also shows that the elastin and collagen fibers are intimately associated (1, 106). Generally the two types of fibers have not been seen joining, but Sobin et al. (121) have described apparent connections between elastin and collagen. Such connections might allow interactions of the two components. Finally, as developed in the chapter by Greaves, Hildebrandt, and Hoppin in this *Handbook*, there is heterogeneity of structure at the level of the terminal ventilatory unit, introducing a further level of complexity to the roles of the connective tissue networks.

INTERFACIAL TENSION

Air-Liquid Interface

It has been known since the experiments of von Neergaard that surface tension contributes substantially to lung recoil. Comparison of pressure-volume curves in air- and liquid-filled states (see Figs. 1 and 2) shows that the air-liquid differences in pressure are greater the higher the lung volume and are greater for inflation than deflation (4). This systematic volume dependency of the surface-tension effects has been attributed to a prominent surface-area dependency and hysteresis of surface tension (γ), reflecting in particular the peculiar properties of pulmonary surfactant (100, 101). The biochemical and physical nature of the alveolar lung lining and of pulmonary surfactant are extensively treated in the chapter by Goerke and Clements in this *Handbook*. Our interest in this chapter is restricted to the magnitude of surface tension and to how it contributes to lung recoil.

For years the surface tension of lung extracts or lung washings has been determined by various techniques, but the question has remained open about the applicability of such measurements to the in situ situation where the subphase in particular is different. Two basic approaches have been used to estimate surface tension in situ.

Estimation of Interfacial Tension From Pressure-Volume Curves

The first method for this estimation utilizes the difference in energy states existing between air-filled and saline-filled lungs. The initial work for this approach was begun by Radford (107), who described a method whereby lung surface area could be estimated based on pressure-volume data from air- and saline-filled lungs and an assumed surface tension, but avoiding any assumptions concerning the size or specific configuration of the terminal respiratory structures. Radford equated the change in surface free energy (dF, equal to γdA, where A is the change in surface area) to the work done by the interface during lung deflation Ps(dV), where Ps is the recoil pressure difference between air and saline deflation curves (Fig. 7A). In the absence of information to the contrary, he assumed that γ was constant and equal to 50 dyn·cm^{-1}. Integrating over the whole deflation limb gives

$$A = (1/\gamma) \int_{TLC}^{RV} Ps(dV) \qquad (3)$$

He drew the interesting conclusion from the calculated results that morphological estimates of lung surface area were too large by a factor of ~10. In retrospect, the discrepancy can readily be explained if one recognizes that γ is not constant and may have a mean value of only ~5 dyn·cm^{-1} instead of the assumed value of 50 dyn·cm^{-1}.

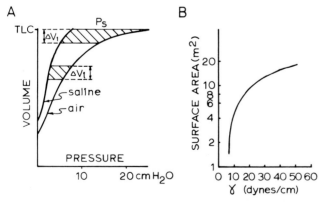

FIG. 7. *A*: volume-pressure deflation curves for air-filled and saline-filled lungs. *B*: surface area–surface tension relationship calculated from differences in pressure of saline-filled and air-filled lungs and assumptions of isotropic deflation and simple summation of tissue and surface contributions.

Brown et al. (10, 11) relaxed the assumption that γ is a constant and instead allowed it to vary

$$\gamma = Ps(\Delta V/\Delta A) \qquad (4)$$

where ΔV is a measured finite volume decrement on deflation (Fig. 7A) and ΔA is the corresponding change of alveolar surface area, estimated from $A = kV^{2/3}$. To find k, γ was assumed to be 50 dyn·cm^{-1} over the first volume decrement ΔV at TLC. At every other volume step (ΔV_n) on the deflation limb, γ_n was calculated using this value of k. Figure 7B shows the γ-A relationship for a dog lung estimated by using this approach.

Further refinements were made by Bachofen et al. (4) and Fisher et al. (40) by eliminating the necessity for stepwise graphical integration. Using the basic equation $\gamma = Ps(dV/dA)$ and obtaining dV/dA by differentiating $A = kV^{2/3}$, they obtained the relationship $\gamma = \frac{3}{2}(Ps/k)V^{1/3}$. The shape factor ($k$) could again be determined by assuming one arbitrary value for γ, for example, γmax = 61 dyn·cm^{-1} at TLC. With this method, γ-A curves could be constructed for inflation as well as for deflation limbs of pressure-volume curves. The results showed that γ fell rapidly to ~10 dyn·cm^{-1} at 90% TLC, 5 dyn·cm^{-1} at 80% TLC, and 2 dyn·cm^{-1} at 50% TLC. The inflation limb generally had a knee at ~20–25 dyn·cm^{-1}, then increased sharply toward 50 dyn·cm^{-1} above 80% TLC. This last feature in particular did not resemble γ-A relationships that had been determined from lung extracts of surfactant in vitro.

A major assumption underlying all of the foregoing energy methods is exact equivalence of detailed alveolar shape in fluid- and air-filled states. In order for Ps to have the meaning of "surface component of elastic recoil," it is essential that the tissue component of recoil is accurately subtracted from total recoil. If alveolar shapes or duct sizes are changed by the presence of surface forces, the stress distribution within the parenchyma must be altered and consequently the saline pressure-volume curve no longer accurately represents tissue retraction in the air-filled lung. This problem has been illustrated by a simplified model of an alveolar duct (57) where tissue elastic deformation and stress were calculated with and without a known interfacial tension. The problem was then inverted and an attempt was made to calculate the known γ from the two sets of calculated mechanical properties representing air- and liquid-filled states. It was shown that the air-saline difference, corresponding to Ps above, was complex in meaning and did not lend itself to the estimation of γ. It was necessary to have additional information about the changes in surface area in relation to pressure and volume.

Recently morphological studies of air- and liquid-filled lungs (45) have permitted graphical analyses for estimating surface tension (138). The relationships among total elastic energy in the air-filled state (E), tissue energy (U), surface energy ($\int \gamma dS$), and surface area (S) at a given lung volume are shown schematically in Figure 8A. Wilson obtained an expression for the difference between air-filled (PA) and saline-filled (Ps) lung recoil pressures in terms of the surface areas of air-filled (SA) and saline-filled (Ss) lungs, the surface tension (γ), and its change with volume ($d\gamma/dV$). The solution for γ was then found graphically by the slope-field method. Briefly, on a plot of γ versus V, a series of line segments with a range of values of γ and the appropriate slopes $d\gamma/dV$ are plotted at each volume. The curve best connecting a series of line segments in such a way that γ continually decreases toward zero at RV is taken as the solution. This approach required that there were only small differences between SA and Ss. To circumvent this limitation, Wilson also developed a more general argument and concluded that

$$\gamma = - \int_{V_s}^{V} \frac{\delta(PA - Ps)}{\delta S} \, dV \qquad (5)$$

Surface tension could then be obtained using a plot of PA − Ps as a function of S.

One problem with these approaches is that a purely elastic behavior is assumed, that is, there is conservation of energy during inflation and deflation. To the extent that hysteresis has not been taken into account, the conclusions may not be totally accurate. Nonetheless Wilson's approach is a significant advance, because it now becomes possible to dispense with assumptions of isotropy. Of particular interest is the conclusion that tissue recoil in air-filled lungs may actually make up as much as 50% of what was previously attributed to the surface component.

Direct Estimation of Interfacial Tension in Situ

Another approach in determining the in situ surface tension utilizes the principle that oil droplets, when placed on an air-liquid interface, spread to thin lenses just as the tension of the surface is raised past a critical value. Schürch et al. (113, 115, 116) applied this technique in excised rat and cat lungs. The theoretical basis of the technique can be derived from the surface-tension relationship in a three-phase system,

as originally described in 1805 by Thomas Young

$$\gamma_{A,C} = \gamma_{B,C} \cos \alpha + \gamma_{A,B} \cos \theta \qquad (6)$$

These force vectors, angles, and three phases (A, B, C) are illustrated in Figure 9.

As the droplet spreads to a thin lens, the angles α and θ become small and their cosines are 1.0. With a series of oils calibrated by directly measuring $\gamma_{A,C}$, the sum $\gamma_{B,C} + \gamma_{A,B}$ could be determined for each oil on agar or saline at the point of spreading. The same oils were then placed as test droplets of ~10 μm diameter on alveolar surfaces by micropipettes with 1- to 3-μm tip diameter. The lung volumes were then found at which each droplet just began to spread. The results are illustrated and compared with other results in Figure 8B. Because the results from the droplet method are the most direct measurements of any that have been attempted to the present time, they have become the standard against which all others must be compared. All methods agree that surface tension decreases to remarkably low levels of 2–3 dyn·cm⁻¹ or less in the region of functional residual capacity. Predictions vary only with respect to the rate at which this low tension is approached.

Cell Medium Interfacial Tension

The possibility that the interface at the epithelial cell surfaces constitutes an important and overlooked energy store has not been addressed in the literature. Although direct measurements on alveolar epithelium

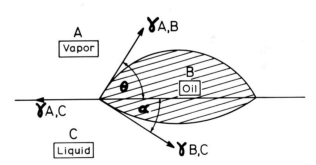

FIG. 9. Schematic relationships among contact angles and interfacial tensions, forming basis for experiments of Schürch and colleagues (114).

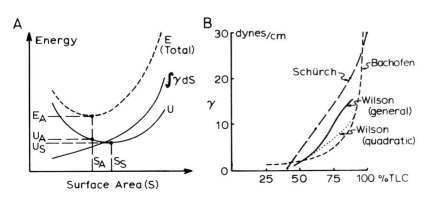

FIG. 8. A: plots of tissue (U), surface ($\int \gamma dS$), and total (E) energies against surface areas (S). B: surface tension–lung volume relationships obtained by Bachofen et al. (4), Schürch (116), and Wilson (138).

have not been reported, the cell medium tensions of several other cell types have been measured and were found to be generally <1 dyn·cm^{-1}. The method involves the application of Young's equation in conjunction with the following empirical equation of state relationship as developed by Neumann et al. (94) between the solid, liquid, and vapor phases

$$\gamma_{B,C} = (\sqrt{\gamma_{A,C}} - \sqrt{\gamma_{A,B}})^2/(1 \\ - 0.015 \sqrt{\gamma_{A,C} - \gamma_{A,B}}) \quad (7)$$

Eliminating $\gamma_{B,C}$ from the two expressions and assuming the contact angle α to be near zero gives

$$\cos\theta = [\gamma_{A,B} + (0.015 \gamma_{A,C} \\ - 2) \sqrt{\gamma_{A,C} - \gamma_{A,B}}]/[\gamma_{A,B}(0.015 \quad (8) \\ \sqrt{\gamma_{A,C} - \gamma_{A,B}} - 1)]$$

Here $\gamma_{A,C}$ is the unknown, to be determined from measurements of the contact angle θ and from the interfacial tension between medium and test drop ($\gamma_{A,B}$). The principle has been verified in lipid-water interfaces, where the lipid was DPPC and the tension could be varied from <0.1 dyn·cm^{-1} to ~6 dyn·cm^{-1} (117). When this principle was applied to human erythrocytes in neutrophils, porcine pulmonary macrophages, and murine lymphoid cells, all $\gamma_{A,C}$ were in the mdyn·cm^{-1} range (113). A separate study of rabbit aortic wall endothelium gave slightly higher $\gamma_{A,C}$ but still <0.1 dyn·cm^{-1} (9). A much larger value, 3.5 dyn·cm^{-1}, has been reported in one study of the blood-endothelial boundary of dog carotid artery and jugular vein (120). The difference may relate in part to the fact that blood was used as the liquid rather than saline or culture medium, as in the previous studies. If present in the lung, tension this large could give rise to several centimeters of water recoil.

CONTRACTILE ELEMENTS

The pressure-volume behavior of the lungs can be rapidly and reversibly changed by several interventions known to affect smooth muscle, namely vagal stimulation (79, 140, 141), intravenous histamine particularly after removing β-adrenergic response (27), atropine (140), and isoproterenol (31, 32, 69). Three types of contractile elements have been thought to participate: smooth muscle of small airways, smooth muscle in alveolar ducts, and interstitial contractile cells.

Airways

Bronchial smooth muscle runs a generally helical course around and along the airways, and contraction causes shortening and narrowing of the airways. This can reduce lung volume directly (by reduction of airway volume) or indirectly (by traction on the paren-

chyma). The effects of peripheral airway constriction are probably more significant than those of central airways, because the peripheral airways contain the greater fraction of airway volume and penetrate throughout the parenchyma.

Alveolar Duct

Smooth muscle is part of the stout fibromuscular band that encircles the mouths of alveoli. Contraction of alveolar duct cells has several effects. *1*) The ducts narrow and the volume of the ducts decreases relative to neighboring alveoli (92). *2*) There is a purse-string effect in which the adjacent alveoli are distorted as the alveolar entrance rings are narrowed and displaced toward the center of the duct. Colebatch and Mitchell (25) have studied freshly excised lungs ventilated with warm, oxygenated Krebs solution. The addition of histamine (a direct constrictor of smooth muscle) to the ventilating solution caused marked decreases in lung volume at all distending pressures; Vmax, for example, decreased ~40% and 20% in cat and dog lungs, respectively. Pressure-volume loops also showed markedly increased hysteresis and increased stress adaptation, features consistent with the properties of contracted smooth muscle. All of these changes were reversed by ventilating the lungs with a solution containing isoproterenol (a smooth muscle relaxant). Because trapped liquid was decreased rather than increased, it was concluded that the airways were not occluded and that the constriction occurred more peripherally, in the alveolar ducts. The displacements of the pressure-volume curve, however, were greater than could be accounted for by the volume of the alveolar ducts alone, ordinarily 25%–30% of lung volume. Contraction of conducting airways would not directly explain the discrepancy, because they account for only 5% of lung volume. More likely the ductal muscle constricts the entire terminal ventilatory unit, because displacement of the alveolar entrance ring network toward the center of the duct would act as a drawstring on the entire unit and cause major effects on its volume.

Septa

Kapanci et al. (73) proposed another possible mechanism for pneumoconstriction and described contractile interstitial cells in the alveolar walls of rats, monkeys, humans, and lambs. Parallel fibrils similar to those in smooth muscle cells were found in up to 50% of the interstitial cells that were previously thought to be fibroblasts. Immunofluorescent staining suggested the presence of actin in these cells in amounts exceeding that in noncontractile cells. Parenchymal strips that were nonresponsive to serotonin showed repeated contraction and relaxation to changes in O_2 tension or exposure to drugs such as epinephrine and papaverine. Anatomical studies showed that these cells oriented generally transverse to the plane of the septum and attached to the opposing epithelial basement membranes. Contraction of these interstitial cells might be expected to indent the epithelium, reducing the free alveolar surface area and thereby constricting the parenchyma. Transverse orientation would generally not be optimal for contracting the parenchyma, and it is uncertain whether these cells actually function as stress-bearing elements within the alveolar wall. At present there is no direct information concerning their mechanical properties or the forces that can actually be generated by their contraction.

There are arguments supporting each of these three sites of contraction. Kapanci et al. favored the interstitial cells, arguing that the nonresponsiveness of his parenchymal strips to serotonin indicated the absence of smooth muscle. An alternative explanation for his findings is that alveolar duct or small airway smooth muscle was present in his parenchymal strips but was not responsive to serotonin. Colebatch and colleagues (22, 25) favor the alveolar ductal muscle theory and have found dramatic histological evidence of puckering of the alveolar duct in barium sulfate embolism (92) to support this possibility. The effects of vagal stimulation and of inhaled histamine, on the other hand, favor a site known to be affected by these agents, namely small airways. The relative importance of these three contractile systems is not at all clear. They all share, however, the potential for changing lung distensibility without importantly affecting total airway resistance.

Functional Implications

Colebatch (22) has proposed that such a system may influence the distribution of ventilation locally. The distribution of ventilation, unlike the distribution of perfusion, need not depend importantly on the distribution of flow resistance among the conduits. Instead, at ordinary breathing frequencies the distribution of ventilation normally depends primarily on the distribution of distensibility among the air spaces served. Why this is true can be seen by considering the mechanics of an airway and its air spaces in terms of airway resistance and the air-space compliance, the product of which is the characteristic time constant for the exponential response to a step input of pressure. For small regions in the lung, compliance and resistance are so small that the time constants are normally short relative to breathing events, and there is no important delay in the response. The local distribution of ventilation therefore is nearly the same as it would be statically and thus is determined by the local compliances. For a further discussion see NON-UNIFORMITIES OF VENTILATION, p. 210. It is intriguing that vagal stimulation or histamine aerosol can reduce compliance substantially during tidal breathing in the dog (82). This may represent global activity of the local contractile mechanism. The physiological importance of this mechanism remains to be clarified.

POSTMORTEM CHANGES

Lung properties are frequently studied after excision, in some cases several hours after circulatory arrest. It is therefore important to consider possible postmortem effects brought about by changes in such factors as temperature, the secretory rate of surfactant, and contractile states. These modifications may influence the mechanical properties of lung tissue, the surface lining, or the airways.

Lung Tissue

Little information is presently available regarding postmortem alterations in connective tissues of the lung. Significant changes in the mechanics of fibers would not be expected soon after excision. Cooling per se could have some effect, as demonstrated by Inoue et al. (71). Figure 4 shows, however, that for saline-filled lungs only minor changes occur between 37°C and 21°C. Wider temperature extremes clearly bring about more significant alterations in recoil, particularly near TLC.

Clinically edema commonly occurs when the circulatory system is intact at the time of death (35, 48). Experimentally the dose and injection site of anesthetics, ambient temperature, elapsed time after death, and vascular and airway pressures can all influence fluid accumulation in the lung (35). For example, high doses of intravenous pentobarbital can enhance edema formation. On the other hand, low temperature, low vascular pressures, and high airway pressures reduce fluid accumulation. Alterations in capillary permeability may be the main mechanism for postmortem lung edema (90). The effects of moderate edema on lung mechanics are apparently not large. Cook et al. (29) felt that although tidal compliance was much reduced by edema, normal pressure-volume curves could be restored by a full inflation that reversed the atelectasis.

Lung Surface

Both anatomical and physiological evidence have shown postmortem changes in the surface component of the lung. Changes in type II cells of mouse lungs can be demonstrated at the electron-microscopic level 30 min after death (103). At 1 h, cytoplasmic vesicles appear, increasing gradually with time; after 8 h at 25°C most cells contain large vesicles, and the cell boundary is disrupted. Surface activity of the lung can be maintained intact for various periods, depending mainly on the storage temperature. For example, mouse lungs still had "normal" surface activity at the following temperatures and time intervals: −10°C for 21 days, 25°C for 3 days, and 37°C for 1 day (102). As the storage time increases the surface activity in the squeezed lung fluid is lost, but the rate of deterioration also depends on temperature: 25°C for 4 days and 37°C for 2 days. The final loss of surface activity may be related to the hydration of surfactant (89, 102).

Airways

Artificial ventilation of the postmortem lung is usually associated with gas trapping. This subject is dealt with in more detail in the chapter by Greaves, Hildebrandt, and Hoppin in this *Handbook*. Another kind of change, massive bronchoconstriction, has recently been found in the guinea pig lung. These lungs become very difficult to inflate soon after killing the animal by pentobarbital overdose, even while the chest is still intact. A slow inflation maneuver results ~20–30 min after excision in a pressure-volume curve showing very high opening pressures compared with a curve in vivo, and V_{30} is reduced 60%. Furthermore virtually all the gas remains trapped on deflation; the small amount that can be withdrawn is not much greater than the dead-space volume (Fig. 10). This implies widespread closure of airways even at V_{30} (Y.-L. Lai, W. J. Lamm, and J. Hildebrandt, unpublished observations).

Grossly these lung lobes open quite unevenly during inflation, that is, some lobes open completely and others remain entirely collapsed. This may signify that the lobar bronchi are intensely constricted, causing the lobes to act as units. However, pieces of peripheral tissue cut from these lungs with extreme gas trapping shrink only slightly, indicating fairly complete peripheral airway obstruction as well. Time-dependent effects of airway constriction also occur: serial measurements of pressure-volume curves show no effect 3–5 min after death by exsanguination, but after 30 min there is evidence of severe bronchoconstriction.

The mechanism of this massive bronchoconstriction is unclear at present. Foam is not found in the airways of these lungs, and bilateral vagotomy before killing the animal has failed to ameliorate the bronchoconstriction. Similarly antemortem treatment of the animal with antihistamines or a smooth muscle relaxant (papaverine) or ventilation with 99% O_2 has no preventive effect. It is possible that release of chemical mediators or rigor mortis while the lungs are collapsed may be responsible (100).

NONUNIFORMITIES OF VENTILATION

The major role of the stress-bearing structures in the lung is the appropriate distribution of gas volume and ventilation throughout the lung. As a point of departure, it has generally been assumed that the mechanical properties of the lung are homogeneous down to the level of the gas-exchanging unit, which is probably the region subserved by the respiratory bronchiole (143). This assumption is based on the observations that the lung parenchyma appears to be made of the same material throughout and that the excised lung appears to inflate and deflate evenly. A major departure from this behavior is seen in situ along the vertical axis and is attributable to the effects of gravity on the lung and chest wall (see the chapter by Rodarte and Fung in this *Handbook*). In addition, there is evidence that ventilation is uneven at a local level, not explainable by the effects of gravity (see the chapter by Engel in this *Handbook*). Opening and closing phenomena or alveolar instability might cause local uneven ventilation, but these features are usually absent during tidal breathing and therefore are not normally expected to influence local ventilation or gas exchange. More likely, variations in airway and parenchymal properties cause units to expand asynchronously and/or disproportionately, and therefore cause abnormal gas exchange.

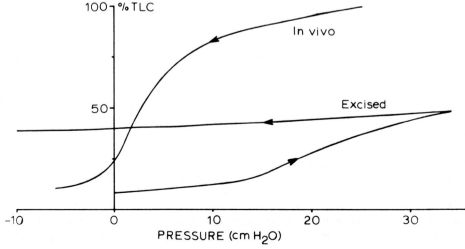

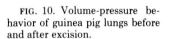

FIG. 10. Volume-pressure behavior of guinea pig lungs before and after excision.

Synchrony of Ventilation

The mechanical determinants for the synchronous ventilation of different lung regions were first described by Otis and colleagues (97), who introduced the concept of time constants of units ventilated in parallel. Units with long time constants would ventilate more slowly than units with shorter time constants. Yet, provided the period of the ventilatory cycle exceeded the longest individual time constants, all units would tend to ventilate synchronously. Increasing the frequency of ventilation such that the period of the ventilatory cycle was of the order of the longest time constants or less would delay and decrease total ventilation in the slowest units. Under these circumstances the lungs would appear to become progressively less compliant, and nonuniformities of ventilation would appear.

In normal humans there is little frequency dependence of total lung compliance up to breathing frequencies of 60–90/min, suggesting that parallel regions within the lungs ventilate fairly synchronously at these frequencies (97, 142). This apparent uniformity of time constants can be explained by three possible mechanisms: *1*) time constants that are short relative to the period of breathing, *2*) collateral ventilation (80), and *3*) mechanical interdependence among adjacent lung units (85). Each is discussed briefly below.

Time constants for adult human lungs are normally short (~0.2–0.4 s) relative to the period of breathing (0.6 s at 100 breaths/min; 6 s at 10 breaths/min). Furthermore, because the major portion of airway resistance resides centrally (in the first few generations of bronchi), the time constants in regions subtended by more peripheral airways should be even shorter. Macklem and Mead (81) have estimated that only 10% of the total airway resistance lies in airways of <2 mm in diameter, implying that peripheral time constants are only ~10% of the time constant for the whole lung. Because time constants are generally so short at the peripheral level, large variations could exist among the individual time constants without asynchronous ventilation occurring at physiological breathing frequencies. Short time constants therefore generally favor uniformity of ventilation among terminal units.

Second, collateral ventilation between parallel units could theoretically promote synchronous ventilation, provided that the time constants of these pathways were sufficiently short. In fact the direct interalveolar pathways, through the pores of Kohn, are probably largely closed and thus have very high resistances, suggesting time constants of the order of several minutes (70, 112). Other collateral channels, through connecting alveolar ducts (85) or perhaps through the canals of Lambert, have lower resistances (112) and therefore shorter time constants, and these channels may in some species promote synchronous ventilation of terminal units (12). Enhanced collateralization, as

in pulmonary emphysema, however, may contribute significantly to local ventilation when the collateral path might constitute the major avenue for gas delivery to some units.

The final mechanism relates to the effects of mechanical interdependence. Mead and co-workers (87) have argued that any deviation in the volume of a hypothetical unit, without similar changes in its neighbors, would be opposed by forces exerted on its outer walls through the anatomical connections with adjacent units. As a result, greater pressures are required to ventilate a unit out of phase with its neighbors than in phase. Mechanical interdependence always acts to reduce nonuniformities and therefore promotes uniform and synchronous ventilation of terminal units.

These three mechanisms, then, favor synchrony, and the third also favors uniformity of ventilation among units subjected to identical pressures and ventilated at physiological frequencies. Hence at first it might be expected that gas concentrations would similarly be uniform at the finer levels of lung structure. Somewhat surprisingly, substantial inhomogeneities of gas concentrations have been described at all levels of lung organization down to and including small subsegments (36, 38, 39, 126).

Gas Dilution

Measurement of N_2 or He expired after a single deep inspiration of O_2 shows a positive slope of the alveolar plateau phase. Generally the rising N_2 or He concentrations have been attributed to differences in N_2 dilution on inspiration coupled with sequential regional emptying, the better ventilated units with the lowest N_2 or He concentrations emptying first. Although this phenomenon could arise mainly from regional differences in compliance and gravity, intraregional concentration gradients have also been found. Engel et al. (38) and Suda et al. (126) passed fine catheters peripherally along the airways and showed that the slope of the alveolar plateau was similar for whole lungs, individual lobes, and small subsegments of the lung subtended by airways of 3 mm diameter. They also found cardiogenic oscillations in gas concentration at all levels sampled down to airways of 3 mm diameter, again indicating nonuniformity of gas concentrations at the local level. These findings were independent of the normal pleural pressure gradient imposed by gravity. Because small subsegments showed as much inhomogeneity of N_2 concentrations as larger regions of the lung, the anatomical basis for the uneven gas compositions must have been more peripheral at the fine level of lung structure (38).

These findings suggest that ventilation varies substantially among individual units or small groups of units, a result contrary to the above mechanical analysis predicting homogeneity peripherally. There are several other possible explanations for the observations: in part the single-breath N_2 test may accentuate nonuniformities because of the deep inspiration required; in another test, the multiple-breath N_2 washout performed while breathing normally, the N_2 concentration in young normals falls quite monoexponentially, indicating a high degree of uniformity of ventilation. It is also possible that the conventional interpretation of the sloping alveolar plateau in terms of nonuniformities of ventilation may not be completely correct. Recent theoretical analyses of gas mixing at the fine level suggest that inequalities of gas concentrations may arise in asymmetrical parallel units even when ventilation is uniform (37, 88). According to this theory, gas mixing by diffusion will occur most rapidly in the shortest units within an acinus, giving the appearance of preferential ventilation to these units. By further proposing diffusive interactions at the branching points between neighboring units, sequential filling and emptying of individual units can be simulated with this model (37). If this theory is substantially correct, geometric asymmetry among units rather than uneven mechanical properties may be the principal reason for local inequalities of gas concentrations and the positive slope of the alveolar plateau. This model is obviously speculative and requires experimental confirmation. Nevertheless, it may help to resolve the contradiction between the conventional interpretation of the observed nonuniformities of gas and the mechanical concepts of ventilation among peripheral lung units.

REFERENCES

1. ADAMSON, J., JR. An electron microscopic comparison of the connective tissue from the lungs of young and elderly subjects. *Am. Rev. Respir. Dis.* 98: 394–406, 1968.
2. BACHOFEN, H., P. GEHR, AND E. R. WEIBEL. Alterations of mechanical properties and morphology in excised rabbit lungs rinsed with a detergent. *J. Appl. Physiol.: Respirat. Environ. Exercise Physiol.* 47: 1002–1010, 1979.
3. BACHOFEN, H., AND J. HILDEBRANDT. Area analysis of pressure-volume hysteresis in mammalian lungs. *J. Appl. Physiol.* 30: 493–497, 1971.
4. BACHOFEN, H., J. HILDEBRANDT, AND M. BACHOFEN. Pressure-volume curves of air- and liquid-filled excised lungs—surface tension in situ. *J. Appl. Physiol.* 29: 422–431, 1970.
5. BACHOFEN, H., AND M. SCHERRER. Lung tissue resistance in healthy subjects and in patients with lung disease. In: *Airway Dynamics, Physiology, and Pharmacology*, edited by A. Bouhuys. Springfield, IL: Thomas, 1970, p. 123–134.
6. BAYLISS, L. E., AND G. W. ROBERTSON. The viscoelastic properties of the lungs. *Q. J. Exp. Physiol.* 29: 27–47, 1939.
7. BIENKOWSKI, R., AND M. SKOLNICK. On the calculation of surface tension in lungs from pressure-volume data. *J. Colloid Interface Sci.* 48: 350–351, 1974.
8. BORST, H. G., E. BERGLUND, J. L. WHITTENBERGER, J. MEAD, M. McGREGOR, AND C. COLLIER. The effect of pulmonary vascular pressures on the mechanical properties of the lungs of anesthetized dogs. *J. Clin. Invest.* 36: 1708–1714, 1957.
9. BOYCE, J. F., S. SCHÜRCH, AND D. J. L. McIVER. Interfacial tensions in healthy and atherosclerotic rabbit aortae. *Atherosclerosis* 37: 361–370, 1980.
10. BROWN, E. S. Lung area from surface tension effects. *Proc. Soc. Exp. Biol. Med.* 95: 168–170, 1957.
11. BROWN, E. S., R. P. JOHNSON, AND J. A. CLEMENTS. Pulmonary surface tension. *J. Appl. Physiol.* 14: 717–720, 1959.
12. BROWN, R., A. J. WOOLCOCK, N. J. VINCENT, AND P. T. MACKLEM. Physiological effects of experimental airway obstruction with beads. *J. Appl. Physiol.* 27: 328–335, 1969.
13. BUTLER, J. The adaptation of the relaxed lungs and chest wall to changes in volume. *Clin. Sci.* 16: 421–433, 1957.
14. CARSON, J. On the elasticity of the lungs. *Philos. Trans. R. Soc. London* Part 1: 29–44, 1820.
15. CARTON, R. W., J. DAINAUSKAS, AND J. W. CLARK. Elastic properties of single elastic fibers. *J. Appl. Physiol.* 17: 547–551, 1962.
16. CLEMENTS, J. A. Surface tension of lung extracts. *Proc. Soc. Exp. Biol. Med.* 95: 170–174, 1957.
17. CLEMENTS, J. A. Surface phenomena in relation to pulmonary function. *Physiologist* 5: 11–28, 1962.
18. CLEMENTS, J. A. Functions of the alveolar lining. *Am. Rev. Respir. Dis.* 115: 67–71, 1977.
19. CLEMENTS, J. A., R. F. HUSTEAD, R. P. JOHNSON, AND I. GRIBETZ. Pulmonary surface tension and alveolar stability. *J. Appl. Physiol.* 16: 444–450, 1961.
20. CLEMENTS, J., AND H. TRAHAN. Effect of temperature on pressure-volume characteristics of rat lungs (Abstract). *Federation Proc.* 22: 281, 1963.
21. CLOETTA, M. Untersuchungen über die Elastizität der Lunge und deren Bedeutung für die Zirkulation. *Pfluegers Arch. Gesamte Physiol. Menschen Tiere* 152: 339–364, 1913.
22. COLEBATCH, H. J. H. The humoral regulation of alveolar ducts. In: *Airway Dynamics, Physiology, and Pharmacology*, edited by A. Bouhuys. Springfield, IL: Thomas, 1970, p. 169–189.
23. COLEBATCH, H. J. H., I. A. GREAVES, AND C. K. Y. NG. Exponential analysis of elastic recoil and aging in healthy males and females. *J. Appl. Physiol.: Respirat. Environ. Exercise Physiol.* 47: 683–691, 1979.
24. COLEBATCH, H. J. H., I. A. GREAVES, AND C. K. Y. NG. Pulmonary mechanics in diagnosis. In: *Mechanisms of Airways Obstruction in Human Respiratory Disease*, edited by M. A. de Kock, J. A. Nadel, and C. M. Lewis. Cape Town, South Africa: Balkema, 1979, p. 25–47.
25. COLEBATCH, H. J. H., AND C. A. MITCHELL. Constriction of isolated living liquid-filled dog and cat lungs with histamine. *J. Appl. Physiol.* 30: 691–702, 1971.
26. COLEBATCH, H. J. H., B. S. NAIL, AND C. K. Y. NG. Computerized measurement of pulmonary conductance and elastic recoil. *J. Appl. Physiol.: Respirat. Environ. Exercise Physiol.* 44: 611–618, 1978.
27. COLEBATCH, H. J. H., C. K. Y. NG, AND N. NIKOV. Use of an exponential function for elastic recoil. *J. Appl. Physiol.: Respirat. Environ. Exercise Physiol.* 46: 387–393, 1979.
28. COMROE, J. H. Retrospectroscope: premature science and immature lungs. I. Some premature discoveries. *Am. Rev. Respir. Dis.* 116: 127–135, 1977.
29. COOK, C. D., J. MEAD, G. L. SCHREINER, N. R. FRANK, AND J. M. CRAIG. Pulmonary mechanics during induced pulmonary edema in anesthetized dogs. *J. Appl. Physiol.* 14: 177–186, 1959.
30. DALE, W., AND H. RAHN. Rate of gas absorption during atelectasis. *Am. J. Physiol.* 170: 606–615, 1952.
31. DE TROYER, A., J. C. YERNAULT, AND D. RODENSTEIN. Influence of beta-2 agonist aerosols on pressure-volume characteristics of the lungs. *Am. Rev. Respir. Dis.* 118: 987–995, 1978.
32. DE TROYER, A., J. C. YERNAULT, AND D. RODENSTEIN. Effects of vagal blockade on lung mechanics in normal man. *J. Appl. Physiol.: Respirat. Environ. Exercise Physiol.* 46: 217–226, 1979.
33. DONDERS, F. C. Bijdrage tot het mechanisme van ademhaling en bloedsomloop in den gezonden en zieken toestand. *Ned.*

Lancet 2: 333–376, 1849.

34. DUNNILL, M. S. Effect of lung inflation on alveolar surface area in the dog. *Nature London* 214: 1013–1014, 1967.

35. DURLACHER, S. H., W. G. BANFIELD, AND A. D. BERGNER. Post-mortem pulmonary edema. *Yale J. Biol. Med.* 22: 565–572, 1950.

36. ENGEL, L. A., H. MENKES, L. D. H. WOOD, G. UTZ, J. JOUBERT, AND P. T. MACKLEM. Gas mixing during breath holding studied by intrapulmonary gas sampling. *J. Appl. Physiol.* 35: 9–17, 1973.

37. ENGEL, L. A., AND M. PAIVA. Analyses of sequential filling and emptying of the lung. *Respir. Physiol.* 45: 309–321, 1981.

38. ENGEL, L. A., G. UTZ, L. D. H. WOOD, AND P. T. MACKLEM. Ventilation distribution in anatomical lung units. *J. Appl. Physiol.* 37: 194–200, 1974.

39. ENGEL, L. A., L. D. H. WOOD, G. UTZ, AND P. T. MACKLEM. Gas mixing during inspiration. *J. Appl. Physiol.* 35: 18–24, 1973.

40. FISHER, M. J., M. F. WILSON, AND K. C. WEBER. Determination of alveolar surface area and tension from in situ pressure-volume data. *Respir. Physiol.* 10: 159–171, 1970.

41. FRANK, N. R., E. P. RADFORD, JR., AND J. L. WHITTENBERGER. Static volume-pressure interrelations of the lungs and pulmonary blood vessels in excised cat's lung. *J. Appl. Physiol.* 14: 167–173, 1959.

42. FRY, D. L. A preliminary lung model for simulating the aerodynamics of the bronchial tree. *Comput. Biomed. Res.* 2: 111–134, 1968.

43. FUKAYA, F., C. J. MARTIN, A. C. YOUNG, AND S. KATSURA. Mechanical properties of alveolar walls. *J. Appl. Physiol.* 25: 689–695, 1968.

44. GIBSON, G. J., N. B. PRIDE, J. DAVIS, AND R. C. SCHROTER. Exponential description of the static pressure-volume curve of normal and diseased lungs. *Am. Rev. Respir. Dis.* 120: 799–811, 1979.

45. GIL, J., H. BACHOFEN, P. GEHR, AND E. R. WEIBEL. Alveolar volume-surface area relation in air- and saline-filled lungs fixed by vascular perfusion. *J. Appl. Physiol.: Respirat. Environ. Exercise Physiol.* 47: 990–1001, 1979.

46. GLAISTER, D. H., R. C. SCHROTER, M. F. SUDLOW, AND J. MILIC-EMILI. Bulk elastic properties of excised lungs and the effect of a transpulmonary pressure gradient. *Respir. Physiol.* 17: 347–361, 1973.

47. GREAVES, I. A., AND H. J. H. COLEBATCH. Elastic behavior and structure of normal and emphysematous lungs post mortem. *Am. Rev. Respir. Dis.* 121: 127–136, 1980.

48. GUMP, F. E., Y. MASHIMA, A. FERENCZY, AND J. M. KINNEY. Pre- and postmortem studies of lung fluids and electrolytes. *J. Trauma* 11: 474–482, 1971.

49. HABER, P. S., H. J. H. COLEBATCH, C. K. Y. NG, AND I. A. GREAVES. Alveolar size as a determinant of pulmonary distensibility in mammalian lungs. *J. Appl. Physiol.: Respirat. Environ. Exercise Physiol.* 54: 837–845, 1983.

50. HAJJI, M. A., T. A. WILSON, AND S. J. LAI-FOOK. Improved measurements of shear modulus and pleural membrane tension of the lung. *J. Appl. Physiol.: Respirat. Environ. Exercise Physiol.* 47: 175–181, 1979.

51. HANCE, A. J., AND R. G. CRYSTAL. The connective tissue of the lung. *Am. Rev. Respir. Dis.* 112: 657–711, 1975.

52. HANSEN, J. E., AND E. P. AMPAYA. Human air space shapes, sizes, areas, and volumes. *J. Appl. Physiol.* 38: 990–995, 1975.

53. HEYNSIUS, A. Über die Grösse des negativem Drucks im Thorax beim rubigen Athmen. *Pfluegers Arch. Gesamte Physiol. Menschen Tiere* 29: 265–311, 1882.

54. HILDEBRANDT, J. Dynamic properties of air-filled excised cat lung determined by liquid plethysmograph. *J. Appl. Physiol.* 27: 246–250, 1969.

55. HILDEBRANDT, J. Pressure-volume data of cat lung interpreted by a plastoelastic, linear viscoelastic model. *J. Appl. Physiol.* 28: 365–372, 1970.

56. HILDEBRANDT, J. Modeles de l'hysteresis pression-volume.

Bull. Physio-Pathol. Respir. 8: 337–350, 1972.

57. HILDEBRANDT, J. Lung surfactant mechanics: some unresolved problems. In: *Regulation of Ventilation and Gas Exchange*, edited by C. D. Davies and G. D. Barnes. New York: Academic, 1978.

58. HILDEBRANDT, J., H. BACHOFEN, AND G. BRANDT. Reduction of hysteresis in liquid-sealed bell type spirometers. *J. Appl. Physiol.* 28: 216–218, 1970.

59. HOFFMAN, L., O. O. BLUMENFELD, R. B. MONDSHINE, AND S. S. PARK. Effect of DL-penicillamine on fibrous proteins of rat lung. *J. Appl. Physiol.* 33: 42–46, 1972.

60. HOFFMAN, L., R. B. MONDSHINE, AND S. S. PARK. Effect of DL-penicillamine on elastic propeties of rat lung. *J. Appl. Physiol.* 30: 508–511, 1971.

61. HOPPIN, F. G., JR., AND J. HILDEBRANDT. Mechanical properties of the lung. In: *Bioengineering Aspects of the Lung*, edited by J. B. West. New York: Dekker, 1977, p. 83–162.

62. HOPPIN, F. G., JR., J. M. B. HUGHES, AND J. MEAD. Axial forces in the bronchial tree. *J. Appl. Physiol.: Respirat. Environ. Exercise Physiol.* 42: 773–781, 1977.

63. HORIE, T., R. ARDILA, AND J. HILDEBRANDT. Static and dynamic properties of excised cat lung in relation to temperature. *J. Appl. Physiol.* 36: 317–322, 1974.

64. HORIE, T., AND J. HILDEBRANDT. Dynamic compliance, limit cycles, and static equilibria of excised cat lung. *J. Appl. Physiol.* 31: 423–430, 1971.

65. HORIE, T., AND J. HILDEBRANDT. Volume history, static equilibrium and dynamic compliance of excised cat lung. *J. Appl. Physiol.* 33: 105–112, 1972.

66. HORIE, T., AND J. HILDEBRANDT. Dependence of lung hysteresis area on tidal volume, duration of ventilation, and history. *J. Appl. Physiol.* 35: 596–600, 1973.

67. HORWITZ, A. L., N. A. ELSON, AND R. G. CRYSTAL. Proteoglycans and elastin. In: *The Biochemical Basis of Pulmonary Function*, edited by R. G. Crystal. New York: Dekker, 1976, p. 273–311.

68. HUTCHINSON, J. Thorax. In: *Cyclopaedia of Anatomy and Physiology*, edited by R. B. Todd. London: Longmans, 1849–1852, vol. 4, pt. 2, p. 1017–1086.

69. INGRAM, R. H., JR., J. J. WELLMAN, E. R. MCFADDEN, JR., AND J. MEAD. Relative contributions of large and small airways to flow limitation in normal subjects before and after atropine and isoproterenol. *J. Clin. Invest.* 59: 696–703, 1977.

70. INNERS, C. R., P. B. TERRY, R. J. TRAYSTMAN, AND H. A. MENKES. Effects of lung volume on collateral and airways resistance in man. *J. Appl. Physiol.: Respirat. Environ. Exercise Physiol.* 46: 67–73, 1979.

71. INOUE, H., C. INOUE, AND J. HILDEBRANDT. Temperature effects on lung mechanics in air- and liquid-filled rabbit lungs. *J. Appl. Physiol.: Respirat. Environ. Exercise Physiol.* 53: 567–575, 1982.

72. JAEGER, M. J., AND A. B. OTIS. Measurement of airway resistance with a volume displacement body plethysmograph. *J. Appl. Physiol.* 19: 813–820, 1964.

73. KAPANCI, Y., A. ASSIMACOPOULOS, C. IRLE, A. ZWAHLEN, AND G. GABBIANI. "Contractile interstitial cells" in pulmonary alveolar septa: a possible regulator of ventilation/perfusion ratio? Ultrastructural immunofluorescence and in vitro studies. *J. Cell Biol.* 60: 375–392, 1974.

74. KARLINSKY, J. B., G. L. SNYDER, C. FRANZBLAU, P. J. STONE, AND F. G. HOPPIN, JR. In vitro effects of elastase and collagenase on mechanical properties of hamster lungs. *Am. Rev. Respir. Dis.* 113: 769–777, 1976.

75. KEITH, A. The mechanism of respiration in man. In: *Further Advances in Physiology*, edited by L. Hill. London: Longmans, 1909, p. 182–207.

76. KNUDSON, R. J., AND W. T. KALLENBORN. Evaluation of lung elastic recoil by exponential curve analysis. *Respir. Physiol.* 46: 29–42, 1981.

77. LEMPERT, J., AND P. T. MACKLEM. Effect of temperature on rabbit lung surfactant and pressure-volume hysteresis. *J. Appl.*

Physiol. 31: 380–385, 1971.

78. LIEBERMEISTER, G. Zur normalen und pathologischen Physiologie der Atmungsorgane. I. Über das Verhältnis zwischen Lungendehnung und Lungenvolumen. *Zentralbl. Allg. Pathol. Pathol. Anat.* 18: 644–650, 1907.

79. LORING, S. H., J. M. DRAZEN, J. C. SMITH, AND F. G. HOPPIN, JR. Vagal stimulation and aerosol histamine increase hysteresis of lung recoil. *J. Appl. Physiol.: Respirat. Environ. Exercise Physiol.* 51: 477–484, 1981.

80. MACKLEM, P. T. Airway obstruction and collateral ventilation. *Physiol. Rev.* 51: 368–436, 1971.

81. MACKLEM, P. T., AND J. MEAD. Resistance of central and peripheral airways measured by a retrograde catheter. *J. Appl. Physiol.* 22: 395–401, 1967.

82. MACKLIN, C. C. Musculature of the bronchi and lungs. *Physiol. Rev.* 9: 1–60, 1929.

83. MARSHALL, R., AND A. B. DuBOIS. The measurement of the viscous resistance of the lung tissue in normal man. *Clin. Sci.* 15: 161–170, 1956.

84. MARSHALL, R., AND J. G. WIDDICOMBE. Stress relaxation of the human lung. *Clin. Sci.* 20: 19–31, 1960.

85. MARTIN, H. B. Respiratory bronchioles as the pathway for collateral ventilation. *J. Appl. Physiol.* 21: 1443–1447, 1966.

86. McILROY, M. B., J. MEAD, N. J. SELVERSTONE, AND E. P. RADFORD, JR. Measurement of lung tissue viscous resistance using gases of equal kinematic viscosity. *J. Appl. Physiol.* 7: 485–490, 1955.

87. MEAD, J., T. TAKISHIMA, AND D. LEITH. Stress distribution in lungs: a model of pulmonary elasticity. *J. Appl. Physiol.* 28: 596–608, 1970.

88. MOOR, E., AND J. S. ULTMAN. Monte Carlo simulation of simultaneous gas flow and diffusion in an asymmetric distal pulmonary airway model. *Bull. Math. Biol.* 38: 161–193, 1976.

89. MORLEY, C. J., A. D. BANGHAM, P. JOHNSON, G. D. THORBURN, AND G. JENKIN. Physical and physiological properties of dry lung surfactant. *Nature London* 271: 162–163, 1978.

90. MORRISS, A. W., R. E. DRAKE, AND J. C. GABEL. Comparison of microvascular filtration characteristics in isolated and intact lungs. *J. Appl. Physiol.: Respirat. Environ. Exercise Physiol.* 48: 438–443, 1980.

91. MURPHY, B. G., AND L. A. ENGEL. Models of the pressure-volume relationship of the human lung. *Respir. Physiol.* 32: 183–194, 1978.

92. NADEL, J. A., H. J. H. COLEBATCH, AND C. R. OLSEN. Location and mechanisms of airway constriction after barium sulfate microembolism. *J. Appl. Physiol.* 19: 387–394, 1964.

93. NAGAO, K., R. ARDILA, AND J. HILDEBRANDT. Rheological properties of excised rabbit lung stiffened by repeated hyperinflation. *J. Appl. Physiol.: Respirat. Environ. Exercise Physiol.* 47: 360–368, 1979.

94. NEUMANN, A. W., R. J. GOOD, C. J. HOPE, AND M. SEJPAL. An equation-of-state approach to determine surface tensions of low-energy solids from contact angles. *J. Colloid Interface Sci.* 49: 291–304, 1974.

95. NIEWOEHNER, D. E., J. KLEINERMAN, AND L. LIOTTA. Elastic behavior of postmortem human lungs: effect of aging and mild emphysema. *J. Appl. Physiol.* 39: 943–949, 1975.

95a. OLDMIXON, E. H., AND F. G. HOPPIN, JR. Comparison of amounts of collagen and elastin in pleura and parenchyma of dog lung. *J. Appl. Physiol.: Respirat. Environ. Exercise Physiol.* 56: 1383–1388, 1984.

96. ORSOS, F. Über das elastische Gerust der normalen und der emphysematosen Lunge. *Beitr. Pathol. Anat. Allg. Pathol.* 41: 95–121, 1907.

97. OTIS, A. B., C. B. McKERROW, R. A. BARTLETT, J. MEAD, M. B. McILROY, N. J. SELVERSTONE, AND E. P. RADFORD, JR. Mechanical factors in distribution of pulmonary ventilations. *J. Appl. Physiol.* 8: 427–433, 1956.

98. PAIVA, M., J. C. YERNAULT, P. van EERDEWEGHE, AND M. ENGLERT. A sigmoid model of the static volume-pressure curve of the lung. *Respir. Physiol.* 23: 317–323, 1975.

99. PARISH, W. E., A. R. AKESTER, AND D. M. GREGG. The demonstration of bronchospasm in anaphylaxis by radiography. *Int. Arch. Allergy Appl. Immunol.* 25: 89–104, 1964.

100. PATTLE R. E. Properties, function and origin of the alveolar lining layer. *Nature London* 175: 1125–1126, 1955.

101. PATTLE, R. E. The cause of the stability of bubbles derived from the lung. *Phys. Med. Biol.* 5: 11–26, 1960.

102. PATTLE, R. E., AND S. M. COOPER. Postmortem changes in the surpellic activity of lung surfactant. *Br. J. Exp. Pathol.* 59: 337–338, 1978.

103. PATTLE, R. E., C. SCHOCK, AND J. M. CREASEY. Post-mortem changes at electron microscope level in the type II cells of the lung. *Br. J. Exp. Pathol.* 55: 221–227, 1974.

104. PENGELLY, L. D. Curve-fitting analysis of pressure-volume characteristics in the lungs. *J. Appl. Physiol.: Respirat. Environ. Exercise Physiol.* 42: 111–116, 1977.

105. PIERCE, J. A. The elastic tissue of the lung. In: *The Lung,* edited by A. A. Liebow and D. E. Smith. Baltimore, MD: Williams & Wilkins, 1968, p. 41–47.

106. PIERCE, J. A., AND R. V. EBERT. Fibrous network of the lung and its change with age. *Thorax* 20: 469–476, 1965.

107. RADFORD, E. P., JR. Method for estimating respiratory surface area of mammalian lungs from their physical characteristics. *Proc. Soc. Exp. Biol. Med.* 87: 58–61, 1954.

108. RADFORD, E. P., JR. Recent studies of mechanical properties of mammalian lungs. In: *Tissue Elasticity,* edited by J. W. Remington. Washington, DC: Am. Physiol. Soc., 1957, p. 177–190.

109. REINBERG, S. A. Roentgen-ray studies on the physiology and pathology of the tracheo-bronchial tree. *Br. J. Radiol.* 30: 451–455, 1925.

110. REMINGTON, J. W. Hysteresis loop behavior of the aorta and other extensible tissues. *Am. J. Physiol.* 180: 83–95, 1955.

111. SALAZAR, E., AND J. H. KNOWLES. An analysis of pressure volume characteristics of lungs. *J. Appl. Physiol.* 19: 97–104, 1964.

112. SASAKI, H., T. TAKISHIMA, AND M. NAKAMURA. Collateral resistance at alveolar level in excised dog lungs. *J. Appl. Physiol.: Respirat. Environ. Exercise Physiol.* 48: 982–990, 1980.

113. SCHÜRCH, S. Surface tension at low lung volumes: dependence on time and alveolar size. *Respir. Physiol.* 48: 339–355, 1982.

114. SCHÜRCH, S., D. F. GERSON, AND D. J. L. McIVER. Determination of cell/medium interfacial tensions from contact angles in aqueous polymer systems. *Biochim. Biophys. Acta* 640: 557–571, 1981.

115. SCHÜRCH, S., J. GOERKE, AND J. A. CLEMENTS. Direct determination of surface tension in the lung. *Proc. Natl. Acad. Sci. USA* 73: 4698–4702, 1976.

116. SCHÜRCH, S., J. GOERKE, AND J. A. CLEMENTS. Direct determination of volume- and time-dependence of alveolar surface tension in excised lungs. *Proc. Natl. Acad. Sci. USA* 75: 3417–3421, 1978.

117. SCHÜRCH, S., AND D. McIVER. Interfacial tension at lipid-water interfaces. Comparison of equation-of-state predictions with direct experimental measurements. *J. Colloid Interface Sci.* 81: 301–304, 1981.

118. SETNIKAR, I., AND G. MESCHIA. Proprieta elastiche del polmone e di modelli meccanici. *Arch. Fisiol.* 52: 288–302, 1953.

119. SHARP, J. T., F. N. JOHNSON, N. B. GOLDBERG, AND P. VAN LITH. Hysteresis and stress adaptation in the human respiratory system. *J. Appl. Physiol.* 23: 487–497, 1967.

120. SHERMAN, I. A. Interfacial tension effects in the microvasculature. *Microvasc. Res.* 22: 296–307, 1981.

121. SOBIN, S. S., Y. C. FUNG, H. M. TREMER, AND T. H. ROSENQUIST. Elasticity of the pulmonary alveolar microvascular sheet in the cat. *Circ. Res.* 30: 440–450, 1972.

122. STANLEY, N. N., R. ALPER, E. L. CUNNINGHAM, N. S. CHERNIACK, AND N. A. KEFALIDES. Effects of a molecular change in collagen on lung structure and mechanical function. *J. Clin. Invest.* 55: 1195–1201, 1975.

123. STENGEL, P., D. FRAZER, AND K. WEBER. Lung degassing: an evaluation of two methods. *J. Appl. Physiol.: Respirat. Environ. Exercise Physiol.* 48: 370–375, 1980.

124. STOREY, W. T., AND N. C. STAUB. Ventilation of terminal air units. *J. Appl. Physiol.* 17: 391–397, 1962.

125. STROMBERG, D. D., AND C. A. WIEDERHIELM. Viscoelastic description of a collagenous tissue in simple elongation. *J. Appl. Physiol.* 26: 857–862, 1969.

126. SUDA, Y., C. J. MARTIN, AND A. C. YOUNG. Regional dispersion of volume-to-ventilation ratios in the lung of man. *J. Appl. Physiol.* 29: 480–485, 1970.

127. SUGIHARA, T., J. HILDEBRANDT, AND C. J. MARTIN. Viscoelastic properties of alveolar wall. *J. Appl. Physiol.* 33: 93–98, 1972.

128. TATTERSALL, S. F., R. P. PEREIRA, D. HUNTER, G. BLUNDELL, AND N. B. PRIDE. Lung distensibility and airway function in intermediate alpha-1-antitrypsin deficiency (PiMZ). *Thorax* 34: 637–646, 1979.

129. TIERNEY, D. F., AND R. P. JOHNSON. Altered surface tension of lung extracts and lung mechanics. *J. Appl. Physiol.* 20: 1253–1260, 1965.

130. VALBERG, P. A., AND J. B. BRAIN. Lung surface tension and air space dimensions from multiple pressure-volume curves. *J. Appl. Physiol.: Respirat. Environ. Exercise Physiol.* 43: 730–738, 1977.

131. VAN DER BRUGH, J. P. Über eine Methode Zur Messung des interpleuralen Druckes. *Pfluegers Arch. Gesamte Physiol. Menschen Tiere* 82: 591–602, 1900.

132. VESALIUS, A. *De humani corporis fabrica libri septem.* 1543.

133. VON BASCH. S. Über eine Function des Capillardruckes in den Lungenalveol. *Wien. Med. Blatter* 10: 465–467, 1887.

134. VON HALLER, A. *Elementa physiologiae.* Lausanne: Grosset, 1776, vol. III.

135. VON HAYEK, H. *The Human Lung,* translated from German by V. E. Krane. New York: Hafner, 1960.

136. VON NEERGAARD, K. Neue Auffassungen über einen Grundbegriff der Atemmechanik. Die Retraktionskraft der Lunge, abhängig von der Oberflachenspannung in den Alveolen. *Z. Gesamte Exp. Med.* 66: 373–394, 1929.

137. WANG, N. S., AND W. L. YING. A scanning electron microscopic study of alkali-digested human and rabbit alveoli. *Am. Rev. Respir. Dis.* 115: 449–460, 1977.

138. WILSON, T. A. Relations among recoil pressure, surface area, and surface tension in the lung. *J. Appl. Physiol.: Respirat. Environ. Exercise Physiol.* 50: 921–926, 1981.

139. WOHL, M. E., J. TURNER, AND J. MEAD. Static volume-pressure curves of dog lungs—in vivo and in vitro. *J. Appl. Physiol.* 24: 348–354, 1968.

140. WOOLCOCK, A. J., P. T. MACKLEM, J. C. HOGG, AND N. J. WILSON. Influence of autonomic nervous system on airway resistance and elastic recoil. *J. Appl. Physiol.* 26: 814–818, 1969.

141. WOOLCOCK, A. J., P. T. MACKLEM, J. C. HOGG, N. J. WILSON, J. A. NADEL, AND J. BRAIN. Effect of vagal stimulation on central and peripheral airways in dogs. *J. Appl. Physiol.* 26: 806–813, 1969.

142. WOOLCOCK, A. J., N. J. VINCENT, AND P. T. MACKLEM. Frequency dependence of compliance as a test for obstruction in the small airways. *J. Clin. Invest.* 48: 1097–1106, 1969.

143. YOUNG, I., R. W. MAZZONE, AND P. D. WAGNER. Identification of functional lung unit in the dog by graded vascular embolization. *J. Appl. Physiol.: Respirat. Environ. Exercise Physiol.* 49: 132–141, 1980.

CHAPTER 14

Micromechanics of the lung

IAN A. GREAVES | Harvard School of Public Health, Boston, Massachusetts

JACOB HILDEBRANDT | Virginia Mason Research Center, University of Washington, Seattle, Washington

FREDERIC G. HOPPIN, JR. | The Memorial Hospital, Brown University, Pawtucket, Rhode Island

CHAPTER CONTENTS

PULMONARY MECHANICS, like alveolar gas exchange, is often introduced with the model of a single representative alveolus. This conceptual alveolus is a spherical elastic balloon with walls that are tense due to stretching of connective tissue elements in the walls and to surface tension at the air-liquid interface. These tensions account for a transmural pressure difference, the pressure inside being greater than that outside with a magnitude (P) given by the Young-Laplace relationship, $P = 2T/r$, where T is the tension within the walls and r is the radius of curvature of the sphere. The contributions of tissue and interfacial tensions to T are additive. The lung parenchyma is considered to be a homogeneous assembly of such alveoli, with inflation-deflation properties deriving from the representative alveolus.

Although this model is still a useful point of departure, it must be modified to explain several well-established observations. These include inhomogeneities of inflation, instability, nonspherical alveoli, interaction of alveoli with alveolar ducts, and network structure of the parenchyma as distinct from a collection of mechanically independent structures.

CONFIGURATION OF TERMINAL AIR SPACES

One approach to understanding the mechanical properties of the parenchyma is to consider the configuration of terminal air spaces when lung volume changes. A wide range of evidence from direct observations, histology, and radiography indicates that the airways, alveolar ducts, and alveoli all expand and contract as the lung inflates and deflates. A fundamental question regarding the behavior of these structures, however, is to what extent they change size proportionately as lung volume changes.

Macroscopic Isotropy and Symmetry of Expansion

The physical science terms *isotropy* and *anisotropy* refer, respectively, to equality of the mechanical properties of a structure in all directions and to inequality of properties when measured along different axes. In the isotropic lung, inflation and deflation are expected to occur by symmetrical expansion and contraction in all directions. Ardila et al. (1) attached markers to the pleural surface of a lung and measured the distance between them as the volume changed. They found that linear dimensions along several axes vary as the cube root of lung volume ($V^{1/3}$), i.e., the pleural surface expands symmetrically. Sittipong and Hyatt (54) used tantalum dust to define the airways (down to 0.4 mm internal diam) and demonstrated that the linear dimensions of these internal structures also varied as $V^{1/3}$. Equally important, they demonstrated that the branching angles of airways were constant over a wide range of lung volumes. Both observations suggest that lung expansion is symmetrical and that the lung properties are isotropic at well below the lobar level. Such macroscopic isotropy, however, does not necessarily imply isotropy at finer levels of lung structure. There is evidence for asymmetrical behavior in the relative volumes of alveolar ducts and alveoli, inhomogeneous distortions of alveolar septa, and instability of alveoli. Such microscopic asymmetry occurring randomly throughout the lung may nonetheless permit expansion to remain symmetrical at a more macroscopic level.

Alveolus–Alveolar Duct Interactions

The first experimental approach to the question of the distribution of volume between ducts and alveoli at different lung volumes (after decades of conjecture) was by Storey and Staub (55). They froze cat lungs at two levels of inflation [~50% and 80% of maximal volume (Vmax)] and found on sectioning that the sizes of alveoli and ducts changed proportionately with volume. Klingele and Staub (31) extended these observations and found a degree of asymmetry at volumes below these levels. Cat lungs were frozen at various volumes reached either during deflation from Vmax or during inflation from 25% Vmax. The shapes of alveoli were quantified by measuring their depth and mouth diameter and by calculating the ratio of depth to mouth diameter. At volumes >40%–50% Vmax the ratio of depth to mouth diameter was constant, but at lower volumes the ratio was increased. Because the diameters of alveolar mouths determine the size of alveolar ducts, the greater decrease in alveolar mouth diameter relative to depth at low volumes implies that alveolar duct volume decreases proportionately more than alveolar volume. These findings delineate one type of asymmetrical behavior at low volumes.

Forrest (15) used a method similar to that of Klingele and Staub (31) and found comparable changes in alveolar shape at low volumes in guinea pig lungs. However, he also used a morphometric method involving point counting of alveoli and ducts, and this method produced different results: alveolar volume changed linearly with total lung volume, whereas alveolar duct volume showed a curvilinear relationship to the total volume. These conflicting findings in the same experimental material must reflect differences in the two methods of measurement. Hansen and Ampaya (27) may have identified the source of the conflict by noting the difficulties in distinguishing between alveolar duct and alveolar air space in micro-

scopic sections and thereby making reliable estimates of volumes of these structures by the point-counting method.

In another approach to describing the configuration of terminal air spaces as lung volume changes, the alveolar surface area (S) and volume (V) were estimated morphometrically and then the exponent n was found by curve fitting in the expression $S = kV^n$, where k and n are constants. If the structure at this level were isotropic, the expansion of air spaces would be symmetrical, alveolar configuration would be preserved, and n would necessarily have a value of $2/3$. (This is because surface area varies as the square and volume varies as the cube of a characteristic linear dimension.) Departure from this hypothetical value must therefore indicate a change of configuration. Various changes of configuration have been postulated and are presented schematically in Figure 1B–E along with the corresponding values of n. Various combinations of such changes could result in a range of values of n.

Unfortunately this approach cannot distinguish clearly among the various postulated configurational changes. Whereas a given configurational change specifies the value of n, the converse is not true because it is possible for various configurational changes to produce a given result (e.g., Fig. 1B, C).

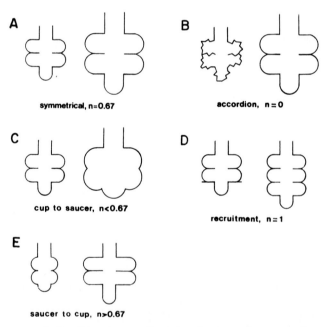

FIG. 1. Possible acinar configuration changes and corresponding values of exponent n. A: isotropic expansion. B: alveolar septa change length by unfolding in an accordion-like manner. Surface area is constant at all volumes. C: surface area is constant as shapes of alveoli change from "cup" to "saucer." D: changes in lung volume result solely from recruitment or derecruitment of alveoli. Surface area and volume appear and disappear proportionately. E: alveoli bud from rigid alveolar duct and surface area increases disproportionately to volume.

Nonetheless the approach has some value because interpretations of configurational changes must be consistent with morphometric results.

Experimental results for n have been conflicting, perhaps due to the use of different animal species but more probably due to differences in methodology and especially to the use of different volume histories before fixing the lungs. The different morphometric and fixation techniques used may also account for some of the discrepancies between studies. In particular, at high magnifications the greater degree of resolution of the alveolar surface results in higher estimates of surface area and therefore greater values for S/V (42). Consequently, if there are changes in the fine configuration of the alveolar surface as alveolar volume changes, S/V would differ when measured at different magnifications. Mechanical fixation is an additional concern; elastin is not well fixed by conventional methods and may contract during processing of tissues, thus changing alveolar configuration from the configuration in the fresh state (41).

Air-Space Morphometry—Light Microscopy

Dunnill (9) instilled formaldehyde into the lungs of dogs and fixed them at various levels of inflation. From measurements of linear intercepts made on standard histologic sections he determined the linear regression of log S on log V to obtain the slope $n = 0.77$. This value did not differ significantly from 0.67, and hence no definite conclusions could be drawn regarding asymmetry of alveolar expansion. Furthermore these results are relevant only to fluid-filled states.

D'Angelo (8) used a different approach. He photographed the subpleural alveoli of intact and excised rabbit lungs through a dissecting microscope and measured alveolar diameters along two axes at various volumes reached during deflation from Vmax. Mean linear dimensions were equal in each direction and changed proportionately over the entire volume range (20%–100% Vmax). From the values obtained for S and V, D'Angelo calculated that $n = 0.67$ (consistent with symmetry of expansion). Flicker and Lee (13) obtained an equivalent result when they measured the average perimeter and average area of subpleural alveoli in dog lobes and showed that the ratio of perimeter to area varied almost exactly as $V^{-1/3}$. Because this ratio is proportional to S/V, this finding is equivalent to showing that S is proportional to $V^{2/3}$. This approach is appealing because problems of tissue fixation inherent in other morphometric methods are avoided. The findings of these two studies seem straightforward, being consistent with the model of alveolar diameters increasing symmetrically over the major proportion of lung volume. However, the applicability of the results may be restricted to subpleural alveoli. Because the pleural surface is known to behave symmetrically (1),

pleural surface area must vary as $V^{2/3}$. The projected areas of the subpleural alveoli that are bound anatomically to the pleura must behave similarly, but deeper alveoli might well behave differently. There is evidence supporting the comparability of dimensions of subpleural and deeper alveoli. D'Angelo (8) examined tangential and vertical histologic sections of several layers of alveoli beneath the pleura and showed that the dimensions of alveoli in the deeper layers were the same as for the first subpleural layer, and Gil et al. (22) more recently confirmed that subpleural alveoli have the same S/V values as alveoli elsewhere in the lung. Nevertheless these results from "subpleural" alveoli may not be comparable to the projection seen through the pleura, particularly because the value found by Gil et al. (22) differed considerably from $V^{2/3}$.

Tsunoda et al. (57), in another approach, measured the thickness of alveolar walls at various inflations. Assuming constant tissue volume, they reasoned that mean alveolar wall thickness (δ) should vary inversely with alveolar wall area (i.e., as $V^{-0.67}$) if alveolar walls behaved in an ideal symmetrical fashion. Air-filled and liquid-filled cat lobes were fixed at various levels of inflation, and thin microscopic sections (0.2 μm) were examined by light microscopy ($\times$ 400). Wall thickness varied curvilinearly with total volume, from a maximum of 10–11 μm in degassed lungs to a minimum of 4 μm at Vmax. The linear regression of log δ on log V had a slope of -0.44, implying that $S \propto V^{0.44}$. This suggests asymmetric changes in which the septa thinned less and area increased less than expected for symmetrical inflation. Again the actual mechanism cannot be specified. It could, for example, be the result of some accordion-like extension (Fig. 1B) or a change in alveolar shape from cup to saucer (Fig. 1C). A similar result ($S \propto V^{0.48}$) was calculated by D'Angelo (8) from the results of Klingele and Staub (31). The results of Tsunoda et al. (57) therefore support the findings of Klingele and Staub. Surprisingly, Tsunoda et al. (57) could not detect obvious differences between air-filled and liquid-filled lungs with respect to the relationship between δ and V. This contrasts with the results of Gil et al. (22), who found that at a given lung volume, S is systematically greater in liquid-filled lungs, particularly in the middle vital capacity range.

Overall the results obtained by light microscopy are conflicting, some being consistent with expansion that is basically symmetrical (8, 9, 13, 15) and some with expansion in which S increased less than expected for the symmetrical case (15, 22, 31, 55, 57).

Air-Space Morphometry—Electron Microscopy

Scanning electron microscopy shows that in the air-filled state the alveolar surfaces are remarkably smooth between 60% and 100% Vmax, and at these volumes the surfaces have been likened to "concave mirrors" (22). At lower volumes, however, the alveolar surface becomes progressively irregular, first by alveolar capillaries bulging into alveolar spaces and then by undulation or folding of the entire septum in an accordion fashion.

Transmission electron microscopy of air-filled lungs fixed by vascular perfusion reveals additional irregularities of the alveolar septal tissues beneath the surface lining. When rat lungs are inflated and deflated from the totally degassed state, the alveolar septa exhibit various degrees of plication of the epithelial cellular layer and deeper structures (2, 60). The folds range from superficial, consisting of invaginations into the capillary spaces by the endothelial and epithelial layers, to a pleating of the full thickness of the septum. Such pleating occurs in the corners of alveolar air spaces near the junctions of septa and results in a thicker mass of septal tissue with a piling up of alveolar capillaries, elastin, and collagen fibers in the corner regions and in a broader, more gentle curve to the alveolar surface.

It is important to note that the early studies were often unphysiological. To some extent the formation of folds and pleats must have been enhanced by the experimental conditions of degassing the lungs initially and then inflating them submaximally. Leith (32) points out that lungs with small alveoli, such as rat lungs (mean alveolar diam at Vmax of ~80 μm), require much greater reinflation pressures than lungs with larger alveoli. This explains why when rat lungs are inflated to only 18 cmH$_2$O there is prominent pleating of the alveolar septa at all volumes and why measurements of S and V (2, 60) suggest that such lungs inflate and deflate by recruitment and derecruitment of alveoli.

Mazzone et al. (36), also in rats, more recently used a rapid-freezing technique and did not degas the lungs initially. They found that intracapillary invaginations disappeared at a transpulmonary pressure of 25 cmH$_2$O but at low lung volumes the depths of folds increased linearly as pressure decreased. Gil et al. (22) used degassed rabbit lungs but took particular care to inflate them several times to higher pressures (25–30 cmH$_2$O) before fixing them by vascular perfusion at various volumes reached on deflation from Vmax. Pleating of septa occurred at all volumes including, surprisingly, at Vmax. At high volumes the pleating of septa was confined to the corners of alveoli where three alveolar walls join. At 40% Vmax, alveolar walls showed sinuous profiles or waviness of the septa called "crumpling" (22). Stereological measurements in these air-filled lungs showed a progressively increasing slope of the log S–log V relationship with increasing lung volume, which is therefore consistent with a change from considerable accordion-like extension of septa in the low volume range ($n < \frac{2}{3}$) to a more symmetrical stretching of septa in the middle volume range ($n \simeq \frac{2}{3}$), and finally to a recruitment of alveoli or septal unpleating near total lung capacity ($n > \frac{2}{3}$). In the liquid-filled lung the slope was more linear, giving n

$\simeq 0.57$ over the volume range 40%–80% Vmax and $n \simeq 0.65$ over the range 40%–110% Vmax. Although Gil's data appear to be the most reliable to date because of the care taken to fix the lungs under physiological conditions, the interpretation of the data is not entirely straightforward. For example, the septa in fluid-filled alveoli appear to become flaccid over most of the volume range, yet $n = 0.58$ suggests nearly symmetrical inflation. It is also possible that prior degassing contributes to the pleating and that a truly physiological preparation has not yet been studied.

MECHANICAL INTERACTIONS OF TISSUE AND SURFACE

Mechanical Models

In the simplest concept, tissue and surface tensions are independent of each other and sum to exert the lung's elastic recoil. This concept underlies the calculations of the surface tension contribution to lung recoil that have been made by the Young-Laplace relationship with an assumed surface tension and either the characteristic alveolar diameter or mean alveolar curvature (23). Until recently this assumption was necessary in attempts to infer surface tension (9) from comparisons of air-filled and liquid-filled pressure-volume curves (3, 59). However, the anatomic relationships of tissue and surface in the terminal ventilatory unit suggest a more complex model, and this is supported by studies of lung configuration (22) and analysis of pressure-volume behavior (61). The stress-bearing structures of the lung parenchyma are depicted in Figure 2. There is an axial duct from which alveoli open radially. The septa bear tensions in their connective tissues and their air-liquid interfaces, and in each septum these tensions are mechanically in parallel. Along one pathway, spanning the unit by the outer septa, the tensed elements are uniform. By another pathway, however, the tensed elements are nonuniform. The radially dispersed septa connect to an inner ring (the cyclindrical net formed of the fibromuscular alveolar entrance rings). As the alveolar entrance rings have negligible air-liquid interface associated with them, the tensions in the inner ring are borne by the fibromuscular tissue alone.

All of these stress-bearing elements act to constrict the unit. However, within the unit, because of the mechanical series relationship of radial septa and entrance rings, configuration depends on the balance among surface and tissue forces. In particular, one can predict from inspection of the model that an increase of surface tension, at any given total volume, will dilate the entrance rings, decreasing septal surface area and decreasing alveolar volume in favor of alveolar duct volume. Conversely, increased tension in the smooth muscle of the alveolar entrance rings, at a given total volume, will constrict the entrance rings, increasing septal surface area and increasing alveolar

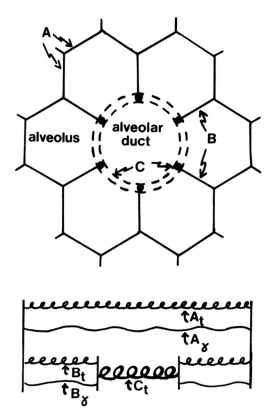

FIG. 2. Schematic representation of the alveolar duct and its surrounding alveoli (*top*). The mechanical relationships of tissue (*coiled lines*) and surface tensions (*wavy lines*) are shown schematically (*bottom*). A, septa forming outer circumferential boundary; B, radially dispersed septa; C, alveolar entrance rings. Subscripts t and γ refer to tensions in the tissue elements and air-liquid interfaces, respectively.

volume at the expense of alveolar duct volume. Hysteresis of any element might also affect configuration; for example, a greater surface tension during inflation would favor a lesser septal surface area during inflation, whereas hysteresis of smooth muscle in the alveolar entrance rings (48) would oppose or reverse this effect.

Morphology in Presence and Absence of Surface Tension

The above theoretical predictions have been tested (22). At high lung volumes, S values in liquid-filled and air-filled lungs tend to approach the same values at the same volumes. This suggests predominance of connective tissue tensions in the air-filled state, due to the increasing stiffness of the connective tissues when extended at high lung volumes. In the middle volume range, however, the air-filled lung has a considerably lower surface area than the liquid-filled lung, which is consistent with predominance of surface tension effects. At very low volumes, the differences between the liquid-filled and air-filled lungs again diminish, although they do not vanish as would be expected with the very low surface tensions that have

been reported at functional residual capacity and below (50).

Gil and colleagues (22) have described an "undulating" appearance of the alveolar septa in the liquid-filled state at all volumes except near Vmax. In addition, scanning electron micrographs show that the free edges of the alveolar mouths, which appear as well-defined linear structures in an air-filled lung, have a "crinkled" appearance after liquid filling. These observations suggest that in the presence of surface tension on the radial septa the alveolar entrance rings are tensed, whereas in the absence of surface tension the alveolar entrance rings are flaccid. Thus in the liquid-filled state, recoil of the unit would be attributable primarily to tension in the elastic elements of the outer boundary, whereas the tissues of the radial septa and of the alveolar entrance rings would not bear much tension. In the air-filled state the surface tensions of the radial septa act to relieve the septal tissue elements, and this may account for the redundant pleating of the septa that has been described in the corners of the alveoli (22, 23). By this concept the radially disposed alveolar septa do not bear tissue tensions in the air-filled lung except at very high lung volumes, a view very different from the conventional one. The observations leading to these conclusions require confirmation. There is, for example, an internal inconsistency between the interpretations of crinkling and undulation of structures and the morphometry of the liquid-filled lung: if alveolar walls are indeed unstressed in the liquid-filled state at volumes < 80% Vmax, S should be relatively constant as volume decreases; however, S decreases nearly proportionally with $V^{2/3}$ in saline-filled lungs (22), which implies that alveolar septa may be stressed elastically despite their flaccid appearance in Gil's preparation.

Effects on Capillaries and Interstitial Fluid

Alveolar capillaries are distorted by surface tension. In contrast to the smoothed alveolar surface of air-filled lungs, electron micrographs of liquid-filled lungs show extensive protrusion of capillaries from the alveolar surface at all volumes, most obviously at low and medium lung volumes. At all volumes below Vmax in liquid-filled lungs, alveolar capillaries are more rounded, more homogenously dilated, and more evenly distributed along the alveolar septa than in air-filled lungs (22).

Theoretically there are opposing mechanical effects of the capillary deformation that is seen in the air-filled state. With capillaries confined beneath a smoothed alveolar surface, the septal connective tissue network interweaving with the capillary network should be deformed, its fibrous bundles following a more circuitous course around the capillaries, and this should stretch and tense the fibrous network. On the other hand, the reduction in septal surface area should shorten radial alveolar septa and this should reduce tissue tensions. Redundancy of alveolar septa in the corner pleats (22, 23) suggests the latter consequence, that septal tissue tensions are reduced rather than increased.

Surface tension may also have direct implications to vascular mechanics. Capillaries in the flat portions of the septa appear somewhat flattened and confined by the alveolar surface; in corner regions where the surface is curved they appear larger and rounder. This suggests greater capillary transmural pressures and lower interstitial pressures in the corners. A likely explanation is as follows. Any tensions in those structures (the air-liquid surface, the fibrous tissue, and epithelial layers) that separate the capillary from alveolar gas will exert forces on the interstitium that depend on the local radii of curvature (r_1 and r_2) of the structures (by the Young-Laplace relationship). In the flat portions of the septum, where r_1 and r_2 are very large, capillaries are exposed essentially to alveolar gas pressure, but in the corners the interstitial pressure should be reduced relative to alveolar gas pressure by a factor of $(\gamma/r_1 + \gamma/r_2)$, where γ is surface tension. The latter effect should be greatest at high lung volumes where γ is greatest and r_1 and r_2 are smallest (see Fig. 5). This effect should also be increased in the presence of an impaired surfactant. At lower lung volumes, as γ approaches zero and corner curvature increases, pericapillary pressures should be more homogeneous throughout the alveolar septa. Indeed, capillaries become more uniform in size and shape as the lung deflates (22). Theoretically these local differences in interstitial pressures might also affect interstitial fluid dynamics.

Clearly the distribution of forces at the fine level of lung structure is not fully resolved. Questions remain regarding the relative roles of the various fiber systems at the level of the alveolar septum and the interactions between surface tension and connective tissue components. It does seem probable, however, that surface forces on septa can exceed tissue forces in the septa, that interfacial tension distorts the configuration of the alveolus–alveolar duct assembly, and that interfacial tension may have important effects on capillary distension and interstitial fluid balance.

CLOSURE

The gas-exchanging function of the lung requires patency of airways and alveoli, yet these structures are at risk of collapsing and there is evidence that closure of these structures occurs in the normal subject as well as in disease.

Airways

Most mammalian lungs, allowed to deflate spontaneously, retain ~0.5 ml of gas per gram lung tissue. Efforts to remove this gas by applying a negative pressure at the airway opening fail, causing the airways to collapse without removing the more distal alveolar gas.

Airways are ordinarily held open by their own intrinsic structure and by radial traction of the surrounding parenchyma. Central airways, because of the cartilage in their walls, are patent at zero transpulmonary pressure and resist collapse at negative transmural pressures. Intraparenchymal airways are exposed to radial traction across a peribronchial limiting membrane centrally and are tethered by direct fibrous continuity in the periphery. As a first approximation, the traction on the intraparenchymal airways is equal to intrapleural pressure and varies with lung volume according to the pressure-volume characteristics of the lung; as lung volume increases, traction increases and airways dilate. Because peripheral airways lack cartilage, to remain patent they may require the radial traction of the surrounding parenchyma. Consequently they collapse near zero transpulmonary pressure.

Traction also changes when, at a given lung volume, an airway narrows or dilates. The change in traction is in the direction to oppose the change of size of the airway. This stabilizing phenomenon, known as mechanical interdependence (38), is inherent in the lung as an elastic network and can be explained by the following general argument. At any given lung volume, the elastic network of the lung is at its lowest energy configuration. Local deformation of a part of an elastic network deforms the surrounding network and changes its stored energy in a direction that opposes the original deformation. Thus, for example, constriction of an airway requires energy to deform both the airway and the surrounding parenchyma. The energy put into the surrounding parenchyma is expressed as an increased tethering and acts to oppose the original constriction. Indeed, airways can be shown to be appreciably less compliant in situ than excised, particularly at the higher inflation pressures (47). At low lung volumes, however, where the radial tensions in the parenchyma are less, the stabilizing effect of mechanical interdependence is also less and consequently airways are at greater risk of undue narrowing and closure.

Dog lung pressure-volume curves have been interpreted as showing that airway closure begins at positive transpulmonary pressures as high as 4 cmH$_2$O (24). The configuration of the pressure-volume curves varies with changes in the minimum pressure to which the lung is deflated on each cycle. In repeated cycles with minimum pressure below ~4 cmH$_2$O, the compliance of the lower portion of the deflation curve decreases and the reinflation curve shows an initially decreased compliance followed by an inflection at higher pressures suggestive of reopening (19). Against this interpretation is the observation that pressure-volume curves of the lungs are essentially unchanged by extensive airway plugging (4). Furthermore a preparation in living rabbits has given evidence of airway patency to −1 or −2 cmH$_2$O (6). Pressure-volume curves, if performed during very careful and slow deflation, reach slightly negative values before the sharp inflection that signifies gas trapping. In addition the deflation volume-pressure curves in this region are the same whether volume is slowly reduced by O$_2$ absorption from the alveoli or by deflation via the airways, suggesting that all air spaces remain in communication with the trachea at these negative pressures. These discrepant findings may be related to differences in gas flow during inflation, because slowly inflated lungs are particularly prone to air trapping (19); in experiments not showing evidence of gas trapping, inflation rates may have been rapid or fewer deflations may have been made to low end-expiratory volumes.

In humans and dogs some airway closure seems to occur normally in situ. There is a terminal rise (phase IV) in the N$_2$ concentration of the expirate of a single-breath N$_2$ washout that is thought to result from closure of airways in the N$_2$-poor lower regions of the lung. It has been argued that this change of N$_2$ concentration may reflect severe regional flow limitation rather than actual closure of airways (30, 46), but several observations support actual airway closure. First, after washing out N$_2$ by breathing 100% O$_2$, maintenance of low lung volumes for several minutes induces absorption atelectasis. Second, significant amounts of N$_2$ are retained when 100% O$_2$ is breathed at low lung volumes (5). Third, radioactive tracers that are ordinarily drawn into most of the lung by N$_2$O absorption at low lung volumes are not drawn into dependent regions if breathing is limited to low lung volumes (10, 14). These observations suggest that substantial regions of the lung are not in continuity with the central airways at low lung volumes. Most of airway closure is presumed to be in the dependent regions where closure occurs because of the lesser degree of inflation and hence the lesser radial traction.

Alveoli

Complete alveolar collapse or atelectasis usually cannot be induced by deflation via the airways but requires gas absorption distal to an occluded airway, the presence of excess fluid in the alveoli, or impaired pulmonary surfactant. To study the mechanics of atelectatic regions, lungs are degassed in vitro by lowering the pressure to below that of water vapor (59) or in vivo by absorption of O$_2$.

The appearance of the atelectatic lung contrasts markedly with that of the air-filled lung. The atelectatic lung is dark red, but one can see into it to a depth of ~1 mm. By contrast the air-filled lung is light pink and the reflective alveolar surfaces impair vision much beyond the first few layers of subpleural alveoli.

Alveolar patency may be expected to require tensile forces in the parenchyma. Nonetheless there is some evidence of "alveolar resistance to collapse" in studies showing that deflation continues down to −1 to −2 cmH$_2$O transpulmonary pressure (6). The structural basis for such behavior is not clear. Unlike central airways, alveolar septa have no stiff cartilage to provide strength in compression. Indeed, at low lung volumes, the wavy and folded appearance of alveolar septa (22) suggests that they are easily broadened or buckled. One possible explanation for alveolar resistance to collapse is the effect of vascular distension; at a given low lung volume, transpulmonary pressure is reduced by vascular distension (16, 25), the erectile effect of which is qualitatively in the right direction to explain the observation.

Sequence of Closure

The trapping of gas in the alveoli during deflation shows that, although both airways and alveoli collapse near zero distending pressure, airways normally close or become blocked before alveoli collapse. To identify the anatomic level at which airway closure occurs, Hughes et al. (29) froze lungs at negative transpulmonary pressures. Following peripheral airways centrally in serial microscopic sections, they noted that the airway lumina disappeared at the level of the terminal bronchiole only to appear again more centrally. This preference for collapse in the peripheral rather than central airways is probably due to intrinsic differences in airway properties. Differences in intrinsic airway properties have been well documented; the collapsibility of excised airways increases peripherally, consistent with the fact that peripheral airways have progressively less cartilage (35), and this probably explains why peripheral airways in situ show more collapsibility than central airways (40).

This usual sequence of closure (airways before alveoli) traps air in the alveolar air spaces. In some diving mammals, however, the sequence is reversed with the result that passive deflation of the excised lung does not trap air in the alveoli but empties the alveoli completely (32). The cause of this reversal appears to be cartilaginous armoring of the airways out to the periphery.

There are two physiologically fortunate consequences of airways closing before alveoli. First, gas exchange can continue for a time in regions with trapping, whereas atelectasis would create instant shunting. Second, for reasons discussed in the next section, it is substantially easier to reinflate a lung with collapsed airways than one with atelectasis.

OPENING

Inflation of lungs to near total lung capacity (~30 cmH$_2$O in humans and dogs) generally reopens all airways and regions of alveolar atelectasis. The pressures at which these structures open, however, can vary considerably depending on the site of closure (airways or alveoli), on the state of the pulmonary surfactant, and on the state of bronchoconstriction.

Airways

Evidence regarding the conditions for airway opening comes from several sources. Regional measurements of radioactive gas during inspiration from residual volume in upright humans show that inspired gas enters into the bases of the lung only after ~20% of the vital capacity has been inhaled (39). Similarly the basilar atelectasis that forms after a few minutes of O_2 breathing at low lung volumes with small tidal excursions can be prevented if the end-inspiratory volumes exceed residual volume by >20% of the vital capacity (5). These results suggest that, although airways at the lung bases may close at low lung volumes, the airways are normally reopened near functional residual capacity. The critical pressures for reopening have also been inferred from regional pressure-volume curves in humans (39) and from lung pressure-volume curves in excised animal lungs (24). In humans, plots of regional volume versus esophageal pressure obtained during stepwise inspirations show a fairly abrupt upward inflection above ~4 cmH$_2$O distending pressure, suggesting that critical opening pressures are exceeded at ~4 cmH$_2$O (38). Somewhat greater opening pressures have been inferred from the configuration of pressure-volume curves in excised dog lungs (24). After these lungs are deflated to low volumes so that some airways close, the reinflation curve is at first relatively noncompliant but then shows an upward inflection or "knee" in the range of 12–20 cmH$_2$O. In confirmation of the interpretation of this knee as airway opening, compliance during the subsequent deflation and reinflation is proportional to how much of the lung has been filled above this knee (i.e., how much had been reopened). The location of the knee was therefore taken as indicating a range of opening pressures of 12–20 cmH$_2$O.

Alveoli

On the other hand, atelectasis may require substantially greater distending pressures for reopening. If complete atelectasis is induced by vacuum degassing or O_2 absorption, the initial inflation of excised dog lungs requires 15–25 cmH$_2$O or more. Lungs with smaller or larger alveoli may require higher or lower pressures, respectively (32). In humans, after breathing 100% O_2 at low lung volumes, compliance is initially low on reinflation and chest pain and cough interrupt inspiration. These signs and symptoms of atelectasis can occur with inspiration to well above 20 cmH$_2$O distending pressure.

Mechanics of Opening

Models have been used to explain the phenomena associated with opening of airways and alveoli (33, 37). Although these models are not fully satisfactory, they provide a useful point of departure. Clearly the major difficulty of reopening airways or alveoli results from the presence of an air-liquid interface. When there is no such interface (as in saline-filled lungs) these opening and closing phenomena do not occur, hysteresis is far less (3), and microscopic evidence of airway or alveolar closure is absent (22).

Macklem (33) compared the effects of surface tension in the open and closed portions of an airway (Fig. 3A). In the open portion of a cylindrical airway, surface tension exerts a constrictive pressure of γ/r. At the point of airway collapse a fluid or mucous plug must exist in the lumen with hemispherical interfaces concave to the air-filled sides (34). On the liquid side of the interfaces (the closed portion of the airway) the liquid pressure is lower than airway air pressure by $2\gamma/r$. The effect of interfacial tension in the closed portion is twice that in the open portion because of

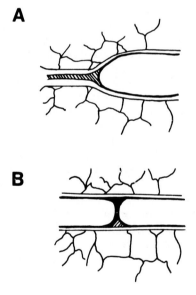

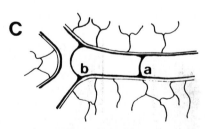

FIG. 3. Air-liquid interfaces at sites of airway closure. *A*: peripheral airway (*left*) is closed by narrowing over a considerable length of airway. *B*: there is only a film across the lumen resulting in only minor narrowing. *C*: film has different surface tension on central and peripheral sides of an air bubble and is shown in straight airway (a) and at bifurcation (b).

the hemispherical versus the cylindrical geometry of the air-liquid interfaces. Consequently, as soon as an airway closes, the pressure in the collapsed segment is lowered further and there is a greater tendency for the airway to remain closed.

Surfactant is probably present in the liquid lining of airways; surfactant-producing cells are present and the airway hysteresis is reduced by rinsing out the lung with polysorbate solution (34). The actual magnitude of interfacial tension in the airways is unknown, but it could be in the vicinity of the equilibrium tension for surfactant (20–25 dyn·cm^{-1}) and could vary with changes of interfacial surface area. Airway surfactant probably originates from alveolar type II cells, moves into the airways under a gradient of film pressure, and then is cleared by mucociliary transport. The γ may be relatively high during opening because, as the locus of closure moves distally in the airways, the S of the central air-liquid interface is greatly expanded, thereby raising γ. For $\gamma = 40$ dyn·cm^{-1} and $r = 200$ μm in terminal bronchioles, the constricting effect of γ is ~2 cmH$_2$O in the air-filled portion and 4 cmH$_2$O in the collapsed portion. Pressure of >4 cmH$_2$O must then be provided in the airway just to overcome this restriction to opening.

The mechanical relationships among the interface, airway, and alveoli as opening progresses are not well described. When the airway is closed and air is trapped distally (as occurs readily at the lung bases), both the distal and proximal air-liquid interfaces must be considered. Macklem (33) believes the proximal interface progresses distally until it backs into the distal interface, thus creating a flat thin fluid film. Because this thin film spans a short portion of the airway, it does not constrict the airway effectively. Furthermore, because of the tight r at the edges of the film, Macklem (33) argues that there is a locally negative fluid pressure that draws fluid from the middle of the film and enhances its rupture (Fig. 3B). Consideration of the phenomenon of progressive gas trapping, however (see GAS TRAPPING, p. 226), supports the notion that under some circumstances such obstructing films are relatively stable and can move in and out through a series of generations of airways during inflation and deflation. If this is the case, there may be an additional impediment to opening associated with expansion of the film when it arrives at a branching of the airways. During inflation a positive central airway pressure must be developed to curve the film before it can progress out the diverging walls (Fig. 3C).

A further impediment to distal progression of the film would be caused by any differences in γ on the two sides of the film. Currently there is no direct evidence regarding the actual values of γ on each side, but it is probable that the surfactant on the central side is spread as the film moves distally during inflation, whereas the surfactant on the distal side is compressed. If this is so, γ on the central side (γ_c) will

be greater than that on the distal side (γ_d). The difference of γ acting at the edges of the film will then oppose inflation by ($\gamma_c - \gamma_d$) times the length of the edge ($2r$) and thus would require a pressure difference across the film of $2(\gamma_c - \gamma_d)/r$.

The pressure difference across the film can be no greater than $2(\gamma_c + \gamma_d)/r_t$, where r_t is the radius of the parent tube (by the Young-Laplace relationship setting r as the smallest dimension possible). For $\gamma = 40$ dyn·cm^{-1} and an airway diameter = 200 μm, the pressure difference could be as high as 16 cmH$_2$O. In practice the pressure difference should be less than this estimate because r of the film would probably be greater than that of the airway and because γ_d would be <40 dyn·cm^{-1}.

By contrast, in atelectasis there is no air distal to the point of airway closure; a single interface must expand as it progresses distally and must assume progressively smaller r_1 and r_2. This process is visualized through the pleural surface of the degassed excised lung (45). The diameters of the air-filled spaces during early reinflation of rat and dog lungs are 200–300 μm. With progressive inflation, new air spaces bud from the original ones and the newer spaces are of smaller diameter so that at full inflation the mean diameter of air-filled units is ~50–80 μm. The absolute values of these dimensions may have been underestimated due to refraction of light by the curved interfaces, but the qualitative observation seems valid that sequentially smaller units are recruited as the atelectatic lung reinflates. This fact accounts qualitatively for the serially greater pressures needed to open more peripheral airways and alveoli. The magnitude of the opening pressures for alveoli, however, is surprisingly large. From the Young-Laplace relationship, the curvature of the advancing air-liquid interface could account for no more than 8 cmH$_2$O collapsing pressure (for $\gamma = 40$ dyn·cm^{-1} and an airway diameter = 200 μm, conservative estimates of the size of a human or dog alveolar duct), and this is only 25%–50% of the measured opening pressures. Presumably there must be substantial restricting tissue tensions in the mass of collapsed alveoli surrounding the advancing air front. This is surprising because these tissues might be expected to be flaccid and redundant when collapsed. Conceivably smooth muscle tone and the presence of viscous adhesive mucus impede airway opening.

Septal Pleats

In a different sense opening and closing may occur at the subalveolar level with infolding of the epithelial surfaces into the pulmonary capillaries and with pleating of the alveolar septa in alveolar corners. Intracapillary folds and pleats have been observed at transpulmonary pressures of 15–20 cmH$_2$O or higher and appear to increase in depth and number as the lungs deflate (23, 36). It is not known whether septal folds and pleats open at significantly higher distending pressures than those at which they form. If they did, these phenomena could contribute to the pressure-volume hysteresis of the lung, along with the opening and closing of airways and alveoli, and may account for some of the hysteresis between S/V and transpulmonary pressure demonstrated in rat lungs (60).

The magnitude of opening pressures for alveolar folds and pleats has received little theoretical or experimental attention. Such structures could open by the separation of infolded surfaces either *1*) evenly along their whole length, *2*) in a wedgelike manner, or *3*) by peeling apart (47). The forces that oppose opening in the first two cases result from γ at the air-liquid interface in the narrow air gap forming in the infolded space; both would require considerable force to initiate separation. The third case seems the most likely because the existence of sharp curvatures of the epithelial sheets implies that these layers do in fact bend easily. In all three cases the surface work involved is $\int \gamma dS$, where dS is the incremental area of the sheet opened by expanding the air-liquid interface. However, in the third case the force required is much less, although the distance over which it acts is increased.

The possibility that there exist cohesive forces between the epithelial sheets, as distinct from those associated with γ, must also be entertained, but this appears unlikely for the following reason. A working concept of a "glue" between the apposed cellular sheets would require considerable strength of the cellular sheet. It is difficult to attribute such strength to cells that consist only of a fluid or gel cytoplasm and a lipid protein surface membrane. Membrane subphase interfacial tension provides very little strength: in cell systems this tension has been found to be much less than 1 dyn·cm^{-1} (51). Thus appreciable surface adhesion would be likely to disrupt cells. There is, however, no direct information regarding this mechanism in the lung.

GAS TRAPPING

An interesting phenomenon occurs when excised lungs are ventilated very slowly between low (-5 to $+5$ cmH$_2$O) and high ($+20$ to $+30$ cmH$_2$O) transpulmonary pressures. With successive inflation-deflation cycles, the volume of gas retained in the lung at low pressures increases progressively and may reach 80% Vmax or more. Once formed this trapped gas cannot be removed by applying a negative pressure to the airways or by pushing on the pleural surface either manually or by positive pressure. Vacuum degassing the lung can abolish all trapped gas, but trapping can be reproduced by again cycling the lung slowly (10). Progressive trapping occurs also in saline-filled lungs.

Foam

In air-filled lungs, foam formation is the most likely mechanism for gas retention. Trapping of gas is associated with a thick white foam in the lumen of smaller airways that exudes into the larger airways. If the parenchyma is cut the lung will not deflate. Faridy and Permutt (11) concluded that a stable foam obstructed the airways and caused gas to be trapped distally. They further showed that depletion of surfactant, caused by ventilating the lungs with small tidal volumes for several hours (12), prevents the formation of bubbles in the airways and abolishes gas trapping when the lungs are again cycled slowly through large volumes.

Mechanism

It has been proposed that trapping occurs when a stable liquid film forms at the site of airway closure and reopening does not rupture the film but instead pushes the film distally into respiratory bronchioles or ducts. Liquid films have been observed to form across the airways during deflation at low lung volumes (34). Such films sometimes form at several cmH$_2$O above zero transpulmonary pressure. If these films account for gas trapping, one would predict that cycling the lungs at greater end-deflation pressures by limiting the formation of new films would decrease the proportion of gas trapped. Frazer et al. (18) ventilated excised lungs with end-deflation pressures ranging from $+6$ to -5 cmH$_2$O and, in confirmation of the prediction, found that gas trapping increases noticeably below $+4$ cmH$_2$O. The rate of increase of trapping is maximal at approximately $+2.2$ cmH$_2$O and trapping is not further increased below zero pressure. Trapping is also sensitive to the peak inflation pressure: lowering peak pressure from 30 cmH$_2$O to 25 cmH$_2$O to 20 cmH$_2$O reduces the volume trapped in 10 ventilatory cycles from 60% to 40% to 20% of the original vital capacity, respectively (19).

An intriguing observation is that the proportion of gas trapped in a given cycle depends primarily on the rate of inflation (18), although there is some influence of deflation rate (Y. Hosokawa and J. Hildebrandt, unpublished observations). The degree of gas trapping also appears to depend on the solubility (α) and molecular weight (M_r) of the gas used to ventilate the lung: Frazer and Weber (19) found a correlation between the amount of gas trapped and $\alpha M_r^{1/2}$ for SF$_6$, N$_2$, and He, although N$_2$O lay off the line. Because $\alpha M_r^{1/2}$ is proportional to the diffusion constant, the results suggest that gaseous diffusion is important in this phenomenon.

To explain the observed dependence of gas trapping on the rate of lung inflation and not on deflation, Frazer and Weber (19) postulated that a pressure difference across a liquid film spanning the airways provides the driving force for gaseous diffusion into and out of the trapped volume of gas and that the pressure difference is greater during inflation than deflation, resulting in an increased trapped gas volume in successive cycles. The basis for their postulate is as follows. As the lung inflates, each film moves peripherally along an airway until a bifurcation is reached. If the film is to move further peripherally, the total area of the liquid film must increase and thus energy must be expended. Frazer and Khoshnood (17) reasoned that the energy would produce a pressure drop of several cmH₂O across the film, thereby generating a driving pressure for gaseous diffusion across the film into the trapped space. The pressure required to increase S of the film would be proportional to γ. The films most likely contain surfactant (11) and therefore exhibit γ-S hysteresis similar to surfactant. This means that the energy required to stretch the film during inflation, when the film is expanding, is greater than that recovered during deflation, when the film is contracting. Thus the forces promoting diffusion of gas into trapped spaces (pressure drop during inflation) should exceed the forces in the opposite direction (pressure drop during deflation), the net result being that trapped gas would accumulate progressively with each inflation-deflation cycle, particularly when inflation is prolonged. This mechanism does not, however, explain the formation of the thick airway foam, which could be the main factor promoting trapping.

Trapping in Vivo

It is likely that this type of gas trapping is largely confined to excised lungs ventilated very slowly with tidal volumes of at least half the vital capacity. Sergysels et al. (53) specifically looked for similar gas trapping in anesthetized, paralyzed dogs. They found only a small degree of trapping during air breathing and only when they cycled the lungs through a full vital capacity at mean flows of 100–150 ml/s. Ventilation with 80% N₂O–20% O₂ in a similar manner increased trapping by ~10% of vital capacity. They attributed this increase to the differential diffusibility (30:1) across the film of N₂O into and N₂ out of the small bubbles of airway foam. As the foam volume expanded, closure occurred slightly earlier during deflation. The experiments, however, are not very physiological; mammals do not take several minutes to inspire, yet films and bubbles do occur and may cause gas trapping in pulmonary edema associated with acute left heart failure. The familiar white frothy fluid that may appear in the airways in this condition resembles the stable foam described in the airways of excised lungs with trapped gas. This may explain in part the findings of increased closing volume in humans during episodes of acute pulmonary edema (26) and in dogs that developed gas trapping (53). Formation of airway films may also be expected to occur in other causes of acute lung edema (such as after inha-

lation of chlorine gas or after cerebral trauma) when massive edema can develop suddenly as well as with aspirations of various liquids into the bronchial tree (such as in drowning or the aspiration of gastric contents).

INSTABILITY

When the lung is inflated from the atelectatic state, filling of air spaces is nonuniform. Observed through the pleural surface, alveoli inflate patchily and appear suddenly, popping open as outpouchings from the underlying alveolar sacs. On deflation, however, normal alveoli do not show such instability but deflate progressively without collapse and remain as discrete units (43). If, however, the alveolar lining layer is depleted or chemically altered, as by rinsing the lung with polysorbate solution or kerosene, the individual alveoli will appear to be unstable during deflation and inflation (44). Similar instability is observed in the lungs of patients with respiratory distress syndromes such as hyaline membrane disease or shock lung.

Negative Pressure-Volume Compliance

Instability implies a region of negative compliance (dV/dP < 0) on the pressure-volume curve: increasing the volume lowers rather than raises the distending pressure (Fig. 4). In a system where pressure is the controlled variable, raising pressure to a critical opening pressure above which dV/dP < 0 will cause the alveolus to open by jumping across the region of negative compliance to the next volume at equilibrium with pressure. Similarly, lowering pressure to the crit-

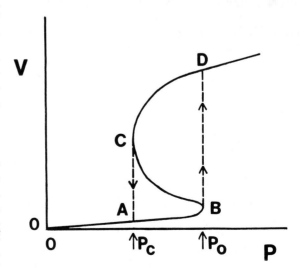

FIG. 4. Theoretical pressure-volume characteristics of alveolus showing region of negative compliance from B to C, causing an alveolus when inflated to critical opening pressure (P_O) to jump from B to D and when deflated to critical closing pressure (P_C) to jump from C to A. [Adapted from Mead (37).]

ical closing pressure will cause a closing jump. Theoretically, constant γ contributes to such instability. For example, at a single spherical interface (e.g., a bubble in water) the distending pressure is $2\gamma/r$, and if γ is constant, the slope of the volume-pressure curve is always negative. (Combining the Young-Laplace relationship with the formula for the volume of a sphere and taking the derivative, one obtains $dP/dV \propto -V^{-4/3}$.) This structure is therefore inherently unstable. Yet alveoli in the healthy lung appear to be stable over the physiological range of volumes. To explain the generally observed stability when faced with this theoretical prediction, physiologists have variously invoked geometric factors, positive elastance of interfacial tension, positive elastance of fibrous structures, and network behavior.

Configurational Stability

Historically the first explanation offered was geometric, although now it is deemed erroneous. Von Neergaard (59) compared the pressure-volume behaviors of liquid-filled and air-filled lungs and noted that the contribution of interfacial tension to transpulmonary pressure increased with increasing lung volume, indicating that on the average the air-liquid interface contributed a positive compliance. He offered the explanation that the appropriate model was not of spherical units, in which r_1 and r_2 must increase with inflation, but of structures less than hemispherical that inflate with decreasing r_1 and r_2 and go from the configurations of shallow saucers to those of deeper cups (see Fig. 1D). Unfortunately this elegant explanation is not borne out by anatomic studies: a large proportion of alveoli are cuplike at low volumes (28, 31) and morphologic results suggest that the change of shape during inflation may well be the converse (see CONFIGURATION OF TERMINAL AIR SPACES, p. 217).

Surface Tension Elastance

Although the physical chemistry of compressible monolayers was well understood at the time, von Neergaard was apparently unaware that γ could change with alveolar surface area. Clements and co-workers (7) postulated area-dependent changes in γ, demonstrated such properties in lung extracts and washings, and pointed to the mechanical implications for stability. They noted that a positive elastance of the γ-S relationship ($d\gamma/dS > 0$) favors stability. It can be shown that the spherical film is inherently unstable at fixed pressure unless surface elastance exceeds $\gamma/2S$.[1] Characterizations of in situ surface

tension elastance (3, 13, 50, 52, 61), however, show only small surface elastances over much of the volume range, particularly at low lung volumes after a deflation from total lung capacity. Thus, for spherical alveoli, surface elastance alone would be unlikely to account for stability.

Positive Tissue Elastance

The simple spherical film, such as a soap bubble blown on the end of a small tube, is an inaccurate representation of the alveolus where the air-liquid interface is spread on the alveolar septum; a model with surface and tissue contributions acting in parallel is more helpful in understanding the effects of tissue elastance on stability (7). Because the tension in the tissue of the alveolar septum is a function of r [$f(r)$] and acts mechanically in parallel with surface tension, a positive tissue elastance [$f'(r) > 0$] favors stability. With this tissue elastance incorporated into the simple spherical model, it can be shown that there is instability unless surface elastance exceeds $[\gamma + f(r) - rf'(r)]/2S$.[2] By inspection, it is apparent that a positive tissue elastance reduces the need for positive surface elastance. Tissue elastance would be particularly important at high lung volumes where the slope of $f(r)$ increases sharply.

Network Behavior (Interdependence)

The third stabilizing influence is network behavior. In the models discussed, "the individual [alveoli] were taken to act independently of one another" (7). This is clearly not the case for alveoli, for larger regions within the parenchyma, or even for lobes within the chest. The independent bubble model is therefore inappropriate. Alveoli are not independent structures but are spaces within a network of alveolar septa. An alveolus or group of alveoli cannot collapse without pulling and distorting the surrounding network. The same principle holds for larger units within the lobes and for whole lobes in situ to the extent that they are interdependent with each other and with the chest wall.

Mead et al. (38) considered two theoretical mechanisms whereby the parenchymal network opposes nonuniform changes in size of one region within the network relative to another: 1) changes of the tension in the elastic elements of the surrounding parenchyma and 2) changes of the effective area on which those tensions are applied. If an alveolus deflates relative to its neighbors, the tensions in the septa of the surrounding parenchyma increase and the alveolar area

---

[1] For a simple spherical film, the derivative of the Young-Laplace relationship gives $dP/dr = -2\gamma/r^2 + (2/r)(d\gamma/dr)$. Therefore for stability (which requires that $dP/dr > 0$) $d\gamma/dr$ must exceed γ/r. Alternatively, because $d\gamma/dS = (d\gamma/dr)(dr/dS)$ and dr/dS for a sphere = $\frac{1}{8}\pi r$, then $d\gamma/dS > \gamma/8\pi r^2 = \gamma/2S$.

[2] From the Young-Laplace relationship, $P = 2[\gamma + f(r)]/r$. The derivative gives $d\gamma/dr = \gamma/r + f(r)/r + (r/2)(dP/dr) - f'(r)$. For stability $dP/dr > 0$. Combining and solving, one obtains $d\gamma/dr > \gamma/r + f(r) - f'(r)$. From $S = kr^2$, $dS/dr = 2kr$. Multiplying both sides of the inequality by dS/dr and substituting, one obtains $d\gamma/dS > [\gamma + f(r) - rf'(r)]/2S$.

into which the septa insert decreases; both factors effectively increase the distending pressure acting on the deflating alveolus and therefore oppose its collapse.

The stabilizing influence of this network behavior is potentially powerful. For example, the inherent instability of the independent bubble model with constant surface tension totally disappears in the interdependent model. Consider the force balance at the boundary of a region within the lung. At equilibrium the tensions in the septa pulling inward (collapsing) and those pulling outward (inflating) balance exactly. If the region is deflated and interfacial tension remains constant (surface elastance zero), the net forces due to surface tensions decrease because the length of septa attaching to the boundary decreases. However, the decrease is equal on the inner and outer sides of the boundary (with constant γ and similar changes of length of inward-acting and outward-acting septa) and therefore the surface forces remain balanced. By this argument the interdependent gas-containing region with constant γ is not inherently unstable, as had been earlier argued for the independent bubble model. Thus any small positive tissue or surface elastance should suffice to stabilize air spaces in such a network. Fung (21) has presented a rigorous mathematical justification for this conclusion for the single alveolus.

An additional aspect of network behavior may lend further stability. The above theory presumes conformed distortions, i.e., the angles of application of outward or inward tensions for the boundary of the region stay the same during distortion. More likely the angles will change with collapse, the outward-directed septa being drawn in toward the axis of collapse and the inward-directed septa deviating away from the axis of collapse. Such changes of angles are stabilizing because they increase the outward component of force and decrease the inward component.

Despite all these theoretical reasons to expect stability, alveolar instability does occur in many circumstances where surface elastance is impaired or alveolar fluid is increased. Instability of small units can be observed through the pleural surface, even though the overall pressure-volume curve of the lung is not unstable, reflecting a range of critical opening and closing pressures for the individual unstable units. Why does the theoretical prediction of stability in the interdependent model fail in these circumstances? Several explanations are offered. 1) Perhaps alveoli seen to pop shut beneath the pleura do not satisfy the requirements of the interdependence model because, unlike deeper alveoli, they are not completely surrounded by the elastic network. However, histologic studies show that atelectasis is not preferentially distributed adjacent to the pleura. 2) The observed instability after rinsing the lung with polysorbate may represent movement of free liquid. Substantial liquid remains in the lung after rinsing, thus increasing lung weight by 50% or more. The movement of such free liquid from one alveolus to the next via pores or across

membranes would allow preferential filling of those alveoli with the smallest radii of surface curvature. Such a mechanism may account partly for the instability seen in pulmonary edema or pneumonia. 3) At low lung volumes, the gathering of tissue into the corners so that the septa are redundant implies that the connective tissue in these septa is flaccid and does not supply a stabilizing positive tissue elastance. 4) At low lung volumes and with increased alveolar fluid, the entire alveolar surface (rather than just the corners) becomes spherical. This introduces a new instability: at high volumes, where part of the septal surface is flat, the radius of curvature in the corner of an alveolus increases with deflation; at low volumes, however, where the entire septal surface is curved, the radius of curvature must decrease with deflation (Fig. 5). This latter situation favors instability because the pressure favoring further collapse now increases with deflation (by the Young-Laplace relationship). The alveolus may become unstable, then, when the alveolar configuration becomes spherical rather than having partly flat regions, a configuration favored by low volumes, high surface tension, and excess fluid.

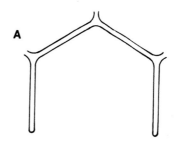

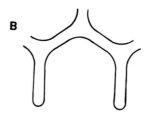

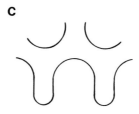

FIG. 5. Alveolar configuration during deflation from high (A) to middle (B) to low (C) volumes. With deflation septa shorten and, as tissue volume is conserved, they widen. Radius of curvature in the corners increases between high and middle volumes but decreases at low volumes, particularly in presence of some alveolar fluid.

REFERENCES

1. ARDILA, R., T. HORIE, AND J. HILDEBRANDT. Macroscopic isotropy of lung expansion. *Respir. Physiol.* 20: 105–115, 1974.
2. ASSIMACOPOULOS, A., R. GUGGENHEIM, AND Y. KAPANCI. Changes in alveolar capillary configuration at different levels of lung inflation in the rat. An ultrastructural and morphometric study. *Lab. Invest.* 34: 10–22, 1976.
3. BACHOFEN, H., J. HILDEBRANDT, AND M. BACHOFEN. Pressure-volume curves of air- and liquid-filled excised lungs—surface tension in situ. *J. Appl. Physiol.* 29: 422–431, 1970.
4. BROWN, R., A. J. WOOLCOCK, N. J. VINCENT, AND P. T. MACKLEM. Physiological effects of experimental airway obstruction with beads. *J. Appl. Physiol.* 27: 328–335, 1969.
5. BURGER, E. J., JR., AND P. MACKLEM. Airway closure: demonstration by breathing 100% O₂ at low lung volumes and by N₂ washout. *J. Appl. Physiol.* 25: 139–148, 1968.
6. CAVAGNA, G. A., E. J. STEMMLER, AND A. B. DUBOIS. Alveolar resistance to atelectasis. *J. Appl. Physiol.* 22: 441–452, 1967.
7. CLEMENTS, J. A., R. F. HUSTEAD, R. P. JOHNSON, AND I. GRIBETZ. Pulmonary surface tension and alveolar stability. *J. Appl. Physiol.* 16: 444–450, 1961.
8. D'ANGELO, E. Local alveolar size and transpulmonary pressure in situ and in isolated lungs. *Respir. Physiol.* 14: 251–266, 1972.
9. DUNNILL, M. S. Effect of lung inflation on alveolar surface area in the dog. *Nature London* 214: 1013–1014, 1967.
10. ENGEL, L. A., A. GRASSINO, AND N. R. ANTHONISEN. Demonstration of airway closure in man. *J. Appl. Physiol.* 38: 1117–1125, 1975.
11. FARIDY, E. E., AND S. PERMUTT. Surface forces and airway obstruction. *J. Appl. Physiol.* 30: 319–321, 1971.
12. FARIDY, E. E., S. PERMUTT, AND R. L. RILEY. Effect of ventilation on surface forces in excised dogs' lungs. *J. Appl. Physiol.* 21: 1453–1462, 1966.
13. FLICKER, E., AND J.-S. LEE. Equilibrium of force of subpleural alveoli: implications to lung mechanics. *J. Appl. Physiol.* 36: 366–374, 1974.
14. FORKERT, L., S. DHINGRA, AND N. R. ANTHONISEN. Airway closure and closing volume. *J. Appl. Physiol.: Respirat. Environ. Exercise Physiol.* 46: 24–30, 1979.
15. FORREST, J. B. The effect of changes in lung volume on the size and shape of alveoli. *J. Physiol. London* 210: 533–547, 1970.
16. FRANK, N. R., E. P. RADFORD, JR., AND J. L. WHITTENBERGER. Static volume-pressure interrelations of the lungs and pulmonary blood vessels in excised cats' lungs. *J. Appl. Physiol.* 14: 167–173, 1959.
17. FRAZER, D. G., AND B. KHOSHNOOD. A model of the gas trapping mechanism in excised lungs. *Proc. N. Engl. Bioeng. Conf.* 7: 482–485, 1979.
18. FRAZER, D. G., P. W. STENGEL, AND K. C. WEBER. Meniscus formation in airways of excised rat lungs. *Respir. Physiol.* 36: 121–129, 1979.
19. FRAZER, D. G., AND K. C. WEBER. Trapped air in ventilated excised rat lungs. *J. Appl. Physiol.* 40: 915–922, 1976.
20. FRAZER, D. G., AND K. C. WEBER. The effects of several gases (He, N₂, N₂O, and SF₆) on gas trapping in excised lungs. *Respir. Physiol.* 40: 323–333, 1980.
21. FUNG, Y.-C. Stress, deformation, and atelectasis of the lung. *Circ. Res.* 37: 481–496, 1975.
22. GIL, J., H. BACHOFEN, P. GEHR, AND E. R. WEIBEL. Alveolar volume-surface area relation in air- and saline-filled lungs fixed by vascular perfusion. *J. Appl. Physiol.: Respirat. Environ. Exercise Physiol.* 47: 990–1001, 1979.
23. GIL, J., AND E. R. WEIBEL. Morphological study of pressure-volume hysteresis in rat lungs fixed by vascular perfusion. *Respir. Physiol.* 15: 190–213, 1972.
24. GLAISTER, D. H., R. C. SCHROTER, M. F. SUDLOW, AND J. MILIC-EMILI. Bulk elastic properties of excised lungs and the effect of a transpulmonary pressure gradient. *Respir. Physiol.* 17: 347–364, 1973.
25. GOLDBERG, H. S., W. MITZNER, K. ADAMS, H. MENKES, S. LICHTENSTEIN, AND S. PERMUTT. Effect of intrathoracic pressure on pressure-volume characteristics of the lung in man. *J. Appl. Physiol.* 38: 411–417, 1975.
26. HALES, C. A., AND H. KAZEMI. Small airways function in myocardial infarction. *N. Engl. J. Med.* 290: 761–765, 1974.
27. HANSEN, J. E., AND E. P. AMPAYA. Lung morphometry: a fallacy in the use of the counting principle. *J. Appl. Physiol.* 37: 951–954, 1974.
28. HANSEN, J. E., AND E. P. AMPAYA. Human air space shapes, sizes, areas, and volumes. *J. Appl. Physiol.* 38: 990–995, 1975.
29. HUGHES, J. M. B., D. Y. ROSENZWEIG, AND P. B. KIVITZ. Site of airway closure in excised dog lungs: histologic demonstration. *J. Appl. Physiol.* 29: 340–344, 1970.
30. HYATT, R. E., G. C. OKESON, AND J. R. RODARTE. Influence of expiratory flow limitation on the pattern of lung emptying in normal man. *J. Appl. Physiol.* 35: 411–419, 1973.
31. KLINGELE, T. G., AND N. C. STAUB. Alveolar shape changes with volume in isolated, air-filled lobes of cat lung. *J. Appl. Physiol.* 28: 411–414, 1970.
32. LEITH, D. E. Comparative mammalian respiratory mechanics. *Physiologist* 19: 485–510, 1976.
33. MACKLEM, P. T. Airway obstruction and collateral ventilation. *Physiol. Rev.* 51: 368–436, 1971.
34. MACKLEM, P. T., D. F. PROCTOR, AND J. C. HOGG. The stability of peripheral airways. *Respir. Physiol.* 8: 191–203, 1970.
35. MARTIN, H. B., AND D. F. PROCTOR. Pressure-volume measurements on dog bronchi. *J. Appl. Physiol.* 13: 337–343, 1958.
36. MAZZONE, R. W., C. M. DURAND, AND J. B. WEST. Electron microscopy of lung rapidly frozen under controlled physiological conditions. *J. Appl. Physiol.: Respirat. Environ. Exercise Physiol.* 45: 325–333, 1978.
37. MEAD, J. Mechanical properties of lungs. *Physiol. Rev.* 41: 281–330, 1961.
38. MEAD, J., T. TAKISHIMA, AND D. LEITH. Stress distribution in lungs: a model of pulmonary elasticity. *J. Appl. Physiol.* 28: 596–608, 1970.
39. MILIC-EMILI, J., J. A. M. HENDERSON, M. B. DOLOVICH, D. TROP, AND K. KANEKO. Regional distribution of inspired gas in the lung. *J. Appl. Physiol.* 21: 749–759, 1966.
40. NAKAMURA, M., H. SASAKI, K. SEKIZAWA, M. ISHII, T. TAKISHIMA, AND F. G. HOPPIN, JR. Series distribution of airway collapsibility in dogs. *J. Appl. Physiol.: Respirat. Environ. Exercise Physiol.* 50: 325–333, 1981.
41. OLDMIXON, E. H., S. SUZUKI, J. P. BUTLER, AND F. G. HOPPIN, JR. Perfusion dehydration fixes elastin and preserves lung air-space dimensions. *J. Appl. Physiol.* 58: 105–113, 1985.
42. PAUMGARTNER, D., G. LOSA, AND E. R. WEIBEL. Resolution effect on the stereological estimation of surface volume and its interpretation in terms of fractal dimensions. *J. Microsc.* 121: 51–63, 1981.
43. RADFORD, E. P., JR. Mechanical factors determining alveolar configuration. *Am. Rev. Respir. Dis.* 81: 743–744, 1960.
44. RADFORD, E. P., JR. Mechanical stability of the lung. *Arch. Environ. Health* 6: 128–133, 1963.
45. RADFORD, E. P., JR., AND M. MCLAUGHLIN. Dependence of lung mechanical properties on anatomic relationships within terminal lung units (Abstract). *Federation Proc.* 15: 147, 1956.
46. RODARTE, J. R., R. E. HYATT, AND D. A. CORTESE. Influence of expiratory flow on closing capacity at low expiratory flow rates. *J. Appl. Physiol.* 39: 60–65, 1975.
47. SANDERSON, R. J., G. W. PAUL, A. E. VATTER, AND G. F. FILLEY. Morphological and physiological basis for lung surfactant action. *Respir. Physiol.* 27: 379–392, 1976.
48. SASAKI, H., AND F. G. HOPPIN, JR. Hysteresis of contracted airway smooth muscle. *J. Appl. Physiol.: Respirat. Environ. Exercise Physiol.* 47: 1251–1262, 1979.
49. SASAKI, H., F. G. HOPPIN, JR., AND T. TAKISHIMA. Peribronchial pressure in excised dog lungs. *J. Appl. Physiol.: Respirat. Environ. Exercise Physiol.* 45: 858–869, 1978.

50. SCHÜRCH, S. Surface tension at low lung volumes: dependence on time and alveolar size. *Respir. Physiol.* 48: 339–355, 1982.

51. SCHÜRCH, S., D. F. GERSON, AND D. J. L. MCIVER. Determination of cell/medium interfacial tensions from contact angles in aqueous polymer systems. *Biochim. Biophys. Acta* 640: 557–571, 1981.

52. SCHÜRCH, S., J. GOERKE, AND J. A. CLEMENTS. Direct determination of surface tension in the lungs. *Proc. Natl. Acad. Sci. USA* 73: 4698–4701, 1976.

53. SERGYSELS, R., R. AMYOT, P. T. MACKLEM, AND R. R. MARTIN. In vivo gas trapping induced by nitrous oxide. *J. Appl. Physiol.: Respirat. Environ. Exercise Physiol.* 43: 414–420, 1977.

54. SITTIPONG, R., AND R. E. HYATT. Static mechanical behavior of bronchi in excised dog lung. *J. Appl. Physiol.* 37: 201–206, 1974.

55. STOREY, W. F., AND N. C. STAUB. Ventilation of terminal air units. *J. Appl. Physiol.* 17: 391–397, 1962.

56. SYBRECHT, G. W., L. GARRETT, AND N. R. ANTHONISEN. Effect of chest strapping on regional lung function. *J. Appl. Physiol.* 39: 707–713, 1975.

57. TSUNODA, S., H. FUKAYA, T. SUGIHARA, C. J. MARTIN, AND J. HILDEBRANDT. Lung volume, thickness of alveolar walls, and microscopic anisotropy of expansion. *Respir. Physiol.* 22: 285–296, 1974.

58. VALBERG, P. A., AND J. D. BRAIN. Lung surface tension and air space dimensions from multiple pressure-volume curves. *J. Appl. Physiol.: Respirat. Environ. Exercise Physiol.* 43: 730–738, 1977.

59. VON NEERGAARD, K. Neue Auffassungen über einen Grundbegriff der Atemmechanik. Die Retraktionskraft der Lunge, Abhängig von der Oberflachenspannung in den Alveolen. *Z. Gesamte Exp. Med.* 66: 373–394, 1929.

60. WEIBEL, R. R., P. UNTERSEE, J. GIL, AND M. ZULAUF. Morphometric estimation of pulmonary diffusion capacity. VI. Effect of varying positive pressure inflation of air spaces. *Respir. Physiol.* 18: 285–308, 1973.

61. WILSON, T. A. Relations among recoil pressure, surface area, and surface tension in the lung. *J. Appl. Physiol.: Respirat. Environ. Exercise Physiol.* 50: 921–926, 1981.

CHAPTER 15

Distribution of stresses within the lung

JOSEPH R. RODARTE | *Departments of Internal Medicine and of Physiology and Biophysics, Mayo Medical School and Mayo Clinic, Rochester, Minnesota*

Y. C. FUNG | *University of California, San Diego, La Jolla, California*

CHAPTER CONTENTS

THE METHOD FOR DEALING WITH MECHANICS of bodies and the concept of stress and strain are discussed in the chapter by Wilson in this *Handbook*. We refer the reader to that chapter for the definitions of stresses and strains. Stresses and strains are coupled by the mechanical properties of a material. The stress distribution in a body is a result of the material properties of the body and the forces or displacements that are imposed on it. Wilson's chapter gives simple examples of stress distributions pertinent to lung mechanics. In principle the techniques of solid mechanics can be used to answer many questions, such as: *1)* how is the lung supported in the thoracic cavity? *2)* what determines the nonuniform distribution of pleural pressure and regional lung volume? and *3)* what is the magnitude of interdependence between the surrounding lung parenchyma and the bronchi, vessels, or segments with occluded airways? However, the geometry of the lung and its material properties are complex, and regional measurements of pressure and volume are difficult. Only recently have any of these problems been studied by using the techniques of solid mechanics. This chapter shows how some important areas of lung mechanics can be viewed as problems of stress distribution. The material properties of the lung are discussed first. Then the effects of gravity and of shape change imposed by the thoracic wall on the regional volume and ventilation distribution in the lung are discussed. Finally, the problem that has been studied most successfully by stress analysis is detailed: the interdependence between the lung parenchyma and the intraparenchymal vessels and bronchi.

WHY IS STRESS DISTRIBUTION NONUNIFORM?

If one lived in a zero-gravity environment and the lung expanded uniformly, and if the lung structure were homogeneous, the stress distribution in the lung would be uniform. In reality these conditions are not met, and stress distribution in the lung is nonuniform.

The principal reasons for nonuniform stress distribution in the lung are illustrated in Figure 1. The springs in Figure 1 are one-dimensional analogues of the lung. The lung parenchyma acts like a nonlinear spring—nonlinear in the sense that the stress is not linearly proportional to the strain. In strips of lung tissue the spring constant (the ratio of force to displacement) increases with increasing force, resulting in a relationship in which the force is approximately an exponential function of the stretch (5). Springs labeled B, C, and D are analogues of the change in stress and strain distribution in the lung caused by the weight of the lung tissue, the effect of chest wall or diaphragm movement, and the effect of bronchi, arteries, or veins on the stress distribution in the lung, respectively.

The lung is made of a three-dimensional network of nonlinear interalveolar septa together with airways and blood vessels. It is enclosed in a pleura over which the pressure distribution is nonuniform. The complexity is obvious, but the necessity of nonuniform stress distribution is evident.

WHY IS IT IMPORTANT TO KNOW STRESS DISTRIBUTION?

The lung is an organ designed for gas exchange between the environment and the blood. Ventilation

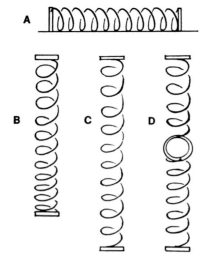

FIG. 1. Linear analogues of pulmonary stress distribution. Three-dimensional parenchymal deformation is illustrated by a spring. *A*: uniform expansion of spring stretched between 2 plates. Stress is distributed uniformly throughout body, and strain is uniform, as indicated by uniform spacing of coils. *B*: vertically oriented spring deformed by its own weight. Superimposed on uniform stress determined by separation of plates, weight of spring causes nonuniform stress and strain manifested by nonuniform spacing of coils. *C*: increased uniform stress by greater separation of end plates changes strain distribution and apparent magnitude of gravitational deformation because of nonlinear length-tension relationship of spring. *D*: either stiff or soft rings can be inserted in body of spring, further changing strain distribution.

is required to bring environmental air into close proximity to the blood. To analyze ventilation, one needs to know how the pressure applied to the pleural surface (resulting in change of lung volume) is distributed through the parenchyma to the air spaces within. Thus one must know the distribution of stress and also the size of the alveoli and how they change during breathing. The distribution of the sizes of the alveoli is proportional to the strain distribution in the lung (analogous to the spacing between the coils of the spring in Fig. 1), and the distribution of ventilation is proportional to the change of strain. Thus one must know the strain.

To analyze gas exchange, one must know the blood flow in the interalveolar septa. The thickness of the septa, and thus the caliber of the capillary blood vessels in the septa, is related to the tension in the septa. The higher the tension the more stretched the septa and the narrower the capillary blood vessels; consequently the resistance to flow becomes higher and blood flow is affected. Thus the stress and strain distributions influence perfusion as well as ventilation. The distribution of ratios of ventilation to perfusion in the lung depends on the stress and strain distributions.

The filtration of water from pulmonary capillaries is dependent on the difference between the capillary blood pressure and the interstitial fluid pressure, which is determined by stress in the septal tissue. The

subsequent movement of water into the bronchial and perivascular interstitium is also related to a pressure gradient in the direction of the flow, which is also determined indirectly by the distribution of parenchymal stress.

To determine the stress and strain distributions, one must know the transpulmonary pressure and thus the pleural pressure. Pleural pressure is nonuniform and very difficult to measure. The boundary condition that is more easily determined is the shape of the chest wall and diaphragm. Thus to determine pleural pressure, the mathematical procedure is to solve the problem of stress distribution for a known chest wall shape, with pleural pressure as an unknown variable.

The effect of heart motion on ventilation and the effect of lung volume on the heart depend similarly on stress distribution in the heart and lung.

Nonuniform stress and strain distributions in the lung that are caused by the weight of the lung exist over large distances and contribute to the regional differences in pleural pressure and lung volume. (See the chapters by Agostoni and by Milic-Emili in this *Handbook*.)

The interaction between the parenchyma and the bronchi, arteries, and veins or one part of the parenchyma and another is known as interdependence. In their chapter in this *Handbook*, Menkes and Macklem discuss interdependence and collateral ventilation, and in his chapter Engel discusses how interdependence influences the dynamic distribution of gas flow.

These remarks illustrate the importance of stress and strain distributions in normal lungs, but there are other applications. In disease states these distributions are altered. In emphysema the mechanical properties of the interalveolar septa are changed, as are the alveolar size and number. In edema and atelectasis the alveolar configuration and mechanical properties are changed. Infections and neoplasia cause local changes in stress and strain. Analysis of stress distribution in disease states should be helpful in understanding the pathophysiology of many pulmonary diseases, especially if the local stress states can be measured.

Stress distribution in the lung is important in environmental physiology: during acceleration or deceleration, space flight at zero gravity, and deep-sea diving and rising to the surface. Why are certain breathing exercises practiced in Yoga? Are they truly beneficial, and if so, how and why? Why do animals exposed to low-level pressure waves from bomb or gun explosions sometimes die of lung injury? The answers to these questions lie in stress distribution. Finally, the long-term growth and resorption of tissues and organs are stress related. Wolff's law is applicable in the bone; the geometric shape of the bone is a result of adaptation to the stress field. A corollary in orthopedics and surgery is that the stress in the bone must be within a specific range—not too large, not too small. An analogue in the lung is shown by Crystal's

(4) experiment, in which he tied off the left bronchus and collapsed the left lung of a rabbit. The right lung was then stressed because it had to expand to fill the chest cavity. An accelerated growth of the right lung occurred during the next 2 wk. A careful study of the growth of tissues that are modulated by stresses is fundamental to the understanding of healing, aging, health, and disease.

SIMPLIFICATIONS INTRODUCED TO ANALYSIS OF STRESS DISTRIBUTION

Two of the most important simplifications introduced into the lung stress analysis are 1) the continuum approach, in which the macroscopic stresses and strains are defined over a sufficiently large number of alveoli, and 2) the incremental approach, in which small changes from a known large deformation are analyzed. These are discussed in detail in the chapter by Wilson in this *Handbook*. Through the continuum approach the details of stress distribution in each interalveolar septum are considered only in the statistical sense and are expressed in terms of local values of macroscopic stresses and strains. Most of the problems in the preceding section can be dealt with this way, but certain details [e.g., the question asked by Karakaplan et al. (16) of how the individual interalveolar septa facing an alveolar duct behave as the tissue is stressed] cannot be dealt with this way. A comparison among some examples given in reference 16 and examples given in references 8, 9, 15, 17, and 19 shows the difference in complexity, with and without the continuum hypothesis.

The incremental approach linearizes the nonlinear differential equations, which are difficult to solve. In the study of the lung this approach has been remarkably successful because the deformations in many problems can be considered as small perturbations of a uniformly inflated state.

RELATIONSHIP BETWEEN MICROSCOPIC STRUCTURE AND MACROSCOPIC PROPERTIES

Stress in the lung results from the tension in solid-tissue elements and that in the air-liquid interface. Alveolar walls have length-tension properties similar to those of other biologic tissue (5). Relationships between surface tension and surface area have been extensively studied in vitro. (See the chapter by Goerke and Clements in this *Handbook*.) Several attempts have been made to derive stress-strain relationships at the continuum level, starting from models of the microstructure (7, 9, 16, 24, 25). Although these models differ in their descriptions of the alveolar shape and the stress-bearing elements, the handling of surface tension, and the analytical methods employed, they all are based on the same principle and employ the same steps. The first step is to calculate the stretching (strains) of the individual interalveolar septa from the overall deformation of the lung tissue (called the macroscopic strains). The next step is to calculate the forces (tissue stresses and surface tension) that act on the interalveolar septa as a consequence of this stretching. The third step is to calculate the force (normal and tangential components) that acts on an arbitrary cross section of the lung tissue as a summation of the contributions from the alveolar septa. If such a cross section is on the order of 1 mm^2, which is much larger than the cross-sectional area of an individual alveolus and much smaller than that of the whole lung, the average force per unit area approaches a stable limit. The normal component of this force per unit area is called the macroscopic tensile stress, whereas the tangential component per unit area is called the macroscopic shear stress. Combining these steps, one obtains a relationship between the macroscopic strains and stresses, which is called the constitutive equation of the lung parenchyma.

The theoretic derivation just outlined is meaningful because it provides a link between the macroscopic constitutive relationship, which is measurable in the laboratory, and the stress-strain relationship of the microscopic interalveolar septa. Through such a link one can study the effect of the ultrastructure of the interalveolar septa (e.g., the collagen and elastin networks, the ground substances, and the attachment of fibroprotein to the ground substances) on the physiology of the lung. Through such a study the surface tension on the interalveolar septa can be assessed. These are important areas for future investigation.

MATERIAL PROPERTIES OF LUNG PARENCHYMA

In vivo the lung is subject to finite deformation. Even if hysteresis and time-dependent effects are neglected, the relationship between stress and strain is nonlinear over the range of physiological deformations. A nonlinear constitutive relationship is described most economically in terms of a strain-energy function. A strain-energy function describes the energy stored in a unit mass of tissue as a function of the strain in the tissue. A strain-energy function represents the work done by the stresses during deformation. A stress can be obtained by taking the derivative of the strain-energy function with respect to the corresponding strain component. The results of two experiments on excised pieces of lung parenchyma have been expressed in terms of strain-energy functions (26, 34). In a study by Lee et al. (26), the lung parenchyma was assumed to be isotropic and, to fit the experimental data, nine material constants were introduced into a polynomial form of strain-energy function. In a study by Vawter, Fung, and West (34), the strain-energy function was assumed to be exponential in form, and only three material constants were used if isotropy was assumed and four if isotropy was not assumed. Other than some simple problems (8, 9, 27), not many solutions have been obtained or tested using these strain-energy functions.

If relatively small deformations are considered, the problem of stress analysis can be linearized. In certain problems it is sufficient to consider relatively small nonuniform deformation superimposed on a uniform volume change, which can be quite large. For these problems the material properties can be described by a linear relationship between the incremental stresses and strains. This is analogous to defining lung compliance as a local pressure-volume relationship, with the value of compliance depending on the initial state of inflation rather than utilizing a nonlinear description of the entire pressure-volume curve. Therefore elastic constants are determined as functions of the initial state (pressure or volume) rather than as true material constants. Because the uniformly inflated state is isotropic, the incremental stress-strain relationship is isotropic, and only two elastic constants are needed to characterize the linearized constitutive equation.

Two basic approaches to the determination of these constants have been taken. The first approach involves both the uniform and the nonuniform deformation of small cubes of parenchyma excised from frozen lobes (12), from which the elastic constants can be obtained. The second approach uses small perturbations of an entire excised lobe to determine two elastic constants, the bulk modulus (K) and the shear modulus (μ). (In English engineering literature, the symbol for the shear modulus is G; in mechanics literature, μ is most common. To avoid confusion with pulmonary conductance, μ is used for the shear modulus in this *Handbook*.) The bulk modulus is the ratio of fractional volume change to the change in uniform pressure and thus is a specific elastance pertaining to uniform inflation. The shear modulus is the ratio of shear stress to shear strain. Pure shear strain does not involve any change in volume, so the shear modulus is an elastance pertaining to pure change of shape. A method to determine the shear modulus of the lung when the bulk modulus is already known is to impose a localized indentation of the surface of excised lobes (11, 23). These moduli are discussed in the chapter by Wilson in this *Handbook*. These two approaches (11, 12, 23) to the determination of elastic properties, although yielding similar results that the shear modulus is less than the bulk modulus, differ in that the indentation data yield a shear modulus substantially less than that obtained from the excised parenchymal cubes. The reason for this discrepancy is not clear, but it may have to do with the nonuniform stress and strain resulting from discrete attachments of experimental apparatus to the parenchymal cubes.

The lung parenchyma is composed of tissue and air, and these two components can move independently.

Thus the lung parenchyma is a two-phase material. The behavior of the gas phase depends on whether the airway is open or closed. If the airway is open and pleural pressure is changed, the pressure in the gas is independent of lung volume. If the airway is closed and lung volume is changed, the pressure in the gas is determined by the compressibility of the gas. Thus the value of the bulk modulus is very different in these two cases. Figure 2 shows the bulk modulus of dog lungs with open airways obtained by small perturbations in volume as a function of inflating pressure and lung volume. In spite of the hysteresis in the pressure-volume curve, the bulk modulus–pressure relationship is essentially the same on the inflation and deflation limbs and is approximately a linear function of the inflating pressure. Figure 3 shows the shear modulus obtained by punch-indentation tests. The shear modulus is also approximately a linear function of the inflating pressure. In fact the statement that the elastic modulus varies linearly with inflating pressure fits the experimental data better for the shear modulus than for the bulk modulus.

MEANING OF OTHER ELASTIC CONSTANTS

In engineering practice, deformations other than volume expansion and pure shear are frequently used to determine material properties and to define two different elastic constants that are related to the shear and bulk moduli. In a rod pulled uniaxially, the ratio of the axial stress to the axial strain of the material is termed *Young's modulus* (E). When a rod is stretched in one direction the dimensions in other directions may be changed. Poisson's ratio (ν) is the ratio of the decrease in normal strain in the direction perpendicular to the axis of the rod to the increase in axial strain. For an infinitesimal deformation this ratio is a

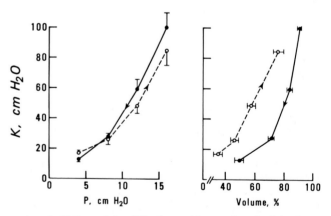

FIG. 2. Bulk modulus (K) of parenchyma of excised dog lungs obtained by small perturbations in volume as a function of trans-pulmonary pressure (P) in *left panel* and as a function of lung volume in *right panel*. Inflation (*open circles*) and deflation (*closed circles*) volume histories are shown; $K \simeq 4P$ during both inflation and deflation maneuvers. [From Lai-Fook (18).]

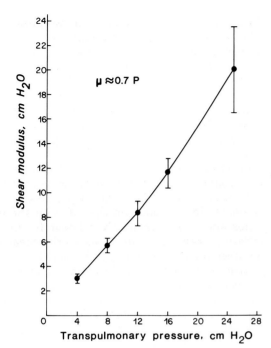

FIG. 3. Shear modulus (μ) of excised dog lungs determined by punch-indentation tests as a function of transpulmonary pressure (P); μ is essentially a linear function of P and is approximated by $\mu \simeq 0.7P$. [From Lai-Fook (17).]

constant. When the strains are finite the ratio varies with all six independent components of strain. Thus Poisson's ratio can represent a material property only if the strains are infinitesimal. When the strains are infinitesimal the values of elastic constants E and ν for different materials are subjected to thermodynamic restrictions

$$E > 0, \qquad -1 < \nu < 0.5 \qquad (1)$$

(See ref. 6, p. 353 for proof.) For simplicity, the following examples of deformations are considered infinitesimal so that ν can be assumed to be constant. The elastic constants E and ν are related to K and μ by the formulas

$$E = 9K\mu/(3K + \mu) \qquad (2)$$

$$\nu = (3K - 2\mu)/2(3K + \mu) \qquad (3)$$

$$K = E/3(1 - 2\nu) = 2\mu(1 + \nu)/3(1 - 2\nu) \qquad (4)$$

In infinitesimal deformation, $\nu = 0$ means that the material does not contract in lateral directions when elongated in one direction, and its change in volume is then directly proportional to the axial lengthening. At the other extreme, as ν approaches 0.5, axial lengthening produces sufficient lateral shortening so that there is essentially no change in volume. When $\nu = 0.5$, the material can be deformed without change of volume. Thus when ν approaches 0.5, μ is small relative to K.

It is important, however, to know that the concept of equating a ν of 0.5 with incompressibility is true only for infinitesimal strains. For finite strains this is generally untrue, even for a material that is isotropic and obeys Hooke's law. A demonstration is very simple (33). The following equation, stating that the volume remains constant, relates the material constants and the principal stresses σ_1, σ_2, and σ_3 for a linearly elastic incompressible material in finite or infinitesimal deformation[1]

$$\left\{ 1 + \frac{2}{E} [\sigma_1 - \nu(\sigma_2 + \sigma_3)] \right\}$$
$$\left\{ 1 + \frac{2}{E} [\sigma_2 - \nu(\sigma_3 + \sigma_1)] \right\} \qquad (5)$$
$$\left\{ 1 + \frac{2}{E} [\sigma_3 - \nu(\sigma_1 + \sigma_2)] \right\} = 1$$

This equation is satisfied by $\nu = 0.5$ if the strains (σ/E) are infinitesimal or if the stresses are uniform ($\sigma_1 = \sigma_2 = \sigma_3$). In all other cases the equation cannot be satisfied for arbitrary loading, whether or not $\nu = 0.5$. Thus $\nu = 0.5$ generally does not guarantee the absence of volume change in finite strain if the load is not uniform.

IMPLICATIONS OF RELATIVE MAGNITUDES OF BULK AND SHEAR MODULI

To define the stress-strain relationship of the lungs, one must know the bulk modulus and the shear modulus. In fact the ratio of the shear modulus to the bulk modulus determines whether the lung responds to certain loading primarily with a change in shape or a change in volume.

One of the examples presented in the chapter by Wilson in this *Handbook* is the gravitational deformation of a cylinder in a rigid container of the same size and shape. In this example the theory of linear elasticity is utilized, and the results illustrate the effect of the ratio of the shear modulus to the bulk modulus on the deformation. For the normal lung at functional

---

[1] By a proper choice of orientation of the coordinate axes, the state of stress at a point can be described by these normal stresses while the shear stresses are zero. These coordinate axes are called the principal axes, and the normal stresses are called the principal stresses. In Equation 5, assume that the stretch ratios λ_1, λ_2, and λ_3 (in which λ is wavelength) in the directions of the principal axes are linearly related to the principal stresses as follows

$$\lambda_1 = 1 + 2/E [\sigma_1 - \nu(\sigma_2 + \sigma_3)]$$
$$\lambda_2 = 1 + 2/E [\sigma_2 - \nu(\sigma_3 + \sigma_1)]$$
$$\lambda_3 = 1 + 2/E [\sigma_3 - \nu(\sigma_1 + \sigma_2)]$$

Assume that these relationships are valid for a certain material, even for finite strain. The ratio of deformed volume to the original volume caused by any deformation is $\lambda_1\lambda_2\lambda_3$. Thus $\lambda_1\lambda_2\lambda_3 = 1$ signifies incompressibility.

residual capacity (FRC), the material density is ~0.13 g/cm³. The data in Figures 2 and 3 indicate that for lung volumes in the physiological range, μ is ~15% of K. According to Equation 4, μ/K ranges from 1.5 to 0 for ν values of 0–0.5. A μ/K value of 0.15 corresponds to a ν value of 0.43.

The significance of the ratio of the shear modulus to the bulk modulus is illustrated by several examples. First, consider the effect of gravity. When external shape is constant (Fig. 4) the gravitational deformation is much less than if the material were not constrained. Even though the external shape is not changed, there is a vertical gradient of regional volume (i.e., volumetric strain) as the upper portion of the material is expanded by the weight of the material below it, and the lower portion is compressed by the weight of the material above it. The axial extension of the upper region tends to decrease the radius, and an increased radial stress is required to maintain the constant shape. (Cylindrical polar coordinates are used to describe the cylinder shown in Fig. 4. The radial stress is denoted by τ_{rr}, and the axial stress is denoted by τ_{zz}.) Dependent regions compressed by the weight above them tend to expand in the radial direction, and a compressive stress is required to prevent this bulging. If the shear modulus were zero, the material would behave like a compressible fluid and the gradient of stress would be equal to density.

The shear modulus also affects the vertical gradient in regional volume (Fig. 4, *right*). Note the gradient in volume that would be predicted by using the vertical gradient in pressure and the pressure-volume curve

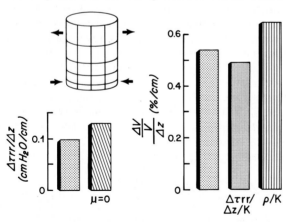

FIG. 4. Gravitational deformation of cylindrical body constrained within rigid container of same size and shape prior to action of gravity. Material properties are those of normal lung parenchyma at functional residual capacity as in Figs. 2 and 3 and density (ρ) of 0.13 g/cm³. *Dotted bars* in *both panels*, gradients predicted by linear-elasticity model using values stated above. *Left*: vertical gradient in radial stress. *Cross-hatched bar*, gradient that would occur if shear modulus (μ) were zero. *Right*: vertical gradient in regional volume. *Finely stippled bar*, gradient that would be predicted from vertical gradient in stress (*dotted bar*) and pressure-volume curve [bulk modulus (K)]. *Vertically hatched bar*, gradient from hydrostatic pressure gradient and pressure-volume curve. [Adapted from Rodarte (31).]

for the material during uniform expansion given by the bulk modulus. This computation would result in a 10% underestimation of volume gradient computed by linear elasticity (dotted bar at *right*). Note the vertical gradient that would be predicted from a hydrostatic gradient, i.e., from a pressure gradient equal to density and the uniform pressure-volume curve, if the shear modulus were zero. The vertical gradient of radial stress (Fig. 4, *left*) obtained in this example is less than that reported in experimental animals (1); the vertical gradient in regional volumes in this example is less than that reported at FRC in humans (29). If the shear modulus were larger and approached the values for the bulk modulus, the material would be much stiffer and gravitational loading would produce smaller gradients in both radial stress and regional volumes than those shown in Figure 4.

The effect of a change in shape (ignoring for the moment the gravitational effect) is illustrated in Figure 5. In this example a cylinder is in a container of the same size and shape. The sides of the container are then rotated with no change in volume. This deformation results in a vertical gradient of both the radial stress and regional volume, the magnitudes of which depend on the properties of the deformed material. For a 1.5° rotation of the sides, the vertical gradient of radial stress is ~0.05 cmH₂O/cm (*left*). The vertical gradient in regional volume for an angular deformation of 1.5° is 0.13%/cm (*right*). The vertical gradient in regional volume that would be predicted from the regional stress and the uniform pressure-volume curve (shown in Fig. 5) is a substantial overestimation of the actual gradient in regional volume. If the shear modulus were increased relative to the bulk modulus, the change in shape would have a much greater effect on both the pressure and volume gradients.

In the undeformed state the pressure (P) on the sides of the cylinder has no axial component, i.e., P = τ_{rr}. The weight of the material is equal to the product of difference between the vertical stress (τ_{zz}) on the top and bottom and the area. When the sides are rotated, the pressure on the sides has a vertical component that bears part of the weight, and the pressure on the top and bottom of the material also is affected by this deformation.

For small deformations the principle of linear superposition applies and different solutions can be added. To illustrate, it is instructive to consider the cylindrical body shown in Figures 4 and 5 again and combine the effects of gravity with that of shape change required to produce a vertical gradient of radial stress of 0.25 cmH₂O/cm vertical height (Fig. 6). An angle of slightly more than 4° is required. This stress distribution produces a vertical gradient of volume of 0.9%/cm. Some of the gradient is caused by gravity, and the rest is caused by shape change. Gravity produces a gradient of radial stress (pleural pressure) that

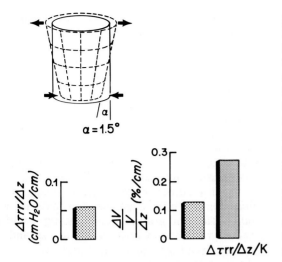

FIG. 5. Effect of change in shape without gravity. Cylindrical body with properties as in Fig. 4 but without gravity is subjected to a rotation of sides of angle (α) of 1.5°. *Left*: vertical gradient in radial stress. *Right*: *dotted bar*, vertical gradient in regional volume; *finely stippled bar*, gradient that would be predicted from regional stress and uniform pressure-volume curve. [Adapted from Rodarte (31).]

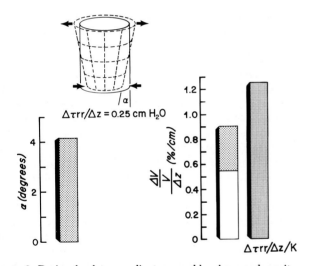

FIG. 6. Regional volume gradients caused by shape and gravity. Cylindrical body with properties as in Figs. 4 and 5 is subjected to gravity and then angular deformation to create vertical gradient of radial stress ($\Delta\tau_{rr}/\Delta z$). *Left*: angle α required to produce vertical gradient of pressure of 0.25 cmH$_2$O/cm height in presence of gravity. *Right*: vertical gradient in regional volume. *Undotted portion* of *left bar*, gradient caused by gravity; *dotted portion*, gradient caused by shape change; *finely stippled bar*, gradient that would be predicted from pressure gradient and uniform pressure-volume curve. [Adapted from Rodarte (31).]

is ~40% of the total, but it produces more than half the gradient of volume.

MACROSCOPIC LUNG STRESS DISTRIBUTION

In static conditions all forces acting on the lung must balance. Under physiological conditions it ap-

pears that there is little tension in the main-stem bronchi (30). During breath holding, significant shear stress at the pleural surface is highly unlikely in normal lungs. Therefore the integral of forces acting on the pleural surface over the entire lung must be equal to the weight of the lung. The effect of gravity on the lung requires a nonuniform stress distribution to balance the body force. Thus the effect of gravity on the lung itself in the absence of other factors may cause a vertical gradient in regional volume and pleural surface pressure. Pleural pressure is further influenced by the relative deformability of the lung parenchyma and chest wall such that the final distribution of regional lung volume and pleural pressure is determined by both the gravitational deformation of the lung and chest wall (including the abdomen) and their interactions. (The physiological data concerning these interactions are presented in the chapters by Agostoni, by Milic-Emili, and by Rehder and Marsh in this *Handbook*.) At present, insufficient detail is available for a rigorous formulation in terms of solid mechanics.

However, a technique that has the potential to provide enough information to determine the distribution of parenchymal strain involves the tracking of displacements of many radiopaque markers embedded in the lung parenchyma (2, 32). If the constitutive relationship of the lung parenchyma were known, stress distribution could be derived.

The gravitational deformation of the lung outside the thorax is schematically illustrated in Figure 7, which shows an idealized lung-shaped object supported from below by a force equal to its weight. The lung is expanded by a uniform inflation pressure. In addition a nonuniform stress is produced by gravity. At each horizontal level the lung is compressed in the vertical direction by the weight of tissue above it. This nonuniform uniaxial stress produces a vertical compression determined by Young's modulus and a radial expansion determined by Poisson's ratio. When $\nu <$ 0.5, this gravitational deformation decreases regional

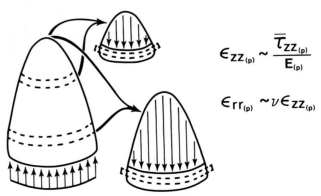

$$\epsilon_{zz_{(p)}} \sim \frac{\bar{\tau}_{zz_{(p)}}}{E_{(p)}}$$

$$\epsilon_{rr_{(p)}} \sim \nu\epsilon_{zz_{(p)}}$$

FIG. 7. Schematic representation of effect of gravity on material with idealized lung shape. ϵ_{zz}, Vertical strain; ϵ_{rr}, radial strain; $\bar{\tau}_{zz}$, vertical stress caused by weight of lungs; E, Young's modulus; ν, Poisson's ratio. Subscript p indicates value is function of pressure.

volume in increasing degree from apex to base. This deformation depends on Young's modulus and Poisson's ratio, or the equivalent bulk modulus and shear modulus. Because of the shape of this idealized lung, the stress at any level is nonuniform, and the actual solution of this problem is far more complex than indicated. Nevertheless the idealized solution illustrates the important features of the problem. As lung volume decreases, the vertical force or weight supported at a level does not change but is distributed over a smaller area, so the vertical stress increases; Young's modulus decreases as the transpulmonary pressure, and thus volume, decreases. Both factors increase the vertical strain. The fractional change in volume is less than the vertical strain because of the radial strain, the magnitude of which is determined by Poisson's ratio. This simple model can be used to compute the relationship between the regional volume as a function of height and the overall lung volume. Nondependent regions change volume less than overall lung volume, and the slope of this relationship between nondependent regional volume and overall lung volume decreases monotonically with decreasing lung volume. Dependent regions change their volumes more than the overall volume, and the slope of the relationship increases monotonically with decreasing volume. This pattern of regional volume and ventilation distribution would cause a single-breath O_2 test to show a decreasing concentration of N_2 with increasing expired alveolar volume. This pattern of decreasing expired N_2 concentration was observed in studies of isolated lower lobes of dogs supported in this manner (15), once intraregional differences in the N_2 concentration were abolished by breath holding. Furthermore there was generally good agreement between lobe shape predicted by the modeling and that observed by computer axial tomography (15). This agreement between modeling and experiment in spite of the geometric simplifications required to achieve an analytic solution constitutes strong support for the applicability of continuum mechanics to problems of regional-volume distribution of the lung.

Analytic solutions have been obtained only for objects with certain special shapes subjected to relatively symmetric forces. For more complex situations a numerical method is preferred. One such method commonly employed in engineering is the finite-element analysis. In this method the body is divided into many elements with simple shapes. The deformation of each element caused by forces applied at the edges is calculated. The coupled algebraic equations that express the conditions of static equilibrium for each element under the action of forces from neighboring elements are simultaneously solved by computer. The geometric complexity that can be approached with this technique is limited only by the amount of time invested in setting up the problem and the size of the computer required to run the program.

A pioneering application of finite-element techniques to lung mechanics was the analysis of the effect of gravity on a lung-shaped paraboloid of revolution enclosed in a rigid container of the same size and shape (36). Subsequent studies examined the effects of selective expansion of the "rib cage" or "diaphragm" (35). These results have been criticized because of the description of the material properties used (8, 27). The pattern of regional volume distribution in these theoretic studies is in marked contrast to the regional volume distribution reported in intact humans utilizing ^{133}Xe (29). The models have all predicted monotonically increasing apex-to-base differences in regional volume, which have a greater-than-linear increase with decreasing lung volume, whereas ^{133}Xe studies in humans indicate gradients in regional volume that increase linearly from total lung capacity (TLC) to ~50% TLC and then increase less than linearly or even decrease below ~50% TLC. A more recent finite-element model utilizing a slightly different lung shape, a strain-energy function description of the material properties, and published values of rib cage and diaphragmatic displacements (27) shows a pattern of regional volume distribution that agrees closely with the data from radioactive gas in intact humans. However, the imposed shape changes in the thoracic cavity in the more recent model (27) rather than the different material properties utilized may be responsible for the different modeling results.

Recent studies of regional lung volume obtained from the localization of multiple radiopaque markers embedded in the lung parenchyma utilizing biplane videofluoroscopy indicate a very complex pattern of regional volume distribution (13). In supine dogs there are gradients of regional volume in both cephalocaudal and vertical directions within lobes and differences between lobes unexplainable by differences in mechanical properties of the lobes. The prone position is not a simple rotation of the supine. It is apparent from these studies that the thoracic cavity does not act like a rigid container of the same general shape as the lung, and at least in the dog the coupling of the lung and rib cage is as important a determinant of regional volume distribution as is the effect of gravity on lung parenchyma. None of the finite-element models to date has utilized realistic shapes or considered the presence of pleural fissures that may be important in allowing the lung to conform to the thoracic cavity (3). The problem of the effect of gravity on regional lung volume and pleural pressure is discussed in greater detail in the chapters by Milic-Emili and by Agostoni in this *Handbook*.

LOCAL STRESS DISTRIBUTION

Mead et al. (28) pointed out that the average stress acting on any plane passing through an inflated lung is equal to the transpulmonary pressure. These investigators coined the term *interdependence* to indicate that the surrounding lung parenchyma would resist any nonuniform distortion that would occur if a lung region had an occluded airway or if the pressure-volume relationship of the airways or vessels were different from that of the parenchyma. Thus the driving force for collateral ventilation, the effect of interdependence on airway and vessel diameter, and the stabilizing influence on the bronchi under conditions of maximal flow are all problems of regional stress distribution. Unfortunately most interdependence problems are very complex. A problem that has been successfully addressed is one of cylindrical structures embedded in the lung parenchyma.

The approach to the problem of the circular cylindrical hole utilizes a classic solution in the theory of elasticity: in cylindrical coordinates the equation of equilibrium for an isotropic linear-elastic material is satisfied by a radial displacement equal to c/r, in which c is a constant and r is the radial distance from the axis of symmetry. (See the chapter by Wilson in this *Handbook*.) This solution defines a stress field that decays rapidly with increasing distance from the axis and, for small deformation, leaves the volume of the material unchanged so that the perturbation stress depends on the shear modulus alone. By matching this solution with the boundary conditions of a bronchus, a blood vessel, or a plain hole, the interdependence problems can be solved. These solutions and their experimental verification are discussed next.

If a circular cylindrical core of parenchyma is bored out, the stress acting on the surface where the tissue was excised is effectively changed from transpulmonary pressure to zero, and this removal of the inward-acting stress supplied by the excised tissue allows the cylindrical hole to expand. Thus an experiment could be performed to confirm the applicability of elasticity theory (20). Cores of tissue were bored from collapsed lungs, the cut surfaces were coated with tantalum, the pleural surfaces were sealed, and pressure-volume experiments were performed. The pressure-diameter behavior of the cylindrical holes was obtained radiographically. From the weight of the tissues removed and the weight and pressure-volume curves of the lobes, the pressure-diameter behavior that the excised cores of tissue would have had in the intact lobe was computed. The radial expansion of the parenchyma produced by removing the tissue and reducing the stress from transpulmonary pressure to zero was then determined. The experimental results agree with the analytic solution. In Figure 8 the displacement of the boundary normalized by the radius that the cylinder would have in the intact lobe is determined by the ratio of the inflation pressure to the shear modulus. Because shear modulus is a linear function of pressure, the normalized expansion is independent of volume, i.e., the pressure-volume curve of the hole is the same as that of the lobe.

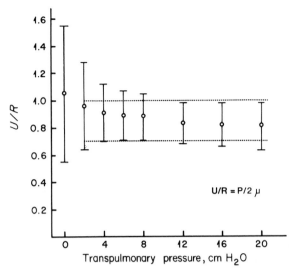

FIG. 8. Fractional radial expansion of cylindrical hole (U/R) and nondimensional displacement of boundary of cylindrical holes in lung parenchyma as function of transpulmonary pressure (P). μ, Shear modulus. Data fall within range predicted by equation $U/R = (P/2) \mu$, as indicated by *dotted lines* for $\mu = 0.7P$ and $\mu = 0.5P$. Because μ is proportional to P, prediction is independent of P. [From Lai-Fook, Rodarte, et al. (20).]

Considering interdependence of the parenchyma with bronchi and blood vessels, one visualizes these tubular structures having a unique pressure-diameter behavior as imbedded in cylindrical holes in the parenchyma whose pressure-diameter behavior is determined by the material properties of the parenchyma. At a fixed lung volume, one can examine the interaction in determining the resulting diameter and can compute the mean peritubular stress in a way that is analogous to the way physiologists utilize the pressure-volume curves of the lung and chest wall to compute lung volume and pleural pressure at any given airway pressure. This problem has been examined for bronchi (19) and blood vessels (17).

Peribronchial pressure may be computed if the pressure-diameter behavior of the excised bronchus, the intact bronchus embedded in the lung parenchyma, and the diameter of the hole in the parenchyma in which the bronchus is embedded when the peribronchial pressure is equal to the pleural pressure are all known. Figure 9 shows the transmural pressure-diameter behavior of the excised bronchus and the pressure-diameter behavior of the hole in the parenchyma when the parenchyma is uniformly expanded (i.e., during uniform changes in volume). In this situation the uniform hole diameter would be proportional to the cube root of the lung volume. If the peribronchial pressure were equal to pleural pressure, the transmural pressure of the bronchus would be equal to transpulmonary pressure. At the lung volume in Figure 9 the diameter of the parenchymal hole (point a) is larger than the diameter of the bronchus at that transmural pressure (point f). Because the diameter of the intact bronchus must equal the parenchymal

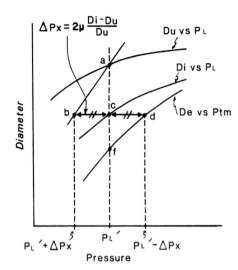

FIG. 9. Graphic representation of relationships among uniform hole diameter (Du), intact bronchial diameter (Di), excised bronchial diameter (De), difference between peribronchial and pleural pressure (ΔPx), and parenchymal shear modulus (μ), when Du > De. Du and Di are plotted against transpulmonary pressure (PL) and De is plotted against transmural pressure (Ptm). Nonuniform behavior of parenchymal hole at constant transpulmonary pressure (PL') is given by line *a–b*. With specific values for Du and Di (*a* and *c*) at PL', *d* on De-Ptm curve is determined. Alternatively, given values for Du and De, value for Di (*c* on line *a–f*) is determined. [From Lai-Fook, Hyatt, and Rodarte (19).]

hole diameter, peribronchial pressure must be less than pleural pressure to expand the bronchus and contract the parenchymal hole. The intact diameter (point c) lies on the line a–f, and its position is determined by the compliance of the bronchus and the compliance of the parenchymal hole at constant lung volume. Line a–b is the pressure-diameter behavior of the uniform hole when peribronchial pressure is reduced at a constant transpulmonary pressure. The slope is steeper than that of the pressure-diameter behavior of the parenchyma during uniform expansion because this pressure-diameter behavior is governed by the shear modulus, which is less than the bulk modulus of lung parenchyma. The location of point c (the equilibrium diameter between points a and f) is such that the change in peribronchial pressure required to reduce the size of the parenchymal hole from point a to point c is the same magnitude as the change in peribronchial pressure required to increase the bronchial diameter from point f to point c (line b–c = line c–d). This analysis can be utilized to predict peribronchial pressure in isolated lobes. To determine peribronchial pressure as a function of lung volume this analysis must be performed at different volumes. When there is no bronchial tone the peribronchial pressure is approximately equal to or 1 cmH2O greater than pleural pressure over most of the physiological volume range in isolated dog lungs (19). With normal or increased tone, peribronchial pressure is less than pleural pressure.

The solution for the pressure-diameter behavior of

the cylindrical hole in the elastic continuum also can be utilized to predict the magnitude of the effect of the lung parenchyma on bronchial diameter at constant lung volume when intraluminal pressure is less than alveolar pressure during expiratory flow. This is illustrated in Figure 10, which shows the diameters of the undeformed parenchyma, the in situ bronchus, and the excised bronchus at a given static transpulmonary pressure. Note the transmural pressure-diameter behavior of the excised bronchus and the static pressure-diameter curve of the intact bronchus as transpulmonary pressure is reduced. However, if intrabronchial pressure is reduced during flow at constant lung volume, the change in diameter of the in situ bronchus is less than during uniform deflation because of the nonuniform distortion of the parenchyma. The total decrease in intrabronchial pressure required to achieve the indicated diameter is the sum of the pressure required to reduce the bronchial diameter (i.e., transmural pressure) and the pressure required to deform the surrounding parenchyma.

Bronchi can be excised and their pressure-diameter relationships can be determined. Thus the diameter of the parenchymal hole can be chosen to reconcile the intact and the excised behavior. Because of the many supernumerary branches, it is very difficult to obtain reliable pressure-diameter curves of excised blood vessels to determine the size of the parenchymal hole. However, if the size of the parenchymal hole under uniform conditions at one transpulmonary pressure is known, the pressure-diameter behavior is defined because the diameter of the hole varies with the

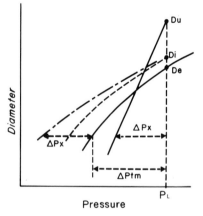

FIG. 10. Comparison of intact bronchial pressure (PL)-diameter (Di) behavior for deflation pressure-volume maneuvers in which lung volume changes with PL (*dashed curve*) and the isovolume case in which lung volume is held at initial PL and intrabronchial pressure is reduced (*dashed-dotted curve*). *Diagonal line* from uniform hole diameter (Du) represents pressure change (ΔPx) required to reduce Du. *Solid curve* (De-Ptm) represents excised bronchial behavior. Reduction of intact bronchial diameter (Di) at constant lung volume requires total reduction in intrabronchial pressure that equals sum of ΔPx required to reduce diameter of lung parenchyma and change in transmural pressure (ΔPtm) required to reduce excised bronchial diameter (De). [From Lai-Fook, Hyatt, and Rodarte (19).]

cube root of lung volume. For any arbitrary size of the parenchymal hole, given an experimentally determined intact vascular pressure-diameter behavior at fixed lung volume, the pressure-diameter behavior of an excised vessel can be computed. If the size of the parenchymal hole is correct, the computed pressure-diameter curve of the excised vessel can be used to compute the pressure-diameter curve of an intact vessel at any other fixed transpulmonary pressure. When the computed intact curve agrees with the experimentally determined curve, it indicates that the excised curve was correct and in turn that the correct uniform hole diameter was used. That is, by an iterative process one can determine a uniform hole size that, when used with intact vascular pressure-diameter curves at various lung volumes, predicts a single excised vascular pressure-diameter curve. If the obtained pressure-diameter behaviors of the excised vessel and the parenchymal hole are consistent with the intact curves at multiple transpulmonary pressures, it is strong evidence that these curves, which cannot be directly measured, are correct.

Figure 11 shows vessel pressure-diameter curves at five different transpulmonary pressures. At a fixed transpulmonary pressure, vessel diameter increases as vessel pressure increases. This effect is less pronounced at high transpulmonary pressure than at low transpulmonary pressure because of greater parenchy-

mal interdependence at high lung volumes caused by the increased shear modulus. At any vessel pressure, vessel diameter increases with increased transpulmonary pressure because of interdependence between the vessel and the surrounding parenchyma.

By an iterative procedure, Lai-Fook (17) determined a size for the uniform parenchymal hole (Fig. 11) that, when combined with the measured intact pressure-diameter behavior of a vessel at one transpulmonary pressure, yields a predicted excised vessel transmural pressure-diameter behavior, which by a graphic analysis similar to that illustrated in Figure 9 predicts intact vessel transmural pressure-diameter behavior at four other transpulmonary pressures that agree with measured values.

If one knows the transmural pressure-diameter behavior of the vessel, the perivascular pressure can be computed from any of the other curves at a given diameter and from the vascular pressure. For example, at a transpulmonary pressure of 16 cmH_2O and a venous pressure of 0 cmH_2O relative to pleural pressure, the intact vein diameter is ~90% of maximum. The curve for intrinsic vessel behavior indicates that at a diameter of 90% the transmural pressure is 9 cmH_2O. Thus at a transpulmonary pressure of 16 cmH_2O and a venous pressure of 0 cmH_2O, the perivascular pressure is 9 cmH_2O less than pleural pressure.

This analysis indicates that for a transpulmonary pressure >4 cmH_2O the diameter of the parenchymal hole is larger than the diameter of the vein at any transmural pressure. This means that in the intact lung the vessel must be pulled outward and the parenchyma pulled inward by a perivascular pressure less than the pleural pressure. The magnitude of the difference between the perivascular pressure and the pleural pressure is determined by the compliances of the vessel and the parenchymal hole. The compliance of the parenchymal hole is determined by the shear modulus and not by the bulk modulus or the pressure-volume curve of the lung. The difference between perivascular and pleural pressure, determined by this technique for arteries and veins in excised dog lobes, is shown in Figure 12. Note that for physiological vascular pressures at volumes near FRC, perivascular pressure is very near pleural pressure, suggesting that the surrounding parenchyma is uniformly expanded. However, with lung inflation, perivascular pressure progressively becomes negative with respect to pleural pressure, and this effect is more pronounced for arteries than for veins. Also with increasing intravascular pressure, perivascular pressure increases as the vessel expands to match more closely the surrounding parenchyma.

There are limits to the magnitude of deformation that may be approximated by linear elasticity. In this analysis of vascular interdependence a nonlinear strain-energy function was used (17). Direct measurements of perivascular pressure near the hilum of the

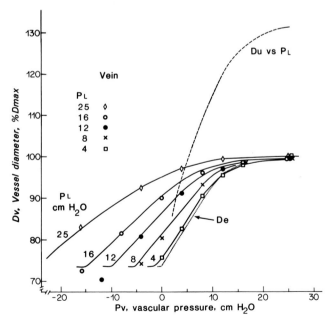

FIG. 11. Representative pressure-diameter behavior for major veins in excised dog lobe at various static values of transpulmonary pressure (PL) indicated on individual curves. *Symbols,* measurements obtained by roentgenograms; *solid curves,* predicted relationships computed from pressure-diameter behavior of uniform hole (Du vs. PL, *dashed curve*) and computed excised pressure-diameter behavior (De, *dotted curve*). Du varies with cube root of lung volume and was chosen so that De computed from Du, and measured Dv at one PL value, when used with Du predicted the measured Dv at the other PL values. [From Lai-Fook (17).]

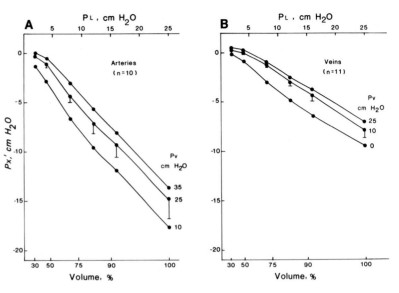

FIG. 12. Difference between perivascular pressure and pleural pressure (Px′) vs. transpulmonary pressure (PL) for constant arterial pressures of 10, 25, and 35 cmH₂O and venous pressures of 0, 10, and 25 cmH₂O. Vascular pressures (Pv) are measured relative to pleural pressure. *A*: data for arteries in 10 lobes. *B*: data for veins in 11 lobes. *Vertical bars*, 1 SE. [From Lai-Fook (17).]

lung are generally consistent with those shown in Figure 12 (10, 14, 22). This agreement suggests that perivascular fluid pressure is a reliable indication of the total stress that couples the larger vessels with the surrounding parenchyma.

The pulmonary artery and bronchi are adjacent to each other as they pass through the lung parenchyma. Under some combinations of airway and vascular pressures, the predicted perivascular and peribronchial pressures are quite different, suggesting that there should be some interaction between the bronchus and artery. Finite-element techniques are required to examine this problem (21). Figure 13 shows the distortion of shape of the luminal surface of the bronchus and the artery under the extreme conditions of an arterial pressure of −40 cmH₂O. The reduction in arterial diameter distorts the bronchus. The apparent gap between the bronchus and the artery is caused by the finite thickness of the wall. The principal stresses are perpendicular and occur in an orientation in which there is no shear stress and therefore are the largest normal stresses. Note that the greatest stress is at the junction of the artery and the bronchus. There is minimal effect on peribronchial stress other than at this junction, although as expected, stress is much greater on the arterial surface. The simulation shown in this figure was at a transpulmonary pressure of 4 cmH₂O. At a higher transpulmonary pressure, when the lung parenchyma is much stiffer, the shape changes of the bronchus are somewhat less pronounced and the magnitude of stress concentration at the arterial bronchial junction is greater.

Other problems of interdependence, such as forces applied to segments of the obstructed airways by surrounding parenchyma and chest wall or the forces involved in lobar atelectasis, have not been addressed in terms of stress analysis because of the geometric complexities. The compliance of an obstructed segment would be the compressibility of air. If the shape

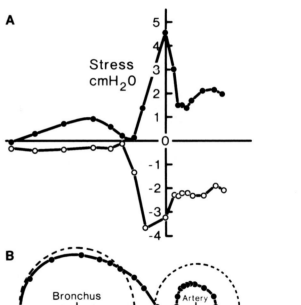

FIG. 13. Interdependence between bronchus and arteries. *A*: distribution of 2 principal stresses (*open* and *closed circles*) for points on walls of deformed bronchus and artery corresponding to *circles* in *B*. Note stress concentration at junction of airway and vessel. *B*: *dashed curves*, luminal surface of bronchus and artery when parenchyma is uniformly expanded at a transpulmonary pressure of 4 cmH₂O; *solid curves*, distortion of shape of luminal surface when arterial pressure is reduced to −40 cmH₂O. [From Lai-Fook and Kallok (21).]

of an occluded segment were spherical and completely embedded in normal parenchyma, an analytic solution would be relatively simple. However, all segments that can be occluded by obstruction of a bronchus are approximately conical and have a pleural surface. The geometric complexities make this a difficult problem to approach analytically.

The applications of the techniques of solid mechanics to questions of physiological interest are still in their infancy. It seems inevitable that the use of these techniques in mechanics of the respiratory system will increase. There is an exciting potential for more rigorous analysis of problems that so far have been approached qualitatively.

REFERENCES

1. AGOSTONI, E., AND G. MISEROCCHI. Vertical gradient of transpulmonary pressure with active and artificial lung expansion. *J. Appl. Physiol.* 29: 705–712, 1970.
2. CHEVALIER, P. A., J. F. GREENLEAF, R. A. ROBB, AND E. H. WOOD. Biplane videoroentgenographic analysis of dynamic regional lung strains in dogs. *J. Appl. Physiol.* 40: 118–122, 1976.
3. CHEVALIER, P. A., J. R. RODARTE, AND L. D. HARRIS. Regional lung expansion at total lung capacity in intact vs. excised canine lungs. *J. Appl. Physiol.: Respirat. Environ. Exercise Physiol.* 45: 363–369, 1978.
4. CRYSTAL, R. G. Lung collagen: definition, diversity and development. *Federation Proc.* 33: 2248–2255, 1974.
5. FUKAYA, H., C. J. MARTIN, A. C. YOUNG, AND S. KATSURA. Mechanical properties of alveolar walls. *J. Appl. Physiol.* 25: 689–695, 1968.
6. FUNG, Y. C. *Foundations of Solid Mechanics.* Englewood Cliffs, NJ: Prentice-Hall, 1965.
7. FUNG, Y. C. A theory of elasticity of the lung. *J. Appl. Mech.* 41: 8–14, 1974.
8. FUNG, Y. C. Stress, deformation, and atelectasis of the lung. *Circ. Res.* 37: 481–496, 1975.
9. FUNG, Y. C., P. TONG, AND P. PATITUCCI. Stress and strain in the lung. *J. Eng. Mech. Div.* 104: 201–223, 1978.
10. GOSHY, M., S. J. LAI-FOOK, AND R. E. HYATT. Perivascular pressure measurements by wick-catheter technique in isolated dog lobes. *J. Appl. Physiol.: Respirat. Environ. Exercise Physiol.* 46: 950–955, 1979.
11. HAJJI, M. A., T. A. WILSON, AND S. J. LAI-FOOK. Improved measurements of shear modulus and pleural membrane tension of the lung. *J. Appl. Physiol.: Respirat. Environ. Exercise Physiol.* 47: 175–181, 1979.
12. HOPPIN, F. G., JR., G. C. LEE, AND S. V. DAWSON. Properties of lung parenchyma in distortion. *J. Appl. Physiol.* 39: 742–751, 1975.
13. HUBMAYR, R. D., B. J. WALTERS, P. A. CHEVALIER, J. R. RODARTE, AND L. E. OLSON. Topographical distribution of regional lung volume in anesthetized dogs. *J. Appl. Physiol.: Respirat. Environ. Exercise Physiol.* 54: 1048–1056, 1983.
14. INOUE, H., C. INOUE, AND J. HILDEBRANDT. Vascular and airway pressures, and interstitial edema, affect peribronchial fluid pressure. *J. Appl. Physiol.: Respirat. Environ. Exercise Physiol.* 48: 177–185, 1980.
15. KALLOK, M. J., T. A. WILSON, J. R. RODARTE, S. J. LAI-FOOK, P. A. CHEVALIER, AND L. D. HARRIS. Distribution of regional volumes and ventilation in excised canine lobes. *J. Appl. Physiol.: Respirat. Environ. Exercise Physiol.* 47: 182–191, 1979.
16. KARAKAPLAN, A. D., M. P. BIENIEK, AND R. SKALAK. A mathematical model of lung parenchyma. *J. Biomech. Eng.* 102: 124–136, 1980.
17. LAI-FOOK, S. J. A continuum mechanics analysis of pulmonary vascular interdependence in isolated dog lobes. *J. Appl. Physiol.: Respirat. Environ. Exercise Physiol.* 46: 419–429, 1979.
18. LAI-FOOK, S. J. Elastic properties of lung parenchyma: the effect of pressure-volume hysteresis on the behavior of large blood vessels. *J. Biomech.* 12: 757–764, 1979.
19. LAI-FOOK, S. J., R. E. HYATT, AND J. R. RODARTE. Effect of parenchymal shear modulus and lung volume on bronchial pressure-diameter behavior. *J. Appl. Physiol.: Respirat. Environ. Exercise Physiol.* 44: 859–868, 1978.
20. LAI-FOOK, S. J., R. E. HYATT, J. R. RODARTE, AND T. A. WILSON. Behavior of artificially produced holes in lung parenchyma. *J. Appl. Physiol.: Respirat. Environ. Exericse Physiol.* 43: 648–655, 1977.
21. LAI-FOOK, S. J., AND M. J. KALLOK. Bronchial-arterial interdependence in isolated dog lung. *J. Appl. Physiol.: Respirat. Environ. Exercise Physiol.* 52: 1000–1007, 1982.
22. LAI-FOOK, S. J., AND B. TOPOROFF. Pressure-volume behavior of perivascular interstitium measured in isolated dog lung. *J. Appl. Physiol.: Respirat. Environ. Exercise Physiol.* 48: 939–946, 1980.
23. LAI-FOOK, S. J., T. A. WILSON, R. E. HYATT, AND J. R. RODARTE. Elastic constants of inflated lobes of dog lungs. *J. Appl. Physiol.* 40: 508–513, 1976.
24. LAMBERT, R. K., AND T. A. WILSON. A model for the elastic properties of the lung and their effect on expiratory flow. *J. Appl. Physiol.* 34: 34–48, 1973.
25. LEE, G. C., AND A. FRANKUS. Elasticity properties of lung parenchyma derived from experimental distortion data. *Biophys. J.* 15: 481–493, 1975.
26. LEE, G. C., A. FRANKUS, AND P. D. CHEN. Small distortion properties of lung parenchyma as a compressible continuum. *J. Biomech.* 9: 641–648, 1976.
27. LIU, J.-T., AND G. C. LEE. Static finite deformation analysis of the lung. *J. Eng. Mech. Div.* 104: 225–238, 1978.
28. MEAD, J., T. TAKISHIMA, AND D. LEITH. Stress distribution in lungs: a model of pulmonary elasticity. *J. Appl. Physiol.* 28: 596–608, 1970.
29. MILIC-EMILI, J., J. A. M. HENDERSON, M. B. DOLOVICH, D. TROP, AND K. KANEKO. Regional distribution of inspired gas in the lung. *J. Appl. Physiol.* 21: 749–759, 1966.
30. MISEROCCHI, G., AND E. AGOSTONI. Longitudinal forces acting on the trachea. *Respir. Physiol.* 17: 62–71, 1973.
31. RODARTE, J. R. Importance of lung material properties in respiratory system mechanics. *Physiologist* 20(5): 21–25, 1977.
32. SMITH, H. C., J. F. GREENLEAF, E. H. WOOD, D. J. SASS, AND A. A. BOVE. Measurement of regional pulmonary parenchymal movement in dogs. *J. Appl. Physiol.* 34: 544–547, 1973.
33. VAWTER, D. L. Poisson's ratio and incompressibility. *Biorheology* 18: 170–171, 1981.
34. VAWTER, D. L., Y. C. FUNG, AND J. B. WEST. Elasticity of excised dog lung parenchyma. *J. Appl. Physiol.: Respirat. Environ. Exercise Physiol.* 45: 261–269, 1978.
35. VAWTER, D. L., F. L. MATTHEWS, AND J. B. WEST. Effect of shape and size of lung and chest wall on stresses in the lung. *J. Appl. Physiol.* 39: 9–17, 1975.
36. WEST, J. B., AND F. L. MATTHEWS. Stresses, strains, and surface pressures in the lung caused by its weight. *J. Appl. Physiol.* 32: 332–345, 1972.

CHAPTER 16

Alveolar surface tension and lung surfactant

JON GOERKE

JOHN A. CLEMENTS

Departments of Physiology and Pediatrics and the Cardiovascular
Research Institute, University of California,
San Francisco, California

CHAPTER CONTENTS

THIS CHAPTER REVIEWS what is known about the lung alveolar surface monolayer. We emphasize the surface chemical aspects of lung surfactant and consider both the sources and sinks of this material. Since the last discussion of the topic in the chapter by Clements and Tierney (36) in the 1965 edition of the *Handbook* section on respiration, there seems to have been a gradual and steady advance in our knowledge. This is reflected in subsequent reviews (31, 64, 132, 193), none of which points to studies demonstrating quantum leaps in our understanding. As in most active research areas the lung surfactant field has produced a growing number of detailed papers dealing with more specialized topics. This has prompted us to limit this chapter to the alveolar monolayer and its immediate spatial and temporal relations to the lung, leaving more detailed discussions of surfactant biochemistry and relevant pulmonary mechanics to others [see the chapter

by King and Clements (96) in the first volume of the *Handbook* section on the respiratory system and the chapters by Greaves, Hildebrandt, and Hoppin, by Rodarte and Fung, and by Wilson in this volume]. Although the field has not been free of controversies, most of the disagreements have arisen in these latter biochemical and lung mechanical areas. Where there remain contentions with what we regard as the majority view of our more circumscribed topic on lung surfactant, references are cited for the conflicting opinions.

BACKGROUND

Early Contributors

Pulmonary physiologists have been aware of the importance of the lung air-water interfacial film since 1929, when von Neergaard (192a) first attributed the difference in the recoil forces between fluid- and air-filled lungs to the action of surface tension (γ), characteristic of an air-water interface. The topic lay dormant for nearly a quarter century, until Radford (156, 157) revived interest with liquid- and air-inflation studies in which he attempted to fix the interfacial tension at a particular value with detergents. Soon thereafter, Mead and associates (116, 117) emphasized the dependence on surface forces of compliance and loss of compliance during shallow breathing.

Concurrently, Pattle (144, 145) showed that lung tissue contained a remarkable material that stabilized microscopic bubbles suspended in water. He hypothesized that the substance reduced the otherwise very large retractive forces of the clean air-water interface in the bubbles and in the lung. Clements and his colleagues (18, 29, 32) used the Langmuir-Wilhelmy surface balance to demonstrate directly the surface tension–lowering property of lung extracts, and Brown (17) identified dipalmitoyl phosphatidylcholine (DPPC) as the active surfactant principle. Avery and Mead (9) pointed out the relation of the material to the respiratory distress syndrome of the newborn.

Relevance of Alveolar Surface Film

Central to the study of the lung surfactant monolayer is the contention that the air-water interface strongly influences lung mechanical properties (156, 157). In this chapter we emphasize that most physiologists who study lung surfactant do so because they believe it is connected with lung compliance and the work of breathing. The strong correlation of surfactant deficiency with pulmonary disease (9, 21, 35, 71) has reinforced this connection and spawned efforts to provide replacements or supplements for the natural material (3, 8, 13, 45, 53–55, 57, 73, 86, 124, 125, 174, 178, 179). An implicit aim of many surfactant monolayer studies is to provide a rational basis for designing adequate artificial lung surfactants.

Current Model of Lung Surfactant Action

As electron-micrographic techniques sharpened over the past 20 years, it became clear that lung surfactant was produced in lung type II cells and stored in lamellar bodies prior to being secreted into the alveolar lumen (23, 204). What stimulates the release of these lamellar bodies is unclear (34), although mechanical (47, 81, 114, 142) and humoral (14, 101, 142) mechanisms have been implicated. Once the lamellar bodies are in the shallow alveolar subphase and are free of their outer membranes, they are converted to a strange-looking form termed *tubular myelin* (60, 74, 148, 164, 165, 194, 197, 198). In vitro this process requires the presence of calcium ions (12a, 60).

It is assumed that when the monolayer surface is significantly expanded, as during an inspiration to total lung capacity, surfactant (tubular myelin) adsorbs in packets to essentially bare surface patches, which are then covered (filled) by very rapid spreading. A segregation or sorting of components in the surface then probably occurs, so that regions especially rich in DPPC exist. On compression of this film during expiration back down to functional residual capacity, the areas of DPPC-poor surface film are squeezed out, leaving a nearly pure DPPC film as the monolayer.

During tidal breathing this tightly packed DPPC-rich film resists rapid collapse, while allowing the very slow exit of material. Because the adsorption of new material is also prevented by this degree of film packing, the total surface area gradually becomes smaller until the next large breath reinitiates the cycle.

Although this model ties together many observations on lung surfactant, there are conflicting theories. These theories should be tested against new experimental evidence as it arises, e.g., the observation that high-frequency assisted ventilation does not seem to produce a progressive stiffening of the lung (loss of monolayer DPPC) even in the absence of deep inspirations (184). This may be related to the fact that such ventilation is usually applied with a continuous positive pressure and that higher transpulmonary pressures have been shown to retard the rate of monolayer loss even without concomitant high-frequency ventilation (196). New material might enter the surface, however, in response to rapid surface expansions, which could transiently raise surface tension above the equilibrium value of 25 mN·m^{-1} and allow adsorption to take place.

DEFINITION AND MEASUREMENT OF SURFACE TENSION

Generation of Interfacial Tension

The existence of surface tension at an air-liquid interface usually means that liquid molecules in the surface are at a higher energy level than those in the bulk (1, 56). Intermolecular attractive forces in the liquid provide a large potential energy for driving molecules from the surface to the bulk and thus for shrinking the interfacial area. Rounded droplets of water are a tribute to this force: their spherical shape offers the least possible surface area and therefore is the configuration with the lowest surface energy. For pure air-saturated water in equilibrium with water vapor–saturated air at 37°C, the surface energy density associated with this shrinking process is 70 mJ·m^{-2} (70 erg·cm^{-2}). The energy involved in the spontaneous removal of a planar patch of water surface 1 cm long by dx cm wide is the negative of that required to pull a bar 1 cm in length against a force of 70 dyn a distance dx cm within the surface. Such a force per length is called the surface tension of water (70 mN·m^{-1} or 70 dyn·cm^{-1} at 37°C); this measurement is assumed to give the surface energy density available for mechanical work.

Suppose that a second substance is present in the water and that water molecules are attracted more strongly to each other than they are to molecules of this substance. Such a substance accumulates in the interface because its arrival there displaces water molecules from the surface. At the surface the water molecules interact less strongly with their new neighbors; in the bulk they interact more strongly. The average attractive force in the interface decreases, as does the potential energy tending to shrink the surface, and the surface tension of the film-covered interface is found to be lower than that of the clean air-water surface.

Suspensions of many naturally occurring lipids, including unsaturated phosphatidylcholines, and lipid mixtures containing saturated phosphatidylcholines spontaneously form films that lower the interfacial tension to ~25 mN·m^{-1}. This value can be considered the equilibrium surface tension (γ_{eq}) for such films in the presence of an excess of the lipid. More tightly packed films with higher concentrations of surface lipid can be achieved only by physical compression, i.e., by reducing the available interfacial area. Films in these overcompressed, nonequilibrium states are not stable, however, and material leaves the surface with varying rapidity until surface tension has risen to ~25 mN·m⁻¹. Films that are rich in DPPC, such as lung surfactant, lose material so slowly that surface tension remains as low as 1 mN·m⁻¹ for hours. This striking metastability of overcompressed lung surfactant films makes breathing easy for the individual and theoretical interpretations difficult for the surface chemist (11, 58, 152). We describe next three of the systems most commonly used to measure the surface tension of lung-related films.

Methods

The classic and most easily understood apparatus for observing surface films is the Langmuir film balance [Fig. 1; (1, 56)]. Surface pressure, measured as the force per length required to keep stationary a linear surface float separating a clean air-water surface from a film-covered surface, gives the difference between the surface tensions of these two surfaces. The trough is hydrophobic and filled with an excess of aqueous subphase, so that the top surface of the water projects above the sides of the container. A hydrophobic barrier, resting on the top edges of the trough, is then used to compress the film toward the float. Unfortunately when interfacial monolayer tensions are reduced by film compression to much below 25 mN·m⁻¹, the previously hydrophobic top edges of the trough become wetted by the film plus aqueous solution and the solution overflows.

Clements et al. (33) modified the system to compress the films with a continuous Teflon ribbon standing on edge in a deeper trough. Presently the most commonly used design is a deep half-filled Teflon trough with a tightly fitting Teflon barrier for compressing the surface film (Fig. 2). Metastable lipid films are often solid or extremely viscous at room

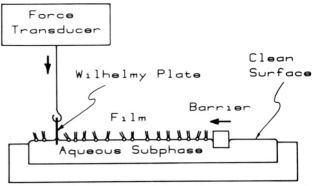

FIG. 2. Modified Wilhelmy film balance. Ends of barrier fit tightly against sidewalls of trough. Surface tension is lowered by moving barrier to left and compressing the film. This is sensed as a decreased force pulling on small, hydrophilic Wilhelmy dipping plate.

temperature and at very low surface tensions (118, 192) and seem to be well contained by this technique. Few investigators have taken the trouble to document monolayer containment and the absence of film leaks, however. In these latter systems, surface tension is usually measured with a platinum Wilhelmy dipping plate (1, 56) attached to a force transducer. The Wilhelmy method relies on the continual presence of a zero contact angle between the vertical dipping plate and the adherent surface of the fluid within the trough (56). Although this is easily achieved during the compression phase of isotherm inscription, it is often difficult to obtain during film expansion, particularly if the meniscus is forced to advance over an unclean, film-coated plate. The result, seen even in published isotherms, is a reversed hysteresis, or a measurement of surface tension during film expansion that is lower than expected.

Lung surfactant films with low surface tension or even DPPC films at 37°C or higher tend to creep over the vertical walls of even these modified troughs, however; treatment of the walls with an alcoholic solution of lanthanum and long-chain saturated phosphatidylcholine has been recommended to help contain the pure lipid films (66). For lung surfactant films, however, we feel that no trough-type surface balance has yet been demonstrated to have a leak-free surface.

Thus some investigators have turned to submerged air bubbles as microtroughs. Pattle (144) first predicted alveolar surface tensions from the properties of isolated air bubbles expressed from lung tissue. Others have extended this technique by forming bubbles on an underwater capillary and measuring transsurface pressures directly (2, 44, 175, 176). When bubbles are used, surface tension is calculated by applying Laplace's law: $\gamma = rP/2$, where r is bubble radius and P is the transmonolayer pressure gradient. Effects of gravity on bubble shape are neglected. The bubble-on-a-tube configuration apparently tends to minimize the effects of film leaks. On the other hand,

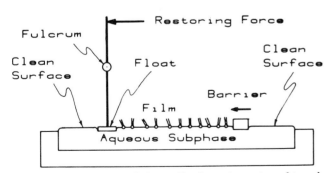

FIG. 1. Langmuir film balance. Barrier rests on top of trough sidewalls. Moving it left compresses the surface film, lowering surface tension (raising the surface pressure). Compressed film pushes on mica float with a force proportional to difference between surface tensions in the clean and film-covered surfaces. Float is kept in a null position by applying an opposing force, which is therefore a measure of film surface pressure. In many applications this force is supplied by a nulled torsion balance.

because surface-active materials usually arrive at the air-water interface by adsorption from the aqueous media, surface concentrations are not known. Schürch (168) surmounted this difficulty with a variation of the bubble technique in which known amounts of film materials are spread from solvents directly onto the surface of large bubbles. After determining bubble surface area, he could calculate the surface concentrations involved. Some of the bubble methods use samples as small as 20 μl in volume (44) and thus seem appropriate to use when native surfactant stability is studied or when small sample sizes are mandatory. In most of these systems, even when material is expected to adsorb onto the surface from the aqueous subphase, no stirring is provided. Diffusion or even sedimentation may thus influence the measured kinetic behavior. Bubble methods, however, are suitable for measuring rapid changes in surface tension and other dynamic properties of films.

A recently developed technique measures surface tension directly at the alveolar surface (168–171). Droplets of certain fluorocarbon liquids with low surface tension are calibrated by their ability to spread on DPPC monolayers compressed to different surface tensions. In general when the droplet's own inherent surface tension is less than that of the monolayer, it rapidly spreads on the surface of the monolayer. Under direct visualization, droplets of a set of these materials are placed by micropipettes on the alveolar surfaces of excised cat lungs and the surface tension is measured at lung volumes from total lung capacity down to functional residual capacity.

The actual time course of surfactant adsorption has also been measured with variations of the Wilhelmy plate and bubble methods. To provide a fresh adsorption surface, the trough surface is first swept or aspirated clean or a new bubble is formed. The subsequent decrease of surface tension must be correlated with tension-area isotherms of the formed film to calculate the amount of material adsorbed.

ADSORPTION AND SPREADING OF SURFACTANT FILMS

Form of Surfactant

For soluble surfactants, adsorption at the air-water interface clearly involves soluble monomers. Because DPPC is so insoluble (177), monomers cannot offer effective vehicles for the apparently large flux of material to the surface, and bulk-surface transfer probably takes place through forms such as tubular myelin (64). There is not much published evidence for this (60), and more information is needed about how surfactant actually moves from the type II cell to the air-water interface. On the other hand, monomers have been implicated in the apparently similar process of lipid transfer from liposome to liposome (115). Some authors have suggested that under certain circumstan-

ces tubular myelin may represent the product of monolayer collapse rather than the immediate source of the monolayer (109–111, 183). Ultimately adsorption has to be an energy-driven mechanism. It will be promoted by high surface tension (high surface energy) and retarded by low surface tension. The lower limit for spontaneous adsorption from suspensions of most phospholipids is a γ_{eq} value of ~25 mN·m^{-1}.

Factors Affecting Adsorption and Spreading

Although the detailed molecular mechanisms are not understood, some of the factors affecting adsorption and spreading of surfactant are known. For example, taking a deep breath expands alveolar surface area, which provides room for more material to be adsorbed from the subphase (59). In this connection the expansion-compression asymmetry of lung surfactant film behavior (206), describable as tension-area hysteresis, is particularly important. It means that relatively small expansions will raise surface tension sufficiently to allow adsorption of new material (131).

The composition of newly secreted surfactant within the subphase probably differs from that in the older, repeatedly compressed alveolar film. The former is best represented by analyses of alveolar samples or lung lavage (94, 98, 162), lamellar bodies, and tubular myelin (60). Presently monolayer composition must be deduced from the physical properties of the alveolar film (31, 80), because the film itself has not been isolated independently of material in the subphase. Analyses show that subphase surfactant contains substantial amounts of negatively charged and unsaturated phospholipids in addition to DPPC. These would tend to fluidize the otherwise solid DPPC film (46, 78, 91, 92, 103, 104, 121). Whether such fluidity promotes adsorption is not well established, but it would also enhance the collapsibility of already formed and compressed monolayers (65). This makes it likely that the working alveolar monolayer is greatly enriched in DPPC (31, 80) and differs from the recently adsorbed but uncompressed monolayer. Supporting evidence for this latter point comes from experiments with heated lungs, whose pressure-volume behavior can best be explained on the basis of a DPPC-rich monolayer (31). The finding of a small negative temperature coefficient for adsorption of lung surfactant components (95) has not yet been related to composition or other physicochemical properties, except to suggest an entropy-driven process.

The apoprotein now commonly found in surfactant preparations has no proven function as yet. Recombination studies have suggested that it does (12a, 97) and does not (122) promote a more rapid adsorption of DPPC and other lipids to the air-water interface.

The aqueous subphase surrounding surfactant obviously must influence adsorption and spreading, but the small size, thinness, and inaccessibility of this compartment have made its measurement particularly difficult. From morphometric analyses (37) it can be calculated that no point on the alveolar surface is farther than ~50 μm from a type II cell. Lamellar bodies issuing from these cells are ~1 μm in diameter (197), and the tubular myelin they form appears to have an even bulkier structure. In addition, the thickness of the aqueous subphase may be thin over most of the alveolar surface (195). All of this leads one to believe that movement of surfactant to the surface is not limited by geometric factors, although one group has stressed the theoretical importance of aqueous bulk viscosity (85).

Reifenrath (158) has attempted the difficult task of directly sampling the alveolar subphase in adult animals with micropipettes, but the relatively high content of serum albumin that he found makes one suspect contamination with interstitial fluid. One group has succeeded in measuring subphase pH by microelectrodes within the alveoli of anesthetized adult rabbits and reports a value of 6.92 (129). Other subphase ion activities will undoubtedly be measured in the near future, because ions are known to interact with and influence the physical properties of phospholipids (75, 76).

Serial sampling of fetal airway fluid provides another means of assessing the concentrations and fluxes of alveolar subphase components (100, 139–141). The data show a pH of 6.27, even more acid than in the adult, a calcium concentration of 0.86 meq·liter^{-1} (misprinted in ref. 141), and a chloride concentration of 157 meq·liter^{-1}. There is very little protein (0.2 g· liter^{-1}) in this fluid.

Because pulmonary edema fluid (30, 163) and other agents in the alveoli (87, 133, 172, 182) are sometimes associated with poor surfactant function, the permeability of alveolar membranes to water and nonelectrolytes has received some attention (42, 43) and certainly warrants more. In addition, one group has reported the isolation of a protein from alveolar lavage that may inhibit surfactant function (88).

Even the alveolar vapor phase has been considered, with the deleterious effects of high oxygen tension being the most thoroughly studied (20, 22, 37, 70). Anesthetic agents have been implicated in the destabilization of the alveolar monolayer (4, 5, 147, 203), and the respreading effect of ethanol has also been investigated (26, 113).

PROPERTIES OF FILMS RELATED TO LUNG SURFACTANT

Low Surface Tension and Other Quasi-Static Film Properties

Pure DPPC monolayers have frequently been studied by surface chemists, largely because phosphatidyl-

cholines are biologically important lipids and because pure DPPC is relatively easy to prepare. Most investigators have not concerned themselves with DPPC films at surface tensions below 25 mN·m^{-1} and hence have avoided studying the very region of most interest to lung physiologists. Such films collapse when compressed to very low surface tensions, and surface tension rises toward 25 mN·m^{-1}. This tendency is enhanced by the presence of even small amounts of impurities or by temperatures above 40°C. Inadequate surface balance design may also confuse the picture by allowing surface leaks to take place and surface tension to rise rapidly. All of these difficulties are magnified when lung surfactant films, which are more complex and inherently less stable, are studied. One should be careful not to attribute to DPPC or lung surfactant films what are really the properties of impurities or leaky balances.

Monolayer isotherms of lung surfactant materials are plotted as surface tension versus area per molecule or versus area per weight of material applied to the surface; they are traditionally used to describe the equilibrium properties of monolayers in general. However, DPPC suspensions may not spontaneously lower aqueous surface tension below 69 mN·m^{-1} at temperatures under 41°C, indicating that this high figure represents their limiting γ_{eq} (152). When studied in similar ways, suspensions of most other phospholipids, particularly those containing unsaturated fatty acids or ionizable head groups, have a limiting γ_{eq} of ~25 mN·m^{-1}. Measurements of γ_{eq} are complicated by the fact that the speed with which equilibrium is reached may be rapid when the suspension is above the temperature for phase transition from the gel to liquid crystal but may be exceedingly slow below this temperature. Because measured surface tensions lower than γ_{eq} do not represent true equilibrium states, those isotherm regions in which $\gamma < \gamma_{eq}$ should be considered merely as convenient devices for describing surface force-area relationships. Equations that presuppose true equilibrium should be applied with caution to such data (152, 181).

Figures 3 and 4 show isotherms of DPPC monolayers studied at various temperatures. The ability of such monolayers to reach low surface tensions is clearly limited to temperatures under ~41°C. Above this temperature, compression causes the films to collapse at surface tensions of ~25 mN·m^{-1}. These DPPC isotherms also show a phase transition from the liquid-condensed to the liquid-expanded state (1), manifested here as a nearly horizontal region or plateau in the isotherm. At higher temperatures the transition occurs at lower surface tensions.

Surface balances have also been used to study films of lung surfactant (Fig. 5) in preparations ranging from unfractionated lung lavage fluid to relatively pure lamellar bodies. There has been no uniformity in the procedures used to spread the material at the interface, and rarely have attempts been made to

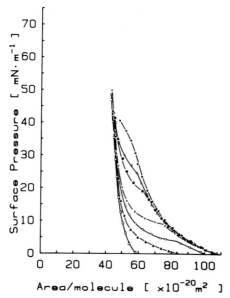

FIG. 3. Surface pressure vs. area for dipalmitoyl phosphatidyl-choline monolayers at various temperatures. ●, 34.6°C; △, 29.5°C; ■, 26.0°C; ×, 21.1°C; ○, 16.8°C; ▲, 12.4°C; □, 6.2°C. [From Phillips and Chapman (149).]

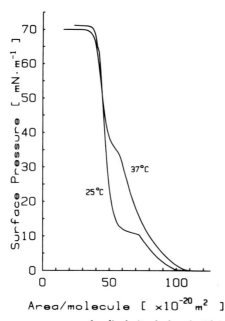

FIG. 4. Surface pressure vs. area for dipalmitoyl phosphatidyl-choline compressed to collapse pressures. Highest surface pressures at each temperature correspond to zero surface tension. (J. Goerke and J. Gonzales, unpublished observations.)

determine the area per molecule of the spread DPPC. One can apply aqueous suspensions of material drop-wise (56) to the surface, in the hope that none falls through to the subphase, or one can allow it to flow down a roughened glass rod into the interface (187). The addition of solvents such as 2-propanol makes spreading of native surfactant faster and more complete (153) but undoubtedly modifies the properties of

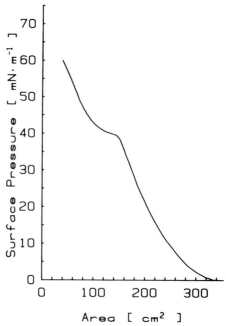

FIG. 5. Surface pressure vs. area for dog lung surfactant at 37°C. Surface pressure of 70 mN·m⁻¹ corresponds to surface tension of 0 mN·m⁻¹. [From King and Clements (93).]

the film itself. Adsorption from surfactant suspensions in the aqueous subphase is also a popular means of forming films for study but forces one to measure the amount reaching the surface by some independent method (67, 112), which is seldom done.

Once in the surface the material is slowly compressed to record an isotherm. Because many natural surfactant films collapse rather quickly at surface tensions below 25 mN·m⁻¹, this process often represents a race against time that can hardly produce an equilibrium isotherm. Repeated compression-expansion cycles are frequently reported for lung surfactant films (50), with the assumption that such films eventually resemble the steady-state alveolar monolayer in situ after many respiratory cycles. This resemblance would be more likely to hold for experiments involving subphase-suspended material present at physiological concentrations, but the results are difficult to interpret because alveolar subphase states are largely unknown.

Isotherms obtained from the first compression of natural surfactant films at the physiologically relevant temperature of 37°C typically show a large shoulder at a surface tension near 30 mN·m⁻¹ (95); this has variously been attributed to the presence of a phase transition (186) or a squeezing out of non-DPPC film components (77, 80). Below this point, surface tension falls more rapidly as the film is compressed to reach values near 0 mN·m⁻¹. Because of the measurement difficulties just discussed, the slope of this portion of the isotherm is highly dependent on compression speed. Withdrawal of the compressing barrier at this point usually gives a steeper slope, corresponding to a

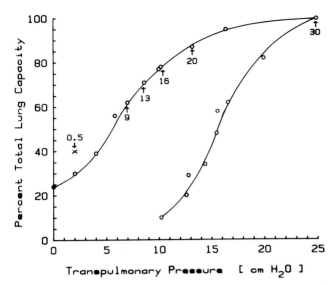

FIG. 6. Volume vs. pressure from isolated rat (o) and cat (x) lungs. Surface tension was directly measured in lungs at selected points on deflation curve as indicated by *arrows*. [Rat data from Schürch et al. (169); cat data from Schürch (168).]

lower value of surface compliance (change in surface tension per fractional change in surface area). This compression-expansion asymmetry produces hysteresis in full-cycle isotherms. It reflects relatively slow film collapse during compression and lagging film formation during expansion.

A more direct but far more difficult way to study the native surfactant has been to measure the surface tension of the alveolar monolayer in situ (168–171). These investigations have confirmed the heretofore theoretical existence of very low surface tensions in the lung but of course were unable to generate tension-area isotherms because surface area was not measured concomitantly (Fig. 6).

Dynamic Film Properties

What happens to the alveolar film once it has been formed and while it is being compressed? These kinetic aspects of the lung surfactant monolayer are even less well understood than its static properties.

Several processes seem to take place in both mixed lipid films containing DPPC and in lung surfactant films. Even during an initial monolayer compression, and certainly as a result of repeated compressions, non-DPPC components are squeezed out of the monolayer, tending to leave a DPPC-rich film at the interface (80, 151). The process is apparently similar to the squeezing out of unsaturated fatty acids from mixed films (52). Where the lost material goes has not been well established, although repeated cycling of the same films suggests that at least portions of the squeezed-out material can reenter the monolayer (136, 167). This squeezing out seems to happen at or below surface tensions of 30 mN·m^{-1} and produces relatively horizontal inflections on isotherms. This same feature

of isotherms has also been interpreted as a phase transition of monolayer material resident in the surface and not as expulsion of material from the surface region (186). If a significant fraction of the expelled material reenters the monolayer as usable surfactant, secreted fluxes of surfactant from type II cells will underestimate true alveolar monolayer turnover. However, if such local recycling does not occur, lipid metabolic rates may have to match the rates of monolayer collapse. This problem clearly needs investigation.

Even before the squeezing out of monolayer components during compression, two other processes may occur: surface sorting and surface relaxation. Sorting refers to the formation of domains or regions of a particular lipid composition within the monolayer. Although there is no evidence yet for the occurrence of this process in lung surfactant monolayers, it would offer a reasonable mechanism for the squeezing out of non-DPPC components as preformed domains having relative instability. Such segregation is known to occur in some mixed phospholipid monolayers (6, 15, 16, 25, 28, 38, 39, 62, 69, 89, 90, 104, 150, 191).

During the relaxation process the surface tension of pure DPPC films appears to rise toward a slightly higher value, with a half time measured in seconds, when compression is abruptly stopped at surface tensions >25 mN·m^{-1} (127, 180). The process is more prominent when the lipid is in its liquid-condensed form, giving a surface tension rise of ~1–3 mN·m^{-1}. The extent of relaxation also seems to be greater when faster barrier advances are employed, although this has not been quantified. Because small area losses are equivalent to large surface tension changes in these low-compressibility monolayers, these observations may represent not molecular rearrangements but merely small amounts of surface film leakage. The extent of the surface tension changes involved probably would not have a significant effect on lung volumes or alveolar stability, particularly because lung surfactant films usually reach a surface tension of 30 mN·m^{-1} via the rapid adsorption of new material from the subphase and not by compression of the existing film (170).

More important is the slow, largely irreversible collapse of DPPC-rich films compressed to surface tensions below the γ_{eq} value of 25 mN·m^{-1}. This is the region where the surfactant film keeps the lung volume and interfacial area from falling. The collapse process has been studied in stearic acid films (154), in DPPC and DPPC-rich films (66, 80, 127, 130, 134, 135, 159), and in films of lung surfactant (105, 146, 185). Pure DPPC films collapse very slowly even at 37°C; the lowest time constants reported are 0.03 h^{-1} for films held at $\gamma = 5$ mN·m^{-1} (80). A much more rapid collapse process occurs in lung surfactant films (185), but the possibility of surface leaks in the apparatus suggests that natural surfactant could actually be more stable. Indeed microdroplet experiments by

Schürch (168) suggest that the alveolar monolayer in situ is much more stable than one would have guessed from surface balance measurements. To reach this conclusion one must assume that in Schürch's experiments under the condition of constant volume, alveolar surface area was also constant. Because Pattle (144) was able to show high film stabilities in alveolar wash using his bubble system, one may expect more reliable (and higher) values of stability to come from bubble studies in the future.

Is monolayer turnover restricted to individual respiratory units, with little or no equilibration of film surface tension between units and little film flow up the airway? The occurrence of focal atelectasis suggests that surface tension is not uniform throughout the lung, but this would be difficult to establish experimentally. Film viscosity is certainly relevant to these questions and has been examined in a variety of ways. The general consensus is that both DPPC and compressed lung surfactant films are highly viscous and almost solid (118–120, 123, 192). Just as surface shear viscosity of highly compressed films keeps them from creeping out of surface balances, it may also keep them from slipping into distant alveolar units or up the airway. High surface dilatational viscosity, on the other hand, serves to explain the asymmetry of DPPC monolayer compressibility on compression versus expansion. During expiration the monolayer is compressed, packing lipid acyl chains more closely together and thereby increasing intermolecular forces. However, the monolayer is assumed to crack apart into condensed "ice floes" and stretches of "open sea" as area is increased during inspiration, because the monolayer patches do not expand proportionally as fast as the total surface area. The result is higher surface tension for a given total area during film expansion than during film compression (7). At least one group believes aqueous drag on the monolayer, rather than monolayer viscosity itself, is the dominant factor in producing this hysteresis (84).

Such interfacial hysteresis is in turn implicated in lung pressure-volume hysteresis (40, 59, 61, 136, 188, 201), although alternative explanations have been proposed (82, 189).

INFLUENCE OF SURFACE TENSION ON LUNG PRESSURE-VOLUME BEHAVIOR

Static Properties

The extraordinarily low surface tensions reached by the alveolar film strongly affect the pressure-volume behavior of the intact lung. This topic is addressed in detail in the chapters by Greaves, Hildebrandt, and Hoppin, by Rodarte and Fung, and by Wilson in this *Handbook*. Suffice it to say here that film surface tension and hysteresis are essential for explaining the difference between air-filled and saline-filled lung pressure-volume curves and for predicting the behav-

ior of pressure-volume curves after lung lavage with detergents that produce more nearly constant interfacial tensions (10, 190, 200, 201).

Dynamic Properties

The contributions of dynamic film properties to lung pressure-volume behavior are also treated in detail elsewhere in this *Handbook* (see the chapters by Greaves, Hildebrandt, and Hoppin, by Rodarte and Fung, and by Wilson). We point out here only that monolayer collapse may help explain the loss of compliance during shallow breathing (116, 205, 206) and the subsequent development of atelectasis (48, 50, 126, 173, 196).

TURNOVER AND RECYCLING OF SURFACTANT COMPONENTS

Possible Recycling Paths

Evidence is accumulating that used lung surfactant is not completely degraded but is recycled within the lung (12, 57, 63, 72, 106, 143, 166). Possible recycling could take place *1*) within the surface film between collapsed and squeezed-out phases and the monolayer itself, *2*) between the monolayer and the old material extruded into the aqueous subphase, *3*) via the subphase and reprocessing mechanisms within type II cells, and *4*) via pathways incorporating other cells, such as type I cells and alveolar macrophages. Magoon et al. (107) have provided data from rabbits that support the idea of surfactant recycling. They studied fractions of tissue lamellar bodies and fractions of alveolar lavage prepared by differential centrifugation. Decreasing sedimentability correlated with later labeling with tracer, lower adsorption rates, smaller particle size, and lower protein and phosphatidylglycerol content. The earlier lavage fractions were enriched in tubular myelin. The data suggest a metabolic sequence in which heavier, denser material is precursor to material that is lighter and less dense. This is a relatively new area of investigation, and the importance of each recycling pathway has not been well established.

Local Monolayer Recycling

If they are not compressed to the point of collapse, monolayers of most biologically relevant lipids show little hysteresis in their isotherms when repeatedly expanded and compressed. This means that the compression-expansion process is essentially reversible in the time scale of isotherm inscription for these lipids. Many of these lipids (particularly unsaturated phospholipids) can be compressed to collapse and yet give essentially identical isotherms on recompression if inscribed slowly enough. This latter property is sensitive to expansion and compression rates but is good evidence for complete surface respreading of the collapsed monolayers. This apparently does not hold for DPPC monolayers below 41°C. There seems to be little or no respreading of collapsed pure DPPC films (80, 130). The respreading of the DPPC content of collapsed mixed DPPC films or of native lung surfactant has not been quantified. This point is important for the adequate description of surfactant turnover; until it is answered satisfactorily, we will not know if only new, rapidly adsorbable surfactant can replace the losses of DPPC and other components from the alveolar surface film.

Extramonolayer Recycling Pathways

Partial or complete degradation of surfactant components within the alveolar subphase has to be considered, because some investigators find lipid hydrolase activity associated with lamellar body preparations (41, 68, 137, 138). However, the evidence is conflicting (79). The processes might resemble what happens in the gut, where triglycerides and phospholipids must be broken down to fatty acids and water-soluble head groups before being absorbed (102). If such lipid products were taken into type II cells, they would be available for resynthesis into new surfactant.

Recent evidence supports the direct internalization of subphase lipids by type II cells (27, 57, 72, 155). This process might resemble the internalization of low-density lipoproteins and chylomicron remnants by hepatic cells (19). One may find specific binding sites for used surfactant on the luminal surfaces of type II cells and a recycling pathway within the cell involving multivesicular bodies and lamellar bodies and perhaps endoplasmic reticulum and Golgi apparatus. Adsorption at the cell surface might require a specific surfactant-associated protein.

Alveolar macrophages contain engulfed myelinic structures that possibly consist of used surfactant (99, 108, 199). This phospholipid pool does not seem to be derived entirely from an extracellular pool (12), and its size and turnover rate are probably not large enough to account for a significant part of the surfactant removal. If a large fraction of the alveolar phospholipid is recycled by type II cells, however, macrophages may take up a very significant part of the material that escapes recycling. The eventual destination of the ingested lipid has not been determined.

Although the monolayer could theoretically flow up the airway from alveoli to trachea, studies designed to sample this escape route have recovered only trivial amounts of phospholipid radioactivity (12, 51). This evidence should encourage investigators to focus their attention on recycling or degradation mechanisms within the alveoli themselves. These metabolic processes, as they are uncovered, should be quantitatively linked to surfactant fluxes into and out of the alveolar monolayer: in the steady state the biochemical and physical kinetics must balance (80).

SUMMARY OF LUNG SURFACTANT PROPERTIES

Some of the more important physical properties attributed to lung surfactant are briefly summarized. Similar properties should be exhibited by lipid mixtures or natural extracts prepared for the treatment of the respiratory distress syndrome of the newborn (49, 53, 123, 130, 134, 160).

Rapid Adsorption and Spreading

A significant fraction of the total potential alveolar monolayer is probably created within the time of a deep breath. Pure DPPC has not been prepared in such a way that it can adsorb and spread so fast, and consequently some of the other components of surfactant serve to get DPPC into the surface film. Unsaturated and negatively charged phospholipids plus an apoprotein may fill this function. The most successful replacement studies in animals and humans have used some form of whole natural surfactant, incorporating all these components, and their success has undoubtedly been due to rapid surface adsorption and spreading. This does not mean that DPPC films can be formed only with the adjuvants present in lung surfactant. An artificial surfactant could conceivably be spread with other agents or solvents (24, 25).

Low Surface Tension When Film is Compressed

Of equal importance is the ability of the monolayer to resist a high compressive force, i.e., to give a surface tension approaching $0 \text{ mN} \cdot \text{m}^{-1}$. This is the most well known and established property of lung surfactant, and its theoretical basis lies in Laplace's law. The lipid DPPC is one of the few compounds of mammalian origin that can serve this function, and all formulations of surfactant replacements to date have been built around it.

Stable Low Surface Tension

The mere presence of a DPPC-enriched monolayer does not guarantee either low surface tensions or the stability of low tensions if they are achieved. A major portion of the adsorption adjuvants are apparently selectively squeezed out of or removed from the monolayer, because their presence would prevent stable, low tensions from being achieved. Although the adsorption and spreading agents leave the monolayer rapidly, the remaining DPPC film collapses much more slowly, with a half time of ~30 min. The asymmetry between the surfactant adsorption processes and DPPC loss processes is therefore important and profound. Significant amounts of DPPC should enter the interface in less than a second but should take many minutes to leave.

FUTURE CONSIDERATIONS

There is much more to learn about the physical properties of lung surfactant. *1*) What is the actual chemical composition of the adsorbing material (presumably tubular myelin), of the initially adsorbed film and the repeatedly compressed film, of material desorbing from the monolayer at different stages of its existence, and of materials removed from the lumen for recycling? *2*) How does the complex lamellar body structure become transformed into the very different but equally complex tubular myelin form? *3*) Can one provide accurate theoretical and physically realized models of the processes of adsorption, squeezing out, and collapse? *4*) Is recycling present at all levels? In particular, does "old" collapsed or squeezed-out monolayer readsorb to the interface and function anew, or must it be reprocessed by intracellular mechanisms?

We thank John Gonzales, Maureen Gallant, and Barbara Ehrlich for their help in preparing this manuscript.

This work was supported in part by Grants HL-24075 and HL-28298 from the Public Health Service. John A. Clements is a Career Investigator of the American Heart Association.

REFERENCES

1. ADAM, N. K. *The Physics and Chemistry of Surfaces.* New York: Dover, 1968.
2. ADAMS, F. H., AND G. ENHORNING. Surface properties of lung extracts. I. A dynamic alveolar model. *Acta Physiol. Scand.* 68: 23–27, 1966.
3. ADAMS, F. H., B. TOWERS, A. B. OSHER, M. IKEGAMI, T. FUJIWARA, AND M. NOZAKI. Effects of tracheal instillation of natural surfactant in premature lambs. I. Clinical and autopsy findings. *Pediatr. Res.* 12: 841–848, 1978.
4. ALARIE, Y., M. A. CHOBY, AND W. E. POEL. Alveolar instability following administration of fluorocarbon (Abstract). *Toxicol. Appl. Pharmacol.* 22: 306, 1972.
5. ALARIE, Y., AND J. QUEALY. Effects of trichlorotrifluoroethane on pressure-volume curves in rat lungs (Abstract). *Physiologist* 15: 69, 1972.
6. ALBRECHT, O., H. GRULER, AND E. SACKMANN. Pressure-composition phase diagrams of cholesterol/lecithin, cholesterol/phosphatidic acid, and lecithin/phosphatidic acid mixed monolayers: a Langmuir film balance study. *J. Colloid Interface Sci.* 79: 319–338, 1981.
7. ARDILA, R., D. POTTER, AND J. HILDEBRANDT. Interfacial hysteresis in lung (Letter to the editor). *J. Appl. Physiol.* 37: 472, 1974.
8. AVERY, M. E. On replacing the surfactant. *Pediatrics* 65: 1126–1177, 1980.
9. AVERY, M. E., AND J. MEAD. Surface properties in relation to atelectasis and hyaline membrane disease. *Am. J. Dis. Child.* 97: 517–523, 1959.
10. BACHOFEN, H., P. GEHR, AND E. R. WEIBEL. Alterations of mechanical properties and morphology in excised rabbit lungs rinsed with a detergent. *J. Appl. Physiol.: Respirat. Environ. Exercise Physiol.* 47: 1002–1010, 1979.
11. BANGHAM, A. D., C. J. MORLEY, AND M. C. PHILLIPS. The physical properties of an effective lung surfactant. *Biochim. Biophys. Acta* 573: 552–556, 1979.
12. BARITUSSIO, A. G., M. W. MAGOON, J. GOERKE, AND J. A. CLEMENTS. Precursor-product relationship between rabbit type II cell lamellar bodies and alveolar surface active material: surfactant turnover time. *Biochim. Biophys. Acta* 666: 382–393, 1981.
12a. BENSON, B. J., M. C. WILLIAMS, K. SUEISHI, J. GOERKE, AND T. SARGEANT. Role of calcium ions in the structure and function of pulmonary surfactant. *Biochim. Biophys. Acta* 793: 18–27, 1984.
13. BERGGREN, P., G. GROSSMANN, R. NILSSON, S. TOLLBOM, AND B. ROBERTSON. A protein-free physiologically active preparation of natural lung surfactant. *IRCS J. Med. Sci.* 9: 283–284, 1981.
14. BERGMAN, B. Beta-mimetics and the preterm neonatal lung. *Acta Physiol. Scand. Suppl.* 497: 1–52, 1981.
15. BOGGS, J. M., M. A. MOSCARELLO, AND D. PAPAHADJOPOULOS. Phase separation of acidic and neutral phospholipids induced by human myelin basic protein. *Biochemistry* 16: 5420–5426, 1977.
16. BOGGS, J. M., D. D. WOOD, M. A. MOSCARELLO, AND D. PAPAHADJOPOULOS. Lipid phase separation induced by a hydrophobic protein in phosphatidylserine-phosphatidylcholine vesicles. *Biochemistry* 16: 2325–2329, 1977.
17. BROWN, E. S. Isolation and assay of dipalmityl lecithin in lung extracts. *Am. J. Physiol.* 207: 402–406, 1964.
18. BROWN, E. S., R. P. JOHNSON, AND J. A. CLEMENTS. Pulmonary surface tension. *J. Appl. Physiol.* 14: 717–720, 1959.
19. BROWN, M. S., P. T. KOVANEN, AND J. L. GOLDSTEIN. Regulation of cholesterol by lipoprotein receptors. *Science* 212: 628–635, 1981.
20. BRUMLEY, G., AND J. D. CRAPO. Oxygen-adapted rats and lung-disaturated lecithin. *J. Pediatr.* 95: 892–895, 1979.
21. BRUMLEY, G. W., W. A. HODSON, AND M. E. AVERY. Lung phospholipids and surface tension correlations in infants with and without hyaline membrane disease and in adults. *Pediatrics* 40: 13–19, 1967.
22. BRUMLEY, G. W., B. TUGGLE, L. LUXNER, AND J. D. CRAPO. Disaturated phosphatidylcholine in rat lungs with altered numbers of type II alveolar epithelial cells. *Am. Rev. Respir. Dis.* 119: 461–470, 1979.
23. BUCKINGHAM, S., AND M. E. AVERY. Time of appearance of lung surfactant in the foetal mouse. *Nature London* 193: 688–689, 1962.
24. CADENHEAD, D. A., AND B. M. J. KELLNER. Some observations on monolayer spreading solvents with special reference to phospholipid monolayers. *J. Colloid Interface Sci.* 49: 143–145, 1974.
25. CADENHEAD, D. A., AND F. MUELLER-LANDAU. Molecular accommodation and molecular interactions in mixed insoluble monomolecular films. *J. Colloid Interface Sci.* 78: 269–270, 1980.
26. CADENHEAD, D. A., AND J. E. OSONKA. The influence of ethanol on both condensed and expanded monomolecular films at the air-water interface. *J. Colloid Interface Sci.* 33: 187–191, 1970.
27. CHANDER, A., J. F. STRAUSS, AND A. B. FISHER. Uptake of phosphatidylcholine (PC) by granular pneumocytes in primary culture (Abstract). *Federation Proc.* 40: 407, 1981.
28. CHAPMAN, D., N. F. OWENS, M. C. PHILLIPS, AND D. A. WALKER. Mixed monolayers of phospholipids and cholesterol. *Biochim. Biophys. Acta* 183: 458–465, 1969.
29. CLEMENTS, J. A. Surface tension of lung extracts. *Proc. Soc. Exp. Biol. Med.* 95: 170–172, 1957.
30. CLEMENTS, J. A. Pulmonary edema and permeability of alveolar membranes. *Arch. Environ. Health* 2: 280–283, 1961.
31. CLEMENTS, J. A. Functions of the alveolar lining. *Am. Rev. Respir. Dis.* 115: 67–71, 1977.
32. CLEMENTS, J. A., E. S. BROWN, AND R. P. JOHNSON. Pulmonary surface tension and the mucus lining of the lungs: some theoretical considerations. *J. Appl. Physiol.* 12: 262–268, 1958.

33. CLEMENTS, J. A., R. F. HUSTEAD, R. P. JOHNSON, AND I. GRIBETZ. Pulmonary surface tension and alveolar stability. *J. Appl. Physiol.* 16: 444–450, 1961.
34. CLEMENTS, J. A., M. J. OYARZÚN, AND A. BARITUSSIO. Secretion and clearance of lung surfactant: a brief review. *Prog. Respir. Res.* 15: 20–26, 1981.
35. CLEMENTS, J. A., A. C. G. PLATZKER, D. F. TIERNEY, C. J. HOBEL, R. K. CREASY, A. J. MARGOLIS, D. W. THIBEAULT, W. H. TOOLEY, AND W. OH. Assessment of the risk of the respiratory-distress syndrome by a rapid test for surfactant in amniotic fluid. *N. Engl. J. Med.* 286: 1077–1081, 1972.
36. CLEMENTS, J. A., AND D. F. TIERNEY. Alveolar instability associated with altered surface tension. In: *Handbook of Physiology. Respiration,* edited by W. O. Fenn and H. Rahn. Washington, DC: Am. Physiol. Soc., 1965, sect. 3, vol. II, chapt. 69, p. 1565–1583.
37. CRAPO, J. D., B. E. BARRY, H. A. FOSCUE, AND J. SHELBURNE. Structural and biochemical changes in rat lungs occurring during exposures to lethal and adaptive doses of oxygen. *Am. Rev. Respir. Dis.* 122: 123–143, 1980.
38. DARKE, A., E. G. FINER, A. G. FLOOK, AND M. C. PHILLIPS. Complex and cluster formation in mixed lecithin cholesterol bilayers, cooperativity of motion in lipid systems. *FEBS Lett.* 18: 326–330, 1971.
39. DAVIS, P. J., K. P. COOLBEAR, AND K. M. W. KEOUGH. Differential scanning calorimetric studies of the thermotropic phase behavior of membranes composed of dipalmitoyllecithin and mixed-acid unsaturated lecithins. *Can. J. Biochem.* 58: 851–858, 1980.
40. DE BOER, J., I. J. HERMANS, AND C. A. P. BAKKER. Contribution of alveolar surface lining to lung mechanics. Analysis of in vivo measurements of air- and fluid-filled lungs. *Acta Physiol. Pharmacol. Neerl.* 14: 231–249, 1967.
41. DIAUGUSTINE, R. P. Lung concentric laminar organelle. Hydrolase activity and compositional analysis. *J. Biol. Chem.* 249: 584–593, 1974.
42. EGAN, E. A., R. M. NELSON, AND R. E. OLVER. Lung inflation and alveolar permeability to non-electrolytes in the adult sheep in vivo. *J. Physiol. London* 260: 409–424, 1976.
43. EGAN, E. A., R. E. OLVER, AND L. B. STRANG. Changes in non-electrolyte permeability of alveoli and the absorption of lung liquid at the start of breathing in the lamb. *J. Physiol. London* 244: 161–179, 1975.
44. ENHORNING, G. Pulsating bubble technique for evaluating pulmonary surfactant. *J. Appl. Physiol.: Respirat. Environ. Exercise Physiol.* 43: 198–203, 1977.
45. ENHORNING, G., AND B. ROBERTSON. Lung expansion in the premature rabbit fetus after tracheal deposition of surfactant. *Pediatrics* 50: 58–66, 1972.
46. EVANS, R. W., M. A. WILLIAMS, AND J. TINOCO. Surface viscosities of phospholipids alone and with cholesterol in monolayers at the air-water interface. *Lipids* 15: 524–533, 1980.
47. FARIDY, E. E. Effect of distension on release of surfactant in excised dogs' lungs. *Respir. Physiol.* 27: 99–114, 1976.
48. FARIDY, E. E. Fetal lung development in surgically induced prolonged gestation. *Respir. Physiol.* 45: 153–166, 1981.
49. FARRELL, E. E., M. A. COX, J. TORDAY, K. KEOUGH, M. ANTON, AND H. W. TAEUSCH. Criteria for exogenous surfactants (Abstract). *Pediatr. Res.* 15: 718, 1981.
50. FINLEY, T. N., W. H. TOOLEY, E. W. SWENSON, R. E. GARDNER, AND J. A. CLEMENTS. Pulmonary surface tension in experimental atelectasis. *Am. Rev. Respir. Dis.* 89: 372–378, 1964.
51. FISHER, H. K., M. H. HYMAN, AND S. J. ASHCRAFT. Alveolar surfactant phospholipids are not cleared via trachea (Abstract). *Federation Proc.* 38: 1373, 1979.
52. FLORENCE, R. T., AND W. D. HARKINS. Molecular interaction in mixed monolayers. II. Unstable mixtures with unsaturated fatty acids. *J. Chem. Phys.* 6: 856–860, 1938.
53. FUJIWARA, T., H. MAETA, S. CHIDA, AND T. MORITA. Surface properties of artificial surfactant in comparison with natural

and synthetic surfactant lipids (Abstract). *IRCS Med. Sci.* 7: 311, 1979.
54. FUJIWARA, T., H. MAETA, S. CHIDA, AND T. MORITA. Improved lung-thorax compliance and prevention of neonatal pulmonary lesion in prematurely delivered rabbit neonates subjected to IPPV after tracheal instillation of artificial surfactant (Abstract). *IRCS Med. Sci.* 7: 313, 1979.
55. FUJIWARA, T., H. MAETA, S. CHIDA, T. MORITA, Y. WATABE, AND T. ABE. Artificial surfactant therapy in hyaline membrane disease. *Lancet* 1: 55–59, 1980.
56. GAINES, G. L. *Insoluble Monolayers at Liquid-Gas Interfaces.* New York: Wiley, 1966.
57. GEIGER, K., M. L. GALLAGHER, AND J. HEDLEY-WHYTE. Cellular distribution and clearance of aerosolized dipalmitoyl lecithin. *J. Appl. Physiol.* 39: 759–766, 1975.
58. GERSHFELD, N. L. Thermodynamics and experimental methods for equilibrium studies with lipid monolayers. In: *Methods in Membrane Biology,* edited by E. D. Korn. New York: Plenum, 1974, p. 69–104.
59. GIL, J., H. BACHOFEN, P. GEHR, AND E. R. WEIBEL. Alveolar volume-surface area relation in air- and saline-filled lungs fixed by vascular perfusion. *J. Appl. Physiol.: Respirat. Environ. Exercise Physiol.* 47: 990–1001, 1979.
60. GIL, J., AND O. K. REISS. Isolation and characterization of lamellar bodies and tubular myelin from rat lung homogenates. *J. Cell Biol.* 58: 152–171, 1973.
61. GIL, J., AND E. R. WEIBEL. Morphological study of pressure-volume hysteresis in rat lungs fixed by vascular perfusion. *Respir. Physiol.* 15: 190–213, 1972.
62. GILBERT, D. B., C. TANFORD, AND J. A. REYNOLDS. Cholesterol in aqueous solution: hydrophobicity and self-association. *Biochemistry* 14: 444–448, 1975.
63. GLATZ, T. H., M. IKEGAMI, AND A. JOBE. Degradation and reutilization of alveolar surfactant (Abstract). *Pediatr. Res.* 14: 642, 1980.
64. GOERKE, J. Lung surfactant. *Biochim. Biophys. Acta* 344: 241–261, 1974.
65. GOERKE, J. Factors affecting adsorption of lipids related to lung surfactant at the air-water interface (Abstract). *Physiologist* 24(4): 104, 1981.
66. GOERKE, J., AND J. GONZALES. Temperature dependence of dipalmitoyl phosphatidylcholine monolayer stability. *J. Appl. Physiol.: Respirat. Environ. Exercise Physiol.* 51: 1108–1114, 1981.
67. GOERKE, J., H. H. HARPER, AND M. BOROWITZ. The interaction of calcium with monolayers of stearic and oleic acid. In: *Surface Chemistry of Biological Systems,* edited by M. Blank. New York: Plenum, 1970, p. 23–35.
68. GOLDFISCHER, S., Y. KIKKAWA, AND L. HOFFMAN. The demonstration of acid hydrolase activities in the inclusion bodies of type II alveolar cells and other lysosomes in the rabbit lung. *J. Histochem. Cytochem.* 16: 102–109, 1968.
69. GRANT, C. W. M., S. HONG-WEI WU, AND H. M. MCCONNELL. Lateral phase separations in binary lipid mixtures: correlation between spin label and freeze-fracture electron microscopic studies. *Biochim. Biophys. Acta* 363: 151–158, 1974.
70. GROSS, N. J. Mechanical properties of mouse lungs: effects of degassing on normal, hyperoxic, and irradiated lungs. *J. Appl. Physiol.: Respirat. Environ. Exercise Physiol.* 51: 391–398, 1981.
71. GRUENWALD, P., R. P. JOHNSON, R. F. HUSTEAD, AND J. A. CLEMENTS. Correlation of mechanical properties of infant lungs with surface activity of extracts. *Proc. Soc. Exp. Biol. Med.* 109: 369–371, 1962.
72. HALLMAN, M., B. L. EPSTEIN, AND L. GLUCK. Analysis of labeling and clearance of lung surfactant phospholipids in rabbit. Evidence of bi-directional surfactant flux between lamellar bodies and alveolar lavage. *J. Clin. Invest.* 68: 742–751, 1981.
73. HALLMAN, M., T. A. MERRITT, H. SCHNEIDER, B. L. EPSTEIN,

F. MANNINO, D. K. EDWARDS, AND L. GLUCK. Isolation of human surfactant from amniotic fluid and a pilot study of its efficacy in respiratory distress syndrome. *Pediatrics* 71: 473–482, 1983.

74. HASSETT, R. J., R. L. SANDERS, A. E. VATTER, AND O. K. REISS. Lamellar bodies: isolation from rat lung, stability and conversion to tubular myelin figures (Abstract). *Federation Proc.* 36: 615, 1977.

75. HAUSER, H., C. HINCKLEY, J. KREBS, B. LEVINE, M. PHILLIPS, AND R. WILLIAMS. The interaction of ions with phosphatidylcholine bilayers. *Biochim. Biophys. Acta* 468: 364–377, 1977.

76. HAUSER, H., AND M. C. PHILLIPS. Ion-binding to phospholipids. Interaction of calcium and lanthanide ions with phosphatidylcholine (lecithin) *Eur. J. Biochem.* 58: 133–144, 1975.

77. HAWCO, M. W., K. P. COOLBEAR, P. J. DAVIS, AND K. M. W. KEOUGH. Exclusion of fluid lipid during compression of monolayers of mixtures of dipalmitoylphosphatidylcholine with some other phosphatidylcholines. *Biochim. Biophys. Acta* 646: 185–187, 1981.

78. HAWCO, M. W., P. J. DAVIS, AND K. M. W. KEOUGH. Lipid fluidity in lung surfactant: monolayers of saturated and unsaturated lecithins. *J. Appl. Physiol.: Respirat. Environ. Exercise Physiol.* 51: 509–515, 1981.

79. HEATH, M. F., AND W. JACOBSON. Phospholipases A1 and A2 in lamellar inclusion bodies of the alveolar epithelium of rabbit lung. *Biochim. Biophys. Acta* 441: 443–452, 1976.

80. HILDEBRAN, J. N., J. GOERKE, AND J. A. CLEMENTS. Pulmonary surface film stability and composition. *J. Appl. Physiol.: Respirat. Environ. Exercise Physiol.* 47: 604–611, 1979.

81. HILDEBRAN, J. N., J. GOERKE, AND J. A. CLEMENTS. Surfactant release in excised rat lung is stimulated by air inflation. *J. Appl. Physiol.: Respirat. Environ. Exercise Physiol.* 51: 905–910, 1981.

82. HILLS, B. A. What is the true role of surfactant in the lung? *Thorax* 36: 1–4, 1981.

84. HORN, L. W. Evaluation of some alternative mechanisms for interface-related stress relaxation in lung. *Respir. Physiol.* 34: 345–357, 1978.

85. HORN, L. W., AND S. H. DAVIS. Apparent surface tension hysteresis of a dynamical system. *J. Colloid Interface Sci.* 51: 459–476, 1975.

86. IKEGAMI, M., T. HESTERBERG, M. NOZAKI, AND F. H. ADAMS. Restoration of lung pressure-volume characteristics with surfactant: comparison of nebulization versus instillation and natural versus synthetic surfactant. *Pediatr. Res.* 11: 178–182, 1977.

87. IKEGAMI, M., A. JOBE, AND T. GLATZ. Surface activity following natural surfactant treatment in premature lambs. *J. Appl. Physiol.: Respirat. Environ. Exercise Physiol.* 51: 306–312, 1981.

88. IKEGAMI, M., A. H. JOBE, AND H. C. JACOBS. Characterization of a protein from immature lambs that inhibits surfactant function (Abstract). *Clin. Res.* 31: 141, 1983.

89. ITO, T., AND S. I. OHNISHI. Ca²⁺-induced lateral phase separations in phosphatidic acid-phosphatidylcholine membranes. *Biochim. Biophys. Acta* 352: 29–37, 1974.

90. ITO, T., S. OHNISHI, M. ISHINAGA, AND M. KITO. Synthesis of a new phosphatidylserine spin-label and calcium-induced lateral phase separation in phosphatidylserine-phosphatidylcholine membranes. *Biochemistry* 14: 3064–3069, 1975.

91. JACOB, J., M. HALLMAN, AND L. GLUCK. Phosphatidylinositol (PI) and phosphatidylglycerol (PG) enhance surface properties of lecithin (PC) (Abstract). *Pediatr. Res.* 14: 644, 1980.

92. JACOB, J., M. HALLMAN, AND L. GLUCK. The effect of phosphatidylglycerol (PG) and phosphatidyl inositol (PI) on dipalmitoyl lecithin (DPPC) monolayer (Abstract). *Pediatr. Res.* 14: 644, 1980.

93. KING, R. J., AND J. A. CLEMENTS. Surface active materials from dog lung. I. Method of isolation. *Am. J. Physiol.* 223: 707–714, 1972.

94. KING, R. J., AND J. A. CLEMENTS. Surface active materials from dog lung. II. Composition and physiological correlations. *Am. J. Physiol.* 223: 715–726, 1972.

95. KING, R. J., AND J. A. CLEMENTS. Surface active materials from dog lung. III. Thermal analysis. *Am. J. Physiol.* 223: 727–733, 1972.

96. KING, R. J., AND J. A. CLEMENTS. Lipid synthesis and surfactant turnover in the lungs. In: *Handbook of Physiology. Circulation and Nonrespiratory Functions*, edited by A. P. Fishman and A. B. Fisher. Bethesda, MD: Am. Physiol. Soc., 1985, sect. 3, vol. I, chapt. 8, p. 309–336.

97. KING, R. J., AND M. C. MACBETH. Physicochemical properties of dipalmitoyl phosphatidylcholine after interaction with an apoprotein of pulmonary surfactant. *Biochim. Biophys. Acta* 557: 86–101, 1979.

98. KING, R. J., AND M. C. MACBETH. Interaction of the lipid and protein components of pulmonary surfactant. Role of phosphatidylglycerol and calcium. *Biochim. Biophys. Acta* 647: 159–168, 1981.

99. KING, R. J., H. MARTIN, D. MITTS, AND F. M. HOLMSTROM. Metabolism of the apoproteins in pulmonary surfactant. *J. Appl. Physiol.: Respirat. Environ. Exercise Physiol.* 42: 483–491, 1977.

100. KITTERMAN, J. A., P. L. BALLARD, J. A. CLEMENTS, E. J. MESCHER, AND W. H. TOOLEY. Tracheal fluid in fetal lambs: spontaneous decrease prior to birth. *J. Appl. Physiol.: Respirat. Environ. Exercise Physiol.* 47: 985–989, 1979.

101. KLASS, D. J. Dibutyryl cyclic GMP and hyperventilation promote rat lung phospholipid release. *J. Appl. Physiol.: Respirat. Environ. Exercise Physiol.* 47: 285–289, 1979.

102. KNOEBEL, L. K. Secretion and action of digestive juices; absorption. In: *Physiology* (4th ed.), edited by E. W. Selkurt. Boston, MA: Little, Brown, 1976, p. 654–658.

103. LAU, M.-J., AND K. M. W. KEOUGH. Lipid composition of lung and lung lavage fluid from map turtles (*Malaclemys geographica*) maintained at different environmental temperatures. *Can. J. Biochem.* 59: 208–219, 1981.

104. LEE, A. G. Lipid phase transitions and phase diagrams: mixtures involving lipids. *Biochim. Biophys. Acta* 472: 285–344, 1977.

105. LEMPERT, J., AND P. T. MACKLEM. Effect of temperature on rabbit lung surfactant and pressure-volume hysteresis. *J. Appl. Physiol.* 31: 380–385, 1971.

106. MAGOON, M. W., A. G. BARITUSSIO, J. GOERKE, AND J. A. CLEMENTS. Precursor-product (PP) relationship between rabbit type II cell lamellar bodies (LB) and alveolar surface active material (SAM) and SAM turnover time (τ) (Abstract). *Federation Proc.* 40: 407, 1981.

107. MAGOON, M. W., J. R. WRIGHT, A. BARITUSSIO, M. C. WILLIAMS, J. GOERKE, B. J. BENSON, R. L. HAMILTON, AND J. A. CLEMENTS. Subfractionation of lung surfactant. Implication for metabolism and surface activity. *Biochim. Biophys. Acta* 750: 18–31, 1983.

108. MASON, R. J. Lipid metabolism. In: *Lung Biology in Health and Disease. The Biochemical Basis of Pulmonary Function*, edited by R. G. Crystal. New York: Dekker, 1976, vol. 2, p. 127–169.

109. MASSARO, D. Clinical implications of the effect of breathing pattern on the lung. *Am. Thorac. Soc. News* 6: 30–35, 1980.

110. MASSARO, D., L. CLERCH, AND G. D. MASSARO. Effect of temperature and ventilatory rate of excised rat lungs on aggregation of surfactant (Abstract). *Federation Proc.* 39: 1065, 1980.

111. MASSARO, D., L. CLERCH, AND G. D. MASSARO. Surfactant aggregation in rat lungs: influence of temperature and ventilation. *J. Appl. Physiol.: Respirat. Environ. Exercise Physiol.* 51: 646–653, 1981.

112. McBAIN, J. W., AND C. W. HUMPHREYS. The microtome method of the determination of the absolute amount of adsorption. *J. Phys. Chem.* 36: 300–311, 1932.

113. McCLENAHAN, J. B., R. MUSSENDEN, AND J. D. OHLSEN.

Effect of ethanol on surfactant of ventilated lungs. *J. Appl. Physiol.* 27: 90–95, 1969.

114. MCCLENAHAN, J. B., AND A. URTNOWSKI. Effect of ventilation on surfactant, and its turnover rate. *J. Appl. Physiol.* 23: 215–220, 1967.

115. MCLEAN, L. R., AND M. C. PHILLIPS. Mechanism of cholesterol and phosphatidylcholine exchange or transfer between unilamellar vesicles. *Biochemistry* 20: 2893–2900, 1981.

116. MEAD, J., AND C. COLLIER. Relation of volume history of lungs to respiratory mechanics in anesthetized dogs. *J. Appl. Physiol.* 14: 669–678, 1959.

117. MEAD, J., J. L. WHITTENBERGER, AND E. P. RADFORD, JR. Surface tension as a factor in pulmonary volume-pressure hysteresis. *J. Appl. Physiol.* 10: 191–196, 1957.

118. MEBAN, C. Surface viscosity of surfactant films from human lungs. *Respir. Physiol.* 33: 219–227, 1978.

119. MEBAN, C. Physical properties of surfactant from the lungs of the tortoise *Testudo hermanni. Comp. Biochem. Physiol. A* 67: 253–257, 1980.

120. MEBAN, C. Surface elastic properties of surfactant from the lungs of neonatal pigs. *Biol. Neonate* 37: 308–312, 1980.

121. MEBAN, C. Effect of lipids and other substances on the adsorption of dipalmitoyl phosphatidylcholine. *Pediatr. Res.* 15: 1029–1031, 1981.

122. METCALFE, I. L., G. ENHORNING, AND F. POSSMAYER. Pulmonary surfactant-associated proteins: their role in the expression of surface activity. *J. Appl. Physiol.: Respirat. Environ. Exercise Physiol.* 49: 34–41, 1980.

123. MORLEY, C. J., A. D. BANGHAM, P. JOHNSON, G. D. THORBURN, AND G. JENKIN. Physical and physiological properties of dry lung surfactant. *Nature London* 271: 162–163, 1978.

124. MORLEY, C. J., A. D. BANGHAM, N. MILLER, AND J. A. DAVIS. Dry artificial lung surfactant and its effect on very premature babies. *Lancet* 1: 64–68, 1981.

125. MORLEY, C., B. ROBERTSON, B. LACHMANN, R. NILSSON, A. BANGHAM, G. GROSSMANN, AND N. MILLER. Artificial surfactant and natural surfactant. Comparative study of the effects on premature rabbit lungs. *Arch. Dis. Child.* 55: 758–765, 1980.

126. MORRIS, G. S., J. A. THLIVERIS, AND E. E. FARIDY. Development of fetal rat lung during prolonged gestation. *Respir. Physiol.* 42: 263–285, 1980.

127. MUNDER, J. W., AND J. SWARBRICK. Time-dependent surface behavior of dipalmitoyllecithin and lung alveolar surfactant monolayers. *Biochim. Biophys. Acta* 291: 344–350, 1973.

129. NIELSON, D. W., J. GOERKE, AND J. A. CLEMENTS. Alveolar subphase pH in the lungs of anesthetized rabbits. *Proc. Natl. Acad. Sci. USA* 78: 7119–7123, 1981.

130. NOTTER, R. H., S. HOLCOMB, AND R. D. MAVIS. Dynamic surface properties of phosphatidylglycerol-dipalmitoyl phosphatidylcholine mixed films. *Chem. Phys. Lipids* 27: 305–319, 1980.

131. NOTTER, R. H., AND R. D. MAVIS. Surface tension hysteresis in lung surfactant films: etiology and physiologic consequence (Abstract). *Pediatr. Res.* 15: 728, 1981.

132. NOTTER, R. H., AND P. E. MORROW. Pulmonary surfactant: a surface chemistry viewpoint. *Ann. Biomed. Eng.* 3: 119–159, 1975.

133. NOTTER, R. H., D. L. SHAPIRO, R. TAUBOLD, AND J. CHEN. Bilirubin interactions with phospholipid components of lung surfactant. *Pediatr. Res.* 16: 130–136, 1982.

134. NOTTER, R. H., S. A. TABAK, S. HOLCOMB, AND R. D. MAVIS. Postcollapse dynamic surface pressure relaxation in binary surface films containing dipalmitoyl phosphatidylcholine. *J. Colloid Interface Sci.* 74: 370–377, 1980.

135. NOTTER, R. H., S. A. TABAK, AND R. D. MAVIS. Surface properties of binary mixtures of some pulmonary surfactant components. *J. Lipid Res.* 21: 10–22, 1980.

136. NOTTER, R. H., R. TAUBOLD, AND R. D. MAVIS. Hysteresis in saturated phospholipid films and its potential relevance for

lung function in vivo. *Exp. Lung Res.* 3: 109–127, 1982.

137. O'HARE, K. H., J. K. NEWMAN, A. E. VATTER, AND O. K. REISS. Esterases in developing and adult rat lung. II. An electrophoretic analysis. *J. Histochem. Cytochem.* 19: 116–123, 1971.

138. O'HARE, K. H., O. K. REISS, AND A. E. VATTER. Esterases in developing and adult rat lung. I. Biochemical and electron microscopic observations. *J. Histochem. Cytochem.* 19: 97–115, 1971.

139. OLVER, R. E. Ion transport and water flow in the mammalian lung. In: *Lung Liquids*, edited by R. Porter and M. O'Connor. New York: Elsevier, 1976, p. 199–209. (Ciba Found. Symp. 38.)

140. OLVER, R. E., E. E. SCHNEEBERGER, AND D. V. WALTERS. Epithelial solute permeability, ion transport and tight junction morphology in the developing lung of the foetal lamb. *J. Physiol. London* 315: 395–412, 1981.

141. OLVER, R. E., AND L. B. STRANG. Ion fluxes across the pulmonary epithelium and the secretion of lung liquid in the foetal lamb. *J. Physiol. London.* 241: 327–357, 1974.

142. OYARZÚN, M. J., AND J. A. CLEMENTS. Ventilatory and cholinergic control of pulmonary surfactant in the rabbit. *J. Appl. Physiol.: Respirat. Environ. Exercise Physiol.* 43: 39–45, 1977.

143. OYARZÚN, M. J., J. A. CLEMENTS, AND A. BARITUSSIO. Ventilation enhances pulmonary alveolar clearance of radioactive dipalmitoyl phosphatidylcholine in liposomes. *Am. Rev. Respir. Dis.* 121: 709–721, 1980.

144. PATTLE, R. E. Properties, function and origin of the alveolar lining layer. *Nature London* 175: 1125–1127, 1955.

145. PATTLE, R. E. Properties, function, and origin of the alveolar lining layer. *Proc. R. Soc. London Ser. B* 148: 217–240, 1958.

146. PATTLE, R. E. Slow collapse in vitro of the alveolar lining film. *J. Physiol. London* 284: 101–102, 1978.

147. PATTLE, R. E., C. SCHOCK, AND J. BATTENSBY. Some effects of anaesthetics on lung surfactant. *Br. J. Anaesth.* 44: 1119–1127, 1972.

148. PAUL, G. W., R. J. HASSETT, AND O. K. REISS. Formation of lung surfactant films from intact lamellar bodies. *Proc. Natl. Acad. Sci. USA* 74: 3617–3620, 1977.

149. PHILLIPS, M. C., AND D. CHAPMAN. Monolayer characteristics of saturated 1,2-diacyl phosphatidylcholines (lecithins) and phosphatidylethanolamines at the air-water interface. *Biochim. Biophys. Acta* 163: 301–313, 1968.

150. PHILLIPS, M. C., AND E. G. FINER. The stoichiometry and dynamics of lecithin-cholesterol clusters in bilayer membranes. *Biochim. Biophys. Acta* 356: 199–206, 1974.

151. PHILLIPS, M. C., D. E. GRAHAM, AND H. HAUSER. Lateral compressibility and penetration into phospholipid monolayers and bilayer membranes. *Nature London* 254: 154–156, 1975.

152. PHILLIPS, M. C., AND H. HAUSER. Spreading of solid glycerides and phospholipids at the air-water interface. *J. Colloid Interface Sci.* 49: 31–39, 1974.

153. PLATZKER, A. C. G., J. A. KITTERMAN, E. J. MESCHER, J. A. CLEMENTS, AND W. H. TOOLEY. Surfactant in the lung and tracheal fluid of the fetal lamb and acceleration of its appearance by dexamethasone. *Pediatrics* 56: 554–561, 1975.

154. RABINOVITCH, W., R. F. ROBERTSON, AND S. G. MASON. Relaxation of surface pressure and collapse of unimolecular films of stearic acid. *Can. J. Chem.* 38: 1881–1890, 1960.

155. RABINOWITZ, J. L., T. CARDWELL, AND D. J. P. BASSETT. Reutilization of fatty acid carbons for lung lipid synthesis. *Am. J. Physiol.* 240 (*Endocrinol. Metab.* 3): E435–E440, 1981.

156. RADFORD, E. P., JR. Method for estimating respiratory surface area of mammalian lungs from their physical characteristics. *Proc. Soc. Exp. Biol. Med.* 87: 58–61, 1954.

157. RADFORD, E. P., JR. Recent studies of mechanical properties of mammalian lungs. In: *Tissue Elasticity*, edited by J. W. Remington. Washington, DC: Am. Physiol. Soc., 1957, p. 177–190.

158. REIFENRATH, R. Chemical analysis of the lung alveolar surfactant obtained by alveolar micropuncture. *Respir. Physiol.*

19: 35–46, 1973.

159. RIES, H. E., JR., M. MATSUMOTO, N. UYEDA, AND E. SUITO. Electron microscopic studies of monolayers of lecithin. *Adv. Chem. Ser.* 144: 286–293, 1975.

160. ROBERTSON, B. Lung surfactant for replacement therapy. *Clin. Physiol.* 3: 97–110, 1983.

162. RYAN, S. F., S. A. HASHIM, G. CERNANSKY, C. R. BARRETT, JR., A. L. L. BELL, JR., AND D. F. LIAU. Quantification of surfactant phospholipids in the dog lung. *J. Lipid Res.* 21: 1004–1014, 1980.

163. SAID, S. I., C. M. BANERJEE, W. R. HARLAN, JR., AND M. E. AVERY. Pulmonary edema as a cause of surfactant deficiency. *Jpn. Heart J.* 8: 742–744, 1967.

164. SANDERS, R. L., R. J. HASSETT, AND A. E. VATTER. Isolation of lung lamellar bodies and their conversion to tubular myelin figures in vitro. *Anat. Rec.* 198: 485–501, 1980.

165. SANDERSON, R. J., AND A. E. VATTER. A mode of formation of tubular myelin from lamellar bodies in the lung. *J. Cell Biol.* 74: 1027–1031, 1977.

166. SCARPELLI, E. M., S. CONDORELLI, G. COLACICCO, AND E. V. COSMI. Lamb fetal pulmonary fluid. II. Fate of phosphatidylcholine. *Pediatr. Res.* 9: 195–201, 1975.

167. SCHULMAN, J. H., AND A. H. HUGHES. Monolayers of proteolytic enzymes and proteins. IV. Mixed monolayer films. *Biochem. J.* 29: 1243–1252, 1935.

168. SCHÜRCH, S. Surface tension at low lung volumes: dependence on time and alveolar size. *Respir. Physiol.* 48: 339–355, 1982.

169. SCHÜRCH, S., J. GOERKE, AND J. A. CLEMENTS. Direct determination of surface tension in the lung. *Proc. Natl. Acad. Sci. USA* 73: 4698–4702, 1976.

170. SCHÜRCH, S., J. GOERKE, AND J. A. CLEMENTS. Direct determination of volume- and time-dependence of alveolar surface tension in excised lungs. *Proc. Natl. Acad. Sci. USA* 75: 3417–3421, 1978.

171. SCHÜRCH, S., AND D. J. L. McIVER. Surface tension at low lung volumes: dependence on time and alveolar size (Abstract). *Biophys. J.* 33, pt. 2: 201, 1981.

172. SCHÜRCH, S. F., AND M. R. ROACH. Interference of bronchographic agents with lung surfactant. *Respir. Physiol.* 28: 99–117, 1976.

173. SEKULIC, S. M., J. HAMLIN, R. ELLISON, AND L. ELLISON. Pulmonary surfactant and lung circulation in experimental atelectasis. *Am. Rev. Respir. Dis.* 97: 69–75, 1968.

174. SHANNON, D. C., H. KAZEMI, E. W. MERRILL, K. A. SMITH, AND P. S.-L. WONG. Restoration of volume-pressure curves with a lecithin fog. *J. Appl. Physiol.* 28: 470–473, 1970.

175. SLAMA, H., W. SCHOEDEL, AND E. HANSEN. Bestimmung der Oberflächeneigenschaften von Stoffen aus den Lungenalveolen mit einer Blasenmethode. *Pfluegers Arch.* 322: 355–363, 1971.

176. SLAMA, H., W. SCHOEDEL, AND E. HANSEN. Lung surfactant: film kinetics at the surface of an air bubble during prolonged oscillation of its volume. *Respir. Physiol.* 19: 233–243, 1973.

177. SMITH, R., AND C. TANFORD. The critical micelle concentration of L-α-dipalmitoylphosphatidylcholine in water and water-methanol solutions. *J. Mol. Biol.* 67: 75–83, 1972.

178. SMYTH, J. A., I. L. METCALFE, P. DUFFTY, F. POSSMAYER, M. H. BRYAN, AND G. ENHORNING. Hyaline membrane disease treated with bovine surfactant. *Pediatrics* 71: 913–917, 1983.

179. STEIM, J. Synthetic substitutes for surfactant. In: *Lung Maturation and the Prevention of Hyaline Membrane Disease*, edited by T. D. Moore. Columbus, OH: Ross Labs., 1976, p. 51–53.

180. TABAK, S. A., R. H. NOTTER, J. S. ULTMAN, AND S. M. DINH. Relaxation effects in the surface pressure behavior of dipalmitoyl lecithin. *J. Colloid Interface Sci.* 60: 117–125, 1977.

181. TAJIMA, K., AND N. L. GERSHFELD. Detection of low levels of lipid contamination of lecithin by equilibrium spreading pressures. *J. Colloid Interface Sci.* 81: 283–284, 1981.

182. TAYLOR, F. B., AND M. E. ABRAMS. Effect of surface active lipoprotein on clotting and fibrinolysis, and of fibrinogen on surface tension of surface active lipoprotein. *Am. J. Med.* 40: 346–350, 1966.

183. THET, L. A., L. CLERCH, G. D. MASSARO, AND D. MASSARO. Changes in sedimentation of surfactant in ventilated excised rat lungs. Physical alterations in surfactant associated with the development and reversal of atelectasis. *J. Clin. Invest.* 64: 600–608, 1979.

184. THOMPSON, W. K., B. E. MARCHAK, A. B. FROESE, AND A. C. BRYAN. High-frequency oscillation compared with standard ventilation in pulmonary injury model. *J. Appl. Physiol.: Respirat. Environ. Exercise Physiol.* 52: 543–548, 1982.

185. TIERNEY, D. F., J. A. CLEMENTS, AND H. J. TRAHAN. Rates of replacement of lecithins and alveolar instability in rat lungs. *Am. J. Physiol.* 213: 671–676, 1967.

186. TRAEUBLE, H., H. EIBL, AND H. SAWADA. Respiration—a critical phenomenon? Lipid phase transitions in the lung alveolar surfactant. *Naturwissenschaften* 61: 344–354, 1974.

187. TRURNIT, H. J. A theory and method for the spreading of protein monolayers. *J. Colloid Sci.* 15: 1–13, 1960.

188. VALBERG, P. A., AND J. D. BRAIN. Lung surface tension and air space dimensions from multiple pressure-volume curves. *J. Appl. Physiol.: Respirat. Environ. Exercise Physiol.* 43: 730–738, 1977.

189. VAWTER, D. L., Y. C. FUNG, AND J. B. WEST. Elasticity of excised dog lung parenchyma. *J. Appl. Physiol.: Respirat. Environ. Exercise Physiol.* 45: 261–269, 1978.

190. VAWTER, D. L., Y. C. FUNG, AND J. B. WEST. Constitutive equation of lung tissue elasticity. *J. Biomech. Eng.* 101: 38–45, 1979.

191. VERVERGAERT, P. H. J. T., B. DE KRUYFF, A. J. VERKLEIJ, J. F. TOCANNE, AND L. L. M. VAN DEENEN. Calorimetric and freeze-etch study of the influence of Mg^{2+} on the thermotropic behaviour of phosphatidylglycerol. *Chem. Phys. Lipids.* 14: 97–101, 1975.

192. VILALLONGA, F. Surface chemistry of L-alpha-dipalmitoyl lecithin at the air-water interface. *Biochim. Biophys. Acta* 163: 290–300, 1968.

192a. VON NEERGAARD, K. Neue Auffassungen über einen Grundbegriff der Atemmechanik. Die Retractionskraft der Lunge, abhängig von der Oberflaechenspannung in den Alveolen. *Z. Gesamte. Exp. Med.* 66: 373–394, 1929.

193. WATKINS, J. C. The surface properties of pure phospholipids in relation to those of lung extracts. *Biochim. Biophys. Acta* 152: 293–306, 1968.

194. WEIBEL, E. R., G. S. KISTLER, AND G. TOENDURY. A stereologic electron microscope study of "tubular myelin figures" in alveolar fluids of rat lungs. *Z. Zellforsch. Mikrosk. Anat.* 69: 418–427, 1966.

195. WEIBEL, E. R., P. UNTERSEE, J. GIL, AND M. ZULAUF. Morphometric estimation of pulmonary diffusion capacity. VI. Effect of varying positive pressure inflation of air spaces. *Respir. Physiol.* 18: 285–308, 1973.

196. WILLIAMS, J. V., D. F. TIERNEY, AND H. R. PARKER. Surface forces in the lung, atelectasis, and transpulmonary pressure. *J. Appl. Physiol.* 21: 819–827, 1966.

197. WILLIAMS, M. C. Conversion of lamellar body membranes into tubular myelin in alveoli of fetal rat lungs. *J. Cell Biol.* 72: 260–277, 1977.

198. WILLIAMS, M. C. Freeze-fracture studies of tubular myelin and lamellar bodies in fetal and adult rat lungs. *J. Ultrastruct. Res.* 64: 352–361, 1978.

199. WILLIAMS, M. C., AND B. J. BENSON. Immunocytochemical localization and identification of the major surfactant protein in adult rat lung. *J. Histochem. Cytochem.* 29: 291–305, 1981.

200. WILSON, T. A. Relations among recoil pressure, surface area, and surface tension in the lung. *J. Appl. Physiol.: Respirat. Environ. Exercise Physiol.* 50: 921–926, 1981.

201. WILSON, T. A. Surface tension-surface area curves calculated from pressure-volume loops. *J. Appl. Physiol.: Respirat. Environ. Exercise Physiol.* 53: 1512–1520, 1982.

203. WOO, S. W., W. BERLIN, U. BUECH, AND J. HEDLEY-WHITE. Altered perfusion, ventilation, anesthesia and lung-surface forces in dogs. *Anesthesiology* 33: 411–418, 1970.

204. WOODSIDE, G. L., AND A. J. DALTON. The ultrastructure of lung tissue from newborn and embryo mice. *J. Ultrastruct.*

Res. 2: 28–54, 1958.

205. WYSZOGRODSKI, I., K. KYEI-ABOAGYE, H. W. TAEUSCH, JR., AND M. E. AVERY. Surfactant inactivation by hyperventilation: conservation by end-expiratory pressure. *J. Appl. Physiol.* 38: 461–466, 1975.

206. YOUNG, S. L., D. F. TIERNEY, AND J. A. CLEMENTS. Mechanism of compliance change in excised rat lungs at low transpulmonary pressure. *J. Appl. Physiol.* 29: 780–785, 1970.

CHAPTER 17

Mechanical properties of airway smooth muscle

NEWMAN L. STEPHENS | *Department of Physiology, Faculty of Medicine, University of Manitoba, Winnipeg, Canada*

FREDERIC G. HOPPIN, JR. | *The Memorial Hospital, Brown University, Pawtucket, Rhode Island*

CHAPTER CONTENTS

THE MECHANICAL PROPERTIES of airway smooth muscle are emphasized in this chapter. These properties have been reviewed in the literature (36, 43, 51, 52, 54). They share many similarities with properties of striated muscle and are readily described by conventional parameters, as is discussed in this chapter. Recent advances in our understanding of the ultrastructure, subcellular mechanisms, and contractile and regulatory protein biochemistry of smooth muscle in general indicate that, although strong similarities exist between striated and smooth muscles, there are differences in the manner that muscle function is regulated. For example, it is now known that in smooth muscle calcium-sensitive regulation of contraction is not mediated via a tropomyosin-troponin system but by a calmodulin-mediated, myosin-linked light chain phosphorylation mechanism (12, 16, 33). Thus the molecular mechanism to be studied in attempting to understand disorders of smooth muscle relaxation, for example, which occur in allergic bronchospasm (48), may be quite different from that in striated muscle.

Much of the work in this chapter is based on studies of canine tracheal smooth muscle. There is evidence that it serves as a model for airway smooth muscle in general (51) down to the level of the sixth generation. The properties of airway smooth muscle from peripheral airways have not been directly studied, but some information about them is available from in vivo or in situ experiments and from studies of lung strips.

AIRWAY SMOOTH MUSCLE

Traditionally two modes of function of smooth muscle are distinguished, that of supporting loads over a range of lengths and that of shortening at different velocities under different loads. It is probably important also to understand how airway smooth muscle behaves in circumstances where its length is rapidly changed by breathing maneuvers.

(Following the practice of the literature on muscles, we use the terms *tension* and *force* interchangeably throughout this chapter. The units are dynes or grams multiplied by the acceleration due to gravity.)

Functional characterization, then, centers on the tension developed with stimulation at a given length (*l*), the dependence of developed tension on velocity, and the tensions during imposed length changes. The properties of tracheal smooth muscle under these several circumstances are emphasized in this chapter.

Length-Tension Relationships

GENERAL CONSIDERATIONS. Measurement of the force developed with activation over a range of lengths provides information about the ability of the muscle to stiffen and support loads. Figure 1 shows isometric

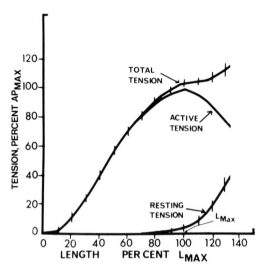

FIG. 1. Mean length-tension curves of canine tracheal smooth muscle. "Resting tension" curve is obtained after using pharmacological relaxants or by inhibiting energy-producing metabolic processes to preclude any spontaneous resting tone. The shape of this curve is typical of noncontractile biological tissues and results primarily from presence of elastin and collagen. With activation at a given length, tension rises to a level shown by the "total tension" curve. Difference in tension between total and resting curves represents activity of contractile element or force generator of muscle and is replotted as "active tension." It is maximum at a unique length, which is arbitrarily defined as l_o (l_{max}). Note: full curve not shown. *Bars* indicate standard errors. [Adapted from Stephens et al. (55).]

length-tension (P) curves for canine tracheal smooth muscle. By analogy with vascular smooth muscle (40), the initial, compliant portion of the resting-tension curve is probably due to elastin, and the final stiffer portion is due to collagen. Repeated length cycling of the resting muscle induces considerable stress relaxation and narrows the hysteresis loop. The magnitude of stress relaxation is a function of the magnitude of length change and the interval of time it is held isometric at high tensions. Any length change greater than 25% of the muscle's initial unloaded length results in stress relaxation.

In skeletal muscle, l_o is defined as maximum length, but has the additional quality of representing the usual functioning length of the muscle in vivo. Whether this is also true for tracheal smooth muscle has not been determined. The maximum active tetanic tension (P_o) that can be elicited by supramaximal alternating current stimulation in a physiological bath is 1.10 kg· cm^{-2} (or 11.00 N·cm^{-2}) ± 0.059. If a correction is made for noncontractile material (this consists of nucleus and organelles and is ∼40%) in the muscle cell, then P_o increases to 3.34 kg·cm^{-2}. These calculations confirm the observation of Aksoy et al. (3) that the contractile elements of smooth muscle can develop approximately the same force as those of skeletal muscle. On the other hand, tracheal smooth muscle can shorten to ∼10% l_o, whereas striated muscles can shorten only to ∼65%. The responsible mechanisms

in smooth muscle are unknown. The ratio of myosin to actin is less in smooth muscle than in striated muscle, and well-defined sarcomeres have not been described. It may be speculated that the myosin filament in smooth muscle can "crawl" along a set of relatively lengthy actin filaments without running into the limiting Z bands.

In measuring length-tension curves, it must be remembered that the maximum isometric tetanic tension developed at any length is affected by the history of the contraction. Curves for the maximum tensions obtained in a series of contractions at different lengths differ if the contractions are isometric, freeloaded, or afterloaded. Figure 2 shows such curves. The isometric curve differs from the three curves in which shortening occurred.

REDUCED ACTIVATION AT NORMAL CALCIUM CONCENTRATIONS AND AT SHORT LENGTHS. The tensions elicited by supramaximal stimulations of tracheal smooth muscle in a physiological bath are less than the maximum. With the muscle at l_o, a higher calcium concentration (4.75 mM) considerably increases tension (P_o) (Fig. 3), indicating that there is less than full activation at normal calcium concentrations. This is unlike skeletal muscle fibers but is like the response seen in cat papillary muscle (22).

The discrepancy is proportionately greater at shorter lengths. In Figure 4, where tension is normalized by the maximum tension developed at that cal-

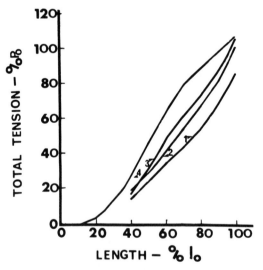

FIG. 2. Mean length–total tension curves elicited in different ways for the tracheal smooth muscle preparations. *Curve 4* is the conventional isometric tetanic length-tension curve, as in Fig. 1. *Curve 3* was obtained from experiments in which the muscle first shortened isotonically from l_o (carrying the preload needed to set it at that length) and then contracted isometrically at a preselected length. *Curve 2* was obtained from conventional afterloaded contractions in which the muscle first contracted isometrically at l_o and then shortened isotonically. *Curve 1* was obtained from freeloaded contractions, in which the muscle was first loaded (and allowed to lengthen in response to the load) before being (isotonically) contracted from the loaded length. [Adapted from Stephens and Van Niekerk (59).]

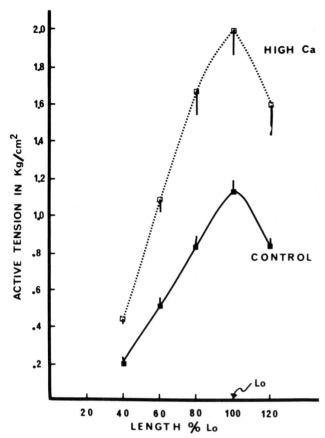

FIG. 3. Mean length-tension curves for tracheal smooth muscle. Ca^{2+} concentration for *upper curve* is 4.75 mM and for *lower curve* is 2.0 mM. *Bars* indicate standard errors. [Adapted from Stephens et al. (58).]

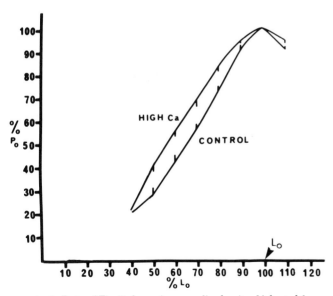

FIG. 4. Data of Fig. 3 shown in normalized units. [Adapted from Stephens et al. (58).]

cium concentration, P_o data show that the two curves differ significantly over the range from 40% l_o to 85% l_o. This difference after adjustment for P_o indicates

that the reduction of activation at physiological concentrations of calcium is even greater when the muscle is short. A similar phenomenon is found in skeletal muscle, and Taylor (61) has described its morphological correlate; at $l < l_o$ the central fibrils of a single amphibian skeletal muscle fiber are wavy, indicating that they are relaxed. This appearance is eliminated by using increased levels of calcium and caffeine and is termed "reduced activation at short lengths."

The mechanism underlying this length-related reduced activation is not known. In skeletal muscles it has been ascribed to the fact that at short lengths the muscle fiber is not only shortened but is also widened, which results in distortion of the T tubule and impairment of excitation-contraction coupling. Indeed, at l_o itself there is no reduced activation. In smooth muscle, however, because there is no T-tubule structure, another explanation must be sought. It is possible that the cells in the middle of the strip are not adequately stimulated in normal calcium concentration, resulting in reduced activation.

Force-Velocity Relationships

AT LOADS LESS THAN MAXIMUM ISOMETRIC TENSION. Measurements of force at various velocities not only provide information regarding the ability of the muscle to support loads but also to shorten and thus do work; they also provide an index of power generation.

Force-velocity curves (curve in Fig. 5) are hyperbolic and can be fitted by Hill's equation (20)

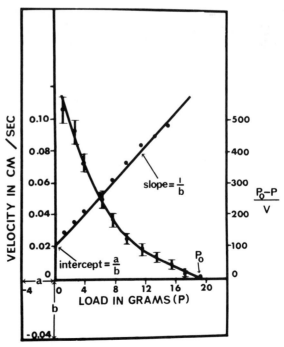

FIG. 5. Mean force-velocity curve of tracheal smooth muscle. All experiments conducted at l_o (l_{max}). *Bars* indicate standard errors. [Adapted from Stephens et al. (55).]

$$(P + a)\ (V + b) = (P_o + a)\ b$$

where V represents velocity, and P_o, a, and b are constants. P_o is the maximum isometric tension, and a and b are the asymptotes of the hyperbola; a has units of force and is an index of numbers of force-generating sites in the cross-sectional area of the muscle; b has units of velocity and is an index of the rate of energy liberation or of actomyosin ATPase activity. The values of a and b can be conveniently obtained from the intercept (a/b) and the slope ($1/b$) of a plot of $(P_o - P)/V$ as a function of P because this represents the linearized transform of

$$(P_o - P)/V = (P/b) + (a/b)$$

The validity of applying this equation to skeletal muscle has been questioned chiefly because the a constant appears to be load dependent. However, Woledge (63) has shown that a is a true constant for smooth muscle.

The velocity of shortening at zero load (V_{max}) is usually extrapolated from data with loads as small as the preload for setting the relaxed muscle at l_o, using either graphical extrapolation or the equation $V_{max} = P_o\ b/a$. Direct measurements have been made using the load clamp of Brutsaert et al. (5), which makes it possible to measure velocity for tracheal smooth muscle down to zero load (N. L. Stephens, unpublished observation); the V_{max} values obtained directly by zero load clamps are not statistically different from those obtained by computation (using the equation given above) from the constants obtained from conventional force-velocity measurements. We conclude, therefore, that in tracheal smooth muscle V_{max} can be accurately measured by either method; the load-clamp technique is much more convenient, however, because it requires only one measurement.

These force-velocity studies show that, although values for P_o are not too dissimilar from those for striated muscle, V_{max} values are much smaller. Table 1 shows force-velocity constants for striated and smooth muscles. After correcting for temperature differences, the conclusion is that tracheal smooth muscle contracts almost 100 times slower than the frog sartorius muscle.

AT LOADS GREATER THAN MAXIMUM ISOMETRIC TENSION. When an active muscle is forcibly lengthened,

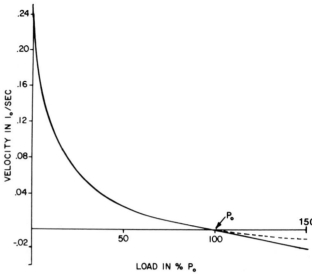

FIG. 6. Mean force-velocity curves elicited during shortening and elongation of activated tracheal smooth muscle. *Broken curve* is extrapolated. [Adapted from Hanks and Stephens (19).]

the load may exceed P_o. This may pertain to airway smooth muscle in vivo during inspiration. It may also occur if contraction is not homogeneous such that parts of the muscle less strongly activated are forcibly lengthened by parts in series with them that are more strongly activated.

Force-velocity curves using quick-release methods, with loads below and above P_o, are shown in Figure 6. The curve for $P < P_o$ is similar to that shown in Figure 5 and was obtained for values of P <150% P_o. At loads >150% P_o, the length changes are too great to permit measurement of maximum velocity of lengthening at constant starting length (l_o). For comparison with the direct measurement, the dashed curve shows an extrapolation based on force-velocity constants obtained from the $P < P_o$ part of the curve. Statistical analysis shows that these two curves are significantly different; the extrapolation is not valid. The force-velocity curve for $P > P_o$ shown here resembles those for the urinary bladder reported by Johansson et al. (24) and skeletal muscle reported by Aubert (4).

Note that at a velocity of lengthening of $\sim 0.03\ l_o \cdot$ s^{-1} the muscle can support a load of 150% P_o, whereas at a similar velocity during shortening the muscle can support a load of only 50% P_o. This testifies to the surprising and considerable strength of the elongating muscle. Measurements of high-energy phosphates [adenosine triphosphate and creatine phosphate] show that the elongating muscle consumes considerably less energy than the shortening muscle at equivalent velocities (19).

Stimulus-Response Relationships

From a practical point of view, stimulus-response relationships are generally elicited to identify maximal stimuli for studies of other mechanical parameters.

TABLE 1. *Dynamic Muscle Constants*

	a, g/cm^2	a/P_o	b, l/s	P_o, kg/cm^2	V_{max}, l/s^*	Ref.
Frog sartorius	399	0.257	0.331	2.0	1.29	20
Cat heart papillary	175	0.22	0.27	0.80	1.24	47
Rabbit uterus		0.44	0.09		0.18	10
Dog trachealis	244	0.21	0.04	1.17	0.17	49

Frog sartorius at 0°C, cat heart muscle at 27°C, pregnant rabbit uterus at 27°C, and canine trachealis at 37°C. P_o, maximum tension; l, muscle length; a, constant with units of force; b, constant with units of velocity. * $V_{max} = P_o\ b/a$. [Adapted from Stephens et al. (55).]

The most convenient electrical stimulus to use is 60 Hz AC. A current density of 400 mA·cm^{-2} is 10% greater than the maximal stimulus. With this density, once the muscle has been equilibrated for 2 h in Krebs-Henseleit solution aerated with 95% O_2 and 5% CO_2 (P_{O_2} 660 Torr, P_{CO_2} 40 Torr, and pH 7.4) at 37°C, a steady unchanging P_o can be elicited at 5-min intervals for 4 h. This may not be true for isotonic shortening, especially at low loads; smooth muscle does not seem to tolerate shortening as well as isometric contraction. Interspersing an isometric contraction between consecutive isotonic contractions seems to preserve the steady state.

Figure 7 shows a mean voltage-response curve of a graded type for tracheal smooth muscle. Unlike skeletal muscle, once the maximal stimulus strength is exceeded by 20%, contractile response diminishes, therefore selection of a stimulus has to be very carefully investigated.

Figure 8 shows active tension and its first derivative versus time at different muscle lengths. Although the maximum tension increases with muscle length, the peak dP/dt is achieved at the same moment at all lengths. From this we conclude that the additional force-generating cross bridges recruited with increasing length (up to l_o) are functionally homogeneous.

Defining a maximal stimulus is not straightforward. We have already discussed the increased tensions apparent when the Ca^{2+} concentration is increased. With either electrical or full K^+ (120 mM) stimulation, the maximum response may be diminished by the

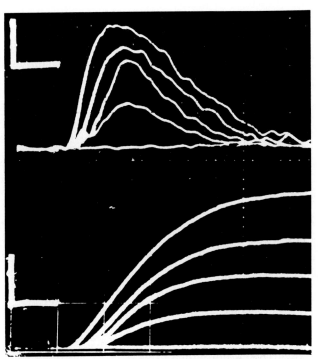

FIG. 8. *Bottom*: active isometric tension records (for typical tracheal smooth muscle) as functions of time. Calibration represents 4 g vertically and 2 s horizontally. Curves from *top* to *bottom* represent tension records obtained with muscle lengths set at l_o, 0.8 l_o, 0.6 l_o, and 0.4 l_o. *Top*: curves represent dP/dt values (P, active tension; t, time) obtained by electrical differentiation of bottom curves. Calibration represents 0.5 g·s^{-1} vertically and 2 s horizontally. [Adapted from Stephens and Kroeger (53).]

concomitant release of negative inotropic substances such as norepinephrine or putative transmitters from the nonadrenergic inhibitory nervous system (39). This suggests that to obtain a maximal response the bathing medium must contain 4.75 mM Ca^{2+} and blockers for any relaxant neurotransmitters. It is noteworthy that physiological frequencies of stimulation are below 10 Hz, yet these do not yield maximal responses in vitro for which frequencies ~100 Hz are optimal.

Myogenic Responses

In so-called single-unit smooth muscle, stretch generally induces contraction (8). The contraction originates at a myogenic level and can be elicited even when motor nerves to the muscle have been blocked. It is most often seen in smaller blood vessels and may aid in the process of autoregulation. The behavior of airway smooth muscle pertinent to the contraction is not clear. Canine tracheal smooth muscle (28), at least in vitro, does not appear to possess a myogenic response. This is not surprising, because tracheal smooth muscle is a multiunit type of smooth muscle with no action potentials or phasic mechanical activity; such muscles do not generally possess myogenic responses. Figure 9, left panel, shows that no myogenic responses can be elicited when applying a quick

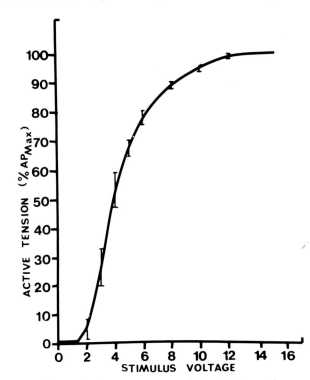

FIG. 7. Mean stimulus-response curve for tracheal muscle. Tension is expressed as percent of P_o. *Bars* indicate standard errors. [Adapted from Stephens (51).]

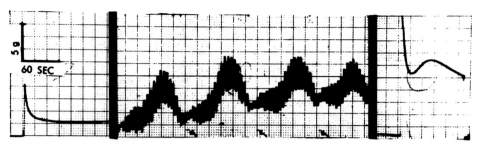

FIG. 9. Active isometric tension traces from spontaneously contracting tracheal smooth muscle. *Left panel* shows absence of a myogenic response before treatment with tetraethylammonium chloride. *Right panel* shows presence of a myogenic response after tetraethylammonium chloride treatment. *Middle panel* shows phasic activity of 2 periodicities. [Adapted from Stephens et al. (54).]

stretch of optimal specifications. However, Suzuki et al. (60), Kirkpatrick (27), and Kroeger and Stephens (28) have reported that application of tetraethylammonium (TEA) bromide induces very strong spontaneous phasic mechanical activity in tracheal smooth muscle. This is seen in the middle panel, in which at least two types of rhythms can be discerned. The right panel shows that a myogenic response is now present in the muscle. The studies of Kroeger and Stephens (28) showed that this is associated with the new development of decrementally conducted complex action potentials. The muscle seems to have developed single-unit potentials. In current injection experiments with an Abe-Tomita bath (1), analysis of the current voltage and voltage-distance plots as a chain of electrical elements shows a space constant (28) that is considerably increased (from 1.4 mm to 3.6 mm). This increase may be partly due to increase in numbers of low-impedance intercellular junctions (25). On the basis of the electrophysiological data, however, it appears that the action potentials result from reduced K^+ conductance. The work of Kannan and Daniel (25) suggests that a myogenic response and development of intercellular junctions in response to TEA can be induced rapidly (perhaps within 10 min), which suggests that their development does not depend on new protein synthesis but on ad hoc assembly of preformed units. Action potentials elicited by TEA are almost completely carried by Ca^{2+} because D-600, a calcium channel blocker, could eliminate them. This could have important implications for therapy of bronchospasm. The problem of whether human and canine airway smooth muscle in vivo is of single-unit type and the possibility that the in vitro multiunit characteristic is artifactual is discussed in the chapter by Stephens in the *Handbook*, which deals with the role of postjunctional factors in the pathophysiology of airway smooth muscle.

The effect of TEA is best explained by its altering K^+ conductance of the membrane. This change converts the multiunit muscle to a single-unit muscle.

Contractility

In carrying out force-velocity studies on smooth muscle, it must be ensured that steady-state contrac-

tility exists; an absence of this would invalidate the measurements. Brutsaert et al. (5) have defined contractility for heart muscle as the instantaneous relationship in a maximally stimulated muscle among force, velocity, length, and time. Its measurement may be difficult. For example, in eliciting force-velocity curves of heart muscle, shortening commences later in the contraction at the heavier loads. At this time the active state of the muscle is changing (tetanization is not normally possible in this muscle) and hence the relationship between load and velocity is obscured by time dependency. The three-dimensional surface obtained by plotting these three variables against each other defines the contractility state of the muscle for a given set of physiological conditions. The effect of inotropic agents on the muscle can be evaluated only in terms of changes in this surface and not as changes of isometric force alone or of isotonic shortening. A further consideration is that the history of muscle loading may influence contractility, for example, in isotonic shortening the contractile element of the muscle passes from an isometric mode to an isotonic mode. This may not be a continuous smooth process but rather a perturbation that could impair contractility. To determine whether perturbations could affect contractility, Brutsaert et al. (5) developed the technique of abrupt load clamping to elicit length-velocity data. Analyzing the resultant length-velocity relationship (phase plane), they found that maximum velocity of shortening (V_{max}) was unchanged for most of the duration of the muscle shortening and for ~13% of the extent of shortening (this would encompass the physiological range) of the muscle. Hence, under these conditions in papillary muscle, V_{max} is an index of contractility. Outside these limits the three-dimensional force-velocity-length surface defines contractility.

In smooth muscle, time dependency is not as severe a problem because the muscle can be tetanized, but the history of loading of the muscle could affect contractility. Figure 10 shows length-velocity phase planes for canine tracheal smooth muscle. Curves 1 and 2 are planes with 8-mN and 28-mN loads imposed on the muscle. In dashed line 3a the load was abruptly changed from 8 to 28 mN at about the midpoint of

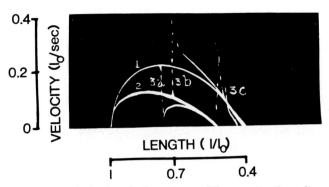

FIG. 10. Velocity-length phase planes of three contractions elicited from canine tracheal smooth muscle. *Curve 1*, plane with 8-mN load imposed on muscle; *curve 2*, plane with 28-mN load. In *dashed line 3a*, load was abruptly changed from 8 to 28 mN at midpoint of shortening, then back to 8 mN near end of shortening. In *dashed line 3b*, load clamped from 8 to 28 mN early in shortening, then changed back to 8 mN at 0.7 l_o. In *dashed line 3c*, load again changed from 8 mN to 28 mN early, then at ~0.5 l_o changed back to 8 mN.

the shortening. After the initial artifact, it is clear that the muscle follows the phase plane for 28 mN. Near the end of the shortening the load was changed back to 8 mN. The shortening now follows the 8-mN curve almost exactly. In dashed line 3b the load was clamped from 8 to 28 mN very early in the shortening; the precise point is not visible. At one point indicated (almost exactly at 0.7 l_o), the load was changed back to 8 mN. Although there is a large artifactual overshoot, the 8-mN curve is regained. In dashed line 3c the load was again changed from 8 to 28 mN very early in the shortening. The appropriate phase plane is closely followed. At ~0.5 l_o the load was again changed to 8 mN. This time the appropriate phase plane is not regained and shows an undershoot. Experiments were conducted for a wide range of loads and for a wide interval of times at which load clamps were applied or removed. From these it was concluded that tracheal smooth muscle resembles heart muscle in its mechanical properties and that the force-velocity-length surface defines its contractility. The V_{max} is another and more convenient index of contractility for the smooth muscle, although it is only valid for shortening less than 25% l_o; fortunately it is valid for most of the duration of shortening. Considerable care has to be taken to ensure steady state.

Series-Elastic Component

Tracheal smooth muscle appears to have a series-elastic component (SEC) with its contractile element (CE). Length-tension properties of the SEC have been discussed in the literature (53). These studies showed that when the isometric muscle developed a force to P_o, the elongation of its SEC was 7.5% l_o. Alterations in the properties of the SEC seen in hypoxia (50) suggest that some of the SEC resides in active components, most likely the cross bridges. Smaller values of the SEC have been reported for vascular smooth

muscle (34). However, generally large values for the SEC have been reported in the past for other types of smooth muscles (15).

Maximum Force Potential (Active State)

The maximum force potential, the ability of a muscle to sustain a maximum load imposed on it by the abrupt load-clamp technique of Brutsaert and Housmans (7), delineates the active-state curve of the contractile element. The abrupt load-clamp technique, because it holds the length of the SEC constant, is superior to the quick-stretch or quick-release method where the length of the SEC is constantly changing, thus obscuring the mechanical behavior of the contractile element.

The application of this approach to a tracheal smooth muscle preparation (58) is shown in Figure 11. The lower curve, designated P_o, is the mean of a series of isometric tetanic contractions. Above it is the maximum force potential curve, designated P_o', obtained with the abrupt load clamp. It has a slow onset (unlike that of skeletal muscle) and a time course much like that of the tetanus itself. Of note, the ratio of P_o'/P_o is 2.86, much higher than that of skeletal muscle, reported as 2.0 by Hill (21), and cardiac muscle, reported as 1.2 by Brutsaert and Housmans (7). This high ratio for tracheal smooth muscle suggests remarkably strong cross bridges. Why tracheal smooth muscle should have strong bridges is not immediately obvious. Of further interest, although the tetanic force returns to zero at ~400% of contraction time (i.e., 52 s), force potential is still elicitable at 800% contraction time (~104 s). Hence after a single tetanizing stimulus the muscle stays activated for a considerable time. Work by Siegman et al. (45) suggests

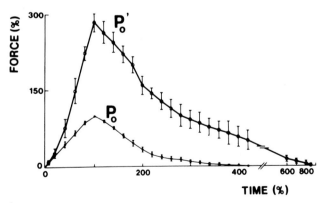

FIG. 11. Time course of maximal force potentials (P_o') in tetanic isotonic contractions of tracheal smooth muscles. Mean values of force development in control isometric contractions (P_o) and force potential (P_o') measured in isotonic contractions are shown. P_o' values obtained from highest possible force level, i.e., where clamped load could be sustained for 100 ms, for load clamps at various times during time course of isotonic tetanic contraction. P_o values obtained from corresponding isotonic control contractions. *Bars* indicate standard errors.

that, at least for *Taenia coli*, this tension requires very little new energy expenditure. The cross bridges involved in such a contraction have been termed "latch bridges" by Dillon et al. (12).

Relaxation

Although contraction of smooth muscle has been fairly well studied, relaxation has received almost no attention. The omission could have serious repercussions. Cardiac muscle physiologists, for example, stress how the magnitude of a contraction depends on the extent to which the muscle has relaxed from a preceding twitch. Furthermore the importance of relaxation in smooth muscle is pointed up by the observation that, although P_o is normal or reduced in vessels from spontaneously hypertensive rats, relaxation time is considerably prolonged (S. Shibata, unpublished observations).

The mechanical characteristics of relaxation can be studied from shortening and force data obtained in the course of conventional afterloaded, isotonic force-velocity experiments (Fig. 12). The region of interest is the relaxation pathway where force falls below the experimentally imposed isotonic level. The inset shows two distinct types of relaxation behavior. Panel A shows curves from cat heart papillary muscle during twitch contractions. It is evident that the relaxation pathways for the different loads differ from each other and from the relaxation pathway for the isometric contraction represented by the topmost curve. This type of relaxation has also been reported for skeletal muscle (22). Brutsaert et al. (6) feel that it represents an efficient calcium-resequestering apparatus whereby the active state is terminated rapidly and relaxation is then dictated by the load. They have termed this "load-dependent relaxation." Panel B of the inset represents force-time records from frog ventricular muscle. It is evident that relaxation for all the curves follows the same pathway. Brutsaert's group (6) ascribes this to a poor complement of sarcoplasmic reticulum for calcium resequestration. Relaxation therefore is load independent and depends on the termination of active state. This has been termed "inactivation-dependent relaxation."

The length and force data comprising the rest of the figure are from similar experiments conducted in tracheal smooth muscle. The force-time curves show that relaxation is of the inactivation-dependent type. This is perhaps to be expected, because there is a paucity of sarcoplasmic reticulum in tracheal smooth muscle. This pattern of relaxation is unaffected by the time at which the isotonic load is applied to the muscle and the manner (abruptly increased or decreased to the value chosen for study) in which it is applied (58).

It must be pointed out that the association between Ca^{2+} resequestration and relaxation in smooth muscle is not straightforward. Contraction in smooth muscle appears to be initiated by the phosphorylation (through a specific kinase) of myosin light chain (37) and terminated by its dephosphorylation through a specific phosphatase (2). This phosphatase is calcium independent. Hence there is a possibility that the rate-limiting step in relaxation may not be calcium resequestration. Because the phosphatase is constantly active at rest and is only inhibited during contraction, however, the likelihood is that the rate-limiting step is the shutting off of the Ca^{2+}-calmodulin–dependent myosin light-chain kinase.

Length Forcing

As diameters of airways change with inspiration and expiration, it becomes important to know how smooth muscle behaves when its length is externally forced, in particular at frequencies and with amplitudes that might be imposed in breathing maneuvers. Such maneuvers are rapid relative to the ability of the smooth muscle to shorten. Considerable force-length hysteresis results, which cannot be predicted in detail from the foregoing force-length and force-velocity plots.

When a strip of tracheal smooth muscle is length cycled over a range approximating that undergone by the trachea in a vital capacity maneuver, length-tension plots (Fig. 13) show complex hysteretic patterns depending on state of activity of the muscle and on the pattern of the imposed length cycles. The relaxed muscle shows little tension. When contracted by carbachol, the muscle increases force to a constant value over several minutes (~10 g in Fig. 13A). If the muscle is then length cycled with a small amplitude, it is very stiff or noncompliant. If, however, the length cycles are large, the muscle shows marked hysteresis or looping, and the force during stretching is severalfold that during shortening.

The tension of the contracted strip depends not

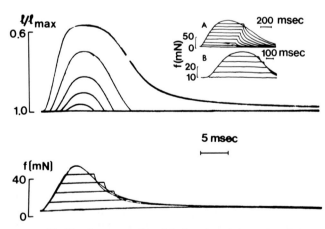

FIG. 12. *Two larger panels at left* show length (*upper*) and force (*lower*) traces of a series of afterloaded isotonic contractions. *Inset panels at right* show contractions with different afterloads up to a full isometric tetanus in cat heart papillary muscle (*A*) and frog ventricular muscle (*B*).

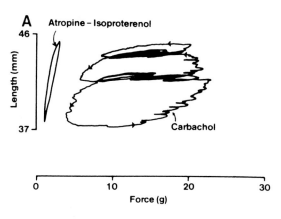

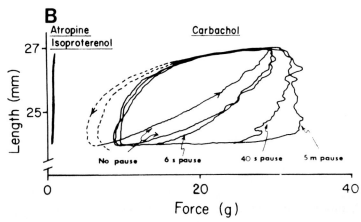

FIG. 13. Length-tension plots in 2 dog trachealis muscle strips. Total range of lengths in sequence is approximately that undergone by trachealis in a vital capacity maneuver. When relaxed with isoproterenol and atropine, tensions were low. Tension in contracted strip is primarily due to active component. When carbachol was added to the bath, with strip held at constant length, tension increased over 1 min to ~10 g. A: muscle was then lengthened from 37 mm to 42 mm, cycled twice over ~0.5 mm, lengthened to 44 mm, cycled twice over ~0.5 mm, and lengthened to 45 mm. It was then shortened with similar pattern of interrupting small cycles. Entire sequence took ~1 min. B: a muscle strip was cycled 5 times over 10% of its length. Each cycle compromised an 8-s lengthening and either an 8-s (*continuous tracing*) or a 4-s (*dashed tracing*) shortening, followed by a pause lasting 0–5 min. During these pauses, force increased isometrically to as much as 20 g at 5 min. Initial slope during subsequent lengthening was lower after longer pauses and was almost indistinguishable from isometric tracings. [Adapted from Sasaki and Hoppin (43).]

only on the pattern of the imposed length cycles but also on their timing. Figure 13*B* shows typical tracings during five cycles, which differ in their timing. In each cycle, an 8-s stretch is immediately followed by a 4- or 8-s shortening and then by a pause of varying duration prior to the next cycle. Tension increases during the pause between cycles, and the longer the pause, the lower the initial compliance when stretch is resumed and more distinct is the inflection during stretching, after which tension is nearly constant. Despite these differences in the pathway during stretch, the tension at peak length remains nearly independent of the duration of the pause. In the shortening phase, initial compliance is low but increases with further shortening. In contrast to the pathway during stretching, the pathway during shortening is not affected by the duration of the pause prior to stretching.

Analogous behavior is seen with continuous length cycling (Fig. 14). There is moderate hysteresis at 0.007 Hz (10-min cycle). At 0.017 Hz, force is greater at the higher length but is less at the lower length (lower overall compliance) and shows greater hysteresis. At still higher cycling frequencies, force is progressively lower during both shortening and stretch phases, and the hysteresis area now becomes less. Hysteresis area is greatest at 0.017 Hz, whereas the mean force decreases and cycling amplitude of force increases as frequency increases. This dynamic behavior is independent of the mean length of the muscle strips over the operating length of the muscle.

These particular patterns of the hysteresis suggest

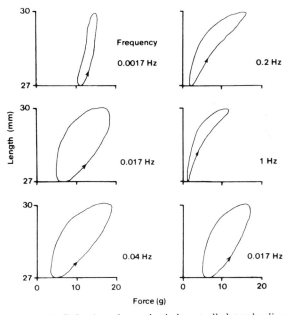

FIG. 14. Behavior of a carbachol-controlled trachealis muscle strip during length cycling at different frequencies. [Adapted from Sasaki and Hoppin (43).]

the operation of two basic properties of the contractile element: *1*) a relatively slow velocity of active shortening and *2*) a critical force for yielding or slipping during stretching. The first is suggested by the precipitous fall of force with imposed shortening and is consistent with the known low V_{max} for tracheal smooth muscle (Table 1). Recovery of force during pause at a given length (Fig. 13) then is in agreement with the slow contractile element "catching up" again. The second property, yielding or slipping of the contractile elements at a critical tension, is suggested by the inflection of the length-tension curve during stretching after a long pause (Fig. 13). The critical tension at which this occurs is dose dependent and is systematically lower and less distinct during stretching after shorter pauses.

The behavior during length cycling can be interpreted in terms of the cross bridges. If the strip is given sufficient time to establish cross bridges and then is forcibly stretched, the cross bridges at first hold on and tension increases sharply because of the strain on the cross bridges and the elastic elements of the muscle. But at a critical tension the cross bridges yield, the filaments slip relative to one another, and further lengthening occurs at a nearly constant tension. With shorter pauses, there is less time for establishing cross bridges. With fewer cross bridges strained, the cross bridges reach their threshold for yielding at a lower total muscle tension. Thus the shorter the pause, the lower the tension in the early stretch phase. The fact that neither the tension at the greatest length of the cycle nor the tension during shortening depend on the duration of the pause before stretching is also consistent with the envisioned mechanism. At the greatest length in repeated cycles, tension is the sum of the characteristic yield forces of all the contractile elements, regardless of whether those elements had all yielded throughout the stretching phase (as after a 5-min pause) or whether they were recruited at various points during stretching, as after shorter pauses. The frequency dependency during continuous length cycling (Fig. 14) is consistent with the same interpretation. During very slow shortening (0.0017 Hz), contractile elements appear to keep up fairly well with the imposed length changes: there is relatively little hysteresis, and tension is well maintained. With more rapid cycling, tension is somewhat higher during lengthening but is particularly lower during shortening. Presumably the contractile element falls somewhat behind during the imposed shortening, but it shortens and is able to exert some tension during stretching. In the most rapid cycles, tension is still lower during shortening and also during lengthening, and the loop develops a boomerang shape, with both phases concave to the force axis and with less hysteresis area than at slower frequencies. Presumably the contractile element, unable to follow the imposed rapid events, simply stays near the length to which it initially yielded. Hysteresis is less in the most rapid cycles because the major contributor to hysteresis, namely the contractile element, is not changing length as much. In more rapid cycles, the compliance of both shortening and lengthening phases approaches the compliance of the series-elastic element (which includes a component due to the established cross bridges themselves): compliance is low

near maximal cycling length where the contractile element is under tension and is high near minimal cycling length because of the extended condition of the contractile element. The series-elastic behavior elicited by very high frequencies and small length excursions has been used in analytical studies of the mechanics of active smooth muscles; it appears that it may also be pertinent at physiological frequencies and length changes.

Airway smooth muscle, then cycled as it may be in vivo during breathing maneuvers, shows great stiffness for small cycles and great hysteresis for large cycles, consistent with the notion that the velocity of shortening of the contractile element is slow relative to the imposed events and that the contractile element slips or yields at a threshold force.

Heterogeneity of Mechanical Properties

Although the qualitative similarity between smooth muscles from different sites in the same animal and from different animals is striking, it is well to be aware that such differences do exist. These differences are generally in the regulatory mechanisms.

DIFFERENCES IN SMOOTH MUSCLE MECHANICS AT DIFFERENT LEVELS OF AIRWAY. Russell (42) investigated the properties of muscle strips from canine trachea and from canine airways 5 mm and 1.5 mm in diameter. In all three, electrical stimulation produced a sustained tonic contraction. The response was dependent on frequency, voltage, and pulse duration. Length–active tension curves for the bronchi were qualitatively similar. Sensitivities (horizontal shifts of dose-response curve) to acetylcholine were also similar for the three sites. The ratio of maximal tension produced by electrical stimulation to that produced by maximal doses of exogenous acetylcholine decreased from the trachea to the 1.5-mm bronchioles; the smaller the airway, the smaller the maximal contraction produced by exogenous acetylcholine. This vertical shift of the dose-response curve is conventionally recognized as a change in reactivity and may indicate a poorer supply of vagal efferent nerve fibers in smaller airways. Alternatively inhibitory innervation (β-adrenergic and/or nonadrenergic inhibitory) increases down the airways.

The pharmacological properties of airway smooth muscle are even more variable than the mechanical properties. Although central airways constrict mainly because of cholinergic activity, a small part of the contraction may stem from α-adrenergic activity. The smallest muscle-containing bronchioles likely contain very few α-adrenoceptors, the main agonist there being histamine.

DIFFERENCES IN AIRWAY SMOOTH MUSCLE MECHANICS IN DIFFERENT ANIMAL SPECIES. The well-recognized existence of this heterogeneity has bedeviled pharmacological studies of airway smooth muscle; care has to be exercised, particularly in extrapolating data obtained from dogs, cats, rats, and guinea pigs to data from humans.

Examples of such heterogeneity are: histamine produces a marked constriction in guinea pig trachea, a relaxation of cat trachea, and no effect on the trachea of the rat and rabbit (13). It seems, from a gross examination, that human bronchi and guinea pig trachea are pharmacologically similar.

One other important consideration relates to mechanisms of relaxation of airway smooth muscle, which may be of relevance to asthma in humans, and that is the role of the nonadrenergic inhibitory nervous system. Richardson and Bouchard (39) presented evidence to suggest that such a system exists in airways in humans. It has been suggested on the analogy of the intestinal system, which has such an innervation also, that the putative transmitter is of purinergic nature. It is speculated that reduced activity of such a system would contribute to bronchial hyperreactivity. Although human tissues appear to possess this system, most workers agree that canine tissues do not possess it. Irvin et al. (21a) have published data indicating that in the cat a nonadrenergic noncholinergic inhibitory system is present and that neither adenosine nor ATPase is the transmitter. Recently vasoactive intestinal polypeptides (VIP) have been suggested as the transmitter.

Current research suggests that part of this heterogeneity of response (30) may result from agents liberated in feedback loops. Examples are the leukotrienes and prostaglandins and the release of transmitters from presynapse. With respect to the latter, histamine appears to interact with presynaptic H_1 receptors in tracheal smooth muscle. This interaction releases acetylcholine, which contributes ~15% to the overall contractile response to histamine.

EFFECTS OF AGE, TEMPERATURE, AND HORMONES. Fleisch et al. (14) have shown that, although aging exerts no effect on β-adrenoceptor activity in rat trachea, it does affect α-adrenoceptors, because norepinephrine-induced α-receptor–mediated tracheal contractions appear greater in tissues from 9-mo-old rats than from 6-wk-old rats.

Kunos and Szentivanyi (29) found that the responses to epinephrine and norepinephrine in rats are blocked by an α-receptor antagonist at low temperatures and by a β-receptor antagonist at higher temperatures. Miller and Marshall (32) showed that adrenoceptors in estrogen-treated myometrium are predominantly of β-type (excitatory), and in progesterone-treated myometrium they are predominantly of α-type.

Mechanics of Lung Strips

The realization that the smaller bronchioles may be significantly involved in asthmatic bronchoconstric-

tion (it must be admitted that definitive proof, by way of static pressure-volume curves, has not yet been provided) has led to the search for a suitable preparation to examine their role in vitro. Lulich et al. (31) have developed the cat lung strip as an in vitro preparation of peripheral airways and have studied its mechanical and pharmacological properties.

The cat lung strip possesses tone that can be reduced by catecholamines, aminophylline, and flufenamate. It is contracted by histamine, prostaglandin $F_{2\alpha}$, and AC field stimulation. The trachea from the same animal does not respond to histamine or prostaglandin $F_{2\alpha}$. Isoproterenol and epinephrine relax the lung strip more powerfully than the trachea. The β_2-adrenoreceptor agonists are more potent in the lung strip than in the trachea. These experiments suggest a predominance of β_2-adrenoreceptors in the lung strip and β_1-adrenoreceptors in the trachea.

Sensitization could be achieved of both the trachea and the lung strip in which a contractile response to a challenge with a specific antigen could be elicited. The initial component of the lung strip contraction is due to histamine; it is not present in the trachea. The delayed, slow phase is seen in both preparations and appears to be mediated by leukotrienes.

CONTRACTILE INTERSTITIAL CELLS OF THE LUNG

The possibility that a substantial portion of the cells in the alveolar interstitium may have a contractile function was first suggested by Kapanci et al. (26). Contractile interstitial cells are located in the alveolar septa around pre- or postcapillary vessels. They look like fibroblasts but contain microfilaments 4–8 nm in diameter and some thicker filaments. They stain with antiactin and antimyosin antibodies and have been proposed as the cause of the contraction of alveolar tissue seen in in vitro studies. These cells are located between the basement membranes of two adjacent alveoli in "pillars" that bridge the intercapillary space.

Kapanci et al. (26) carried out in vitro studies on rat lung parenchymal strips, arterial strips, and bronchial strips. Mechanical responses were assessed under the microscope focused on flexible glass filaments to which the strips were attached. Hypoxia caused significant shortening of the parenchymal strip, as epinephrine and histamine did, whereas serotonin had no effect. By contrast, arterial strips contracted with serotonin and epinephrine but showed no response to hypoxia, and bronchial strips relaxed under hypoxia and epinephrine but contracted very strongly when treated with serotonin. These differences suggest that the contractile mechanism in the parenchyma is neither vascular muscle nor airway smooth muscle. One possibility is that contraction of the parenchyma is due to alveolar duct smooth muscle that is pharmacologically distinct from smooth muscle of the bronchioles. The possibility championed by Kapanci that the interstitial cells have substantial contractile function further rests on an impression, not yet quantified, that these cells have substantially more contractile filaments than are seen in noncontractile cells.

FUNCTIONAL ROLE OF AIRWAY SMOOTH MUSCLE

In contrast to the considerable body of current knowledge about pharmacological, reflex, and mechanical behavior of lung smooth muscle, there is a remarkable mystery about its functional role. Otis' (37) recent statement epitomizes this remarkable situation: "Investigation of bronchial smooth muscle has been going on for over a century. What do we know regarding its functions? About all that is certain is that spasm of bronchial smooth muscle causes asthma." Our ignorance of the reason why smooth muscle is in the lung clouds our perspective on the implications of the mechanical behavior just described.

The functional role of airway smooth muscle probably differs from trachea to alveolar duct not only because of the different roles of the different parts of the airway tree but also because of the different pharmacological behavior, reflex, and anatomical disposition within the structures. The mechanical effects of contraction of the canine tracheal smooth muscle reflects its disposition transversely in the posterior membranous sheath: smooth muscle contractions oppose distension, but when the trachea is submitted to negative transmural pressures (as during forced expiration), tension in the smooth muscle opposes invagination of the posterior membranous sheath and stabilizes the structure against narrowing (36). Bronchi differ somewhat, having helically disposed smooth muscle. Both radial and axial tensions increase with contraction. All bronchi are narrowed by contraction, but particularly in the periphery. As in the trachea, collapsibility of the cartilaginous bronchi is reduced by smooth muscle contraction (36). It has been postulated that the more peripheral, noncartilaginous airways might also be stabilized against collapse by contraction of smooth muscle in their walls (64), but experimental evidence is lacking. The most peripheral elements in this continuous system of smooth muscle are the respiratory bronchioles and alveolar ducts; here constriction can be shown to draw in on (and presumably tense) the surrounding alveolar septa (35).

Functional consequences of smooth muscle contraction (e.g., on airway resistance, ventilatory dead space, lung recoil) are easily demonstrated, but the arguments for utility of these effects are not strong. Narrowing the airways directly increases resistance to airflow and decreases ventilatory dead space. Is there a functional utility in controlling these two opposing characteristics? In quiet breathing, resistance to flow in the airways is small, and an increase in resistance is of little consequence, whereas a reduction in dead space directly reduces the ventilation required. At high ventilation, however, the resistive load becomes appreciable and, because of the high tidal volumes, the dead space becomes relatively unimportant, in which case dilation might be advantageous, decreasing resistance at a minor cost of increasing dead space. If the notion is correct, one might expect to find substantial airway tone at rest and inhibition of tone in fight-or-flight response. Indeed, there is resting tone, mediated by cholinergic vagal pathways, and the airways are generally dilated by adrenergic agents (62).

Another effect of contracting airway smooth muscle is reduction of maximum expiratory flows. Stabilization of airways against collapse might be expected to increase maximum expiratory flow rate (11), but apparently this effect is overcome by the effects of decreased cross-sectional area of the airway at the point of flow limitation and the decreased conductance of the airways upstream from this point (11). The effects of relaxation (as distinct from contraction) of the airway on forced expiration are uncertain. If maximum flow is increased, the functional utility of the airway smooth muscle again may lie in relaxation of resting tone to achieve greater ventilation in a fight-or-flight circumstance. Alternatively, smooth muscle constriction might serve to change the position of the flow-limiting segment along the airways and thereby somehow optimize cough.

The effects of airway smooth muscle contraction on the parenchyma (pneumoconstriction) are intriguing. Lung recoil is increased and compliance is reduced by vagal stimulation and various agents that contract smooth muscle (9, 30, 64). The mechanism probably relates to both axial tensions along the length of the bronchial tree and radial constriction of the airways that tenses the surrounding parenchyma. Modeling these mechanisms suggests that the effects are insignificant unless the most peripheral airways and particularly the alveolar ducts are included (J. C. Smith, J. P. Butler, and F. G. Hoppin, Jr., unpublished observations). It has been suggested that such pneumoconstriction could serve to adjust ventilation-perfusion ($\dot{V}A/\dot{Q}$) relationships on a local level by reducing parenchymal compliance (9). The plausibility of this suggestion, however, is reduced by the observations that bronchial smooth muscle (62) and parenchymal strips (31) constrict with exposure to low oxygen. These actions would have the adverse effect of lowering $\dot{V}A/\dot{Q}$ in hypoxic regions.

It has been hypothesized that airways might have peristaltic behavior, but the evidence is thin. Peristalsis might conceivably aid in unplugging peripheral airways, but, as Widdicombe (62) has pointed out, "it is likely to be far less effective than coughing or ciliary movement."

How might the mechanical properties of airway smooth muscle relate to such functional roles? Whereas the force-velocity output of striated muscle is the very essence of its function, this is not true for airway smooth muscle; it is difficult to see a direct functional implication, for example, in the rapidity with which airways narrow in response to a vagal stimulus. Smooth muscle is slow relative to striated muscle and relative to breathing frequencies; its function therefore is probably to assume a state of contraction while dynamic breathing events go on, rather than to participate actively in the breathing event. From this perspective, the prominent stiffness of contracted airway smooth muscle undergoing limited length cycles (Fig. 13) implies that it can hold a given length (thus limiting ventilatory dead space or local parenchymal compliance, for example) against the cycling tensions of quiet breathing. The property of yielding with longer stretches, on the other hand, explains the temporary dilation (enhanced cough?) following a deep inspiration.

CONCLUSION

It is clear that a considerable amount of information about the mechanical properties of canine tracheal smooth muscle is available. The application of these data to the in vivo muscle needs to be carried out; it awaits development of appropriate technology.

The properties of airway smooth muscle down to the smallest muscle-containing airways need to be studied to determine to what extent tracheal smooth muscle is a model for airway smooth muscle in general. The development of techniques to study the mechanics of single cells will help. These have been developed by Fay (13) for single smooth muscle cells of the toad stomach. The method of Halpern et al. (18) for studying 200-μm-wide arterioles could also be used.

Information regarding subcellular (i.e., cross-bridge level) mechanics is becoming available and will advance our understanding of smooth muscle mechanics in depth. The abrupt load-clamping techniques described in *Force-Velocity Relationships*, p. 265, provide data that can be evaluated in terms of cross-bridge properties.

REFERENCES

1. ABE, Y., AND T. TOMITA. Cable properties of smooth muscle. *J. Physiol. London* 196: 87–100, 1968.
2. ADELSTEIN, R. S., M. A. CONTI, S. P. SCORDILIS, S. CHACKO, B. BARYLKO, AND J. A. TROTTER. Myosin phosphorylation as a regulatory mechanism. In: *Excitation-Contraction Coupling in Smooth Muscle*, edited by R. Casteels, T. Godfraind, and J. C. Ruegg. Amsterdam: Elsevier/North-Holland, 1977, p. 359–366.
3. AKSOY, M. O., S. MRAS, K. E. KAMM, AND R. A. MURPHY. Ca^{2+}, cAMP, and changes in myosin phosphorylation during contraction of smooth muscle. *Am. J. Physiol.* 245 (*Cell Physiol.* 14): C255–C270, 1983.
4. AUBERT, X. *Le couplage energetrique de la contraction musculaire*. Brussels: Arscia, 1956, p. 1–315.
5. BRUTSAERT, D. L., V. A. CLAES, AND E. H. SONNENBLICK. Effects of abrupt load alterations on force-velocity-length and time relations during isotonic contractions of heart muscle: load clamping. *J. Physiol. London* 216: 319–330, 1971.
6. BRUTSAERT, D. L., N. M. DE CLERCK, M. A. GOETHALS, AND P. R. HOUSMANS. Relaxation of ventricular cardiac muscle. *J. Physiol. London* 283: 469–480, 1979.
7. BRUTSAERT, D. L., AND P. R. HOUSMANS. Load clamp analysis of maximal force potential of mammalian cardiac muscle. *J. Physiol. London* 271: 587–603, 1977.
8. BURNSTOCK, G., AND C. L. PROSSER. Responses of smooth muscles to quick stretch; relation of stretch to conduction. *Am. J. Physiol.* 198: 921–925, 1960.
9. COLEBATCH, H. J. H. The humoral regulation of alveolar ducts. In: *Airway Dynamics: Physiology and Pharmacology*, edited by A. Bouhuys. Springfield, IL: Thomas, 1970, 169–189.
10. CSAPO, A. Smooth muscle as a contractile unit. *Physiol. Rev.* 42, Suppl. 5: 7–33, 1962.
11. DAWSON, S. V., AND E. A. ELLIOTT. Wave-speed limitation on expiratory flow—a unifying concept. *J. Appl. Physiol.: Respirat. Environ. Exercise Physiol.* 43: 498–515, 1977.
12. DILLON, P. F., M. O. AKSOY, S. P. DRISKA, AND R. A. MURPHY. Myosin phosphorylation and the cross-bridge cycle in arterial smooth muscle. *Science* 211: 495–497, 1981.
13. FAY, F. S. Mechanics of single isolated smooth muscle cells. In: *Excitation-Contraction Coupling in Smooth Muscle*, edited by R. Casteels, T. Godfraind, and J. C. Ruegg. Amsterdam: Elsevier/North-Holland, 1977, p. 433–439.
14. FLEISCH, J. H., K. M. KENT, AND T. COOPER. Drug receptors in smooth muscle. In: *Asthma: Physiology, Immunopharmacology, and Treatment*, edited by K. F. Austen and L. Lichtenstein. New York: Academic, 1973, p. 139–167.

15. GORDON, A. R., AND M. J. SIEGMAN. Mechanical properties of smooth muscle. I. Length-tension and force-velocity relations. *Am. J. Physiol.* 221: 1243–1249, 1971.
16. GORECKA, A., M. O. AKSOY, AND D. J. HARTSHORNE. The effect of phosphorylation of gizzard myosin on actin activation. *Biochem. Biophys. Res. Commun.* 71: 325–331, 1974.
17. HAHN, H. L., P. D. GRAF, AND J. A. NADEL. Effect of vagal tone on airway diameters and on lung volume in anesthetized dogs. *J. Appl. Physiol.* 41: 581–589, 1976.
18. HALPERN, W., M. J. MULVANY, AND D. M. WARSHAW. Mechanical properties of smooth muscle cells in the walls of arterial resistance vessels. *J. Physiol. London* 275: 85–101, 1978.
19. HANKS, B. S. R., AND N. L. STEPHENS. Mechanics and energetics of lengthening of active airway smooth muscle. *Am. J. Physiol.* 241 (*Cell Physiol.* 10): C42–C46, 1981.
20. HILL, A. V. The heat of shortening and the dynamic constants of muscle. *Proc. R. Soc. London Ser. B* 126: 136–195, 1938.
21. HILL, A. V. *First and Last Experiments in Muscle Mechanics*. Cambridge, UK: Cambridge Univ. Press, 1970.
21a.IRVIN, C. G., R. BOILEAU, J. TREMBLAY, R. R. MARTIN, AND P. T. MACKLEM. Bronchodilatation: noncholinergic, nonadrenergic mediation demonstrated in vivo in the cat. *Science* 207: 791–792.
22. JEWELL, B. R. Discussion remarks. In: S. R. Taylor. Decreased activation in skeletal muscle fibers at short lengths. In: *Physiological Basis of Starling's Law of the Heart*, edited by R. Porter and D. W. Fitzsimons. Amsterdam: Elsevier/North-Holland, 1974, p. 114–116. (Ciba Found. Symp. 24, New Ser.)
23. JEWELL, B. R., AND D. R. WILKIE. The mechanical properties of relaxing muscle. *J. Physiol. London* 152: 30–47, 1960.
24. JOHANSSON, R., P. HELLSTRAND, AND B. UVELIUS. Responses of smooth muscle to quick load change studied at high time resolution. *Blood Vessels* 15: 65–82, 1978.
25. KANNAN, M. S., AND E. E. DANIEL. Formation of gap junctions by treatment in vitro with potassium conductance blockers. *J. Cell Biol.* 78: 338–348, 1978.
26. KAPANCI, Y., P. M. COSTABELLO, AND G. GABBIANI. Location and function of contractile interstitial cells of the lungs. In: *Lung Cells in Disease*, edited by A. Bouhuys. Amsterdam: Elsevier/North-Holland, 1976, p. 69–84.
27. KIRKPATRICK, C. T. Excitation and contraction in bovine tracheal smooth muscle. *J. Physiol. London* 244: 263–281, 1975.
28. KROEGER, E. A., AND N. L. STEPHENS. Effect of tetraethylammonium on tonic airway smooth muscle: initiation of phasic electrical activity. *Am. J. Physiol.* 228: 633–636, 1975.

29. KUNOS, G., AND M. SZENTIVANYI. Evidence favouring the existence of a single adrenergic receptor. *Nature London* 217: 1077–1078, 1968.

30. LORING, S. H., J. M. DRAZEN, J. C. SMITH, AND F. G. HOPPIN, JR. Vagal stimulation and aerosol histamine increase hysteresis of lung recoil. *J. Appl. Physiol.: Respirat. Environ. Exercise Physiol.* 51: 477–484, 1981.

31. LULICH, K. M., H. W. MITCHELL, AND M. P. SPARROW. The cat lung strip as an in vitro preparation of peripheral airways: a comparison of β-adrenoceptor agonists, autacoids and anaphylactic challenge on the lung strip and trachea. *Br. J. Pharmacol.* 58: 71–79, 1976.

32. MILLER, M. D., AND J. M. MARSHALL. Uterine response to nerve stimulation; relation to hormonal status and catecholamines. *Am. J. Physiol.* 209: 859–865, 1965.

33. MRWA, U., AND J. C. RUEGG. Myosin-linked calcium regulation in vascular smooth muscle. *FEBS Lett.* 60: 81–84, 1975.

34. MULVANY, M. J. The undamped and damped series elastic components of a vascular smooth muscle. *Biophys. J.* 26: 401–413, 1979.

35. NADEL, J. A., H. J. H. COLEBATCH, AND C. R. OLSEN. Location and mechanism of airway constriction after barium sulfate microembolism. *J. Appl. Physiol.* 19: 387–394, 1964.

36. OLSEN, C. R., A. E. STEVENS, N. B. PRIDE, AND N. C. STAUB. Structural basis for decreased compressibility of constricted tracheae and bronchi. *J. Appl. Physiol.* 23: 35–39, 1967.

37. OTIS, A. B. A perspective of respiratory mechanics. *J. Appl. Physiol.: Respirat. Environ. Exercise Physiol.* 54: 1183–1187, 1983.

38. RICHARDSON, J. B. The neural control of human tracheobronchial smooth muscle. In: *Asthma: Physiology, Immunopharmacology, and Treatment*, edited by K. Austen and L. Lichtenstein. New York: Academic, 1977, p. 237–247.

39. RICHARDSON, J. B., AND T. BOUCHARD. Demonstration of a nonadrenergic inhibitory nervous system in the trachea of the guinea pig. *J. Allergy Clin. Immunol.* 56: 473–480, 1975.

40. ROACH, N. R., AND A. C. BURTON. The reason for the shape of the distensibility curves of arteries. *Can. J. Biochem. Physiol.* 35: 681–690, 1957.

41. RUDEL, R., AND S. R. TAYLOR. Striated muscle fibers: facilitation of contraction at short lengths by caffeine. *Science* 172: 387–389, 1971.

42. RUSSELL, J. A. Response of isolated canine airways to electric stimulation and acetylcholine. *J. Appl. Physiol.: Respirat. Environ. Exercise Physiol.* 45: 690–698, 1978.

43. SASAKI, H., AND F. G. HOPPIN, JR. Hysteresis of contracted airway smooth muscle. *J. Appl. Physiol.: Respirat. Environ. Exercise Physiol.* 47: 1251–1262, 1979.

44. SASAKI, H., F. G. HOPPIN, JR., AND T. TAKISHIMA. Peribronchial pressure in excised dog lungs. *J. Appl. Physiol.: Respirat. Environ. Exercise Physiol.* 45: 858–869, 1978.

45. SIEGMAN, M. J., T. M. BUTLER, S. U. MOOERS, AND R. E. DAVIES. Mechanical and energetic correlates of isometric relaxation in mammalian smooth muscle. In: *Excitation-Contraction Coupling in Smooth Muscle*, edited by R. Casteels, T. Godfraind, and J. C. Ruegg. Amsterdam: Elsevier/North-Holland, 1977, p. 449–453.

46. SOBIESZEK, A., AND J. V. SMALL. Regulation of the actin-myosin interaction in vertebrate smooth muscle: activation via a myosin light-chain kinase and the effect of tropomyosin. *J. Mol. Biol.* 112: 559–576, 1977.

47. SONNENBLICK, E. H. Implications of muscle mechanics in the heart. *Federation Proc.* 21: 975–990, 1962.

48. SOUHRADA, J. F., AND J. LOADER. Changes of airway smooth muscle in experimental asthma. In: *Mechanisms of Airway Obstruction in Human Respiratory Disease*, edited by M. A. De Kock, J. A. Nadel, and C. M. Lewis. Cape Town: Balkema, 1979, p. 195–207.

49. STEPHENS, N. L. The mechanics of isolated airway smooth muscle. In: *Airway Dynamics: Physiology and Pharmacology*, edited by A. Bouhuys. Springfield, IL: Thomas, 1970, p. 191–208.

50. STEPHENS, N. L. Mechanism of action of hypoxia in tracheal smooth muscle (TSM) with a note on the role of a series elastic component. In: *Vascular Smooth Muscle*, edited by E. Betz. Berlin: Springer-Verlag, 1972, p. 153–156.

51. STEPHENS, N. L. Physical properties of contractile systems. In: *Methods in Pharmacology. Smooth Muscle*, edited by E. E. Daniel and D. M. Paton. New York: Plenum, 1975, vol. 3, p. 265–296.

52. STEPHENS, N. L. Airway smooth muscle: biophysics, biochemistry and pharmacology. In: *Asthma: Physiology, Immunopharmacology, and Treatment*, edited by K. F. Austen and L. M. Lichtenstein. New York: Academic, 1977, p. 147–167.

53. STEPHENS, N. L., AND E. A. KROEGER. Ultrastructure, biophysics and biochemistry of airway smooth muscle. In: *Lung Biology in Health and Disease. Physiology and Pharmacology of the Airways*, edited by J. A. Nadel. New York: Dekker, 1980, vol. 15, p. 31–121.

54. STEPHENS, N. L., E. A. KROEGER, AND U. KROMER. Induction of a myogenic response in tonic airway smooth muscle by tetraethylammonium. *Am. J. Physiol.* 228: 628–632, 1975.

55. STEPHENS, N. L., E. KROEGER, AND J. A. MEHTA. Force-velocity characteristics of respiratory airway smooth muscle. *J. Appl. Physiol.* 26: 685–692, 1969.

56. STEPHENS, N. L., AND U. KROMER. Series elastic component of tracheal smooth muscle. *Am. J. Physiol.* 220: 1890–1895, 1971.

57. STEPHENS, N. L., R. W. MITCHELL, L. A. ANTONISSEN, U. KROMER, B. HANKS, E. A. KROEGER, AND W. KEPRON. Airway smooth muscle: physical properties and metabolism. In: *Airway Reactivity*, edited by F. E. Hargreaves. Mississauga, Canada: Astra, 1981.

58. STEPHENS, N. L., R. W. MITCHELL, AND D. L. BRUTSAERT. Nature of contractile unit: shortening inactivation, maximum force potential, relaxation, contractility. In: *Smooth Muscle Contraction*, edited by N. L. Stephens. New York: Dekker, 1982, p. 91–112.

59. STEPHENS, N. L., AND W. VAN NIEKERK. Isometric and isotonic contractions in airway smooth muscle. *Can. J. Physiol. Pharmacol.* 55: 833–838, 1977.

60. SUZUKI, H., K. MORITA, AND H. KURIYAMA. Innervation and properties of the smooth muscle of the dog trachea. *Jpn. J. Physiol.* 26: 303–320, 1976.

61. TAYLOR, S. R. Decreased activation in skeletal muscle fibres at short lengths. In: *Physiological Basis of Starling's Law of the Heart*, edited by R. Porter and D. W. Fitzsimons. Amsterdam: Elsevier/North-Holland, 1974, p. 93–116. (Ciba Found. Symp. 24, New Ser.)

62. WIDDICOMBE, J. G. Regulation of tracheobronchial smooth muscle. *Physiol. Rev.* 43: 1–37, 1963.

63. WOLEDGE, R. C. The energetics of tortoise muscle. *J. Physiol. London* 197: 685–707, 1968.

64. WOOLCOCK, A. J., AND P. T. MACKLEM. Mechanical factors influencing collateral ventilation in human, dog, and pig lungs. *J. Appl. Physiol.* 30: 99–115, 1971.

CHAPTER 18

Pressure-flow relationships in the lungs

ROLAND H. INGRAM, JR.

Departments of Medicine, Brigham and Women's Hospital and Beth Israel Hospital, Harvard Medical School, Boston, Massachusetts

T. J. PEDLEY

Department of Applied Mathematics and Theoretical Physics, University of Cambridge, Cambridge, England

CHAPTER CONTENTS

AS A GENERAL TERM, resistance means opposition to motion. In the context of the flow of air into and out of the lungs it could be defined as the ratio of the pressure difference driving the flow to the flow rate. However, some of this pressure difference is required to distend elastic structures and to overcome inertia, in addition to overcoming frictional or viscous forces. It is the latter contribution to the pressure drop, in phase with the flow rate and representing dissipation of energy, that should be used in defining resistance; we shall adhere to that definition. Nevertheless, measurements of pressure drop involve the other contributions, and means must be found of assessing them.

HISTORICAL PERSPECTIVES

Galen understood that active expansion of the chest wall was necessary for the lungs to inflate, though a series of fanciful controversies on this point continued for centuries. Despite this early understanding, quantitative attention to the process of lung inflation was paid only in the early part of this century when Rohrer (60), using existing measurements of the trachea and bronchi, calculated the pressures required to produce laminar and nonlaminar flow through the airways. He presented a formula that described the relationships between frictional pressure losses and flow rate

$$\Delta P = K_1\dot{V} + K_2\dot{V}^2 \qquad (1)$$

where ΔP is the pressure difference in phase with flow rate, $\dot{V}$ is the flow rate, and K_1 and K_2 are constants.

Rohrer postulated that K_1 is proportional to gas viscosity and K_2 proportional to gas density, but their values must be determined empirically. This formula, though still usable to describe frictional pressure losses in any tube or series of tubes with fixed geometry, is now known not to have the firm basis in fluid mechanics that Rohrer originally supposed.

Rohrer also calculated the pressures required to overcome the elastic recoil of the lungs, thus providing a unifying and quantitative approach to the subject. These principles were applied by his pupil Wirz (76) in 1923 and by von Neergaard and Wirz (73) in 1927. These investigators utilized the recently developed pneumotachograph for measuring airflow rate, and they punctured the parietal pleura in human subjects to obtain dynamic measurements of pleural pressure. They neglected inertial phase shifts, which are unmeasurable at normal breathing frequencies, and they subtracted the elastic component and calculated pulmonary resistance (Fig. 1). They recognized that invasion of the pleural space would not be acceptable for general clinical usage and also developed a rapid, transient occlusion method for assessing alveolar pressure (Fig. 2). The intent was not only to avoid invasive techniques but, by obtaining alveolar pressure, to have a measure of airway resistance rather than pulmonary resistance, which includes tissue viscance. Their theory was that the transient interruption of flow allows

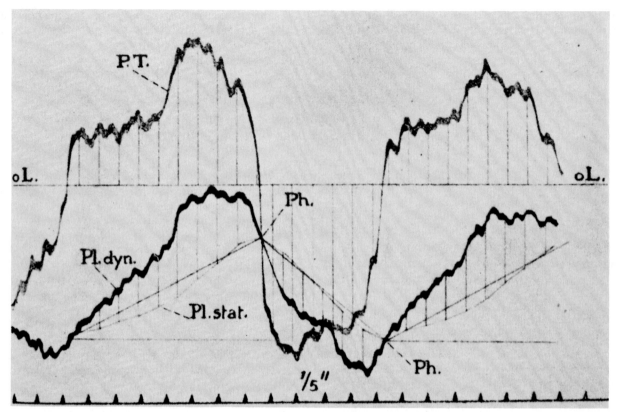

FIG. 1. Measurement of pulmonary resistance showing airflow rate (P.T. denotes pneumotacho-graph) and both static (Pl.stat) and dynamic (Pl.dyn) components of pleural pressure during breathing. Zero pressure level for pleural pressure denoted by 0L; Ph. indicates pleural pressure points at instants of zero flow. Resistance is pressure difference between Pl.dyn and Pl.stat divided by simultaneous airflow rate. [From von Neergaard and Wirz (73).]

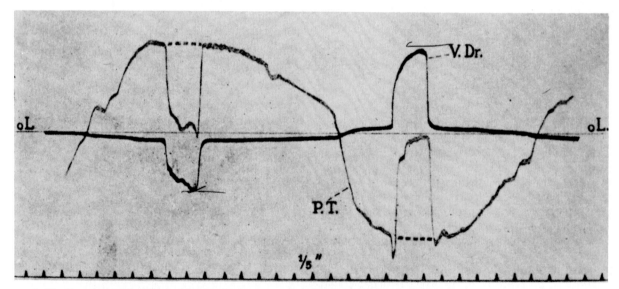

FIG. 2. Mouth pressure (*dark line*) with the zero pressure and airflow levels (0L) and airflow rate (*lighter line*, P.T. denotes pneumotachograph). V.Dr. indicates mouth pressure during occlusion. Note that during occlusion, airflow drops to zero and mouth pressure falls during inspiration or rises during expiration. Airway resistance was thought to be represented by ratio of mouth pressure to airflow rate either just before or after occlusion. See AIRWAY RESISTANCE, p. 289, for criticism of the authors' interpretation. [From von Neergaard and Wirz (73).]

pressures to equilibrate throughout the lung and airways; hence mouth pressure during the brief occlusion represents the alveolar pressure that was producing the flow immediately before and after the occlusion.

Despite development of these techniques, very few measurements were made until the early 1950s, when Mead and Whittenberger (47) measured pulmonary resistance utilizing intraesophageal pressure as an index of pleural pressure and thus brought us into the modern era.

Well before all this, Bert (2) in 1870 had recognized the principle that the volume changes associated with gas compression and decompression during breathing would give a signal proportional to alveolar pressure. However, it was not until 1923 that these principles were applied by Sonne (69), who used whole-body plethysmography to monitor breathing in normal subjects. Sonne's efforts at quantitation were frustrated when he realized that thermal exchange between gas in the lungs and the plethysmographic volume change were in the same sign as alveolar pressure. The problem was not solved until 1956 when DuBois and co-workers (10) approached the thermal exchange problem by limiting tidal excursions to less than the volume of the mouthpiece-flowmeter assembly. With such small tidal volumes, flow rates needed to be increased by increasing frequency; such a panting method has become widely used because of its rapidity, noninvasiveness, and simplicity. DuBois and co-workers recognized also that thermal exchange can be eliminated by rebreathing from a bag containing air at body temperature, ambient pressure, and saturated with water vapor (BTPS) within the plethysmograph. It was Jaeger and Otis (37) in 1964, however, who first successfully used this rebreathing technique for measuring airway resistance similar to the manner tried by Sonne. Because it is technically more demanding, this method is not used nearly as often as the panting technique.

This brief historical review is provided merely to illustrate how recently quantitative approaches to pulmonary pressure-flow relationships have been developed. In no way is it an exhaustive survey of concepts and techniques nor does it provide an adequate description of those techniques mentioned. After considering the physical basis of airway resistance, we return to a more detailed discussion of specific methods, what they measure, the advantages of each, and the potential pitfalls in their interpretation.

PHYSICAL BASIS OF AIRWAY RESISTANCE

General Principles

The chapter by Pedley and Drazen in this *Handbook* considers more completely aerodynamic theory as applied to airway resistance. This chapter briefly reiter-

ates the physical principles before examining how they can be applied quantitatively to the complex, varying, and variable structure of airways.

Pressure drop in any system of tubes can be divided into two components. One component provides the kinetic energy changes associated with acceleration (increasing fluid velocity going from a larger to a smaller cross-sectional area) or deceleration (decreasing fluid velocity going from a smaller to a larger cross-sectional area). This contribution is recoverable because energy is simply transferred between stored energy (pressure) and kinetic energy (associated with flow). The other contribution to pressure drop represents an irrecoverable dissipation of energy due to viscosity. It is this latter term that must be considered in a discussion of resistance. The ratio of viscous pressure loss to kinetic energy per unit volume, under conditions of steady or quasi-steady flow, is a dimensionless quantity known as the coefficient of friction or friction factor (C_F)

$$C_F = \frac{\Delta P}{\frac{1}{2}\rho V^2} \qquad (2)$$

where ΔP is viscous pressure loss [$N \cdot m^{-2}$ (1 Newton per square meter = 1 Pascal $\simeq$ 1/98 cmH$_2$O)], ρ is gas density (kg $\cdot$ m^{-3}), and V is average flow velocity (m $\cdot$ s^{-1}), e.g., in the trachea.

For steady flow in a given system of tubes, there is a unique relationship between C_F and Reynolds number (Re $= \rho V d/\mu$, where d is tube diameter and μ is fluid viscosity). For this reason it is convenient to plot C_F versus Re in the parent tube (i.e., to the trachea) using a log-log plot (Fig. 3). Such a dimensionless representation takes into account differences in conduit size and in physical properties of the gases, and

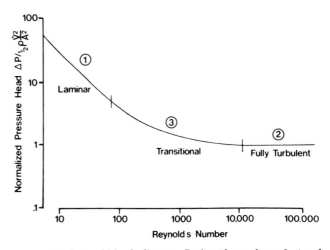

FIG. 3. Idealized Moody diagram. *Region 1* has a slope of −1 and indicates laminar flow. *Region 2* has a slope of zero and represents fully turbulent flow. *Region 3* has a variable slope between −1 and zero (average −½) representing transitional flow regimes. [From Drazen et al. (7).]

hence is particularly useful for examining experimental results in relation to theoretical predictions.

What follows is an attempt to compare predictions with experimental results from airways both in casts and in vivo. Given the very different anatomy of upper (from airway opening through the larynx) and lower (from below the larynx) airways, they will be handled separately. Also inspiratory pressure drops, because they have received much more theoretical attention, are discussed separately from expiratory events. Even so, it becomes apparent that little confidence can be placed in purely theoretical predictions of pressure drop in such complex biological systems.

Predictions of Inspiratory Pressure Drop

UPPER AIRWAYS. Finucane and Mead (14) reported that ~50% of the viscous resistance to breathing is normally provided by the upper airways. Because of the tortuous and variable geometry of these airways, it is impossible to make an accurate quantitative prediction of pressure drop in a given subject. Qualitative predictions can be made, however; during mouth breathing all the protuberances obstructing airflow (e.g., teeth, tongue) are sites of flow separation and hence of energy dissipation, and their contribution to viscous pressure loss is approximately proportional to the square of the velocity, as in a jet flow (see the chapter by Pedley and Drazen in this *Handbook*). Similarly the larynx forms a constriction at which the flow separates and forms a turbulent jet in the trachea, which spreads to the walls and causes the flow further down the trachea to be completely turbulent, even at Reynolds numbers below the usual critical value of ~2,000. It has been observed that the cross-sectional area of the laryngeal aperture varies with lung volume, flow rate, and the frequency of breathing (52, 70). Thus it is not possible to derive a simple formula relating the resistance of the larynx alone to the flow rate. All we can say is that, for a given aperture, the viscous pressure loss is proportional to the square of the velocity, as for flow through an orifice. Thus for the upper airways as a whole, we predict that at realistically large Reynolds numbers the C_F will be constant (slope of zero on a Moody diagram). During nose breathing there will be an additional contribution to the viscous pressure drop because of the convoluted course that the air must traverse.

LOWER AIRWAYS. The simplest model of the human bronchial tree for which quantitative predictions can be made is the completely symmetrical one of Weibel (74), in which every airway of a given generation has the same length (l), diameter (d), and average velocity ($\bar{V}$): the flow rate divides equally at each bifurcation. Because each pathway is identical, only one calculation has to be made for each generation at each flow rate ($\dot{V}$), and the overall viscous pressure drop is readily calculated by summing the contributions from different generations. The dimensions of various airways according to Weibel's model and the Reynolds number of airflow in them at two flow rates (0.16 liter· s^{-1} and 1.67 liters·s^{-1}) are given in Table 1 in the chapter by Pedley and Drazen in this *Handbook*.

This was the procedure followed by Pedley et al. (55), who used their entry-flow model to predict viscous pressure drop on inspiration for each generation of bronchi except the trachea, where turbulent flow is always expected, and in the smallest bronchi where Poiseuille flow was assumed for Re < 33. The basis of the entry-flow model is the observation that there are thin boundary layers in the entrance region of each tube (i.e., on the flow dividers of bifurcations) during inspiration, if the tube Reynolds number is high enough. In such layers the rate of energy dissipation is higher than in Poiseuille flow at the same flow rate, and it increases more rapidly with flow rate (the entry flow viscous pressure drop is proportional to $\dot{V}^{3/2}$, whereas the Poiseuille flow value is proportional to $\dot{V}$). The friction factor is proportional to Re^{-1} for Poiseuille flow and to $Re^{-\frac{1}{2}}$ for entry flow (see Eq. 3).

These calculations led to a prediction of how airway resistance is partitioned among the successive generations of airways at different flow rates (Fig. 4). The resistance of a particular generation is defined as the ratio of the viscous pressure drop down that generation to the overall flow rate into the lung. Results for the trachea (generation 0) have been excluded from this figure because its contribution to lower airway resistance depends in practice on the point within it from which pressure drop is measured. The lowest set of points in Figure 4 represents the distribution of resistance predicted on the assumption that Poiseuille flow is present in every airway (20). Successively higher curves represent greater airflow rates. It can be seen that, especially at the higher flow rates, the resistance of the lung as a whole is predicted to be dominated by the first six generations. This means that most of the pressure drop occurs in them, and relatively little of it occurs in the smaller, more peripheral airways (despite the fact that the resistance per unit length of airway is predicted to be greater in the latter). The peak in the resistance seen at generation 4 is a consequence of the narrowing in total airway cross-sectional area that occurs in the first four generations of Weibel's model. This is almost certainly an artifact of Weibel's averaging process, because in a real asymmetric lung the total cross-sectional area increases regularly with distance from the carina (30). It should also be borne in mind that Weibel's measurements were made on a lung whose volume was 75% of total lung capacity (TLC), thus these predictions apply quantitatively only to a lung at such a volume and to a lung without bronchial smooth muscle tone.

Pedley et al. (55) put together the predictions for every generation and computed the viscous pressure

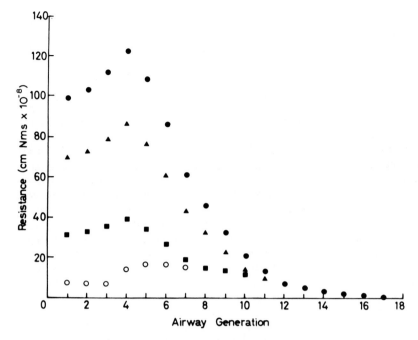

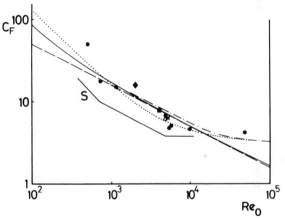

FIG. 4. Predicted variation of viscous flow resistance down the bronchial tree at airflow rates of 0.17 (■), 0.83 (▲), and 1.67 (●) liters·s⁻¹. Also shown on the same scale is the Poiseuille resistance (○). [From Pedley et al. (55).]

drop for the whole bronchial tree, from the start of the trachea to the alveoli, as a function of inspiratory flow rate. Their results have been replotted in the form of a Moody plot and are given in Figure 5. The straight broken line that coincides with the model predictions for tracheal Reynolds number (Re_0) between 3,000 and 30,000 has slope $-\frac{1}{2}$

$$C_F = 500 \; Re_0^{-\frac{1}{2}} \qquad (3)$$

and represents the complete dominance of the pressure drop by that in the larger bronchi where the entry-flow model is used. The more negative slope at smaller Reynolds numbers represents the influence of the linear pressure-flow relationship in the smallest airways. The slightly less negative slope of the solid curve at large Reynolds numbers reflects the contribution of turbulence in the trachea.

A procedure similar to that outlined above was followed by Jaffrin and Kesic (38), who modified it to take better account of turbulence at very high Reynolds numbers (such as those experienced in the rapid breathing of dense gases). They used a formula essentially the same as that for rough tube turbulence in any airway of Weibel's model in which Re exceeded 5,000. The use of a rough tube formula reflects the disturbances introduced into the flow by the frequent branching and agrees with the findings of Douglass and Munson (6). The modified predictions of this model are also shown in Figure 5. For sufficiently large values of tracheal Reynolds number, the friction factor tends to be a constant value of ~3.2.

Another fluid mechanical prediction of airway pressure drop was made by Olson et al. (51), who recognized that the pressure drop is affected by 1) changes in cross-sectional area, 2) curvature of the airways, 3)

FIG. 5. Log-log (Moody) plot of friction factor for the lower airways (C_F) against tracheal Reynolds number (Re_0). *Solid curve*: as predicted from theory of Pedley et al. (55); *broken line*: straight line of slope $-\frac{1}{2}$; *dash-dot curve*: theory modified according to proposals of Jaffrin and Kesic (38); *dotted curve*: best fit according to Rohrer's equation; *three lines marked S*: results of Slutsky et al. (66). Experimental points: ●, adapted from Jaeger and Matthys (36); ×, from Hyatt and Wilcox (33); ■, from Ferris et al. (12), corrected for tracheal diameter; △, from Vincent et al. (72); ◆, from Blide et al. (3).

entrance region character of the flow, and 4) turbulence. However, they merely estimated the four effects separately on the basis of separate experiments and added the four contributions to the pressure drop without consideration of their mutual interaction. Their predictions show a dependence of C_F on Re_0 similar to that in Figure 5, but at a higher value of C_F for any Re_0 (38).

Finally, we note that Rohrer's equation, although not thoroughly based on physical principles like the predictions already described, is the simplest equation with which to try and fit nonlinear pressure-flow relationships. In dimensionless terms it reduces to

$$C_F = \frac{K_1}{Re_0} + K_2 \qquad (4)$$

Because of its simplicity and ubiquity, we question if values of K_1 and K_2 can be found to make this equation agree with the other predictions, for example, the Jaffrin and Kesic curve in Figure 5. The natural choice for K_2 is the large Re_0 limit, 3.2. A value of K_1 of 12,700 gives agreement at $Re_0 = 700$, and the resulting curve is also shown in Figure 5. The agreement is not bad, although the Rohrer curve has too much curvature in the middle region, where a difference of ~25% occurs. Given the inevitability of experimental error, this suggests that Rohrer's equation can give acceptable accuracy when used to fit experimental data, although evaluating the constants K_1 and K_2 does not give much insight into the physical processes at work.

The above predictions have all been made on the assumption that the human bronchial tree is symmetric, as in the Weibel model. Because, in fact, it is not symmetric, the question arises as to what modifications the asymmetry introduces into the predictions. To give the answer one must know two further facts: 1) the lengths, diameters, and other geometrical properties of the real airways and 2) what difference asymmetry makes to the prediction formulas. The former are given by Horsfield et al. (30), at least for the major branches where most of the pressure drop occurs, so we have the data to put into the formulas. However, there has not been a thorough investigation of energy dissipation in asymmetric branched tubes from which a new formula to replace Equation 3 can be deduced

[some limited estimates of the rate of energy dissipation in the central airways were made by Olson et al. (52) from measurements of velocity profiles in a cast]. One might expect, because the human bronchial tree is not systematically asymmetric, that the entry-flow model still applies. However, the multiplicative constant varies from junction to junction according to the degree of asymmetry. Pedley et al. (56) used their equation with the geometrical data of Horsfield et al. to calculate the viscous pressure drop as a function of distance along the first four or five generations of every bronchial pathway, on the assumption that the flow rate into a branch was proportioned to the lung volume subtended by it. The results are shown in Figure 6, where they are compared with the predictions of a symmetric model constructed in the manner of Weibel from the data of Horsfield et al. The predicted variation between pathways is not large, apart from the significant difference between the right and left main bronchus, the former being narrower and shorter than the latter.

It is important to point out that these predictions all refer to the viscous pressure drop from the trachea to the alveoli. The pressure actually measured in the trachea is usually likely to be the static pressure, so that correction must be made for the kinetic energy of flow in the trachea by adding a kinetic term to the tracheal pressure before subtracting alveolar pressure. This kinetic energy term is equal to $\frac{1}{2}\beta\rho\dot{V}^2/A^2$, where A is the tracheal cross-sectional area and β is a constant that is equal to 1 if the velocity profile in the trachea is flat (56). That will be approximately true if the larynx is wide open, but the profile is very peaked if it is not (5a), with the result that β may be as large as 2 (as for Poiseuille flow) or even larger. It was the difficulty of assessing β in vivo that led Isabey and

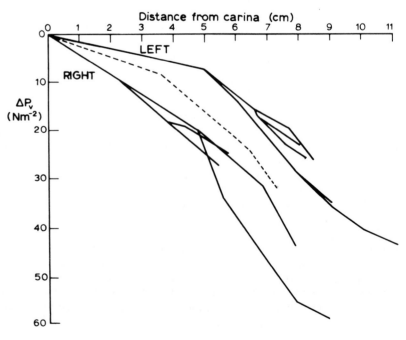

FIG. 6. Predicted variation of viscous pressure down different pathways of asymmetric model of bronchial tree given by Horsfield et al. (30). Viscous pressure drops were plotted at points representing downstream ends of all airways in model, and points joined by straight lines. *Broken line* is prediction for corresponding symmetric model. Flow rate = 1 liter·s^{-1}; 100 N·m^{-2} ≃ 1 cmH$_2$O. [From Pedley et al. (56).]

Chang (34) to prefer not to try to separate the kinetic from the truly resistive pressure drop; they presented steady inspiratory, steady expiratory, and unsteady pressure drops for gas flow in an airway cast.

COMPARISON OF PREDICTIONS WITH EXPERIMENT. The most thorough measurements of the viscous pressure drop in a cast of the human lower airways have been made by Slutsky et al. (66). Their cast, very similar to that used by Isabey and Chang (34), terminated with branches of 3–4 mm diameter, but the absence of the small airways would be unlikely to affect the overall pressure drop significantly (cf. Fig. 4). Also the diameters and lengths of the airways in their cast were significantly larger than those reported by both Weibel (74) and Horsfield et al. (30), suggesting that it had been taken at a larger volume. They achieved a wide range of Reynolds numbers by using both air and helium as flowing gases; helium has a comparable viscosity but a much smaller density than air, so the tracheal Reynolds number is smaller in helium than in air by a factor of 7.8 for the same flow rate.

Their results were presented in the form of a Moody plot of friction factor against tracheal Reynolds number and are reproduced in Figure 5. The most remarkable feature of these results is that they fit very closely to three straight lines (of slopes -1, $-\frac{1}{2}$, and 0) on the Moody plot. This strongly suggests that, as predicted, the entry-flow mechanism dominates the pressure drop in the intermediate Reynolds number range, that turbulent flow in a rough tube is a good model at large tracheal Reynolds number, and that a linear pressure-flow relationship is to be expected for small Reynolds numbers. The differences between these data and the predictions are that the transitions between the three regimes are sharp, that the transition to an approximately constant value of C_F occurs at a much smaller Reynolds number than predicted from the Weibel model, and that although the final constant value of C_F is comparable to that predicted, the measured value of C_F (i.e., of pressure drop) is significantly less than predicted for all $Re_0 < 20,000$. These discrepancies between predictions and measurements may be accounted for by the volume differences and the oversimplifications involved in using Weibel's model and in applying the same entry-flow equation to predict viscous losses for each asymmetric airway.

Human lower airway resistance has been measured in vivo by many workers (3, 7, 12, 33, 36, 72) at various flow rates and lung volumes and using various gas mixtures and methods. Most authors made corrections both for the kinetic energy of flow in the trachea and for the resistance associated with the viscous properties of lung tissue. Ferris et al. (12) found viscous resistance to be only 2% of total pulmonary resistance, whereas others have found values of up to 30% of the total (42). Because the measurements were made at several lung volumes, a suitable correction has been made where possible (see the next section) and the results are plotted in Figure 5. There is naturally much scatter, but on the whole the prediction agrees well with observation, both in absolute value and in Reynolds number variation. Similar conclusions were reached by Jaffrin and Kesic (38).

In experimental animals, it is possible to insert pressure-measuring catheters, either directly or retrogradely, into airways as small as 2–3 mm diameter, so that the resistance of the central and peripheral parts of the lower airways can be distinguished. This has been done by a number of workers (7, 41, 77), who all agree that the resistance of the larger, more central airways dominates that of the smaller, peripheral ones in the normal lung at all flow rates. This is in qualitative agreement with the predictions (Fig. 4), but quantitatively the agreement is not as good. For example, Wood et al. (77) found that the pressure-flow relationship in peripheral airways (of diameter <4 mm) was approximately linear in all cases studied, although the Reynolds number in the 4-mm airways could be as high as 380 while a dense SF_6-air mixture was being breathed. This suggests that something equivalent to Poiseuille flow exists at a much larger Reynolds number than the predicted cutoff value of 33. On the other hand, the pressure-flow relationship in the central airways was consistent with the entry-flow model at all but the lowest values of the tracheal Reynolds number.

EFFECT OF VARYING LUNG VOLUME. The cast from which Weibel made his measurements of airway dimensions was fixed at a lung volume of ~75% TLC. The predicted values of airway resistance therefore apply to this lung volume, and corrections must be made if they are to be compared with values measured at other volumes. If it is assumed that the lung is elastically homogenous, so that the lengths and diameters of all bronchi vary as the cube root of lung volume, which changes with transpulmonary pressure (31), then this correction is easy to make because the viscous pressure drop in any airway is predicted by the entry-flow model to be proportional to $l^{1/2}d^{-4}$. This in turn is proportional to $V^{-7/6}$. Predictions of the dependence of airway resistance on lung volume made in this way were shown by Pedley et al. (55) to agree well with measurements of lower airway resistance made by Vincent et al. (72) on atropinized subjects, where the effects of bronchomotor tone are minimized.

In an experimental plot with considerable scatter, it is difficult to distinguish the expressions $V^{-7/6}$, as predicted, and V^{-1}, which is commonly held to be a good fit to experimental data (3, 23).

Predictions of Expiratory Pressure Drop

In this section we consider quiet expiration in which airway collapse and flow limitation do not occur; these topics are dealt with in the chapters by Wilson, Rodarte, and Butler, by Peslin and Fredberg, and by Bryan and Wohl in this *Handbook*. As has been discussed, the pressure drop during quiet expiratory flow has received considerably less theoretical attention than that during inspiration. The main predictions are that expiratory pressure drop exceeds inspiratory pressure drop both because the velocity profiles are such that viscous energy dissipation is greater and also because the kinetic energy term has to be added to the viscous pressure drop, not subtracted from it, because fluid is accelerated during expiration. This was confirmed by the cast measurements of Isabey and Chang (34). In the chapter by Pedley and Drazen in this *Handbook*, a model was proposed on the basis of the observation that the laminar flow in a tube fed by several generations of smaller tubes is similar to fully developed turbulent flow in a long smooth tube, even at Reynolds numbers of only a few hundred. This led to the prediction that the pressure drop is proportional to $Re_0^{1.75}$, which is close to the measured relationship (in a Perspex model) of $Re_0^{1.7}$ (54) or $Re_0^{1.6}$ (24), where Re_0 is the Reynolds number at the exit, in the largest tube of the system. At larger Reynolds numbers one expects rough tube turbulence to take over (as for inspiration), in which case one would expect $\Delta P \propto Re_0^{2.0}$, and this again is close to the observations of Hardin et al. (24) for $Re_0 > 4,500$ ($\Delta P \propto Re_0^{1.93}$). After taking proper account of the kinetic energy of the flow emerging from their model, Hardin et al. used their data to predict expiratory pressure drop as a function of flow rate for the whole bronchial tree. However, their predictions give considerably lower values than those measured in vivo by Hyatt and Wilcox (33), and expiratory fluid mechanics is less well understood than inspiratory.

Validity of the Quasi-Steady Assumption for Pressure-Flow Relationships for Oscillatory Flow

Throughout this section it has been assumed that although the flow rate through the airways varies with time, the associated pressure drop is the same at any time as it would be for steady flow with the same instantaneous flow rate. The criteria by which quasi steadiness can be assessed are discussed in the chapter by Pedley and Drazen in this *Handbook*. Features of the flow governing the pressure drop in a single airway (the boundary layers on flow dividers and turbulence) are quasi-steady if the time scale within which the flow adjusts itself to changes in the driving pressure gradient is significantly less than the time scale of the unsteadiness itself (e.g., the period of an oscillation). This requires that the dimensionless quantities ϵ (for laminar flow) and α^* (for turbulent flow) are significantly less than 1, where

$$\epsilon = \omega l / \bar{V} \quad \text{and} \quad \alpha^* = \left(\frac{\omega d}{0.03\, \bar{V}} \right)^{1/2} \quad (5)$$

Here ω is a representative angular frequency of the unsteady flow, l and d are the length and diameter of the airway, and $\bar{V}$ is the cross-sectionally averaged instantaneous velocity of flow in it. In fact, a more appropriate barometer than ϵ, of which ϵ is a simplified version for sinusoidal oscillations, is

$$\epsilon' = \frac{l(d\bar{V}/dt)}{\bar{V}^2} \quad (6)$$

where ϵ' represents the ratio of local to convective acceleration in the airway concerned (34), whereas α^{*2} represents the ratio of local to fluctuating (turbulent) accelerations. The values of ϵ and α^* have been calculated for various airways and for two states of breathing (Table 1). One, representing quiet breathing, has a frequency of 0.25 Hz ($\omega = \pi/2$) and a flow rate of 0.5 liter·s^{-1}, and the other, representing rapid breathing, has a frequency of 3.0 Hz ($\omega = 6\pi$) and a flow rate of 2.0 liters·s^{-1}. The values of l and d were taken from Weibel's model, and $\bar{V}$ was calculated accordingly. In all cases ϵ is much less than 1, whereas α^* is close to 1 for the largest airways during rapid breathing. This means that the pressure drop is quasi-steady in all airways where there is laminar flow, but unsteadiness may be important (but not dominant, because α^* is not large) in those larger airways where turbulence occurs.

Apparently, then, the oscillatory nature of the normal breathing cycle does not have a marked effect on pressure-flow relationships in the lung. However, this conclusion must be treated with caution because the quoted values for ϵ and α^* were calculated on the assumption that the flow rate can be represented adequately by a typical value (0.5 liter·s^{-1}), whereas at the end of inspiration and of expiration the flow rate becomes zero. That means that however small ϵ and α^* are most of the time, they must become very large twice per cycle (because $\bar{V}$ goes to zero), and unsteadiness must be important then. Isabey and Chang (34) have demonstrated this very clearly in their experiments on oscillatory flow in a five-gener-

TABLE 1. *Values of ϵ and α^* for Several Airways and Two States of Breathing*

Airway	0.25 Hz, 0.5 liter·s^{-1}		3.0 Hz, 2.0 liters·s^{-1}	
	ϵ	α^*	ϵ	α^*
Trachea	0.096	0.69	0.29	1.20
Primary bronchus	0.035	0.55	0.10	0.95
Lobar bronchus	0.013	0.43	0.038	0.74
Generation 3	0.005	0.34	0.014	0.59
Generation 4	0.010	0.34	0.030	0.59
Generation 5	0.010	0.34	0.031	0.59
Generation 10	0.019	0.42	0.057	0.74

Quasi-steady flow dimensionless numbers: ϵ is the product of angular frequency and tube length divided by average velocity for laminar flow; α^* is proportional to the square root of the product of angular frequency times tube diameter divided by average velocity.

ation lung cast, obtaining a different curve for both inspiration and expiration on the Moody diagram for each frequency used, for each tidal volume used, and for each gas breathed. Their results show that quasi-steady behavior cannot be assumed if ϵ or $\epsilon' > 0.1$ (our $\epsilon = \frac{1}{2}\,\beta^2$ in their notation). The unsteady pressure drop is invariably higher than the quasi-steady one. Moreover resistance measurements using gases of different physical properties in normal subjects also show a different Moody plot for each gas breathed (40a), again suggesting that parameters other than Reynolds number are important.

Unsteadiness may also be significant in certain experimental circumstances when relatively high frequency oscillations are superimposed on the normal breathing cycle. Important examples are the forced-oscillation technique for the measurement of airway resistance (11) and the technique by which gas mixing is enhanced by the imposition of oscillations (68). Some aspects of these techniques are discussed in the chapter by Brody and Thurlbeck in this *Handbook*; here we note that in the forced-oscillation technique the lung is assumed to behave linearly, so that at all times the overall pressure drop (ΔP) is related to lung volume (V), flow rate ($\dot{V}$), and rate of change of flow rate ($\ddot{V}$) by

$$\Delta P = V/C + R\dot{V} + I\ddot{V} \qquad (7)$$

where C, R, and I are constants (the compliance, resistance, and inertance, respectively). It is usually assumed that C, R, and I are independent of volume, flow rate, and frequency, although there is no a priori reason why they should be (63). It follows that if the amplitude of the oscillations is sufficiently small, these quantities are approximately independent of volume and flow rate for a given frequency. However, it is known that they do depend on frequency, especially in patients with diseased lungs. The frequency dependence of compliance and resistance follows from the asymmetry of different lung regions, which therefore are ventilated asynchronously even if the driving pressure is the same for each (53, 66a). Frequency dependence of resistance and inertance is also a consequence of the fluid mechanics of oscillatory flow in tubes because of the change in velocity profile as frequency is increased. The detailed theory of oscillatory flow with angular frequency (ω) in a long straight tube (see the chapter by Pedley and Drazen in this *Handbook*) can be used to show that, for such a tube, R remains approximately independent of frequency until the Womersley parameter α (defined by $\alpha = \frac{1}{2} d\sqrt{\rho\omega/\mu}$, where μ and ρ are gas viscosity and density) exceeds ~6, when it begins to rise in proportion to $\sqrt{\omega}$. On the other hand, I varies very little with frequency, falling from $16\rho l/3\pi^2$ at very low frequency to three-fourths of this value at very high frequency. When the contributions to I are added from all airways (according to Weibel's model) one obtains a value of

I for the whole lung of ~0.01 cmH$_2$O$\cdot$liter$^{-1}\cdot$s^2. This corresponds closely to the value proposed by Mead (43) and is somewhat larger than that reported by DuBois et al. (11) when using static versus dynamic compliance.

If the frequency can be kept low in airway resistance measurements, as in the method proposed by Goldman et al. (18), those measurements are more likely to be representative of normal breathing. The more usual method (11) relies on ascertaining the resonant frequency of the lung at which the compliance and inertia in Equation 7 exactly cancel out, and this is normally in the range of 4–7 Hz. A frequency of 7 Hz corresponds to a tracheal value for α^* of 3.6 and a primary bronchus value for ϵ of 1.0 (assuming that the oscillations are superimposed on a fairly slow inspiration of 500 cm$^3\cdot$s^{-1}). At or above this frequency, therefore, increasing resistance with higher frequencies is to be expected on fluid mechanical grounds. It should be noted that this effect of frequency on resistance is independent of and has the opposite sign of the effects introduced by unequal distribution of time constants (resistance times compliance) in parallel pathways (53).

RESISTANCE IN NORMAL SUBJECTS

Physiological Factors Influencing Measurements

Resistance measurements give different values and functional assessments, depending on the pressures measured, the maneuver or technique used to produce the flow, the lung volume at which the assessment is made, and the lung volume history (hence the elastic recoil pressure) preceding the measurement. Because resistance is the ratio of the frictional pressure losses between the points of pressure measurement to the flow rate, the contribution of each component of the lung between these points is included. For example, if the pressure difference is between alveoli and the mouth, the supraglottic airways, the glottis, the subglottic extrathoracic airways, and the subglottic intrathoracic airways contribute to the pressure losses. When pressure difference in phase with flow rate is taken between the pleural space and the mouth, there is an additional pressure loss due to lung tissue viscance. Pressure differences between the mouth and the body surface, such as produced by forced oscillations at the mouth or by negative-pressure fluctuations surrounding the chest wall, add a component of tissue viscance of the chest wall.

If the predominant aim for measuring resistance is that of assessing the caliber of intrathoracic airways, a consideration of the rather large and variable contribution of upper airways to the result is necessary. Initially Hyatt and Wilcox (32, 33), and subsequently other investigators (3, 12, 64, 72), partitioned pulmo-

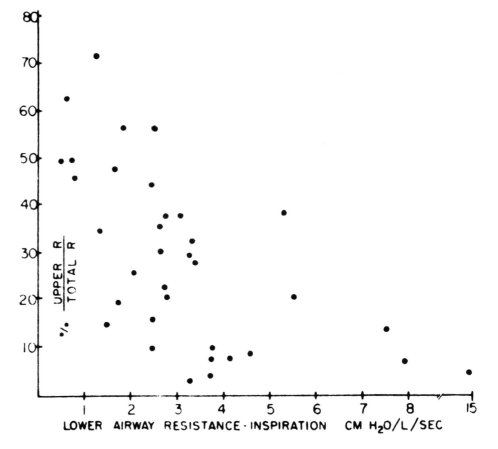

FIG. 7. Ratio × 100 of upper to lower airway resistance plotted against absolute values of lower airway resistance. Note that with increasing lower airway resistance there is decrease in relative contribution of upper airways to total resistance. [From Hyatt and Wilcox (32).]

nary resistance into upper and lower airway components by measuring intratracheal pressure 2–3 cm below the cricoid cartilage. Hyatt and Wilcox found larger inter- and intrasubject variations in the upper airway contribution, but it approximated 50% in normal subjects and 20% in subjects with chronic airway obstruction. More informative, however, is their plot of the ratio of upper airway to total pulmonary resistance versus lower pulmonary resistance (Fig. 7). The logic is simple. Because the absolute values of upper airway resistance were approximately the same in all subjects, their relative contribution to overall resistance lessened in direct proportion to the elevation of lower airway resistance. From this it is possible to conclude that resistance measurements will be most valuable in assessing either acute increases in intrathoracic airway caliber in those subjects with high intrathoracic resistance values or the decrease in caliber with induced bronchoconstriction. However, it has been demonstrated that changes in glottic aperture, the major source of upper airway variability, are in the same sign as intrathoracic airway caliber change (25). Thus it is often not possible to accept changes in total airway resistance as representative of intrathoracic airway events.

There are ways, however, to maximize the glottic aperture and hence to minimize its contribution to resistive pressure losses. Hyatt and Wilcox demon-

strated that the upper airway component decreased ~40% with hyperventilation (32). Stănescu and co-workers (70) extended this observation by direct laryngoscopy and demonstrated that the glottic aperture was wider during panting. Further, Jackson and colleagues (35) showed, also by direct visualization, that glottic aperture was maximized by having the subject pant with no restriction of tidal volume. It may be that the DuBois technique, which requires restricted panting because of thermal effects, cannot always provide accurate information regarding intrathoracic airway changes, especially when subtle effects in normal or near-normal subjects are being examined. However, DuBois et al. (11) reported that the larynx remained open in the two subjects they examined by indirect laryngoscopy. One recent study by Goldstein and Mead (19) offered an alternative solution for studies in normal subjects. These authors used forced oscillations at the mouth immediately after unrestricted panting during the interval when the glottis remained widely open.

These considerations of variations in upper airway configuration and their effects on measured resistance mean that quantitative fluid mechanical predictions of a pressure-flow relationship in the upper airways cannot be made. Moreover casts, with their fixed structure, can provide data of only very limited physiological significance. When there are cyclic variations in glottic aperture size within each breath during quiet breathing, any serious attempt to test fluid mechanical predictions for inspiratory versus expiratory submaximal flow, for example, would need to bypass the upper airways. In studies where this has been done (12), inspiratory intrathoracic airway resistance has been found to be 15%–20% lower than the expiratory values.

An additional complexity introduced by change in glottic aperture is that it varies with lung volume and hence contributes to the volume dependency of overall airway and pulmonary resistance (70). In studies where lower airway resistance has been examined in relation to lung volume, however, there remained a distinct, inverse power relationship of resistance to lung volume (a linear relationship of conductance to lung volume) that is caused by the mechanical interdependence of parenchyma and airways (5). Thus the slope and position of this relationship between conductance and volume obviously is strongly influenced by airway smooth muscle tone and the volume-dependent recoil properties of the lung parenchyma. Vincent and co-workers (72) found a distinct decrease in lower pulmonary conductance at volumes approaching TLC; the explanation is not readily available, but two possibilities must be considered. One is that the increase in tissue viscance at high lung volumes more than offsets the increase in airway caliber, as proposed by Hoppin et al. (28) to explain a similar finding in dog lungs. The other is that at high lung volumes the longitudinal stretching of large airways produces a decrease in caliber. Neither of these eminently testable possibilities has been explored to date.

Because both airways and parenchyma exhibit volume hysteresis, which is dependent on both volume history and time, the exact result of their interaction depends on their relative degrees of hysteresis. Hence the failures of predictions mentioned in PHYSICAL BASIS OF AIRWAY RESISTANCE, p. 279, should come as no surprise. These failures do not reflect the inadequacies of our understanding and application of the physical sciences as much as the enormous biological variability seen within and between subjects and the impossibility of making precise anatomical measurements in vivo. Several clear, qualitative statements can be made, however, to guide the physiologist who wishes to evaluate the significant influence of volume history on resistance measurements. First, when there is a nearly uniform static distending pressure of airways and lung parenchyma and a much greater volume of lung parenchyma, the overall pressure-volume relationship of lung and airways is heavily dominated by the lung. Second, when airway hysteresis exceeds that of the parenchyma, airway dimensions are greater at a given volume when that volume is reached from TLC than when it is reached from residual volume (Fig. 8). This was the most common pattern seen by Froeb and Mead (17). Yet the studies of Vincent et al.

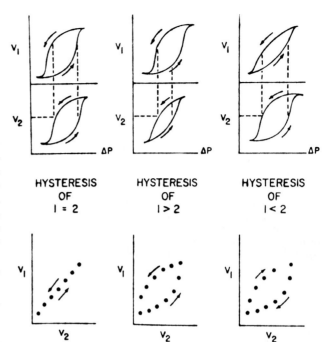

FIG. 8. Schematic drawing showing how relative volume changes of volume-pressure systems exposed to identical pressure cycles can be used to assess relative volume-pressure hysteresis. V_1, airway volume measured as anatomical dead space; V_2, lung volume. Note in *middle panel,* for example, that airways are larger at same lung volume when volume is reached from deflation than when reached from inflation if airway hysteresis exceeds that of lung. [From Froeb and Mead (17).]

(72) showed some subjects with opposite patterns. Because the degree of airway hysteresis is directly related to bronchomotor tone (28, 72), constriction of airway smooth muscle tends to exaggerate the effect of volume history by decreasing resistance greatly after a full inflation (50). Decreases in bronchomotor tone to produce less airway than parenchymal hysteresis result in higher resistance after full inflation. Although this latter pattern has not been directly looked for in this context, Vincent et al. (72) found that after atropine administration pulmonary resistance was slightly greater after inflation to total lung capacity. Of course, equal degrees of hysteresis result in no effect of volume history at all. Because hysteresis mostly reflects viscoelastic properties and because elastic energy is dissipated by flow in the viscous elements, the relative time-dependent behavior of airways and parenchyma becomes important. There is not a large body of literature on this subject, but available data suggest that the time-dependent airway events are less rapid than those of the parenchyma (21). When there is a strong interdependence of airways and parenchyma, the practical message is that volume history and timing sequences must be rigidly standardized if variability between and within subjects is to be minimized.

Central Versus Peripheral Airway Contribution
to Lower Pulmonary Resistance

As mentioned in PHYSICAL BASIS OF AIRWAY RESIS-
TANCE, p. 279, most of the resistance to flow is in the
central airways >2 mm internal diameter; hence
the contributions to overall resistance of smaller airways are normally quite small. To date no submaximal
flow technique has been useful for partitioning lower
airway resistance in human subjects. Although a catheter could be passed retrogradely into intrathoracic
airways, if it were passed into airways <2 mm internal
diameter, the catheter itself would undoubtedly alter
pressure-flow relationships sufficiently to interfere
with interpretation. Macklem and Mead (41) were able
to minimize that problem with dog lungs by pulling a
retrograde catheter through the pleural surface until
the flared central end was wedged snugly in a bronchus
of ~2 mm internal diameter, allowing lateral pressure
to be measured in adjacent, patent bronchi of similar
size. Although this technique has been used to partition resistance in excised human lungs (27), it clearly
has no place in the study of intact human subjects.

Several alternative approaches have been suggested,
but because of the large and variable contribution of
upper airways to overall resistance each approach
could only be applied to the study of lower airway
resistance, which would require a direct pressure measurement below the larynx. Drazen et al. (8), using
intubated dogs, compared partitioned resistance values obtained with a retrograde catheter with overall
pressure-flow measurements using gases of different
physical properties at different flow rates before and
during either peripheral or central airway constriction.
Their idea was that large tracheal Reynolds numbers
produced by very dense gases and high flow rates
would produce large resistance changes with central
airway resistance increases and that large resistance
changes with low tracheal Reynolds numbers produced by low flow rates and less-dense gases would
indicate peripheral airway resistance increases, thus
obviating the need for retrograde catheters. Their data
on central versus peripheral constriction, as validated
by retrograde catheters, supported their idea. This
approach for the localization of airway responses has
not been applied to the study of human subjects to
date.

Another approach that has not been evaluated by
an independent partitioning technique was used by
Pimmel et al. (57). These authors evaluated frequency
dependence of resistance and analyzed their results
on the basis of an electrical analogue that assumed
pressure-flow relationships to be linear and that excluded parallel time-constant differences. The slope
of the graph of log resistance against log frequency
was used to evaluate the ratios of central and peripheral resistance (57). In addition to the questions raised
by the many assumptions of their analogue, a major
problem in using their technique for overall pressure-

flow measurements in intact human subjects (75) is
that the anatomic location of their central and peripheral resistors is unknown. It may be that the central
one is located in the upper airways and that the
peripheral one is in the lower airways, in which case
a great deal could be learned by the technique. The
same can be said about the more exact approach to
the same model proposed by Slutsky and Drazen (67).
It is fair to state that no one has yet developed and
tested a submaximal pressure–flow rate technique for
partitioning central versus peripheral components of
lower airway resistance in normal subjects.

Tissue Viscance

Although the major forces required to distend lung
tissue and expand the chest wall are elastic, there is a
component of viscous pressure loss across these structures that is in phase with flow rate and thus is added
to airway resistance when either pulmonary or respiratory resistance is measured. Alternative designations for this tissue component have been tissue resistance (28), tissue viscous resistance (76), tissue
hysteresis (49), volume-pressure hysteresis, quasi-
static hysteresis, and tissue flow resistance (61). We
have chosen the term *tissue viscance* because it does
not imply any mechanism and serves to distinguish it
from airway resistance, about which a great deal more
is known. Not only is the mechanism difficult to
isolate, but the difficulty in measuring this quantity
is reflected in the wide range of values found in normal
subjects. For example, Ferris et al. (12) found that
lung tissue viscance varied between −6% (a negative
value) and +11% of respiratory system resistance, but
on average contributed 1% to the resistance of the
total system and 2% to the pulmonary resistance.
Others have found pulmonary tissue viscance values
up to 30% of pulmonary resistance in normal subjects
(42). Such wide variability comes from substantial
background noise of both electrical and biological
origins, especially the latter, mainly produced by cardiovascular events that can produce large pressure
signals in the esophageal balloon tracings. The contribution of the viscance of the chest wall, on the other
hand, has been found to be consistently higher in
relation to respiratory system resistance, varying between 27% and 50% and averaging 39% in the study
by Ferris et al. (12). Although there are very few
systematic studies of chest wall viscance, the work of
Hildebrandt (26) and Hoppin et al. (28) on animal
lungs can serve as a useful guide in considering pulmonary tissue viscance. They showed that pulmonary
tissue viscance increases directly with lung volume;
hence the error in attributing resistance values to
airways will be potentially large only at high lung
volumes. Moreover the contribution of tissue viscance
to total respiratory resistance decreases with increased
frequency.

A practical guide for the physiologist comes from

the comparison of airway, pulmonary, and total resistance values in normal subjects by Frank et al. (15). Excluding quiet breathing, during which the variable laryngeal component is large, we can conclude that the total viscous pressure drop in normal subjects is ~70% across the airways, 10% across pulmonary tissue, and 20% across the chest wall. With modest doses of a bronchoconstrictor, the airway component rose to 80% (12), and it is reasonable to assume that further constriction of the airways would render the tissue contribution even smaller.

Inertance

DuBois and colleagues (11) estimated the inertance (I) of the respiratory system in 1955 by determining the damped natural frequency (f_n) and total static compliance (C) of the total respiratory system. Treating it as a simple, linear mechanical system during forced oscillations, and using the relationship by which natural frequency relates to inertance and compliance, $f_n = (2\pi)^{-1}(C/I)^{1/2}$, they calculated inertance to be 5.8×10^{-3} cmH$_2$O$\cdot$liter$^{-1}\cdot$s^2, a value small enough to be neglected in normal subjects breathing air at ambient conditions. A short time later Mead (43) found values for the lungs and airways (excluding chest wall) that were approximately twice as great as the values found by DuBois and colleagues for the total system. By changing the physical properties of the respired gas, Mead concluded that the measured inertance is predominantly due to acceleration and deceleration of respired gases rather than of lung tissue. The low values calculated by DuBois et al. resulted from the use of static rather than dynamic compliance during oscillations. Nonetheless, even the higher inertance values are sufficiently small at normal breathing frequencies to be ignorable. However, high gas density, high cycling frequency, or large body weight of subjects (65) gives inertance values great enough that they should be taken into account. This is not onerous, because by using proper instrumental and display techniques and by using pressure in phase with flow to derive resistance, the correction is automatically made.

Frequency Dependence

In the preceding paragraph and in *Validity of the Quasi-Steady Assumption for Pressure-Flow Relationships for Oscillatory Flow*, p. 284, and *Central Versus Peripheral Airway Contribution to Lower Pulmonary Resistance*, p. 288, the importance of frequency on the measurement and interpretation of resistance has been introduced. The earliest attempt at assessing frequency-dependent behavior of the lung was made by Otis and colleagues (53), who utilized a model of the respiratory system comprising many parallel units, each with a resistance and a compliance in series. In such a system, with different time constants (resistance times compliance) in parallel units, the overall resistance and compliance both decreased with increasing frequency, because the lower time-constant regions received a greater portion of the flow. Hence such frequency-dependent behavior was taken as evidence for nonhomogeneous distribution of inspired gas. Mead (45) modified the model so that the parallel compliances represented the parenchyma and proximal airways, and there was a resistor in series with the parenchymal compliance. From his analysis it became clear that uniform increases in peripheral airway resistance can produce frequency-dependent behavior as the distension of more proximal airways dominates at higher frequencies. Such analyses and interpretations are based on simple linear models that assign single compliance and resistance values to each of the units. Note that the models can be easily modified to include inertances of the parallel pathways, and the predicted overall resistance can thereby be made to increase with frequency. This increase is in addition to that predicted on fluid mechanical grounds.

Techniques for Measuring Resistance

In this final section we wish to list, categorize, and evaluate several techniques for measuring resistance. This requires a brief recapitulation of some of the points made earlier in the chapter. Our purpose is to present in one place a summary guide for a student or beginning investigator who wishes to select the most appropriate technique for the problem under investigation or to evaluate methods reported in the literature. Every method discussed includes the variable contribution of the upper airways, although this can be directly assessed by using appropriate partitioning techniques. Although we have not discussed instrumentation in any detail here, it should be strongly emphasized that with any technique the measuring systems for the pressure and flow rate should be carefully matched for both amplitude and frequency response. It is only after this is assured that changes or differences in pressure-flow relationships can be interpreted in fluid mechanical or physiological terms.

AIRWAY RESISTANCE. Airway resistance is most frequently measured using the technique of DuBois and colleagues (10), which employs a constant-volume, variable-pressure, whole-body plethysmograph (Fig. 9A). The plethysmographic (or box) pressure signal is calibrated so as to represent lung volume changes (ΔPbox = ΔVL). During respiratory efforts with the mouth shutter closed, the pressure at the mouth (Pm) equals pressures throughout the communicating airways and alveoli (PA). During such maneuvers the box pressure varies as the lung volume changes owing to the compression and decompression of gas (Fig. 9A). Now, the ratio of ΔPbox to PA allows calibration of ΔVL in terms of PA and a calculation of lung volume by the Boyle's law technique. The shutter is then opened and the subject pants at ~2 Hz. The relation-

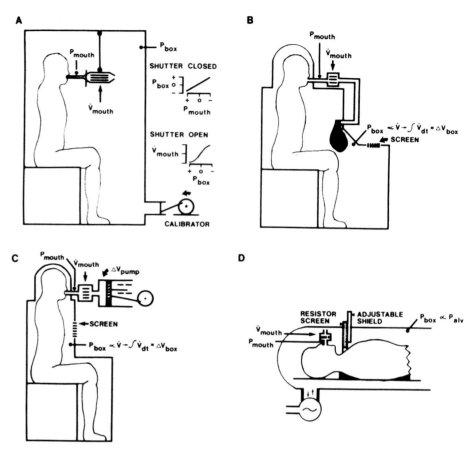

FIG. 9. Four plethysmographic methods for measuring airway resistance. P_{mouth}, mouth pressure; P_{box}, pressure within plethysmograph; $\dot{V}_{mouth}$, airflow rate at mouth. *A*: most commonly used technique. [Adapted from DuBois et al. (10).] *B*: bag contains air at BTPS conditions to avoid thermal effects. [Adapted from Jaeger and Otis (37).] *C*: ΔV_{pump} is volume change of pump at mouth. [Adapted from Finucane et al. (13).] *D*: barospirator technique. [Adapted from Schwaber and Mead (64).]

ship of Pbox (PA) to Pm and flow rate defines the resistance of the airways. The use of a panting maneuver causes the thermal boundary to be maintained within the mouthpiece-flowmeter assembly and minimizes the laryngeal resistance. The rapidity and ease of this method with the concurrent lung volume measurement have made it a popular and useful one for both physiological investigation and clinical applications.

Whole-body plethysmography has been adapted in several other ways for airway resistance measurements. Jaeger and Otis (37) and Jonson and Bouhuys (39) avoided the thermal effects that interfered with Sonne's technique by having their subjects (while seated in a variable-volume plethysmograph) respire from a closed circuit with gas kept at BTPS conditions. Hence the volume signal of the box was directly proportional to PA (Fig. 9B). This technique can be used to assess resistance during quiet breathing, panting, or forceful maneuvers, and thus offers some flexibility. Yet despite these theoretical advantages it is technically complex and cumbersome, so that few studies have used this method.

A further technical refinement was offered by Finucane and Mead (14), who used forced oscillations (1–10 Hz, volume displacements up to 130 ml) at the mouth while subjects were seated in a variable-volume, whole-body plethysmograph (Fig. 9C). Their rationale was that measurements during oscillatory flow at frequencies greater than those seen during panting or quiet breathing have the advantage of increased resolution of the primary signals (PA and V̇) in time. As an added bonus, their method also allowed a continuous measurement of lung volume. This technique was used to study the frequency dependence of resistance in healthy subjects to determine that part of the overall resistance that is related to the distributions of both resistance and reactance within the lung, not simply to the sum of the resistances of individual airway generations (13). Despite that fruitful use, the technical demands are sufficiently great that this method too is likely to be of use only to those with specific questions that cannot be answered in other ways.

A somewhat novel adaptation of whole-body plethysmography combined with forced oscillation was described by Schwaber and Mead (64). They used the Thunberg barospirator originally devised in 1926 for the purpose of applying external positive and negative pressures that ventilated the subject by gas compression and decompression (71). The initial rationale was to rest the lungs of patients with cavitary pulmonary tuberculosis. Schwaber and Mead had their subject lie supine in the device (Fig. 9D), and a partition with a variable flow resistor was placed between the head and the remainder of the body. The head portion was oscillated at 12–20 cycles/min at ± 80 cmH₂O. When the resistor of the partition was adjusted to give a parallel time constant equal to that of the subject, cyclic motion of the lungs ceased and ventilation was maintained by compression and decompression. Pressure in the body compartment equaled alveolar pressure in these conditions, and so airway resistance was derived. Although this is an intriguing technique, it has not been used subsequently because the equipment is difficult to assemble and preparation of the subject is time consuming.

As noted in HISTORICAL PERSPECTIVES, p. 277, von Neergaard and Wirz devised a nonplethysmographic method for assessing airway resistance. Their idea was that during a brief interruption of airflow, mouth pressure quickly equilibrates with alveolar pressure, which in turn is related to flow rate immediately before and after that occlusion. Mead and Whittenberger (48), however, by using a force-balance equation, have correctly argued that this technique will theoretically measure the pressure generated by the muscles in overcoming airway as well as lung tissue and chest wall viscance (i.e., it will theoretically measure total respiratory system resistance). Their experimental test of this revealed values slightly greater than pulmonary resistance (but less than total system resistance). They attributed this to a damping effect of chest wall on sudden changes in intrapleural pressure. Thus the interrupter technique gives values that cannot be easily categorized or considered as representative of airway, pulmonary, or total system resistance.

PULMONARY RESISTANCE. Evaluation of pulmonary resistance depends on a valid measurement of intrapleural pressure and its change during the breathing cycle. Pressure differences in phase with volume are subtracted either visually, by the isovolume method used by von Neergaard and Wirz (73) and by Mead and Whittenberger (47), or by electronic means to leave pressure in phase with flow rate, representing pulmonary resistance. At low frequencies (<0.4 Hz), inertial pressure changes are sufficiently small that they can be ignored. However, at higher frequencies, corrections for volume acceleration must be made; this can be easily accomplished electronically by subtracting from pulmonary pressure quantities proportional to both acceleration and tidal volume. Thus this method can be used for quiet breathing, during panting, or during forced oscillations. The disadvantages

are that the subject must swallow an esophageal balloon on the end of a catheter, and the resultant value includes an unpredictable and variable contribution from tissue viscance.

RESPIRATORY SYSTEM RESISTANCE. Because resistance of the entire system is obtained by relating in-phase pressure difference between mouth and body surface to simultaneous flow rate, values could be derived by imposing sinusoidal pressure fluctuations either at the body surface (44) or at the mouth. The latter technique is the most often used and was initially introduced by Brody and DuBois in 1956 (4). It has been applied because it eliminates the need for an esophageal balloon, requires little cooperation, and can be used during spontaneous breathing. It is based on the theory that the respiratory system has a resonant frequency at which compliance and inertial factors are equal and of opposite sign, thus canceling to leave a pressure signal in phase with flow rate (11). In normal adult subjects, both DuBois et al. (11) and Grimby et al. (22) found this frequency to be between 5 and 7 Hz.

Two methods have been proposed to measure respiratory resistance at frequencies other than the resonant frequency, which otherwise has to be determined for each subject. Grimby et al. simulated the conditions of resonant frequency by electrically subtracting from mouth pressure a signal proportional to either volume or volume acceleration, depending on whether the oscillation frequency was above or below the resonant value. This required oscilloscopic X-Y display of pressure and flow rate, the loop of which was closed electrically and the slope then determined. Goldman and colleagues (18) described a method that could be applied to a strip-chart recording. They reasoned that the inertial contribution would be zero at peak flow rates when the volume acceleration is zero. Also, with sinusoidal forcing, the lung volume is always the same at peak flow rates; hence elastic pressures should cancel out. When these two methods were compared in normal subjects there was good agreement, yet in obstructive lung disease the simulated resonant frequency method of Grimby et al. appeared to be superior, because it correlated better with other tests of pulmonary function (40).

CONCLUDING REMARKS

Despite a long history of physiological insight, quantitative approaches have only recently appeared for the measurement of pulmonary pressure-flow relationships. The precise application of fluid mechanical principles to predict these relationships has been hampered by the large physiological variability both within and between subjects and by the impossibility of measuring airway dimensions accurately in vivo. The evolution of technique reflects the efforts that have been made to minimize the more predictable sources of variability, such as the glottic aperture. However, this evolution has resulted in more complex, technically demanding, and cumbersome methods that have served the specific purpose for which they were designed but have not proved suitable for routine use in clinical pulmonary function laboratories. Undoubt-

edly more modifications and newer techniques will appear. We suspect that new approaches will improve our ability to correlate measurements of pressure-flow relationships with particular aspects of lung geometry and function and thereby enable abnormalities in the latter to be more easily and accurately diagnosed.

REFERENCES

1. ALBRIGHT, C. D., AND S. BONDURANT. Some effects of respiratory frequency on pulmonary mechanics. *J. Clin. Invest.* 44: 1362-1370, 1965.
2. BERT, P. *Leçons sur la physiologie comparée de la respiration.* Paris: Ballière, 1870, p. 381-389.
3. BLIDE, R. W., H. D. KERR, AND W. S. SPICER, JR. Measurement of upper and lower airway resistance and conductance in man. *J. Appl. Physiol.* 19: 1059-1069, 1964.
4. BRODY, A. W., AND A. B. DUBOIS. Determination of tissue, airway and total resistance to respiration in cats. *J. Appl. Physiol.* 9: 213-218, 1956.
5. BUTLER, J., C. G. CARO, R. ALCALA, AND A. B. DUBOIS. Physiological factors affecting airway resistance in normal subjects and in patients with obstructive respiratory disease. *J. Clin. Invest.* 43: 584-591, 1960.
5a.CHANG, H. K., AND O. A. EL MASRY. A model study of flow dynamics in human central airways. Part I. Axial velocity profiles. *Respir. Physiol.* 49:75-95, 1982.
6. DOUGLASS, R. W., AND B. R. MUNSON. Viscous energy dissipation in a model of the human bronchial tree. *J. Biomech.* 7: 551-557, 1974.
7. DRAZEN, J. M., S. H. LORING, AND R. H. INGRAM, JR. Distribution of pulmonary resistance: effects of gas density, viscosity, and flow rate. *J. Appl. Physiol.* 41: 388-395, 1976.
8. DRAZEN, J. M., S. H. LORING, AND R. H. INGRAM, JR. Localization of airway constriction using gases of varying density and viscosity. *J. Appl. Physiol.* 41: 396-399, 1976.
10. DUBOIS, A. B., S. Y. BOTELHO, AND J. H. COMROE, JR. A new method for measuring airway resistance in man using a body plethysmograph: values in normal subjects and in patients with respiratory disease. *J. Clin. Invest.* 35: 327-335, 1956.
11. DUBOIS, A. B., A. W. BRODY, D. H. LEWIS, AND B. F. BURGESS, JR. Oscillation mechanics of lungs and chest in man. *J. Appl. Physiol.* 8: 587-594, 1955.
12. FERRIS, B. G., JR., J. MEAD, AND L. H. OPIE. Partitioning of respiratory flow resistance in man. *J. Appl. Physiol.* 19: 653-658, 1964.
13. FINUCANE, K. E., S. V. DAWSON, P. D. PHELAN, AND J. MEAD. Resistance of intrathoracic airways of healthy subjects during periodic flow. *J. Appl. Physiol.* 38: 517-530, 1975.
14. FINUCANE, K. E., AND J. MEAD. Estimation of alveolar pressure during forced oscillation of the respiratory system. *J. Appl. Physiol.* 38: 531-537, 1975.
15. FRANK, N. R., J. MEAD, AND J. L. WHITTENBERGER. Comparative sensitivity of four methods for measuring changes in respiratory flow resistance in man. *J. Appl. Physiol.* 31: 934-938, 1971.
16. FREDBERG, J. J., AND J. MEAD. Impedance of intrathoracic airway models during low-frequency periodic flow. *J. Appl. Physiol.: Respirat. Environ. Exercise Physiol.* 47: 347-351, 1979.
17. FROEB, H. F., AND J. MEAD. Relative hysteresis of the dead space and lung in vivo. *J. Appl. Physiol.* 25: 244-248, 1968.
18. GOLDMAN, M., R. J. KNUDSON, J. MEAD, N. PETERSON, J. R. SCHWABER, AND M. E. WOHL. A simplified measurement of respiratory resistance by forced oscillation. *J. Appl. Physiol.* 28: 113-116, 1970.
19. GOLDSTEIN, D., AND J. MEAD. Total respiratory impedance immediately after panting. *J. Appl. Physiol.: Respirat. Environ. Exercise Physiol.* 48: 1024-1028, 1980.

20. GREEN, M. How big are the bronchioles? *St. Thomas' Hosp. Gaz.* 63: 136-139, 1965.
21. GREEN, M., AND J. MEAD. Time dependence of flow-volume curves. *J. Appl. Physiol.* 37: 793-797, 1974.
22. GRIMBY, G., T. TAKISHIMA, W. GRAHAM, P. T. MACKLEM, AND J. MEAD. Frequency dependence of flow resistance in patients with obstructive lung disease. *J. Clin. Invest.* 47: 1455-1461, 1968.
23. GUYATT, A. R., AND J. H. ALPERS. Factors affecting airways conductance: a study of 752 working men. *J. Appl. Physiol.* 24: 310-316, 1968.
24. HARDIN, J. C., J. C. YU, J. L. PATTERSON, AND W. TRIBLE. The pressure/flow relation in bronchial airways on expiration. In: *Biofluid Mechanics*, edited by D. J. Schneck. New York: Plenum, 1980, vol. 2, p. 39-55.
25. HIGENBOTTAM, T. Narrowing of glottis opening in humans associated with experimentally induced bronchoconstriction. *J. Appl. Physiol.: Respirat. Environ. Exercise Physiol.* 49: 403-407, 1980.
26. HILDEBRANDT, J. Dynamic properties of air-filled excised cat lung determined by liquid plethysmograph. *J. Appl. Physiol.* 27: 246-250, 1969.
27. HOGG, J. C., J. WILLIAMS, J. B. RICHARDSON, P. T. MACKLEM, AND W. M. THURLBECK. Age as a factor in the distribution of lower-airway conductance and in the pathologic anatomy of obstructive lung disease. *N. Engl. J. Med.* 282: 1283-1287, 1970.
28. HOPPIN, F. G., JR., M. GREEN, AND M. S. MORGAN. Relationship of central and peripheral airway resistance to lung volume in dogs. *J. Appl. Physiol.: Respirat. Environ. Exercise Physiol.* 44: 728-737, 1978.
29. HORSFIELD, K., AND G. CUMMING. Morphology of the bronchial tree in the dog. *Respir. Physiol.* 26: 176-182, 1976.
30. HORSFIELD, K., G. DART, D. E. OLSON, G. F. FILLEY, AND G. CUMMING. Models of the human bronchial tree. *J. Appl. Physiol.* 31: 207-217, 1971.
31. HUGHES, J. M. B., F. G. HOPPIN, JR., AND J. MEAD. Effect of lung inflation on bronchial length and diameter in excised lungs. *J. Appl. Physiol.* 32: 25-35, 1972.
32. HYATT, R. E., AND R. E. WILCOX. Extrathoracic airway resistance in man. *J. Appl. Physiol.* 16: 326-330, 1961.
33. HYATT, R. E., AND R. E. WILCOX. The pressure-flow relationship of the intrathoracic airways in man. *J. Clin. Invest.* 42: 29-39, 1963.
34. ISABEY, D., AND H. K. CHANG. Steady and unsteady pressure-flow relationships in central airways. *J. Appl. Physiol.: Respirat. Environ. Exercise Physiol.* 51: 1338-1348, 1981.
35. JACKSON, A. C., P. J. GULESIAN, JR., AND J. MEAD. Glottal aperture during panting with voluntary limitation of tidal volume. *J. Appl. Physiol.* 39: 834-836, 1975.
36. JAEGER, M. J., AND H. MATTHYS. The pressure-flow characteristics of the human airways. In: *Symposium on Airway Dynamics*, edited by A. Bouhuys. Springfield, IL: Thomas, 1969.
37. JAEGER, M. J., AND A. B. OTIS. Measurement of airway resistance with a volume displacement body plethysmograph. *J. Appl. Physiol.* 19: 813-820, 1964.
38. JAFFRIN, M. Y., AND P. KESIC. Airway resistance: a fluid mechanical approach. *J. Appl. Physiol.* 36: 354-361, 1974.
39. JONSON, B., AND A. BOUHUYS. Measurement of alveolar pressure. *J. Appl. Physiol.* 22: 1081-1085, 1967.

40. LANDAU, L. I., AND P. D. PHELAN. Evaluation of two techniques for measurement of respiratory resistance by forced oscillation. *Thorax* 28: 136–141, 1973.

40a.LISBOA, C., L. D. H. WOOD, J. JARDIM, AND P. T. MACKLEM. Relation between flow, curvilinearity, and density dependence of pulmonary pressure-flow curves. *J. Appl. Physiol.: Respirat. Environ. Exercise Physiol.* 48: 878–885, 1980.

41. MACKLEM, P. T., AND J. MEAD. Resistance of central and peripheral airways measured by a retrograde catheter. *J. Appl. Physiol.* 22: 395–401, 1967.

42. MCILROY, M. B., J. MEAD, N. J. SELVERSTONE, AND E. P. RADFORD. Measurement of lung tissue viscous resistance using gases of equal kinematic viscosity. *J. Appl. Physiol.* 7: 485–490, 1955.

43. MEAD, J. Measurement of inertia of the lungs at increased ambient pressure. *J. Appl. Physiol.* 9: 208–212, 1956.

44. MEAD, J. Control of respiratory frequency. *J. Appl. Physiol.* 15: 325–336, 1960.

45. MEAD, J. Contribution of compliance of airways to frequency-dependent behavior of lungs. *J. Appl. Physiol.* 26: 670–673, 1969.

46. MEAD, J., AND C. COLLIER. Relation of volume history of lungs to respiratory mechanics in anesthetized dogs. *J. Appl. Physiol.* 14: 669–678, 1959.

47. MEAD, J., AND J. L. WHITTENBERGER. Physical properties of human lungs measured during spontaneous respiration. *J. Appl. Physiol.* 5: 779–796, 1953.

48. MEAD, J., AND J. L. WHITTENBERGER. Evaluation of airway interruption technique as a method for measuring air-flow resistance. *J. Appl. Physiol.* 6: 408–416, 1954.

49. MOUNT, L. E. The ventilation flow-resistance and compliance of rat lungs. *J. Physiol. London* 127: 157–167, 1955.

50. NADEL, J. A., AND D. F. TIERNEY. Effect of a previous deep inspiration on airway resistance in man. *J. Appl. Physiol.* 16: 717–719, 1961.

51. OLSON, D. E., G. A. DART, AND G. F. FILLEY. Pressure drop and fluid flow regime of air inspired into the human lung. *J. Appl. Physiol.* 28: 482–494, 1970.

52. OLSON, D. E., L. D. ILIFF, AND M. F. SUDLOW. Some aspects of the physics of flow in the central airways. *Bull. Physio-Pathol. Respir.* 8: 391–408, 1972.

53. OTIS, A. B., C. B. MCKERROW, R. A. BARTLETT, J. MEAD, M. B. MCILROY, N. J. SELVERSTONE, AND E. P. RADFORD. Mechanical factors in distribution of pulmonary ventilation. *J. Appl. Physiol.* 8: 427–443, 1956.

54. PACOME, J.-J. Structures d'écoulement et pertes de charge calculées dans le modèle d'arbre bronchique de Weibel. Toulouse, France: Paul Sabatier Univ., 1975. Dissertation.

55. PEDLEY, T. J., R. C. SCHROTER, AND M. F. SUDLOW. The prediction of pressure drop and variation of resistance within the human bronchial airways. *Respir. Physiol.* 9: 387–405, 1970.

56. PEDLEY, T. J., R. C. SCHROTER, AND M. F. SUDLOW. Gas flow and mixing in the airways. In: *Lung Biology in Health and Disease. Bioengineering Aspects of the Lung*, edited by J. B. West. New York: Dekker, 1977, vol. 3, chapt. 3, p. 163–265.

57. PIMMEL, R. L., M. J. TSAI, D. C. WINTER, AND P. A. BROMBERG. Estimating central and peripheral respiratory resistance. *J. Appl. Physiol.: Respirat. Environ. Exercise Physiol.* 45: 375–380, 1978.

58. PROCTOR, D. F., AND D. SWIFT. The nose—a defence against the atmospheric environment. In: *Inhaled Particles and Vapours III*, edited by W. H. Walton. Old Woking, UK: Unwin, 1971, vol. 1.

59. REYNOLDS, D. B., AND J.-S. LEE. Steady pressure-flow relationship of a model of the canine bronchial tree. *J. Appl. Physiol.: Respirat. Environ. Exercise Physiol.* 51: 1072–1079, 1981.

60. ROHRER, F. Der Strömungswiderstand in den menschlichen Atemwegen und der Einfluss der unregelmässigen Verzweigung des Bronchialsystems auf den Atmungsverlauf verschiedenen Lungenbezirken. *Pfluegers Arch. Gesamte Physiol. Menschen Tiere* 162: 225–229, 1915.

61. SAIBENE, F., AND J. MEAD. Frequency dependence of pulmonary quasi-static hysteresis. *J. Appl. Physiol.* 26: 732–737, 1969.

62. SASAKI, H., AND F. G. HOPPIN, JR. Hysteresis of contracted airway smooth muscle. *J. Appl. Physiol.: Respirat. Environ. Exercise Physiol.* 47: 1251–1262, 1979.

63. SCHMID-SCHÖNBEIN, G. W., AND Y. C. FUNG. Forced perturbation of respiratory system. A. The traditional model. *Ann. Biomed. Eng.* 6: 194–211, 1978.

64. SCHWABER, J., AND J. MEAD. Use of a modified Thunberg barospirator to determine airway resistance in man. *J. Appl. Physiol.* 25: 328–332, 1968.

65. SHARP, J. T., J. P. HENRY, S. K. SWEANEY, W. R. MEADOWS, AND R. J. PIETRAS. Total respiratory inertance and its gas and tissue components in normal and obese man. *J. Clin. Invest.* 43: 503–509, 1964.

66. SLUTSKY, A. S., G. G. BERDINE, AND J. M. DRAZEN. Steady flow in a model of human central airways. *J. Appl. Physiol.: Respirat. Environ. Exercise Physiol.* 49: 417–423, 1980.

66a.SLUTSKY, A. S., G. G. BERDINE, AND J. M. DRAZEN. Oscillatory flow and quasi-steady behavior in a model of human central airways. *J. Appl. Physiol.: Respirat. Environ. Exercise Physiol.* 50: 1293–1299, 1981.

67. SLUTSKY, A. S., AND J. M. DRAZEN. Estimating central and peripheral respiratory resistance: an alternative analysis. *J. Appl. Physiol.: Respirat. Environ. Exercise Physiol.* 47: 1325–1331, 1979.

68. SLUTSKY, A. S., J. M. DRAZEN, R. H. INGRAM, JR., R. D. KAMM, A. H. SHAPIRO, J. J. FREDBERG, S. H. LORING, AND J. LEHR. Effective pulmonary ventilation with small-volume oscillations at high frequency. *Science* 209: 609–611, 1980.

69. SONNE, C. Untersuchungen über die relative Weite der Broncholen bei der verschiedenen Luftspannung der Lungen. *Acta Med. Scand.* 58: 313–341, 1923.

70. STĂNESCU, D. C., J. PATTIJN, J. CLÉMENT, AND K. P. VAN DE WOESTIJNE. Glottis opening and airway resistance. *J. Appl. Physiol.* 32: 460–466, 1972.

71. THUNBERG, T. Der Barospirator, ein neuer Apparat für künstliche Atmung. *Skand. Arch. Physiol.* 48: 80–98, 1926.

72. VINCENT, N. J., R. KNUDSON, D. E. LEITH, P. T. MACKLEM, AND J. MEAD. Factors influencing pulmonary resistance. *J. Appl. Physiol.* 29: 236–243, 1970.

73. VON NEERGAARD, K., AND K. WIRZ. Die Messung der Strömungswiderstände in den Atemwegen des Menschen, insbesondere bei Asthma und Emphysem. *Z. Klin. Med.* 105: 51–82, 1927.

74. WEIBEL, E. R. *Morphometry of the Human Lung*. Berlin: Springer-Verlag, 1963.

75. WILLIAMS, S. P., R. L. PIMMEL, J. M. FULLTON, M. J. TSAI, AND A. M. COLLIER. Fractionating respiratory resistance in young children. *J. Appl. Physiol.: Respirat. Environ. Exercise Physiol.* 47: 551–555, 1979.

76. WIRZ, K. Das Verhalten des Druckes im Pleuraraum bei der Atmung und die Ursachen seiner Veränderlichkeit. *Pfluegers Arch. Gesamte Physiol. Menschen Tiere* 199: 1–12, 1923.

77. WOOD, L. D. H., L. A. ENGEL, P. GRIFFIN, P. DESPAS, AND P. T. MACKLEM. Effect of gas physical properties and flow on lower pulmonary resistance. *J. Appl. Physiol.* 41: 234–244, 1976.

CHAPTER 19

Forced expiration

R O B E R T E. H Y A T T | *Mayo Medical School and Mayo Clinic, Rochester, Minnesota*

CHAPTER CONTENTS

FORCED EXPIRATION IS WIDELY USED in the assessment of pulmonary function. Its origin can be traced to the measurement of vital capacity (VC) by Hutchinson (49) in 1846. It became apparent, however, that VC measurements did not evaluate the predominant ventilatory defect in conditions such as asthma, bronchitis, and emphysema, namely a decreased ability to exhale air at normal rates. Tiffeneau and Pinelli (140) in 1947 and Gaensler (37) in 1951 made this possible with their description of the measurement of volumes exhaled during a given period of time from a maximally forced expiratory VC breath. In the basic procedure the subject inspires maximally and then immediately exhales as rapidly and completely as possible. This maneuver is referred to as forced vital capacity (FVC). Recently additional methods for measuring expiratory flow limitation based on the FVC have become available.

This chapter presents a physiological evaluation of forced expiration and considers the main approaches to quantifying the FVC.

MECHANISM OF EXPIRATORY FLOW LIMITATION

It has long been known that measurements during forced expiration were useful in detecting obstructive lung disease. The reasons for this, however, were not initially appreciated. Dayman (24) emphasized the importance of the lung's elastic recoil in determining maximal flow, but Fry et al. (35) made the crucial observation leading to the concept of expiratory flow limitation. They measured pressure-flow relations at isovolume [isovolume pressure-flow (IVPF) curve] and showed that during expiration flow becomes limited at modest, positive transpulmonary pressures (PL). This observation led directly to the description of the maximal expiratory flow-volume (MEFV) curve (56), which emphasized that at most lung volumes there was a limit to maximal expiratory flow ($\dot{V}$max). The existence of expiratory flow limitation explains why the FVC maneuver had proven so useful. The functional relationships between PL, respiratory gas flow, and lung inflation (36) are illustrated in Figure 1, *right*, where three IVPF curves from a normal subject are plotted. The subject was seated in a body plethysmograph and breathed repeatedly with increasing effort. Flow and PL values at specific volumes were used to construct the IVPF curves (56).

The relations of pressure (P) to flow (F) at given lung volumes are basic to the interpretation of the FVC. The $\dot{V}$ would be preferable to F to represent flow, and these curves could be designated P$\dot{V}$ curves. Because F was used in previous publications, it will be retained in this section. The IVPF curves in Figure 1, *right*, demonstrate three important points.

1. Expiratory flow on PF curve A, measured at high inflation, increases as pressure increases. No easily defined limit to expiratory flow exists at volumes near total lung capacity (TLC). Therefore, the $\dot{V}$max near TLC is highly dependent on the subject's effort.

2. Curves B and C, measured at lesser lung inflations, have expiratory maxima. Flow increases with pressure until maxima are reached (points B and C) beyond which further increases in pressure are associated with essentially no change in flow; i.e., the lung is flow limited. Flow values at the maxima decrease with decreasing lung inflation. Maxima have been recorded over approximately the lower 80% of VC.

3. Evidence has been presented that expiratory flow on the plateau of an IVPF curve is uniquely determined by the characteristics of the intrathoracic pulmonary system and the physical properties of the gas (33). During the FVC, $\dot{V}$max over the range of

lung volumes associated with IVPF curve maxima requires less than maximal subject effort and represents a limiting value that cannot be exceeded. However, Leith and Mead (71) showed that young normal subjects at low lung volumes may not be able to maintain sufficient force to keep the lung flow limited. In this situation V̇max near residual volume (RV) becomes dependent on effort.

It is possible to construct from IVPF curves a three-dimensional surface that graphically describes the interrelationships among pressure, flow, and volume. This surface can be used to analyze the FVC but is tedious to construct (36). Fortunately the expiratory IVPF curve maxima provide a simplified approach to the evaluation of the FVC. Because each IVPF curve relates flow to pressure at a given lung volume, it is possible to plot the maximal flows from the IVPF curves against the volumes at which they are measured. This has been done in the left panel of Figure 1 for the three curves in the right panel. The greatest expiratory flow (point A) achieved on curve A is plotted against its corresponding volume, 0.8 liter from TLC. Flow points from the curves with plateaus have been plotted against their corresponding volumes (points B and C). If one recorded IVPF curves over a wide range of lung inflations and plotted the expiratory flow and volume values in this manner, the MEFV plot in Figure 1, *left*, could be constructed. (Alternate methods of plotting would be to present volume as a percent of VC or as absolute thoracic gas volume. It would be preferable to call these V̇V plots.) The solid line relates expiratory flow to volume when expiration is maximally forced, as during the FVC, because pressures in excess of those occurring at the expiratory IVPF maxima are almost invariably developed (50, 56).

In practice one does not construct MEFV diagrams from IVPF curves. Instead the subject breathes into a system that records flow and volume simultaneously. The flow signal is placed on the *y*-axis of a suitable recorder (e.g., oscilloscope) and the volume signal on the *x*-axis. The subject performs the FVC while flow and volume are plotted simultaneously, yielding the MEFV curve. The important physiological aspects of the MEFV projection of the FVC maneuver may now be interpreted in light of the preceding discussion of the interrelationships of pressure, flow, and volume.

The initial portion of the FVC (solid expiratory curve in Fig. 1) near TLC is not associated with recognizable IVPF curve maxima. Because of the force-velocity behavior of the respiratory muscles, sufficient pressure presumably cannot be developed during the high flows achievable at these large lung inflations (1, 54). The V̇max here is largely dependent on patient effort and is sensitive to changes in extrathoracic airway resistance (36, 87); hence it is potentially subject to wide variability.

Over the volume range corresponding to approximately the lower 80% of the expiratory plot, maximal flow does not require maximal effort. Moreover flow does not vary appreciably with effort because forced respiratory maneuvers correspond to pressures existing on the plateau. It follows that the MEFV relations of the FVC are quite reproducible at these volumes.

The V̇max is a function of lung inflation. Hence it is essential to specify the volume at which V̇max is quantified.

The phenomenon of expiratory flow limitation and the mechanisms producing it have intrigued physiologists since it was first described. Mead et al. (92) analyzed forced expiration in terms of the equal pressure point (EPP) concept. Briefly this approach said

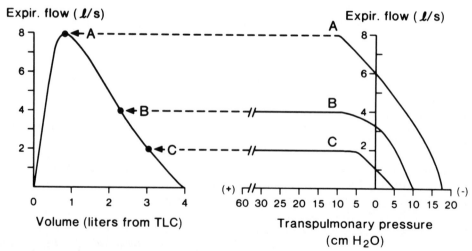

FIG. 1. *Left*: flow-volume plot for normal subject. V̇max values are plotted against their corresponding volume at A, B, and C and define the MEFV curve (*solid line*). *Right*: three isovolume pressure-flow curves from same subject. *Curves A, B, and C* were measured at volumes of 0.8, 2.3, and 3.0 liters from total lung capacity (TLC), respectively. Transpulmonary pressure is the difference between pleural (estimated by an esophageal balloon) and mouth pressures.

that, once flow was limited at a given lung volume, there was a site in the intrathoracic airways where intrabronchial and intrapleural pressures were equal—the EPP. The driving pressure from alveolus to the EPP was the elastic recoil pressure of the lung (Pel,L). Airways downstream (toward the mouth) of the EPP would be compressed, whereas those upstream (toward the alveoli) would not be. Thus when the flow is limited the system could be considered to consist of an elastic element emptying through a fixed resistance in series with a variable resistance. In addition flow could be described by a driving pressure (Pel,L) and the fixed resistance. An upstream resistance (Rus) was defined as Pel,L divided by $\dot{V}$max. The factors determining Rus were analyzed in a very productive fashion. In a series of demanding studies, Macklem and associates (80, 81, 83) defined the anatomic location of the EPP in normal subjects and in patients with obstructive lung disease.

Pride et al. (118) likened flow limitation to the behavior of a Starling resistor with the upstream driving pressure being Pel,L plus a critical transmural pressure (Ptm′). If Ptm′ equals zero, this is the same as the EPP formulation. This analysis emphasized the importance of the compressibility and tone of the flow-limiting segment. This approach has also been widely used to obtain information about the site of flow limitation and its behavior in various disease states and experimental situations.

However, these analyses did not explain the mechanism of flow limitation. Fry (33, 34) took a formal approach to the problem and outlined a mathematical model of flow limitation. He pointed out that if 1) the total cross-sectional area of the bronchial tree (A) could be defined as a function (g) of PL and position along the tree (x)

$$A = g(\text{PL}, x) \qquad (1)$$

and 2) the pressure gradient (dP/dx) in the airways could be described as a function of area, position, and flow

$$dP/dx = g(A, x, \dot{V}) \qquad (2)$$

then for a given flow this coupled set of equations could in principle be integrated from the alveoli, where $x = 0$ and $P = $ Pel,L, to the trachea. Fry (34) showed that for some airway pressure-area curves, there is a maximum value of expiratory flow for which a solution of these equations exists. Unfortunately not enough was known about the flow or the airway properties to implement Fry's approach with confidence. Furthermore one had to deal with the fact that at flow limitation an increase in pleural pressure decreased Ptm and airway area by just the right amount to compensate for the increased pressure difference driving the flow, thus maintaining $\dot{V}$max constant on the IVPF curve plateau.

It seemed there might be localized mechanisms that were dominant in producing flow limitation. Simpli-fied models were proposed. Pardaens et al. (111), Lambert and Wilson (67), and Pedersen et al. (112) postulated that most of the frictional pressure loss occurred in the periphery and that the convective acceleration pressure drop occurred primarily in the central airways. These assumptions could be expressed by

$$P = \text{Pel,L} - \Delta\text{Pfr} - \tfrac{1}{2}\frac{\rho\dot{V}^2}{A^2} \qquad (3)$$

where P is lateral airway pressure at a point in the central airways, ΔPfr is the frictional pressure loss, and ρ is gas density; the third term on the right is the Bernoulli equation. Combining this approach with measures of ΔPfr and central airway pressure-area plots in excised human lungs, a graphical solution (see the next section) for $\dot{V}$max was obtained (57). Agreement with measured maximal flows was quite good at high and middle volumes but poor at low volumes, where it was suggested that other mechanisms dominated the flow-limiting process (57). Indeed it now appears likely that there are two basic flow-limiting mechanisms. One is the wave-speed mechanism that results from the coupling between airway compliance and the pressure drop due to the convective acceleration of the flow. The other is the coupling between airway compliance and viscous flow losses. Normally the first mechanism appears to dominate over approximately the upper two-thirds of the VC and the second at lower lung volumes. These fundamentally important mechanisms are developed in detail in the chapter by Wilson, Rodarte, and Butler in this *Handbook* and are discussed briefly in the next section.

Wave-Speed Limitation

Dawson and Elliott (23) made a major step toward our present understanding of flow limitation when they recognized that the lung, like other systems, could not carry a greater flow than the flow for which the fluid velocity equals wave speed at some point in the system. The pertinent wave speed is the speed at which a small disturbance travels in a compliant tube filled with fluid. In the arteries this is the speed at which the pulse propagates. In the airway the speed is higher mainly because the fluid density is lower. The wave speed (c) in a compliant tube with an area A that depends on lateral pressure P, filled with a fluid of density ρ, is given by

$$c = \left(\frac{A\,dP}{\rho\,dA}\right)^{\!\tfrac{1}{2}} \qquad (4)$$

where dP/dA is the slope of the pressure-area curve for the airway. Maximal flow is the product of the fluid velocity at wave speed and airway area, cA.

The equation for the wave speed and its significance in limiting flow can be derived from the partial differential equations describing the physical laws that gov-

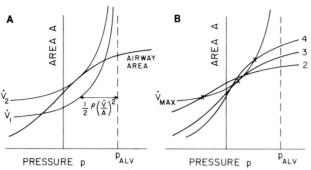

FIG. 2. Representation of flow limitation at wave speed. *A*: typical curve of airway area (A) as a function of p, the difference between lateral airway pressure and pleural pressure. If dissipative pressure losses are neglected, p can be calculated by subtracting the Bernoulli term $\rho \dot{V}^2/2A^2$ from alveolar pressure (P_{ALV}). Because P_{ALV} (or PA) is measured relative to pleural pressure, it is equivalent to static recoil pressure. The intersection of this curve with the airway pressure-area curve determines pressure and airway area at a given flow. There is a maximal flow for which a point common to both curves exists. *B*: airway pressure-area curves for generations 2, 3, and 4 and the Bernoulli curve for maximal flow. Flow limitation occurs in generation 3, but there is an additional pressure drop because of compression downstream of the flow-limiting site in generation 2. [From Wilson et al. (149).]

ern flow. A mathematical analysis in that style has been presented (23, 55). The mechanism can also be described graphically. A typical pressure-area curve of an airway is shown in Figure 2*A* in which the pressure axis describes lateral pressure relative to pleural pressure. If convective acceleration were the only cause of a pressure drop, the following modification of Equation 3 could be used to describe the relation between lateral pressure (P), alveolar pressure (PA), and airway area (*A*) for a given flow rate ($\dot{V}$)

$$P = PA - \tfrac{1}{2}\rho\frac{\dot{V}^2}{A^2} \qquad (5)$$

This equation can also be plotted in Figure 2*A* for different values of $\dot{V}$. The airway area and pressure that would occur in this airway at $\dot{V}$ are the coordinates of the intersection of this curve with the bronchial pressure-area curve. That point represents the simultaneous solution of the airway and flow pressure-area relations. For larger flows the pressure-area curve of Equation 5 shifts upward and to the left. It is clear that there is a maximum flow (V_2 in Fig. 2*A*) for which a single solution exists. At that flow the two curves are tangent at the common value of *A* and P. Because the curves are tangent, they have the same slope at the tangency point. If Equation 5 is differentiated for P, with PA, ρ, and $\dot{V}$ held constant, Equation 6 is obtained

$$1 = \rho \frac{\dot{V}^2}{A^3}\frac{dA}{dP} \qquad (6)$$

The slope d*A*/dP is equal to the slope of the bronchial

pressure-area curve. Solving Equation 6 for $\dot{V}$, Equation 7 is obtained for maximal flow

$$\dot{V}max = A\left(\frac{A\,dP}{\rho\,dA}\right)^{1/2} \qquad (7)$$

This is the same as Equation 4 for flow limitation at wave speed, where $\dot{V}max$ equals cA, wave-speed flow ($\dot{V}_c$).

At high lung volumes where the recoil pressure is relatively large, lateral pressure in the peripheral airways is positive and the airway pressure-area curves are nearly horizontal. Also in the periphery the total cross-sectional area of the parallel flow paths is large, and a line representing the Bernoulli equation in Figure 2*A* is nearly vertical if *A* is large. The two curves are far from having common slopes in the periphery. As flow increases, a tangency point will appear first in the central airways where the total cross-sectional area is small and the pressure has fallen to a value for which the airways are more compliant. Therefore at high lung volumes flow is determined primarily by convective losses, wave speed, and area of the central airways.

In Figure 2*B* representative pressure-area curves for the total cross-sectional area of the airways of the second, third, and fourth generations of the Weibel model of the bronchial tree are shown (144). The Bernoulli curve for maximal flow is also shown. The pressures and areas in each generation are shown by the points labeled *x*. The flow-limiting site, a choke point in wave-speed terminology, is in the third generation where the tangency condition is satisfied. Additional pressure drops through the bronchial tree occur because of additional compression of the airways downstream from the choke point (see the chapter by Wilson, Rodarte, and Butler in this *Handbook*).

At lower lung volumes, the Bernoulli curves originate from a lower PA. The Bernoulli curve in Figure 2*B* is shifted down and to the left. Tangency occurs at a lower flow and the point of tangency shifts to a higher generation (i.e., toward the periphery).

Elliott and Dawson (28) confirmed that the pressure distribution through a compliant channel was consistent with wave-speed theory. Mink et al. (100, 101) and Hyatt et al. (57) showed that properties of maximal flow at middle and high lung volumes in dog lungs and excised human lungs are consistent with this model.

Equation 7 is not, however, a complete predictive statement. Airway area, compliance, and wave speed are functions of Ptm. Therefore the maximal flow that an airway can carry is a function of lateral pressure within the airway. In the real situation, in addition to the convective pressure drop, frictional or dissipative pressure losses contribute to determining the pressure distribution. However, if the dissipative losses are known, the flow-limiting site and the value of maximal flow can be predicted by the graphical method utilizing the wave-speed concept (57). A useful, clear discussion of the interrelation among the factors determining flow limitation is found in a paper by Mead (90).

The concept of flow limitation at wave speed is an essential feature of a complete model and provides insight about maximal flow. One can obtain an intuitive appreciation for wave-speed limitation from the following considerations. Essentially one wishes to understand how the wave-speed mechanism produces plateaus on IVPF curves. The critical point to keep in mind is that on the plateau, flow is independent of the downstream pressure; this is the so-called "waterfall" or Starling resistor effect. In the isovolume condition, it is clear from Equation 7 that at low flows, wave speed is high because the airways show little compression (area large) and are on the flat part of their pressure-area characteristic (they are stiff). A drop in pressure at the outlet will be transmitted upstream at a speed that is diminished only slightly by the countering effect of airflow velocity. As flow increases, the speed at which a downstream pressure disturbance (a drop in pressure) can be transmitted upstream will fall because 1) wave speed is decreasing and 2) the opposing effect of the airflow velocity is increasing. When the speed (predicted by the wave-speed equation) no longer exceeds the speed of expiratory flow, the pressure disturbance can no longer propagate upstream and affect the flow. In essence the downstream pressure change is no longer seen by the upstream driving pressure and flow becomes independent of, or uncoupled from, downstream pressure. When this occurs, the system is flow limited and the waterfall phenomenon and a choke point develop. Further decreases in downstream pressure only compress the airways downstream of the choke point and, of course, have no effect on the flow.

As seen from Equation 7, given the pressure-area behavior of an individual airway, one can compute its $\dot{V}_c$ at all Ptm values. When the airway is distended, $\dot{V}_c$ is high. As Ptm falls, the airway narrows and wave speed falls. Narrowing occurs for two reasons. 1) As lung volume decreases, the tethering force of the lung parenchyma decreases. 2) As flow increases, the pressure losses cause narrowing. At high lung volumes the total cross-sectional area of the peripheral airways is large, as is their $\dot{V}_c$. In contrast, central airway area is relatively small. In addition the large increases in velocity as flow reaches the central airways leads to further narrowing. Therefore it is not surprising that flow limitation has been shown to occur first near the outlet of the system (83). At lower lung volumes, lung recoil decreases, the area of the peripheral airway decreases dramatically, their compliance increases, their wave speed falls, and the choke point moves toward the periphery. In the manner of Figure 2 this is the same as the tangency point shifting to more peripheral bronchi.

With wave-speed theory and some modest assump-

tions about the nature of the dissipative losses, it has been possible to deduce that the viscosity and density dependence of maximal flow must be related in a particular way (135). Also the difference between the typical shapes of canine and human flow-volume curves can be related to the differences between their airway properties by means of the wave-speed concept (82). The flow-limiting site in the canine occurs in the trachea over most of the volume range (60). The trachea is not very compliant, and the tangency point occurs at a negative pressure of the order of −15 to −20 cmH₂O relative to pleural pressure. A change in recoil pressure with a changing lung volume produces a relatively small fractional change in the total pressure drop to the flow-limiting site and a relatively small change in maximal flow. Therefore the canine flow-volume curve is fairly flat until low volumes, at which point the flow-limiting site shifts rapidly to more compliant intraparenchymal airways. The flow-limiting site in human lungs is typically in the second and third generations at higher lung volumes and the pressure at the critical point is ~0. Therefore the EPP hypothesis is a good approximate description of flow limitation in humans at high volumes in contrast to the canine (92). As lung volume decreases, the change in recoil pressure has a significant effect. Flow decreases and the flow-limiting site moves peripherally more rapidly and more continuously than in canines. Humans who have canine-like flow-volume curves probably have flow limitation in the trachea or at the carina, and the flow-volume curves of these individuals should be more sensitive to the head position and the change of compliance that axial tension produces in the trachea [(83, 95); see also *Axial Bronchial Tension*, p. 309].

Viscous Flow Limitation

At low lung volumes the density dependence of maximal flow is small, the viscosity dependence is large, and the wave-speed concept is less useful. Shapiro (129) has described a purely viscous flow limitation in a compliant tube. Suppose a compliant tube with the pressure-area properties shown in Figure 3A were attached to rigid supporting tubes at the ends, a distance l apart. If the cross section of the tube remained circular and the tube area and flow were small enough, the pressure drop in the tube would be described by the Poiseuille equation

$$\frac{dP}{dx} = -a\frac{\mu\dot{V}}{A^2} \qquad (8)$$

where a is a numerical constant and μ is gas viscosity. By multiplying both sides by $A^2 dx/a\mu$ and integrating from $x = 0$ (the upstream end of the tube where pressure is P_1) to $x = l$ (the downstream end of the tube where pressure is P_2) the following expression for $\dot{V}$ is obtained

$$\dot{V} = -\frac{1}{a\mu l} \int_{P_1}^{P_2} A^2 dP \qquad (9)$$

That is, the flow is $1/a\mu l$ times the area under the curve of A^2 versus P between P_1 and P_2. If P_1 is held fixed and P_2 is decreased, $\dot{V}$ increases, but if A^2 approaches zero fast enough as P_2 becomes negative, the integral approaches a finite limit as P_2 becomes infinitely negative. Therefore if P_1 is held fixed and P_2 is reduced, $\dot{V}$ approaches a limiting value. The curve of $\dot{V}$ versus P_2 corresponding to the tube properties and the value of P_1 shown in Figure 3A is shown in Figure 3B. If A^2 approaches zero fast enough for the integral to remain finite as P becomes large and negative, the wave-speed limit on the flow cA approaches zero as P becomes large and negative. The wave-speed limit would be reached at some negative value of P_2. However, if the tube and flows are small, flow reaches its maximal value and becomes independent of P_2 by the viscous mechanism at a value of P_2 much higher than the value at which wave speed is eventually reached. The limiting flow is essentially established by the coupling between viscous losses and tube compliance, and limitation at wave speed is not the significant mechanism.

Computational Model

A computer can be used to obtain a more complete model that includes convective acceleration, laminar and turbulent dissipation in the flow, and airway compliance and from these can predict the pressure distribution in the airways, IVPF curves, and maximal flow-volume curves. Lambert et al. (68) described such a model. It consists of an equation for the pressure gradient in the flow and airway pressure-area curves for 17 generations of the bronchial tree. The pressure gradient in the flow is described by the equation

$$\frac{dP}{dx} = -\frac{1}{2}\rho \frac{d}{dx}\left(\frac{\dot{V}}{A}\right)^2 - f \qquad (10)$$

where the dissipation pressure loss (f) is described by an equation of the form of Rohrer's equation

$$f = a\mu \frac{\dot{V}}{A^2} + b\rho \frac{\dot{V}^2}{A^2} \qquad (11)$$

This expression and values for the constants a and b were obtained from data on the dissipative pressure losses in flow through a cast of a canine bronchial tree (120, 121). The choice of airway pressure-area curves was constrained by data on human airway pressure-area curves of the central airways (57) and Weibel's description of the maximum area for all generations (144). For a given lung volume and a given value of $\dot{V}$, Equation 11 was integrated from the periphery to the end of the trachea. Flow was increased and the integration repeated until a maximum flow was reached

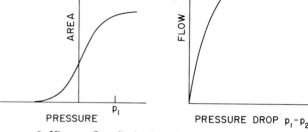

FIG. 3. Viscous flow limitation. *A*: pressure-area curve of a smaller airway. *B*: if the pressure gradient in the flow is described by the Poiseuille equation, then for a fixed pressure at the upstream end of the tube (p_1), flow will depend on the pressure at the downstream end of the tube (p_2). [From Wilson et al. (149).]

for which wave speed occurred at some point in the airways or the pressure at the end of the trachea was $-100 \text{ cmH}_2\text{O}$.

By making the peripheral airways quite compliant, it was possible to match the average air-MEFV curves of five human lungs. The predicted curves for He-O_2 and SF_6 also matched the data for these lungs. General features of the predictions (e.g., lung conductance, density and viscosity dependence of maximal flow, and pressure required to reach maximal flow) were similar to published data.

By altering certain parameters of the model it is possible to mimic characteristics frequently seen in individual MEFV curves. For example, decreasing the area of the third generation results in the flow-limiting site remaining in that generation to a lower lung volume and produces a knee in the MEFV curve. Decreasing the area of the peripheral airways results in a decreased density dependence, especially at lower lung volume, and an increase in the volume at isoflow (66).

It remains to be seen whether the benefits that would be expected from such a quantitative model can be realized. First, the sensitivity of the MEFV curve to each of the parameters of the model should be determined. Second, the uniqueness of the relationship between the model parameters and the predicted MEFV curves should be investigated.

An important objective is to model disease. This appears to be a significantly more difficult task because inhomogeneities are expected. In modeling flow through an inhomogeneous bronchial tree, a method must be developed for finding different regional flows for which the pressures match at common points in the branching network. Furthermore inhomogeneous emptying introduces time as an independent variable, and flow at a given lung volume cannot be analyzed independently of the flow at preceding volumes.

The above model for normal lungs has potential limitations in that, for example, it uses a symmetric model of the airways and does not directly take into account bronchial-parenchymal interdependence (91) or viscoelastic behavior of the airways (123). Nor does it predict negative effort dependence, which occurs in a minority of normal subjects. In such cases flow on an IVPF curve (Fig. 1) actually falls below the maximum value with increasing PL. Nevertheless it appears to provide a basis for modeling more complicated problems such as flow limitation in abnormal lungs.

MEASUREMENT AND ANALYSIS

The FVC maneuver is conventionally recorded by having the subject breathe into a spirometer with an attached recording device that provides a volume-time tracing of the forced expiration. Spirometers vary in their recording characteristics, and attention is directed to several studies of these instruments (5, 146). Based on the harmonic analysis of various respiratory maneuvers (72, 86), instruments with good dynamic response of ~6–12 cycles/s should adequately record the FVC. Recommendations for standardization of spirometry have recently been published (134). The FVC maneuver can also be recorded by various other devices to provide a flow-volume record.

Because the volume-time spirometric tracing and the flow-volume plot are both widely used, it is pertinent to consider the interrelations of these methods of recording. Figure 4 illustrates a normal FVC recorded for flow versus volume (Fig. 4, *top*) and volume versus time (Fig. 4, *bottom*). Both plots contain the same basic information, and one can be derived from the other. The MEFV trace can be converted to the volume-time tracing. The MEFV plot is divided into equal volume increments, in this case 0.2 liter each. Only the first five increments are shown. The mean expiratory flow ($\bar{V}$ in liters/s) for each increment is then determined. The time in seconds to exhale each volume increment equals 0.2 liter divided by the mean flow for that particular increment. The volume increments and their corresponding times are summed and plotted as points on the volume-time graph in Figure 4. Conversely the volume-time trace could be converted to an MEFV plot by determining the slope at many volume points and plotting this flow against volume. It is quite feasible to record the relations between volume and both flow and time simultaneously during the FVC maneuver. The figure is merely to show the interrelations of the plots and permit the physiological features of the MEFV plot to be related to the usual spirogram.

The FVC has been quantified in a number of ways. The terms and symbols used in Table 1 follow the recommendations of a committee of the Commission on Respiratory Physiology. The common methods of quantifying the FVC are listed in Table 1. These can be divided into three general categories of tests.

The first category (test 2) measures the peak flow occurring during the initial part of the FVC with a variety of instruments (40, 46, 151, 152). The charac-

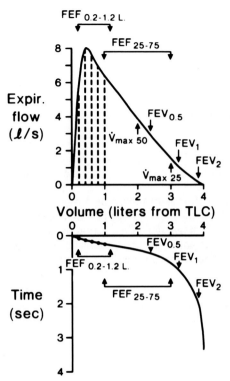

FIG. 4. *Top*: flow-volume plot of a forced expired vital capacity maneuver from a normal subject. *Bottom*: derived volume-time trace of the same breath. $\dot{V}$max, maximum expiratory flow; TLC, total lung capacity; FEF, mean forced expiratory flow between two designated volume points in FVC; FEV, forced expiratory volume in time interval. [Adapted from Hyatt (51).]

teristics of the instruments differ, leading to somewhat different normal values. Because of the marked volume dependence of $\dot{V}$max, it is important that these tests are initiated from the full inspiratory position.

The second category measures the volume of air exhaled after a given time has elapsed. Time intervals varying from 0.43 to 3.2 s have been advocated, with the 1-s volume (FEV_1) being most widely used. The result is given either as the absolute volume exhaled (FEV_t, test 3), preferably corrected to body temperature, barometric pressure, and water-vapor saturation [BTPS (99)], or as the volume exhaled expressed as a percent of the FVC (test 4). The volumes exhaled in 0.5, 1, and 2 s are indicated on both curves in Figure 4. Because peak flows are not achieved instantly during the FVC (Fig. 4), there is always some problem in knowing where to begin measurement of the various FEV values. To circumvent this problem it is common to extrapolate the steepest part of the volume-time trace back to TLC and measure from this point (134).

The third category relates expiratory flow to lung volume. Two types of flow have been measured. One measures $\bar{V}$ during the FVC. Two such tests are described under test 5 in Table 1. Their positions are shown in Figure 4. They should also be corrected to BTPS. Another one records absolute flow at a specified

TABLE 1. *Nomenclature*

Test Description	Recommended Term	Symbol
1. Volume of gas expired after full inspiration, expiration being as rapid and complete as possible (i.e., forced)	Forced vital capacity	FVC
2. Peak expiratory flow (liter/min or liter/s) measured by various instruments	Peak expiratory flow, qualified by name of instrument used	PEF
3. Volume of gas exhaled over a given time interval during a complete forced expiration	Forced expiratory volume, qualified by time interval in s	FEV_t
4. FEV_t expressed at % of FVC	Percent of FVC expired in time interval t	$FEV_t/FVC\%$
5. Volume of air exhaled over a specified volume range of the FVC divided by the time to exhale this volume, expressed as liter/min or liter/s. Examples:	Mean forced expiratory flow between two designated volume points in FVC	
Volume between 0.2 and 1.2 liters of the FVC/time	Mean forced expiratory flow, 0.2–1.2 liters	$FEF_{0.2–1.2\ liters}$
Volume between 25% and 75% of the FVC/time	Mean forced expiratory flow, 25%–75% of FVC	$FEF_{25\%–75\%}$
6. Maximal expiratory flow at a specific volume during FVC expressed in liter/min or liter/s. Examples:	Maximal expiratory flow qualified at xx percent of VC (note: 100% VC is at TLC; 0% VC is at RV)	
Flow at point when 75% of FVC remaining	Maximal expiratory flow, 75% of VC	$\dot{V}max_{75}$
Flow at point when 50% of FVC remaining	Maximal expiratory flow, 50% of VC	$\dot{V}max_{50}$
Flow at point when 25% of FVC remaining	Maximal expiratory flow, 25% of VC	$\dot{V}max_{25}$

TABLE 2. *Range of Normal Values for Average Adult Male*

Test	Liters	Percent	Liters/min	Liters/s	Ref.
$FEV_{0.5}$ and $FEV_{0.5\%}$*	2.8–3.2	58–66			2, 39, 69, 99
$FEV_{0.75}$ and $FEV_{0.75\%}$	2.9–3.8	70–80			17, 99
FEV_1 and $FEV_{1\%}$	3.0–4.0	80–85			2, 29, 37, 39, 65, 73, 99, 113
FEV_2 and $FEV_{2\%}$	3.4–4.4	94–95			37, 73, 105
FEV_3 and $FEV_{3\%}$	3.5–4.8	97–99			2, 37, 73
PEF			500–622		152
PEF			315–420		40
$FEF_{0.2–1.2\ liters}$			350–550		2, 14, 16, 65, 78, 85
$FEF_{25\%–75\%}$				2.7–5.4	16, 21, 32, 65, 73, 102
$\dot{V}max_{75}$				4.8–8.4	50
$\dot{V}max_{50}$				3.7–5.3	50, 125
$\dot{V}max_{25}$				1.4–2.4	50, 125

* FEV_t expressed as percent of FVC.

volume during the FVC. Examples of this method are given under test 6 in Table 1. These values are obtained with ease from an MEFV record (Fig. 4).

No attempt is made to summarize all reported normal values. Normal ranges for an average adult white male are listed in Table 2 and representative references. Precise evaluation of normal values requires consideration of the following factors.

1. Age. The forced expiratory volumes decrease with age in adults, but this age effect is either lost (2, 65, 73, 99, 113) or decreased (103, 125) when these volumes are expressed as a percent of VC. In children through adolescence there is a positive age correlation of the FEV and the $FEF_{25\%–75\%}$ (21, 39, 78). Peak expiratory flows in adults generally show a negative correlation with age (47, 77, 127, 141). The $FEF_{0.2–1.2\ liters}$ test, with one exception (65), also shows a negative age correlation in adults (2, 85) and a positive correlation in children (78). A similar negative age correlation in adults is reported for the $FEF_{25\%–75\%}$ (65, 73).

2. Sex. Adult males have greater FEV and FEF values than females of the same height. The study of Strang (136) indicates that in children, if height is taken into account, differences in FEV_1 between sexes disappear.

3. Size. Size may be viewed either in terms of body size (i.e., height, weight, or body surface area) or in terms of lung size [i.e., VC, TLC, or functional residual capacity (FRC)]. The consensus is that FEV values show a positive correlation with height (3, 17, 39, 65, 99, 105). This correlation is generally lost or decreased when the volumes are expressed as a percent of FVC (125). Most studies also show a positive correlation between height and peak expiratory flow, although this is not found consistently in both sexes (40, 77, 127, 131, 141). The $FEF_{0.2–1.2\ liters}$ varies directly with height in children (78) but not in adults (2, 65). The $FEF_{25\%–75\%}$ shows a positive height correlation in children (21) and adults (102).

4. Race. A number of studies have demonstrated differences related to ethnic background for several

measures of the FVC. The altitude of residence must also be considered (22). Generally blacks have been found to have smaller values for the FVC and FEV_1 than whites (22, 125). However, when comparing similar thoracic dimensions (22) or TLC (69), these differences apparently disappear. Lapp et al. (69) point out the practical value of appreciating racial differences when evaluating individuals for employment.

Europeans tend to have relatively large FEV (133), whereas those of Orientals are variously reported as being lower (110) or equal (128) to those of blacks. Williams et al. (147) suggest that ventilatory function may vary even within a geographic area where large ethnic differences would not be anticipated. Additional data on ethnic effects can be found in references 11, 22, and 30.

5. Intrasubject variability. Part of this variability will reflect the skill of the technician as well as subject training. Nickerson et al. (107) controlled these variables and defined in 15 normal subjects the percent change in various tests that would represent a significant change in function. For the FVC the value was 5%, whereas it was 8%–9% for the FEV_1, $FEF_{25\%-75\%}$, and $\dot{V}max_{50}$ and 12% for $\dot{V}max_{25}$. These values are close to those reported by Lebowitz et al. (70). In patients with cystic fibrosis the change required to be significant was approximately twice that of the normals (107).

Thus consideration must be given to age, sex, size, race, and intrasubject variability when interpreting these measurements. Differences in instrumentation and data acquisition have hindered the comparison and pooling of data from different laboratories. Another problem is that smoking alters ventilatory function. Certain important age, sex, size, and race correlations may be lost for the more sensitive tests if smokers are included in a normal population.

Volume-Time

The usual approaches to quantifying volume-time relations have been discussed above. The volume expired in a given time is reported as an absolute value or as a percent of the FVC. From the spirogram, estimates of mean flow rate are obtained, such as the $FEF_{25\%-75\%}$ (Table 1). In addition a number of studies have proposed measuring the time required to exhale either part (126) or all of the FVC (13, 61).

Permutt and associates (114, 142) have taken a more formal approach to analysis of forced expiration in the time domain. Because airway obstruction is associated with decreased maximal flows at given volumes, the time of expiration becomes important, and because the spirogram is best at showing the time course of expiration, they analyzed the spirogram with time as the primary variable. In a manner analogous to quantifying an indicator injected into the circulation, they developed a moment analysis of the spirogram. This analysis is particularly sensitive to events occurring at the end of expiration where early airway disease is felt to have its major effect. They presented data suggesting that the distribution of transit times reflects anatomic inhomogeneity. This analysis was quite sensitive in distinguishing between smoking and nonsmoking males. Indeed these workers suggest that analysis of the spirogram in the time domain that emphasizes "the terminal events of a forced expiration is as sensitive as any other test now available in estimating the degree of regional inhomogeneity of the small airways" (114). Of interest is their finding that the oft-maligned $FEV_3/FVC\%$ was as sensitive as the moment or slope-ratio (88) analysis (see the next section) in detecting differences between young smokers and nonsmokers (114).

A number of studies have attested to the sensitivity of the moment analysis (59, 75, 106) in detecting early abnormalities, and more experience is being gained with this procedure (76, 107, 119). Clearly the terminal events of the FVC are more readily appreciated from the spirogram than from the MEFV curve. This analysis holds considerable promise and warrants careful investigation as well as evaluation of its reproducibility (107). The terminal portion of the spirogram is especially sensitive to subject effort and gas-compression effects (58). The influence of these factors on the value of this analysis also needs to be determined.

Flow-Volume

Flow-volume curves are generally quantified by measuring $\dot{V}max$ at various normalized volumes in the VC, for example, at 75%, 50%, and 25% of the VC remaining to be exhaled. Hyatt et al. (55) has termed these curves *free-floating* in contrast to *volume-based* curves, which are related to absolute lung volume, where $\dot{V}max$ is expressed as a percent of TLC, either observed or predicted but generally the former (7).

Because measurement of TLC is time consuming and adds an additional potential measurement error, free-floating curves are used almost exclusively. However, the volume-based curves are particularly valuable when following either acute (8, 109) or chronic changes in a given subject.

Flow is most often expressed in absolute terms, liter/s. In certain instances normalization of $\dot{V}max$ by dividing by observed VC or TLC, yielding VC or TLC values per second, is useful, particularly for intrasubject comparisons such as before and after pneumonectomy. However, this normalization in compensating for individual differences in lung size has not proven very useful (7, 44).

Hyatt et al. (55) has analyzed the advantages and limitations of free-floating and volume-based curves. Based on the usual changes in MEFV curves encountered in disease, Mead concludes there is no single best test. He suggests two measurements as useful descriptions of MEFV curves. One is the RV/TLC ratio, which estimates the fraction of the largest achievable lung volume that cannot be expired at all. The second is the ratio of the rate constants at 50% and 25% VC, namely $\frac{1}{2}(\dot{V}max_{50}/\dot{V}max_{25})$, which gives an estimate of the shape of the MEFV curve, being unity for a linear curve. More attention should be directed to evaluating these approaches to describing the MEFV curve. It was hoped that the average slope of the MEFV curve over a given volume range would discriminate between normal and abnormal curves (51). However, a number of studies have shown a single slope measurement to be a poor discriminator (63) partly due to its large variability among normals (7).

There are still unresolved problems in defining normal values for the MEFV curve. The greatest appears to be the large intersubject variability with or without normalization of flow and volume (7, 44). These differences undoubtedly reflect differences in the mechanical properties of the lung among normals that may be of prognostic value. However, this knowledge is of small comfort to the investigator attempting to establish normal standards.

Another problem is that all MEFV measurements based on volumes measured at the mouth do not reflect lung volume changes caused by gas compression. During forced expiration, P_A values in excess of 100 cmH_2O are not uncommon, and the resulting gas compression of over 10% distorts the true relations between $\dot{V}max$ and volume (58). This distortion can be overcome by measuring volume changes with the subject in a body plethysmograph, but in routine studies this is impractical; there are few data on normal MEFV curves obtained using a body box (7). The values presented in Table 2 were from MEFV curves measured at the mouth and hence include the compression artifact (58). It has been suggested that including the compression effect aids in separating normal from abnormal subjects; P_A in the latter tends to be greater during the FVC, thus maximizing decreases in $\dot{V}max$ (153). Unfortunately relatively small changes in effort (and hence gas compression) can have dramatic effects on MEFV curves measured at the mouth [Fig. 5; (62)]. The subject must be urged to make a maximal effort with each FVC for maximal reproducibility. Yet this can be a very difficult problem, particularly when studying subjects over time.

Another problem is that of determining the true MEFV curve obtained by measuring volume either at the mouth or with a plethysmograph. Assume one obtained five MEFV curves on the same subject at one sitting and the curves showed moderate variation in VC, peak flows, and slope. (Flow differences are not nearly as apparent when dealing with spirograms.) How does one obtain the most reproducible and hopefully the true MEFV curve? A number of approaches have been suggested, and Peslin et al. (115) systematically evaluated eight of these methods. They concluded that the most reproducible, and probably the least biased, data were obtained from composite curves

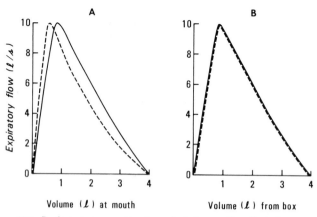

FIG. 5. *A*: two consecutive forced vital capacity efforts by same subject with flow and volume measured at the mouth. *B*: same efforts with volume measured from body plethysmograph. Efforts are identical because gas compression has been corrected for. [From Hyatt (52).]

constructed by superimposing efforts either at TLC or on the descending limb. The latter method is based on the assumption that there is a unique $\dot{V}max$ at a given volume. With this assumption, several studies (12, 139) have utilized a computer for smoothing and averaging MEFV curves. As seen from Figure 6 these curves are quite reproducible in subjects studied on two occasions, and the method reveals previously unrecognized irregularities of $\dot{V}max$ that may reflect sudden changes in the location of the choke point. This method of handling MEFV curves appears very promising.

Another problem is that $\dot{V}max$ is highly dependent on the Pel,L. At 50% VC, Pel,L was shown to vary from 5 to 11.4 cmH_2O in 40 nonsmoking males 19–35 yr old (18). In turn a significant positive correlation existed between Pel,L_{50} and $\dot{V}max_{50}$. It would be ideal, but totally unrealistic, to obtain static pressure curves of the lung along with MEFV curves in establishing normal values.

Are there practical physiological methods of quantifying MEFV curves? Mention was made in this section that the RV/TLC ratio and the ratio of expiratory rate constants warranted study (55). Mead (88) has also suggested that the configuration of the MEFV curve contains important information regarding the homogeneity of emptying. Many normal individuals have linear MEFV curves that are believed to reflect homogeneous emptying. Mead suggests that nonhomogeneous emptying indicates disease, and this leads to curvilinearity of the effort-independent portion of the MEFV curve. Curvilinearity can actually arise from two sources: the nonlinear behavior of the flow-limiting process itself (92) and the parallel nonuniformities in the process. Lung recoil pressures and pulmonary airway resistance, both important determinants of $\dot{V}max$ (18), vary nonlinearly with lung volume. Resistance also varies nonlinearly with flow. It would not be surprising that a lung, even when

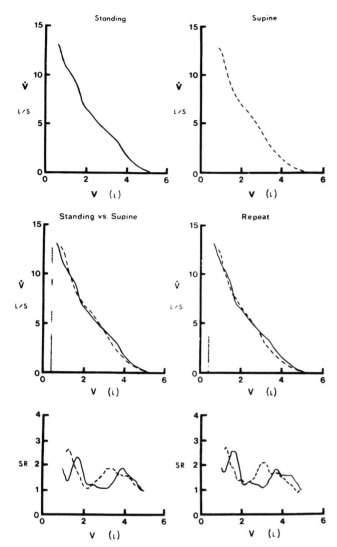

FIG. 6. Averaged flow-volume curves for normal subject. *Upper panels*: initial standing (*left*) and supine (*right*) curves. *Middle panels*: comparison of standing (*solid lines*) and supine (*dashed lines*) average flow-volume curves obtained initially (*left*) and 3 mo later (*right*). *Lower panels*: comparison of standing (*solid lines*) and supine (*dashed lines*) slope ratios (SR) versus volume (V) plots obtained initially (*left*) and 3 mo later (*right*). $\dot{V}$, flow. [From Castile et al. (19).]

emptying as a unit, might produce a curvilinear MEFV curve (92). When the lung is not behaving in a homogeneous fashion, additional sources of nonlinearity exist: regions that empty rapidly contribute disproportionately to both flow and volume change early in expiration, whereas slow regions account for most of the flow and volume change later in expiration.

The problem is to distinguish between these sources of curvilinearity. Two approaches have been suggested: an analysis of the MEFV configuration and the implications of time.

To examine the configuration, Mead (88) looked at the relationship between two rate-constant slopes: the slope of a line drawn from RV through a point on the curve (the chord slope) and the slope of the line tangent to the curve at the point in question. The ratio of tangent to chord slope has been called the slope ratio (SR) (88). A graph of this SR versus volume, i.e., the SR-V graph, is sensitive to configuration (Fig. 6). For a linear MEFV curve, the ratio is unity at all points. For a curve bowed toward the volume axis, the tangent slope exceeds the chord slope and SR is greater than unity at all points.

The SR-V relationship shows both the range and progression of configuration with volume change. The latter aspect allows the distinction between homogeneous and nonhomogeneous emptying. It can be shown that for systems that empty homogeneously over the effort-independent volume range, there is an upper limit to SR of ~2.5 and a lower limit of ~0.5 (88). In nonhomogeneous systems there is no upper limit. Furthermore nonhomogeneous emptying should be associated with a systematic fall in SR with volume, whereas homogeneous emptying, although it might show systematic fluctuations, would not show progressive reduction in SR with volume.

The SR analysis has received only limited clinical evaluation. In one study the SR and moment analysis were equally sensitive in detecting early abnormalities (114). Other studies have emphasized the large variability of the SR method and found it less sensitive than the moment analysis (59, 107, 119). However, further study is warranted.

Another approach to distinguishing homogeneous from nonhomogeneous emptying involves the relative sensitivity of MEFV configuration to time when curves are initiated from volumes less than TLC. Theoretically a homogeneous MEFV curve has a configuration that depends directly on recoil and flow-resistive parameters (which, in turn, are both tightly coupled to lung volumes), and timing depends on these parameters. In contrast, a system that empties nonhomogeneously, in the sense of having some regions that deflate more rapidly than others, has MEFV curves that depend on timing: whatever the volume is at which a forced expiration is initiated, the fast regions will contribute disproportionately at first. One anticipates that in homogeneous systems, if expirations were interrupted and then allowed to start up again after the initial nonhomogeneous displacements from airways undergoing compression (64), which would be substantially completed within ~20 ms, these MEFV curves would superimpose uninterrupted ones. Indeed this is seen to be the case for normal lungs. In contrast, for lungs that empty nonhomogeneously, if expirations are interrupted for a sufficient period and then allowed to start again, flows will exceed those at the same volume for an uninterrupted curve and for periods longer than can be accounted for by displacements from compressed airways (96).

Both methods for detecting nonhomogeneous emptying depend on measurable rates of emptying. They do not detect nonhomogeneous behavior of regions that empty so slowly that within the time span of an FVC their contributions go unmeasured. It must be remembered that MEFV curves reflect the behavior of lungs over a fairly restricted time span. The RV/TLC ratio contains the very slow regions, if they are present.

Finally, it should be noted that there are statistical techniques that can be applied to all measurements from the FVC. For example, Pimmel et al. (116) derived two parameters from the FVC by a feature-extraction technique. This approach can be expanded to analyze a large number of tests from the FVC and compress the data into a few nonredundant, empirical parameters. These parameters may prove useful in assessing the change in a subject's pulmonary function with time and in automating the interpretation of pulmonary function data.

RELATIVE MERITS OF PRESENTATIONS

Volume-Time

A major value of the volume-time trace is the ease of measuring time-based events, such as the FEV_t and $FEF_{25\%-75\%}$, from the spirogram. As noted in *Volume-Time*, p. 303, a spirogram with an adequate time base is the best way of visualizing the time course of expiration. It is particularly useful in detecting terminal slowing.

Flow-Volume

The presentation of forced expiration in the MEFV mode played a major role in advancing the understanding of flow limitation. The major value of the MEFV presentation is that it focuses directly on $\dot{V}max$ as a function of the pertinent, independent variable (volume), the relationship of most interest during forced expiration in both health and disease. In addition there are practical advantages in using the MEFV curve.

From inspection of a series of consecutive MEFV curves, a quick judgment can be made as to their reproducibility. One assumes that $\dot{V}max$ is a unique function of volume. By superimposing repeated efforts one can easily assess poor efforts where either $\dot{V}max$ is not consistently achieved or the VC is truncated at either end. It is rare that an individual consistently produces reproducible, submaximal efforts. If a serious question exists as to whether a person is exerting sufficient effort to achieve $\dot{V}max$, an esophageal balloon can resolve the issue by determining whether pressure in excess of that usually required to produce $\dot{V}max$ is being generated (108, 117). Of course one must keep in mind the problems related to the gas-compression artifact when volume is measured at the mouth (Fig. 5). False negative effort dependence of IVPF curves is seen when measuring volume at the mouth due to the gas-compression artifact. True neg-

ative effort dependence is occasionally seen on curves generated in a plethysmograph and can add to the complexity of evaluating reproducibility (92). However, in all instances the MEFV presentation appears superior to the volume-time tracing in judging reproducibility. The use of SR values (Fig. 6) appears to be a very sensitive method for judging reproducibility (19, 139).

It is often instructive to relate tidal breathing and maximal voluntary ventilation to flows developed during the FVC (50, 138). This is accomplished by superimposing these breathing patterns on an MEFV curve (53, 138); this provides a visual impression of the total flow available to the person. The MEFV loop, which includes forced inspiration, has been particularly useful in the detection and analysis of lesions of the major airway (38, 97, 98). The configuration of the loop depends on the type and location of the lesion. A fixed lesion will have the same effect on the loop whether exposed to intra- or extrathoracic pressure. Variable lesions that respond to Ptm have quite different contours depending on their location (Fig. 7).

Occasionally a subject cannot produce a continuously forced expiratory effort because the subject lacks coordination or comprehension or is malingering. A reasonable idea of the MEFV curve frequently can be obtained by the continuous recording of the subject's efforts, even though none is truly maximal (Fig. 8A). Another approach is to record a series of coughs and to define the MEFV envelope from them (Fig. 8B). Although they use different volume histories, these maneuvers closely approximate the subject's true MEFV curve. The examples in Figure 8 were obtained with the subject in a body plethysmograph and the flow transients (64) were filtered for sake of clarity.

The MEFV curve is also useful in evaluating the effect of bronchodilator drugs. One compares $\dot{V}max$ at the same lung volume on curves obtained before and after therapy. If TLC has been measured, the curves can be aligned in terms of absolute lung

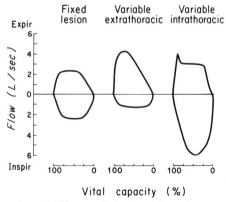

FIG. 7. Characteristic flow-volume loops produced by major airway lesions. Fixed lesion resulted from fracture of larynx. Variable extrathoracic lesion was due to bilateral vocal cord paralysis. Variable intrathoracic pattern was produced by malignancy of trachea at carina. [From Hyatt and Black (53).]

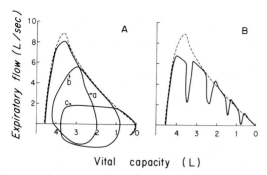

FIG. 8. *A*: maximal expiratory flow-volume curve (*dashed curve*) obtained from series of expiratory efforts, none of which represented an acceptable flow-volume curve effort. Sequence was effort *a* (initiated from full inspiration) followed by effort *b* and then effort *c*. *B*: lower two-thirds of maximal expiratory flow-volume curve can be reliably estimated from a series of coughs initiated from full inspiration. For clarity flow transients have been filtered out. [From Hyatt and Black (53).]

volume. Alternately one could use magnetometers to volume-reference flow-volume curves as described by Goldstein and Mead (41). If TLC has not been measured, one assumes that TLC has not changed and the curves are aligned at points of maximal inspiration. Response to therapy is readily visualized by this approach. Similarly it has been shown that MEFV curves are useful in identifying the onset of bronchoconstriction induced by inhalation of allergens [Fig. 9; (109)] or pharmacological agents.

Useful information has come from relating the MEFV curve to the static expiratory pressure-volume plot of the lung. It has been shown that the driving force of lung recoil during forced expiration is adequately modeled by using the static pressure-volume relation (143). Thus $\dot{V}max$ is plotted as a function of Pel,L. Mead and associates (92) termed this relationship *the maximum flow–static recoil (MFSR) curve*. This approach is an extension of the work of Caro and associates (15), who demonstrated that Pel,L rather than lung volume was a major determinant of airway resistance. Similarly it has been shown that Pel,L is more directly related to $\dot{V}max$ than volume is. Recently MFSR curves have been applied in clinical and experimental studies as a method of characterizing the cause of flow limitation (6, 27, 137). If loss of lung recoil is the sole cause of a reduced $\dot{V}max$, then a normal, although foreshortened, MFSR curve results (6). If elevated airway resistance is a major cause of the reduction in $\dot{V}max$, an abnormal MFSR curve will result even with correction for any loss of recoil. However, it is pertinent to reemphasize the original warning (92) against applying MFSR curves in conditions where substantial nonhomogeneous emptying occurs. Finally, from a consideration of the merits of the MEFV curve and spirogram it would seem ideal to record simultaneously FVC efforts in both the volume-time and flow-volume mode, as in the fashion of Figure 4.

ADDITIONAL CONSIDERATIONS

Volume and Time History

For some time it has been known that expiratory flow-volume curves initiated from middle VC can be more sensitive than the usual MEFV curves in detecting acute changes in lung mechanics. These maneuvers, called partial expiratory flow-volume (PEFV) curves, are not preceded by a maximal inspiration to TLC. Frank et al. (31) suggested using PEFV curves for the detection of mild degrees of bronchoconstriction because Nadel and Tierney (104) had shown that a maximal inspiration transiently reduced the degree of induced bronchoconstriction in normal individuals. However, care must be taken in evaluating PEFV curves because they exhibit initial transients in flow that can contribute appreciably to the curve (64).

Bouhuys et al. (8) compared PEFV to MEFV curves in evaluating induced bronchoconstriction in normal subjects and induced bronchodilatation in subjects with asthma. These authors related flow on both curves to absolute lung volume (60% of the control TLC) and found in both groups that PEFV curves were more sensitive in detecting changes than MEFV curves.

Recent studies have documented the importance of considering both time and volume histories with MEFV and PEFV curves to evaluate changes in airway caliber in normal subjects. Green and Mead (43) compared MEFV to PEFV curves. The PEFV curves were preceded by a maximal inspiration. The subject exhaled to a specified volume, paused for varying periods, and then performed the PEFV maneuver. The PEFV curves obtained immediately after a maximal inspiration had higher flows at 50% and 75% of expired VC than PEFV curves preceded by a 10- to 20-s pause. Furthermore flows on the delayed PEFV curves were lower than those of the MEFV curve, indicating that a maximal inspiration temporarily reduces normal resting bronchomotor tone. This explanation was further supported by the fact that delayed

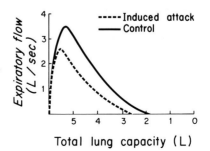

FIG. 9. Maximal expiratory flow-volume curves from patient with asthma. Patient was asymptomatic during control period. Symptoms including wheezing were induced by inhaling an extract of ragweed. Resulting change in lung mechanics is readily identified from maximal expiratory flow-volume curves. [From Hyatt and Black (53).]

PEFV curves were more sensitive in detecting the effects of isoproterenol in normal subjects than were MEFV curves. In another study PEFV curves were as sensitive as changes in airway conductance, a test not preceded by a maximal inspiration (41).

A report by Wellman et al. (145) indicated that in normal subjects, flows on a PEFV curve performed just after exhaling to RV were higher than those of a PEFV curve initiated from middle VC. The expiration to RV increased static lung recoil, which the authors concluded caused the increased flow at 50% TLC. Again the effect was dependent on time, disappearing in ~10 s.

The value of PEFV curves relative to MEFV curves in estimating tone and airway caliber changes has not been established in subjects with chronic obstructive airway disease. Melissinos et al. (96) have utilized interrupted PEFV curves; the subjects breathe neither to TLC nor RV. They examined the time dependence of $\dot{V}$max in subjects with bronchitis, smokers, and nonsmokers and found evidence of nonhomogeneous lung emptying in the first two groups.

However, a considerable problem appears to exist in establishing normal values for partial maneuvers of any kind. Obviously standardization of volume and time history will be difficult if comparison among individuals is attempted. On the other hand the partial maneuvers would appear to be ideally suited to 1) detecting acute changes in bronchial tone within an individual and 2) assessing the presence or absence of nonhomogeneous emptying (96).

Effects of Changing Gas Properties

It has long been recognized (33) that the effect on MEFV curves of changing the physical properties of inspired gas was likely to yield additional information about flow regimes during $\dot{V}$max. Clearly, changing gas properties is the easiest way of perturbating the system. Recently MEFV curves made with the subject breathing air (air-MEFV curves) and with the subject equilibrated with 80% He and 20% O_2 (He-MEFV curves) have been compared to elucidate the mechanism for reduced flows in patients with definite airway obstruction, to detect obstructive disease at a time when flows on air are still normal, and to estimate the site of action of bronchoactive agents.

Flow in a long, straight, smooth-walled tube at a low Reynolds number is laminar; pressure losses are directly proportional to flow and gas viscosity but independent of gas density. In the converging flow pattern in the airways, however, velocity profiles become distorted at bifurcations and, as more parabolic velocity profiles are reestablished, there are additional pressure losses related to gas density and viscosity. Even in long, straight tubes there is no simple equation for turbulent flow, but for a fixed driving pressure flow should vary with gas density to the −0.43 to −0.50 power, depending on the Reynolds number. At

intermediate Reynolds numbers there is a weak dependence on gas viscosity. At very high Reynolds numbers flow is independent of gas viscosity and proportional to density to the −0.50 power, as in convective acceleration.

Schilder et al. (124) examined MEFV curves in normal subjects breathing gases with densities and viscosities differing from air. The effect of viscosity was most apparent at low lung volumes, whereas the effect of density was greatest at middle and high lung volumes. Wood and Bryan (150) used a compression chamber that permitted a 10-fold increase in density with no change in viscosity. Log $\dot{V}$max varied linearly with gas density. There was a fairly constant dependence of maximal flow on density down to 25% VC. These and other data (124, 135, 150) suggest that above 25%–30% VC in normal individuals the pressure loss between the alveoli and the choke point is predominantly due to turbulent flow and convective acceleration.

The small airways normally contribute a relatively small portion of total airway resistance. Increased resistance of the small airways may not alter total airway resistance but should reduce maximal flow. Because of the great variability of MEFV curves in normal individuals, flows may not be reduced below the normal range. However, disease in the small airways should increase the relative contribution of viscosity-dependent flow regimes to the total pressure drop between the alveoli and the choke point. The He-MEFV curves in these individuals would show a less-than-normal increase in flow when compared with air-MEFV curves. Many cigarette smokers show this effect (26, 48, 84).

Although comparing He-MEFV curves with air-MEFV curves may be more sensitive in the detection of early small airways obstruction than air-MEFV curves alone, there are certain practical considerations in using the He-MEFV curves. The lung should be completely equilibrated with the He-O_2 mixture (48). When MEFV curves are measured with expired volume measured at the mouth, errors may be introduced because of thoracic gas compression. At the same expired gas volume, thoracic gas volume may be lower during air-MEFV curves than during He-MEFV curves because the force-velocity characteristics of the respiratory muscles result in a higher PA (1, 54). Accordingly use of expired volumes rather than thoracic gas volume should exaggerate $\Delta\dot{V}$max$_{50}$, the increase in $\dot{V}$max at 50% VC on He-MEFV curves compared with air curves. The force-velocity relationship of the respiratory muscles also explains why comparing the ratio of peak flows underestimates density dependence (150). A vexing problem in determining density dependence is aligning MEFV curves when the VC values are not identical. This is particularly critical in the determination of VisoV̇, the volume at which He-MEFV and air-MEFV curves coincide (48), because the air-MEFV and He-MEFV curves frequently converge gradually. Most authors accept only maneuvers where the two VC values are within 5% and align the curves at RV. MacDonald and Cole (79) studied a group of 25 normal subjects twice daily on 5 consecutive days. They found sufficient intrasubject variability in density dependence and VisoV̇ to make them question the value of the He-MEFV curves. However, these results apply only to normal subjects, and the study did not utilize smoothing and averaging techniques (12, 139). Li et al. (74) have reported a substantial intertechnician variability. A detailed evaluation should be undertaken in subjects with disease.

On the whole the comparison of He-MEFV curves with air-MEFV curves shows promise in detecting early obstructive lung disease and in elucidating the site of increased airway resistance and the response to therapeutic interventions. However, interpretation of the He response is complex. Mink et al. (100, 101) studied the factors leading to an increased V̇max when breathing He-O_2. They determined the site of flow limitation (i.e., the choke point) in the lungs of open-chest dog preparations and in excised human lungs ventilated with both air and He-O_2. Although there was considerable variability in ΔV̇max$_{50}$ in these normal lungs the results could be interpreted on the basis of the wave-speed theory modified to account for peripheral viscous losses (23). When, as in most cases, the choke point on air and He-O_2 occurred at the same site, the results depended on the relative proportion of viscosity to density-dependent pressure losses. Mink et al., like others (18, 93), pointed out that ΔV̇max$_{50}$ cannot be a precise method for distinguishing between obstruction of peripheral and central airways. Indeed the full potential of the He-MEFV curve will not be realized until the determinants of V̇max are understood, at least qualitatively, in terms of an analytic model as discussed in *Computational Model*, p. 300. Finally, gas mixtures other than He-O_2 may prove more informative.

Dysanaptic Growth

There is a large intersubject variability in V̇max in normal individuals (7, 44). Noting that this variability was not significantly reduced by normalizing for lung volumes, Green et al. (44) suggested that differences in airway dimensions in relation to overall lung size might develop during growth. They suggested that this dissociation between parenchymal and airway size might be partly responsible for the wide variations of V̇max in normal humans. They termed this differential growth process *dysanaptic* growth (44), and it has been suggested that disparities in lung and airway size might be predisposing factors in disease (89).

The studies of Brody et al. (10) on Peruvian natives and hamsters raised in hypoxic environments (20) or on protein-deficient diets (9) are consistent with the concept that dysanaptic growth occurs and can significantly alter V̇max. The study of De Troyer et al.

(25) in children is also consistent with this concept. In a later publication Mead (89) presented data that appear consistent with airway diameter being independent of lung size. Mead's analysis needs further evaluation because some data indicate that at least large airway size may be positively correlated with TLC (R. G. Castile, personal communication). Nevertheless the concept of dysanaptic growth is quite useful. For example, Castile et al. (18) presented data generally consistent with this concept. In addition these investigators (18) suggested that part of the variability in V̇max reflected a dissociation between central and peripheral airway size—another reflection of dysanaptic growth.

Axial Bronchial Tension

One of the important parameters determining wave speed, and hence flow limitation, is the elastance of the bronchi at the choke point (see Eq. 4). Griffiths (45) and Dawson and Elliott (23) have argued that localized increased axial tension at the choke point causes negative effort dependence. Wilson (148) presented a theoretical analysis showing that a localized increase in axial tension has the effect of increasing V̇max and can produce negative effort dependence. Briefly the argument is as follows. Axial tension or shear stresses in the airway walls that act between adjacent segments of the airway have the effect of coupling the deformation at neighboring points along the airway. A localized choke point first appears at a point of minimum area. The airway on both sides of the choke point would pull outward and tend to increase the area at the choke point. At higher PL when the airway is compressed downstream of the choke point, this supporting effect would be smaller and V̇max would decrease. Thus changes in axial tension in the airways near the choke point could have the effect of both increasing maximal flow and introducing negative effort dependence on the IVPF curves.

In contrast to localized changes in axial tension the effect of altering overall longitudinal tension in the central airways was examined by Melissinos and Mead (95) in 15 normal young adults. Eleven subjects had consistently higher V̇max during neck hyperextension at high volumes accompanied by changes in the MEFV curve configuration. They suggested that at these volumes in young subjects the choke point resides in the trachea and that neck hyperextension lengthens and stiffens the trachea, which in turn increases its wave speed. The observation was confirmed in dogs.

Thoracoabdominal Mechanics

There have been relatively few studies of thoracoabdominal mechanics during the FVC, and there are essentially no data relating the patterns of deformation to V̇max. Sharp et al. (130) found no paradoxical motion at a given body level during the FVC; lateral motion was less than anteroposterior motion, but they did note phase differences between the two diameters. They found overwhelming dominance of rib cage motion in both sitting and supine postures. In the supine position abdominal volume during a FVC was larger than during quiet breathing; the converse was true in the upright position.

Siafakas et al. (132) recorded transdiaphragmatic pressure during forced expiration as well as diameter measurements of the lower chest and abdomen. Like Sharp et al. (130) they found distortion with the anteroposterior diameters shifted to the left of the relaxation curve, and in most cases the rib cage contribution was greater. However, they noted initially an outward movement of the anteroposterior diameter of the rib cage while the lateral diameters moved in opposite directions. These changes were highly reproducible in each subject. In addition transdiaphragmatic pressure was positive to varying degrees in all subjects during the FVC. They suggested that the diaphragm contracts in order to modulate the intrathoracic pressure and this can influence the pattern of emptying.

Melissinos et al. (94) also found that early during the FVC the lower anteroposterior rib cage tended to increase; this was at a time when the upper chest was decreasing in size. This paradoxical rib cage motion tends to support the observation by Bashoff et al. (4) of a preferential emptying of the upper lobes early in the FVC with later, more homogeneous emptying compared with the slow VC maneuver. They also noted

that lower abdominal diameter decreased rapidly at the onset of the FVC, suggesting that the diaphragm moves upward (94). This perhaps explains their finding that early during the FVC thoracic dimensions changed less than those of the abdomen. These workers also found that estimates of volume change from magnetometers during the FVC were quite inaccurate.

The changes in thoracic shape observed by Melissinos et al. (94) were sufficient to alter the pleural pressure gradient (42). These workers speculated that these changes may affect the pattern of lung emptying during the FVC either directly (in terms of driving pressure) or indirectly by altering the longitudinal tension of the airway at the choke point (94).

In summary the pattern of chest wall deformation during the FVC is complex and varies among subjects. Furthermore there are some unresolved differences among the studies cited. Nevertheless in a given individual the pattern of shape change appears to be highly reproducible as does the transdiaphragmatic pressure. It will be interesting to learn if these varying patterns are reflected in different patterns of lung emptying. Can individuals alter the manner in which they perform the FVC and will this produce predictable changes in V̇max? Regional RV is larger in the nondependent lung (122) after a forced expiration, but there is no satisfactory explanation for this occurrence. Perhaps further studies of the type discussed in this chapter will clarify this question.

REFERENCES

1. AGOSTONI, E., AND W. O. FENN. Velocity of muscle shortening as a limiting factor in respiratory air flow. *J. Appl. Physiol.* 15: 349–353, 1960.
2. ARKINS, J. A., M. R. GLASER, AND R. J. TRETTEL. The maximal expiratory flow rate of normal individuals. *Dis. Chest* 37: 496–498, 1960.
3. ASHFORD, J. R., D. P. DUFFIELD, AND J. W. J. FAY. A search for simple combinations of F.E.V. (1 second) and F.V.C. independent of age and physique in coal miners. *Ann. Occup. Hyg.* 4: 68–81, 1961.
4. BASHOFF, M. A., R. H. INGRAM, JR., AND D. P. SCHILDER. Effect of expiratory flow rate on the nitrogen concentration vs. volume relationship. *J. Appl. Physiol.* 23: 895–901, 1967.
5. BERNSTEIN, L., AND D. MENDEL. The accuracy of spirographic recording at high respiratory rates. *Thorax* 6: 297–309, 1951.
6. BLACK, L. F., R. E. HYATT, AND S. E. STUBBS. Mechanism of expiratory airflow limitation in chronic obstructive pulmonary disease associated with alpha-1-antitrypsin deficiency. *Am. Rev. Respir. Dis.* 105: 891–899, 1972.
7. BLACK, L. F., K. OFFORD, AND R. E. HYATT. Variability in the maximal expiratory flow volume curve in asymptomatic smokers and in nonsmokers. *Am. Rev. Respir. Dis.* 110: 282–292, 1974.
8. BOUHUYS, A., V. R. HUNT, B. M. KIM, AND A. ZAPLETAL. Maximum expiratory flow rates in induced bronchoconstriction in man. *J. Clin. Invest.* 48: 1159–1168, 1969.
9. BRODY, J. S., AND B. N. CONNELL. Dietary protein deficiency and postnatal lung growth (Abstract). *Federation Proc.* 34: 934, 1975.
10. BRODY, J. S., S. LAHIRI, M. SIMPSER, E. K. MOTOYAMA, AND T. VELASQUEZ. Lung elasticity and airway dynamics in Pe-

ruvian natives to high altitude. *J. Appl. Physiol.: Respirat. Environ. Exercise Physiol.* 42: 245–251, 1977.
11. BROWN, P., D. SADOWSKY, AND D. C. GAJDUSEK. Ventilatory lung function studies in Pacific Island Micronesians. *Am. J. Epidemiol.* 108: 259–265, 1978.
12. BRUCE, E. N., AND A. C. JACKSON. Smoothing of MEFV curves by digital filtering of flow as a function of volume. *J. Appl. Physiol.: Respirat. Environ. Exercise Physiol.* 48: 202–206, 1980.
13. BURKI, N. K., AND M. C. DENT. The forced expiratory time as a measure of small airway resistance. *Clin. Sci. Mol. Med.* 51: 53–58, 1976.
14. CANDER, L., AND J. H. COMROE, JR. A method for the objective evaluation of bronchodilator drugs. Effects of dapanone, isuprel, and aminophylline in patients with bronchial asthma. *J. Allergy* 26: 210–218, 1955.
15. CARO, C. G., J. BUTLER, AND A. B. DUBOIS. Some effects of restriction of chest cage expansion on pulmonary function in man: an experimental study. *J. Clin. Invest.* 39: 573–583, 1960.
16. CARO, C. G., AND A. B. DUBOIS. Pulmonary function in kyphoscoliosis. *Thorax* 16: 282–290, 1961.
17. CARPENTER, R. G., A. L. COCHRANE, J. C. GILSON, AND I. T. T. HIGGINS. The relationship between ventilatory capacity and simple pneumoconiosis in coal workers. The effect of population selection. *Br. J. Ind. Med.* 13: 166–176, 1956.
18. CASTILE, R. G., R. E. HYATT, AND J. R. RODARTE. Determinants of maximal expiratory flow and density dependence in normal humans. *J. Appl. Physiol.: Respirat. Environ. Exercise Physiol.* 49: 897–904, 1980.
19. CASTILE, R., J. MEAD, A. JACKSON, M. E. WOHL, AND D. STOKES. Effects of posture on flow-volume curve configuration

in normal humans. *J. Appl. Physiol.: Respirat. Environ. Exercise Physiol.* 53: 1175–1183, 1982.

20. CELLI, B. R., E. LUCEY, AND J. S. BRODY. Physiological consequences of dysanaptic lung growth (Abstract). *Federation Proc.* 36: 469, 1977.

21. CHERNIACK, R. M. Ventilatory function in normal children. *Can. J. Med.* 87: 80–81, 1962.

22. COTES, J. E. *Lung Function: Assessment and Application in Medicine* (4th ed.). Oxford, UK: Blackwell Scientific, 1979, p. 347–352.

23. DAWSON, S. V., AND E. A. ELLIOTT. Wave-speed limitation on expiratory flow—a unifying concept. *J. Appl. Physiol.: Respirat. Environ. Exercise Physiol.* 43: 498–515, 1977.

24. DAYMAN, H. Mechanics of airflow in health and in emphysema. *J. Clin. Invest.* 30: 1175–1190, 1951.

25. DE TROYER, A., J.-C. YERNAULT, M. ENGLERT, D. BARAN, AND M. PAIVA. Evolution of intrathoracic airway mechanics during lung growth. *J. Appl. Physiol.: Respirat. Environ. Exercise Physiol.* 44: 521–527, 1978.

26. DOSMAN, J., F. BODE, J. URBANETTI, R. MARTIN, AND P. T. MACKLEM. The use of a helium-oxygen mixture during maximum expiratory flow to demonstrate obstruction in small airways in smokers. *J. Clin. Invest.* 55: 1090–1099, 1975.

27. DUFFELL, G. M., J. H. MARCUS, AND R. H. INGRAM, JR. Limitation of expiratory flow in chronic obstructive pulmonary disease: relation of clinical characteristics, pathophysiological type, and mechanisms. *Ann. Intern. Med.* 72: 365–374, 1970.

28. ELLIOTT, E. A., AND S. V. DAWSON. Test of wave-speed theory of flow limitation in elastic tubes. *J. Appl. Physiol.: Respirat. Environ. Exercise Physiol.* 43: 516–522, 1977.

29. ENGSTROM, I., F. E. ESCARDO, P. KARLBERG, AND S. KRAEPELIEN. Respiratory studies in children. VI. Timed vital capacity in healthy children and in symptom-free asthmatic children. *Acta Paediatr.* 48: 114–120, 1959.

30. FEMI-PEARSE, D., AND E. A. ELEBUTE. Ventilatory function in healthy adult Nigerians. *Clin. Sci.* 41: 203–211, 1971.

31. FRANK, N. R., M. O. AMDUR, J. WORCESTER, AND J. L. WHITTENBERGER. Effects of acute controlled exposure to SO_2 on respiratory mechanics in healthy male adults. *J. Appl. Physiol.* 17: 252–258, 1962.

32. FRANKLIN, W., AND F. C. LOWELL. The expiratory rate during the third quarter of a maximal forced expiration (E_{50-75}). *J. Allergy* 32: 162–168, 1961.

33. FRY, D. L. Theoretical considerations of the bronchial pressure-flow-volume relationships with particular reference to the maximum expiratory flow-volume curve. *Phys. Med. Biol.* 3: 174–194, 1958.

34. FRY, D. L. A preliminary lung model for simulating the aerodynamics of the bronchial tree. *Comput. Biomed. Res.* 2: 111–134, 1968.

35. FRY, D. L., R. V. EBERT, W. W. STEAD, AND C. C. BROWN. The mechanics of pulmonary ventilation in normal subjects and in patients with emphysema. *Am. J. Med.* 16: 80–97, 1954.

36. FRY, D. L., AND R. E. HYATT. Pulmonary mechanics. A unified analysis of the relationship between pressure, volume and gasflow in the lungs of normal and diseased human subjects. *Am. J. Med.* 29: 672–689, 1960.

37. GAENSLER, E. A. Analysis of the ventilatory defect by timed capacity measurements. *Am. Rev. Tuberc.* 64: 256–278, 1951.

38. GAMSU, G., D. B. BORSON, W. R. WEBB, AND J. H. CUNNINGHAM. Structure and function in tracheal stenosis. *Am. Rev. Respir. Dis.* 121: 519–531, 1980.

39. GANDEVIA, B. Normal standards for single breath tests of ventilatory capacity in children. *Arch. Dis. Child.* 35: 236–239, 1960.

40. GOLDSMITH, J. R. A simple test of maximal expiratory flow for detecting ventilatory obstruction. *Am. Rev. Tuberc. Pulm. Dis.* 78: 180–190, 1958.

41. GOLDSTEIN, D., AND J. MEAD. Use of magnetometers to volume-reference flow-volume curves. *J. Appl. Physiol.: Respirat. Environ. Exercise Physiol.* 48: 731–736, 1980.

42. GRASSINO, A. E., AND N. R. ANTHONISEN. Chest wall distortion and regional lung volume distribution in erect humans. *J. Appl. Physiol.* 39: 1004–1007, 1975.

43. GREEN, M., AND J. MEAD. Time dependence of flow-volume curves. *J. Appl. Physiol.* 37: 793–797, 1974.

44. GREEN, M., J. MEAD, AND J. M. TURNER. Variability of maximum expiratory flow-volume curves. *J. Appl. Physiol.* 37: 67–74, 1974.

45. GRIFFITHS, D. J. Negative resistance effects in flow through collapsible tubes. *Med. Biol. Eng.* 13: 758–802, 1975.

46. HADORN, W. Über die Bestimmung des Exspirationsstosses (maximale Ausatmungsstromstärke). *Z. Klin. Med.* 140: 266–290, 1942.

47. HIGGINS, I. T. T. Respiratory symptoms, bronchitis, and ventilatory capacity in random sample of an agricultural population. *Br. Med. J.* 2: 1198–1203, 1957.

48. HUTCHEON, M., P. GRIFFIN, H. LEVISON, AND N. ZAMEL. Volume of isoflow. A new test in detection of mild abnormalities of lung mechanics. *Am. Rev. Respir. Dis.* 110: 458–465, 1974.

49. HUTCHINSON, J. On the capacity of lungs and on the respiratory function with view of establishing a precise and easy method of detecting diseases by spirometer. *Trans. Med. Soc. London* 29: 137–252, 1846.

50. HYATT, R. E. The interrelationships of pressure, flow and volume during various respiratory maneuvers in normal and emphysematous subjects. *Am. Rev. Respir. Dis.* 83: 676–683, 1961.

51. HYATT, R. E. Dynamic lung volumes. In: *Handbook of Physiology. Respiration*, edited by W. O. Fenn and H. Rahn. Washington, DC: Am. Physiol. Soc., 1965, sect. 3, vol. II, chapt. 54, p. 1381–1397.

52. HYATT, R. E. Effort independence and forced expiratory flow (Letter to the editor). *Chest* 77: 246–247, 1980.

53. HYATT, R. E., AND L. F. BLACK. The flow-volume curve. A current perspective. *Am. Rev. Respir. Dis.* 107: 191–199, 1973.

54. HYATT, R. E., AND R. E. FLATH. Relationship of air flow to pressure during maximal respiratory effort in man. *J. Appl. Physiol.* 21: 477–482, 1966.

55. HYATT, R. E., J. R. RODARTE, J. MEAD, AND T. A. WILSON. Changes in lung mechanics: flow-volume relations. In: *Lung Biology in Health and Disease. The Lung in the Transition Between Health and Disease*, edited by P. T. Macklem and S. Permutt. New York: Dekker, 1979, vol. 12, p. 73–112.

56. HYATT, R. E., D. P. SCHILDER, AND D. L. FRY. Relationship between maximum expiratory flow and degree of lung inflation. *J. Appl. Physiol.* 13: 331–336, 1958.

57. HYATT, R. E., T. A. WILSON, AND E. BAR-YISHAY. Prediction of maximal expiratory flow in excised human lungs. *J. Appl. Physiol.: Respirat. Environ. Exercise Physiol.* 48: 991–998, 1980.

58. INGRAM, R. H., JR., AND D. P. SCHILDER. Effect of gas compression on pulmonary pressure, flow, and volume relationship. *J. Appl. Physiol.* 21: 1821–1826, 1966.

59. JANSEN, J. M., R. PESLIN, A. B. BOHADANA, AND J. L. RACINEUX. Usefulness of forced expiration slope ratios for detecting mild airway abnormalities. *Am. Rev. Respir. Dis.* 122: 221–230, 1980.

60. JONES, J. G., R. B. FRASER, AND J. A. NADEL. Prediction of maximum expiratory flow rate from area-transmural pressure curve of compressed airway. *J. Appl. Physiol.* 38: 1002–1011, 1975.

61. JORDANOGLOU, J., E. KOURSOUBA, C. LALENIS, T. GOTSIS, J. KONTOS, AND C. GARDIKAS. Effective time of the forced expiratory spirogram in health and airways obstruction. *Thorax* 34: 187–193, 1979.

62. KNUDSON, R. J., M. D. LEBOWITZ, AND B. BURROWS. Effort independence and forced expiratory flow (Letter to the editor). *Am. Rev. Respir. Dis.* 122: 990–991, 1980.

63. KNUDSON, R. J., J. MEAD, M. D. GOLDMAN, J. R. SCHWABER, AND M. E. WOHL. The failure of indirect indices of lung elastic recoil. *Am. Rev. Respir. Dis.* 107: 70–82, 1973.

64. KNUDSON, R. J., J. MEAD, AND D. E. KNUDSON. Contribution of airway collapse to supramaximal expiratory flows. *J. Appl. Physiol.* 36: 653–667, 1974.

65. KORY, R. C., R. CALLAHAN, H. G. BOREN, AND J. C. SYNER. The Veterans Administration-Army cooperative study of pulmonary function. *Am. J. Med.* 30: 243–258, 1961.

66. LAMBERT, R. K. The use of a computation model for expiratory flow to simulate the effects of two airway abnormalities. *Aust. Physiol. Eng. Sci. Med.* 4: 100–108, 1981.

67. LAMBERT, R. K., AND T. A. WILSON. A model for the elastic properties of the lung and their effect on expiratory flow. *J. Appl. Physiol.* 34: 34–48, 1973.

68. LAMBERT, R. K., T. A. WILSON, R. E. HYATT, AND J. R. RODARTE. A computational model for expiratory flow. *J. Appl. Physiol.: Respirat. Environ. Exercise Physiol.* 52: 44–56, 1982.

69. LAPP, N. L., H. E. AMANDUS, R. HALL, AND W. K. C. MORGAN. Lung volumes and flow rates in black and white subjects. *Thorax* 29: 185–188, 1974.

70. LEBOWITZ, M. D., R. J. KNUDSON, G. ROBERTSON, AND B. BURROWS. Significance of intraindividual changes in maximum expiratory flow volume and peak expiratory flow measurements. *Chest* 81: 566–570, 1982.

71. LEITH, D. E., AND J. MEAD. Mechanisms determining residual volume of the lungs in normal subjects. *J. Appl. Physiol.* 23: 221–227, 1967.

72. LEMEN, R. J., C. B. GERDES, M. J. WEGMANN, AND K. J. PERRIN. Frequency spectra of flow and volume events for forced vital capacity. *J. Appl. Physiol.: Respirat. Environ. Exercise Physiol.* 53: 977–984, 1982.

73. LEUALLEN, E. C., AND W. S. FOWLER. Maximal midexpiratory flow. *Am. Rev. Tuberc. Pulm. Dis.* 72: 783–800, 1955.

74. LI, K. Y., L. T. TAN, P. CHONG, AND J. A. DOSMAN. Between-technician variation in the measurement of spirometry with air and helium. *Am. Rev. Respir. Dis.* 124: 196–198, 1981.

75. LIANG, A., A. E. MACFIE, E. A. HARRIS, AND R. M. L. WHITLOCK. Transit-time analysis of the forced expiratory spirogram during clinical remission in juvenile asthma. *Thorax* 34: 194–199, 1979.

76. LIGAS, J. R., F. P. PRIMIANO, JR., G. M. SAIDEL, AND C. F. DOERSHUK. Comparison of measures of forced expiration. *J. Appl. Physiol.: Respirat. Environ. Exercise Physiol.* 42: 607–613, 1977.

77. LOCKHART, W., D. H. SMITH, A. MAIR, AND W. A. WILSON. Practical experience with the peak flow meter. *Br. Med. J.* 1: 37–38, 1960.

78. LYONS, H. A., R. W. TANNER, AND T. PICCO. Pulmonary function studies in children. *Am. J. Dis. Child.* 100: 196–207, 1960.

79. MACDONALD, J. B., AND T. J. COLE. The flow-volume loop: reproducibility of air and helium-based tests in normal subjects. *Thorax* 35: 64–69, 1980.

80. MACKLEM, P. T., R. G. FRASER, AND W. G. BROWN. Bronchial pressure measurements in emphysema and bronchitis. *J. Clin. Invest.* 44: 897–905, 1965.

81. MACKLEM, P. T., R. G. FRASER, AND W. G. BROWN. The detection of the flow-limiting bronchi in bronchitis and emphysema by airway pressure measurements. *Med. Thorac.* 22: 220–230, 1965.

82. MACKLEM, P. T., AND J. MEAD. Factors determining maximum expiratory flow in dogs. *J. Appl. Physiol.* 25: 159–169, 1968.

83. MACKLEM, P. T., AND N. J. WILSON. Measurement of intrabronchial pressure in man. *J. Appl. Physiol.* 20: 653–663, 1965.

84. MALO, J. L., AND P. LEBLANC. Functional abnormalities in young asymptomatic smokers with special reference to flow volume curves breathing various gases. *Am. Rev. Respir. Dis.* 111: 623–629, 1975.

85. MARCH, H. W., AND H. A. LYONS. A study of the maximal ventilatory flow rates in health and disease. *Dis. Chest* 37: 602–614, 1960.

86. MCCALL, C. B., R. E. HYATT, F. W. NOBLE, AND D. L. FRY. Harmonic content of certain respiratory flow phenomena of normal individuals. *J. Appl. Physiol.* 10: 215–218, 1957.

87. MCDERMOTT, M., AND C. B. MCKERROW. The effect of an external resistance on hyperventilation (Abstract). *Proc. Int. Congr. Physiol. Sci., 20th, Brussels, 1956,* p. 628.

88. MEAD, J. Analysis of the configuration of maximum expiratory flow-volume curves. *J. Appl. Physiol.: Respirat. Environ. Exercise Physiol.* 44: 156–165, 1978.

89. MEAD, J. Dysanapsis in normal lungs assessed by the relationship between maximal flow, static recoil, and vital capacity. *Am. Rev. Respir. Dis.* 121: 339–342, 1980.

90. MEAD, J. Expiratory flow limitation: a physiologist's point of view. *Federation Proc.* 39: 2771–2775, 1980.

91. MEAD, J., T. TAKISHIMA, AND D. LEITH. Stress distribution in lungs: a model of pulmonary elasticity. *J. Appl. Physiol.* 28: 596–608, 1970.

92. MEAD, J., J. M. TURNER, P. T. MACKLEM, AND J. B. LITTLE. Significance of the relationship between lung recoil and maximum expiratory flow. *J. Appl. Physiol.* 22: 95–108, 1967.

93. MEADOWS, J. A., III, J. R. RODARTE, AND R. E. HYATT. Density dependence of maximal expiratory flow in chronic obstructive pulmonary disease. *Am. Rev. Respir. Dis.* 121: 47–53, 1980.

94. MELISSINOS, C. G., M. GOLDMAN, E. BRUCE, E. ELLIOTT, AND J. MEAD. Chest wall shape during forced expiratory maneuvers. *J. Appl. Physiol.: Respirat. Environ. Exercise Physiol.* 50: 84–93, 1981.

95. MELISSINOS, C. G., AND J. MEAD. Maximum expiratory flow changes induced by longitudinal tension on trachea in normal subjects. *J. Appl. Physiol.: Respirat. Environ. Exercise Physiol.* 43: 537–544, 1977.

96. MELISSINOS, C. G., P. WEBSTER, Y.-K. TIEN, AND J. MEAD. Time dependence of maximum flow as an index of nonuniform emptying. *J. Appl. Physiol.: Respirat. Environ. Exercise Physiol.* 47: 1043–1050, 1979.

97. MILLER, R. D., AND R. E. HYATT. Obstructing lesions of the larynx and trachea: clinical and physiologic charcteristics. *Mayo Clin. Proc.* 44: 145–161, 1969.

98. MILLER, R. D., AND R. E. HYATT. Evaluation of obstructing lesions of the trachea and larynx by flow-volume loops. *Am. Rev. Respir. Dis.* 108: 475–481, 1973.

99. MILLER, W. F., R. L. JOHNSON, JR., AND N. WU. Relationships between fast vital capacity and various timed expiratory capacities. *J. Appl. Physiol.* 14: 157–163, 1959.

100. MINK, S. N., AND L. D. H. WOOD. How does HeO_2 increase maximum expiratory flow in human lungs? *J. Clin. Invest.* 66: 720–729, 1980.

101. MINK, S., M. ZIESMANN, AND L. D. H. WOOD. Mechanisms of increased maximum expiratory flow during HeO_2 breathing in dogs. *J. Appl. Physiol.: Respirat. Environ. Exercise Physiol.* 47: 490–502, 1979.

102. MORRIS, J. F., A. KOSKI, AND L. C. JOHNSON. Spirometric standards for healthy nonsmoking adults. *Am. Rev. Respir. Dis.* 103: 57–67, 1971.

103. MORRIS, J. F., W. P. TEMPLE, AND A. KOSKI. Normal values for the ratio of one-second forced expiratory volume to forced vital capacity. *Am. Rev. Respir. Dis.* 108: 1000–1003, 1973.

104. NADEL, J. A., AND D. F. TIERNEY. Effect of a previous deep inspiration on airway resistance in man. *J. Appl. Physiol.* 16: 717–719, 1961.

105. NEEDHAM, C. D., M. C. ROGAN, AND I. MCDONALD. Normal standards for lung volumes, intrapulmonary gas-mixing, and maximum breathing capacity. *Thorax* 9: 313–325, 1954.

106. NEUBURGER, N., H. LEVISON, A. C. BRYAN, AND K. KRUGER. Transit time analysis of the forced expiratory spirogram in growth. *J. Appl. Physiol.* 40: 329–332, 1976.

107. NICKERSON, B. G., R. J. LEMEN, C. B. GERDES, M. J. WEGMANN, AND G. ROBERTSON. Within-subject variability and per cent change for significance of spirometry in normal sub-

jects and in patients with cystic fibrosis. *Am. Rev. Respir. Dis.* 122: 859–866, 1980.

108. OLAFSSON, S., AND R. E. HYATT. Ventilatory mechanics and expiratory flow limitation during exercise in normal subjects. *J. Clin. Invest.* 48: 564–573, 1969.

109. OLIVE, J. T., JR., AND R. E. HYATT. Maximal expiratory flow and total respiratory resistance during induced bronchoconstriction in asthmatic subjects. *Am. Rev. Respir. Dis.* 106: 366–376, 1972.

110. OSCHERWITZ, M., S. A. EDLAVITCH, T. R. BAKER, AND T. LARBOE. Differences in pulmonary functions in various racial groups. *Am. J. Epidemiol.* 96: 319–327, 1972.

111. PARDAENS, J., K. P. VAN DE WOESTIJNE, AND J. CLÉMENT. A physical model of expiration. *J. Appl. Physiol.* 33: 479–490, 1972.

112. PEDERSEN, O. F., B. THIESSEN, AND S. LYAGER. Airway compliance and flow limitation during forced expiration in dogs. *J. Appl. Physiol.: Respirat. Environ. Exercise Physiol.* 52: 357–369, 1982.

113. PEMBERTON, J., AND E. G. FLANAGAN. Vital capacity and timed vital capacity in normal men over forty. *J. Appl. Physiol.* 9: 291–296, 1956.

114. PERMUTT, S., AND H. A. MENKES. Spirometry: analysis of forced expiration within the time domain. In: *Lung Biology in Health and Disease. The Lung in the Transition Between Health and Disease,* edited by P. T. Macklem and S. Permutt. New York: Dekker, 1979, vol. 12, p. 113–152.

115. PESLIN, R., A. BOHADANA, B. HANNHART, AND P. JARDIN. Comparison of various methods for reading maximal expiratory flow-volume curves. *Am. Rev. Respir. Dis.* 119: 271–277, 1979.

116. PIMMEL, R. L., M. J. TSAI, AND J. F. DONOHUE. Forced expiratory spirometric parameters derived by feature-extraction techniques. *Am. Rev. Respir. Dis.* 120: 1245–1250, 1979.

117. POTTER, W. A., S. OLAFSSON, AND R. E. HYATT. Ventilatory mechanics and expiratory flow limitation during exercise in patients with obstructive lung disease. *J. Clin. Invest.* 50: 910–919, 1971.

118. PRIDE, N. B., S. PERMUTT, R. L. RILEY, AND B. BROMBERGER-BARNEA. Determinants of maximal expiratory flow from the lungs. *J. Appl. Physiol.* 23: 646–662, 1967.

119. RACINEUX, J. L., R. PESLIN, AND B. HANNHART. Sensitivity of forced expiration indices to induced changes in peripheral airway resistance. *J. Appl. Physiol.: Respirat. Environ. Exercise Physiol.* 50: 15–20, 1981.

120. REYNOLDS, D. B., AND J.-S. LEE. Modeling study of the pressure-flow relationship of the bronchial tree (Abstract). *Federation Proc.* 38: 1444, 1979.

121. REYNOLDS, D. B., AND J.-S. LEE. Steady pressure-flow relationship of a model of the canine bronchial tree. *J. Appl. Physiol.: Respirat. Environ. Exercise Physiol.* 51: 1072–1079, 1981.

122. RUFF, F., R. R. MARTIN, AND J. MILIC-EMILI. Previous volume history of the lung and regional distribution of residual volume. *J. Appl. Physiol.: Respirat. Environ. Exercise Physiol.* 51: 313–316, 1981.

123. SASAKI, H., T. TAKISHIMA, AND T. SASAKI. Influence of lung parenchyma on dynamic bronchial collapsibility of excised dog lungs. *J. Appl. Physiol.: Respirat. Environ. Exercise Physiol.* 42: 699–705, 1977.

124. SCHILDER, D. P., A. ROBERTS, AND D. L. FRY. Effect of gas density and viscosity on the maximal expiratory flow-volume relationships. *J. Clin. Invest.* 42: 1705–1713, 1963.

125. SCHOENBERG, J. B., G. J. BECK, AND A. BOUHUYS. Growth and decay of pulmonary function in healthy blacks and whites. *Respir. Physiol.* 33: 367–393, 1978.

126. SEGALL, J. J., AND B. A. BUTTERWORTH. The maximal mid-expiratory flow time. *Br. J. Dis. Chest* 62: 139–146, 1968.

127. SELBY, T., AND J. READ. Maximal expiratory flow rates in Australian adults. *Australas. Ann. Med.* 10: 49–51, 1961.

128. SELTZER, C. C., A. B. SIEGELAUB, D. G. FRIEDMAN, AND M. F. COLLEN. Differences in pulmonary function related to smoking habits and race. *Am. Rev. Respir. Dis.* 110: 598–608, 1974.

129. SHAPIRO, A. H. Steady flow in collapsible tubes. *J. Biomech. Eng.* 99: 126–147, 1977.

130. SHARP, J. T., N. B. GOLDBERG, W. S. DRUZ, AND J. DANON. Relative contributions of rib cage and abdomen to breathing in normal subjects. *J. Appl. Physiol.* 39: 608–618, 1975.

131. SHEPHARD, R. J. Some observations on peak expiratory flow. *Thorax* 17: 39–48, 1962.

132. SIAFAKAS, N. M., A. J. R. MORRIS, AND M. GREEN. Thoracoabdominal mechanics during relaxed and forced vital capacity. *J. Appl. Physiol.: Respirat. Environ. Exercise Physiol.* 47: 38–42, 1979.

133. SIDOR, R., AND J. M. PETERS. Differences in ventilatory capacity of Irish and Italian fire fighters. *Am. Rev. Respir. Dis.* 108: 669–671, 1973.

134. Snowbird workshop on standardization of spirometry: a statement by the American Thoracic Society. *Am. Rev. Respir. Dis.* 119: 831–838, 1979.

135. STAATS, B. A., T. A. WILSON, S. J. LAI-FOOK, J. R. RODARTE, AND R. E. HYATT. Viscosity and density dependence during maximal flow in man. *J. Appl. Physiol.: Respirat. Environ. Exercise Physiol.* 48: 313–319, 1980.

136. STRANG, L. B. The ventilatory capacity of normal children. *Thorax* 14: 305–310, 1959.

137. STUBBS, S. E., AND R. E. HYATT. Effect of increased lung recoil pressure on maximal expiratory flow in normal subjects. *J. Appl. Physiol.* 32: 325–331, 1972.

138. TAKISHIMA, T., G. GRIMBY, W. GRAHAM, R. KNUDSON, P. T. MACKLEM, AND J. MEAD. Flow-volume curves during quiet breathing, maximum voluntary ventilation, and forced vital capacities in patients with obstructive lung disease. *Scand. J. Respir. Dis.* 48: 384–393, 1967.

139. TIEN, Y.-K., E. A. ELLIOTT, AND J. MEAD. Variability of the configuration of maximum expiratory flow-volume curves. *J. Appl. Physiol.: Respirat. Environ. Exercise Physiol.* 46: 565–570, 1979.

140. TIFFENEAU, R., AND PINELLI. Air circulant et air captif dans l'exploration de la fonction ventilatrice pulmonaire. *Paris Med.* 133: 624–628, 1947.

141. TINKER, C. M. Peak expiratory flow measured by the Wright peak flow meter. Distribution of values in men aged 30–59 who denied respiratory symptoms. *Br. Med. J.* 1: 1365–1366, 1961.

142. TOCKMAN, M., H. MENKES, B. COHEN, S. PERMUTT, J. BENJAMIN, W. C. BALL, JR., AND J. TONASCIA. A comparison of pulmonary function in male smokers and nonsmokers. *Am. Rev. Respir. Dis.* 114: 711–722, 1976.

143. WEBSTER, P. M., S. H. LORING, J. P. BUTLER, AND F. G. HOPPIN, JR. Lung recoil during rapid vital capacity expirations simulated by gas compression. *J. Appl. Physiol.: Respirat. Environ. Exercise Physiol.* 49: 142–149, 1980.

144. WEIBEL, E. R. *Morphometry of the Human Lung.* New York: Academic, 1963, p. 110–143.

145. WELLMAN, J. J., R. BROWN, R. H. INGRAM, JR., J. MEAD, AND E. R. MCFADDEN, JR. Effect of volume history on successive partial expiratory flow-volume maneuvers. *J. Appl. Physiol.* 41: 153–158, 1976.

146. WELLS, H. S., W. W. STEAD, T. D. ROSSING, AND J. OGNANOVICH. Accuracy of an improved spirometer for recording of fast breathing. *J. Appl. Physiol.* 14: 451–454, 1959.

147. WILLIAMS, D. E., R. D. MILLER, AND W. F. TAYLOR. Pulmonary function studies in healthy Pakistani adults. *Thorax* 37: 243–249, 1978.

148. WILSON, T. A. Modeling the effect of axial bronchial tension on expiratory flow. *J. Appl. Physiol.: Respirat. Environ. Exercise Physiol.* 45: 659–665, 1978.

149. WILSON, T. A., R. E. HYATT, AND J. R. RODARTE. The

mechanisms that limit expiratory flow. *Lung* 158: 193–200, 1980.

150. WOOD, L. D. H., AND A. C. BRYAN. Effect of increased ambient pressure on flow-volume curve of the lung. *J. Appl. Physiol.* 27: 4–8, 1969.

151. WRIGHT, B. M. A miniature Wright peak-flow meter. *Br. Med. J.* 2: 1627–1628, 1978.

152. WRIGHT, B. M., AND C. B. MCKERROW. Maximum forced expiratory flow rate as a measure of ventilatory capacity. With a description of a new portable instrument for measuring it. *Br. Med. J.* 2: 1041–1047, 1959.

153. ZAMEL, N., I. KASS, AND G. J. FLEISCHLI. Relative sensitivity of maximal expiratory flow-volume curves using spirometer versus body plethysmograph to detect mild airway obstruction. *Am. Rev. Respir. Dis.* 107: 861–863, 1973.

CHAPTER 20

Cough

D A V I D   E .   L E I T H

J A M E S   P .   B U T L E R

S T E V E N   L .   S N E D D O N

J O S E P H   D .   B R A I N

Anesthesia Department, Brigham and Women's Hospital, Boston, Massachusetts

Department of Environmental Science and Physiology, Harvard School of Public Health, Boston, Massachusetts

COUGH IS A WIDE FIELD that has been reviewed extensively (10, 18, 54, 55, 73, 80, 89, 111). This chapter, however, is narrow for it addresses primarily the mechanics of cough, conceived as the junction of two topics: *1*) forced expiration, which is physiology, and *2*) two-phase cocurrent flow, which is fluid mechanics. This approach emphasizes the opportunities for those with competence in both fields to advance the current understanding of cough mechanics, cough clearance, and cough failures.

The existing descriptions and insights into basic mechanisms of forced expiration and cough are reasonably satisfactory, but knowledge of local mechanisms involved in cough clearance is rudimentary. It is desirable to know more about how, and how well, materials with various properties in airways are moved, and removed, by cough; what the necessary conditions are and how and where they arise; as well as what can impair the operation of the cough mechanism and what are the consequences of, and what can be done about, its impairment.

More complete discussions are available that focus on neural organization of cough (32, 125, 157, 158); airway physiology (108); mucociliary clearance and other defense mechanisms (10, 17, 25, 27, 30, 84, 95, 107, 115, 116, 121, 146, 151); the effects of cough on the circulatory and cerebrospinal fluid (CSF) systems (80, 96, 137–139, 159, 160); and on clinical (6, 13, 18, 54, 55, 86, 133, 151), developmental (82, 85, 103), pharmacological (2, 5, 10, 108, 117, 163), and epidemiological and historical (19, 51, 58, 128) aspects of cough.

GENERAL CONSIDERATIONS

Cough has several practical functions. It is usually an occasional and casual matter, associated with insignificant respiratory infections or aspiration of ingested materials. Such coughs are elicited by stimulation of receptors within central airways and reflect the clearance function that is the focus of this chapter. A second function appears to be served by laryngopharyngeal coughs (73) and by the expiration reflex elicited by stimulation of the vocal folds (73), which are not preceded by inspiration and presumably serve to prevent or minimize aspiration of foreign materials into the airway. A third function appears to be served when cough is elicited by application of high distending pressures to the lung. Such coughs set limits to maximal inspiration, for example, in the presence of atelectasis (21), presumably protecting the lung from overdistension and mechanical disruption.

However, cough is also a sign or symptom of well over 100 diseases and other conditions of medical significance and thus is a source of deeper concern. For physicians it is both a problem and a tool in differential diagnosis. In epidemiology its association with smoking and chronic bronchitis deserves special mention. Cough can signal such serious processes as neoplasms and infections, some of the latter communicable (126) by cough, or it can be benign from the point of view of the lung, representing social signals, symbols, habits, or tics. The causes may be obvious or as rare and obscure as neurilemomas of the vagus, hairs touching the tympanic membrane, and transvenous pacemakers.

For millions of people (and their associates) chronic or paroxysmal cough may be a more or less severe nuisance. For some it is socially incapacitating (as when it is incessant or causes urinary incontinence), and it can be exhausting, debilitating, and even life threatening (as when cough syncope occurs during such ordinary activities as driving). Thus suppression of cough is the basis for a whole field of pharmacology and commerce. The absence of cough, or its failure to be effective, however, can also be threatening, for example, in the newborn, in comatose or paralyzed individuals, in patients with chronic obstructive lung diseases, or in individuals whose pain after surgery may limit expiratory effort. Thus the developmental aspects of cough, the mechanisms of its failure, and the methods to stimulate it, to evaluate and enhance its effectiveness, and to replace it with various therapeutic maneuvers or devices (7, 9, 12, 14, 31) are of interest.

Cough results in substantial stresses on the body wall, which makes voluntary cough a useful maneuver in physical diagnosis and reflex cough a problem during and after surgical procedures on the thorax, abdomen, pelvic floor, and spine. Cough can result in body wall trauma such as torn muscles and fractured ribs and vertebrae. Although it does not overdistend the lungs, it can cause lung disruption, with passage of air into interstitial spaces of the lung (92), mediastinum (106, 127), body wall, and body cavities (pleural, pericardial, and peritoneal), but apparently not into the circulation (a deadly complication of lung overdistension) (60).

High thoracoabdominal pressures, transient or sustained, occur during cough and are transmitted to the circulatory and CSF systems, producing a range of important although incompletely understood effects (46, 96, 138, 139, 160). Multiple sites of flow limitation are established in the vascular system ("vascular waterfalls") at the boundaries of the thoracoabdominal cavities and of the central nervous system (CNS). Venous return, right and left heart filling and afterloads, systemic arterial flow distributions, and vascular reflexes are profoundly influenced. Cough syncope (66, 80, 97, 118, 138) and related phenomena [e.g., weight-lifters' blackout (33) and micturition syncope (45, 134)] are due partly to these mechanisms and partly to increases in CSF pressure that are nearly equal to and simultaneous with increases in thoracoabdominal pressure, with consequent decreases in cerebral perfusion pressure. These relationships are important during the so-called new cardiopulmonary resuscitation (CPR) and cough-induced CPR (15, 34) but are not yet well understood. Changes in CSF pressure contribute to other complications of cough in the presence of some CNS abnormalities (77, 105, 147, 159) and during CNS and eye surgery. A variety of circulatory complications are associated with cough: cardiac rhythm abnormalities, dislodged venous or cardiac mural thrombi, and malfunctioning central venous or right heart catheters [including ventriculoatrial shunts for hydrocephalus (109)], which can become kinked or knotted, sometimes, but rarely, around papillary muscles.

COUGH DESCRIPTION

This section outlines a typical cough and describes in more detail each of its four phases: inspiration, compression, expiration, and cessation. This discussion is based on several descriptive papers, which are well worth reading (20, 76, 78, 88, 128, 129, 139, 156, 164).

Whether cough is initiated voluntarily or by stimulation of receptors in the lower airways, the first action is usually inspiration of a variable volume of air (Fig. 1). Next the glottis is closed simultaneously with or just after the onset of forceful expiratory muscle activity that quickly raises thoracoabdominal pressures to 100 cmH_2O or more above ambient pressure. About 0.2 s after the glottis closes, it is actively opened; subglottic pressure falls and expiratory flow begins. Intrathoracic pressures, however, usually continue to rise (Fig. 2); thus peak pressure usually occurs after peak flow. Expiratory flow quickly rises to (and may briefly exceed) "maximal" flow (see *Expiration*, p. 319) as central intrathoracic airways collapse. Their narrowed cross section is associated with high gas linear velocities and therefore with high shearing forces at airway walls and high kinetic energies. These conditions are probably important in suspending and clearing materials adherent to the walls. After a widely variable volume of air is expired, expiratory muscle activity diminishes abruptly, perhaps with the onset of antagonistic activity of the diaphragm and other muscles; alveolar pressure (P_A) falls toward ambient pressure and flow drops toward zero, sometimes interrupted finally by glottis closure. Several coughs may follow in immediate series from high to low lung volumes without intervening inspirations, or inspirations, sometimes near maximal, may precede subsequent coughs. There are wide variations.

Inspiration

As with most inspirations, there is active abduction of the glottis during the inspirations that precede

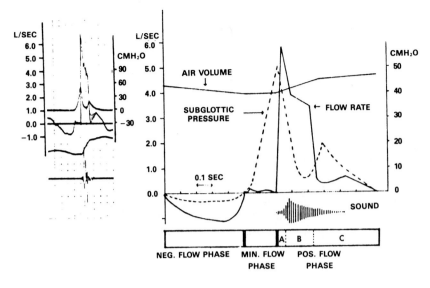

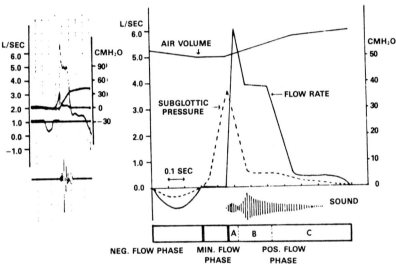

FIG. 1. Flow at airway opening (flow rate), spirometric volume change (air volume), subglottic pressure, and sound level during two representative coughs (*top* and *bottom*). Recordings on *left* are diagrammed on *right*. Positive flow phase is divided into increasing (*A*), constant (*B*), and decreasing (*C*) phases. [From Yanagihara et al. (164).]

cough (150). The inspired volume is quite variable; in voluntary cough it appears to depend on the anticipated forcefulness of the expiratory phase. Yanagihara et al. (164) observed that when subjects were instructed to "produce a single gentle cough in a natural manner," they generally inspired an amount approximately equal to the tidal volume; one subject inspired only ~90 ml. On the other hand, Harris and Lawson (48, 78) observed that when subjects were instructed to cough three times with maximal effort they inspired much more deeply, as much as 50% of their vital capacity (VC). During spontaneous cough it is not uncommon for humans to respond to difficulty in raising secretions by initiating coughs from progressively higher lung volumes until they are finally able to raise whatever is causing them to cough. By contrast the entry of foreign material into the laryngeal approaches may trigger an immediate cough without prior inspiration, presumably minimizing the probability of its penetration deeper into the airway. Korpás and Tomori (73) review evidence for an expiration

reflex that has this function and is distinct from cough.

Different investigators attribute varying degrees of importance to the inspiratory phase of a cough. Langlands (76) does not emphasize it: "At the beginning of a cough the glottis closes." Bucher (20) attaches a great deal of importance to the inspiratory phase, calling it "an integral part of the act of coughing" and "an important connecting link between the stimulus and the resulting response: the deeper the inspiration the stronger the expiratory thrust." Perhaps the difference reflects experience with different types of coughs. In any case greater pressures (due to longer expiratory muscles) and greater expiratory flow rates are available at high lung volumes; both are thought to increase cough effectiveness.

Compression

The onset of expiratory muscle activity and the nearly simultaneous closure of the glottis mark the

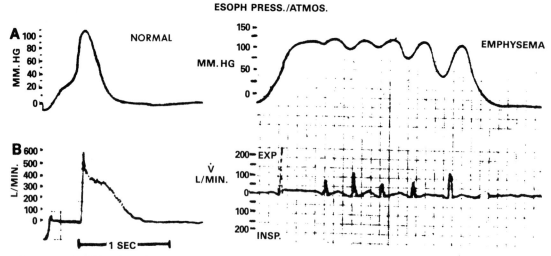

FIG. 2. Flow ($\dot{V}$) at airway opening (*B*) and esophageal pressure (*A*) during single cough in normal subject (*left*) and in subject with emphysema (*right*). Peak time derivative of pressure is ~1,200 and 500 cmH$_2$O/s for on and off transients, respectively, in normal subject but is less in emphysematous subject. In latter, esophageal pressure stays high throughout series of maneuvers that appears to include 6 or 7 glottis closures and reopenings. EXP, expiration; INSP, inspiration. [From Whittenberger and Mead (156).]

beginning of the compressive phase, which is sometimes characterized by a brief initial period of expiratory flow and a voiced "huh" sound (76, 164). Closure of the glottis is achieved by contraction of the adductor muscles of the arytenoid cartilages. According to Von Leden and Isshiki (150), closure is reinforced by supraglottic structures: "the ventricular folds obscure the vocal folds, except in a very gentle cough, and often the epiglottis covers the laryngeal inlet."

The glottis remains closed for ~0.2 s, during which the abdominal, pleural, alveolar, and subglottic pressures rise rapidly, and lung volume decreases as alveolar gas is compressed. The rate and extent of the change in lung volume during this time may be surprisingly great. For example, if PA rises to 200 cmH$_2$O in 0.2 s and if thoracic gas volume (VTG) is initially 5 liters, then the volume decrement is ~1 liter and the mean rate of change of VTG due to compression ($\dot{V}c$) is 5 liters/s. Observed values of the time derivative of pressure (dP/d*t*) range between 600 and 1,600 cmH$_2$O/s (102), with $\dot{V}c$ of ~9 liters/s (40). The effects of gas compression on VTG and $\dot{V}c$ are greater at altitude (59) and less under hyperbaric conditions. If the glottis had been open during the 0.2 s, airflow out at the airway opening ($\dot{V}ao$) would have added to the change, and rate of change, of VTG ($\dot{V}TG = \dot{V}c + \dot{V}ao$). Evans and Jaeger (40) report that $\dot{V}TG$ is ~18 liters/s at sea level. Because expiratory muscle length and contraction velocity are related to VTG and $\dot{V}TG$, respectively, and because the force-length and force-velocity relationships of these muscles are like those of other skeletal muscles (3, 67), their external contractile force, and therefore the intrathoracic pressures achieved, would be smaller throughout an open-

glottis maneuver than during a closed-glottis maneuver. By separating the compressive and expiratory phases of a cough, use of the glottis decreases VTG during the expiratory phase and permits that phase to occur at higher lung volumes and $\dot{V}ao$ than would otherwise be achieved (40), with pressures 30%–180% greater than those observed during voluntary forced expirations at the same lung volumes (100, 102). Higher pressure and flow presumably enhance cough effectiveness. Note, however, that flow rises no faster at the onset of cough than at the onset of forced expiration (72).

The contraction of muscles during compression is a coordinated event. In each of the two pathways for change of lung volume, i.e., the rib cage and the abdomen-diaphragm, there are substantial agonist-antagonist interactions between the inspiratory and expiratory muscles, which are less during cough than during forced vital capacity (FVC) maneuvers (100, 102). The diaphragm thus opposes the development of positive pleural pressure (Ppl) during the compressive phase. This opposition ceases with the opening of the glottis, at which point the diaphragm relaxes and allows full positive-pressure development in the thorax. It is not known why the maneuver is organized this way.

The maximal intrathoracic pressures observed in some people during voluntary and reflexly stimulated cough exceed the static maximal voluntary pressures that they can achieve. Such a relationship cannot be explained by current understanding of expiratory muscle force-length-velocity characteristics; thus it has been suggested that the reflex act engages more neural drive and perhaps less antagonistic activity. This view is supported by the observation that rectus muscle tears and fractures of ribs and vertebrae are associated with cough but never, to our knowledge, with voluntary forced expiration, Valsalva maneuvers, or expulsive maneuvers.

The duration of glottis closure presumably should match the length of time required for expiratory muscle activity to bring about the necessary changes in intrathoracic pressure. Glottis timing is centrally controlled and the rate of pressure rise is a complex function of motor unit recruitment, muscle properties [e.g., maximal rate of tension development (94, 104)], chest wall shape changes, and gas compressibility (volume). It is not known how, or how well, these two times are matched or what adjustments, if any, are made in the former to adapt to changes in the latter, for example, in pathological states.

The closing and subsequent abrupt reopening of the glottis is a basic feature that distinguishes cough from simple forced expiration and, although it has the effects and probable significance to cough outlined in this section, its actual importance in airway clearance is uncertain (20, 110, 150, 164). Occasionally an intubated or tracheotomized patient can cough effectively, and both normal and diseased humans sometimes clear lower airways by voluntary short, sharp forced expirations without glottis closure (123). Negus (110) calls this a "bovine" cough and chest physiotherapists call it "huffing" (130).

Expiration

The glottis is opened by active abduction in 20–40 ms (75, 150). Pressure in the larger (central) airways falls abruptly toward (or even *below*) atmospheric pressure, whereas Ppl and PA remain high or continue to rise. Two related but distinct events then occur simultaneously. Expiratory flow from the lung periphery rises rapidly to maximal values as great as 10 liters/s (depending on lung volume) and central intrathoracic airways abruptly collapse, causing volume decrements of ~100 ml in as little as 20 ms; substantial transient "supramaximal" flow spikes may thus be superimposed on the flow coming from the lung parenchyma. The instantaneous flow through the airway opening ($\dot V$ao) is the sum of these two flows, which come from and through central airways as they collapse. (There is also a negligible contribution from airway gas decompression.) Violent accelerations of airway walls are associated with these events and are thought to contribute to formation and suspension of droplets (99).

After airway collapse is complete, there may be a phase of sustained expiration lasting up to a few hundred milliseconds, during which airway walls may flutter. Lung volume and flow rate decrease approximately exponentially in time, with a time constant of ~0.5 s. Thus flow is maximal and decreases along the maximal expiratory flow-volume (MEFV) curve of the lung in rough proportion to lung volume above residual

volume (RV). Total expired volumes range from a few tens of milliliters to over a liter.

Another pattern of expiration was seen in 70% of coughs examined by Melissinos et al. (102). Shortly after the glottis opened, expiratory muscle activity ceased abruptly, causing intrathoracic pressure to fall by 40% within 0.1 s after peak pressure was reached; dP/dt was −500 to −1,500 cmH2O/s. Thoracic gas expansion, i.e., $\dot V$c, occurred at a rate nearly equal but opposite in sign to $\dot V$ao, so that $\dot V$TG was nearly zero and lung volume remained nearly constant or even increased during this time. As long as intrathoracic pressure was high enough to keep subjects on their MEFV curves, $\dot V$ao remained constant or even increased (100–102).

Flow rates approaching 10 liters/s, through central airways with total cross-sectional area of ~2 cm^2, imply linear velocities of ~5,000 cm/s in uncompressed regions. Some intrathoracic airways, however, are compressed during cough, and higher velocities exist in these compressed regions. These aspects of cough and their relation to clearance mechanisms are considered in AIRFLOW, this page, and TWO-PHASE COCURRENT FLOW, p. 325.

Cessation

Cessation of cough begins when expiratory muscles relax; this sometimes occurs simultaneously with the onset of or an increase in antagonistic activity of inspiratory muscles. Gastric or abdominal pressure (Pab) as well as Ppl and PA drop toward ambient pressure. Expiratory flow becomes submaximal. Transmural pressures (Ptm) applied to central intrathoracic airways rise from highly negative (collapsing) pressures toward the slightly positive values set by lung recoil under static conditions. The glottis may close as the final event; there may be, instead, a voiced "huh" sound or simply quiet cessation of flow as antagonistic activity of inspiratory and expiratory muscles and elastic recoil of the respiratory system come into balance and PA falls to ambient pressure.

AIRFLOW

This section considers the magnitudes and distributions of volume flows and linear velocities in the lung during the expiratory phase of cough as well as some aspects of regional and local flow patterns. This requires attention to regional cross-sectional areas, to the timing of events during cough, and, importantly, to the mechanism by which limits are set to maximal expiratory flows from the lung. This mechanism is reviewed concisely by Hyatt (52) and is treated more fully by Hyatt et al. (53) and in the chapters by Hyatt and by Wilson, Rodarte, and Butler in this *Handbook*. This section provides only enough background in the physics and physiology of forced expiration to set the stage for TWO-PHASE COCURRENT FLOW, p. 325, which covers the movement of complex liquid and semisolid materials through airways by expiratory airflow.

Forced Expiration

During expiratory FVC maneuvers, mammalian lungs empty along approximately exponential curves of volume (therefore also of flow) in time. When maximal flow is plotted against volume, the idealized MEFV curve is a straight line; the volume-flow ratio is the time constant for the maneuver and is ~0.5 s in normal humans. This implies peak expiratory flows approaching 2 VC/s, or ~10 liters/s for an individual with a VC of 5 liters.

The MEFV curves are highly repeatable because of the operation of an effort-independent expiratory flow-limiting mechanism that resides in the lung. These curves outline a flow-volume domain within which all expiratory events must lie (with some exceptions). Surprisingly modest expiratory effort suffices to reach the outer limits of the domain, making forced expiration an easy, reproducible feature of such unphysiological maneuvers as pulmonary function tests. From the point of view of normal physiology, it is likely that these limits are reached during maximal exercise only by elite athletes, whereas they are reached routinely during cough. Thus Mead et al. (99) suggest that in normal humans, expiratory flow limitation is pertinent to "expectoration rather than ventilation."

Flow Limitation

Expiratory flow limitation is one of several important biological examples of the operation of a more generally applicable mechanism that sets upper limits to gas or liquid flow through collapsible tubes, and by analogy, to liquid flow in open channels and to gas flow in converging nozzles (Table 1). These general and particular mechanisms are addressed by Shapiro (136); their applications to expiratory flow were advanced by Dawson and Elliott (35, 36, 38).

Consider a flimsy elastic tube filled with water; neglect gravity and viscous losses. If one end of the tube is struck, a wavelike disturbance propagates along the tube by the progressive local exchange of kinetic energy (in moving liquid) with potential energy (in elastic deformation of the wall). The speed of wave propagation in the tube (c) depends on the associated inertial forces (thus on fluid density) and elastic forces [thus on stiffness of the tube wall (Y)]. For example, if the fluid is very dense and the tube is very compliant, then c is low.

If the downstream pressure (Pds) of the model is lowered so that the fluid flows steadily through the tube toward the point of origin of the pressure disturbance (i.e., wave disturbance), the net velocity of the wave's upstream propagation now is the difference

TABLE 1. *Examples of Wave-Speed Concepts in One-Dimensional Flows*

	Compressible Flow	Open-Channel Hydraulics	Elastic Tube Flow
Propagating wave	Sound	Shallow water	Pulse
Energy storage	Gas compression	Water level (gravity)	Tube recoil
Wave speed	$\sqrt{\gamma P/\rho}$	$\sqrt{\rho g H/\rho} = \sqrt{gH}$	$\sqrt{Y/\rho}$
Velocity greater than wave speed	Supersonic flow	Shooting flow	Supercritical velocity
Ratio of velocity to wave speed	Mach number	Froude number	Speed ratio (S)
Discontinuity	Shock	Hydraulic jump	Elastic jump

γ, Specific heat ratio; P, absolute pressure; ρ, density of fluid; g, acceleration of gravity; H, height of liquid above bottom of channel; Y, elastic modulus of tube cross section. [From Dawson and Elliott (35).]

between the fluid flow velocity and c. An interesting limit is reached when Pds is sufficiently low that the fluid flow velocity = c. Under these conditions, pressure disturbances (changes) can no longer propagate upstream. This implies that further decrements in Pds (Fig. 3B, lines 4–7) cannot influence flow or geometry in the upstream region. An analogy with flow over a dam is clear and precise; flow through both systems is ultimately independent of changes in Pds. Increasing the heights of the dam and the upstream water level by equal amounts (keeping their difference constant) produces the same effect as decreasing the downstream water level by that amount. In our tube analogy, as in the lung, lowering Pds is equivalent to increasing upstream and surrounding pressures by equal amounts. That is, equal increases in Ppl and PA with fixed Pao are equivalent to decreases in Pao alone with Ppl and PA fixed.

Shapiro (136) extends the analogy by defining a speed index (S) equal to the ratio of the fluid flow velocity to c "whose central role is comparable in significance to that of the Mach number and the Froude number" (Table 1); at a point in a tube or airway where the fluid flow velocity = c, $S = 1$. Shapiro (136) and Wilson et al. (161) consider an additional viscous flow limitation that is not addressed in this chapter.

Suppose that the tube's specific compliance [$(1/A)(dA/dPtm)$, where A is cross-sectional area] is everywhere the same function of Ptm, but its resting cross section is not uniform along its length. Because volume flow is everywhere the same (a continuity condition that follows from conservation of mass in incompressible fluids), velocity varies inversely with cross section, thus local flow velocity becomes critical (i.e., reaches c) first (if at all) at the narrowest point. A flow maximum has been achieved in the sense that lowering Pds will not increase flow. The magnitude of the flow maximum equals the product of c and the tube cross section at this so-called choke point. Low-

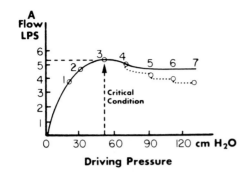

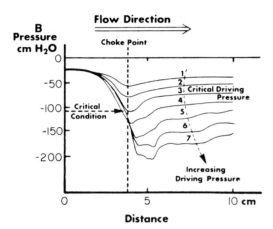

FIG. 3. *A*: progressive decreases in pressure at the downstream end of an excised dog trachea result in increasing flows only to critical condition. *Dotted line* connects *open circles* that show time-dependent effects of stress relaxation (increased compressibility) of tracheal wall. *B*: further increases in driving pressure (i.e., decreases in downstream pressure) do not increase flow or change pressure-distance profile upstream of choke point but do decrease pressures (and cause decreases in cross-sectional area) downstream from choke point (note downstream pressure recovery). Numbered points in *A* correspond to numbered lines in *B*. LPS, liters per second. [From Elliott and Dawson (38).]

ering Pds tends to collapse (i.e., compress) downstream regions of the tube, resulting in increased (perhaps supercritical) velocities there; but ideally it cannot increase volume flow or change the location of the choke point, or influence the geometry or pressure and velocity distributions in regions upstream of the choke point.

Downstream from regions of tube compression and supercritical velocity, another phenomenon relevant to cough may appear. At some point, velocity abruptly falls from supercritical to subcritical and, although violent turbulence and high frictional energy losses might exist, substantial pressure recovery can occur. The lower velocity and higher pressure are linked to one another and associated with increased cross-sectional area. Mathematically a discontinuity exists at such locations. These relationships are observed in hydraulic jumps (e.g., at the foot of spillways) and elastic jumps, for example, in collapsible-tube models

(39, 43, 136, 153) and isolated dog tracheas. In the naive analysis such jumps are quasi-steady. Secondary effects, however, may play a role in causing oscillations in this regime (38, 155). It has been suggested, however, that elastic jumps and pressure recovery do not occur in airways (154).

When flow is maximal, the locations of elastic jumps can vary with Pds, whereas those of choke points do not. Thus both the length and the degree of narrowing of the region of tube compression are effort dependent, as is velocity in this region.

By contrast to the above, suppose that the tube's resting cross section is everywhere the same, but that its elastic properties, which are described by the "tube law" (i.e., the Ptm-*A* relationship), vary along its length. Tube wave speed is lowest where tube wall compliance is highest, and as a first approximation, this point is expected to be the location of the choke point (if one exists).

In the models described above, influences of the tube law are separated from those of the tube cross section for illustrative purposes; in actuality, however, they interact via positive feedback. As flow rises from zero toward a maximal value (due to lowering Pds), pressures within the tube fall and compliant regions tend to narrow more than less compliant ones. As a result, local velocities rise even further in the narrower regions, causing local pressures to fall further; additional local deformation (i.e., narrowing) occurs until equilibrium is reached.

Changes in velocity that are associated with motion from place to place (e.g., from larger to smaller cross sections in a tube) involve convective acceleration, as distinguished from temporal acceleration. Volume flow throughout the model and linear velocity at any given point within it do not change with time (i.e., conditions of quasi-steady flow exist); velocity, however, is not the same at all points in the model. Depending on the relationships between the convective accelerative pressure drops (Pca) (see Table 2) and the local tube laws (which can vary from point to point) near a region of minimal cross section, the system may not exhibit flow limitation, may approach a critical flow asymptotically, or may even show negative effort dependence (i.e., a decrease in flow due to a downstream shift in choke point location) when Pds is lowered.

The situation becomes unavoidably complicated when this simple model is applied to the lung. Airway Ptm-*A* curves are markedly nonlinear, differ among airway regions (e.g., due to the variable presence of cartilage rings), and vary in time-dependent and volume history–dependent ways (e.g., due to smooth muscle activity and hysteresis). They differ with lung volume because of radial and longitudinal forces that arise from mechanical interdependence between airways and surrounding parenchyma and, in extrapulmonary airways, because of changes in Ppl and airway length and tension. At high positive and negative Ptm, central airways are stiff and c is high; but when Ptm is near zero, the same airways are compliant and c is low. Thus choke points tend to reside where Ptm is near zero.

Influenced by exterior and interior pressure distributions, Ptm varies along the length of airways during forced expiration. Peribronchial pressures may be less than Ppl, are not uniformly distributed, and are influenced by mechanical interdependence between airways and parenchyma. Interior pressures depend on inlet pressures (i.e., PA) and thus on overall and regional lung volume and elasticity and expiratory effort as well as on the nonuniform distributions of Pca and frictional pressure drops (Pfr).

At high lung volumes, choke points tend to reside near the tracheal bifurcation, and as lung volume diminishes, they move into more peripheral airways in a discontinuous manner (98); how far upstream they move is uncertain. Some authors find that they move into 2nd or 3rd generation branches (trachea = zero) at lung volumes near RV (141), whereas other authors estimate that they move as far as 5th or 6th generation branches (74, 75). The distance they move surely varies with age, among species, and in diseases.

A more realistic model requires use of a trumpet-shaped conduit (i.e., one that narrows sharply from inlet to outlet) whose wall stiffness increases progressively toward the outlet. A relationship between tube size and fluid density and viscosity is assumed that allows Pca to be large in relation to Pfr at high flows (161). The cross-sectional area of the conduit at any point along its length is taken to be the sum of the cross-sectional areas of all branches at that level in the branching hierarchy.

TABLE 2. *Air Velocity and Convective Accelerative Pressure*

v_a, cm/s	Pca, cmH₂O
1,000	0.7
2,000	3
3,000	6
4,000	11
5,000	18
6,000	26
7,000	35
10,000	71
15,000	161
20,000	286
25,000	446
30,000	643

v_a, Velocity of air; Pca, convective accelerative pressure (Pca = ½ $\rho_a v_a^2$, where ρ_a is density of air). Pressure is often expressed in units of cmH₂O, rationalized as follows. The pressure exerted by a water column = $\rho_\omega g$H, where H is the height of the water column, ρ_ω is the density of water, and g is acceleration of gravity. At sea level, g = 980 cm/s² and ρ_ω = 1 g/cm³. A water column of H = 1 cm thus exerts a pressure of 980 dyn/cm², which is defined to be a pressure of 1 cmH₂O. For ρ_a = 0.0014 g/cm³ (at sea level and body temperature, ambient pressure saturated with water vapor) and v_a in cm/s, Pca (in cmH₂O) is numerically = $(7.14 \times 10^{-7})v_a^2$.

More detailed modeling and analysis are possible but difficult (74, 75) and unnecessary for present purposes. In this chapter it suffices to understand *1*) that the lung displays flow limitation associated with the existence of one or more choke points, which if multiple are in parallel and perhaps in series; *2*) that the locations of the choke points vary with lung volume and depend on gas density and viscosity, and on airway and lung geometry and mechanical properties, including effects of smooth muscle activity and hysteresis and the presence of secretions and other materials, in complex time-varying relationships; *3*) that downstream from such choke points there is a region of supercritical flow whose length and degree of narrowing (therefore gas velocity at any given volume flow) are effort dependent; and *4*) that there may be an elastic jump, where pressure and cross-sectional area increase and velocity drops from supercritical (above c) to subcritical (below c).

Flow Velocities

Cough clearance (see TWO-PHASE COCURRENT FLOW, p. 325) depends partly on the linear velocity of gas flow in airways. Regional magnitudes of these velocities can be estimated in several ways. Rough estimates can be made by dividing volume flow by regional (summed) airway cross section (79). These values range up to ~5,000 cm/s in uncompressed central airways if volume flow is 10 liters/s and cross-sectional area is 2 cm². For comparison the speed of sound in air is ~38,000 cm/s at sea level and at body temperature, saturated with water vapor. Estimates in compressed regions downstream from choke points have ranged up to 28,000 cm/s (129). Uncertainty about actual cross-sectional areas, however, limits our confidence in many of these estimates. Furthermore available pressures appear inadequate to reach such high velocities (see later in this section).

More direct estimates come from measurements of local Pitot pressure [i.e., the difference between static and dynamic pressure (90)], which is equivalent to local Pca (Table 2). Further insights about the range of velocities that may exist at choke points and in compressed regions can be drawn from Table 2. Suppose that near total lung capacity (TLC) lung recoil pressure were 35 cmH₂O, and all (and only) this pressure were available to accelerate gas to the choke point (53); then maximal velocity (v_{max}) at the choke point would be 7,000 cm/s. To the extent that Pfr is greater than zero, available Pca and v_{max} would be lower.

The same approach can be extended to compressed regions. In this case the total driving pressure of interest is PA, which is effort dependent. To establish an upper limit, suppose that all (and only) the maximal PA were available for Pca. If PA were 160 cmH₂O, v_{max} could not exceed 15,000 cm/s. For people with extremely high cough pressures [i.e., 400 (97) to 600

(137) cmH$_2$O], velocities as high as 30,000 cm/s would be a limit. At these velocities—which approach sonic velocities—gas compressibility can no longer be neglected (124); this issue is not addressed in this chapter.

Actual Pca could theoretically be greater than PA because pressure recovery can occur as gas decelerates (i.e., as cross-sectional area increases) between compressed regions and airway opening (e.g., at elastic jumps). Thus pressure within compressed airways could conceivably be subatmospheric. Actual measurements as well as realistic estimates that consider Pfr, however, show lower values of Pca. For example, Macklem and Wilson (91) found tracheal Pca to be ~40 cmH$_2$O in a normal human during forced expi-

ration at 75% VC with PA > 80 cmH$_2$O; the corresponding velocity was ~7,500 cm/s. In one subject during forced expiratory maneuvers at a tracheal Ptm of −120 cmH$_2$O (91) (see Fig. 10B), tracheal cross-sectional area was ~1 cm^2 near TLC and decreased in proportion to the fraction of VC remaining (e.g., 0.75 cm^2 at 75% VC). If a similar proportionality is assumed for maximal flow of 10 liters/s at TLC, tracheal velocities of ~10,000 cm/s can be estimated, remaining nearly constant through much of the VC.

Similar measurements are shown in Figure 4 (50) during a series of graded expiratory efforts by another subject. Figure 4A shows minimal pressure in the trachea of ~7 cmH$_2$O at a point 7 cm mouthward from the carina. The increase in pressure from this point toward the mouth indicates gas deceleration and pressure recovery in excess of frictional losses. It is not usefully interpreted as "negative resistance" and it does not indicate backward shear stress at the wall. Figure 4B shows that as effort increases, the Pca peak is located slightly farther downstream, and the region of high Pca (therefore high velocity and low cross-sectional area) extends farther mouthward (see Fig. 3). Peak Pca rises <10 cmH$_2$O for each 20 cmH$_2$O increment in PA; thus when PA is 85 cmH$_2$O and Pca is 32 cmH$_2$O, v_{max} reaches 7,000 cm/s in a short segment of compressed trachea. Even if PA approached 250 cmH$_2$O it would be hard to envision Pca >100 cmH$_2$O in this individual; that would correspond to a v_{max} of ~12,000 cm/s. Interestingly Pca at the carina does not change with driving pressure; thus the choke point in this person is located at or mouthward from the carina even at a relatively low lung volume (specifically 50% VC). Furthermore Pca is low, corresponding to v_{max} of <2,000 cm/s in the uncompressed region.

Thus we and others (89) think it likely that in ordinary cough, v_{max} nowhere exceeds 10,000–15,000 cm/s, which is less than some earlier estimates.

In summary, at a choke point when flow is maximal, the linear velocity of the fluid equals tube wave speed

$$v_{max} = c \qquad (1)$$

The terms on the left and right, respectively, may be rewritten (52) as

$$\dot{V}max/A = \rho^{-1/2}(A\ dPtm/dA)^{1/2} \qquad (2)$$

where $\dot{V}max$ is the maximal volume flow and ρ is fluid density. When the density is constant, v_{max} is dependent only on the specific elastance of the airway (A dPtm/dA), thus the specific elastance has special significance. Airway elasticity is an important consideration in computational models of forced expiration (74, 75). It is regionally variable intrinsically, and may also vary with pressure, time, mechanical history, and smooth muscle activity (63, 64, 71, 113, 114, 140). In addition it varies during growth and development [low values exist in the fetus and newborn (81)] and with age and disease. It may, however, be about the same

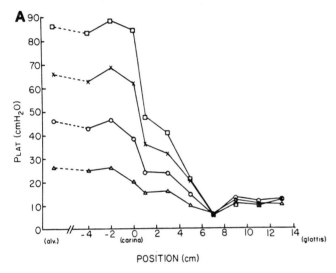

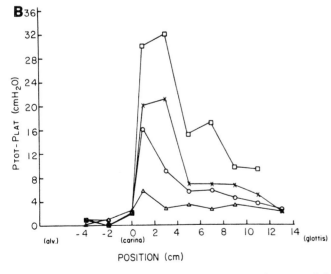

FIG. 4. *A:* airway pressure (PLAT) vs. position during graded expiratory efforts in a normal subject at ~50% vital capacity. *Dashed lines,* unknown pressure-distance function from alveoli to first measured data points (note break in position axis). *B:* difference between stagnation pressure (PTOT) and PLAT vs. position during same maneuvers. PTOT − PLAT, pressure associated with convective acceleration; alv, alveolus. [From Hoppin et al. (50).]

in the trachea of adult mammals over a wide range of body size (81).

Flow Transients

The previous discussion is based on the implicit assumption that quasi-steady conditions exist during forced expiration, i.e., conditions under which temporal accelerations (and related effects) can be neglected because other processes dominate [e.g., convective accelerations and viscous (frictional) energy losses]. Forced expirations are ordinarily long in relation to the time required for airways to collapse and for flow limitation to develop fully; thus the assumption of quasi-steady flow appears to be justified. Quasi-steady flow is probably also applicable to the later phases of experimental cough in the presence of normally small amounts of airway secretions (72).

Whether, and when, air and liquid flow can be considered quasi-steady in cough events that may be brief and involve large amounts of secretions, however, remains to be shown. Liquid flow may take time to develop and it may significantly influence gas flow development. Furthermore the abrupt temporal accelerations of airway walls at the onset of cough and during wall fluttering, when it occurs (11, 42, 43, 153–155), may be important in cough clearance. Thus some unsteady features of interest exist in cough. These can be expected to have wavelike characteristics that are more complicated than those of interest during steady flow, influenced, for example, by wall mass.

Complex flow transients at the onset of cough and forced expiration have been observed for a long time (37, 41) and their origin was clearly understood, although measurement errors (e.g., inertial bouncing in spirometers) introduced confusion at times. Using measuring systems that had very fast response times and the ability to exclude changes in volume of the upper airway (especially the cheeks) from the flow signal, Knudson et al. (72) examined voluntary forced expirations, cough, and flow transients triggered by the rapid release of a shutter at the mouth. They found that the expiratory flow rate during cough rose rapidly to, and beyond, the limits described by the MEFV curve (Fig. 5). This transient overshoot in volume flow was frequently as much as twice the maximal flow obtained at the same volume during the FVC maneuver. The flow transients were most obvious when maximal flows were low, i.e., at low lung volumes. Greater peak flows were achieved by triggering a fast shutter while the subject was exerting expiratory effort (Fig. 6). If expiratory efforts persisted, flow rates fell back to the MEFV curve within 100 ms and were superimposable on it for the duration of the maneuver (Fig. 7). Thus, except for the magnitude of the initial supramaximal flow transient, flow appears to be limited during cough in much the same way as it is limited during forced expiration.

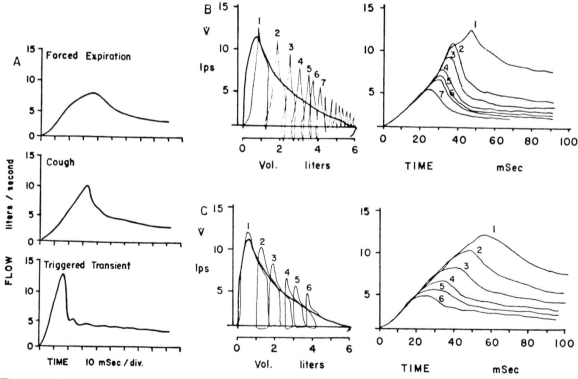

FIG. 5. Flow-time plots for 3 maneuvers at same lung volume (A), coughs (B), and forced expirations (C) initiated at different lung volumes. Flow-volume plots for maneuvers in B and C are superimposed on maximal expiratory flow-volume curves. Same subject provided all data shown. [From Knudson et al. (72).]

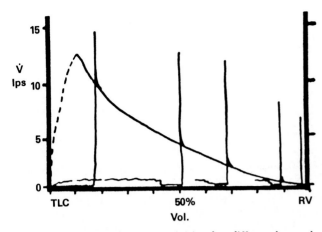

FIG. 6. Five triggered transients initiated at different lung volumes (Vol), superimposed on subject's maximal expiratory flow-volume curve. Amplitude of the supramaximal flow transient decreases less with lung volume than does maximal flow. RV, residual volume; TLC, total lung capacity, $\dot{V}$, flow. [From Knudson et al. (72).]

The flow transient and associated wall motions may be important in cough, but the relationship between them and cough effectiveness is unknown. Recognizing that linear gas velocity was probably important, Harris and Lawson (48) measured airway dimensions from radiographs and volume flow with a pneumotachograph. They found in one example that $\dot{V}ao$ peaked between 0.5 and 1.0 s after flow onset, with a calculated fluid flow velocity of 3,200 cm/s within the observed central airways. Maximal airway narrowing occurred ~0.5 s later, and although $\dot{V}ao$ was lower at that time, fluid flow velocity was higher (6,300 cm/s). They concluded that cough effectiveness could not be usefully judged from peak $\dot{V}ao$. The transient flows and perhaps the velocities are greater at the downstream end of the segment undergoing compression than at its upstream end, which receives only the flow from the lung periphery. The validity of Harris and Lawson's (48) flow measurements can be questioned because Knudson et al. (72) reported much greater flow-transient amplitudes. Even if Harris and Lawson measured flow rates during the flow transient that were too low by a factor of two, the true linear velocities during the flow transient were no greater than those during the flow-limited portion. This makes a study of cough under steady-flow conditions all the more reasonable, with the reservation that the previous arguments only consider the flow of gas, although liquid and airway wall motion also may be important.

Indeed, an additional feature of the period of airway collapse is that the airway walls undergo rather violent motion. This might greatly facilitate the interaction between gas and liquid that causes mucus movement. The studies of Knudson et al. (72) provide data that can be used to estimate the magnitude of the radial acceleration of the liquid-lined airway walls. Their analysis of the shutter-triggered flow transients shows

that the time constant for airway collapse is ~3–8 ms. Thus the majority of the collapse occurs within 10–15 ms after the opening of the glottis. Initially the wall is accelerated radially inward; to stop this inward motion, an accleration acting radially outward must be applied. If the distance moved by the airway wall is ~0.5 cm, its accelerations are roughly 2×0.5 cm/$(0.01$ s$)^2$ or as much as 10 times the acceleration of gravity. This large radial wall acceleration suggests that the flow transient must be included when considering the mechanisms for removal of secretions by cough. Moving the airway wall this way may be like shaking out a rug in a stiff wind. Without the quick shake of the rug, the wind is essentially unable to sweep away the dust, but with shaking, the inertia of the dust particles allows them to move across gas streamlines, out of the slowly moving boundary layer, and into the high-velocity windstream that is very effective at removing them. The precise interactions between wall motion and flow through the airway are unclear, but a critical pattern may exist that is important for mucus droplet formation and transport.

With the exception of the supramaximal flow transients, wall motions presumably do not directly affect maximal volume flow, whereas they do affect local patterns of gas and mucus flow. Any effects on the volume flow of gas are indirect (i.e., through gas-liquid interaction) and are addressed in the next section.

TWO-PHASE COCURRENT FLOW

Although there are gross descriptions of gas flow during experimental cough, less is known about the transport of other materials by cough. How does mucus get to the pharynx during cough? Is it dragged along airway walls as a film, or is it carried in the airstream as droplets? In either case, momentum must be transferred from gas moving at high velocity to the initially stationary, much denser materials adhering

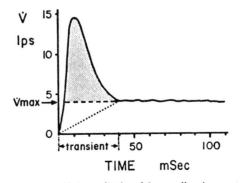

FIG. 7. Volume displaced from collapsing central airways is represented by total area under flow-time curve ($\int \dot{V}dt$) for supramaximal transient, less the area that represents volume coming from parenchyma during same time. Magnitude of latter is uncertain, however, because time course of rise in parenchymal flow to maximum flow ($\dot{V}max$) is uncertain (e.g., as shown by *dashed* and *dotted lines*). *Stippled area* shows probable minimum value of change in airway volume. [From Knudson et al. (72).]

to the airway walls. How does this coupling occur, and how do the physical properties of the two fluids and the conduit interact in the process? These and related questions are the province of two-phase cocurrent flow.

Two-phase flow is important in various industrial processes, including pumping, mixing, and creating fine suspensions of reactant materials. Thus it receives substantial attention in the literature of chemical engineering (119) and physicochemical hydrodynamics (120), and considerable study has been devoted to the relationships between gas and liquid flow rates and the pressures required to drive them.

In 1968 Leith (79) pointed out the relevance of two-phase flow to cough. There are problems in using engineering data for this purpose (83, 112), especially when considering both small and collapsible conduits and complex materials (e.g., airway secretions) and when examining the transition from annular to mist flow (see *Two-Phase Flow Regimes*, this page). Nevertheless progress toward understanding cough requires analyzing it as a process involving two-phase flow (16, 26, 28, 61, 62, 131, 132).

Mucus Properties

The physical properties of materials cleared by cough are widely variable, incompletely described, and unusual in some respects. They influence the mechanical coupling of gas and secretions during cough. This section presents some of these properties; however, their relevance to clearance of abnormal secretions is speculative and normal secretions are not thought to be cleared by cough (24).

Mucus is a non-Newtonian fluid, i.e., its shear strain rate is not directly proportional to shear stress (Fig.

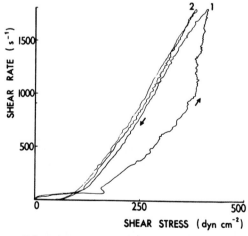

FIG. 8. Sequential measurements on mucus sample, showing complex shear stress–shear strain behavior, including shear thinning (decrease in viscosity with increasing shear rate) and shear destruction (changes in behavior after first exposure to high shear rates). For comparison, mucus shear rates are <10 s^{-1} during ciliary transport and may range well over 1,000 s^{-1} during cough. [From Lopez-Vidriero et al. (84), by courtesy of Marcel Dekker, Inc.]

8). Special methods are required to measure its viscoelastic properties (70, 84, 95), which can change dramatically and sometimes permanently, depending on the frequency, velocity, and amplitude of the deformation to which it is being or has been subjected. Thus, for example, mucus viscosity may range from 10 to 1,000 centipoise (cp) (the viscosity of water = 1 cp). Mucus shows marked shear thinning, i.e., its viscosity may decrease by 3 orders of magnitude at high shear rates (146). King and Macklem (68, 70) suggest that such behavior may permit secretions to move much farther mouthward under the high shear stresses of cough than in the opposite direction during inspiration, when velocities and shear rates are lower. On the other hand mucus also shows shear destruction; its highly nonlinear shear stress–shear strain rate curve is markedly less curved (and shows less hysteresis) after exposure to high shear rates (95).

During high-frequency low-amplitude deformation, mucus behaves as an elastic material; perhaps this has the effect of holding it together during transport by brief cough transients. This view appears to conflict with the idea that shear thinning of mucus enhances cough transport. If high-frequency flutter of airway walls occurs during forced expiration (43,153), it is reasonable to wonder if such elasticity perhaps increases the tendency for materials to accumulate at internodes of standing waves and be thrown off (155).

The roles of elasticity, shear thinning, and shear destruction (and of their dependence on mechanical history) in mucus transport by viscous flow and droplet-suspension mechanisms during cough are uncertain. The effects of surface tension (and its hysteretic changes with surface area) and of the variable thickness and nonuniform structure of the mucus-serous layer are also uncertain. The uncertainty about the significance of these properties (and their departures from normality) to cough means that our attempts to facilitate cough [e.g., by physical maneuvers (130, 148) or by changing the properties of secretions] have been empirical. Better understanding of the cough mechanism may lead to more effective treatments.

Two-Phase Flow Regimes

There are four primary flow regimes: bubble, slug, annular, and mist (Fig. 9). Bubble flow is not relevant to cough and is not discussed in this chapter. Slug flow appears to be very effective in removing large plugs of semisolid sputum, which can be shot out of the airway at high velocity. Slug flow may have greater importance in real cough than is suggested by the space devoted to it in this chapter.

In annular flow the liquid occupies an annular sleeve along the sides of the tube and the gas flows as a high-velocity central core. In mist flow liquid droplets are suspended as an aerosol and move with the gas. Between these two pure regimes there is a broad transition in which waves are present on the liquid surface

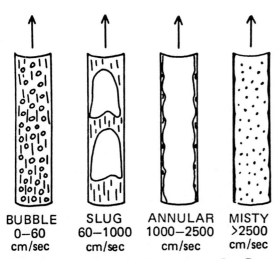

BUBBLE
0–60
cm/sec

SLUG
60–1000
cm/sec

ANNULAR
1000–2500
cm/sec

MISTY
>2500
cm/sec

FIG. 9. Four basic regimes in two-phase cocurrent flow. Range of associated gas velocities taken from engineering literature (119) for large rigid conduits and ordinary Newtonian liquids. There is reason to think that lower velocities apply in the lung. *Arrows,* direction of flow. [From Leith (79).]

and disorganized flow patterns are observable in the liquid. These flow regimes have been well described qualitatively, and empirical predictive equations have been proposed for the conditions during which each type of flow might exist (42, 43, 153). There also have been several attempts at theoretical analysis of the flow (4, 22, 93, 145). Typically these give reasonable predictions of the liquid flow rate and the thickness of the liquid annulus, but often the predictions for the gas flow rate are wrong by an order of magnitude. Scherer and Burtz (132) used dimensional analysis to obtain a parameter that they used to predict the "fraction coughed out" of a glycerin-lined rigid cylindrical test section by a compressed gas source. Their analysis balanced shear forces at the gas-liquid interface against viscous forces in the liquid. They implicitly assumed steady conditions and stratified flow (i.e., no suspended droplets), although the experiments used transient flows and a substantial amount of the transport was in liquid droplets. Despite these simplifications their dimensionless parameter accounted for the effects of changing gas properties and liquid viscosity quite well, but failed to explain the results for different-sized tubes.

Engineering analyses generally do not consider three important aspects of cough. First, many are concerned with steady flow but not with transient flow. Second, the mechanisms of particle generation and suspension involve instabilities at the transition between annular and mist flow, which are of interest in cough. Third, and perhaps most important, airways collapse during forced expiration, more greatly in the presence of liquid that causes increased resistance and decreased intraluminal pressure; thus the gas-liquid interaction may greatly influence the gas flow rate and the distributions of pressure, area, and velocity. These aspects are dealt with in the next three sections.

Transient and Steady Flow

Does the brevity of cough influence its effectiveness? From the point of view of gas flow, maximal flow from the periphery is established very rapidly; thus it might be tempting to assume quasi-steady conditions to the choke point. Interactions between gas and liquid, however, may take time to develop and may influence gas flow and choke-point locations (see later in this section). In central airways, airway collapse at the onset of cough introduces supramaximal flow transients whose amplitude and duration may be relatively large and whose significance to mucus transport is unknown.

From the point of view of mucus transport, one must consider both mist and annular flow regimes. Significant time may be necessary for the development of the conditions required for particle generation, suspension, and acceleration (i.e., mist flow); these processes are considered in the next section. Once particles are suspended and traveling at the high velocities at which the gas moves (i.e., thousands of centimeters per second), they can move long distances in short times if they do not deposit on airway walls downstream.

Annular flow is another matter. How long does it take for a liquid annulus that is dragged along the airway wall to reach steady-flow conditions, and how fast and how far does it move?

The imposition of a shear stress at the surface of a fluid that was initially at rest is a source of vorticity in the fluid. Quite generally, vorticity propagates away from boundaries as a diffusive process, with the kinematic viscosity of the fluid [i.e., ratio of fluid viscosity to fluid density (μ/ρ)] playing the role of a diffusion coefficient. Thus the temporal approach of the velocity profile to its steady-state spatial configuration is, in leading order, exponential in time, with a time constant proportional to $(\rho/\mu)h^2$, where h is the fluid thickness. For a viscosity of 0.01 p, a density of 1 g/cm^3, and a thickness of 0.01 cm, this time constant is on the order of 0.01 s; thus there does appear to be sufficient time for complete development of the velocity profile in the mucus during shear flow in an annulus.

That being the case, how far might the mucus be carried by this mechanism? The average distance traveled ($\bar{d}$) by the mucus in annular flow is the product of the average liquid velocity ($\bar{v}_l$) and the duration of flow (T), which is assumed equal to cough duration. Thus

$$\bar{d} = \bar{v}_l T \qquad (3)$$

If mucus were a Newtonian fluid and its thickness were small in relation to the radius of the tube, then the velocity at any point in the mucus layer would be approximately a linear function of distance from the wall, and

$$\bar{v}_l = v_{l,i}/2 \qquad (4)$$

where $v_{l,i}$ is the velocity of the mucus at the gas-liquid interface. Furthermore

$$v_{l,i} = (h/\mu_l)\tau \qquad (5)$$

where h is the thickness of the mucus layer, μ_l is mucus viscosity, and τ is the shear stress, which is uniform within the mucus and therefore at the mucus surface. By continuity τ is also the shear stress in the gas at the interface. Assuming fully developed turbulent flow with gas density ρ_g and mean gas velocity $\bar{v}_g$, then

$$\tau = \tfrac{1}{2}k\rho_g\bar{v}_g^2 \qquad (6)$$

where k is a numerical constant whose value is ~0.002, derived from the friction factor for fully developed turbulent flow in a rough-walled conduit.

By successively eliminating $\bar{v}_l$, $v_{l,i}$, and τ from Equations 3–6, the average distance traveled by the mucus annulus as it is dragged along the wall in simple viscous flow during a single cough (or forced expiration) of duration T is found to be

$$\bar{d} \sim \mathrm{T}(h/\mu_l)0.001\rho_g\bar{v}_g^2 \qquad (7)$$

Thus the average distance traveled is presumably proportional to cough duration, mucus thickness, gas density, and gas velocity squared, and inversely proportional to mucus viscosity. Attempts may be made to estimate each of these terms during cough. If T were 0.25 s, mucus thickness were 1 mm, viscosity were 100 cp (100 times that of water), volume flow rate were 4 liters/s, and airway cross-sectional area were 2 cm², then the average distance traveled would be ~1.0 cm (a very modest distance).

However, 1 mm is ~100 times the usual mucus thickness, so for normal airway lining layers, the average distance traveled is 100 times less than the 1.0 cm calculated above. Perhaps this is why normal subjects do not have productive coughs (24). On the other hand, if the fluid viscosity were closer to that of water (10 cp) (as it is for serous secretions) and the airways were collapsed to one-tenth of the 2 cm² assumed above, so that gas velocity were 10 times greater, then the average distance traveled would be ~1,000 times greater than the 1.0 cm calculated earlier. The linear gas velocity has by far a greater effect than gas viscosity, because the shear forces in the gas vary as linear gas velocity squared. Thus in the collapsed regions downstream from flow-limiting segments, annular flow may be an effective transport mechanism. However, in the absence of airway compression, and particularly in regions near the lung periphery, where linear velocities rapidly decrease as total cross-sectional area increases, annular flow has been thought to have little potential to transport mucus during a single cough. But Scherer (131), using the same analysis, supposes that the shear occurs in an underlying serous layer and that the overlying mucus travels as a slab. He too concludes that mucus

transport increases linearly with the ratio of thickness to viscosity (see Eq. 5) for the serous layer. Scherer also considers boundary shear stress during laminar flow in the gas phase ($\tau_{g,lam}$)

$$\tau_{g,lam} = \mu_g(0.332/D)v_g\mathrm{Re}_g^{1/2} \qquad (8)$$

where D is diameter, μ_g is gas viscosity, and Re_g is the gas Reynolds number. He suggests that "under conditions of excess mucus production where the serous layer has low viscosities close to those of water, the effect of cough can extend down to the level of the respiratory bronchioles." If this is true, manipulation of gas density and viscosity could increase annular transport in the periphery. Increased gas viscosity and decreased density allow higher gas flow rates at high lung volumes; thus higher gas velocities and shear forces may be achieved in small airways. Camner (23) showed that 1–2 min of cough did not clear radiolabeled particles from the lungs of normal humans, but did clear them from the lungs of patients with increased sputum. He commented, "It is tempting to suggest that one main function of the submucosal glands is to produce mucus in order to make coughing effective." Warwick (152), presumably applying similar analyses to the different shear stresses applied to airway walls (and their mucus lining) during inspiration and expiration, concludes that ordinary breathing constitutes a mucus pump toward the airway opening; the pump's effectiveness increases with minute ventilation (162).

The second of the three limitations regarding the application of simple engineering analyses to cough (see the previous section) is that annular flow is probably unstable under certain conditions. During annular flow the pressure gradient along the tube can induce curvature in the velocity profile in the mucus layer. Such flow is inertially unstable (8, 165, 166), i.e., any infinitesimal disturbance grows in time because of the nonlinear Navier-Stokes equations that govern fluid flow. Furthermore the non-Newtonian nature of mucus, particularly the fact that its viscosity decreases with increasing shear rate, accentuates the instabilities, which are probably important in the generation of particles during the development of mist flow. Particle generation and mist flow are presumably important mechanisms in cough and are discussed in more detail in the next section.

Particle Generation

Annular flow has many features of unstable flow. As gas velocity increases, wavelets appear on the surface. At first these are small, with short wavelengths. They are associated with increased resistance to gas flow; it appears that substantial transfer of momentum and energy begins to take place between gas and liquid. Much of the additional energy must be dissipated by viscous losses in the liquid. As the gas velocity increases further, the flow pattern in the liquid becomes increasingly disorganized and the waves become larger. Gas flow resistance increases sharply (28, 62) and probably influences the local operation of the mechanisms that limit gas flow. The Navier-Stokes equations are difficult to solve when the amplitude of the disturbances is small, and become almost unmanageable when the amplitude increases. The only analyses that have progressed beyond this point have been those that used gross simplifications of the shape of the wavy-flow patterns (56, 57, 65). Nonetheless the transition from wavy annular flow to mist flow is accompanied by an even larger increase in the momentum transfer between gas and liquid. Thus, although difficult to deal with analytically, this transition appears to be important to the cough process.

With further increases in linear velocity, particle generation at the liquid surface begins (56, 57); three mechanisms may be involved. In the first mechanism, a roll wave (similar in shape to an ocean wave) may have interfacial instabilities due to surface tension in the liquid; i.e., near the peak of the waves, small droplets of fluid may be sheared or pinched off from thin liquid processes and become suspended in the airstream. In the second mechanism, the surface wave induces gas flow that is directed toward the base of the next wave, causing material to be lifted from the liquid surface (56). This wave-undercutting mechanism is particularly relevant because it is especially effective in viscous fluids. In the third mechanism, a "liquid bridge" between the tube walls is disintegrated. Such bridges can be created by waves on opposite sides of the tube reaching a crest at the same point or by dipping of one side of an airway wall into the mucus layer on the opposite side as a result of unsteady wall motions. This mechanism is considered further in the next section.

The importance of these mechanisms is difficult to assess. Discussion of transport distances during annular flow noted that liquid velocities could vary over at least five orders of magnitude, liquid thickness could vary over three orders of magnitude, and depending on shear rate, liquid viscosity could also vary over three orders of magnitude. Thus the liquid Reynolds number (Re_l) may vary over a tremendous range. Because Re_l is presumably important in determining the flow profile within the liquid, a unified analysis based on any single mechanism of droplet production and entrainment is not possible. For wave undercutting and roll-wave shearing, which are probably the most important mechanisms for particle generation, something can be said, first, about the conditions under which entrainment occurs and second, when it does, which mechanism predominates. There is quantitative uncertainty about applying existing theories to cough, because they deal with Newtonian fluids (57, 65); however, their qualitative features might be applicable. The relevant variables are Re_g and Re_l, the

ratios of gas and liquid densities and viscosities, and the surface tension of the gas-liquid interface.

First, if the gas velocity is below a critical value, then no entrainment occurs no matter how high Re_l may be; if Re_l is below a critical value, no entrainment occurs for any gas velocity. For sufficiently viscous liquids (e.g., mucus) these no-entrainment conditions are condition A

$$Re_l = \text{any value}$$
$$v_g \lesssim 0.11(\sigma/\mu_l)(\rho_l/\rho_g)^{1/2}$$

and condition B

$$v_g = \text{any value}$$
$$Re_l \lesssim 150(\rho_l/\rho_g)^{3/4}(\mu_g/\mu_l)^{3/2}$$

where σ is the surface tension of the gas-liquid interface and ρ_l is the density of the liquid. The relationships under condition A show that entrainment is more unlikely with high surface tension, low viscosity liquids, and high liquid-to-gas density ratios. Condition B shows that entrainment is more unlikely with high liquid-to-gas density ratios and high gas-to-liquid viscosity ratios. When both conditions A and B are violated, i.e., when gas velocity and Re_l both exceed critical values, droplet entrainment occurs. Critical values appear to be as low as 600 cm/s for gas velocity and 2 for Re_l.

Second, the mechanism of entrainment appears to be governed simply by Re_l. For cocurrent flow the transition between wave undercutting (low Re_l) and roll-wave shearing (high Re_l) appears to occur at a Re_l of ~160. For gas velocity near critical values (see preceding paragraph) and for mucus layers 10 μm thick, Re_l is ~10, suggesting that wave undercutting occurs.

Another important aspect of entrainment involves the orientation of the tube with respect to gravity. The Re_l at which roll waves appear is 2 when the flow is directed vertically downward, but when the flow is directed either horizontally or vertically upward roll waves do not occur until Re_l is >160. Thus liquid is much more susceptible to entrainment when annular flow is directed vertically downward. Also, the inlet conditions are important in engineering experiments; there is a great variety of incoming flow profiles at different points along the airways. Finally, the results described in the preceding paragraphs are from engineering experiments whose applicability to cough has not been substantiated.

Once the particles are formed, they need to be entrained into the gas flow and accelerated. This process involves additional momentum transfer between gas and liquid as the particles approach freestream velocity. Because the initial velocities of the particles do not equal the gas velocities, the particles may be subjected to substantial shearing forces and may be shattered into many smaller particles (1, 44, 49); the consequences to transport are not clear. Particles may rapidly impact on the wall at a short distance from their point of formation. This may disturb the local liquid flow at that point, perhaps resulting in small droplet formation at the point of impact.

To examine some of these questions, aerosolization of viscous gelatin solutions in excised dog lungs under isovolume constant-flow conditions was studied (143, 144). Small amounts of solution were instilled at localized positions along the airways of dried and fresh lungs and the aerosol in the gas stream was collected at the airway outlet.

Only when Re_g in the trachea exceeded a certain critical threshold ($Re_{g,c}$) was there any removal of liquid as an aerosol. The $Re_{g,c}$ was usually between 750 and 2,000 when the amount of material instilled into the airways was <0.5 ml. When larger amounts of simulated mucus were present, aerosolization occurred at lower flows with $Re_{g,c}$ between 500 and 1,000. When the amount instilled was 0.2 ml and the tracheal Re_g was 5,000, only 10% of the first instillation was recovered, but that percentage gradually increased to 79% by the fourth instillation. Direct observation of the trachea showed that the early instillations were splattered against the airway wall, mouthward from the instillation site (in this case the carina). With subsequent instillations, material gradually accumulated at downstream sites and began to be reaerosolized from these positions. There appears to be a critical mass or thickness of liquid below which there is little tendency to form aerosols. Of the amount recovered as aerosol, >95% was collected during the first 2 s after instillation.

In a fresh preparation in which airways were collapsible, the results differed slightly. First, the aerosolization started at a lower volume flow rate. The airways, however, were compressed at these same flow rates; thus the tracheal gas velocity and Re_g are not as easily estimated as they were in the rigid lungs and they varied along the trachea. In rigid lungs it did not matter whether the liquid was placed on the anterior or the posterior portion of the trachea. In the fresh lung, however, the aerosolization started at a slightly (20%) lower flow rate if the material was placed on the posterior part of the airway. These differences suggest that wall motion facilitates formation of particles. Direct observations in tracheal models support this idea. Webster et al. (155) smeared grease on the outside of a rubber membrane that was stretched over a channel to make such a model. Downstream from choke points, wall flutter was observed with oscillation frequencies of ~800 Hz and standing-wave amplitudes that could exceed channel depth (see the next section). Within 1 s, the grease collected at antinodes of the standing waves and was thrown as far as 1 m.

In our studies, suspended gelatin particles were large (up to 0.1–0.5 mm diameter), in accord with engineer-

ing data for similar fluids (65, 149). Even at flow rates >5 liters/s and gelatin viscosities of only 1 cp, there was very little mass in particles <20 μm diameter.

Clarke and colleagues (26, 28) showed that the flow-resistive properties of liquid-lined tubes are vastly different from those of a dry tube of the same size (Fig. 10). The difference is dramatic above certain flow rates, suggesting a qualitative change in the coupling of gas and liquid. Jones et al. (62) showed similar interactions in branched tubes, in which Re_g values of ~900 are associated with fully turbulent flow.

King et al. (69) on the other hand found no important interaction between gas and mucus-simulant layers within an acrylic tube during steady or oscillatory flow at low Re_g; but at Re_g near critical values of ~10,000–15,000, standing waves formed in the gel, pressure drop increased sharply, and droplet suspension began. Perhaps inertial effects [e.g., secondary flows, which are present even at low Re_g in branched systems (29, 62, 135)] influence the gas-liquid coupling. For their tube with an inside diameter of 1.85 cm and gel layers 0.5–1 mm thick, increase in gas-liquid coupling occurred with flow rates of ~2.5 liters/s, i.e., critical velocities were ~1,200 cm/s. The magnitude of the pressure drop was quite sensitive to gel thickness. The standing waves and the increase in pressure drop developed over several seconds (longer than a cough); this development process was slowed by increased cross-linking in the gel.

The conditions for droplet suspension might extend

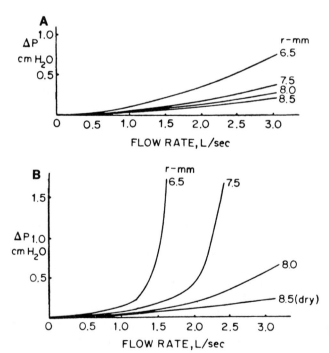

FIG. 10. *A*: pressure (ΔP)-flow curves for dry tubes of various radii (*r*). *B*: pressure-flow curves for 8.5-mm-radius tube with fluid annulus that reduces inner radius to values indicated. Human tracheal radius is similar. [From Clarke et al. (28).]

upstream from choke points, i.e., not be limited to regions of airway compression (79). Previously it was supposed that as total cross section increased further upstream, velocities fell below the critical values, which were supposedly ~2,500 cm/s, with Re_g ~25,000 in 1.5-cm-diameter airways. King et al. (69), however, indicate that critical velocity and Re_g may be half these values; Sneddon's experiments (143) and those of Jones et al. (62) suggest even lower values. King et al. (69) suggest further that critical velocity and Re_g diminish with tube diameter and that airway geometry is such that critical and achieved values of velocity and Re_g diminish by similar amounts as airway size decreases from central to peripheral regions of the lung. Thus critical interactions between gas and mucus may occur even in small airways.

Taken together, the results of Scherer (131), Clarke (26, 28), King (69), Jones (62), Sneddon (143) and their colleagues suggest that annular and mist flow may provide effective mucus transport much farther out in the lung than had been supposed. This suggestion needs to be explored.

Finally, the time dependence found by King et al. (69) for development of critical gas-liquid interaction and droplet suspension is different from the time dependence of transport by shear flow in an annulus. Thus there may be sites and conditions in which prolonged maneuvers (e.g., forced expirations) are more effective for droplet transport of secretions than is a series of coughs (122, 148).

Airway Deformation

The third issue mentioned in *Two-Phase Flow Regimes*, p. 326, that is not dealt with in engineering research but must be considered in cough is the complex mechanical and geometrical characteristics of airways. These characteristics introduce at least three ways in which two-phase flow in the lung may differ from that described. *1)* Unsteady wall motions may drastically alter the stability of the gas-liquid interface. *2)* Opposite sides of the airway wall may transiently flap together, so that the liquid transiently spans the space between the walls and is subjected to the impact of the oncoming gas stream. *3)* The entrainment of large amounts of liquid into the airstream requires substantial momentum transfer from gas to liquid, with an associated substantial reduction in gas pressure (i.e., increase in pressure drop). Thus collapsible-tube mechanics may be fundamentally altered by the presence of liquid along the walls.

The magnitude of airway wall acceleration during cough was estimated to be as high as 10 times that of gravity (see *Flow Transients*, p. 324). During the initial phase of the collapse, when the wall is being accelerated from rest, the acceleration is directed toward the opposite wall and thus tends to oppose any surface instabilities. Conversely to bring the wall to its steady-

state position it must again experience an acceleration, this time in the opposite direction. Under these conditions the acceleration tends to destabilize the fluid surface, enhancing the creation of surface distortions that can lead to particle generation. Furthermore these considerations need not be confined to the initial flow transients; i.e., wall flutter may occur throughout the maneuver (42). Unsteady wall motions can lead to extreme accelerations of the liquid, which may destabilize the surface (155). These considerations are probably most important downstream from the site of flow limitation, in airways that collapse during the flow transient, and where unsteady wall motion may be a means of energy dissipation downstream from a region of supercritical flow (35, 154).

The second way in which two-phase flow in collapsible tubes may differ from that reflected in engineering studies is the dipping phenomenon. Airway walls may transiently flap together and then move apart, lifting a bridge of mucus between them that is exposed to the flowing gas. A similar situation has been observed in engineering studies during annular flow when the liquid thickness is so large that surface waves on opposite walls come together at some point along the tube. The resultant liquid bridge is associated with a substantial increase in the rate of particle formation; it is unstable due to surface tension, so it shatters into droplets (44, 49, 56). The dipping phenomenon is expected to be most prominent in the region downstream from a point of flow limitation (155). We know of no directly relevant measurements in lungs.

A third way that collapsibility can influence two-phase flow in tubes is through decreases in the maximal gas flow rate. There are several ways that this can happen. Because mucus is usually quite viscous, it can dissipate substantial amounts of energy as heat. This energy must be supplied by the gas; its dissipation decreases potential energy (gas pressure). Like laminar or turbulent frictional losses in the gas, these losses, if they occur upstream of the flow-limiting segment, reduce the maximal gas flow rate. Thus the presence of mucus in upstream airways might reduce cough effectiveness in downstream airways. Also the acceleration of liquid to the velocity of the gas will require transfer of momentum from gas to liquid. This will reduce the gas pressure, lower the airway Ptm, and tend to collapse the airway. This narrowing may increase the frictional losses and further reduce the gas pressure, leading to more narrowing, and so on. Thus the site of flow limitation may migrate upstream toward more distal locations where liquid is present, possibly enhancing mucus transport. Finally, if liquid is suspended in the gas stream, the density of the resulting aerosol may be substantially higher than the density of the air alone. For example, suspending an aerosol with a concentration of 0.1% by volume doubles the density of the flowing medium. If this more dense "fluid" must be accelerated through a constriction, it will require a larger Pca than does air alone; this will tend to reduce the maximal flow rate. Specifically, if the wave-speed equation for flow rate still holds, then wave speed will be reduced in proportion to the square root of density.

Particle Deposition in Expiration

If removal of secretions from the airway includes production of an aerosol, the distance the material travels in the aerosol state before depositing again on the airway wall (if it does) is critical. Any change in an airway's ability to generate particles must be weighed against any changes in the aerosol collection efficiency of airways mouthward from that point. Thus collapsing an airway may cause aerosol generation to increase, but if it also increases the mouthward deposition of mucus aerosols there may be little net improvement in cough efficiency.

Of the factors influencing particle deposition in the expiratory direction, the most important is particle size, which depends on the mechanism of particle formation. At high Re_l, the dominant mechanisms of particle formation may be the shearing of roll waves and the possible shattering of particles as they are entrained. The particle sizes generated under these conditions have been studied experimentally (57) and several theoretical analyses, based on the instability of liquid jets and sheets, have been attempted. Thus Kataoka et al. (65) obtained an expression for the volume-median particle size

$$D = 0.028(v_g^2 \cdot \sigma/\rho_g)\mathrm{Re}_l^{-1/6}\mathrm{Re}_g^{2/3}(\rho_g/\rho_l)^{-1/3}(\mu_g/\mu_l)^{2/3} \quad (9)$$

The combination of the gas velocity and the Re_g terms indicates that the particle diameter depends on the gas flow rate to the $-4/3$ power. Thus particle size decreases rapidly with increasing flow rate. This is in contrast to the rate of liquid entrainment discussed above, which increases with increasing gas flow rate. Also these analyses are applicable to large Re_l, thus they might not be applicable to cough.

Although there are data on the sizes of particles formed, particle deposition in the expiratory direction has not been carefully explored. It is likely, however, that deposition during expiration is qualitatively similar to that during inspiration. If so, particles >20–50 μm diameter can be predicted to deposit quickly by sedimentation and by impaction, particularly just beyond (i.e., mouthward from) bifurcations. Very small particles (i.e., those <0.1 μm diameter) would deposit due to turbulent mixing in the gas. Particles in the intervening range of 0.1–20 μm diameter might remain suspended. This is in accord with the observations of Loudon and Roberts (87), who measured the size of particles expelled from the airways during speech, laughter, and cough. The bulk of the aerosol, expressed in number of particles, was in the intervening size range. Measuring particle sizes at the mouth, however,

does not reflect how the material is being transported in the trachea and major airways. Perhaps much larger particles are continuously generated, deposited, and regenerated, traveling only a short distance in the aerosol state each time. They might clear the larynx but still not appear at the airway opening. The mass of a particle is proportional to its diameter cubed; thus particles of 10 μm diameter would need to be 1,000 times more numerous than particles of 100 μm diameter to account for the same mass.

To define how deposition in the expiratory direction varies with changing particle size, we conducted experiments with a test aerosol introduced into the airways via a retrograde catheter (143). For particles of 0.5–2 μm diameter introduced at the carina, there was very little tracheal deposition, even at the highest flow rates. There was also little deposition in the first few airway generations when the flow was laminar. When particles were introduced in small airways beyond the carina, however, they appeared to be influenced by effects such as turbulence or secondary flows in the gas stream and deposited much more readily. Particle entrainment during cough may be very different from particle injection via a catheter, but it may be tentatively predicted that particle deposition is an increasing function of gas flow rate and that it depends on the site of aerosol production.

Smaldone et al. (142) showed that "cough produced a significant increase in deposition of 1 μm particles in the region immediately downstream from the flow-limiting segment." They also showed that after 50–100 coughs, ciliary transport of mucus decreased to zero at the main flow-limiting segment. The responsible mechanisms were not determined but might include damage to the mucus membrane (47) and stripping of the mucus layer. Transport was slowed upstream, perhaps by transit of the flow-limiting segment through these regions at low lung volumes. It was hardly influenced in downstream regions because, Smaldone et al. (142) suggest, shear stresses there were lower; it is not clear that this suggestion is plausible, thus this observation is puzzling.

CONCLUSIONS

In recent years progress has been made toward understanding the mechanics of cough, particularly with regard to flow limitation during forced expiration and the basics of two-phase cocurrent flow in rigid tubes. At least two challenges remain. The first is to extend the current knowledge of two-phase flow to include non-Newtonian fluids in branching systems of collapsible tubes. The second is to explore the mechanisms of cough failure and discover what can be done about them. The ubiquity of cough and the serious consequences of cough failures make these potentially rewarding areas of investigation.

Excellent assistance in manuscript preparation was provided by Patrice Ayers, Virginia Bardzik, Steven Zeogas, Les Phillips, Eleanor Dowling, and Emil Millet.

This work was supported in part by National Heart, Lung, and Blood Institute, Specialized Center of Research Grant HL-31970.

REFERENCES

1. Acrivos, A. The breakup of small drops and bubbles in shear flows. *Ann. NY Acad. Sci.* 404: 1–11, 1983.
2. Agnew, J. E., J. R. M. Bateman, N. F. Sheahan, A. M. Lennard-Jones, D. Pavia, and S. W. Clarke. Effect of oral corticosteroids on mucus clearance by cough and mucociliary transport in stable asthma. *Bull. Eur. Physiopathol. Respir.* 19: 37–41, 1983.
3. Agostoni, E., and W. O. Fenn. Velocity of muscle shortening as a limiting factor in respiratory air flow. *J. Appl. Physiol.* 15: 349–353, 1960.
4. Anderson, G. H., and B. G. Mantzouranis. Two-phase (gas-liquid) flow phenomena. I. Pressure drop and hold-up for two-phase flow in vertical tubes. *Chem. Eng. Sci.* 12: 109–126, 1960.
5. Aviado, D. M. Regulation of bronchomotor tone during anesthesia. *Anesthesiology* 42: 68–80, 1975.
6. Banyai, A. L. A symptom connoting many causes and sequels. *Chest* 60: 355, 1971.
7. Barach, A. L., G. J. Beck, H. A. Bickerman, and H. E. Seanor. Physical methods simulating mechanisms of the human cough. *J. Appl. Physiol.* 5: 85–91, 1952.
8. Batchelor, G. K. *Introduction to Fluid Dynamics.* New York: McGraw-Hill, 1969.
9. Beck, G. J., and L. A. Scarrone. Physiological effects of exsufflation with negative pressure (E.W.N.P). *Dis. Chest* 29: 80–95, 1956.
10. Berglund, E., B. S. Nilsson, B. Mossberg, and B. Bake (editors). Cough and expectoration. *Eur. J. Respir. Dis. Suppl.* 110: 1–262, 1980.
11. Bertram, C. D., and T. J. Pedley. A mathematical model of unsteady collapsible tube behaviour. *J. Biomech.* 15: 39–50, 1982.
12. Bickerman, H. A. Exsufflation with negative pressure (E.W.N.P). Elimination of radiopaque material and foreign bodies from bronchi of anesthetized dogs. *Arch. Intern. Med.* 93: 698–704, 1954.
13. Bickerman, H. A. Bronchial drainage and phenomena of cough. In: *Clinical Cardiopulmonary Physiology* (2nd ed.), edited by B. L. Gordon. New York: Grune & Stratton, 1960, chapt. 31, p. 494–506.
14. Bickerman, H. A., G. J. Beck, C. Gordon, and A. L. Barach. Physical methods simulating mechanisms of the human cough: elimination of radiopaque material from the bronchi of dogs. *J. Appl. Physiol.* 5: 92–98, 1952.
15. Bircher, N., P. Safar, G. Eshel, and W. Stezoski. Cerebral and hemodynamic variables during cough-induced CPR in dogs. *Crit. Care Med.* 10: 104–107, 1982.
16. Blake, J. On the movement of mucus in the lung. *J. Biomech.* 8: 179–180, 1975.
17. Brain, J. D., D. F. Proctor, and L. M. Reid (editors). *Lung Biology in Health and Disease. Respiratory Defense Mechanisms.* New York: Dekker, 1977, vol. 5.
18. Brashear, R. E. Cough: diagnostic considerations with normal chest roentgenograms. *J. Fam. Pract.* 15: 979–985, 1982.
19. Brown, A. L., and E. Archibald. The action of cough upon material in the tracheobronchial tract. *Annu. Rev. Tuberc.* 16: 111–122, 1927.
20. Bucher, K. Pathophysiology and pharmacology of cough. *Pharmacol. Rev.* 10: 43–58, 1958.
21. Burger, E. J., Jr., and J. Mead. Static properties of lungs after oxygen exposure. *J. Appl. Physiol.* 27: 191–197, 1969.
22. Calvert, S., and B. Williams. Upward cocurrent annular flow of air and water in smooth tubes. *AIChE J.* 1: 78–86, 1955.

23. Camner, P. Studies on the removal of inhaled particles from the lungs by voluntary coughing. *Chest* 80, Suppl. 6: 824–827, 1981.
24. Camner, P., B. Mossberg, K. Phillipson, and K. Strandberg. Elimination of test particles from the human tracheobronchial tract by voluntary coughing. *Scand. J. Respir. Dis.* 60: 56–62, 1979.
25. Ciba Foundation. *Respiratory Tract Mucus.* New York: Excerpta Med., 1978. (Ciba Found. Symp. 54.)
26. Clarke, S. W. The role of two-phase flow in bronchial clearance. *Bull. Physio-Pathol. Respir.* 9: 359–372, 1973.
27. Clarke, S. W. Physical defences of the respiratory tract. *Eur. J. Respir. Dis. Suppl.* 126: 27–30, 1983.
28. Clarke, S. W., J. G. Jones, and D. R. Oliver. Resistance to two-phase gas-liquid flow in airways. *J. Appl. Physiol.* 29: 464–471, 1970.
29. Clarke, S. W., J. G. Jones, and D. R. Oliver. Factors affecting airflow through branched tubes. *Bull. Physio-Pathol. Respir.* 8: 409–428, 1972.
30. Clarke, S. W., and D. Pavia (editors). Lung mucociliary clearance and the deposition of therapeutic aerosols. *Chest* 80, Suppl. 6: 789–924, 1981.
31. Colebatch, J. Artificial coughing for patients with respiratory paralysis. *Aust. NZ J. Med.* 10: 201–212, 1961.
32. Coleridge, J. C. G., and H. M. Coleridge. Afferent vagal C fibre innervation of the lungs and airways and its functional significance. *Rev. Physiol. Biochem. Pharmacol.* 99: 2–110, 1984.
33. Compton, D., P. M. Hill, and J. D. Sinclair. Weightlifters' blackout. *Lancet* 2: 1234–1237, 1973.
34. Criley, J. M., A. H. Blaufuss, and G. L. Kissel. Cough-induced cardiac compression. Self-administered form of cardiopulmonary resuscitation. *J. Am. Med. Assoc.* 236: 1246–1250, 1976.
35. Dawson, S. V., and E. A. Elliott. Wave-speed limitation on expiratory flow—a unifying concept. *J. Appl. Physiol.: Respirat. Environ. Exercise Physiol.* 43: 498–515, 1977.
36. Dawson, S. V., and E. A. Elliott. Use of the choke point in the prediction of flow limitation in elastic tubes. *Federation Proc.* 39: 2765–2770, 1980.
37. Dayman, H. Mechanics of airflow in health and in emphysema. *J. Clin. Invest.* 30: 1175–1190, 1951.
38. Elliott, E. A., and S. V. Dawson. Test of wave-speed theory of flow limitation in elastic tubes. *J. Appl. Physiol.: Respirat. Environ. Exercise Physiol.* 43: 516–522, 1977.
39. Elliott, E. A., and S. V. Dawson. Fluid velocity greater than wavespeed and the transition from supercritical to subcritical flow in elastic tubes. *Med. Biol. Eng. Comput.* 17: 192–198, 1979.
40. Evans, J. N., and M. J. Jaeger. Mechanical aspects of coughing. *Pneumonologie* 152: 253–257, 1975.
41. Gandevia, B. The spirogram of gross expiratory tracheobronchial collapse in emphysema. *Q. J. Med.* 32: 23–31, 1962.
42. Glaister, D. H., S. W. Clarke, and J. G. Jones. Oscillations in expiratory gas flow during a forced vital capacity manoeuvre (Abstract). *Clin. Sci.* 37: 567–568, 1969.
43. Grotberg, J. B., and S. H. Davis. Fluid-dynamic flapping of a collapsible channel: sound generation and flow limitation. *J. Biochem.* 13: 219–230, 1980.
44. Haas, F. C. Stability of droplets suddenly exposed to a high velocity gas stream. *AIChE J.* 10: 920–924, 1964.
45. Haldane, J. H. Micturition syncope: two case reports and a review of the literature. *Can. Med. Assoc. J.* 101: 712–713, 1969.

46. HAMILTON, W. F., R. A. WOODBURY, AND H. T. HARPER, JR. Arterial, cerebrospinal and venous pressures in man during cough and strain. *Am. J. Physiol.* 141: 42–50, 1944.

47. HAMOSH, P. Effect of shearing stress (SS) on the tracheal mucosa (Abstract). *Am. Rev. Respir. Dis.* 109: 694, 1974.

48. HARRIS, R. S., AND T. V. LAWSON. The relative mechanical effectiveness and efficiency of successive voluntary coughs in healthy young adults. *Clin. Sci.* 34: 569–577, 1968.

49. HINZE, J. O. Fundamentals of the hydrodynamic mechanism of splitting in dispersion processes. *AIChE J.* 1: 289–295, 1955.

50. HOPPIN, F. G., JR., J. M. B. HUGHES, AND J. MEAD. Axial forces in the bronchial tree. *J. Appl. Physiol.: Respirat. Environ. Exercise Physiol.* 42: 773–781, 1977.

51. HUIZINGA, E. The "tussive squeeze" and the "bechic blast" of the Jacksons. *Ann. Otol. Rhinol. Laryngol.* 76: 923–934, 1967.

52. HYATT, R. E. Expiratory flow limitation. *J. Appl. Physiol.: Respirat. Environ. Exercise Physiol.* 55: 1–7, 1983.

53. HYATT, R. E., J. MEAD, J. R. RODARTE, AND T. A. WILSON. Changes in lung mechanics: flow-volume relationship. In: *Lung Biology in Health and Disease. The Lung in the Transition Between Health and Disease*, edited by P. T. Macklem and S. Permutt. New York: Dekker, 1979, vol. 12, chapt. 5, p. 73–112.

54. IRWIN, R. S., W. M. CORRAO, AND M. R. PRATTER. Chronic persistent cough in the adult: the spectrum and frequency of causes and successful outcome of specific therapy. *Am. Rev. Respir. Dis.* 123: 413–417, 1981.

55. IRWIN, R. S., M. J. ROSEN, AND S. S. BRAMAN. Cough. A comprehensive review. *Arch. Intern. Med.* 137: 1186–1191, 1977.

56. ISHII, M., AND M. A. GROLMES. Inception criteria for droplet entrainment in two-phase concurrent film flow. *AIChE J.* 21: 308–318, 1975.

57. ISHII, M., AND K. MISHIMA. Liquid transfer and entrainment correlation for droplet-annular flow. *Proc. Int. Heat Transfer Conf., 7th, Munich, 1982*, vol. 5, p. 307–312.

58. JACKSON, C. Cough: bronchoscopic observations on the cough reflex. *J. Am. Med. Assoc.* 79: 1399–1404, 1922.

59. JAEGER, M. J. Coughing and forced expiration at reduced barometric pressure (Abstract). *Federation Proc.* 31: 322, 1972.

60. JAMES, R. E. *Extra-Alveolar Air Resulting from Submarine Escape Training: A Post-Training Roentgenographic Survey of 170 Submariners*. Groton, CT: US Navy Bureau of Medicine and Surgery, 1968. (Submarine Med. Res. Lab. Naval Submarine Med. Center Rep. No. 550.)

61. JONES, J. G., AND S. W. CLARKE. Dynamics of cough. *Br. J. Anaesth.* 42: 280–285, 1970.

62. JONES, J. G., S. W. CLARKE, AND D. R. OLIVER. Two-phase gas-liquid flow in airways. *Br. J. Anaesth.* 41: 192–193, 1969.

63. JONES, J. G., R. B. FRASER, AND J. A. NADEL. Prediction of maximum expiratory flow rate from area-transmural pressure curve of compressed airway. *J. Appl. Physiol.* 38: 1002–1011, 1975.

64. JONES, J. G., R. B. FRASER, AND J. A. NADEL. Effect of changing airway mechanics on maximum expiratory flow. *J. Appl. Physiol.* 38: 1012–1021, 1975.

65. KATAOKA, I., M. ISHII, AND K. MISHIMA. Generation and size distribution of droplet in annular two-phase flow. *J. Fluids Eng.* 105: 230–238, 1983.

66. KATZ, R. M. Cough syncope in children with asthma. *J. Pediatr.* 77: 48–51, 1970.

67. KIKUCHI, Y., H. SASAKI, K. SEKIZAWA, K. AIHARA, AND T. TAKISHIMA. Force-velocity relationship of expiratory muscles in normal subjects. *J. Appl. Physiol.: Respirat. Environ. Exercise Physiol.* 52: 930–938, 1982.

68. KING, M. Rheological requirements for optimal clearance of secretions: ciliary transport versus cough. *Eur. J. Respir. Dis. Suppl.* 110: 39–45, 1980.

69. KING, M., H. K. CHANG, AND M. E. WEBER. Resistance of mucus-lined tubes to steady and oscillatory airflow. *J. Appl. Physiol.: Respirat. Environ. Exercise Physiol.* 52: 1172–1176, 1982.

70. KING, M., AND P. T. MACKLEM. Rheological properties of microliter quantities of normal mucus. *J. Appl. Physiol.: Respirat. Environ. Exercise Physiol.* 42: 797–802, 1977.

71. KNUDSON, R. J., AND D. E. KNUDSON. Effect of muscle constriction on flow-limiting collapse of isolated canine trachea. *J. Appl. Physiol.* 38: 125–131, 1975.

72. KNUDSON, R. J., J. MEAD, AND D. E. KNUDSON. Contribution of airway collapse to supramaximal expiratory flows. *J. Appl. Physiol.* 36: 653–667, 1974.

73. KORPÁS, J., AND Z. TOMORI. *Progress in Respiration Research. Cough and Other Respiratory Reflexes*, Basel: Karger, 1979, vol. 12.

74. LAMBERT, R. K. The use of a computational model for expiratory flow to simulate the effects of two airway abnormalities. *Aust. Phys. Eng. Sci. Med.* 4: 100–108, 1981.

75. LAMBERT, R. K., T. A. WILSON, R. E. HYATT, AND J. R. RODARTE. A computational model for expiratory flow. *J. Appl. Physiol.: Respirat. Environ. Exercise Physiol.* 52: 44–56, 1982.

76. LANGLANDS, J. The dynamics of cough in health and in chronic bronchitis. *Thorax* 22: 88–96, 1967.

77. LARSON, S. J., A. SANCES, JR., J. B. BAKER, AND D. H. REIGEL. Herniated cerebellar tonsils and cough syncope. *J. Neurosurg.* 40: 524–528, 1974.

78. LAWSON, T. V., AND R. S. HARRIS. Assessment of the mechanical efficiency of coughing in healthy young adults. *Clin. Sci.* 33: 209–224, 1967.

79. LEITH, D. E. Cough. *Phys. Ther.* 48: 439–447, 1968.

80. LEITH, D. E. Cough. In: *Lung Biology in Health and Disease. Respiratory Defense Mechanisms*, edited by J. D. Brain, D. F. Proctor, and L. M. Reid. New York: Dekker, 1977, vol. 5, pt. II, chapt. 15, p. 545–592.

81. LEITH, D. E. Mammalian tracheal dimensions: scaling and physiology. *J. Appl. Physiol.: Respirat. Environ. Exercise Physiol.* 55: 196–200, 1983.

82. LEITH, D. E. Cough development. *Am. Rev. Respir. Dis.* 131: S39–S42, 1985.

83. LOCKHART, R. W., AND R. C. MARTINELLI. Proposed correlation of data for isothermal two-phase two-component flow in pipes. *Chem. Eng. Prog.* 45: 39–49, 1949.

84. LOPEZ-VIDRIERO, M. T., I. DAS, AND L. M. REID. Airway secretion: source, biochemical and rheological properties. In: *Lung Biology in Health and Disease. Respiratory Defense Mechanisms*, edited by J. D. Brain, D. F. Proctor, and L. M. Reid. New York: Dekker, 1977, vol. 5, pt. I, chapt. 9, p. 289–356.

85. LORIN, M. I. Mechanical defense mechanisms of the respiratory system. In: *Pulmonary Physiology of the Fetus, Newborn and Child*, edited by E. M. Scarpelli. Philadelphia, PA: Lea & Febiger, 1975, chapt. 10, p. 220–238.

86. LOUDON, R. G. Cough in health and disease. In: *Current Research in Chronic Obstructive Lung Disease*. Washington, DC: US Govt. Printing Office, 1968, p. 41–53. (Proc. 10th Aspen Emphysema Conf., Arlington, VA, 1968.)

87. LOUDON, R. G., AND R. M. ROBERTS. Droplet expulsion from the respiratory tract. *Am. Rev. Respir. Dis.* 95: 435–442, 1967.

88. LOUDON, R. G., AND G. B. SHAW. Mechanics of cough in normal subjects and in patients with obstructive respiratory disease. *Am. Rev. Respir. Dis.* 96: 666–677, 1967.

89. MACKLEM, P. T. Physiology of cough. *Ann. Otol. Rhinol. Laryngol.* 83: 761–768, 1974.

90. MACKLEM, P. T., R. G. FRASER, AND W. G. BROWN. Bronchial pressure measurements in emphysema and bronchitis. *J. Clin. Invest.* 44: 897–905, 1965.

91. MACKLEM, P. T., AND N. J. WILSON. Measurement of intrabronchial pressure in man. *J. Appl. Physiol.* 20: 653–663, 1965.

92. MACKLIN, M. T., AND C. C. MACKLIN. Malignant interstitial emphysema of the lungs and mediastinum as an important occult complication in many respiratory diseases and other conditions: interpretation of clinical literature in light of laboratory experiment. *Medicine Baltimore* 23: 281–357, 1944.

93. MAHALINGAM, R., AND M. A. VALLE. Momentum transfer in two-phase flow of gas-pseudoplastic liquid mixtures. *Ind. Eng.*

Chem. Fundam. 11: 470–477, 1972.

94. MARAZZINI, L., F. VEZZOLI, AND G. RIZZATO. Intrathoracic pressure development in chronic airways obstruction. *J. Appl. Physiol.* 37: 575–578, 1974.

95. MARRIOTT, C. The viscoelastic nature of mucus secretion. *Chest* 80, Suppl. 6: 804–808, 1981.

96. MATTHAY, R. A., M. A. MATTHAY, AND D. R. DANTZKER (editors). Cardiovascular-pulmonary interaction in normal and diseased lungs. In: *Clinics in Chest Medicine.* Philadelphia, PA: Saunders, 1983, vol. 4, p. 99–325.

97. MCINTOSH, H. D., E. H. ESTES, AND J. V. WARREN. The mechanism of cough syncope. *Am. Heart J.* 52: 70–82, 1956.

98. MEAD, J. Expiratory flow limitation: a physiologist's point of view. *Federation Proc.* 39: 2771–2775, 1980.

99. MEAD, J., J. M. TURNER, P. T. MACKLEM, AND J. B. LITTLE. Significance of the relationship between lung recoil and maximum expiratory flow. *J. Appl. Physiol.* 22: 95–108, 1967.

100. MELISSINOS, C., E. BRUCE, AND D. LEITH. Factors affecting pleural pressure during cough in normal man (Abstract). *Clin. Res.* 24: 643A, 1976.

101. MELISSINOS, C. G., E. N. BRUCE, D. E. LEITH, AND J. MEAD. Flow and pressure during cough in normal subjects (Abstract). *Clin. Res.* 25: 421A, 1977.

102. MELISSINOS, C. G., D. E. LEITH, J. S. BRODY, E. BRUCE, AND J. MEAD. Thoracoabdominal mechanics in spontaneous cough (Abstract). *Am. Rev. Respir. Dis.* 117: 372, 1978.

103. MILLER, H. C., G. O. PROUD, AND F. C. BEHRLE. Variations in the gag, cough, and swallow reflexes and tone of the vocal cords as determined by direct laryngoscopy in newborn infants. *Yale J. Biol. Med.* 24: 284–291, 1952.

104. MOGNONI, P., F. SAIBENE, G. SANT'AMBROGIO, AND E. AGOSTONI. Dynamics of the maximal contraction of the respiratory muscles. *Respir. Physiol.* 4: 193–202, 1968.

105. MORGAN-HUGHES, J. A. Cough seizures in patients with cerebral lesions. *Br. Med. J.* 2: 494–496, 1966.

106. MUNSELL, W. P. Pneumomediastinum. *J. Am. Med. Assoc.* 202: 689–693, 1967.

107. MYGIND, N., M. H. NIELSEN, AND M. PEDERSEN (editors). Kartagener's syndrome and abnormal cilia. *Eur. J. Respir. Dis. Suppl.* 127: 1–167, 1983.

108. NADEL, J. A. (editor). *Lung Biology in Health and Disease. Physiology and Pharmacology of the Airways.* New York: Dekker, 1980, vol. 15.

109. NATELSON, S. E., AND W. MOLNAR. Malfunction of ventriculoatrial shunts caused by the circulatory dynamics of coughing. *J. Neurosurg.* 36: 283–286, 1972.

110. NEGUS, V. E. *The Comparative Anatomy and Physiology of the Larynx.* New York: Grune & Stratton, 1949.

111. NEWHOUSE, M., J. SANCHIS, AND J. BIENENSTOCK. Lung defense mechanisms. *N. Engl. J. Med.* 295: 990–998, 1976.

112. O'CONNOR, G. E., AND T. W. F. RUSSELL. Heat transfer in tubular fluid-fluid systems. *Adv. Chem. Eng.* 10: 1–53, 1978.

113. OLSEN, C. R., A. E. STEVENS, N. B. PRIDE, AND N. C. STAUB. Structural basis for decreased compressibility of constricted tracheae and bronchi. *J. Appl. Physiol.* 23: 35–39, 1967.

114. PALOMBINI, B., AND R. F. COBURN. Control of the compressibility of the canine trachea. *Respir. Physiol.* 15: 365–383, 1972.

115. PAVIA, D., J. R. M. BATEMAN, AND S. W. CLARKE. Deposition and clearance of inhaled particles. *Bull. Eur. Physiopathol. Respir.* 16: 335–366, 1980.

116. PAVIA, D., P. P. SUTTON, J. E. AGNEW, M. T. LOPEZ-VIDRIERO, S. P. NEWMAN, AND S. W. CLARKE. Measurement of bronchial mucociliary clearance. *Eur. J. Respir. Dis. Suppl.* 127: 41–56, 1983.

117. PAVIA, D., P. P. SUTTON, M. T. LOPEZ-VIDRIERO, J. E. AGNEW, AND S. W. CLARKE. Drug effects on mucociliary function. *Eur. J. Respir. Dis. Suppl.* 128: 304–317, 1983.

118. PEDERSEN, A., E. SANDOE, E. HVIDBERG, AND M. SCHWARTZ. Studies on the mechanism of tussive syncope. *Acta Med. Scand.* 179: 653–661, 1966.

119. PERRY, R. H., C. H. CHILTON, AND S. D. KIRKPATRICK (editors). *Chemical Engineers' Handbook* (4th ed.). New York: McGraw-Hill, 1963.

120. PFEFFER, R. (editor). Fourth international conference on physicochemical hydrodynamics. *Ann. NY Acad. Sci.* 404: 1–536, 1983.

121. PHIPPS, R. J. The airway mucociliary system. In: *Respiratory Physiology III*, edited by J. G. Widdicombe. Baltimore, MD: University Park, 1981, vol. 23, chapt. 5, p. 213–260. (Int. Rev. Physiol. Ser.)

122. PRYOR, J. A., B. A. WEBBER, M. E. HODSON, AND J. C. BATTEN. Evaluation of the forced expiration technique as an adjunct to postural drainage in treatment of cystic fibrosis. *Br. Med. J.* 2: 417–418, 1979.

123. RAYL, J. E. Tracheobronchial collapse during cough. *Radiology* 85: 87–92, 1965.

124. RICE, D. A. Sound speed in pulmonary parenchyma. *J. Appl. Physiol.: Respirat. Environ. Exercise Physiol.* 54: 304–308, 1983.

125. RICHARDSON, P. S., AND A. C. PEATFIELD. Reflexes concerned in the defence of the lungs. *Bull. Eur. Physiopathol. Respir.* 17: 979–1012, 1981.

126. RILEY, R. L. Disease transmission and contagion control. *Am. Rev. Respir. Dis.* 125: 16–19, 1982.

127. ROE, P. F., AND B. N. KULKARNI. Pneumomediastinum in children with cough. *Br. J. Dis. Chest* 61: 147–150, 1967.

128. ROHRER, F. Die Mechanik des Hustens. *Schweiz. Med. Wochenschr.* 2: 765–767, 1921.

129. ROSS, B. B., R. GRAMIAK, AND H. RAHN. Physical dynamics of the cough mechanism. *J. Appl. Physiol.* 8: 264–268, 1955.

130. ROSSMAN, C. M., R. WALDES, D. SAMPSON, AND M. T. NEWHOUSE. Effect of chest physiotherapy on the removal of mucus in patients with cystic fibrosis. *Am. Rev. Respir. Dis.* 126: 131–135, 1982.

131. SCHERER, P. W. Mucus transport by cough. *Chest* 80, Suppl. 6: 830–833, 1981.

132. SCHERER, P. W., AND L. BURTZ. Fluid mechanical experiments relevant to coughing. *J. Biomech.* 11: 183–187, 1978.

133. SCHNEIDER, A. P., II, W. R. DAWS, AND R. D. ADAMS. The coughing child. *Postgrad. Med.* 74: 258–260, 1983.

134. SCHOENBERG, B. S., J. F. KUGLITSCH, AND W. E. KARNES. Micturition syncope—not a single entity. *J. Am. Med. Assoc.* 229: 1631–1633, 1974.

135. SCHROTER, R. C., AND M. F. SUDLOW. Flow patterns in models of the human bronchial airways. *Respir. Physiol.* 7: 341–355, 1969.

136. SHAPIRO, A. H. Steady flow in collapsible tubes. *J. Biomech. Eng.* 99: 126–147, 1977.

137. SHARPEY-SCHAFER, E. P. Effects of coughing on intrathoracic pressure, arterial pressure, and peripheral blood flow. *J. Physiol. London* 122: 351–357, 1953.

138. SHARPEY-SCHAFER, E. P. The mechanism of syncope after coughing. *Br. Med. J.* 2: 860–863, 1953.

139. SHARPEY-SCHAFER, E. P. Effect of respiratory acts on the circulation. In: *Handbook of Physiology. Circulation*, edited by W. F. Hamilton. Washington, DC: Am. Physiol. Soc., 1965, sect. 2, vol. III, chapt. 52, p. 1875–1886.

140. SIMONSSON, B. G., F. M. JACOBS, AND J. A. NADEL. Role of autonomic nervous system and the cough reflex in the increased responsiveness of airways in patients with obstructive airway disease. *J. Clin. Invest.* 46: 1812–1818, 1967.

141. SMALDONE, G. C., AND E. H. BERGOFSKY. Delineation on flow-limiting segment and predicted airway resistance by movable catheter. *J. Appl. Physiol.* 40: 943–952, 1976.

142. SMALDONE, G. C., H. ITOH, D. L. SWIFT, AND H. N. WAGNER, JR. Effect of flow-limiting segments and cough on particle deposition and mucociliary clearance in the lung. *Am. Rev. Respir. Dis.* 120: 747–758, 1979.

143. SNEDDON, S. L. Fluid Mechanics and Physiology of Cough. Boston, MA: Harvard School of Public Health, 1979. PhD thesis.

144. SNEDDON, S. L., AND J. D. BRAIN. Steady expiratory flow in dog lungs: an isovolume preparation. *J. Appl. Physiol.: Respirat. Environ. Exercise Physiol.* 51: 1331–1337, 1981.

145. SRIVASTAVA, R. P. S. Liquid film thickness in annular flow. *Chem. Eng. Sci.* 28: 819–824, 1973.
146. STURGESS, J., A. J. PALFREY, AND L. REID. Rheological properties of sputum. *Rheol. Acta* 10: 36–43, 1971.
147. SUTHERLAND, J. M., AND J. H. TYRER. "Cough syndrome" with suggestions as to the possible role played by cerebral atherosclerosis. *Med. J. Aust.* 1: 39–42, 1965.
148. SUTTON, P. P., R. A. PARKER, B. A. WEBBER, S. P. NEWMAN, N. GARLAND, M. T. LOPEZ-VIDRIERO, D. PAVIA, AND S. W. CLARKE. Assessment of the forced expiration technique, postural drainage and directed coughing in chest physiotherapy. *Eur. J. Respir. Dis.* 64: 62–68, 1983.
149. TATTERSON, D. F., J. C. DALLMAN, AND T. J. HANRATTY. Drop sizes in annular gas-liquid flow. *AIChE J.* 23: 68–76, 1977.
150. VON LEDEN, H., AND N. ISSHIKI. An analysis of cough at the level of the larynx. *Arch. Otolaryngol.* 81: 616–625, 1965.
151. WANNER, A. Clinical aspects of mucociliary transport. *Am. Rev. Respir. Dis.* 116: 73–125, 1977.
152. WARWICK, W. J. Mechanisms of mucous transport. *Eur. J. Respir. Dis. Suppl.* 127: 162–167, 1983.
153. WEAVER, D. S., AND M. P. PAIDOUSSIS. On collapse and flutter phenomena in thin tubes conveying fluid. *J. Sound Vib.* 50: 117–132, 1977.
154. WEBSTER, P. M., R. P. SAWATZKY, V. HOFFSTEIN, R. LEBLANC, M. J. HINCHEY, AND P. A. SULLIVAN. Aeroelastic modelling of expiratory flow limitation (Abstract). *Federation Proc.* 42: 1008, 1983.
155. WEBSTER, P. M., N. ZAMEL, M. HINCHEY, AND P. A. SULLIVAN. Clearance of viscous material from artificial trachea by flow-limitation induced wall oscillation (Abstract). *Am. Rev.*

Respir. Dis. 123: 178, 1981.
156. WHITTENBERGER, J. L., AND J. MEAD. Research in tuberculosis and related subjects. Respiratory dynamics during cough. *Transactions Natl. Tuberc. Assoc., 48th Annu. Meet., New York, 1952,* p. 414–418.
157. WIDDICOMBE, J. G. Respiratory reflexes. In: *Handbook of Physiology. Respiration,* edited by W. O. Fenn and H. Rahn. Washington, DC: Am. Physiol. Soc., 1964, sect. 3, vol. I, chapt. 24, p. 585–630.
158. WIDDICOMBE, J. G. Mechanism of cough and its regulation. *Eur. J. Respir. Dis. Suppl.* 110: 11–15, 1980.
159. WILLIAMS, B. Cerebrospinal fluid pressure changes in response to coughing. *Brain* 99: 331–346, 1976.
160. WILLIAMS, B. Cough headache due to craniospinal pressure dissociation. *Arch. Neurol.* 37: 226–230, 1980.
161. WILSON, T. A., R. E. HYATT, AND J. R. RODARTE. The mechanisms that limit expiratory flow. *Lung* 158: 193–200, 1980.
162. WOLFF, R. K., M. B. DOLOVICH, G. OBMINSKI, AND M. T. NEWHOUSE. Effects of exercise and eucapnic hyperventilation on bronchial clearance in man. *J. Appl. Physiol.: Respirat. Environ. Exercise Physiol.* 43: 46–50, 1977.
163. World Health Organization. *Opiates and Their Alternates for Pain and Cough Relief.* Geneva: World Health, 1972, p. 1–19. (Tech. Rep. Ser. No. 495.)
164. YANAGIHARA, N., H. VON LEDEN, AND E. WERNER-KUKUK. The physical parameters of cough: the larynx in a normal single cough. *Acta Oto-Laryngol.* 61: 495–510, 1966.
165. YIH, C. Stability of a non-Newtonian liquid flowing down an inclined plane. *Phys. Fluids.* 8: 1257–1262, 1965.
166. YIH, C. *Fluid Mechanics.* New York: McGraw-Hill, 1969.

CHAPTER 21

Collateral flow

HAROLD A. MENKES | *Department of Environmental Health Sciences, School of Hygiene and Public Health, The Johns Hopkins University, Baltimore, Maryland*

PETER T. MACKLEM | *Department of Medicine, McGill University and Royal Victoria Hospital, Montreal, Canada*

ALTHOUGH INTERALVEOLAR COMMUNICATIONS were described more than 100 years ago (70), the functional significance of ventilation through pathways that bypass the airways has been largely ignored. In fact alveolar pathways or pores of Kohn were commonly thought to be artifacts of fixation (74). If so, they were of no functional significance. However, in 1930 Van Allen et al. (125) noted that if a lobar bronchus was obstructed, atelectasis resulted. On the other hand, if a segmental airway was obstructed, not only did atelectasis not occur, but ventilation distal to the obstruction was surprisingly effective (67). They attributed this to "collateral respiration," which they concluded resulted from mass flow or diffusion from the adjacent unobstructed lung. Although these investigators were familiar with interalveolar pores of Kohn and presumed that pores provided communications for collateral flow, subsequent reports by Lambert (65), Duguid

and Lambert (24), and Martin (76) indicated that alternative pathways exist.

COMMUNICATIONS FOR COLLATERAL FLOW

Potential pathways for collateral flow are illustrated in Figure 1. Unlike interalveolar pores, which are 5–10 μm in diameter, Lambert's bronchoalveolar channels may be 25 μm in diameter, and Martin's interbronchiolar or interductal communications may be up to 120 μm in diameter. Thus alternative pathways are larger than alveolar pores; however, there are other differences as well. Pores of Kohn, which are surrounded by capillaries (4, 69), are mechanically linked to the alveolar walls that they penetrate. In contrast, alternative pathways, whether bronchoalveolar, interbronchiolar, or interductal communications, are structurally similar to small airways or alveolar ducts. The smooth muscle reported in their walls as well as their surrounding tissue attachments suggest that they should function like small airways.

Alveolar Pores

Alveolar pores have been found in the lungs of virtually all mammalian species examined to date (69). Because they are lined by alveolar epithelium and have, in a large percentage of cases, epithelial junctions on one or both sides of the openings, Boatman and Martin (10) concluded that they were developmental in origin and did not represent alveolar tears. They are 3–13 μm in diameter and were described by Loosli (69) to vary in shape. He found that some were cylindrical, whereas others looked like funnels or hourglasses. Loosli also noted that they were more numerous in the septa adjacent to pleura. This observation was later confirmed by Ranga and Kleinerman (99), who used the scanning electron microscope in studies of mouse lungs. Macklin (74) observed alveolar communications more frequently in alveolar walls attached to the bronchi and larger blood vessels. Ranga

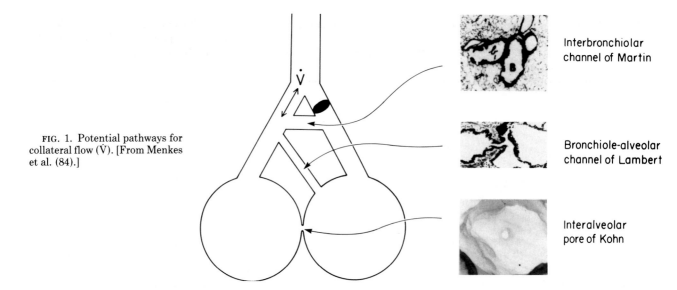

FIG. 1. Potential pathways for collateral flow (V̇). [From Menkes et al. (84).]

Interbronchiolar channel of Martin

Bronchiole-alveolar channel of Lambert

Interalveolar pore of Kohn

and Kleinerman also noted more pores in peribronchial alveoli. Indeed, Macklin concluded that this distribution might be related to the "subjection of the walls to greater strain on account of the functional movements of these tubes." This is especially intriguing in view of Caradonna's report (cited in ref. 69) that alveolar communications appear earlier and are more numerous in guinea pigs molested and excited during development. Therefore it is possible that they are the product of excessive effort and dilation of the alveolar walls during the act of ventilation.

According to Loosli (69), the size of alveolar pores is dependent on lung volume and the capillary network in alveolar walls. According to Kuno and Staub (60), microholes in alveolar walls are closed at a transpulmonary pressure of zero and open with lung inflation. Their size is a direct function of lung volume and independent of transpulmonary pressure. Lai-Fook et al. (64) reported that the volume of spherical and cylindrical holes cut in the parenchyma of isolated dog lobes also was a function of lobe volume and independent of transpulmonary pressure. Unfortunately, quantitative assessments of pore size as a function of either lung volume or transpulmonary pressure have not been reported.

There are semiquantitative reports of pore size and number as functions of age and species. Caradonna (cited in ref. 69) reported that pores did not appear in the lungs of normal guinea pigs and rabbits until ~8 mo of age. Martin (75) reported an increase in the number of pores per alveolar wall in dogs between the time of birth and 1 yr of age but found that the pores remained constant in size and number thereafter. Ranga and Kleinerman (99) also failed to find an increase in the number of pores in mice between the ages of 3 mo and 26 mo after an initial increase between 1 mo and 3 mo. However, in studies in postmortem human lungs, Pump (98) reported a positive

correlation between age and the area of alveolar holes or fenestrae in patients who had denied respiratory symptoms. If, as postulated by Pump, pores of Kohn are part of the degenerative emphysematous process, they could represent the initial stages of disease.

Comparisons of numbers of pores in different species have been reported by several investigators. Pores appear to be more numerous in the dog and less common in the pig and sheep. Human lungs have intermediate numbers (70). However, most studies are based on observations of relatively few lungs, and because of a large amount of variability in size and distribution of pores, comparisons between species are difficult to interpret. Furthermore it is not clear whether the pores assessed in a random examination of the lung by current methods are functionally significant. For example, Parra et al. (94) recently reported that when an intratracheal route of fixation is used, pores are numerous and appear to be patent. However, when an intravenous route of fixation is used, most alveolar pores are filled with an extracellular material (Fig. 2). Thus many previous reports of pore numbers and size might be misleading in view of the usual intratracheal route of fixation. A further complication of the interpretation of anatomic assessments of collateral communications is that the location of those communications as well as their size and number is important. Clearly it is those communications joining adjacent portions of lung supplied by different airways that provide potential pathways for collateral flow. Martin (76) speculated that interalveolar pores would require close to 200 cmH₂O pressure to open once closed; he concluded that although they could be easily seen in lungs, their functional significance was limited. Therefore he sought and found alternative pathways; he was able to define those pathways by injecting material (India ink particles) that deposited in them when collateral flow occurred.

Alternative Pathways for Collateral Flow

In search of alternative pathways for collateral flow, Martin (76) demonstrated the deposition of aerosolized India ink particles in interbronchiolar or interductal communications in dog lungs. Deposition failed to occur in alveolar pores. In addition he passed polystyrene spheres as large as 120 μm in diameter through collateral pathways; these spheres were obviously too large to pass through alveolar pores. He concluded that collateral flow occurs through communications between respiratory bronchioles and not through smaller pathways such as pores of Kohn in dogs. It was unknown whether larger communications are present in normal human lungs until Raskin and Herman (100) demonstrated short tubular interacinar ducts in human lungs. These were ~200 μm in diameter.

A second alternative pathway was first described by Lambert (65) when she discovered bronchiolar alveolar communications that appear to join respiratory bronchioles to alveolar ducts and sacs subtended by the bronchioles of adjacent acini. These communications were up to 25 μm in diameter (24) and have been found in infant and adult humans and in rabbits, cats, and sheep (12, 59). However, it is unlikely that communications reported by Lambert are responsible for the movement of microspheres of 120 μm in dog lungs (76) and 50 μm in human lungs (39) through collateral channels because they are too small.

Other reports with descriptions of interacinar communications at the level of the alveolar duct emphasize the numerous potential collateral pathways (12, 70). It is not clear whether interalveolar communications or larger openings are responsible for collateral flow at that level. However, it is apparent that there are different types of collateral channels that communicate between alveoli, between regions within the acinus, between acini, between segments, and even between lobes (111).

Collateral Communications and Disease

Both alveolar and alternative pathways for collateral ventilation have been demonstrated in normal lungs from humans as well as experimental animals. Because collateral communications provide necessary routes of flow when airways are obstructed, investigators have attempted to assess numbers and types of collateral communications in disease characterized by chronic obstruction, e.g., emphysema; however, investigators such as Martin (75) and Ranga and Kleinerman (99) considered alveolar pores to be normal structures and discounted the possibility that they represented degenerative or disease processes. Pump (96, 98) claimed that pores of Kohn are part of the degenerating emphysematous process and are the first stage in the formation of larger fenestrae. It is not clear

whether large interalveolar communications or fenestrae begin as smaller pores as claimed by Boren (11). However, there is no doubt that the size and/or number of alveolar communications are increased with emphysema both in humans (11) and experimental animals (27, 33, 94, 107). Because of the decreased number and size of small airways in emphysema (70), it is reasonable to expect collateral communications to assume a prominent role in the distribution of airflow in that disease.

Few studies of alternative pathways in disease have been reported. Lambert's channels may be increased in certain patients with emphysema and honeycomb lungs (66). Interbronchiolar communications have also been described in disease (93, 113). However, their functional significance in the diseased lung remains to be determined. Thus the quantitative assessments of collateral communications are limited not only because of the scarcity of studies but also because the structure has not been related to function. Whereas it is possible for communications between adjacent airways to provide channels for ventilation, it is not obvious how interalveolar pores adjacent to the pleural surface could function. For quantitative morphologic assessments to be meaningful one must consider the position of collateral channels with respect to adjacent units that might be obstructed. Thus interalveolar pores could provide pathways for collateral flow, whether obstruction occurs in larger sublobar airways or in very peripheral bronchi, as long as the pores were strategically situated along planes separating the adjacent units. In contrast, interbronchiolar communications would not be useful if obstruction occurred in terminal bronchioles beyond the collateral channels, and Lambert's communications would be functionally insignificant for obstruction that occurred in airways central to their position. In attempting to relate structure and function, Martin injected an aerosol containing India ink particles that passed through and deposited on collateral channels. In the dog those particles deposited in bronchiolar and interductal communications. More recently, Rosenberg and Lyons (105) repeated this experiment with human lungs and found that tantalum particles deposited along openings in alveolar walls. Because there are gross anatomic differences between canine and human lungs, it would not be surprising if the major pathways for collateral flow differed in the two species.

Other attempts to relate structure to function were reported by Sasaki et al. (110) and Takishima et al. (117). In their studies these investigators progressively filled the airways with silicone rubber. They found that when the cast of the airways progressed to terminal bronchioles but not into alveoli, resistance to collateral flow (Rcoll) became extremely high. They used this evidence to conclude that major pathways for collateral flow were at the bronchiolar level in the canine lung.

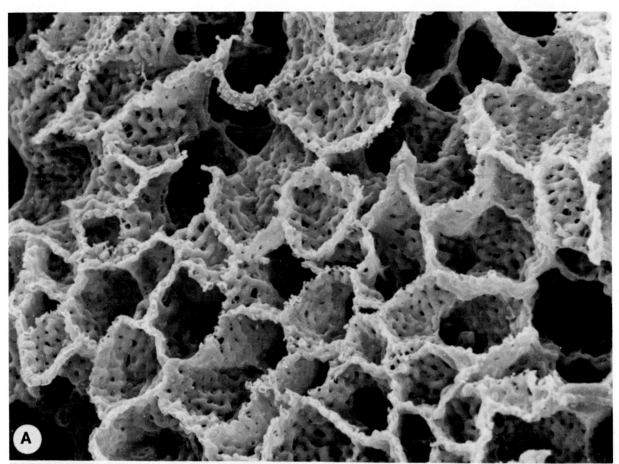

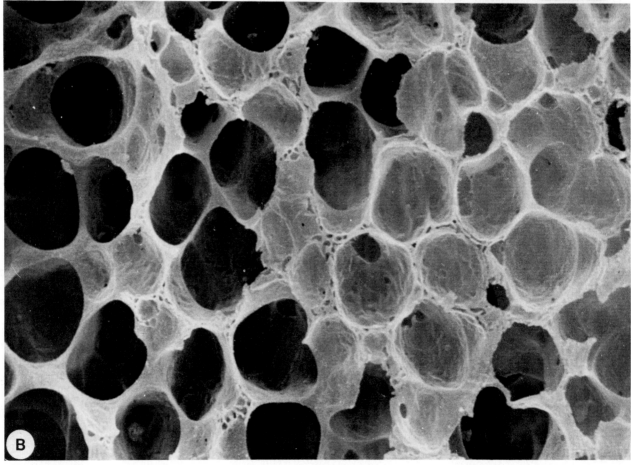

RESISTANCE TO COLLATERAL FLOW

Measurements of Collateral Flow

From their classic series of studies, Van Allen and Jung (124) concluded that an obstructed lobule was able to "breathe from the side through the adjacent free parts of the lung." To study "collateral respiration" they developed a special dilatable cannula that obstructed airways of varying size. Through this cannula they collected air that passed into the obstructed unit through collateral communications from the surrounding unobstructed lung. They measured the effects of various factors on collateral flow, including respiratory rate, tidal volume, and pharmacological agents such as histamine. Other investigators have modified their approach and have used tracer gases (e.g., ^{133}Xe and Ar) to assess the flow of gas distal to obstructed airways (25, 39).

An indirect method of measuring Rcoll was described by Woolcock and Macklem (130). In their studies they calculated Rcoll by measuring the compliance of a sublobar unit of lung and dividing it into the time constant for collateral ventilation (τcoll). Both compliance and τcoll will be discussed in *Time Constants for Collateral Ventilation*, p. 347. The method involved the rapid injection of a bolus of air beyond a wedged catheter and the oscillation of the lung around the obstructed unit. Calculations of Rcoll were dependent on several questionable assumptions, including homogeneity within the obstructed segment and in the surrounding lung. Nevertheless they showed that collateral flow was much more rapid than had previously been realized.

The most direct method for measuring Rcoll is to assess the relationship between steady-state flow through collateral channels (V̇coll) and the pressure drop across them. This approach was used by Baarsma and Dirken in studies of intact rabbits (4) and humans and by Hogg, Macklem, and Thurlbeck (43), Robotham, Menkes, et al. (104), and Henderson et al. (39) in excised lungs. The most simple and versatile way to make this measurement was described by Hilpert (40) in a thesis written in 1970. Hilpert wedged a double-lumen catheter into a peripheral airway. (A fiberoptic bronchoscope can be used to obstruct an airway under visual control.) Through one lumen of the obstruction catheter, V̇coll is injected through the collateral system. Through the other lumen, pressure at the site of the obstruction is measured (Fig. 3). Under steady-state conditions, resistance through the collateral system equals (Pb − PA)/V̇coll, where Pb is pressure at the point of bronchial obstruction and PA

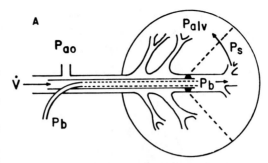

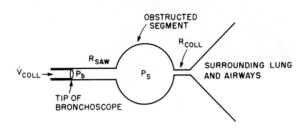

ELECTRICAL ANALOGUE

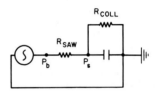

FIG. 3. *A*: method for measurements of resistance in small airways and collateral channels. V̇, flow; Pb, pressure in airway at point of obstruction; Ps, pressure in alveoli of obstructed segment; Palv, pressure in alveoli of the lung surrounding obstructed segment; Pao, pressure at airway opening. [From Menkes et al. (84).] *B*: model of collateral system. V̇coll, flow through collateral system; Rsaw, resistance of small airways; Rcoll, resistance of collateral communications.

is pressure in the lung surrounding the obstructed unit (alveolar pressure). This resistance has two components. The first reflects resistance in small airways (Rsaw) distal to the obstruction but proximal to alveoli of the obstructed segment. The second reflects Rcoll. When V̇coll is stopped, Pb falls toward the pressure in the compliant units of the obstructed segment (Ps). Because the compliance and resistance of small airways are small, their product, which is the time constant for deflation of small airways, is also small. Therefore with stop V̇coll, Pb falls immediately to Ps, and Rcoll then equals (Ps − PA)/V̇coll. In most studies of normal lungs, Rsaw is small compared to Rcoll and is frequently immeasurable. However, in

---

FIG. 2. Scanning electron micrographs of dog lung. *A*: intratracheal fixation at instillation pressure of 30 cmH$_2$O with 2.5% glutaraldehyde solution, stained with uranyl acetate, dehydrated, critical-point dried, and coated with gold. Note numerous interalveolar communications. × 230. *B*: perfusion fixation with 1% osmium tetroxide solution and processed as in *A*. Note paucity of interalveolar communications. × 230. (Photographs courtesy of Dr. Peter Gehr.)

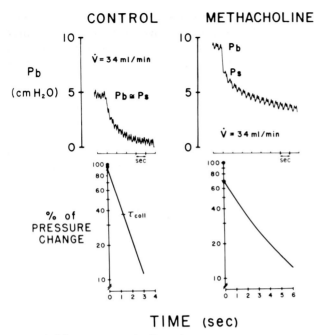

FIG. 4. Measurements of collateral mechanics after injection of methacholine in dog. After methacholine, a stop in flow ($\dot{V}$) is followed by an abrupt decrease in pressure at bronchial obstruction (Pb) to level of pressure in obstructed segment (Ps). Difference between Pb and Ps is related to resistance in constricted airways distal to obstruction. τcoll, Time constant for collateral flow. [From Menkes and Traystman (83).]

disease (120) or after local administration of methacholine in solution (114) or ozone (Fig. 4), Rsaw is measurable and equals (Pb − Ps)/$\dot{V}$coll.

Figure 4 shows that after stop $\dot{V}$coll, Ps falls exponentially toward PA. The rate at which Ps falls as the obstructed segment empties into the surrounding lung through collateral channels is governed by Rcoll and the compliance of the obstructed segment.

Effects of Species, Location, Size, and Age

To compare Rcoll expressed in absolute terms for different species or locations in the lung, it is necessary to relate the measurement to some index of the amount of lung served. One method for doing this is to use the product of Rcoll and volume of lung subtended. However, in most studies the volume of obstructed lung is not known. Thus other approaches and approximations have been used. The most common approach has been to obstruct airways of the same size at similar transpulmonary pressures. When marked differences in values are found, e.g., when the same technique is applied to dogs and pigs, results can be interpreted. However, when smaller differences in absolute values for Rcoll are found, conclusions must be drawn with caution.

Marked species variations in Rcoll have been reported. However, because of differences in techniques used by different investigators, it is frequently difficult to compare one study with another. Dogs have well-

developed collateral communications and have been reported to have lower Rcoll than horses (103) and humans (130). Pigs have high Rcoll (130). In general, species with well-developed intralobular septa have high resistances to collateral flow (e.g., pigs), whereas those with poorly developed septa have lower resistances (e.g., dogs). Calculations by Inners, Menkes, et al. (54) suggested that in young normal subjects, resistance through collateral communications supplying a sublobar portion of lung is ~50 times as great as the resistance through airways supplying that portion. Thus in the normal individual, Rcoll far exceeds resistance through the airways and little tendency for collateral flow is expected.

Widely varying values of Rcoll have not only been reported among species but also between animals within a species; Rcoll varies by an order of magnitude when airways of similar size are obstructed in different dogs (121, 130). This is not too surprising because of the anatomy of the dog's tracheobronchial tree, which has the configuration of a pine tree and does not have symmetrical dichotomous branches. However, one might expect Rcoll to vary as a function of segment size or area of apposition with the surrounding lung. According to the report by Menkes, Macklem, et al. (81) it does not; however, major differences between the lobes have been reported. The middle lobe in both dogs (102) and humans (53) has a higher Rcoll than other lobes. This observation led Inners, Menkes, et al. (53) to speculate that the propensity of the right middle lobe to become diseased and atelectatic may be related to a failure of collateral flow to prevent this. It is noteworthy that the two segments of the right middle lobe in humans are the only ones with only a single interface with another segment and are surrounded on all other sides by pleura.

Systematic studies of the relationship between Rcoll and age have not been reported. Rosenberg and Lyons (105) were unable to detect collateral flow in six lungs obtained from premature deliveries up to the age of 4 wk. Because flow was easily measured in lungs from older subjects, the investigators concluded that the potential for collateral flow develops with age. However, this is inconsistent with individual reports indicating that with segmental bronchial atresia the segment without an airway may still contain air soon after birth (104). Thus it appears that even if well-defined collateral communications are not present at birth, they may develop soon after.

Mechanical Factors

The caliber of collateral channels is affected by stresses of the surrounding tissues, tension within the walls of the channels, and the surface-active material at air-liquid interfaces.

VOLUME. As the lung inflates, Rcoll falls (40, 130). Inasmuch as alveolar micropunctures (60) expand and small airways (48) increase in size in proportion to the cube root of lung volume, Rcoll should fall whether alveolar pores or alternative pathways provide for collateral flow. However, if both pores and alternative pathways increase in size isotropically with the rest of the lung, resistance to flow through pores should fall more rapidly than resistance through alternative pathways (83). In fact it has been shown that Rcoll falls more with lung inflation than resistance through the airways (81, 130). Furthermore increases in resistance of airways with increases in lung volume at high volumes (71, 126), although disputed by some investigators (45), have never been shown for Rcoll. Thus one might conclude that alveolar pores rather than alternative pathways are responsible for collateral flow; however, if alveolar pores are filled largely by extracellular material at low lung volumes (94), it is possible that with lung inflation the recruitment of new channels accounts for the decreases in Rcoll that have been observed. Another possibility is that alternative pathways for collateral flow are oriented in a different direction than airways and thus are subjected to different distending pressures. Because of the isotropic nature of lung inflation, this is unlikely.

Although it is clear that as the whole lung (including collaterally ventilated regions) increases in volume, Rcoll falls, it is not clear whether the caliber of collateral channels is determined primarily by the size of the collaterally ventilated region or by the surrounding lung. If the size of an obstructed segment affects collateral communications, one would expect the channels to distend with increases in Ps at a constant transpulmonary pressure and thus result in lower resistance at high flows. Studies reported by Baarsma and Dirken (4) as well as Baker and Daly (6) suggest that pressure-flow relationships through collateral channels are surprisingly linear. Robinson and Sorenson (103) reported increased Rcoll with increases in flow. Although an increase in Rcoll could be related to nonlaminar flow, these studies strongly support the notion that collateral communications are primarily regulated by the size of the surrounding lung.

The importance of transpulmonary pressure of the surrounding lung on the caliber of collateral channels might explain observations originally reported by Lindskog and Bradshaw (68) when they found that there was "no essential difference in the pressure threshold" necessary for inflation via the airways or collateral channels. Because inflation via the airways results in distension of the surrounding lung, collateral channels supplying uninflated adjacent portions could be distended by the inflated portions. Thus whether they were alveolar communications that have been reported to close at low lung volumes (60) or alternative channels that, like terminal bronchioles, should close at low volumes (50), stresses from the adjacent lung tending to distend them may be as important for their opening as gas pressures within them.

VASCULAR VOLUME. Vascular volume may affect Rcoll in two ways. *1)* With increases in vascular volume, lung volume at a constant recoil pressure will increase at low volumes and decrease at high volumes (30, 34). Because Rcoll is a function of lung volume, any change in vascular volume may then affect Rcoll indirectly. *2)* With increases in vascular volume, small airways and extra-alveolar collateral channels, which are contained within the same interstitial compartments as the vessels, may be affected (42). Similarly, alveolar communications are surrounded by capillary networks so that any change in vascular volume could affect pore size. It is, however, not obvious whether inflation of the wall surrounding a pore should increase or decrease its caliber (83).

In their pioneering studies on the control of collateral respiration, Johnson and Lindskog (56) and Call et al. (15) reported that pulmonary arterial or venous occlusion reduced collateral ventilation. Ankeney et al. (3) confirmed these results but added the observation that with blood transfusions resulting in increased pulmonary artery pressure, V̇coll fell. The latter observation is surprising. More recent direct measurements of the relationship between Rcoll and pulmonary vascular pressures (31, 122) indicate that if partial pressure of CO_2 (P_{CO_2}) values are controlled, the direct effects of vascular pressures on Rcoll are trivial. For example, Traystman, Terry, and Menkes (122) showed that if pulmonary vascular flow ceases, Rcoll increases. However, because V̇coll persists in the absence of perfusion, P_{CO_2} falls in that situation. Further studies by this group indicated that if P_{CO_2} values were maintained, most of the effect of changing pulmonary vascular pressures on Rcoll was abolished. Thus P_{CO_2} rather than intravascular pressure changes could explain previous studies on the effects of the pulmonary circulation on collateral flow. However, this still does not explain observations by Ankeney et al. (3). One possibility is that the decrease in collateral flow that they observed after transfusion was related to the presence of "moderate focal intra-alveolar hemorrhage and partial atelectasis." Thus it is reasonable to conclude that intravascular pressures and volume play a minor role in determining Rcoll. This supports the hypothesis that alveolar pores play a secondary role in the distribution of collateral flow, at least at low lung volumes.

SURFACTANT. Surfactant lines small airways (72) and interalveolar pores of Kohn (94). After inactivating surfactant, Macklem et al. (72) demonstrated that higher pressures were necessary to move a fluid meniscus in small airways of excised lungs. In that case increased opening pressures were necessary to initiate flow; however, no studies have shown whether surfactant, which lines alveolar pores, is necessary for pores to open. As discussed by Boren (11) an alveolar pore has two radii of curvature, one around its edge that results in a tension tending to open the pore and another across its opening that results in a tension tending to close the pore. Thus, depending on the relative size of these two radii of curvature, surface forces may tend to open or close pores. Therefore increased surface tension is expected to close pores if they are small, e.g., at low lung volume (64), or to open them if they are large, e.g., at higher volumes or with disease (11). Change of surface tension may also affect the caliber of alternative pathways. Fluid that lines the pathways should tend to close them, whereas fluid that lines structures surrounding the pathways should tend to open them. In studies designed to investigate the role of surface tension in collateral ventilation, Menkes, Macklem, et al. (80) measured Rcoll before and after inactivating surfactant with kerosene. They found that Rcoll decreased whether measured at the same lung volume or transpulmonary pressure. They concluded that pores provided the primary channels for collateral flow, assuming that the radius of the pore wall was small relative to the radius of the pore opening. As pointed out by Mead (77), these investigators failed to consider the possibility that alveolar structures surrounding alternative pathways provided a greater outward-acting pull when surfactant was inactivated. However, even at the same transpulmonary pressure when the outward pull should have been the same, Rcoll was lower. This did not support the conclusion that extra-alveolar communications provide the major pathways for collateral ventilation; other studies do. Bachofen et al. (5) demonstrated that after the inactivation of surfactant with a detergent, there was a progressive collapse of alveoli during deflation. In fact they found that most alveoli were collapsed at ~40% total lung capacity. At those volumes most air was contained by overexpanded ducts. If alveoli were collapsed it is unlikely that pores were open. Further support that extra-alveolar communications supply the major pathways for collateral flow is provided by a report by Nakamura et al. (89) that increased lung surface tension decreased bronchial collapsibility and a later report by Sasaki et al. (110) that during the nonhomogeneous deflation of airways at a constant lung volume, airway pressures were lower than during quasi-static deflation. These reports indicate that increased surface tension should increase the size of alternative pathways for collateral flow. Thus there is ample reason to believe that increased surface tension should reduce resistance to flow through alternative pathways, especially at low lung volumes.

Because increased surface tension lowers Rcoll, it should be lower during inflation than during deflation at the same lung volume. Conflicting results have been reported. Woolcock and Macklem (130) found that this was the case; however, Hogg et al. (43) and Robinson and Sorenson (103) found the opposite. One explanation for a lower Rcoll during deflation is that collateral communications that could be opened or recruited during inflation remain open even at lower pressures during deflation.

Pharmacological and Neural Control

In general, agents that constrict small airways or increase lung elastic recoil increase Rcoll. Agents that dilate the airways or decrease lung recoil decrease Rcoll. For example, histamine (2, 15, 56) and methacholine (16, 56, 114) decrease collateral flow, whereas isoproterenol (56), atropine (8, 56), and epinephrine (16) increase collateral flow. Similarly, vagal stimulation, which has been reported to constrict peripheral airways and increase lung recoil (132), also causes increased resistance to collateral flow (92). Although this may be modulated by β-adrenergic activity (131), increases in Rcoll are produced in the absence of β-blockade (130). Because cholinergic blockade reduces Rcoll (8) it is likely that cholinergic tone has a continuous modulating effect on collateral flow. When an agent is delivered to the lung periphery, through the collateral system, small airways or collateral channels (114) may respond. For example, cigarette smoke and histamine, when delivered in aerosol form, increase Rcoll without measurable effects on Rsaw (32, 58). It is possible that the failure to detect increases in Rsaw is related to the insensitivity of its measurements, i.e., in a large proportion of studies, Rsaw is immeasurable by the stop-Vcoll method. Other agents or methods of administration, however, have profound effects on Rsaw with or without effects on Rcoll. For example, methacholine delivered in solution to a point just beyond the obstruction in the collateral system increases Rsaw (114). Presumably this effect is related to deposition of the agent in small airways and its failure to penetrate more distally into collateral channels. Ozone, when delivered in relatively high concentrations (e.g., 1.5 ppm) for short periods (1–2 min), may increase in Rsaw with trivial effects of Rcoll (A. Gertner, unpublished observations). Reasons for this are not clear. It is possible that very soluble agents are absorbed by small airways upstream to the collateral system. Other explanations depend on differences between collateral channels and small airways, differences in the distribution of nerves (91), receptor populations (1) and cell types (37), as well as anatomic differences (23). These differences may be especially important when considering changes in the lung periphery and comparing those changes with large airways. In 1971 Johnson and Lindskog (56) wrote that "the rate of collateral ventilation is a sensitive tool for studying small changes in the peripheral air passages whether induced by pharmacologic agents or hemodynamic alterations." To the extent that the collateral system reflects the function of the lung periphery, it provides an approach to the study of peripheral function bypassing the large airways.

Respiratory Gases

In 1970 Chen et al. (16) reported that hypercapnia increased collateral flow. This effect was confirmed by Johnson and Lindskog (56) and extended by Sealy and Seaber (112). The latter investigators reported that dilation of collateral channels occurred when inspired CO_2 increased from 2.5% to 6% with little further change when it was increased to 15%. Sealy and Seaber also reported that effects of CO_2 were seen in a denervated, unperfused, excised lung. Traystman, Batra, and Menkes (121), using Hilpert's method for assessing collateral flow, found that when 5% CO_2 was infused through the collateral system, Rcoll fell close to 50% compared with Rcoll measured with the infusion of air. When 10% instead of 5% CO_2 was used, Rcoll fell another 9%. They concluded that the local concentration of CO_2 has marked effects on Rcoll and that it provides a potent mechanism for the local regulation of ventilation in the presence of airway obstruction. In later studies, Traystman, Terry, and Menkes (122) reported that similar effects of CO_2 were obtained whether CO_2 was administered locally or whether air was infused locally and CO_2 administered to the whole lung. In fact a combination of local CO_2 and whole-lung CO_2 had no more effect than either one alone. This is surprising and suggests that collateral communications are either maximally dilated by CO_2 at any given lung volume or that CO_2 penetrates to the critical site in the plane between segment and surrounding lung whatever the route of administration.

It has been shown that the effects of CO_2 are related to the lung volume at which measurements are made and are modified by parasympathetic tone. Batra, Menkes, et al. (8) reported that the effects of CO_2 were greater in nondependent than dependent regions of lung and that these effects were diminished after atropine. They concluded that relative hypocapnia in nondependent regions where ventilation-perfusion ($\dot{V}/\dot{Q}$) relationships were increased was responsible for the increased effect of 5% CO_2 and that the effects of hypocapnia were mediated at least partly by vagal reflexes. Because hypocapnia increases resistance through airways (20, 51, 52, 90, 115) and because atropine lowers the response of airways to hypocapnia (20, 90), the studies of Batra, Menkes, et al. (8) suggest that alternative pathways for collateral ventilation are responsible for collateral flow. Chen et al. (16) concluded that because of the "dynamic changes" produced by CO_2, pores of Kohn were less likely responsible for collateral flow than alternative channels; however, this logic breaks down when one considers that hypocapnia may also decrease lung compliance (20, 51). Therefore if elastic recoil increases in the presence of a low P_{CO_2}, there should be a decrease in size of alveolar pores as well as alternative communications.

Whereas changes in P_{CO_2} have marked effects on collateral flow, changes in the partial pressure of O_2 (P_{O_2}) have relatively trivial effects whether P_{O_2} values are raised or lowered (16, 121). In their report that hypoxia increased Rcoll, Traystman, Batra, and Menkes (121) showed that this effect was abolished with local administration of CO_2. In addition, because hypoxia affects Rcoll in dependent regions of lung more than in nondependent regions (8), it is likely that the effects of hypoxia are mediated through vascular constriction, an increased $\dot{V}/\dot{Q}$ relationship, and the resultant fall in P_{CO_2}.

COLLATERAL FLOW

The flow of gas through collateral channels is a function of Rcoll and the pressure gradient for flow. In this section we discuss the gradient for flow, which equals Ps − PA. This gradient depends first on the degree of nonhomogeneity between the segment and surrounding lung and then on the magnitude of interdependence. The degree of nonhomogeneity refers to the difference in elastic recoil pressures of adjacent portions of the lung. For example, if the lung is surrounded by a common pressure (pleural pressure) and one region of the lung is more distended than its neighbors, alveolar pressure within it will exceed pressure in the surrounding lung and a gradient for flow will result. The second factor that contributes to the gradient for collateral flow is interdependence.

Pulmonary Interdependence

Interdependence is a mechanical property of the lung that determines how the movements of one portion of the lung affect adjacent units. According to a model of pulmonary elasticity proposed by Mead et al. (78), the distending pressure of units within a uniformly or homogeneously expanded lung equals transpulmonary pressure. However, in a nonuniformly or nonhomogeneously expanded lung, pressures that tend to reduce the nonuniformity are generated. For example, if a unit of lung is obstructed at a fixed volume, when the surrounding lung inflates, the stresses on the obstructed unit produced by tissue attachments from the surrounding lung tend to inflate the unit. These stresses depend on the degree of nonhomogeneity between adjacent segments.

Interdependence between lung and pulmonary blood vessels has been appreciated since Whittenberger et al. (129) reported that lung inflation affected pulmonary vascular resistance and Macklin (73) showed that ventilation of the lungs affected pulmonary blood vessels. Subsequent reports indicate that changes in lung volume affect alveolar and extra-alveolar vessels differently (47), that with lung inflation perivascular pressure falls relative to pleural pressure (35, 62), and that interdependence between alveolar structures and blood vessels differs in different species (9, 57). Even as the recoil of the lung affects the caliber of blood vessels, the volume of blood vessels affects the recoil of the lungs (30). Just as pulmonary blood vessels are interdependent with the surrounding lung, the airways are also interdependent. Several investigators have shown that the elastic properties of the airways are regulated by the surrounding lung (46, 48, 49, 63, 108, 119). Direct measurements indicate that with lung inflation, peribronchial fluid pressure falls, although this effect is diminished when edema collects in the peribronchial space (55).

Like a blood vessel or airway, the movements of which are restrained relative to movements of the surrounding lung, a segment of lung exhibits interdependence with surrounding structures. The magnitude of interdependence can be measured in two ways. First, the compliance of a portion or segment of lung can be measured under homogeneous and nonhomogeneous conditions. Under homogeneous conditions its elastic recoil is the same as the elastic recoil of the adjacent lung. Under nonhomogeneous conditions this is not the case. When Woolcock and Macklem (130) measured the nonhomogeneous compliance (C′s) of obstructed units, they found that it was substantially lower than the homogeneous compliance (Cs). Although their rapid-injection method for measuring C′s probably underestimated it, their report encouraged others to develop other methods for its measurement. Menkes, Macklem, et al. (79) and Takishima and Mead (118) reported comparisons of Cs and C′s in excised dog, goat, and cow lungs. In those experiments C′s was lower than Cs at transpulmonary pressures greater than zero. Both groups observed that where an obstructed segment extended to the pleura, its surface could pucker in relation to adjacent pleura when nonhomogeneous movements occurred. This observation suggested that the chest wall might be an important mediator of the forces of interdependence, and to mimic the effects of the chest wall, other lobes were glued to pleural surfaces of obstructed segments. They found that C′s fell in relationship to Cs when this was done.

A second method for measuring interdependence involves obstructing a portion of the lung so that its volume is fixed. When the surrounding lung ventilates, forces of interdependence affect the pressure applied to the outer surface of the obstructed unit, which results in changes in Ps within that unit or changes in elastic recoil of that unit. Under these conditions it is possible to define an index of interdependence (K) that equals Δ(Ps − Ppl)/ΔPL, where the volume of a sublobar segment is fixed, Ppl is pleural pressure, and PL is transpulmonary pressure in the unobstructed lung.

It has been shown that K can also be calculated from comparisons of Cs and C′s where K = (Cs/C′s) −1 (9). From the two methods for measuring K it is

evident that if there is no interdependence, i.e., K = 0, then Cs = C′s, and the value of Ps − Ppl does not change with inflation of unobstructed lung. However, when K is finite, nonhomogeneous inflation results in a deviation of the pressure surrounding the obstructed unit from Ppl. This deviation then results in a lowering of C′s, or in the case where volume is fixed, a fall in Ps.

Several factors affect pulmonary interdependence, including species, the chest wall, lung volume, and surface tension. (Fig. 5).

Measurements of pulmonary interdependence have been made in several species by utilizing different techniques. Comparable methods applied to dogs and pigs indicate that at functional residual capacity (FRC), K in dogs is approximately two times greater than that measured in pigs (82, 116). Less interdependence in pigs may be related to their extensive lobulation, which permits slippage between units, like slippage between lobes. If so, human lungs should exhibit more interdependence than pig lungs and less

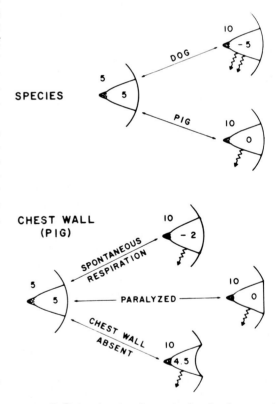

FIG. 5. Determinants of magnitude of pulmonary interdependence (K). *Top*: in dog, when the lung surrounding an obstructed segment inflates from a pressure of 5 to 10 cmH$_2$O, an outward-acting pull results in a decrease of pressure from 5 to −5 cmH$_2$O within segment. This corresponds to K = 2. In pig, in which K = 1, pressure in segment decreases from 5 to 0 cmH$_2$O. *Bottom*: in spontaneously breathing pig, when the lung surrounding an obstructed segment inflates from a pressure of 5 to 10 cmH$_2$O, pressure in segment decreases from 5 to −2 cmH$_2$O (K = 1.4). With paralysis, K = 1. When the lung is excised, K = 0.1. Shape changes of obstructed segment may be responsible for low K values in the excised lung. [From Menkes and Traystman (83).]

than dog lungs, and lobes should exhibit less interdependence than sublobar units.

Zidulka et al. (134) demonstrated higher K for sublobar units than lobes. However, measurements of intralobar interdependence in humans have not been reported, although Woolcock and Macklem's (130) studies suggested a greater degree of interdependence in dogs than in postmortem human lungs. It should be noted that measurements of vascular interdependence in postmortem human lungs indicate substantially lower degrees of interdependence in human than in dog lungs (57).

The chest wall increases the effects of interdependence. For example, K may be an order of magnitude lower in excised lungs compared with lungs in the chest wall (82, 116). In addition, even with the chest wall intact, there may be a reduction in K with muscle paralysis (134). This may partly account for differences in the distribution of ventilation when positive pressure is compared with spontaneous respiration or electrophrenic pacing (14, 86, 87). The reason that the chest wall is important for maintaining homogeneous ventilation is probably related to its role in preserving lung shape. When nonhomogeneous movements occur, a portion of the stresses generated by interdependence may be opposed by changes in recoil pressure resulting from shape changes. For example, if the lung inflates around an obstructed unit, forces of interdependence tend to lower Ps. However, if changes in shape at a free pleural surface increase recoil of the segment, the fall in Ps and thus the driving pressure for flow into the obstructed unit decrease.

The effects of lung and segment volume on K have been systematically studied in the pig. Sylvester, Menkes, and Stitik (116) measured the effects of interdependence while changing lung and segment volumes independently. Their first major finding was that when lung volume increased, K decreased. This occurred when both the obstructed segment and the unobstructed lung were at high transpulmonary pressures. This also occurred when the obstructed segment was maintained at a small lung volume and the surrounding lung inflated to high transpulmonary pressures. The latter finding is unexpected. If forces of interdependence act over a smaller surface area, their effects should be increased (78). Sylvester, Menkes, and Stitik (116) interpreted this finding to indicate that the lung and segment resist shape changes to a greater extent at high lung volumes and when there is a greater degree of nonhomogeneity. If, under those conditions, tissues are more resistant to strain (21, 101), changes in Ps resulting from interdependence will be dampened by changes in tissue recoil pressures. Thus gradients for flow may be modified by shape changes.

The effects of surface tension on interdependence have been assessed in several studies. Nakamura et al. (88) found that airways were larger and less collapsible when surrounded by air-filled compared to liquid-filled lungs. Menkes, Macklem, et al. (80) reported that the inactivation of surfactant appeared to decrease interdependence. To explain this they suggested that in the presence of surfactant, as a segment inflated nonhomogeneously, fiber attachments on its surface shortened, decreasing surface tension and their outward pull. Without surfactant and a fixed surface tension, this would not occur and K would be less. Other studies showing hysteresis in measurements of interdependence (82) and increased stability of airways under dynamic conditions support this interpretation (119). However, in their studies of interdependence, Sylvester, Menkes, and Stitik (116) did not observe hysteresis in measurements of K in porcine lungs. This suggests that at least in the pig, changes in surface tension at the interface between nonhomogeneous units independent of surface tension in the whole lung play relatively minor roles in generating stresses of interdependence.

Time Constants for Collateral Ventilation

Whether collateral channels can be effective in providing ventilatory pathways depends on τcoll, which equals Rcoll·C's. The relation between τcoll and tidal volume of a collaterally ventilated space is shown in Figure 6. This important relationship, which was described for ventilation through the airways by Dixon and Brodie (22) in 1903, was examined for ventilation through collateral channels by Nakamura et al. (89) in 1964. Brown, Macklem, et al. (13) pointed out that ventilation through collateral channels could occur very rapidly. They noted that widespread obstruction of small airways with 2-mm beads in dogs did not reduce pulmonary compliance even at a ventilatory function close to 1 cycle/s. They concluded that extensive collateral channels beyond the 2-mm obstructed airways provided for efficient movement of air and no decrease in tidal volume entering obstructed areas compared with the tidal volume entering unobstructed areas. That is, τcoll in relation to frequency was short. The most direct method for measuring τcoll was described by Hilpert (40). With stop V̇coll, τcoll can be calculated from the decay in Ps after the initial fall of Pb to Ps. If that decay follows a single exponential course, τcoll equals the time for it to fall ~63% $(1 - 1/e$, where e is the base of the natural logarithm) toward base line. Because τcoll = Rcoll·C's, the decay in Ps will be a function of Rcoll and C's and will not follow a single exponential course if either one changes during inflation of the nonhomogeneously inflated segment. The decay in Ps follows an exponential course surprisingly well, although deviations occur even in a healthy dog lung. In spite of these deviations, several investigators have reported τcoll from measurements in horse, dog, and human lungs. In dog lungs at FRC, τcoll varies widely but usually in the range of 0.5–2.5 s (40, 43, 154). In humans, τcoll was reported to be as low as 0.3 s by Bartels (7) but much

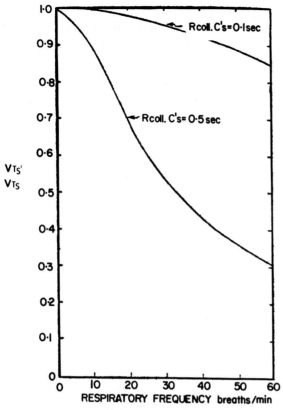

FIG. 6. Effect of respiratory frequency on ventilation of collaterally ventilated units (VTs′) compared to unobstructed units (VTs) with Rcoll·C′s (τcoll) = 0.1 s and 0.5 s. [From Macklem (70).]

higher by Terry, Menkes, et al. (120) and Inners, Menkes, et al. (53). Part of the variation in results may reflect lobar differences; τcoll is at least five times larger in the middle lobe than the upper lobe in young normal subjects (53) and differs widely from lobe to lobe in dogs (102). Part of the variation may also reflect differences in the size of obstructed units (130).

In general those factors that are associated with increased Rcoll (e.g., lobulated lungs, low lung volume, hypocapnea, and edema) are also associated with higher τcoll. However, this is not always the case. For example, factors such as vagal stimulation (130), methacholine administration (114), and kerosene to inactivate surfactant (80) may change Rcoll with relatively small effects on τcoll. The reason is that each of them affects C′s in the opposite direction. It is not known whether this is related to recruitment of parallel units or a change in elastic properties of the distended region.

GAS EXCHANGE AND COLLATERAL FLOW

Gas Exchange in Obstructed Units

In their initial studies of collateral flow, Van Allen et al. (125) concluded that ventilation distal to an obstructed airway occurred by diffusion or by the passage of gas through alveolar communications. Baker and Daly (6) measured the rate of flow of helium from apical to basilar segments in excised dog lungs and concluded that the "driving force of collateral ventilation is the pressure differential between segments." They were unable to detect flow occurring as a result of a diffusion gradient alone. Hogg, Macklem, et al. (44), using excised dog lungs, observed that after obstruction of peripheral airways with 2-mm beads the distribution of ventilation was disturbed. It returned to preobstruction values only after a 5-min breath hold. They concluded that diffusion of gas through collateral communications or alveolar walls occurs slowly. In a theoretical analysis of the movement of helium through alveolar walls under a diffusion gradient or through alveolar pores under a pressure gradient, Hilpert (41) calculated that transfer by collateral ventilation is ~10^4 times as effective as diffusion. Thus it is likely that diffusion across boundaries separating obstructed and unobstructed units in excised canine lungs is relatively unimportant compared to collateral flow. However, it remains possible that respiratory gases diffuse more rapidly through alveolar walls because they are more soluble than inert gas (28). Furthermore grossly dilated alveolar communications found in emphysematous lungs may facilitate diffusion through air spaces. This might be important especially if pressure gradients for mass flow are small in emphysema.

The efficiency of collateral flow to ventilate obstructed regions has been assessed by several investigators. In 1934 Lindskog and Bradshaw (67) reported that with lobar obstruction, gas tensions beyond the obstruction equilibrated at mixed venous levels. However, with sublobar obstruction, gas sampled from the obstructed area never had CO_2 levels above arterial P_{CO_2} (Pa_{CO_2}) and P_{O_2} values were above arterial levels. Flenley, Welchel, and Macklem (29) also reported that P_{O_2} values in gas sampled beyond wedged subsegmental airways in dogs were high and that they lie between alveolar tensions in the rest of the lung and arterial tension. They also showed that the $\dot{V}/\dot{Q}$ relationship of the collaterally ventilated unit was lower than that for the whole lung. Further evidence that collateral flow is contaminated by alveolar gas during inspiration was reported by Metcalf et al. (85). In their studies they found that the P_{O_2} and P_{CO_2} of gas entering a collaterally ventilated space were very close to end-tidal P_{O_2} and P_{CO_2} values of unobstructed lung. Thus with collateral flow the obstructed unit inspires from an adjacent region. As shown by West (128) this "parasitic" unit has a grossly impaired CO_2 output but maintains a relatively unaffected O_2 uptake. On the basis of their findings, Flenley, Welchel, and Macklem (29) concluded that the functional collateral channels in the dog are more likely to communicate between alveoli than between small airways; however, this need not be so. Engel, Menkes, Macklem, et al. (26) reported that when gas is sampled in small airways, alveolar gas contaminates the gas even during inspiration. This occurs because the churning action of the heart increases the rate of diffusion from the alveoli down the airway against the convection of gas in the opposite direction. Thus ventilation through airways as well as ventilation through collateral channels may be contaminated by alveolar gas from surrounding regions. Therefore contamination of inspired gas by alveolar gas in a collaterally ventilated region does not imply that alveolar communications are responsible for flow.

Collateral Flow and Local Regulation of Ventilation-Perfusion Relationships

With obstruction of small airways, $\dot{V}/\dot{Q}$ relationships are better preserved in species with well-developed collateral channels, e.g., dogs, than those without collateral communications, e.g., pigs (28). However, even in those species with collateral communications there is a price to pay. Wagner et al. (127) and Rubinfeld et al. (106) reported a bimodal distribution of $\dot{V}_A/\dot{Q}$ (where $\dot{V}_A$ is alveolar ventilation) in patients with asthma and in dogs with bronchoconstriction induced with *Ascaris* serum extract (an antigen), methacholine, or histamine. The low $\dot{V}/\dot{Q}$ units were centered on a ratio of 0.7 in the humans with essentially no shunt and a ratio of 0.14 in the dogs. In both cases they concluded that collateral flow beyond obstructed airways maintained ventilation, albeit at a reduced level, and prevented the development of true shunt. However, Wagner et al. also noted that after the administration of isoproterenol, blood flow to the low $\dot{V}_A/\dot{Q}$ mode increased and arterial P_{O_2} (Pa_{O_2}) fell. Thus in addition to factors that increase collateral flow to obstructed units (e.g., P_{CO_2}, increased volume, and interdependence), there are factors that reduce perfusion to obstructed units. Grant et al. (36) investigated the effects of local hypoxia on perfusion in the coatimundi, which is a small mammal from Central and South America that has well-developed interlobular fibrous septa. Because collateral flow is poor in these animals, it is possible to wedge a catheter in a

peripheral airway and produce local hypoxia in the lungs. When this was done there was a 22% reduction in local perfusion (as percent of flow at P_{O_2} of 100 mmHg) per 10 mmHg fall in P_{O_2} over the range of 150–36 mmHg. Thus the local regulation of perfusion in addition to the local regulation of ventilation should be considered in any assessment of gas exchange with obstruction of small airways. In considering the regulation of $\dot{V}/\dot{Q}$ with hypoxia, Kuriyama and Wagner (61) have hypothesized that species with well-developed collateral communications (e.g., dogs) have less need for a vasoconstrictor response to hypoxia, whereas species with poorly developed collateral channels (e.g., pigs) have a greater need for vascular responses when airways are obstructed. As these investigators pointed out, this may explain why dogs exhibit relatively feeble pulmonary vascular responses to hypoxia compared to pigs.

The usual method for modeling the match of ventilation to perfusion in the lungs is illustrated in Figure 7A. Inasmuch as capillary flow through the lungs has been compared to sheet flow (31a), perhaps peripheral airflow through the lungs should also be compared to sheet flow (Fig. 7B).

For the vascular system, Young et al. (133) reported that spherical beads 100 μm in diameter or less did not give rise to high $\dot{V}/\dot{Q}$ regions when injected intravenously into dogs. They concluded that the functional gas-exchange units in those lungs was the volume subtended by the vessels 150 μm in diameter (vessels associated with respiratory bronchioles). In studies reported by Flenley, Macklem, et al. (28), obstruction of airways with 2-mm beads resulted in no decrease in $\dot{V}/\dot{Q}$ in either pigs or dogs. However, the anatomic shunt increased in the pig and not in the dog. Thus it is likely that many factors, including species and the presence of disease, will have to be considered when assessing $\dot{V}/\dot{Q}$.

Airway Obstruction and Collateral Flow

Whether flow into an obstructed unit occurs at all depends on τcoll relative to respiratory frequency.

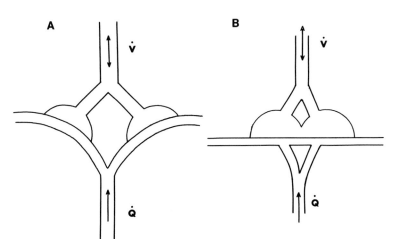

FIG. 7. Models for gas exchange. *A*: separate pathways for ventilation ($\dot{V}$) and perfusion ($\dot{Q}$). *B*: collateral communications for flow of blood and gas are included.

Whether it occurs through airways or collateral channels depends on the relative magnitudes of Rcoll and Rsaw serving the unit. At FRC in the dog, Rcoll may be 15 times as great and in humans it may be 50 times as great as resistance to flow through airways serving the same volume of lung. Thus there should be little reason for flow to pass through collateral channels. However, with disease and increases in Rsaw caused by narrowing or complete obliteration of airways, collateral communications may play a major role in distributing ventilation (70). This has been shown by Hogg, Macklem, and Thurlbeck (43) in postmortem human lungs from patients with emphysema and confirmed by Terry, Menkes, et al. (120) in patients during life. In both studies, airway resistance was high and Rcoll was low in emphysema, compared to normal. Thus increases in number or size of collateral communications occur in emphysema. It is not known whether decreased collateral flow contributes to abnormalities in disease (e.g., interstitial fibrosis), although the long τcoll in middle lobes is thought to contribute to the development of the middle lobe syndrome (17–19, 53). Aside from what is discussed here, little is known about the role of collateral ventilation in the diseased lung, even though collateral flow must assume a more important role in the maintenance of gas exchange in the presence of airway obstruction.

In normal lungs, collateral flow may help to maintain synchronous filling and emptying of adjacent air spaces whose time constants are different. In addition it provides a mechanism for maintaining gas exchange when airways are obstructed and serves to prevent adverse mechanical consequences secondary to gas absorption. Inasmuch as clearance mechanisms and cough depend on alveolar or airway distension, collateral communications provide a route for inflation distal to the obstruction. In their description of pulmonary interdependence, Mead et al. (78) speculated on possible detrimental vascular effects resulting from low pressure, secondary to atelectasis, of small portions of lung. Although it is still unknown whether fluid flux out of vessels or vascular disruption results under these conditions, this possibility exists and illustrates the potential importance of collateral flow for mechanical and gas-exchange functions in the lung.

REFERENCES

1. AHMED, T., P. EYRE, A. J. JANUSZKIEWICZ, AND A. WANNER. Role of H_1- and H_2-receptors in airway reactions to histamine in conscious sheep. *J. Appl. Physiol.: Respirat. Environ. Exercise Physiol.* 49: 826–833, 1980.
2. ALLEY, R. D., AND G. E. LINDSKOG. Pharmacologic factors influencing collateral respiration: possible relation to the etiology of pulmonary complications. *Ann. Surg.* 128: 497–508, 1948.
3. ANKENEY, J. L., C. HUBAY, AND F. TILLOTSON. Effects of change in pulmonary circulation on collateral ventilation. *Surg. Forum* 1: 25–33, 1950.
4. BAARSMA, P. R., AND M. N. J. DIRKEN. Collateral ventilation. *J. Thorac. Surg.* 17: 238–251, 1948.
5. BACHOFEN, H., P. GEHR, AND E. R. WEIBEL. Alterations of mechanical properties and morphology in excised rabbit lungs rinsed with a detergent. *J. Appl. Physiol.: Respirat. Environ. Exercise Physiol.* 47: 1002–1010, 1979.
6. BAKER, D. H., AND W. J. DALY. Collateral ventilation demonstrated by helium transfer. *J. Appl. Physiol.* 26: 321–325, 1969.
7. BARTELS, M. Kollaterale Ventilation beim menschen Habilitationsschrift aus der Medizinischen. Tübingen, West Germany: Tübingen Universitätsklinik, 1972. Thesis.
8. BATRA, G., R. TRAYSTMAN, H. RUDNICK, AND H. MENKES. Effects of body position and cholinergic blockade on mechanics of collateral ventilation. *J. Appl. Physiol.: Respirat. Environ. Exercise Physiol.* 50: 358–362, 1981.
9. BENJAMIN, J. J., P. S. MURTAGH, D. F. PROCTOR, H. A. MENKES, AND S. PERMUTT. Pulmonary vascular interdependence in excised dog lobes. *J. Appl. Physiol.* 37: 887–894, 1974.
10. BOATMAN, E. S., AND H. D. MARTIN. Electron microscopy of the alveolar pores of Kohn. *Am. Rev. Respir. Dis.* 88: 779–784, 1963.
11. BOREN, H. G. Alveolar fenestrae: relationship to the pathology and pathogenesis of pulmonary emphysema. *Am. Rev. Respir. Dis.* 85: 328–344, 1962.
12. BOYDEN, E. A. The structure of the pulmonary acinus in a child of six years and eight months. *Am. J. Anat.* 132: 275–299, 1971.
13. BROWN, R., A. J. WOOLCOCK, N. J. VINCENT, AND P. T. MACKLEM. Physiological effects of experimental airway obstruction with beads. *J. Appl. Physiol.* 27: 328–335, 1969.
14. BYNUM, L. J., J. E. WILSON III, AND A. K. PIERCE. Comparison of spontaneous and positive-pressure breathing in supine normal subjects. *J. Appl. Physiol.* 41: 341–347, 1976.
15. CALL, E. P., G. LINDSKOG, AND A. LIEBOW. Some physiologic and pharmacologic aspects of collateral ventilation. *J. Thorac. Cardiovasc. Surg.* 49: 1015–1025, 1965.
16. CHEN, C., W. C. SEALY, AND A. SEABER. The dynamic nature of collateral ventilation. *J. Thorac. Cardiovasc. Surg.* 59: 518–529, 1970.
17. CULINER, M. M. Obliterative bronchitis and bronchiolitis with bronchiectasis. *Chest* 44: 351–360, 1963.
18. CULINER, M. M. The right middle lobe syndrome, a nonobstructive complex. *Dis. Chest* 50: 57–66, 1966.
19. CULINER, M. M., AND C. A. WALL. Collateral ventilation in "intralobar pulmonary sequestration." Report of a case. *Dis. Chest* 47: 118–122, 1965.
20. CUTILLO, A., E. OMBONI, R. PERONDI, AND F. TANA. Effect of hypocapnia on pulmonary mechanics in normal subjects and in patients with chronic obstructive lung disease. *Am. Rev. Respir. Dis.* 110: 25–33, 1974.
21. D'ANGELO, E., AND S. MICHELINI. Alveolar morphology under localized distorting forces. *J. Appl. Physiol.* 34: 809–815, 1973.
22. DIXON, W. E., AND T. G. BRODIE. Contributions to the physiology of the lungs. I. The bronchial muscles, their innervation and the action of drugs upon them. *J. Physiol. London* 29: 97–173, 1903.
23. DUBOIS, A. B., AND R. M. ROGERS. Respiratory factors determining the tissue concentrations of inhaled toxic substances. *Respir. Physiol.* 5: 34–52, 1968.
24. DUGUID, J. B., AND M. W. LAMBERT. The pathogenesis of coal miners' pneumoconiosis. *J. Pathol. Bacteriol.* 88: 389–403, 1964.

25. EFFMANN, E. L., G. S. FREEDMAN, AND R. C. LANGE. ^{133}Xe studies of collateral ventilation and air trapping following endobronchial occlusion. *Radiology* 105: 85–91, 1972.

26. ENGEL, L. A., H. MENKES, L. D. H. WOOD, G. UTZ, J. JOUBERT, AND P. T. MACKLEM. Gas mixing during breath holding studied by intrapulmonary gas sampling. *J. Appl. Physiol.* 35: 9–17, 1973.

27. FISK, D. E., AND C. KUHN. Emphysema-like changes in the lungs of the blotchy mouse. *Am. Rev. Respir. Dis.* 113: 787–797, 1976.

28. FLENLEY, D. C., J. PICKEN, L. WELCHEL, F. RUFF, P. M. CORRY, AND P. T. MACKLEM. Blood gas transfer after small airway obstruction in the dog and minipig. *Respir. Physiol.* 15: 39–51, 1972.

29. FLENLEY, D. C., L. WELCHEL, AND P. T. MACKLEM. Factors affecting gas exchange by collateral ventilation in the dog. *Respir. Physiol.* 15: 52–69, 1972.

30. FRANK, N. R., E. P. RADFORD, JR., AND J. L. WHITTENBERGER. Static volume-pressure interrelations of the lungs and pulmonary blood vessels in excised cats' lungs. *J. Appl. Physiol.* 14: 167–173, 1959.

31. FULLER, S. D., N. E. ROBINSON, AND J. B. SCOTT. Effect of pulmonary venous pressure on steady-state collateral resistance. *J. Appl. Physiol.: Respirat. Environ. Exercise Physiol.* 49: 643–648, 1980.

31a. FUNG, Y. B., AND S. S. SOBIN. Pulmonary alveolar bloodflow. In: *Lung Biology in Health and Disease. Bioengineering Aspects of the Lung*, edited by J. B. West. New York: Dekker, 1977, vol. 3, p. 267–360.

32. GERTNER, A., B. BROMBERGER, R. TRAYSTMAN, AND H. MENKES. Histamine and pulmonary responses to cigarette smoke in periphery of the lung. *J. Appl. Physiol.: Respirat. Environ. Exercise Physiol.* 53: 582–588, 1982.

33. GLAUSER, E. M. Experimental emphysema in piglet lungs due to periodic hypoxia and hypercapnia. *Am. Rev. Respir. Dis.* 98: 444–448, 1968.

34. GOLDBERG, H. S., W. MITZNER, K. ADAMS, H. MENKES, W. LICHTENSTEIN, AND S. PERMUTT. Effect of intrathoracic pressure on pressure-volume characteristics of the lung in man. *J. Appl. Physiol.* 38: 411–417, 1975.

35. GOSHY, M., S. J. LAI-FOOK, AND R. E. HYATT. Perivascular pressure measurements by wick-catheter technique in isolated dog lobes. *J. Appl. Physiol.: Respirat. Environ. Exercise Physiol.* 46: 950–955, 1979.

36. GRANT, B. J. B., E. E. DAVIES, H. A. JONES, AND J. M. B. HUGHES. Local regulation of pulmonary blood flow and ventilation-perfusion ratios in the coatimundi. *J. Appl. Physiol.* 40: 216–228, 1976.

37. GUERZON, G. M., P. D. PARÉ, M. C. MICHOUD, AND J. C. HOGG. The number and distribution of mast cells in monkey lungs. *Am. Rev. Respir. Dis.* 119: 59–66, 1979.

38. GURTNER, G. H. Evidence for facilitated O_2 and CO_2 transport. In: *Pulmonary Gas Exchange*, edited by J. West. New York: Academic, 1980, p. 205–239.

39. HENDERSON, R., K. HORSFIELD, AND G. CUMMING. Intersegmental collateral ventilation in the human lung. *Respir. Physiol.* 6: 128–134, 1968.

40. HILPERT, P. Kollaterale Ventilation Habilitationsschrift, aus der Medizinischen. Tübingen, West Germany: Tübingen Universitätsklinik, 1970. Thesis.

41. HILPERT, P. He-Auswaschung aus stenosierten Lungensegmenten durch kollaterale Ventilation. *Respiration* 33: 112–122, 1976.

42. HOGG, J. C., J. B. AGARAWAL, A. J. S. GARDINER, W. H. PALMER, AND P. T. MACKLEM. Distribution of airway resistance with developing pulmonary edema in dogs. *J. Appl. Physiol.* 32: 20–24, 1972.

43. HOGG, J. C., P. T. MACKLEM, AND W. M. THURLBECK. The resistance of collateral channels in excised human lungs. *J. Clin. Invest.* 48: 421–431, 1969.

44. HOGG, W., J. BRUNTON, M. KRYGER, R. BROWN, AND P. MACKLEM. Gas diffusion across collateral channels. *J. Appl. Physiol.* 33: 568–575, 1972.

45. HOPPIN, F. G., JR., M. GREEN, AND M. S. MORGAN. Relationship of central and peripheral airway resistance to lung volume in dogs. *J. Appl. Physiol.: Respirat. Environ. Exercise Physiol.* 44: 728–737, 1978.

46. HOPPIN, F. G., JR., J. M. B. HUGHES, AND J. MEAD. Axial forces in the bronchial tree. *J. Appl. Physiol.: Respirat. Environ. Exercise Physiol.* 42: 773–781, 1977.

47. HOWELL, J. B. L., S. PERMUTT, D. F. PROCTOR, AND R. L. RILEY. Effect of inflation of the lung on different parts of pulmonary vascular bed. *J. Appl. Physiol.* 16: 71–76, 1961.

48. HUGHES, J. M. B., F. G. HOPPIN, JR., AND J. MEAD. Effect of lung inflation on bronchial length and diameter in excised lungs. *J. Appl. Physiol.* 32: 25–35, 1972.

49. HUGHES, J. M. B., H. A. JONES, A. G. WILSON, B. J. B. GRANT, AND N. B. PRIDE. Stability of intrapulmonary bronchial dimensions during expiratory flow in excised lungs. *J. Appl. Physiol.* 37: 684–694, 1974.

50. HUGHES, J. M. B., D. Y. ROSENZWEIG, AND P. B. KIVITZ. Site of airway closure in excised dog lungs: histologic demonstration. *J. Appl. Physiol.* 29: 340–344, 1970.

51. INGRAM, R. H., JR. Effects of airway versus arterial CO_2 changes on lung mechanics in dogs. *J. Appl. Physiol.* 38: 603–607, 1975.

52. INGRAM, R. H., JR., G. D. FINLAY, AND J. M. BRADFORD, JR. Relationship of AaDo$_2$ to airway Pco$_2$ in dog lungs. *J. Appl. Physiol.* 40: 720–724, 1976.

53. INNERS, C. R., P. B. TERRY, R. J. TRAYSTMAN, AND H. A. MENKES. Collateral ventilation and the middle lobe syndrome. *Am. Rev. Respir. Dis.* 118: 305–310, 1978.

54. INNERS, C. R., P. B. TERRY, R. J. TRAYSTMAN, AND H. A. MENKES. Effects of lung volume on collateral and airways resistance in man. *J. Appl. Physiol.: Respirat. Environ. Exercise Physiol.* 46: 67–73, 1979.

55. INOUE, H., C. INOUE, AND J. HILDEBRANDT. Vascular and airway pressures, and interstitial edema, affect peribronchial fluid pressure. *J. Appl. Physiol.: Respirat. Environ. Exercise Physiol.* 48: 177–185, 1980.

56. JOHNSON, R., AND G. LINDSKOG. Further studies on factors influencing collateral ventilation. *J. Thorac. Cardiovasc. Surg.* 62: 321–329, 1971.

57. KALK, J., J. BENJAMIN, H. COMITE, G. HUTCHINS, R. TRAYSTMAN, AND H. MENKES. Vascular interdependence in postmortem human lungs. *Am. Rev. Respir. Dis.* 112: 505–511, 1975.

58. KAPLAN, J., G. C. SMALDONE, H. A. MENKES, D. L. SWIFT, AND R. J. TRAYSTMAN. Response of collateral channels to histamine: lack of vagal effect. *J. Appl. Physiol.: Respirat. Environ. Exercise Physiol.* 51: 1314–1319, 1981.

59. KRAHL, V. E. Microscopic anatomy of the lungs. *Am. Rev. Respir. Dis.* 80 (Pt. 2): 24–44, 1959.

60. KUNO, K., AND N. C. STAUB. Acute mechanical effects of lung volume changes on artificial microholes in alveolar walls. *J. Appl. Physiol.* 24: 83–92, 1968.

61. KURIYAMA, T., AND W. W. WAGNER, JR. Collateral ventilation may protect against high-altitude pulmonary hypertension. *J. Appl. Physiol.: Respirat. Environ. Exercise Physiol.* 51: 1251–1256, 1981.

62. LAI-FOOK, S. J. A continuum mechanics analysis of pulmonary vascular interdependence in isolated dog lobes. *J. Appl. Physiol.: Respirat. Environ. Exercise Physiol.* 46: 419–429, 1979.

63. LAI-FOOK, S. J., R. E. HYATT, AND J. R. RODARTE. Effect of parenchymal shear modulus and lung volume on bronchial pressure-diameter behavior. *J. Appl. Physiol.: Respirat. Environ. Exercise Physiol.* 44: 859–868, 1978.

64. LAI-FOOK, S. J., R. E. HYATT, J. R. RODARTE, AND T. A. WILSON. Behavior of artificially produced holes in lung parenchyma. *J. Appl. Physiol.: Respirat. Environ. Exercise Physiol.*

43: 648–655, 1977.

65. LAMBERT, M. W. Accessory bronchiole-alveolar communications. *J. Pathol. Bacteriol.* 70: 311–314, 1955.

66. LIEBOW, A. A. Recent advances in pulmonary anatomy. In: *Pulmonary Structure Function*, edited by A. V. S. DeReuck and M. O'Conner. London: Churchill, 1962. (Ciba Found. Symp.)

67. LINDSKOG, G. E., AND H. H. BRADSHAW. Collateral respiration: the chemical composition and volume of the collaterally respired gases. *Am. J. Physiol.* 108: 581–592, 1934.

68. LINDSKOG, G. E., AND H. H. BRADSHAW. The reinflation of atelectatic lung. An experimental study. *J. Thorac. Surg.* 3: 333–340, 1934.

69. LOOSLI, C. G. Interalveolar communications in normal and pathologic mammalian lungs: review of literature. *Arch. Pathol.* 24: 743–776, 1937.

70. MACKLEM, P. T. Airway obstruction and collateral ventilation. *Physiol. Rev.* 51: 368–436, 1971.

71. MACKLEM, P. T., AND J. MEAD. Resistance of central and peripheral airways measured by a retrograde catheter. *J. Appl. Physiol.* 22: 395–401, 1967.

72. MACKLEM, P. T., D. F. PROCTOR, AND J. C. HOGG. The stability of peripheral airways. *Respir. Physiol.* 8: 191–203, 1969.

73. MACKLIN, C. C. X-ray studies on bronchial movements. *Am. J. Anat.* 35: 303–329, 1925.

74. MACKLIN, C. C. Alveolar pores and their significance in the human lung. *Arch. Pathol.* 21: 202–216, 1936.

75. MARTIN, H. B. The effect of aging on the alveolar pores of Kohn in the dog. *Am. Rev. Respir. Dis.* 88: 773–778, 1963.

76. MARTIN, H. B. Respiratory bronchioles as the pathway for collateral ventilation. *J. Appl. Physiol.* 21: 1443–1447, 1966.

77. MEAD, J. Respiration: pulmonary mechanics. *Annu. Rev. Physiol.* 35: 169–192, 1973.

78. MEAD, J., T. TAKISHIMA, AND D. LEITH. Stress distribution in lungs: a model of pulmonary elasticity. *J. Appl. Physiol.* 28: 596–608, 1970.

79. MENKES, H., G. GAMSU, R. SCHROTER, AND P. T. MACKLEM. Interdependence of lung units in isolated dog lungs. *J. Appl. Physiol.* 32: 675–680, 1972.

80. MENKES, H., A. GARDINER, G. GAMSU, J. LEMPERT, AND P. T. MACKLEM. Influence of surface forces on collateral ventilation. *J. Appl. Physiol.* 31: 544–549, 1971.

81. MENKES, H., D. LINDSAY, G. GAMSU, L. WOOD, A. MUIR, AND P. T. MACKLEM. Measurement of sublobar lung volume and collateral flow resistance in dogs. *J. Appl. Physiol.* 35: 917–921, 1973.

82. MENKES, H., D. LINDSAY, L. WOOD, A. MUIR, AND P. T. MACKLEM. Interdependence of lung units in intact dog lungs. *J. Appl. Physiol.* 32: 681–686, 1972.

83. MENKES, H. A., AND R. J. TRAYSTMAN. State of the art: collateral ventilation. *Am. Rev. Respir. Dis.* 116: 287–309, 1977.

84. MENKES, H. A., R. J. TRAYSTMAN, AND P. TERRY. Collateral ventilation. *Federation Proc.* 38: 22–26, 1979.

85. METCALF, J. F., P. D. WAGNER, AND J. B. WEST. Effect of local bronchial obstruction on gas exchange in the dog. *Am. Rev. Respir. Dis.* 117: 85–95, 1978.

86. MINH, V.-D., G. F. DOLAN, N. KURIHARA, P. J. FRIEDMAN, R. G. KONOPKA, AND K. M. MOSER. Stability in lobar ventilation distribution during change in thoracic configuration. *J. Appl. Physiol.* 39: 462–468, 1975.

87. MINH, V.-D., N. KURIHARA, P. J. FRIEDMAN, AND K. M. MOSER. Reversal of the pleural pressure gradient during electrophrenic stimulation. *J. Appl. Physiol.* 37: 496–504, 1974.

88. NAKAMURA, M., H. SASAKI, AND T. TAKISHIMA. Effect of lung surface tension on bronchial collapsibility in excised dog lungs. *J. Appl. Physiol.* 47: 692–700, 1979.

89. NAKAMURA, T., T. TAKISHIMA, R. TAKASUGI, AND T. SASAKI. Collateral ventilation in excised dog lungs. *J. Appl. Physiol.* 19: 1081–1085, 1964.

90. NEWHOUSE, M. T., M. R. BECKLAKE, P. T. MACKLEM, AND M. McGREGOR. Effect of alterations in end-tidal CO_2 tension on flow resistance. *J. Appl. Physiol.* 19: 745–749, 1964.

91. OLSEN, C. R., H. J. H. COLEBATCH, P. E. MEBEL, J. A. NADEL, AND N. C. STAUB. Motor control of pulmonary airways studied by nerve stimulation. *J. Appl. Physiol.* 20: 202–208, 1965.

92. OLSON, L. E., AND N. E. ROBINSON. Effect of vagal stimulation on collateral flow resistance in dog lungs. *J. Appl. Physiol.: Respirat. Environ. Exercise Physiol.* 49: 287–293, 1980.

93. ORICCHIO, D. Contributo allo studio delle anastomosi inerbronchiali. *Ann. Ist. Carlo Forlanini* 11: 597–604, 1948.

94. PARRA, S. C., L. R. GADDY, AND T. TAKARO. Ultrastructural studies of canine interalveolar pores (of Kohn). *Lab. Invest.* 38: 8–13, 1978.

95. PARRA, S. C., L. R. GADDY, AND T. TAKARO. Early ultrastructural changes in papain-induced experimental emphysema. *Lab. Invest.* 42: 277–289, 1980.

96. PUMP, K. K. The pattern of development of emphysema in the human lung. *Am. Rev. Respir. Dis.* 108: 610–620, 1973.

97. PUMP, K. K. Fenestrae in the alveolar membrane of the human lung. *Chest* 65: 431–436, 1974.

98. PUMP, K. K. Emphysema and its relation to age. *Am. Rev. Respir. Dis.* 114: 5–13, 1976.

99. RANGA, V., AND J. KLEINERMAN. Interalveolar pores in mouse lungs. *Am. Rev. Respir. Dis.* 122: 477–481, 1980.

100. RASKIN, S. P., AND P. G. HERMAN. Interacinar pathways in the human lung. *Am. Rev. Respir. Dis.* 111: 489–495, 1975.

101. ROBERTSON, C. H., D. L. HALL, AND J. C. HOGG. A description of lung distortion due to localized pleural stress. *J. Appl. Physiol.* 34: 344–350, 1973.

102. ROBINSON, N. E., AND R. MILAR. Lobar variations in collateral ventilation in excised dog lungs. *Am. Rev. Respir. Dis.* 121: 827–834, 1980.

103. ROBINSON, N. E., AND P. R. SORENSON. Collateral flow resistance and time constants in dog and horse lungs. *J. Appl. Physiol.: Respirat. Environ. Exercise Physiol.* 44: 63–68, 1978.

104. ROBOTHAM, J. L., H. A. MENKES, B. E. CHIPPS, C. R. INNERS, P. ALDERSON, G. M. HUTCHINS, J. J. TEPAS, AND J. A. HALLER. A physiologic assessment of segmental bronchial atresia. *Am. Rev. Respir. Dis.* 121: 533–540, 1980.

105. ROSENBERG, D. E., AND H. A. LYONS. Collateral ventilation in excised human lungs. *Respiration* 37: 125–134, 1979.

106. RUBINFELD, A. R., P. D. WAGNER, AND J. B. WEST. Gas exchange during acute experimental canine asthma. *Am. Rev. Respir. Dis.* 118: 525–536, 1978.

107. SAHEBJAMI, H., AND C. L. VASSALLO. Influence of starvation on enzyme-induced emphysema. *J. Appl. Physiol.: Respirat. Environ. Exercise Physiol.* 48: 284–288, 1980.

108. SASAKI, H., F. G. HOPPIN, JR., AND T. TAKISHIMA. Peribronchial pressure in excised dog lungs. *J. Appl. Physiol.: Respirat. Environ. Exercise Physiol.* 45: 858–869, 1978.

109. SASAKI, H., T. TAKISHIMA, AND M. NAKAMURA. Collateral resistance at alveolar level in excised dog lungs. *J. Appl. Physiol.: Respirat. Environ. Exercise Physiol.* 48: 982–990, 1980.

110. SASAKI, H., T. TAKISHIMA, AND T. SASAKI. Influence of lung parenchyma on dynamic bronchial collapsibility of excised dog lungs. *J. Appl. Physiol.: Respirat. Environ. Exercise Physiol.* 42: 699–705, 1977.

111. SCANLON, T. S., AND J. L. BENUMOF. Demonstration of interlobar collateral ventilation. *J. Appl. Physiol.: Respirat. Environ. Exercise Physiol.* 46: 658–661, 1979.

112. SEALY, W. C., AND A. SEABER. The action of carbon dioxide on the collateral pathways of pulmonary ventilation. *J. Thorac. Cardiovasc. Surg.* 69: 533–538, 1975.

113. SLAGTER, B., AND H. HEEMSTRA. Limiting factors of expiration in normal subjects. *Acta Physiol. Pharmacol. Neerl.* 4: 419–421, 1955.

114. SMITH, L. J., C. R. INNERS, P. B. TERRY, H. A. MENKES, AND R. J. TRAYSTMAN. Effects of methacholine and hypocapnia on airways and collateral ventilation in dogs. *J. Appl. Physiol.: Respirat. Environ. Exercise Physiol.* 46: 966–972, 1979.

115. STERLING, G. M. The mechanism of bronchoconstriction due to hypocapnia in man. *Clin. Sci.* 34: 277–285, 1968.

116. SYLVESTER, J. T., H. A. MENKES, AND F. STITIK. Lung volume and interdependence in the pig. *J. Appl. Physiol.* 38: 395–401, 1975.

117. TAKISHIMA, T., K. ISHIKAWA, T. SASAKI, H. SASAKI, AND T. NAKAMURA. Measurement of collateral flow at quasialveolar level in excised dog lung. *Tohoku J. Exp. Med.* 105: 405–406, 1971.

118. TAKISHIMA, T., AND J. MEAD. Tests of a model of pulmonary elasticity. *J. Appl. Physiol.* 33: 576–581, 1972.

119. TAKISHIMA, T., H. SASAKI, AND T. SASAKI. Influence of lung parenchyma on collapsibility of dog bronchi. *J. Appl. Physiol.* 38: 875–881, 1975.

120. TERRY, P. B., R. J. TRAYSTMAN, H. H. NEWBALL, G. BATRA, AND H. A. MENKES. Collateral ventilation in man. *N. Engl. J. Med.* 298: 10–14, 1978.

121. TRAYSTMAN, R. J., G. K. BATRA, AND H. A. MENKES. Local regulation of collateral ventilation by oxygen and carbon dioxide. *J. Appl. Physiol.* 40: 819–823, 1976.

122. TRAYSTMAN, R. J., P. B. TERRY, AND H. A. MENKES. Carbon dioxide—a major determinant of collateral ventilation. *J. Appl. Physiol.: Respirat. Environ. Exercise Physiol.* 45: 69–74, 1978.

124. VAN ALLEN, C. M., AND T. S. JUNG. Postoperative atelectasis and collateral respiration. *J. Thorac. Surg.* 1: 3–14, 1931.

125. VAN ALLEN, C. M., G. E. LINDSKOG, AND H. G. RICHTER. Gaseous interchange between adjacent lung lobules. *Yale J. Biol. Med.* 2: 297–300, 1930.

126. VINCENT, N. J., R. KNUDSON, D. E. LEITH, P. T. MACKLEM, AND J. MEAD. Factors influencing pulmonary resistance. *Appl. Physiol.* 29: 236–243, 1970.

127. WAGNER, P. D., D. R. DANTZKER, V. E. IACOVANI, W. C. TOMLIN, AND J. B. WEST. Ventilation-perfusion inequality in asymptomatic asthma. *Am. Rev. Respir. Dis.* 118: 511–524, 1978.

128. WEST, J. B. Gas exchange when one lung region inspires from another. *J. Appl. Physiol.* 30: 479–487, 1971.

129. WHITTENBERGER, J. L., M. MCGREGOR, E. BERGLUND, AND H. G. BORST. Influence of state of inflation of the lung on pulmonary vascular resistance. *J. Appl. Physiol.* 15: 878–882, 1960.

130. WOOLCOCK, A. J., AND P. T. MACKLEM. Mechanical factors influencing collateral ventilation in human, dog, and pig lungs. *J. Appl. Physiol.* 30: 99–115, 1971.

131. WOOLCOCK, A. J., P. T. MACKLEM, J. C. HOGG, AND N. J. WILSON. Influence of autonomic nervous system on airway resistance and elastic recoil. *J. Appl. Physiol.* 26: 814–818, 1969.

132. WOOLCOCK, A. J., P. T. MACKLEM, J. C. HOGG, N. J. WILSON, J. A. NADEL, N. R. FRANK, AND J. BRAIN. Effect of vagal stimulation on central and peripheral airways in dogs. *J. Appl. Physiol.* 26: 806–813, 1969.

133. YOUNG, I., R. W. MASSONE, AND P. D. WAGNER. Identification of functional lung unit in the dog by graded vascular embolization. *J. Appl. Physiol.: Respirat. Environ. Exercise Physiol.* 49: 132–141, 1980.

134. ZIDULKA, A., J. T. SYLVESTER, S. NADLER, AND N. R. ANTHONISEN. Lung interdependence and lung-chest wall interaction of sublobar and lobar units in pigs. *J. Appl. Physiol.: Respirat. Environ. Exercise Physiol.* 46: 8–13, 1979.

CHAPTER 22

Development, growth, and aging of the lung

JEROME S. BRODY | *Pulmonary Center and Department of Medicine, Boston University School of Medicine, Boston, Massachusetts*

WILLIAM M. THURLBECK | *Department of Pathology, University of British Columbia School of Medicine, Vancouver, Canada*

CHAPTER CONTENTS

THIS CHAPTER is concerned with the anatomical and biochemical features of lung growth and aging and their relationship to the mechanical properties of the lung. The physiological aspects of lung growth and aging are covered in depth in other chapters in this *Handbook* and are discussed here only to illustrate specific points. We examine the interrelated topics of the lung's development and growth, its connective tissue, and its mechanical properties.

With exceptions to be noted, the major aspects of lung growth and aging are generally similar in all mammals studied to date, although the timing of events varies from species to species. For example, both rats and humans undergo a period of rapid alveolar formation, but these events, which take place during the first few weeks of life in the rat (44, 45), occur in late gestation and the first few years of life in humans (81, 241). Similarly the increase in the volume of the lung formed by alveolar ducts (a characteristic

of aging lung) takes place between 1 and 10 yr of age in the dog (205) but between 20 and 70 yr of age in humans (242). Although fetal development has been studied extensively in humans, most of the data relating to the perinatal period have been obtained in animals. Little anatomical and biochemical information relating to early postnatal growth in humans is available. The most extensive correlative information covering this period has been obtained from studies of small rodents, especially the rat. In contrast, a large amount of information is available relating to the aging lung in humans. Thus in this chapter we use data from several species to illustrate general principles of lung growth and aging.

LUNG GROWTH AND MATURATION

It is only now becoming apparent that growth and maturation may progress separately in the lung. Because growth is a quantitative phenomenon and maturation is qualitative, there is no reason why either an increase or a decrease in lung growth should necessarily be accompanied by a similar change in maturation. For example, the administration of glucocorticoids in late gestation results in maturation of the epithelial cells of the alveolar wall, so that there are increased proportions of cells containing lamellar bodies and of flattened cells (254). Functionally, surface activity and alveolar stability increase (150, 161). However, this may be accompanied by decreases in the number of cells and in lung weight (50, 152). This may be a dose-dependent phenomenon, with low doses of steroids leading to maturation without suppressing lung growth but with high doses suppressing lung weight (138). That is, lungs may be mature but hypoplastic. Tracheal ligation in fetal sheep results in increased lung tissue mass, but type II cells are infrequent and contain few lamellar bodies (4), an example of hyperplastic, immature lungs. It has been suggested that human lungs may be either hyperplastic and immature or hypoplastic and mature (262).

Growth and maturation are terms that can be ap-

TABLE 1. *Phases of Human Intrauterine Development*

Dubreuil et al. (80)	Loosli and Potter (164)	*Nomina Embryologica* (126a)	Boyden and Tompsett (26)	Brody and Thurlbeck
Glandular, up to 6 mo	Embryonic Glandular, 5 wk–4 mo	Day 26–52 Pseudoglandular, day 52–16 wk	Embryonic Pseudoglandular, 5–17 wk	Day 26–52 Pseudoglandular, day 52–16 wk
Canalicular, 7 mo–birth	Canalicular, 4–7 mo	Canalicular, 17 wk–26 wk	Canalicular, 13–25 wk	Canalicular, 16–28 wk
Alveolar, after birth	Alveolar, 7 mo–birth	Terminal sac, 26 wk–birth	Terminal sac, 24 wk–birth	Saccular, 28–36 wk
				Alveolar, 36 wk–birth

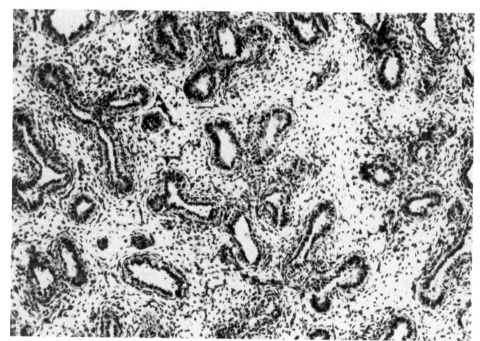

FIG. 1. Pseudoglandular phase of lung development in 16-wk-old fetus. × 159.

plied to either cells or tissues. The lung undergoes a series of complex structural changes during late fetal and early postnatal life, changes that are related to the formation of alveoli. These structural changes are accompanied by cell multiplication (increase in numbers of interstitial, epithelial, and endothelial cells) and cell maturation (differentiation of epithelial and interstitial cells), as well as by tissue growth (increase in lung wt) and tissue maturation (alveolar multiplication, thinning, and restructuring of alveolar wall).

Growth implies an increase in size that may be brought about by an increase in cell number and/or cell size. The lung also has the unique ability to increase in size without necessarily increasing in weight, by increasing its air content per gram of tissue. This occurs at birth, when the lungs contain ~3 ml air/g lung tissue, and increases until 6 yr to reach the adult value of 8 ml/g lung tissue (227).

AIRWAY AND ALVEOLAR DEVELOPMENT

Intrauterine Events

It should be remembered that the lung is a piece of gut modified for gas exchange, because this draws attention to the homology of the nerve supply and cellular constituents of the lung and gut. The lung develops from the laryngotracheal groove in the endodermal tube. In humans the ventral groove appears at 26 days of fetal age and evaginates to form the lung bud, which then branches at 26–28 days. A formal terminology for the phases of human lung development has been suggested (126a), but the described stages are not fully satisfactory. This and other terminologies are shown in Table 1. The first 8 wk after ovulation constitute the embryonal phase, during which the proximal part of the bronchial tree develops. This is followed by the pseudoglandular phase (6–16 wk), during which the bronchial buds continue to subdivide by asymmetric dichotomy. About 65%–75% of bronchial branching occurs between the 10th and 14th wk of fetal life, and by the 16th wk bronchial and bronchiolar development are complete as far as the terminal bronchioles (41). At this stage histologic sections of the lung have a distinctly glandular appearance with the "glands" (in reality tubular airways) lined by columnar, glycogen-containing cells and separated from each other by primitive mesenchyme (Fig. 1).

The pseudoglandular phase is succeeded by the canalicular phase (16–30 wk), which is characterized by a further branching and a thinning of the epithelium, a decrease in the relative amount of mesenchyme, and decreased vascularization [hence the term "canalicular" (80)]. The epithelium becomes irregularly thinned. A rich vascular supply develops and capillaries approach the respiratory epithelium. Progressive thinning leads to flattening of the epithelium and capillary protrusion results in many areas of close approximation of the capillary lumen to the airway surface (Fig. 2). This proceeds until most of the distal airways are lined by flattened epithelium, with only the very terminal spaces lined by cuboidal epithelium

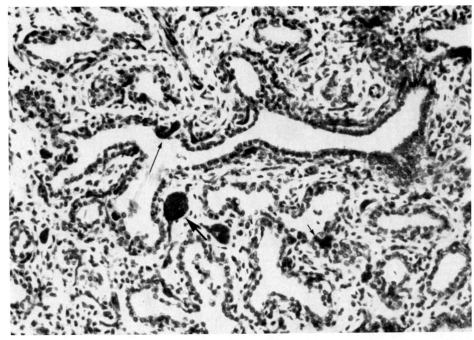

FIG. 2. Early canalicular phase (20 wk of gestation). Note developing blood vessel (*thick arrow*) and appearance of capillaries in epithelium (*thin arrows*). × 263.

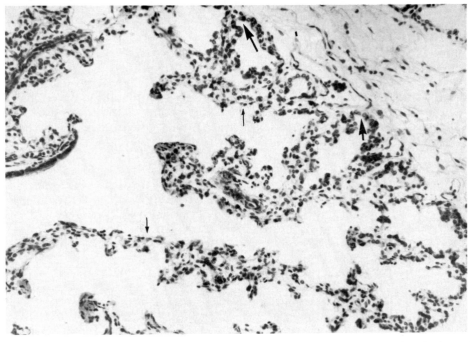

FIG. 3. Late canalicular/early saccular phase (30 wk of gestation). Most of epithelium lining future acinus is flattened (*thin arrows*) but terminal lining of acinus is still cuboidal (*thick arrows*). Some secondary crests can be seen (see Figs. 5 and 6). × 159.

(Fig. 3). A capillary net surrounds each airway (or "saccule"), and as the saccules approach each other and the interstitium thins, the saccular walls develop a double capillary layer, one layer derived from each saccule. Surprisingly the precise sequence of events at the periphery of the lung has not been established. Presumably the primitive acini (structures distal to terminal bronchioles) are formed by further subdivision of the airways during the canalicular period. The number of subdivisions is low because the unit beyond the terminal bronchiole is very simple. The saccules develop a sawtooth appearance due to the further branching that produces the short saccules. This occurs at ~24–26 wk of gestation, when low cuboidal epithelium is present and the mesenchyme is abundant (Fig. 4). Toward the end of the canalicular stage (~28 wk of gestation) the epithelium thins and both type I and type II cells are visible. Scattered osmiophilic bodies can be seen in the type II cells (48) and at this time gas exchange can be maintained.

No further development occurs in utero in rats and mice whose lungs lack alveoli at birth (8, 44, 45). However, their lungs differ in appearance at birth from human lungs at ~28 wk of gestation in that the interstitium is thicker in humans and the saccules are shorter and stubbier.

Small, low subdivisions begin to appear in the saccules at 28–32 wk gestation (Figs. 5 and 6), and these correspond closely to the secondary crests documented in rats in whom the process of alveolarization is well described. These subdivisions elongate and produce small, multifaceted air spaces that may or may not have a double capillary layer. It is not known exactly when these structures can be termed alveoli, but struc-

tures resembling alveoli are found in nearly all lungs at 32 wk of gestation and alveoli are clearly present at 36 wk (Figs. 7 and 8). The number of alveoli at birth in humans varies greatly, with a mean of ~55 million and a range of 10–149 million (156). It has been suggested that alveoli are absent at birth (118) and that the 17×10^6 units present at birth in this case were saccules rather than alveoli (74). The infant on whom these observations were made was below the third percentile in weight and therefore may have been very premature. The number of alveoli reported at birth by other authors has been very variable. Dunnill (81) found 20×10^6 alveoli in one infant, Hieronymi (114, 115) reported 70×10^6 alveoli, and Thurlbeck and Angus (242) found 71×10^6 alveoli. The cause of the wide variation in total alveolar number at birth is not known. It does not seem to be due to interobserver variation because considerable variation in the total alveolar number has been found by a single observer (156). Three papers have suggested that abnormal lung development (hypoplasia) may be more common than was generally thought (189, 231, 263). They point out that whereas pulmonary hypoplasia is a well-recognized association of a variety of congenital anomalies (e.g., renal agenesis and congenital diaphragmatic hernia), similar findings (reduced lung wt, cell number, and radial alveolar counts—an assessment of acinar complexity) may also occur without associated anomalies. Wigglesworth and Desai (262) have stressed that lung development may be critically dependent on the amount of amniotic fluid and on intrauterine respiration and that these quantities may be influenced by such factors as catecholamines, smoking, maternal hypoglycemia, alcohol, and barbi-

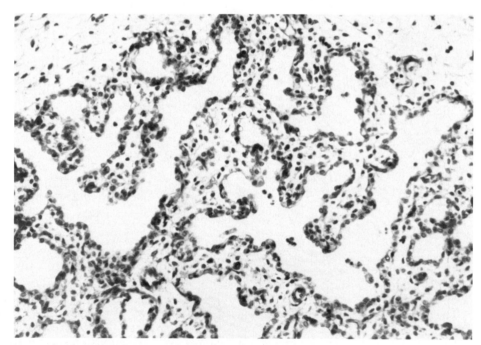

FIG. 4. Middle-to-late canalicular phase (26 wk of gestation) showing further branching to form future acinus. Epithelium is still mostly cuboidal and no secondary crests can be seen. × 263.

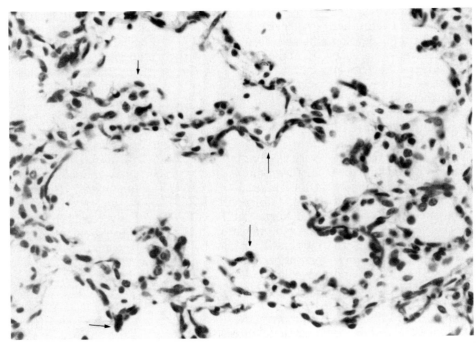

FIG. 5. Many low secondary crests (*arrows*) can be seen in late canalicular/early saccular phase (30 wk of gestation). × 384.

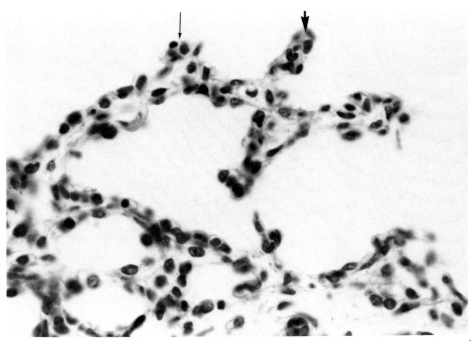

FIG. 6. Low (*thin arrow*) and high (*thick arrow*) secondary crest (30 wk of gestation). × 525.

turates. Thus it is possible that intrauterine lung development may be very sensitive to external stimuli and that the wide variation in total alveolar number at birth reflects this sensitivity.

The changes in the lung that occur during gestation can be quantitated. One of the most dramatic changes is the rapid fall in average thickness of connective tissue between adjacent air spaces (Fig. 9). The aver-

age thickness drops remarkably between 20 and 32 wk of gestation, with relatively little change from then to term. The respiratory surface area increases exponentially (Fig. 10*A*), with little change between 20 and 28 wk of gestation and a fourfold increase from then to term. This increase corresponds to the appearance of secondary crests and alveoli.

As indicated previously, the classic phases describ-

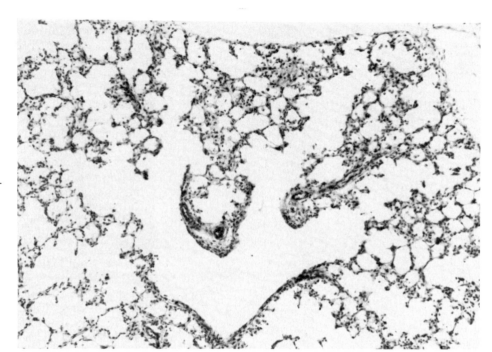

FIG. 7. Alveoli are clearly visible (36 wk of gestation). × 159.

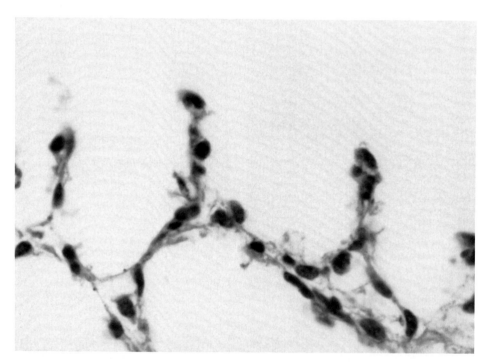

FIG. 8. Thin-walled alveoli in higher-power view of lung in Fig. 7. × 686.

ing intrauterine lung development do not adequately describe human lung growth, and therefore we suggest the terms noted on Table 1.

The term "terminal saccular phase" has been suggested for the period succeeding the canalicular phase up to term (117), but we prefer our terminology. Terminal saccular implies only the terminal structures and omits the intrauterine alveolar phase. The term "saccule" describes the gas exchanging structures in newborn rat lungs (44). As we have indicated, although there is a resemblance to animal lungs at birth at this stage, there are also distinct differences, but the similarity is sufficient to use the term saccular to describe this phase. In addition, we suggest "subsaccules" be used to describe the spaces (before they become alveoli) formed by the secondary crest.

Differentiation of Alveolar Epithelium

Comroe (60–62) has reviewed the discoveries related to recognizing the functional significance of alveolar

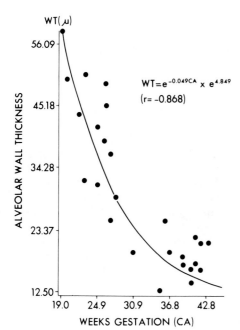

FIG. 9. Thickness of interstitium (WT) between air spaces drops dramatically between 20 and 32 wk of gestation, then changes relatively little to term. [From Langston and Thurlbeck (156).]

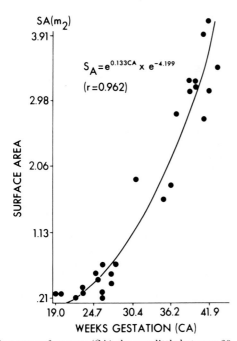

FIG. 10. Respiratory surface area (SA) changes little between 20 and 28 wk of gestation, then increases rapidly to term. [From Langston and Thurlbeck (156).]

type II cells and surfactant in the fetus. In 1959 Avery and Mead (11) found the link between properties that lower surfactant surface tension, lung maturity, and the ability of newborns to negotiate the transition between liquid breathing and air breathing at birth. Gruenwald (108) had shown that surface tension

played an important role in the resistance of newborn lungs to aeration and later linked abnormal patterns of aeration to gestational age (109). In the middle 1960s, several groups of investigators, working with fetal rabbits (125, 146) and lambs (39, 145, 188), established the relationship among fetal age, type II cell morphology, lamellar inclusions, phospholipid concentration, surface tension, and the mechanical properties of air-filled lungs.

Lung distensibility (vol/g lung wt at transpulmonary pressure of 35 cmH$_2$O) and lung stability (% vol retained at given pressure) increase late in gestation in all species; for example, Kotas and Avery (150) found that distensibility increased from 1.5 to 3.5 between days 25 and 31 (term) in the rabbit, and that the percent volume on deflation increased from 14% to 80% of total lung capacity during this period (Fig. 11). Both cell and tissue maturation account for these changes. The increase in lung stability precedes the increase in lung distensibility. The increase in the latter is likely due to tissue maturation because the volume-pressure curve of the lung filled with saline also changes at this time, whereas the change in stability is likely due to maturation of the alveolar type II cell.

The gestational age at which the respiratory epithelium differentiates into type II cells and the age at which lung surfactant synthesis begins vary consid-

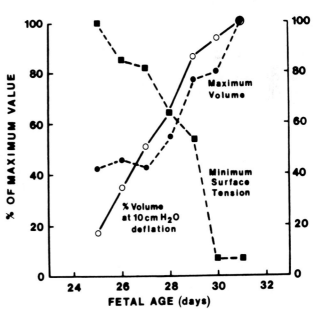

FIG. 11. Changes in parameters of lung maturation vs. fetal age in rabbit. Percent volume, a measure of lung stability, increased rapidly between 25 and 29 days, then slowed to birth (31 days). Maximum volume, an apparent measure of maturation of peripheral lung tissue, does not begin to change until day 28 and increases linearly thereafter. Minimum surface tension of lung mince, an apparent measure of type II cell maturation and surfactant production, changes slowly between days 25 and 29, then rapidly between days 29 and 30, reaching adult values on day 31. [Adapted from Kotas and Avery (151).]

erably among the species studied, but the general sequence of events is apparently identical (53). Differentiated type II cells containing lamellar bodies appear at 60%–65% of gestation (6 mo) in humans, at 80% of gestation in fetal lambs, at 85% of gestation in rabbits, and by 90%–95% of gestation (day 19 or 20) in the rat. In each instance there is a lag between the appearance of the lipoprotein that lowers surface tension in lung tissue and its secretion into the alveolus. This lag lasts several weeks in humans but only 24 h in the rat (53). At birth there is a 10- to 15-fold increase in alveolar surfactant associated with lung expansion and air breathing. Thus it would appear that surfactant is synthesized and stored until its surface tension–lowering functions are required.

The sequence of events associated with the differentiation of fetal alveolar type II cells and the formation of the lamellar body containing surfactant lipoprotein has been described in several species. Williams and Mason (266) have provided an excellent description of this process in the rat (Fig. 12). Between 17 and 19 days of gestation, undifferentiated epithelial cells begin to accumulate glycogen. The glycogen is visible, often displacing cell organelles, and there is a twofold increase in its content per cell (as measured in fetal lung homogenates). During this time, epithelial cells rest on a continuous basement membrane. Between days 19 and 21 of gestation the epithelial cells begin to differentiate and cell proliferation slows; future type II cells diminish in size, glycogen is depleted, and lamellar bodies appear in the cytoplasm. Lysosomal enzymes (acid phosphatase) and phospholipid bilayers first appear within dense granules at the

base of differentiating cells. As the lamellar body enlarges, phospholipid is added, often in association with multivesicular bodies containing both lysosomal enzymes and phospholipid that fuse with the developing granule. The number of trilaminate lamellae increases as the lamellar body enlarges and moves toward the apex of the cell.

There is an inverse relationship between glycogen and phospholipid content with lung glycogen/DNA falling 60% and lung phospholipid/DNA rising 60% between days 19 and 21 of gestation. By day 21 many type II cells have acquired adult characteristics, epithelial type I cells have begun to evolve, and the myelin figures of secreted lamellar bodies begin to appear in the alveolus.

The details of surfactant synthesis, packaging, and secretion are covered in the chapter by Goerke and Clements in this *Handbook* and in several reviews (94, 190, 219). Briefly, 80%–90% of the surfactant complex that lowers surface tension and thus establishes alveolar stability is made up of lipids, and of these, 75% are phospholipids. The primary phospholipids present are highly saturated phosphatidylcholine and a lipid unique to the lung, phosphatidylglycerol. Approximately 10% of the surfactant consists of unique apoproteins, which, together with the phospholipids, form a lipoprotein complex. The synthesis of surfactant lipids occurs primarily through a cytidine 5'-diphosphate choline pathway, although there is an alternate methylation pathway through phosphatidylethanolamine. The actual mechanism by which phosphatidylcholine and phosphatidylglycerol are remodeled to form the surfactant lipoprotein is unclear. In all of the

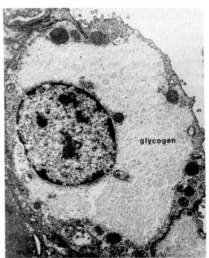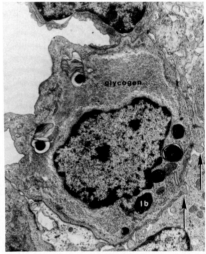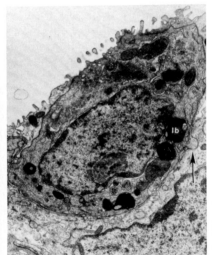

FIG. 12. Increasingly mature alveolar type II cells. Cells were taken from fetal rat lung at 22 days of gestation. *Left*: immature type II cell filled with glycogen, which displaces cell organelles. *Middle*: type II cell containing large amounts of glycogen, but with at least 6 lamellar bodies (*lb*) and several multivesicular bodies. *Arrows* point to epithelial foot processes, which extend through basement membrane and come in close approximation to interstitial cell. *Right*: mature type II cell contains no glycogen, has multiple lamellar bodies, and has many surface microvilli. *Arrow* points to basilar foot process.

species studied, surfactant synthesis increases late in gestation, and this is associated with dramatic changes in the enzymes associated with phospholipid synthesis.

The control of perinatal type II cell differentiation and of the accelerated synthesis and discharge of lung surfactant is unclear, although it has been the topic of considerable investigation. Smith (218) has found that corticosteroid administration to fetal lung fibroblasts results in secretion of a substance that stimulates surfactant synthesis by alveolar type II cells and accelerates lung maturation. This biochemical epithelial-mesenchymal interaction may be influenced by the physical proximity of cells. Grant et al. (106) have shown that the basement membrane, which is continuous beneath the undifferentiated epithelial cells of a rat fetus 18–19 days of age, becomes discontinuous, allowing the penetration of cytoplasmic foot processes from epithelial cells toward interstitial cells. These discontinuities do not appear to correlate directly with the degree of cell surfactant system maturation (as judged by the number of lamellar bodies) and therefore may relate to other potential roles of type II cells at this time, such as the control of interstitial cell function or differentiation into type I cells.

A variety of hormones influence alveolar wall and epithelial cell maturation and the release of type II cell surfactant in the fetal lung (Table 2). Glucocorticoids have been studied in detail and are in widespread clinical use in the treatment of fetuses at high risk of developing respiratory distress syndrome [RDS; (58, 94)]. While studying ways of shortening gestation in sheep, Liggins (161) noted that injections of a glucocorticoid into the fetal lamb advanced lung maturation. He suggested that surfactant production might also be enhanced. This observation was confirmed in the fetal lamb by DeLemos et al. (75) and in the fetal rabbit by Kotas and Avery (150), Wang et al. (254), and Motoyama and co-workers (179). Most investigators have concentrated on the glucocorticoid-induced acceleration of type II cell maturation, although Kikkawa et al. (144) and Kauffman (138) have also emphasized the effect of glucocorticoid on tissue maturation. Kauffman (138) found that tissue maturation occurred at lower doses of dexamethasone than

did type II cell maturation. Indeed, Beck, Mitzner, and co-workers (19, 175, 176) have shown that glucocorticoid administration to pregnant monkeys 3 days before delivery causes an increase in lung volume, not because of a change in surface tension or lung phosphatidylcholine related to type II cell maturation but because of increased lung distensibility associated with changes in connective tissue and lung morphology related to tissue maturation. The mechanism responsible for this acceleration in tissue maturation remains to be determined.

Buckingham and Avery (42), studying the fetal gut, were the first to suggest that corticosteroids may influence epithelial cell maturation. Many investigators have confirmed that glucocorticoids *1)* increase the incorporation of choline into phosphatidylcholine, *2)* increase the activity of choline pathway enzymes (although there is disagreement about which enzymes are involved), *3)* hasten the depletion of type II cell glycogen, *4)* accelerate the appearance of lamellar bodies in type II cells, and *5)* accelerate the appearance of amniotic fluid and alveolar lavage surfactant (93, 119, 219, 249). These agents probably act via cell receptors that stimulate the de novo synthesis of specific proteins. Fetal lung contains cytoplasmic and nuclear receptors for corticosteroids, which increase in number in late gestation (15). Although corticosteroids act directly on fetal lung cells in culture, it is not clear whether they act directly on type II cells. Smith and Tanswell (218, 234) have shown that these agents can induce the synthesis and secretion of the "fibroblast-pneumocyte factor" from fetal lung fibroblasts and that this factor could be responsible for stimulating surfactant synthesis in type II cells. One collaborative study has again demonstrated the efficacy of antenatal glucocorticoids in preventing RDS in high-risk pregnancies (58). This study also confirmed prior suspicions that sex hormones might moderate the effects of glucocorticoids, because only females responded to antenatal treatment with a diminished incidence of RDS. Kotas and Avery (151) provided evidence for a sex-hormone effect on lung maturation by showing that fetal lungs mature more rapidly in females than in males. Nielsen et al. (183) demonstrated that injecting testosterone into pregnant rabbits retards the appearance of fetal lung lavage surfactant, whereas antiandrogens eliminate sex-related differences in fetal surfactant production.

The corticosteroid effect does not appear to be limited to the fetus; one study in adult mice has shown an accumulation of type II cell lamellar bodies and shifts in lung volume-pressure curves after chronic steroid administration (193), and another study has shown an increased accumulation of lamellar bodies in type II cells after the repair of acute lung injury (222). In the latter study, corticosteroids were associated (as in the fetus) with decreases in cell proliferation and in the formation of type I cells. The study suggests that even though glucocorticoids accelerate

TABLE 2. *Factors That Influence Fetal Lung Maturation*

Physical	Hormonal*	Local Mediators*
Respiratory movements	Glucocorticoids	cAMP
Fetal lung liquid	Thyroid hormone	Methylxanthines
Thoracic volume	Insulin	Fibroblast pneumonocyte factor
	Sex hormones	
	Prolactin	Epidermal growth factor

* See Smith and Bogues (219) for a review of these topics.

tissue and cell maturation, they also appear to inhibit tissue and cell growth. Several studies have shown a decreased number of lung cells in fetal rabbits and guinea pigs treated with hydrocortisone (50, 138), and other studies have noted diminished tissue growth (138, 175). It appears that these adverse effects on growth are quickly compensated for in the postnatal period (152).

A wide variety of other agents influence type II cell maturation in the fetus. Some of these agents are hormones that have been associated with clinical evidence of lung immaturity and RDS (e.g., diabetes), some agents seem to act via the cAMP system (e.g., aminophylline), and others appear to be associated with additional specific lung cell receptors (e.g., thyroid hormone; see Table 2). The data supporting thyroid hormone's influence on epithelial cell maturation are similar to but less extensive than those dealing with glucocorticoids. Hitchcock (119) has reviewed these studies. Hitchcock and co-workers (120) have shown that the lung can concentrate thyroid hormone, and Lindberg et al. (162) have demonstrated the existence of pulmonary epithelial thyroid hormone receptors. Exogenous thyroid hormone or thyroid releasing hormone can accelerate several parameters of type II cell maturation (206, 270), whereas fetal thyroidectomy retards lung maturation (90). Hitchcock (119) has also suggested that glucocorticoids and thyroid hormone may interact, perhaps via cAMP. Nijjar (185) has detailed perinatal alterations in fetal and neonatal whole-lung levels of cAMP and has shown that they increase markedly as type II cells begin to mature, although the exact significance of these observations remains to be determined.

Postnatal Events

ANIMALS. Postnatal events are best described in animals (8, 44, 45, 139, 214, 215). In the rat there is little increase in either lung weight (8) or volume (214) during the first day of life, and the rate of [3H]thymidine incorporation into DNA is also low during the first few days of life (68, 139, 187). Both lung weight (8, 185) and the rate of [3H]thymidine incorporation then increase rapidly. Interestingly, in mice [3H]thymidine incorporation (71) and the frequency of mitoses (72) reach maximum values at night in early postnatal life.

Postnatal development of the rat lung is described as occurring in three phases (44, 45): lung expansion, tissue proliferation, and equilibrated growth. During the phase of lung expansion (days 1–4) the lung grows primarily by distension. Morphometric data suggest that little tissue is added during this period (45), but the rapid increase in lung weight noted above suggests that tissue must be added.

During the phase of tissue proliferation [days 7–10 (45)] there is intense DNA synthesis (signifying cell proliferation), a doubling of lung weight, and a two-

to threefold increase in the number of lung cells. Endothelial cell labeling with [3H]thymidine is also intense throughout this period, whereas interstitial cell labeling occurs actively early in the period but then diminishes later (139). The transition of type II cells into type I cells is brisk while the alveolar surface area increases. Alveolar wall thickness initially increases and then falls, primarily due to changes in the interstitium (45).

The rate of growth, expressed as a change in lung weight, is not greatest during this phase. In fact the rate of increase in lung weight, expressed as a percentage of lung weight, steadily decreases after the first few days of life. The onset of the phase of tissue proliferation, however, is indicated by an inflection in the plot of lung volume versus either body size or age (78). Lung volume increases faster than body weight, so that the specific lung volume (vol/unit body wt) increases. Because of the increase in complexity of the lung surface, the alveolar surface area increases rapidly. It increases to the 1.6 power of lung volume (45). If the lung grew by expansion only, the surface area would increase to the two-thirds power of the change in lung volume.

The phase of tissue proliferation is characterized by the transformation of primary saccules (smallest peripheral units in rats and mice) into alveoli. The primary saccules are simple tubular structures whose length greatly exceeds their diameter. They are lined by type I and type II alveolar epithelium and characteristically have a double capillary layer in their walls (45, 214, 256). If the wall of one primary saccule does not abut the wall of another, such as when they are adjacent to lobular septa and vessels, there is only a single capillary layer. The two capillary layers disappear during the postnatal period, but it is not clear how the single capillary that is characteristic of the adult alveolus forms. However, endothelial cell proliferation and the formation of new capillaries (37) accompany tissue proliferation, suggesting that factors regulating angiogenesis may be involved in this crucial phase of lung development. Brody and co-workers (37) have noted changes in alveolar (epithelial) basement membrane proteoglycans and in capillary (endothelial) basement membrane continuity that suggest that these collagenous structures play a key role in the organization of the developing alveolar wall.

The subdivision of primary saccules is caused by the secondary crests (44). The crests characteristically have an elastic fiber, with attached collagen and basal lamina, at their free margins (Fig. 13). Initially the crests are low but they rapidly increase in height, subdividing the primary saccules. The process of subdivision is best shown by scanning electron microscopy (Figs. 14–17). The crests have a single capillary layer and many interstitial cells. The cells in the crest have a labeling rate 1.4 times greater than that of cells in other parts of the saccule (139). Many type II cells are seen in the septa, and oblique septal sections often

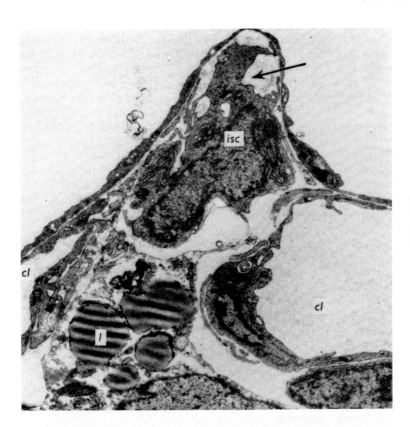

FIG. 13. Electron micrograph of secondary crest. Elastic fiber and collagen are near free margin of crest (*arrow*) and lie in bay of interstitial cell (*isc*). Note lipid droplet (*l*) in lipid-containing interstitial cell. *cl*, Capillary lumen. Scale = 1 μm. [From Amy, Thurlbeck, et al. (8).]

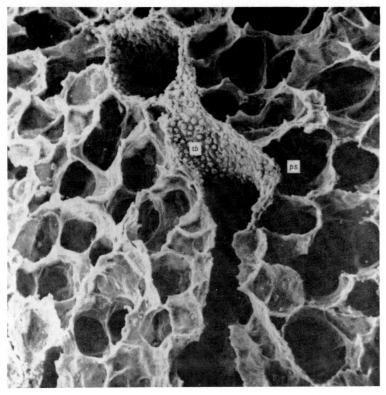

FIG. 14. Terminal bronchiole (*tb*) in 1-day-old mouse; bronchiole leads into a developing acinus. Large, smooth-walled structures surrounding bronchiole are primary saccules (*ps*). × 300. [From Amy, Thurlbeck, et al. (8).]

give the impression that type II cells are situated in the middle of a septum. It has been suggested that there may be both high crests and low crests (182). The high septa were thought to be responsible for making larger subdivisions, resulting in additional large units (e.g., alveolar sacs), whereas the low septa produce alveoli. Elastic tissue apparently plays a central role in alveolar development. An elastic fiber

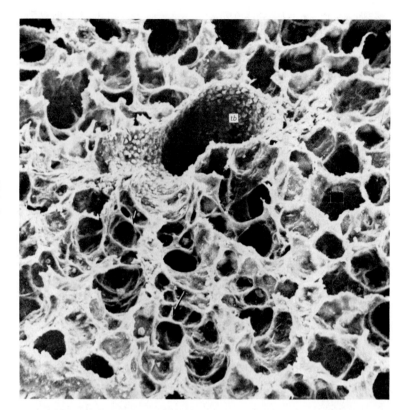

FIG. 15. Primary saccules leading from terminal bronchioles (*tb*) of 3-day-old mouse are being subdivided by low secondary crests (*arrows*). × 300. [From Amy, Thurlbeck, et al. (8).]

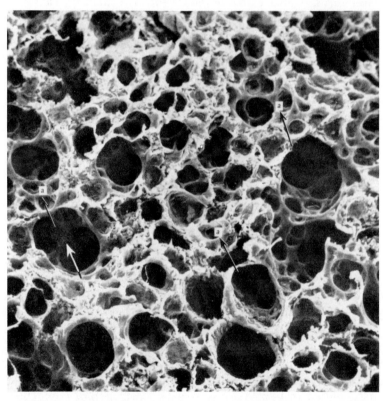

FIG. 16. Most of the primary saccules of 6-day-old mouse have shallow alveoli in their walls (*a; dark arrows*). Some primary saccules (*light arrow*) appear less divided than others. × 300. [From Amy, Thurlbeck, et al. (8).]

demarcates the margin of each crest and the mouth of each alveoli. In newborn infants these elastic fibers resemble a fishnet (86, 87, 89). Emery and Fagan (87) have suggested that this fishnet causes the formation of alveoli. They thought that elastic tissue was formed in such a way "that parts of alveolar walls are increasingly held away from the air sacs and as the lung expands, the alveoli become subdivided. There is thus,

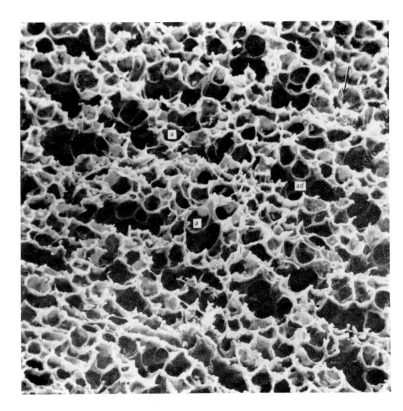

FIG. 17. Alveoli (*a*) are well developed in 14-day-old mouse and alveolar ducts (*ad*) are visible. *Arrow* points to a rare pore of Kohn. × 300. [From Amy, Thurlbeck, et al. (8).]

after birth, a progressive development of a 'fishnet' type of elastic structure, the apertures of which form the mouths of alveoli." To simplify, it is as if the elastic network represented a semirigid fishnet through which a very compliant balloon was blown to form alveoli. Thus the key to understanding alveolar multiplication lies in a detailed knowledge of the connective tissue of the lungs.

Alveoli are probably also produced by the alveolarization of distal bronchioles. If this happens the number of generations of nonalveolated airways should diminish in the postnatal period as the number of alveolated generations within the acinus increases. These data are controversial, with some studies suggesting that there were more generations between the main bronchus and alveoli and more nonalveolated generations in adults versus newborns in both cows and mice (28, 267). Boyden and Tompsett (26), however, showed that there were fewer generations of nonalveolated airways in adult versus newborn dogs. It has been pointed out that the large amount of individual variation in the number of generations in the same pathway of the cat accounts for the variations previously described between young and old animals (212). In the human, however, the great increase in the number of generations within the acinus and the appearance of respiratory bronchioles in the postnatal period suggest that alveolarization of the bronchioles must occur (45, 78).

Equilibrated growth (~2 wk after birth) is the third phase of alveolar growth described in the rat (45). The rate of cell proliferation falls during this period (139)

and the thickness of the alveolar walls decreases dramatically, due primarily to a decrease in the cellular components of the interstitial compartment (45). Alveolar type I cells increase in size 3–4 times between 1 and 6 wk of age (195); lung weight continues increasing but at a slower rate (45). This period is also characterized by a slowing of the rate of increase in lung volume to 0.7 power of body weight, as compared with the 0.99 power in the previous phase, and an increase in surface area to the 0.71 power of lung volume, which is very close to the 0.67 power that would result from simple distension of the lung. However, Holmes and Thurlbeck (123) found that alveolar multiplication in the rat occurred between 4 and 10 wk of age and that the surface area increased directly with lung volume between 4 and 14 wk of age.

A fourth phase exists in some if not most species, beginning after alveolar multiplication ends. This would be the phase of simple expansion. It is not clear when this phase occurs in most species. Our studies suggest that it starts at ~10–14 wk of age in rats (43, 123). Indirect evidence has suggested that alveolar multiplication in rats may continue to 133 days of age (256). It has been suggested that alveolar multiplication in the rabbit ends at 3 mo of age (215).

HUMANS. Even though there are ~50 million alveoli in the human lung at birth on average (see previous section), the major postnatal event is alveolar multiplication. This process rapidly increases the postnatal alveolar surface area. It is believed that alveolar multiplication is very rapid in the first few years of life

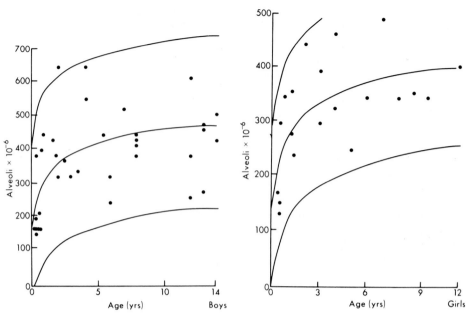

FIG. 18. Total number of alveoli in boys and girls. Note wide range of values (mean ± 2 SD). [From Thurlbeck (241).]

and then decreases exponentially so that it is slow at 4 yr of age and has ceased at 8 yr of age. Dunnill (81) came to these conclusions in his classic study of lung growth. He found that one 4-yr-old child had 257×10^6 alveoli and that one 8-yr-old child had 280×10^6 alveoli. At that time it was thought that all adults had almost precisely 300×10^6 alveoli; therefore because the latter value fell within the adult range, he concluded that alveolar multiplication had stopped by 8 yr of age. However, Angus and Thurlbeck (10) found that normal adult values are in the range of $225-600 \times 10^6$ alveoli, suggesting that these deductions were not necessarily correct. For example, the 4-yr-old child might have had the same number of alveoli when it was an adult, falling as it does within the normal range; thus one could argue that alveolar multiplication had ceased in that child. Alternatively the 8-yr-old child might have had 560×10^6 alveoli as an adult, so one could argue that half of its total number of alveoli were added after 8 yr of age. Radial counts,[1] a function of the number of alveoli in the acinus (88), suggest that alveolar multiplication continues until somatic growth ceases, but the wide standard errors in this study make it hard to come to definite conclusions. Cooney and Thurlbeck (64) studied radial counts and found a small but significant increase between 2 and 8 yr of age. However, a collection of cases larger than Dunnill's (81) showed such a wide variation in alveolar number in children that no conclusion could be drawn about when alveolar multipli-

[1] Measured by counting the number of alveoli on a histologic slide that intersect a line dropped perpendicular from a respiratory bronchiole to the edge of the acinus; see ref. 64 for an examination of the validity and meaning of this method.

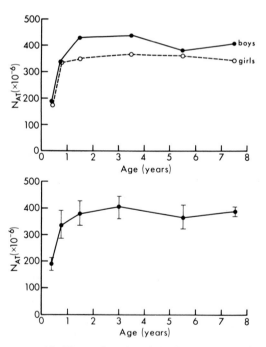

FIG. 19. Mean value of total number of alveoli (N_{AT}) in children of various ages. *Top*: mean value for boys and girls. *Bottom*: mean and SE for both sexes together. Each age group contained similar proportion of each sex. The lower panel shows that no significant differences exist in children between ages 1–2 and 7–8 yr. [From Thurlbeck (241).]

cation stopped (242). This study suffered because a substantial number of the children died after illnesses of some duration and because no distinction was made between the sexes. Studies of the lungs of children who died suddenly (241) showed just as much variation in alveolar number (Fig. 18). These data are equally hard to interpret, but the great bulk of alveoli are apparently formed before 2 yr of age with few if any added subsequently (Fig. 19).

Alveolar surface area increases rapidly in the first 5 yr of life (Fig. 20). Individual lung units (alveolar dimensions and number of alveoli/unit area and vol) are the same in both sexes, but boys had bigger lungs than girls at the same stature (Fig. 21). Thus for a given age and stature the total number of alveoli and the alveolar surface area (Figs. 19 and 20) were greater in boys than girls (241). There have been few studies of lung growth at puberty and therefore the events associated with it are not known. It is apparent, however, that the dimensions must increase during puberty. Regression equations for alveolar surface area derived from children are best fitted by logarithmic equation (241), which predicts a smaller alveolar surface area than is found in adults (237).

GROWTH AND DEVELOPMENT OF CONNECTIVE TISSUE

Intrauterine Period

The major connective tissue components of the fetal lung appear to play separate and distinct roles in the early structuring of the lung. Collagen is involved in the branching morphogenesis of the bronchial tree early in fetal life, whereas elastin is involved in the organization of the distal lung parenchyma late in fetal life.

Collagen appears in a linear, highly organized fashion adjacent to airways that have completed branching but appears in a disordered, random distribution at the sites of new airway buds (259). It has been shown that collagen synthesis, but not necessarily cross-linking, is a necessary prerequisite for airway branching (224). It is not known which type of collagen (i.e., interstitial or basement membrane collagen) is in-

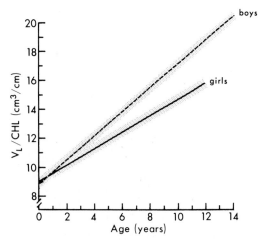

FIG. 21. Lung volumes are larger in boys than girls, a difference that becomes significant at 2–3 yr of age. *Stippled* areas represent mean ± 2 SE. VL, lung volume at full inflation; CHL, crown-heel length. [From Thurlbeck (241).]

volved in this process. Analogies to the development of other branching structures (e.g., salivary or mammary glands) suggest that basement membrane collagen and other extracellular matrix proteins (e.g., glycosaminoglycans) may play an important role in regulating the development of the bronchial tree (21).

Collagen continues to be the dominant connective tissue element in air passages, blood vessels, pleura, and septa during fetal life (85). Several investigators have explored the development of airway connective tissue after the period of airway branching. Bucher and Reid (41) found that the extension of cartilage through the bronchial tree was complete by the 25th wk of gestation in the human, although recent studies suggest that cartilage-bearing bronchi and cartilage fragments increase in number throughout fetal life (217). Bhutani and co-workers (22) demonstrated the physiological effect of these airway tissue changes: they found a threefold fall in specific compliance of the fetal rabbit trachea during the last trimester (21–31 days of gestation). Croteau and Cook (69) found a similar relationship between increasing compliance and increasing immaturity in human fetuses. The change in airway compliance late in gestation may be related to the appearance of elastin, not collagen, in these airways.

Bradley and co-workers (27) reported a dramatic increase in both collagen synthesis and collagen concentration late in fetal life in the rabbit; the location of this new collagen is uncertain because there is little recognizable interstitial collagen present in the distal lung parenchyma of humans or the rat during this period (251). Grant and co-workers (106) have shown that basement membrane collagen in the rat is complete beneath the large airway epithelium but is fragmented and incomplete beneath the developing peripheral airways as late as the 18th day of gestation. Although epithelial basement membranes are well de-

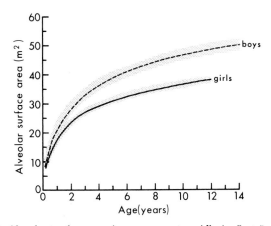

FIG. 20. Alveolar surface area increases most rapidly in first 5 yr of life. *Stippled* areas represent mean ± 2 SE. [From Thurlbeck (241).]

veloped in distal lung parenchyma during the later days of fetal life, endothelial basement membranes are incomplete and discontinuous.

Elastin does not appear in the airways until the 20th–25th wk of gestation in humans, well after large airway branching is complete (153). Although elastin is seen in the pleura and around the airways and blood vessels, its predominant site during late fetal life is in the mouths of developing alveoli. Between the 26th and 32nd wk of gestation in the human there is an increase in elastin in the peripheral parenchyma with deposition predominating at the sites of future alveolar crests or ducts (164). Scattered elastin fibrils are seen in the alveolar walls, but late in fetal life elastin accumulates mainly as isolated segmental deposits. This pattern of elastin deposition in the peripheral lung remains constant during the last few weeks of gestation (164). Collet and Des Biens (59) have detailed the ultrastructural appearance of elastin in the fetal rat lung. They described elastin in association with smooth muscle cells surrounding large airways on the 15th day of gestation, after large airways have formed. On the 19th day elastin appears in association with fibroblasts in the region of respiratory bronchioles. On the 20th and 21st days fibroblasts continue to differentiate into cells actively synthesizing connective tissue in the alveolar zone of the lung. Elastin fibers appear in the cytoplasmic bays of these fibroblasts, first as small bundles of microfilaments and then as a mature, amorphous fiber. This description of microfibrillar protein followed by elastin fibers is supported by biochemical studies of human fetuses by Keeley et al. (140). They found that alkali-insoluble residues of fetal lungs were contaminated by large amounts of polar amino acids that were thought to represent the microfibrillar protein associated with early elastogenesis. This protein, present as early as the 20th–25th week of gestation, accounted for up to 20% of the dry weight of the lung in the fetus, whereas true elastin accounted for only 6% of the dry weight.

Thus collagen appears early in fetal development in association with airway morphogenesis and later as a basement membrane component during alveolar development. Elastin appears relatively late in fetal life, primarily in an immature microfibrillar form, with mature elastin deposited at the margins of secondary crests and around the mouths of alveoli. Neither connective tissue component appears in abundance in the walls of distal lung parenchyma, and this suggests that the fetal lung has little elastic recoil and is easily ruptured.

Postnatal Period

There are few mature collagen fibers in the alveolar walls during early postnatal life. In the rat, cross-linked collagen occurs in scattered areas during the period of alveolar formation, but the bulk of collagen fibers appear after 20 days of age, after most of the

alveoli have formed (251). Probably both epithelial and endothelial basement membrane collagen increase in proportion to the increase in surface area, which is most rapid between 4 and 13 days of age in the rat (45). The study of Bradley and co-workers (27) in rabbits shows that the accumulation of lung collagen that begins in late fetal life continues in early postnatal life and then slows, although the amount of collagen continues to increase (expressed as percent of lung wt) throughout the first 3 yr of the rabbit's life. It is unclear how much of the increased collagen measured in biochemical studies is interstitial and how much is airway, vessel, or basement membrane collagen. The activity of lung lysyl oxidase (main extracellular cross-linking enzyme for both collagen and elastin) is high in rabbit lung tissue in early postnatal life and falls by 50% after 3 wk of age (35). Figure 22 shows that lung collagen concentration in the rat increases in a more linear fashion over the first 6 wk of postnatal life (181). Little information exists relating to postnatal changes in airway collagen. Brody et al. (35) found that the activity of large airway lysyl oxidase decreases more slowly than that of the lung enzyme, remaining high for the first 10 wk of life in the rabbit. These observations suggest that the active synthesis of airway connective tissue components occurs over a longer period than in the lung parenchyma.

Postnatal changes in lung elastin have been more

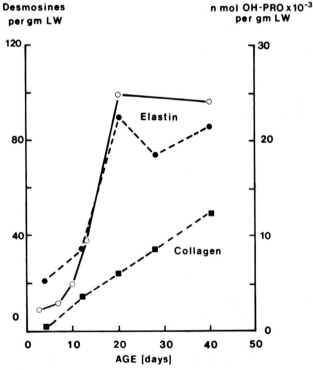

FIG. 22. Age-related changes in lung connective tissue of rat pups, per g lung wt (LW). Data for elastin (desmosines): ●, adapted from Nardell and Brody (181); ○, adapted from Powell and Whitney (198). ■, Data for collagen [nmol OH-PRO (hydroxyproline) × 10⁻³] from Nardell and Brody (181).

completely described than changes in collagen because of the strong suspicion that elastin is causally related to the formation of alveoli. The late prenatal pattern of elastin deposition at the margins of developing alveoli continues through early postnatal life (8, 164, 251). The scattered fine elastin fibers in alveolar walls at birth become thicker and more evenly spaced. The tips of the alveoli initially contain a mixture of microfibrillar and amorphous elastin, often enclosed in the bays of synthetically active fibroblasts. In time the amorphous elastin component assumes predominance as the microfibrillar material is incorporated into the elastic fiber. The only biochemical study of elastin during postnatal growth in humans has shown a rapid postnatal increase in lung elastin content that reaches an adult level of 12% of dry weight of the lung by 6 mo of age (140). During this time there is a concomitant fall in the percentage of microfibrillar protein in the lung. In the rat there is a dramatic increase in lung elastin between 12 and 20 days of age (Fig. 22), after the period of rapid alveolar proliferation (181, 198). After 20 days of age the concentration of lung elastin reaches adult levels (expressed per g of lung wt) and remains constant thereafter.

It would appear from ultrastructural studies that both collagen and elastin are produced primarily by fibroblasts within the pulmonary interstitium. Vaccaro and Brody (251) have described two types of interstitial fibroblasts. One appears within the alveolar buds and is associated with the deposition of microfibrillar and amorphous components of elastin in association with the formation of new alveoli. A second type of fibroblast lies in alveolar walls and is characterized by an accumulation of lipid droplets (168). This cell appears to be less associated with connective tissue deposition but contains actinlike filaments, which often traverse the alveolar wall, indenting the epithelial basement membranes that seemingly serve as anchor points for the growing lung. Such anchor points have been implicated in the budding process of analogous organs, such as the salivary gland (21). The lipid-filled interstitial cell appears in greatest number and contains the most lipid during the period of rapid alveolar formation. The lipid in this cell then vanishes from the rat lung as alveolar formation ceases. The origin and role of these cells and their lipid is uncertain. The cell has been found to contain lipoprotein lipase and likely is the source of the endothelial chylomicron degrading enzyme (167). The lipid within this cell may also influence connective tissue deposition, because fatty acids have been shown to modulate the effect of lysyl oxidase on connective tissue substrates (132).

The factors that regulate the synthesis and deposition of connective tissue proteins and alveolar formation, as well as the relationship existing between these processes, are unclear. Many investigators have commented on the possible link between elastin and alveolar formation (8, 44, 89, 164, 251). Loosli and

Potter (164) and later Emery and Wilcock (89) put forth the fishnet theory, which suggested that the elastic fibers at the mouths of alveoli form a constricting network through which new alveoli grow. Studies by Kida and Thurlbeck (141, 142) support the elastin concept of alveolar formation. These authors treated growing rats with the cross-link enzyme inhibitor β-aminoproprionitrile (BAPN). They found that BAPN interfered with elastic tissue formation and produced hypercompliant lungs with fewer than normal alveoli. Collagen seemed to be less affected by BAPN than elastin.

Blotchy mice and copper-deficient mice, neither of which can form cross-linked connective tissue, have lungs with few or large alveoli similar to those in the BAPN experiment (98, 187). Although these experiments support morphologic studies suggesting a causal link between elastin and alveolar formation, it is unlikely that impaired cross-linking interfered with the fine structure of other connective tissue elements in the lung, particularly the basement membrane collagen. These studies have shown that basement membranes may be involved in the capillary proliferation that accompanies the period of alveolar formation, suggesting that the control of angiogenesis may play an important role in the alveolarization of the lung (37).

MECHANICAL PROPERTIES OF GROWING LUNG

Intrauterine and Perinatal Period

The changes that occur in mechanical properties of the fetal lung are detailed in *Differentiation of Alveolar Epithelium*, p. 360. One of these changes, relating to increased distensibility (i.e., increased vol/g of tissue), is associated with maturation of the alveolar wall tissue and continues into the postnatal period. The other, relating to increased stability of the air-filled lung, is associated with the maturation of the alveolar type II cell and is a uniquely perinatal event.

The mechanical events associated with birth and the first breath are not completely understood. Clearly the efficient release of surfactant from mature type II cells is a prerequisite for the successful transition to breathing air instead of liquid. The details of perinatal surfactant release have been the subject of several studies. In all of the species studied, lung surfactant lipid accumulates in tissue prior to its appearance in the alveolus (or amniotic fluid). This time lag in surfactant appearance ranges from several weeks (in humans) to several hours (in small rodents) (53). Most studies of surfactant release have relied on the appearance of phospholipid in the amniotic fluid; indeed this appearance of surfactant in amniotic fluid provides physicians with a means of determining the state of fetal lung maturity in infants at high risk for developing RDS (94). Torday and Nielsen (246) have shown that alveolar surfactant obtained by lung lavage can be detected 1–2 days before surfactant appears in the amniotic fluid, suggesting that the release of type II cell surfactant may precede birth by several days. Faridy and co-workers (92) have examined the process of perinatal surfactant secretion in the rat using electron microscopy to measure type II cell lamellar bodies as an index of intracellular surfactant and using biochemical analysis of whole-lung disaturated phosphatidylcholine as an index of the total surfactant content. They found that the linear relationship between intracellular and total phospholipid content was dramatically altered 1–2 h before birth, in a fashion compatible with a massive movement of intracellular surfactant into the alveolus. This release of surfactant could be prevented by inhibiting parturition with progesterone, suggesting that a prelabor change in circulating hormone levels might induce surfactant release. Type II cell lamellar material appears to increase both during and immediately after birth, followed by a wave of lamellar body extrusion between 5 min and 2 h after birth. Faridy et al. (92) also found that lung lavage may itself induce surfactant release, suggesting that type II cell release might not occur as early as the studies of rabbit alveolar lavage material implied.

Several investigators have documented increases in whole-lung cAMP/cGMP ratios (185, 247), whole-lung β-adrenergic membrane receptors, adenyl cyclase, and adenyl cyclase's responsiveness to isoproterenol late in fetal life (260). Although it is assumed that the differentiating type II cell is responsible for these changes, other cells may be involved. The complex nature of hormonal interactions in the fetal lung is illustrated by studies that have shown that glucocorticoids increase the number of whole-lung receptors (52) and stimulate the formation of fetal lung fibroblast receptors (100). The physiological significance of these biochemical observations relates in part to the influence that β-adrenergic agents have on the in vitro release of surfactant by type II cells in cultures of type II cells, and in vivo as measured by the amniotic fluid lecithin/sphingomyelin ratio and increasing fetal lung stability (38, 79, 221). Whether the major stimulus for surfactant release is biochemical (associated with sudden rise in epinephrine) or mechanical (associated with lung expansion) is unclear. The two-phase release of type II cell lamellar bodies found by Faridy and co-workers (92) may support both mechanisms. The prenatal release phase might be related to biochemical events, whereas the postnatal phase might be related to lung expansion. The increased incidence of RDS in babies born by cesarean section suggests that the stimuli associated with vaginal delivery may also play a role in the surfactant release process (94).

It has long been recognized that fluid exists in the alveolar spaces of the fetal lung, although the mechanisms of its formation and postnatal absorption and its potential morphologic and mechanical significance

have been defined only recently. In 1913 Addison and How (2) pointed out that this fluid was "drawn into the lungs" with the first few postnatal breaths. Several investigators have shown that ligation of the fetal trachea leads to an accumulation of fetal lung fluid, suggesting continued secretion of this fluid, and that tracheal pressures as high as 12–19 cmH$_2$O can be generated in the ligated lung (4, 49, 130, 157).

The mechanism of prenatal secretion and postnatal absorption of alveolar fluid has been investigated in a series of studies by Strang and co-workers (see ref. 228 for a review). Virtually all of these studies have been performed in the lamb. The lamb lung contains 30 ml/kg alveolar fluid, a value similar to the functional residual capacity (FRC) of the newborn lamb. This fluid forms at the rate of 2–4 ml·h^{-1}·kg^{-1} (or 250 ml/day) during the latter part of fetal life, leaving the lungs via the trachea, and is then either swallowed or appears in the amniotic fluid. This lung liquid is not an ultrafiltrate of plasma and differs from amniotic fluid. Its constitution is best explained by the presence of epithelial pumps that actively transport chloride in one direction and potassium in the other. Thus chloride is transported from the plasma to the alveolar fluid in excess of a reverse bicarbonate flux, sodium follows the electrochemical gradient set up by chloride, and water movement into the alveoli is attributed to the osmotic force of sodium chloride. Studies of tracer movement into the lung liquid have established that the epithelium acts as a rather tight barrier for nonelectrolytes, with a functional pore radius of 0.5–0.6 nm. There appear to be separate functional channels for nonpolar (lipid soluble) and polar substances. The exact site of the epithelial pump(s) and the mechanism of macromolecular transport are unknown.

The lung liquid is absorbed rapidly after birth, the process being complete in <6 h (125). Interstitial spaces appear distended after birth, and lung lymph flow increases 3- or 4-fold within the first 30 min (228). Egan et al. (84) have calculated that the effective epithelial pore radius increases to 3.4–5.6 nm (6- or 7-fold) after birth and postulate that this increase is caused by the increased lung volume, which effectively stretches epithelial pores. In the adult the effective alveolar pore radius increases from 0.9 nm at FRC to 4.0 nm at total lung capacity (83). Ion transport also changes after birth because the lung stops filling with fluid after postnatal airway obstruction. Walters and Olver (253) have shown that isoproterenol decreases ion transport and fluid formation as the lamb approaches term and actually reverses the fluid movement producing resorption at term. They postulate that fluid resorption results from the increased number of membrane β-receptors (noted above) and the discharge of epinephrine that occurs at birth. Indeed in vaginal delivery this process begins before air breathing. Morphologists have been unable to find structural changes in epithelial barriers associated with the functional changes in epithelial pore size. Williams (265) and Schneeberger et al. (211) have found that epithelial tight junctions appear early in the last trimester and that they do not change in the postnatal period during alveolar fluid resorption. Thus the anatomical pathway by which postnatal fluid resorption occurs is not known.

Karlberg et al. (133–136) have reported the events associated with the first postnatal breath in humans. They found that during vaginal delivery, the compliant rib cage was compressed by forces as high as 50 cmH₂O, thereby displacing liquid from the lungs (134). After delivery the chest returned to its resting volume, drawing 7–42 ml of air into the lungs (135). These events, although useful in preparing for subsequent breaths, are not essential because normal aeration occurs even after cesarean delivery. Karlberg found that in the majority of infants studied, the initial inspiratory effort associated with the first breath resulted in a negative intrathoracic pressure of 10–70 cmH₂O, with initial inspiratory volumes of 12–67 ml. The major sources of resistance to inflation appear to be surface forces caused by the air-liquid interface and the frictional forces resulting from the movement of the column of liquid in the airway (3). Some of the infants in Karlberg's study, and others in a later study by Milner and Saunders (174), required much lower initial inspiratory pressures to aerate their lungs, either because partial aeration occurred during vaginal delivery or because pharyngeal "frog breathing" (25) or pulmonary capillary erection (128) may have begun aeration prior to the first measured breath. These phenomena may also explain the fact that Mortola et al. (178) found the first breath in infants delivered by cesarean section to be similar in volume to that reported in vaginally delivered infants: mean first breath tidal volume was 39.6 ml and 42.0 ml in cesarean and vaginal deliveries, respectively. Karlberg found that the initial expiration was prolonged and incomplete, perhaps because the upper airway was partially obstructed, resulting in a continuous positive thoracic pressure, which presumably aided the even opening of the distal lung units. Subsequent breaths followed a pattern similar to the first breath, although inspiratory pressure swings and inspiratory work were less. Mortola et al. (178) found that the FRC rose by an average of 2.8 ml/breath or 41.9 ml over the first 60 min, a rate similar to the 10 ml/kg found by Karlberg in vaginally delivered infants. A steady-state value of 30 ml/kg is reached by 2 days of life (196). The initial low compliance gradually increases over the first several days while resistance gradually falls (136).

Postnatal Period

The mechanics of the growing lung and chest wall are covered in detail in the chapter by Bryan and Wohl in this *Handbook*. Most of their discussion relates to human studies. There is a gap between birth and 6–8 yr of age in human studies, therefore the changes in lung mechanics that accompany alveolar formation and the organization of connective tissue elements within the lung are not known.

Setnikar (213) and Mead (173) have discussed the physiological consequences of elastin and collagen deposition in the lung. They proposed that the volume-pressure curve of the lung could be separated into two parts: one at middle and low volumes, where elastin determines recoil, and one at high lung volumes, where collagen provides recoil and limits lung distensibility. This concept has been supported by the selective enzyme degradation of connective tissue components of whole lungs and alveolar strips in vitro (137, 171). In each instance, elastase degradation diminishes recoil or its correlate, resting length, whereas collagenase degradation influences the lung volume-pressure curve at high lung volumes or its correlate, the stop function at the alveolar wall. Preventing the maturation of connective tissue elements produces similar conclusions. Stanley et al. (226) exposed weanling rats to semicarbazide, an agent that interferes with collagen synthesis, and noted an increased susceptibility to lung rupture. Nardell and Brody (181) studied the volume-pressure characteristics of the rat lung filled with saline, exploring the changes that occur in connective tissue elements during early postnatal growth. As might be expected, increased elastin content correlates with increased lung recoil, whereas increased collagen content correlates with increased structural integrity, as judged by its resistance to rupture (Fig. 23). Thus elastic recoil at a given lung volume increases most dramatically between 12 and 20 days of age, the time when lung elastin concentration increases, whereas the pressure needed to rupture the lung on inflation increases in a linear fashion throughout postnatal lung growth (as does collagen concentration). The hysteresis ratio of the saline-filled lung, a measure of lung viscoelastic properties, is 4–5 times higher at 4 days of age than at 12 days. Thus the newborn rat lung with thick cellular alveolar saccules is mechanically inefficient, has little elastic recoil, and ruptures easily. Lung volume appears to be a complex function that may in part be limited at older ages by the collagen-related stop function.

Lung elastin concentration increases rapidly during postnatal life, reaching adult values early, and is then distributed in a fashion suggesting a close relationship to the formation of new alveoli (Table 3). The increase in elastin content results in increased lung recoil in middle and low lung volume ranges. Collagen content increases more slowly over a longer period. The distribution of interstitial collagen does not appear to be directly related to the formation of alveoli. Collagen concentration correlates most closely with the postnatal increase in distending pressure the growing lung can sustain.

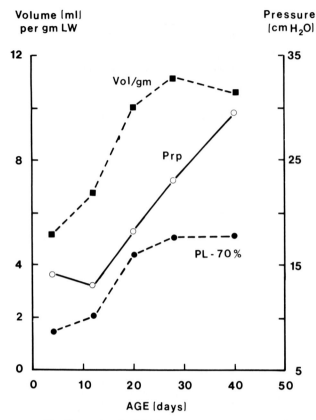

FIG. 23. Change in physiological measures of saline-filled lungs in rat pups from 4 to 40 days of age. Vol/gm, volume at 10 cmH₂O inflation/g lung tissue; Prp, pressure at which saline-filled lung ruptures; PL, deflation recoil pressure at 70% of vol at 10 cmH₂O. Both Vol/gm and PL rise over first 20 days of life, then plateau. Prp is stable over first 12 days of life, then rises in a linear fashion thereafter. [Adapted from Nardell and Brody (181).]

CONTROL OF LUNG GROWTH

Intrauterine Period

EARLY. The constancy of the branching pattern of the bronchial tree suggests that there must be an effective mechanism controlling it. Mesenchymal-epithelial interactions are important in determining branching patterns. The branching of the airways in culture requires mesoderm, which also determines the way in which the branching occurs. For example, chick mesoderm applied to mouse endoderm produces the branching pattern of the chick, not of the mouse (233). The origin of the mesenchyme also influences the way the endoderm develops. Gut mesoderm can cause bronchial budding, but bronchial mesoderm is needed for bronchial branching. Bronchial and gut mesoderm induce budding in tracheal epithelium, but tracheal mesoderm inhibits both bronchial budding and branching (224, 259). An epithelial growth factor has been found in mesenchyme that affects epithelial growth (7). It is not known whether this relationship depends on the cell-to-cell contacts between epithelium and mesenchyme that have been described (24)

or on a secreted factor, such as the fibroblast-pneumonocyte factor that is described elsewhere (see *Differentiation of Alveolar Epithelium*, p. 360). Collagen can also affect the development of airways, because the administration of a proline analogue that depresses collagen synthesis results in a diminished number of bronchial buds (6).

LATE. Many factors have been established, both clinically and experimentally, as being important in controlling lung growth and development in the latter part of gestation. These include the amount of amniotic and lung fluid, the distortion of the lungs by external pressure, and intrauterine respiration. Some suggestions can be made about a common pathway but the evidence is incomplete.

The simplest notion is that lung development can be disturbed by compression (or lack of stretch) of the lung. Both clinically (147, 203) and experimentally (76), hypoplasia occurs in association with diaphragmatic hernia, and the ipsilateral lung is more affected than the contralateral lung. The exact nature of the hypoplasia is still in dispute. Some authors believe that the number of alveoli in each acinus is normal (147) and thus the number of units is too small. These authors documented a striking loss of bronchial and bronchiolar divisions, as well as arterial divisions. Support for this idea comes from the observation that the lung does not recover architecturally after the successful repair of a diaphragmatic hernia (118, 244). Reale and Esterly (203) found a diminished radial count compared with their own control data; however, the reduction in the radial count was insufficient to account for the large reduction in lung volume, indicating that there must have been a loss of major units. Cooney and Thurlbeck (64) have confirmed the observations of Reale and Esterly (203) by finding a reduction in the radial count and alveolar number in congenital diaphragmatic hernia that did not account for the diminished size of the lungs. Compression of the lung is also the likely cause of hypoplasia in a reported case of thoracic dystrophy in which it was thought that alveolar hypoplasia was present (96) and in examples of diaphragmatic atrophy (29, 103). A diminution in the number of airway generations was demonstrated in the latter study, which was associated with the absence of the phrenic nerve (103). Diminished radial counts have been found in anencephaly (203), and these authors attributed this abnormality to anencephaly. The thorax is frequently small, shortened, or abnormal in anencephaly, but Reale and Esterly (203) felt that this was not the cause of hypoplasia, because the alveolar counts were the same in anencephalics with and without chest wall abnormalities. However, in cases of anencephaly and hydrocephaly with hypoplasia, Cooney and Thurlbeck (63) found some other cause for the hypoplasia and found normal lungs in the only subject without a separate cause for the hypoplasia.

TABLE 3. *Postnatal Growth of the Rat Lung*

Stage	Age, days	Structure	Connective Tissue	Physiology
Expansion	0–4	Large saccules Alveolar walls thick and cellular	Little elastin Little collagen	Low vol/g Little recoil Low Prp* High HR†

Proliferation	4–12	More, but smaller
		  air spaces
		Alveolar walls thick
		  and cellular
			Elastin ↑ 50%
			Collagen measurable
				Vol/g ↑ 25%
				Little recoil
				Low Prp
				Low HR

Elastin accumulation	12–20	Alveolar walls thinner
		  and less cellular
			Elastin ↑ 300%
			Collagen ↑ 50%
				Vol/g ↑ 50%
				Recoil doubles
				Prp begins to
				  increase

Proportionate growth	20–40	Few new alveoli Alveolar walls thin slightly	Elastin plateaus Collagen doubles	Stable vol/g Recoil stable Prp increasing

* Pressure at which lung ruptures.   † Hysteresis ratio.   [Adapted from data of Burri et al. (45) and Nardell and Brody (181).]

Some workers have stressed the importance of the amount of lung fluid on lung development. Alcorn et al. (4) found that tracheal ligation in sheep produced abnormally large lungs, due to an increase in fluid levels and an increased amount of tissue. In these animals the alveolar walls were thinner, type II cells were infrequently observed, and there were few lamellar bodies. Thus the lungs enlarged without any increased differentiation. The state of alveolarization is uncertain but it may have increased. Chronic tracheal drainage resulted in the reverse changes in the lungs. Earlier studies (49, 130, 248) had shown that tracheal ligation resulted in big lungs, but its effect on lung tissue itself was not studied because the main interest was the secretion of lung fluid. Similar changes occur in studies of human tracheal and bronchial atresia (107, 197), although the precise effect of atresia on alveoli is not known. Oligohydramnios may be somewhat similar to the tracheal drainage experiment in that diminished amniotic fluid levels may be connected with diminished lung weight. Lung hypoplasia is a well-recognized complication of this condition (13, 191, 235). Indeed, it has been suggested that the non-renal features of Potter's syndrome (pulmonary hypoplasia, facial and ear anomalies, fetal growth deficiency, and limb positioning defects) should be referred to as the "oligohydramnios tetrad," because they may all be found in oligohydramnios without renal anomalies (235). This suggestion is further supported by the observation that the oligohydramnios tetrad is absent in those rare examples of renal agenesis or other renal abnormalities not associated with oligohydramnios (149, 192, 235). When amniotic drainage was performed on days 16 and 17 of gestation in the rat, there was a marked reduction in lung weight, although the lungs were alleged to be histologically normal (232).

The importance of fetal respiration in lung development has recently become apparent. Wigglesworth et al. (264) found that high spinal cord section in fetal rabbits resulted in a 43% loss of wet lung weight (fluid plus tissue) and a 16% reduction in cell number. In a subsequent paper, Wigglesworth and Desai (261) showed that intrauterine cervical cord section at C_1–C_3 in rabbits reduced lung growth by 70%, whereas section at C_5–C_8 reduced lung growth by 40%. They attributed this difference to the greater effect of sectioning above the origin of the phrenic nerve on fetal respiratory movement. The injection of tubocurarine caused an 8% loss of lung weight (wet wt) in fetal rats (177), and bilateral phrenic nerve section resulted in a cessation of subsequent lung growth and structural development in fetal sheep, although epithelial differentiation appeared to be normal (5). Interestingly the effect of sectioning the cord above the phrenic nerve origin in rabbits could be reversed by ligating the trachea (26).

There is a unifying hypothesis, however, and that is that stretch is necessary to promote proper lung development. Thus the intermittent expansion caused by respiration stimulates lung development and in its absence lung development ceases. Compression of the lung, as in diaphragmatic hernia and thoracic abnormalities, diminishes the distending force, and oligohydramnios or tracheal drainage diminishes the distending pressure.

Regrettably it may not be that simple. It is important to recognize that the details of the descriptions of the lungs in various situations are not entirely satisfactory. Furthermore the slowing of growth and maturation need not necessarily proceed together, and the information available on lung hypoplasia is still incomplete. Wigglesworth et al. (262, 263) have indicated that the lung may be structurally and functionally either mature or immature in hypoplastic lungs. They found that oligohydramnios was associated with retarded tissue growth and diminished phospholipid concentrations. On the other hand, hypoplastic lungs from infants with normal or increased amniotic fluid levels were structurally mature and had normal phospholipid concentrations. There are other indications that the control of lung growth may be more complex. Hislop et al. (116) studied eight infants with renal anomalies and found a diminished number of preacinar airways and arteries. Radial counts of alveoli, although consistently low, fell within 2 SD of the predicted value. Similarly, Reale and Esterly (203) found that lung weight was more abnormal than radial counts in 16 of 20 patients with renal anomalies. Thus these observations suggest that there are too few preacinar airways. The process that affects lung growth must be operative between the 12th and 16th wk of gestation, the period when most of the distal airways develop. It seems unlikely that the amount of amniotic fluid could play a part at this time. The kidney and lung begin their development at the same time and it has been suggested that an insult during this period might affect them both. Thus anomalies of the kidney and lung may be associated defects, and previous investigators have suggested that Potter's syndrome is a congenital mesodermal defect (99). Alternately, it has been suggested that the kidney is involved in the normal development of the lung. Injection of nephrotoxins into chick embryos results in lung hypoplasia and decreased proline and collagen production (55). During fetal development the kidney is an important source of proline, which is produced by a renal arginase. Because collagen may be involved in the budding and branching of airways, collagen deficiencies, caused by an inadequate supply of proline and not the associated oligohydramnios, may be the cause of hypoplasia in renal disease. The hypoplastic lungs associated with Rh isoimmunization are also said to be associated with a loss of preacinar airways (51), and because the cause of hypoplasia occurs early in gestation (when airways are developing), some factor other than compression by ascites or hydrothorax must be involved. An immunological mechanism for this has been proposed.

Postnatal Period

Alterations in the chest wall may also have a substantial effect on postnatal lung growth and alveolar multiplication, and one major hypothesis concerning the control of postnatal lung growth involves stretch (56). Leung and co-workers (160) have suggested that the amount of connective tissue produced by smooth muscle cells in culture can be influenced by stretching the cells. These authors grew smooth muscle cells on an elastic membrane and measured collagen and protein synthesis when the cells were at rest (or unstretched). When the membrane was rhythmically stretched, they found a 25% increase in collagen synthesis. Whether a similar control of elastin synthesis by smooth muscle cells or fibroblasts existed is not clear. Lung weight in rats diminished ipsilaterally after the injection of wax into the pleural cavity, after thoracoplasty, and after phrenic nerve avulsion (56).

In another study the alveolar number in rats was not obviously altered after phrenectomy (57). Studies on pneumonectomized animals also provide evidence for a primary mechanical stimulus for lung growth. Performing plombage on the pneumonectomized side abolished the increase in weight and collagen synthesis in the contralateral lung and suppressed and delayed the mitotic response after pneumonectomy (56, 67, 97). Brody et al. (37) have shown that plombage diminishes rather than ablates DNA synthesis and that there is a topographical variation of DNA synthesis within the lung after pneumonectomy. Mesothelial cells are the first cells to label; peripheral alveoli label more than central alveoli 2 days after pneumonectomy and then the response becomes more or less uniform in the alveoli. There are conflicting data concerning the first response to pneumonectomy. Brody (30) has found that the initial response to pneumonectomy is an increase in weight, whereas Das and Thurlbeck (73) found the initial response to be an increase in volume. Thus although mechanical forces may play an important role in controlling lung growth, the evidence for it is less than complete. In addition, mechanical forces are not the only factors involved. After pneumonectomy a somatomedin-like substance appears in the blood that can make type II cells synthesize DNA in culture (220), indicating that humoral factors might be mediating lung growth. Furthermore, the individual lobes of the lung respond differently after pneumonectomy (123, 243). In dogs the cardiac lobe has significantly fewer alveoli per unit volume than the lower and middle lobes. We initially interpreted this to mean that the lower lobe stretched the most and thus responded more completely. However, it is now known that the cardiac lobe expands the most (N. Anthonisen, unpublished data), and thus there may be a humorally induced response that produces alveolar multiplication, which cannot compensate in the most expanded lobe.

Weibel (257) has suggested that lung growth may be largely determined by oxygen consumption. He showed that the morphologically determined diffusing capacity (which is mainly dependent on alveolar and capillary surface area) is closely related to oxygen consumption. Thus the Etruscan shrew, which has an innate high metabolic level, also has a relatively high alveolar surface area (258). Japanese waltzing mice, which exhibit excess motor activity because of a congenital defect in their vestibular apparatus, also have a high alveolar surface area (101). The alveolar surface area is increased in drug-induced motor hyperactivity (121) and in young rats raised at low temperatures (102). Thompson (236) has shown that increased oxygen consumption in hamsters, caused by the administration of triiodothyronine and exposure to cold, resulted in increased lung volumes, surface area, and alveolar number. The most effective way of increasing surface area is to increase the complexity of the alveolar surface, and the most effective way to do this is to have more alveoli per unit volume (increased surface-to-volume ratio). The hypothetical importance of oxygen consumption is not as clear-cut as it might be; one experiment, in which young rats were raised at low temperatures, showed that the increase in the morphologically determined diffusing capacity was primarily caused by increases in lung and capillary volumes, without an increase in alveolar wall complexity (102). Other observations are also controversial. In one study, altered oxygen consumption after administration of thyroxine did not affect lung structure (17); in another study, administration of antithyroid drugs did not affect lung growth (236). It seems unlikely that growth is brought about by hyperventilation associated with increased oxygen consumption, because no increase in lung growth was noted in animals raised in an atmosphere with a high level of ambient CO_2 (18).

The effect of inspired oxygen tension on lung growth remains open to debate. It is well known that natives of high altitudes have larger lungs and chest cages than sea-level controls (126), and it was thought that these were genetic differences (66). Studies by Lahiri and co-workers (154) and Brody and co-workers (36) have shown that the large lungs and depressed hypoxic drive often found in highlanders are environmentally rather than genetically determined. Several investigators have found that young animals exposed to an ambient P_{O_2} in the range of 80–100 Torr have increased physiological and morphometric parameters of lung size (16, 18, 46, 70). However, this increase in lung size was only noted when values were corrected for body weight. Because body weight is decreased in hypoxic exposure, it has been argued that hypoxia does not stimulate lung growth but suppresses body growth instead (238). One study of young guinea pigs exposed to a hypoxic atmosphere for up to 14 wk showed that when corrected for body weight, lung volumes and alveolar surface area increased after 3 wk of exposure but that differences between hypoxic and control animals vanished in adult animals exposed for 14 wk (159). The authors suggest that hypoxia does indeed stimulate lung growth but that factors related to body size (particularly chest cage size) might ultimately limit this growth. The fact that early postoperative exposure to hypoxia accentuates postpneumonectomy lung growth supports this conclusion (30). The mechanism of this lung growth is unclear, although Brody et al. (35) have shown a rapid two- to threefold increase in lung lysyl oxidase, suggesting that increased connective tissue synthesis is involved.

The fact that elevated concentrations of inspired oxygen suppress lung growth is more readily accepted. Burri and Weibel (46) and Bartlett (18) have shown that exposing weanling rats to as little as 40% oxygen resulted in a slowing of lung growth. Because the young lung is more resistant to hyperoxic lung damage (40), it is likely that this effect is not the result of lung injury. Bucher and Roberts (40) have shown that

lung DNA is depressed in newborn rats exposed to 40% oxygen for 12 days, a setting associated with decreased lung tissue maturation. It is known that increased oxygen tensions suppress DNA synthesis in isolated lung cells (14) as well as in lung tissue (91), and it is likely that diminished cell proliferation is involved in this process, although the specific cells involved are not clear. It is interesting that exposure to as little as 35% oxygen suppresses postpneumonectomy lung growth (30) and that oxygen also suppresses lung repair after an injury (111, 268). In the latter instance, Witschi and co-workers (268) have suggested that hyperoxia may selectively interfere with the type II cell proliferation associated with lung repair.

Food deprivation has been shown to markedly depress cellular multiplication in alveoli (110). Emphysema-like changes have been described in starved rats (208, 210), and food deprivation also aggravates emphysema caused by elastase (209). The changes induced by starvation can perhaps be interpreted as interfering with lung growth rather than producing emphysema, although the experiments were performed at a time when alveolar multiplication had probably ceased. The mechanism for this is unknown; it is worth pointing out that starvation diminishes oxygen consumption. Subtle alterations in lung growth and architecture may also occur in animals receiving intraperitoneal injections of saline (141, 142), suggesting that the growing lung may be very sensitive to perturbation.

Growth hormone is likely an important modulator of lung growth. Early studies of fetal lung development showed that fetal hypophysectomy or decapitation impaired lung development (23). Most of these studies concentrated on the role that depressed adrenal or thyroid function played in this process, so that the specific role of growth hormone in fetal lung development is uncertain. Brody and co-workers (34, 127) have suggested that growth hormone is important in maintaining adult lung size, because acromegalics have large lungs with normal mechanical properties, whereas patients with adult onset hypopituitarism have small lungs. The influence of growth hormone on lung size in both mature and growing lungs has been confirmed in animals (31, 32). Smith et al. (220) found that serum from pneumonectomized rats stimulates thymidine incorporation into isolated type II cells but not into fibroblasts. A partial purification of the responsible factor suggested that somatomedin C, a mediator stimulated by growth hormone, may be the major cause of cell proliferation after pneumonectomy. This observation fits with the study by Brody and Buhain (32) showing that a deficit of growth hormone suppresses postpneumonectomy compensatory lung growth. Further evidence that somatomedins may be a key factor in regulating at least some of the cell proliferation associated with lung growth comes from studies by A. J. D'Ercole (personal communication), who has shown that somatomedin C production is extremely high in the fetal lung during late gestation, that the levels peak just before birth, and that they remain high during the early postnatal period of active lung cell proliferation. These workers have shown that somatomedin C can be regulated locally within tissues (77), and Clemmons et al. (54) have found that lung fibroblasts are capable of making somatomedin C. Thus it may be that the lung fibroblast in both fetal and postnatal lung development, as well as in post-pneumonectomy growth, when stimulated (perhaps by stretch) produces somatomedin C, which acts as a mitogen inducing the lung cell proliferation necessary for growth.

AGING OF LUNG

Anatomy

A number of changes occur in the anatomy of the lung with age, and although these changes involve the lungs of most subjects, not every lung is equally affected. Lungs change in shape with age. Anderson et al. (9) showed an increase in their anteroposterior diameter and in their height up to 59 yr of age, after which only the anteroposterior diameter increased. Prior to 60 yr of age the anteroposterior diameter increased more than the lung height, so the net effect was a continual increase in the "index of rounding" (anteroposterior diam/ht) with age. These data were derived from paper-mounted, whole-lung sections from lungs inflated approximately to total lung capacity. It is interesting to speculate why the shape of the lungs changes at this volume when the lung is mainly at FRC. Another change in inflated lung specimens can be seen with the naked eye: the smallest visible spaces increase in size with age. Weibel (255) quantitated this change and noted that the proportion of air in the alveoli was smaller in two older subjects than in three younger ones and that there was an increased proportion of alveolar duct air in the older subjects. Ryan et al. (207) also documented this change by comparing the lungs of an old and young subject. The data of Thurlbeck (239) are shown in Figure 24. The low-order correlations indicate that although these changes are significantly related to age, there is considerable variation between subjects.

The rearrangement of the internal anatomy of the lung results in an increase in the interalveolar wall distance (47, 112, 237). This means that the surface-to-volume ratio of the lung decreases with age and hence the surface area also decreases. The proportion of the lung formed by parenchyma (alveolar walls) also declines steadily with age (Fig. 25). It is not known which component of the alveolar wall diminishes with age, but studies of other organ systems indicated that it may be the capillary bed. Overinflation of the lungs could account for the increase in alveolar wall distance and the decline in the relative proportion of alveolar wall. These measurements are

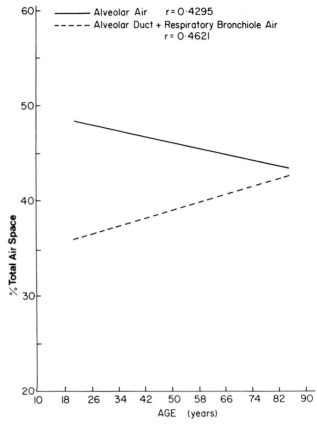

FIG. 24. Proportion of core of air inside alveoli in alveolar ducts, sacs, and respiratory bronchioles increases with age; proportion of alveolar air decreases with age. [From Thurlbeck (241).]

made on excised lungs inflated to a standard transpulmonary pressure, and it is possible that the loss of recoil that occurs with age might result in overinflation of the lungs. However, it has been shown that there is no increase with age in lung volumes of lungs prepared in this way (240). We have unpublished data that show that the number of alveoli per unit volume decreases with age in humans. The fact that lung volume does not increase with age suggests that the loss of alveoli may also account for the diminution of alveolar wall tissue.

Pinkerton et al. (195) conducted the first quantitative ultrastructural and morphologic analysis of age-related changes in the rat lung. They showed that alveolar and capillary surface area in specific pathogen-free rats did not decrease between 5 and 26 mo of age. The endothelial compartment remained unchanged during this period while the ratio of type II to type I cells lining the alveolar surface decreased. The greatest change noted with age during this period was in the interstitial matrix volume (vol of noncellular connective tissue components), which increased 39% in males and 89% in females. Why these findings differ from those noted for humans is unclear. Not all species show age-related changes in alveolar wall mechanics, though (170).

In the human the size and/or number of pores of

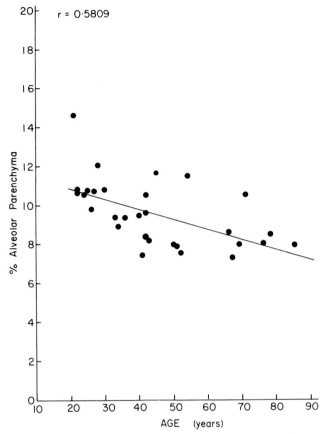

FIG. 25. Volume proportion of lung formed by alveolar wall (% alveolar parenchyma) decreases with age. [From Thurlbeck (241).]

Kohn increase steadily with age (200). Earlier studies indicated that the pores of Kohn were absent in young and numerous in old mammals (163, 165, 166), but a study in mice (201) has shown that there is a rapid increase in the number of pores of Kohn in early life with no significant increase thereafter. In dogs the number of pores increases until 1 yr of age with no change thereafter (169).

An early subjective description of elastic tissue indicated that the elastic fibers decreased in thickness and number with age in humans (269), but a more recent quantitative study showed no change in the number of elastic fibers (184). No alterations were seen in either collagen or elastin in electron-microscopic examinations of human lungs (1). However, in mice the amount of elastin diminished (measured chemically), although the total length of the elastic fibers did not change with age. This suggested either that the fibers were thinned or that some fibers were lost and the remainder were stretched (202). Emphysema, defined as an enlargement of the gas-exchanging portion of the lung accompanied by a destruction of lung tissue, increases in frequency with age (239). This is true even in nonsmokers. Studies of excised lung have shown that even mild degrees of emphysema are associated with a striking loss of elastic recoil and increases in lung volume (20, 216, 240), and because

changes in recoil in excised lungs associated with age alone are small (20, 216), it is possible that the changes described so far that occur with age in intact humans are associated with emphysema, rather than with aging itself. The type of emphysema found in old, nonsmoking subjects is usually a localized, mild panacinar emphysema (239).

Connective Tissue

Lung connective tissue consists of a mixture of collagen, elastin, and proteoglycans. These three components probably interact in some as yet undefined fashion to produce the mechanical properties of lung parenchyma and airways. Each component is likely to have its own rate of synthesis and degradation (i.e., turnover). These varying rates of turnover are probably also influenced by age, and this in turn influences connective tissue interactions and lung mechanical properties. Much information is available about aging's effects on lung collagen, with less available on lung elastin and very little on lung proteoglycans.

Most authors have found that lung collagen content remains constant with age in humans (194). In these studies collagen content is expressed per milligram of lung weight. The best way to compare collagen content in lungs of different ages and weights is not known. Some authors have felt that because the other elements in the lung that affect weight may also change with age, expressing the collagen content per milligram of lung weight can be misleading, and they suggest that collagen content should be expressed for the whole lung (105). Others point out that whole lung contains large vessels and airways and thus can be misleading as regards the parenchymal collagen content. Lung collagen increases with age in the rat (131) and hamster (104) and remains constant in the mouse (202). Only one study examined possible age-related changes in the distribution of collagen, and it found no shift in parenchymal versus airway collagen. None of these studies has characterized age-related changes in different types of collagen.

All of the studies that have measured lung collagen solubility have found that soluble collagen decreases and insoluble collagen increases with age (199, 204). Collagen also becomes more stable, more resistant to thermal and chemical denaturation, and less susceptible to digestion by collagenase (252). These changes have been attributed to an increased number of intermolecular collagen cross-links with fewer reducible cross-links available (12).

Age-related changes in lung elastin have been less extensively characterized than those found in collagen. Elastin's insolubility and our lack of understanding of the role of its microfibrillar components have made studies of elastin maturation difficult. Lung parenchymal elastin levels apparently remain constant with age, although pleural and septal elastin increase and airway and vessel elastin decrease (129, 194). The amino acid composition of elastin changes with age, with increased amounts of polar amino acids suggesting that nonelastin components of elastic tissue become more difficult to separate (129). The mechanical effect of this observation is unknown. Like collagen, elastin becomes more resistant to enzymatic digestion with age.

Mechanical Properties

Physiological changes in lung mechanical properties are covered in detail in other chapters in this *Handbook* and are only summarized here. A common set of physiological changes with aging has been noted in all mammalian species studied, although the magnitude of these changes varies among the species (172, 180). The magnitude of these changes also varies in humans, depending in part on how rigorous the authors have been in excluding smoking and other variables that might confound the influence of age alone. It has also been noted that age-related changes occur more rapidly in males than in females. The physiological changes have been attributed almost exclusively to age-related alterations in lung connective tissue. Lung elastic recoil diminishes with increasing age (250), and this decrease in retractive forces results in airway closure at higher lung volumes (158), an increase in residual volume, diminished maximum expiratory flow rates (147), and altered regional ventilation-perfusion relationships (122) that lead to widened alveolar-to-arterial oxygen gradients (223). Balancing these decreases in lung recoil is an increase in chest wall recoil

inward, so that the total lung capacity stays relatively constant with age and vital capacity falls [because residual volume rises while total lung capacity stays constant (250)]. These changes tend to occur in a linear fashion with increasing age.

Age-related alterations in whole-organ physiology also occur in isolated strips of the alveolar wall. Martin and co-workers (170) have examined the length-tension characteristics of human alveolar walls and found that the maximal extensibility ratio (predicted final length/initial length) decreased with age primarily because the initial or resting length increases. The authors postulate that the change in initial resting length is a permanent deformation that results from elastin deformation. They also noted an age-related change in alveolar wall viscoelastic properties but no change in either tissue compliance or in the breaking force of alveolar walls. Although the increase in resting length correlates with the increased FRC and residual volume seen in whole lungs, the problem is compounded by the fact that not all species demonstrate age-related alveolar wall changes similar to those seen in humans. In particular, there was no change in resting length with age in horses, rabbits, or rats despite the fact that whole-lung physiology in horses and rats changes in a fashion similar to that in humans. Martin and co-workers (170) produced increased connective tissue cross-links in vitro by exposing alveolar walls to weak solutions of aldehyde in an attempt to mimic the increased cross-linking seen in aging, but they were unable to duplicate the changes noted in normal lungs (229).

REFERENCES

1. ADAMSON, J. S. An electron microscopic comparison of the connective tissue from the lungs of young and elderly subjects. *Am. Rev. Respir. Dis.* 98: 399–406, 1968
2. ADDISON, W. H. F., AND H. W. HOW. On the prenatal and neonatal lung. *Am. J. Anat.* 15: 199–214, 1913.
3. AGOSTONI, E., A. TAGLIETTI, A. FERRARIO AGOSTONI, AND I. SETNIKAR. Mechanical aspects of the first breath. *J. Appl. Physiol.* 13: 344–348, 1958.
4. ALCORN, D., T. M. ADAMSON, T. E. LAMBERT, J. E. MALONEY, B. C. RITCHIE, AND P. M. ROBINSON. Morphological effects of chronic tracheal ligation and drainage in the fetal lamb lung. *J. Anat.* 123: 649–660, 1977.
5. ALCORN, D., T. M. ADAMSON, J. E. MALONEY, AND P. M. ROBINSON. Morphological effects of chronic bilateral phrenectomy or vagotomy in the fetal lamb lung. *J. Anat.* 130: 683–695, 1980.
6. ALESCIO, T. Effect of a proline analogue, azetidine-2-carboxylic acid, on the morphogenesis in vitro of mouse embryonic lung. *J. Embryol. Exp. Morphol.* 29: 439–451, 1973.
7. ALESCIO, T., AND M. DiMICHELE. Relationship of epithelial growth to mitotic rate in mouse embryonic lung developing in vitro. *J. Embryol. Exp. Morphol.* 19: 227–237, 1968.
8. AMY, R. W., D. BOWES, P. H. BURRI, J. HAINES, AND W. M. THURLBECK. Postnatal growth of the mouse lung. *J. Anat.* 124: 131–151, 1977.
9. ANDERSON, W. F., A. E. ANDERSON, JR., J. A. HERNANDEZ, AND A. G. FORAKER. Topography of aging and emphysematous lungs. *Am. Rev. Respir. Dis.* 90: 411–423, 1964.
10. ANGUS, G. E., AND W. M. THURLBECK. Number of alveoli in the human lung. *J. Appl. Physiol.* 32: 483–485, 1972.

11. AVERY, M. E., AND J. MEAD. Surface properties in relation to atelectasis and hyaline membrane disease. *Am. J. Dis. Child.* 97: 517–523, 1959.
12. BAILEY, A. J., S. P. ROBINS, AND G. BALIAN. Biological significance of the intermolecular crosslinks of collagen. *Nature London* 251: 105–109, 1974.
13. BAIN, A. D., I. I. SMITH, AND I. K. GAULD. Newborn born after prolonged leakage of liquor amnii. *Br. Med. J.* 5409: 598–599, 1964.
14. BALIN, A. K., D. B. P. GOODMAN, H. RASMUSSEN, AND V. J. CRISTOFALO. Oxygen-sensitive stages of the cell cycle of human diploid cells. *J. Cell Biol.* 78: 390–400, 1978.
15. BALLARD, P. L. Glucocorticoid receptors in the fetal lung. In: *Lung Biology in Health and Disease. Development of the Lung*, edited by W. A. Hodson. New York: Dekker, 1977, vol. 6, chapt. 11, p. 419–444.
16. BARTELS, H., R. BARTELS, A. M. RATHSCHLAG-SCHAEFER, H. RÖBBEL, AND S. LÜDDERS. Acclimatization of newborn rats and guinea pigs to 3000 to 5000 m simulated altitudes. *Respir. Physiol.* 36: 375–389, 1979.
17. BARTLETT, D., JR. Postnatal growth of the mammalian lung: influence of exercise and thyroid activity. *Respir. Physiol.* 9: 50–57, 1970.
18. BARTLETT, D., JR. Postnatal growth of the mammalian lung: influence of low and high oxygen tensions. *Respir. Physiol.* 9: 58–64, 1970.
19. BECK, J. C., W. MITZNER, J. W. C. JOHNSON, G. M. HUTCHINS, J. M. FOIDART, W. T. LONDON, A. E. PALMER, AND R. SCOTT. Betamethasone and the rhesus fetus: effect on lung morphometry and connective tissue. *Pediatr. Res.* 15: 235–240,

1981.

20. BEREND, N., C. SKOOG, AND W. M. THURLBECK. Pressure-volume characteristics of excised human lungs: effects of sex, age, and emphysema. *J. Appl. Physiol.: Respirat. Environ. Exercise Physiol.* 49: 558–565, 1980.

21. BERNFIELD, M. R., AND S. D. BANERIEE. The basal lamina in epithelial-mesenchymal morphologic interactions. In: *Biology and Chemistry of Basement Membranes*, edited by N. A. Kefalides. New York: Academic, 1978, p. 137–148.

22. BHUTANI, V. K., S. D. RUBENSTEIN, AND T. H. SHAFFER. Pressure-volume relationships of tracheae in fetal newborn and adult rabbits. *Respir. Physiol.* 43: 221–231, 1981.

23. BLACKBURN, W. R., H. TRAVERS, AND D. M. POTTER. The role of the pituitary-adrenal-thyroid axis in lung differentiation. I. Studies of the cytology and physical properties of anencephalic fetal rat lung. *Lab. Invest.* 26: 306–318, 1972.

24. BLUEMINK, J. G., P. VAN MAURIK, AND K. A. LAWSON. Intimate cell contact at the epithelial/mesenchymal interface in embryonic mouse lung. *J. Ultrastruct. Res.* 55: 257–270, 1976.

25. BOSMA, J. F., J. LIND, AND N. GENZ. Motions of the pharynx associated with initial aeration of the lungs of the newborn infant. *Acta Paediatr. Scand. Suppl.* 117: 117–122, 1959.

26. BOYDEN, E. A., AND D. H. TOMPSETT. The postnatal growth of the lung in the dog. *Acta Anat.* 47: 185–215, 1961.

27. BRADLEY, K. H., S. D. MCCONNELL, AND R. G. CRYSTAL. Lung collagen composition and synthesis: characterization and changes with age. *J. Biol. Chem.* 249: 2674–2683, 1974.

28. BREMER, J. L. Postnatal development of alveoli in the mammalian lung in relation to the problem of the alveolar phagocyte. *Contrib. Embryol. Carnegie Inst.* 25: 83–118, 1935.

29. BRIGGS, V. A., B. J. REILLY, AND K. LOEWIG. Lung hypoplasia and membranous diaphragm in the congenital rubella syndrome—a rare case. *J. Can. Assoc. Radiol.* 24: 126–127, 1973.

30. BRODY, J. S. Time course of and stimuli to compensatory growth of the lung following pneumonectomy. *J. Clin. Invest.* 56: 897–904, 1975.

31. BRODY, J. S., AND W. J. BUHAIN. Hormone-induced growth of the adult lung. *Am. J. Physiol.* 223: 1444–1450, 1972.

32. BRODY, J. S., AND W. J. BUHAIN. Hormonal influence on postpneumonectomy lung growth in the rat. *Respir. Physiol.* 19: 344–355, 1973.

33. BRODY, J. S., R. BURKI, AND N. KAPLAN. Deoxyribonucleic acid synthesis in lung cells during compensatory lung growth after pneumonectomy. *Am. Rev. Respir. Dis.* 117: 307–316, 1978.

34. BRODY, J. S., A. B. FISHER, A. GOCMEN, AND A. B. DUBOIS. Acromegalic pneumonomegaly: lung growth in the adult. *J. Clin. Invest.* 49: 1051–1060, 1970.

35. BRODY, J. S., H. KAGAN, AND A. MANALO. Lung lysyl oxidase activity: relation to lung growth. *Am. Rev. Respir. Dis.* 120: 1289–1295, 1979.

36. BRODY, J. S., S. LAHIRI, M. SIMPSER, E. K. MOTOYAMA, AND T. VELASQUEZ. Lung elasticity and airway dynamics in Peruvian natives to high altitude. *J. Appl. Physiol.: Respirat. Environ. Exercise Physiol.* 42: 245–251, 1977.

37. BRODY, J. S., C. A. VACCARO, P. J. GILL, AND J. E. GILBERT. Alterations in alveolar basement membranes during postnatal lung growth. *J. Cell Biol.* 95: 394–402, 1982.

38. BROWN, L. A. S., AND W. J. LONGMORE. Adrenergic and cholinergic regulation of lung surfactant secretion in the isolated perfused rat lung and in the alveolar type II cell in culture. *J. Biol. Chem.* 256: 66–72, 1981.

39. BRUMLEY, G. W., V. CHERNIAK, W. A. HODSON, C. NORMAND, A. FENNER, AND M. E. AVERY. Correlations of mechanical stability, morphology, pulmonary surfactant and phospholipid content in the developing lamb lung. *J. Clin. Invest.* 46: 863–873, 1967.

40. BUCHER, J. R., AND R. J. ROBERTS. The development of the newborn rat lung in hyperoxia: a dose-response study of lung growth, maturation and changes in antioxidant enzyme activities. *Pediatr. Res.* 15: 999–1008, 1981.

41. BUCHER, U., AND L. REID. Development of the intrasegmental bronchial tree. The pattern of branching and development of cartilage at various stages of intrauterine life. *Thorax* 16: 207–218, 1961.

42. BUCKINGHAM, S., AND M. E. AVERY. Time of appearance of lung surfactant in the foetal mouse. *Nature London* 193: 688–689, 1962.

43. BUHAIN, W. J., AND J. S. BRODY. Compensatory growth of the lung following pneumonectomy. *J. Appl. Physiol.* 35: 898–902, 1973.

44. BURRI, P. H. The postnatal growth of the rat lung. III. Morphology. *Anat. Rec.* 180: 77–98, 1974.

45. BURRI, P. H., J. DBALY, AND E. R. WEIBEL. The postnatal growth of the rat lung. I. Morphometry. *Anat. Rec.* 178: 711–730, 1974.

46. BURRI, P. H., AND E. R. WEIBEL. Morphometric estimation of pulmonary diffusion capacity. II. Effect of P_{O_2} on the growing lung, adaptation of the growing rat lung to hypoxia and hyperoxia. *Respir. Physiol.* 11: 247–264, 1971.

47. BUTLER, C. Lung surface area in various morphologic forms of human emphysema. *Am. Rev. Respir. Dis.* 114: 347–352, 1976.

48. CAMPICHE, M. A., A. GAUTIER, E. I. HERNANDEZ, AND A. REYMOND. An electron microscope study of the fetal development of the human lung. *Pediatrics* 32: 660–663, 1963.

49. CARMAL, J. A., F. FRIEDMAN, AND F. H. ADAMS. Fetal tracheal ligation and lung development. *Am. J. Dis. Child.* 109: 452–456, 1965.

50. CARSON, S. H., H. W. TAEUSCH, JR., AND M. E. AVERY. Inhibition of lung cell division after hydrocortisone injection into fetal lambs. *J. Appl. Physiol.* 34: 660–663, 1973.

51. CHAMBERLAIN, D., A. HISLOP, E. HEY, AND L. REID. Pulmonary hypoplasia in babies with severe rhesus isoimmunisation: a quantitative study. *J. Pathol.* 122: 43–52, 1977.

52. CHENG, J. B., A. GOLDFIEN, P. L. BALLARD, AND J. M. ROBERTS. Glucocorticoids increase pulmonary β-adrenergic receptors in fetal rabbit. *Endocrinology* 107: 1646–1648, 1980.

53. CLEMENTS, J. A., AND W. H. TOOLEY. Kinetics of surface-active material in the fetal lung. In: *Lung Biology in Health and Disease. Development of the Lung*, edited by W. A. Hodson. New York: Dekker, 1977, vol. 6, chapt. 8, p. 349–366.

54. CLEMMONS, D. R., L. E. UNDERWOOD, AND J. J. VAN WYK. Hormonal control of immunoreactive somatomedin production by cultured human fibroblasts. *J. Clin. Invest.* 67: 10–19, 1981.

55. CLEMMONS, J. J. W. Embryonic renal injury: a possible factor in fetal malnutrition (Abstract). *Pediatr. Res.* 11: 404, 1977.

56. COHN, R. Factors affecting the postnatal growth of the lung. *Anat. Rec.* 75: 195–205, 1938.

57. COHN, R. The postnatal growth of the lung. *J. Thorac. Surg.* 9: 274–277, 1940.

58. Collaborative Group on Antenatal Steroid Therapy. Effect of antenatal dexamethasone administration on the prevention of respiratory distress syndrome. *Am. J. Obstet. Gynecol.* 141: 276–287, 1981.

59. COLLET, A. J., AND G. DES BIENS. Fine structure of myogenesis and elastogenesis in the developing rat lung. *Anat. Rec.* 179: 343–360, 1974.

60. COMROE, J. H., JR. Premature science and immature lungs. Part I. Some premature discoveries. *Am. Rev. Respir. Dis.* 116: 127–135, 1977.

61. COMROE, J. H., JR. Premature science and immature lungs. Part II. Chemical warfare and the newly born. *Am. Rev. Respir. Dis.* 116: 311–323, 1977.

62. COMROE, J. H., JR. Premature science and immature lungs. Part III. The attack on immature lungs. *Am. Rev. Respir. Dis.* 116: 497–518, 1977.

63. COONEY, T. P., AND W. M. THURLBECK. Lung growth and development in anencephaly and hydrancephaly. *Am. Rev. Respir. Dis.* 132: 596–601, 1985.

64. COONEY, T. P., AND W. M. THURLBECK. The radial alveolar count of Emery and Mithal: a reappraisal. I. Postnatal lung

growth. *Thorax* 37: 572–579, 1982.

66. COTES, J. E. Genetic factors affecting the lung. *Bull. Physio-Pathol. Respir.* 10: 109–117, 1974.

67. COWAN, M. J., AND R. G. CRYSTAL. Lung growth after unilateral pneumonectomy: quantitation of collagen synthesis and content. *Am. Rev. Respir. Dis.* 111: 267–277, 1975.

68. CROCKER, T. T., A. TEETER, AND B. NIELSEN. Postnatal cellular proliferation in mouse and hamster lung. *Cancer Res.* 30: 357–361, 1970

69. CROTEAU, J. R., AND C. D. COOK. Volume-pressure and length-tension measurements in human tracheal and bronchial segments. *J. Appl. Physiol.* 16: 170–172, 1961.

70. CUNNINGHAM, E. L., J. S. BRODY, AND B. P. JAIN. Lung growth induced by hypoxia. *J. Appl. Physiol.* 37: 362–366, 1974.

71. DAS, R. M., M. JAIN, AND W. M. THURLBECK. Diurinal variation of deoxyribonucleic acid synthesis in murine alveolar wall cells and airway epithelial cells. *Am. Rev. Respir. Dis.* 119: 81–86, 1979.

72. DAS, R. M., M. JAIN, AND W. M. THURLBECK. Circadium rhythm and proliferation of lung alveolar wall cells during postnatal growth in mice. *Am. Rev. Respir. Dis.* 121: 367–371, 1980.

73. DAS, R. M., AND W. M. THURLBECK. The events in the contralateral lung following pneumonectomy in the rabbit. *Lung* 156: 165–172, 1979.

74. DAVIES, G., AND L. REID. Growth of the alveoli and pulmonary arteries in childhood. *Thorax* 25: 669–681, 1970.

75. DeLEMOS, R. A., D. W. SHERMETA, J. H. KNELSON, R. KOTAS, AND M. E. AVERY. Acceleration of appearance of pulmonary surfactant in the fetal lamb by administration of corticosteroids. *Am. Rev. Respir. Dis.* 102: 459–461, 1970.

76. DeLORIMIER, A. A., D. F. TIERNEY, AND H. R. PARKER. Hypoplastic lungs in fetal lambs with surgically produced congenital diaphragmatic hernia. *Surgery* 62: 12–17, 1967.

77. D'ERCOLE, A. J., G. T. APPLEWHITE, AND L. E. UNDERWOOD. Evidence that somatomedin is synthesized by multiple tissues in the fetus. *Dev. Biol.* 75: 315–328, 1980.

78. DINGLER, E. C. Wachstum der Lunge nach der Geburt. *Acta Anat. Suppl.* 30: 1–86, 1958.

79. DOBBS, L. G., AND R. J. MASON. Pulmonary alveolar type II cells isolated from rats. Release of phosphatidylcholine in response to β-adrenergic stimulation. *J. Clin. Invest.* 63: 378–387, 1979.

80. DUBREUIL, G., A. LACOSTE, AND R. RAYMOND. Observations sur le développement du poumon humain. *Bull. Histol. Appl. Physiol. Pathol.* 13: 235–245, 1936.

81. DUNNILL, M. S. Postnatal growth of the lung. *Thorax* 17: 329–333, 1962.

82. EGAN, E. A., R. M. NELSON, AND E. F. BEALE. Lung solute permeability and lung liquid absorption in premature ventilated fetal goats. *Pediatr. Res.* 14: 314–318, 1980.

83. EGAN, E. A., R. M. NELSON, AND R. E. OLVER. Lung inflation and alveolar permeability to non-electrolytes in the adult sheep in vivo. *J. Physiol. London* 260: 409–424, 1976.

84. EGAN, E. A., R. E. OLVER, AND L. B. STRANG. Changes in non-electrolyte permeability of alveoli and the absorption of lung liquid at the start of breathing in the lamb. *J. Physiol. London* 244: 161–179, 1975.

85. EMERY, J. L. Connective tissue and lymphatics. In: *The Anatomy of the Developing Lung*, edited by J. L. Emery. Lavenham, UK: Heinemann, 1969, p. 49–73.

86. EMERY, J. L. The postnatal development of the human lung and its implications for lung pathology. *Respiration* 27, Suppl.: 41–50, 1970.

87. EMERY, J. L., AND D. G. FAGAN. New alveoli—where and how? *Arch. Dis. Child.* 45: 145, 1970.

88. EMERY, J. L., AND A. MITHAL. The number of alveoli in the terminal respiratory unit of man during late intrauterine life and childhood. *Arch. Dis. Child.* 35: 544–547, 1960.

89. EMERY, J. L., AND P. F. WILCOCK. The postnatal development of the lung. *Acta Anat.* 65: 10–29, 1966.

90. ERENBERG, A., M. L. RHODES, M. M. WEINSTEN, AND R. L. KENNEDY. The effect of fetal thyroidectomy on ovine fetal lung maturation. *Pediatr. Res.* 13: 230–235, 1979.

91. EVANS, M., J. HACKNEY, AND R. BILS. Effects of high concentration of oxygen on cell renewal in the pulmonary alveoli. *Aerosp. Med.* 40: 1365–1368, 1969.

92. FARIDY, E. E., J. A. THLIVERIS, AND G. S. MORRIS. Relationship between lung intra and extracellular DSPC in fetal and neonatal rats. *Respir. Physiol.* 45: 55–66, 1981.

93. FARRELL, P. M. Fetal lung development and the influence of glucocorticoids on pulmonary surfactant. *J. Steroid Biochem.* 8: 463–470, 1977.

94. FARRELL, P. M., AND M. E. AVERY. Hyaline membrane disease. *Am. Rev. Respir. Dis.* 111: 657–688, 1975.

95. FARRELL, P. M., AND T. E. MORGAN. Lecithin biosynthesis in the developing lung. In: *Lung Biology in Health and Disease. Development of the Lung*, edited by W. A. Hodson. New York: Dekker, 1977, vol. 6, chapt. 7, p. 309–348.

96. FINEGOLD, M. J., H. KATZEW, N. B. GENIESER, AND M. H. BECKER. Lung structure in thoracic dystrophy. *Am. J. Dis. Child.* 122: 153–159, 1971.

97. FISHER, J. M., AND J. D. SIMNETT. Morphogenetic and proliferative changes in the regenerating lung of the rat. *Anat. Rec.* 176: 389–395, 1973.

98. FISK, D. E., AND C. KUHN III. Emphysema-like changes in the lung of the blotchy mouse. *Am. Rev. Respir. Dis.* 113: 787–798, 1976.

99. FITCH, N., AND R. C. LACHANCE. The pathogenesis of Potter's syndrome of renal agenesis. *Can. Med. Assoc. J.* 107: 653–656, 1972.

100. FRASER, C. M., AND J. C. VENTER. The synthesis of β-adrenergic receptors in cultured human lung cells: induction by glucocorticoids. *Biochim. Biophys. Res. Commun.* 94: 390–397, 1980.

101. GEELHAAR, A., AND E. R. WEIBEL. Morphometric estimation of pulmonary diffusion capacity. III. The effect of increased oxygen consumption in Japanese waltzing mice. *Respir. Physiol.* 11: 354–366, 1971.

102. GEHR, P., C. HUGONNAUD, P. H. BURRI, H. BACHOFEN, AND E. R. WEIBEL. Adaptation of the growing lung to increased V_{O_2}. III. The effect of exposure to cold environment in rats. *Respir. Physiol.* 32: 345–353, 1978.

103. GOLDSTEIN, J. D., AND L. M. REID. Pulmonary hypoplasia resulting from phrenic nerve agenesis and diaphragmatic amyoplasia. *J. Pediatr.* 97: 282–287, 1980.

104. GOLDSTEIN, R. H. The response of the aging hamster lung to elastase injury. *Am. Rev. Respir. Dis.* 125: 295–298, 1982.

105. GOLDSTEIN, R. H., E. C. LUCEY, C. FRANZBLAU, AND G. L. SNIDER. Failure of mechanical properties to parallel changes in lung connective tissue composition in bleomycin-induced pulmonary fibrosis in hamsters. *Am. Rev. Respir. Dis.* 120: 67–73, 1979.

106. GRANT, M. M., N. R. CUTTS, AND J. S. BRODY. Alterations in lung basement membrane during fetal growth and type II cell development. *Dev. Biol.* 97: 173–183, 1983.

107. GRISCOM, N. T., G. B. S. HARRIS, M. E. WOHL, G. F. VAWTER, AND A. J. EKRALIS. Fluid-filled lung due to airway obstruction in the newborn. *Pediatrics* 48: 383–390, 1969.

108. GRUENWALD, P. Surface tension as a factor in the resistance of neonatal lungs to aeration. *Am. J. Obstet. Gynecol.* 53: 996–1007, 1947.

109. GRUENWALD, P. Normal and abnormal expansion of the lungs of newborn infants obtained at autopsy. III. The pattern of aeration as affected by gestational and postnatal age. *Anat. Rec.* 146: 337–352, 1963.

110. HACKNEY, J. D., M. J. EVANS, R. F. BILS, C. E. SPIER, AND M. P. JONES. Effect of oxygen at high concentration and food deprivation on cell division in lung alveoli of mice. *Exp. Mol. Pathol.* 26: 350–358, 1977.

111. HACKNEY, J. D., M. J. EVANS, C. E. SPIER, U. T. ANZAR, AND K. W. CLARK. Effect of high concentrations of oxygen on

reparative regeneration of damaged alveolar epithelium in mice. *Exp. Mol. Pathol.* 34: 338–344, 1981.
112. HASLETON, P. S. The internal surface area of the adult human lung. *J. Anat.* 112: 391–400, 1972.
113. HEBER, A. R. Some effects of altitudes on the human body. *Lancet* 1: 1148–1150, 1921.
114. HIERONYMI, G. Veranderungen der Lungenstruktur in verschiedenen Lebensalteren. *Verh. Dtsch. Ges. Pathol.* 44: 129–130, 1960.
115. HIERONYMI, G. Über den durch das Alter bedingten Formwandel menschlicher Lungen. *Ergeb. Allg. Pathol. Pathol. Anat.* 41: 1–62, 1961.
116. HISLOP, A., E. HEY, AND L. REID. The lungs in congenital bilateral renal agenesis and dysplasia. *Arch. Dis. Child.* 54: 32–38, 1979.
117. HISLOP, A., AND L. REID. Development of the acinus in the human lung. *Thorax* 29: 90–94, 1974.
118. HISLOP, A., AND L. REID. Persistent hypoplasia of the lung after repair of congenital diaphragmatic hernia. *Thorax* 31: 450–455, 1976.
119. HITCHCOCK, K. R. Lung development and the pulmonary surfactant system: hormonal influences. *Anat. Rec.* 198: 13–34, 1980.
120. HITCHCOCK, K. R., J. HARNEY, AND S. REICHLIN. Hormones and the lung. III. Thyroid hormones in the perinatal rat lung. *Endocrinology* 107: 294–299, 1980.
121. HOGONNAUD, C., P. GEHR, E. R. WEIBEL, AND P. H. BURRI. Adaptation of the growing lung to increased oxygen consumption. II. Morphometric analysis. *Respir. Physiol.* 29: 1–10, 1977.
122. HOLLAND, J., J. MILIC-EMILI, P. T. MACKLEM, AND D. V. BATES. Regional distribution of pulmonary ventilation and perfusion in elderly subjects. *J. Clin. Invest.* 47: 81–92, 1962.
123. HOLMES, C. W. M., AND W. M. THURLBECK. Normal lung growth and response after pneumonectomy in the rat at various ages. *Am. Rev. Respir. Dis.* 120: 1125–1136, 1979.
124. HUMPHREYS, P. W., I. C. S. NORMAND, E. O. R. REYNOLDS, AND L. B. STRANG. Pulmonary lymph flow and the uptake of liquid from the lungs of the lamb at the start of breathing. *J. Physiol. London* 193: 1–29, 1967.
125. HUMPHREYS, P. W., AND L. B. STRANG. Effects of gestation and prenatal asphyxia on pulmonary surface properties of the foetal rabbit. *J. Physiol. London* 192: 53–62, 1967.
126. HURTADO, A. Respiratory adaptation in the Indian natives of the Peruvian Andes. Studies at high altitude. *Am. J. Phys. Anthropol.* 17: 137–165, 1932.
126a.International Anatomical Nomenclature Committee. *Nomina Embryologica.* Bethesda, MD: Fed. Am. Soc. Exp. Biol., 1970.
127. JAIN, B. P., J. S. BRODY, AND A. B. FISHER. The small lung of hypopituitarism. *Am. Rev. Respir. Dis.* 108: 49–55, 1973.
128. JAYKKA, S. Capillary erection and the structure appearance of fetal and neonatal lungs. *Acta Paediatr. Stockholm* 47: 484–488, 1958.
129. JOHN, R., AND J. THOMAS. Chemical composition of elastins isolated from aortas and pulmonary tissues of humans of different ages. *Biochem. J.* 127: 261–269, 1972.
130. JOST, A., AND A. POLICARD. Contribution experimental a l'étude du développement prenatal du poumon chez le lapin. *Arch. Anat. Microsc. Morphol. Exp.* 37: 323–332, 1948.
131. JURICOVA, M., AND Z. DEYL. Aging processes in collagens from different tissues of rats. *Adv. Exp. Med. Biol.* 53: 351–357, 1975.
132. KAGAN, H. M., L. TSENG, AND D. E. SIMPSON. Control of elastin metabolism by elastin ligands. Reciprocal effects on lysyl oxidase activity. *J. Biol. Chem.* 256: 5417–5421, 1981.
133. KARLBERG, P. The adaptive changes in the immediate postnatal period with particular reference to respiration. *J. Pediatr.* 56: 585–604, 1962.
134. KARLBERG, P., F. H. ADAMS, F. GEUBELLE, AND G. WALLGREN. Alteration of the infant's thorax during vaginal delivery. *Acta Obstet. Gynecol. Scand.* 41: 223–229, 1962.
135. KARLBERG, P., R. B. CHERRY, F. E. ESRARDO, AND G. KOCH. Respiratory studies in newborn infants. II. Pulmonary ventilation and mechanics of breathing in the first minutes of life, including the onset of ventilation. *Acta Paediatr. Scand.* 51: 121–136, 1962.
136. KARLBERG, P., AND G. KOCH. Respiratory studies in newborn infants. III. Development of mechanics of breathing the first week of life. A longitudinal study. *Acta Paediatr. Suppl.* 135: 121–129, 1962.
137. KARLINSKY, J. B., G. L. SNIDER, C. FRANZBLAU, P. J. STONE, AND F. G. HOPPIN, JR. In vitro effects of elastase and collagenase on mechanical properties of hamster lungs. *Am. Rev. Respir. Dis.* 113: 769–777, 1976.
138. KAUFFMAN, S. L. Acceleration of canalicular development in lungs of fetal mice exposed transplacentally to dexamethasone. *Lab. Invest.* 36: 395–401, 1977.
139. KAUFFMAN, S. L., P. H. BURRI, AND E. R. WEIBEL. The postnatal growth of the rat lung. II. Autoradiography. *Anat. Rec.* 180: 63–76, 1974.
140. KEELEY, F. W., D. G. FAGAN, AND S. I. WEBSTER. Quantity and character of elastin in developing human lung. Parenchymal tissues of normal infants and infants with respiratory distress syndrome. *J. Lab. Clin. Med.* 90: 981–989, 1977.
141. KIDA, K., AND W. M. THURLBECK. The effects of β-aminoprionitrile on the growing rat lung. *Am. J. Pathol.* 101: 693–710, 1980.
142. KIDA, K., AND W. M. THURLBECK. Lack of recovery of lung structure and function after the administration of β-aminoproprionitrile in the postnatal period. *Am. Rev. Respir. Dis.* 122: 467–475, 1980.
143. KIDA, K., AND W. M. THURLBECK. Tracheal banding in weanling rats diminishes lung growth and alters lung architecture. *Pediatr. Res.* 15: 269–277, 1981.
144. KIKKAWA, Y., M. KAIBARA, E. K. MOTOYAMA, M. M. ORZALESI, AND C. D. COOK. Morphologic development of fetal rabbit lung and its acceleration with cortisol. *Am. J. Pathol.* 64: 423–433, 1971.
145. KIKKAWA, Y., E. K. MOTOYAMA, AND C. D. COOK. The ultrastructure of the lungs of lambs. *Am. J. Pathol.* 47: 877–904, 1965.
146. KIKKAWA, Y., E. K. MOTOYAMA, AND L. GLUCIC. Study of the lungs of fetal and newborn rabbits. Morphologic, biochemical and surface physical development. *Am. J. Pathol.* 52: 177–209, 1968.
147. KITAGAWA, M., A. HISLOP, E. A. BOYDEN, AND L. REID. Lung hypoplasia in congenital diaphragmatic hernia. Quantitative study of airway, artery and alveolar development. *Br. J. Surg.* 58: 342–346, 1971.
148. KNUDSON, R. J., R. C. SLATIN, AND M. D. LEBOWITZ. The maximum expiratory flow volume curve. Normal standards variability and effects of age. *Am. Rev. Respir. Dis.* 113: 587–600, 1976.
149. KOHLER, H. G., K. R. PEEL, AND R. A. HOAR. Extramembranous pregnancy and amniorrhea. *J. Obstet. Gynaecol. Br. Commonw.* 77: 809–812, 1970.
150. KOTAS, R. V., AND M. E. AVERY. Accelerated appearance of pulmonary surfactant in the fetal rabbit. *J. Appl. Physiol.* 30: 358–361, 1971.
151. KOTAS, R. V., AND M. E. AVERY. The influence of sex on fetal lung maturation and on the response to glucocorticoids. *Am. Rev. Respir. Dis.* 121: 377–380, 1980.
152. KOTAS, R., L. MIMS, AND L. HART. Reversible inhibition of lung cell numbers after glucocorticoid injection. *Pediatrics* 53: 358–361, 1974.
153. KRAHL, V. E. Anatomy of the mammalian lung. In: *Handbook of Physiology. Respiration*, edited by W. O. Fenn and H. Rahn. Washington, DC: Am. Physiol. Soc., 1964, sect. 3, vol. I, chapt. 6, p. 213–284.
154. LAHIRI, S., R. G. DELANEY, J. S. BRODY, M. SIMPSER, T. VELASQUEZ, E. K. MOTOYAMA, AND G. POLGAR. Relative roles of environmental and genetic factors in respiratory adaptation to high altitudes. *Nature London* 261: 133–135, 1976.

155. LANGSTON, C., P. SACHDEVA, M. J. COWAN, J. HAINES, R. G. CRYSTAL, AND W. M. THURLBECK. Alveolar multiplication in the contralateral lung after unilateral pneumonectomy in rabbits. *Am. Rev. Respir. Dis.* 115: 7–13, 1977.

156. LANGSTON, C., AND W. M. THURLBECK. Lung growth and development in late gestation and early postnatal life (lung growth in utero and in the neonate). In: *Perspectives in Pediatric Pathology*, edited by H. C. Rosenberg. Chicago, IL: Year Book, 1982, chapt. 8, p. 203–235.

157. LANMAN, J. T., A. SCHAFFER, L. HEROD, Y. OGAWA, AND R. CASTELLANOS. Distensibility of the fetal lung with fluid in the sheep. *Pediatr. Res.* 5: 586–590, 1971.

158. LEBLANC, P., F. RUFF, AND J. MILIC-EMILI. Effects of age and body position on "airway closure" in man. *J. Appl. Physiol.* 28: 448–451, 1970.

159. LECHNER, A. J., AND N. BANCHERO. Lung morphometry in guinea pigs acclimated to hypoxia during growth. *Respir. Physiol.* 42: 155–169, 1980.

160. LEUNG, D. Y. M., S. GLAGOV, AND M. B. MATHEWS. A new in vitro system for studying cell response to mechanical stimulation. Different effects of cyclic stretching and agitation on smooth muscle biosynthesis. *Exp. Cell Res.* 109: 285–298, 1977.

161. LIGGINS, G. C. Premature delivery of foetal limbs infused with glucocorticoids. *J. Endocrinol.* 45: 515–523, 1969.

162. LINDBERG, J. A., A. BREHIER, AND P. L. BALLARD. Triiodothyronine nuclear binding in fetal and adult rat lung and cultured lung cells. *Endocrinology* 103: 1725–1731, 1978.

163. LOOSLI, C. G. Interalveolar communications in normal and pathologic mammalian lungs: review of the literature. *Arch. Pathol.* 24: 743–776, 1937.

164. LOOSLI, C. G., AND E. L. POTTER. Pre- and postnatal development of the respiratory portion of the human lung. *Am. Rev. Respir. Dis.* 80: 5–23, 1959.

165. MACKLEM, P. T. Airway obstruction and collateral ventilation. *Physiol. Rev.* 51: 368–436, 1971.

166. MACKLIN, C. C. Alveolar pores and their significance in the human lung. *Arch. Pathol.* 21: 202–226, 1936.

167. MAKSVYTIS, H., L. SIMANOVIAN, M. MINNASIAN, J. S. BRODY, AND W. H. J. DOUGLAS. In vitro studies of the lipid interstitial cell (LIC) of the developing lung. *J. Cell. Physiol.* 118: 113–123, 1984.

168. MAKSVYTIS, H. J., C. A. VACCARO, AND J. S. BRODY. Isolation and characterization of the lipid-containing interstitial cell from the developing rat lung. *Lab. Invest.* 45: 248–259, 1981.

169. MARTIN, H. B. The effect of aging on the alveolar pores of Kohn in the dog. *Am. Rev. Respir. Dis.* 88: 773–778, 1963.

170. MARTIN, C. J., S. CHIHARA, AND D. B. CHANG. A comparative study of the mechanical properties in aging alveolar wall. *Am. Rev. Respir. Dis.* 115: 981–988, 1977.

171. MARTIN, C. J., AND T. SUGIHARA. Stimulation of tissue properties in irreversible diffuse obstructive pulmonary syndromes. *J. Clin. Invest.* 52: 1918–1924, 1973.

172. MAUDERLY, J. L. Effect of age on pulmonary structure and function of immature and adult animals and man. *Federation Proc.* 38: 173–177, 1979.

173. MEAD, J. Mechanical properties of lungs. *Physiol. Rev.* 41: 281–330, 1961.

174. MILNER, A. D., AND R. A. SAUNDERS. Pressure and volume changes during the first breath of human neonates. *Arch. Dis. Child.* 52: 918–924, 1977.

175. MITZNER, W., J. W. C. JOHNSON, J. BECK, W. LONDON, AND D. SLY. Influence of betamethasone on the development of mechanical properties in the fetal rhesus monkey lung. *Am. Rev. Respir. Dis.* 125: 233–238, 1982.

176. MITZNER, W., J. W. C. JOHNSON, R. SCOTT, W. T. LONDON, AND A. E. PALMER. Effect of betamethasone on pressure-volume relationship of fetal rhesus monkey lung. *J. Appl. Physiol.: Respirat. Environ. Exercise Physiol.* 47: 377–382, 1979.

177. MOESSINGER, A. C., P. MARONE, L. S. JAMES, AND W. A. BLANC. Fetal akinesia and lung growth (Abstract). *Lab Invest.* 42: 175a, 1980.

178. MORTOLA, J. P., J. T. FISHER, J. B. SMITH, G. S. FOX, S. WEEKS, AND D. WILLIS. Onset of respiration in infants delivered by cesarean section. *J. Appl. Physiol.: Respirat. Environ. Exercise Physiol.* 52: 716–724, 1982.

179. MOTOYAMA, E., M. ORZALESI, Y. KIKKAWA, M. KAIBARA, B. WU, C. ZIGAS, AND C. COOK. Effect of cortisol on the maturation of fetal rabbit lungs. *Pediatrics* 48: 547–555, 1971.

180. MUIESON, G., C. SORBINI, AND V. GRASSI. Respiratory function in the aged. *Bull. Physio-Pathol. Respir.* 7: 973–1009, 1971.

181. NARDELL, E. A., AND J. S. BRODY. Determinants of mechanical properties of rat lung during postnatal development. *J. Appl. Physiol.: Respirat. Environ. Exercise Physiol.* 53: 140–148, 1982.

182. NEUHAUSER, G. Beitrag zur Morphogenese der Lunge. *Verh. Anat. Ges.* 52: 277–284, 1961.

183. NIELSEN, H. C., H. M. ZINMAN, AND J. S. TORDAY. Dihydrotestosterone inhibits fetal rabbit pulmonary surfactant production. *J. Clin. Invest.* 69: 611–616, 1982.

184. NIEWOEHNER, D. E., AND J. KLEINERMAN. Morphometric study of elastic fibers in normal and emphysematous human lungs. *Am. Rev. Respir. Dis.* 115: 15–21, 1977.

185. NIJJAR, M. S. Role of cyclic AMP and related enzymes in rat lung growth and development. *Biochim. Biophys. Acta* 586: 454–472, 1979.

186. O'DELL, B. L., K. H. KILBURN, W. N. McKENZIE, AND R. J. THURSTON. The lung of the copper-defiicent rat. A model for developmental pulmonary emphysema. *Am. J. Pathol.* 91: 413–432, 1978.

187. O'HARE, K. H., AND P. L. TOWNES. Morphogenesis of albino rat lung. An autoradiographic analysis of the embryological origin of the Type I and II pulmonary epithelial cells. *J. Morphol.* 132: 69–87, 1970.

188. ORZALESI, M. M., E. K. MOTOYAMA, H. N. JACOBSON, Y. KIKKAWA, E. O. R. REYNOLDS, AND C. D. COOK. The development of the lungs of lambs. *Pediatrics* 35: 373–381, 1965.

189. PAGE, D. V., AND J. T. STOCKER. Anomalies associated with pulmonary hypoplasia. *Am. Rev. Respir. Dis.* 125: 216–221, 1982.

190. PERELMAN, R. H., M. J. ENGLE, AND P. M. FARRELL. Perspectives on fetal lung development. *Lung* 159: 53–80, 1981.

191. PERLMAN, M., AND M. LEVIN. Fetal pulmonary hypoplasia, anuria, and oligohydramnios: clinicopathologic observations and review of the literature. *Am. J. Obstet. Gynecol.* 118: 1119–1123, 1974.

192. PERLMAN, M., J. WILLIAMS, AND M. HIRSCH. Neonatal pulmonary hypoplasia after prolonged leakage of amniotic fluid. *Arch. Dis. Child.* 51: 349–353, 1976.

193. PICKEN, J., M. LURIE, AND J. KLEINERMAN. Mechanical and morphologic effects of long term corticosteroid administration on the rat lung. *Am. Rev. Respir. Dis.* 110: 746–753, 1974.

194. PIERCE, J. A., AND J. B. HOCOTT. Studies on the collagen and elastin content of the human lung. *J. Clin. Invest.* 39: 8–14, 1960.

195. PINKERTON, K. E., B. E. BARRY, J. J. O'NEIL, J. A. RAUB, P. C. PRATT, AND J. D. CRAPO. Morphologic changes in the lung during the lifespan of Fischer 344 rats. *Am. J. Anat.* 164: 155–174, 1982.

196. POLGAR, G., AND T. R. WENG. The functional developmental of the respiratory system. *Am. Rev. Respir. Dis.* 120: 625–695, 1979.

197. POTTER, E. L., AND G. P. BOHLENDER. Intra-uterine respiration in relation to development of fetal lung. *Am. J. Obstet. Gynecol.* 42: 14–22, 1941.

198. POWELL, J. T., AND P. L. WHITNEY. Postnatal development of rat lung. Changes in lung lectin, elastin, acetylcholinesterase and other enzymes. *Biochem. J.* 188: 1–8, 1980.

199. PROCKOP, D. J., K. I. KIVIRIKKO, L. TUDERMAN, AND N. GUZMAN. The biosynthesis of collagen and its disorders. *N. Engl. J. Med.* 301: 77–85, 1979.

200. PUMP, K. K. Emphysema and its relation to age. *Am. Rev. Respir. Dis.* 114: 5–13, 1976.

201. RANGA, V., AND J. KLEINERMAN. Interalveolar pores in mouse lungs. Regional distribution and alterations with age. *Am. Rev. Respir. Dis.* 122: 477–481, 1980.

202. RANGA, V., J. KLEINERMAN, M. P. C. IP, AND J. SORENSON. Age-related changes in elastic fibers and elastin of lung. *Am. Rev. Respir. Dis.* 119: 369–381, 1979.

203. REALE, F. R., AND J. R. ESTERLY. Pulmonary hypoplasia: a morphometric study of the lungs of infants with diaphragmatic hernia, anencephaly and renal malformations. *Pediatrics* 51: 91–96, 1973.

204. RICKERT, W. S., AND W. F. FORBES. Changes in collagen with age. VI. Age and smoking related changes in human lung connective tissue. *Exp. Gerontol.* 11: 89–101, 1976.

205. ROBINSON, N. E., AND J. R. GILLESPIE. Morphologic features of the lungs of aging beagle dogs. *Am. Rev. Respir. Dis.* 108: 1192–1199, 1973.

206. ROONEY, S. A., P. A. MARINO, L. I. GOBRAN, I. GROSS, AND J. B. WARSHAW. Thyrotropin-releasing hormone increases the amount of surfactant in lung lavage from fetal rabbits. *Pediatr. Res.* 13: 623–625, 1979.

207. RYAN, S. F., T. N. VINCENT, R. S. MITCHELL, G. F. FILEY, AND G. DART. Ductectasia: an asymptomatic pulmonary change related to age. *Med. Thorac.* 22: 181–187, 1965.

208. SAHEBJAMI, H., AND C. L. VASSALLO. Effects of starvation and refeeding on lung mechanics and morphometry. *Am. Rev. Respir. Dis.* 119: 443–451, 1979.

209. SAHEBJAMI, H., AND C. L. VASSALLO. Influence of starvation on enzyme-induced emphysema. *J. Appl. Physiol.: Respirat. Environ. Exercise Physiol.* 48: 284–288, 1980.

210. SAHEBJAMI, H., AND J. A. WIRMAN. Emphysema-like changes in the lungs of starved rats. *Am. Rev. Respir. Dis.* 124: 619–624, 1981.

211. SCHNEEBERGER, G. E., D. V. WALTERS, AND R. E. OLVER. Development of intercellular junctions in the pulmonary epithelium of the foetal lamb. *J. Cell. Sci.* 32: 307–324, 1978.

212. SCHWEILER, G. H., AND S. SKOGLUND. Individual variations in the bronchial tree in cats of different ages with special reference to the post-natal development. *Acta Anat.* 56: 70–78, 1964.

213. SETNIKAR, I. Origine e significato della proprieta meccaneche del pomone. *Arch. Fisiol.* 55: 349–357, 1955.

214. SHORT, R. H. D. Alveolar epithelium in relation to growth of the lung. *Philos. Trans. R. Soc. London Ser. B* 235: 35–86, 1951.

215. SHORT, R. H. D. Aspects of comparative lung growth. *Proc. R. Soc. London Ser. B* 140: 432–441, 1952.

216. SILVERS, G. W., T. L. PETTY, AND R. E. STANFORD. Elastic recoil changes in early emphysema. *Thorax* 35: 490–495, 1980.

217. SINCLAIR-SMITH, C. C., J. L. EMERY, D. GADSDON, F. DINSDALE, AND J. BADDELEY. Cartilage in children's lungs: a quantitative assessment using the right middle lobe. *Thorax* 31: 40–43, 1976.

218. SMITH, B. T. Lung maturation in the fetal rat: acceleration by injection of fibroblast-pneumonocyte factor. *Science* 204: 1094–1095, 1979.

219. SMITH, B. T., AND W. G. BOGUES. Effects of drugs and hormones on lung maturation in experimental animal and man. *Pharmacol. Ther.* 9: 51–74, 1982.

220. SMITH, B. T., W. GALAUGHER, AND W. M. THURLBECK. Serum from pneumonectomized rabbits stimulates alveolar type II cell proliferation in vitro. *Am. Rev. Respir. Dis.* 121: 701–707, 1980.

221. SMITH, D. M., S. E. SHELLEY, AND J. U. BALIS. The maturation of the rabbit fetal lung following maternal administration of pilocarpine. *Am. J. Anat.* 154: 163–178, 1979.

222. SMITH, L. J., AND J. S. BRODY. Influence of methylprednisolone on mouse alveolar type 2 cell response to acute lung injury. *Am. Rev. Respir. Dis.* 123: 459–464, 1981.

223. SORBINI, C. A., V. GRASSI, E. SALINAS, AND G. MUIESAN. Arterial oxygen tension in relation to age in healthy subjects. *Respiration* 25: 3–13, 1968.

224. SPOONER, B. S., AND J. M. FAUBIORI. Collagen involvement in branching morphogenesis of embryonic lung and salivary gland. *Dev. Biol.* 77: 84–102, 1980.

225. SPOONER, B. S., AND WESSELS, N. K. Mammalian lung development: interactions in primordium formation and bronchial morphogenesis. *J. Exp. Zool.* 175: 445–454, 1970.

226. STANLEY, N. N., R. ALPER, E. L. CUNNINGHAM, N. S. CHERNIACK, AND N. A. KEFAHDES. Effects of a molecular change in collagen on lung structure and mechanical function. *J. Clin. Invest.* 55: 1195–1201, 1975.

227. STIGOL, L. C., G. F. VAWTER, AND J. MEAD. Studies on elastic recoil of the lung in a pediatric population. *Am. Rev. Respir. Dis.* 105: 552–563, 1972.

228. STRANG, L. B. Growth and development of the lung: fetal and postnatal. *Annu. Rev. Physiol.* 39: 253–276, 1977.

229. SUGIHARA, T., AND C. J. MARTIN. Simulation of lung tissue properties in age and irreversible obstructive syndromes using an aldehyde. *J. Clin. Invest.* 56: 23–29, 1975.

230. SUGIHARA, T., C. J. MARTIN, AND J. HILDEBRANDT. Length-tension properties of alveolar wall in man. *J. Appl. Physiol.* 30: 874–878, 1971.

231. SWISCHUK, L. E., C. J. RICHARDSON, M. M. NICHOLS, AND M. J. INGMAN. Primary pulmonary hypoplasia in the neonate. *J. Pediatr.* 95: 573–577, 1979.

232. SYMCHYCH, P. S., AND P. WINCHESTER. Animal model of human disease: Potter's Syndrome. Animal model: amniotic fluid deficiency and fetal lung growth in the rat. *Am. J. Pathol.* 90: 779–782, 1978.

233. TADERERA, J. V. Control of lung differentiation in vitro. *Dev. Biol.* 16: 489–512, 1967.

234. TANSWELL, A. K., AND B. T. SMITH. Human fetal lung type II pneumonocytes in monolayer culture: the influence of oxidant stress, cortisol environment and soluble fibroblast factors. *Pediatr. Res.* 13: 1097–1100, 1979.

235. THOMAS, I. T., AND D. W. SMITH. Oligohydramnios, cause of the nonrenal features of Potter's syndrome, including pulmonary hypoplasia. *J. Pediatr.* 84: 811–815, 1974.

236. THOMPSON, M. E. Lung growth in response to altered metabolic demand in hamsters: influence of thyroid function and cold exposure. *Respir. Physiol.* 40: 335–347, 1980.

237. THURLBECK, W. M. The internal surface area of non-emphysematous lungs. *Am. Rev. Respir. Dis.* 95: 765–776, 1967.

238. THURLBECK, W. M. The state of the art: postnatal growth and development of the lung. *Am. Rev. Respir. Dis.* 111: 803–844, 1975.

239. THURLBECK, W. M. *Chronic Airflow Obstruction in Lung Disease.* Philadelphia, PA: Saunders, 1976.

240. THURLBECK, W. M. Postmortem lung volumes. *Thorax* 34: 735–739, 1979.

241. THURLBECK, W. M. Post-natal human lung growth. *Thorax* 37: 564–571, 1982.

242. THURLBECK, W. M., AND G. B. ANGUS. Growth and aging of the normal lung. *Chest* 67, Suppl.: 3S–7S, 1975.

243. THURLBECK, W. M., W. GALAUGHER, AND J. MATHERS. Adaptive response to pneumonectomy in puppies. *Thorax* 36: 424–427, 1981.

244. THURLBECK, W. M., K. KIDA, C. LANGSTON, M. J. COWAN, J. A. KITTERMAN, W. TOOLEY, AND H. BRYAN. Postnatal lung growth after repair of diaphragmatic hernia. *Thorax* 34: 338–343, 1979.

245. THURLBECK, W. M., R. C. RYDER, AND N. STERNBY. A comparative study of the severity of emphysema in necropsy populations in three different countries. *Am. Rev. Respir. Dis.* 109: 239–248, 1974.

246. TORDAY, J. S., AND H. C. NIELSEN. Surfactant phospholipid ontogeny in fetal rabbit lung lavage and amniotic fluid. *Biol. Neonat.* 39: 266–271, 1981.

247. TORDET, C., R. BERTIN, C. GARDEY, M. O. RICHARD, F. DAMERON, AND L. MARIN. Lung catecholamines and cyclic nucleotides during perinatal development in the rat. Possible relationships with biochemical and morphological differentiation. *Pediatr. Res.* 15: 787–793, 1981.

248. TOWERS, B. Amniotic fluid and the fetal lung. *Nature London*

183: 1140–1141, 1959.

249. TSAO, F. H., G. R. GUTCHER, AND R. D. ZACHMAN. Effect of hydrocortisone on the metabolism of phosphatidylcholine in maternal and fetal rabbit lungs and livers. *Pediatr. Res.* 13: 997–1001, 1979.

250. TURNER, J. M., J. MEAD, AND M. E. WOHL. Elasticity of human lungs in relation to age. *J. Appl. Physiol.* 25: 664–671, 1968.

251. VACCARO, C. A., AND J. S. BRODY. Ultrastructure of developing alveoli. I. The role of the interstitial fibroblast. *Anat. Rec.* 192: 467–479, 1978.

252. VIIDIK, A. Connective tissue—possible implications of the temporal changes for the aging process. *Mech. Ageing Dev.* 9: 267–285, 1979.

253. WALTERS, D. V., AND R. E. OLVER. The role of catecholamines in lung liquid absorption at birth. *Pediatr. Res.* 12: 239–242, 1978.

254. WANG, N. S., R. V. KOTAS, M. E. AVERY, AND W. M. THURLBECK. Accelerated appearance of osmiophilic bodies in fetal lungs following steroid injection. *J. Appl. Physiol.* 30: 362–365, 1971.

255. WEIBEL, E. R. *Morphometry of the Human Lung.* Heidelberg, West Germany: Springer-Verlag, 1963.

256. WEIBEL, E. R. Post-natal growth of the lung and pulmonary gas-exchange capacity. In: *Development of the Lung,* edited by A. V. S. de Reuck and R. Porter. Boston, MA: Little, Brown, 1967, p. 131–148. (Ciba Found. Symp.)

257. WEIBEL, E. R. Fleischner lecture. Looking into the lung. What can it tell us? *Am. J. Roentgenol.* 113: 1021–1031, 1979.

258. WEIBEL, E. R., P. H. BURRI, H. CLAASSEN, P. GEHR, AND S. SEHOVIC. Size and structure of the respiratory system of the smallest mammal. In: *Comparative Physiology. Primitive Mammals,* edited by K. Schmidt-Nielsen, L. Bolis, and C. R. Taylor. New York; Cambridge Univ. Press, 1979, p. 181–191.

259. WESSELS, N. K. Mammalian lung development: interactions in formation and morphogenesis of tracheal buds. *J. Exp. Zool.*

175: 455–466, 1970.

260. WHITSETT, J. A., M. A. MANTON, C. DAROVEC-BECKERMAN, K. G. ADAMS, AND J. J. MOORE. β-Adrenergic receptors in the developing rabbit lung. *Am. J. Physiol.* 240 (*Endocrinol. Metab.* 3): E351–E357, 1981.

261. WIGGLESWORTH, J. S., AND R. DESAI. Effect on lung growth of cervical cord section in the rabbit fetus. *Early Hum. Dev.* 3: 51–65, 1979.

262. WIGGLESWORTH, J. S., AND R. DESAI. Is fetal respiratory function a major determinant of perinatal survival? *Lancet* 1: 264–267, 1982.

263. WIGGLESWORTH, J. S., R. DESAI, AND P. GUERRINI. Fetal lung hypoplasia: biochemical and structural variations and their possible significance. *Arch. Dis. Child.* 56: 606–615, 1981.

264. WIGGLESWORTH, J. S., R. M. L. WINSTON, AND K. BARTLETT. Infuence of the central nervous system on fetal lung development. *Arch. Dis. Child.* 52: 965–967, 1977.

265. WILLIAMS, M. C. Development of the alveolar structure of the fetal rat in late gestation. *Federation Proc.* 36: 2653–2659, 1977.

266. WILLIAMS, M. C., AND R. J. MASON. Development of the type II cell in the fetal rat lung. *Am. Rev. Respir. Dis.* 115: 37–47, 1977.

267. WILLSON, H. G. Postnatal development of the lung. *Am. J. Anat.* 44: 97–122, 1928.

268. WITSCHI, H. R., W. W. HASCHEK, A. J. P. KLEIN-SZANTO, AND P. J. HAKKINEN. Potentiation of diffuse lung damage by oxygen: determining of variables. *Am. Rev. Respir. Dis.* 123: 98–103, 1981.

269. WRIGHT, R. R. Elastic tissue of normal and emphysematous lungs—tridimensional histologic study. *Am. J. Pathol.* 39: 355–367, 1961.

270. WU, B., Y. KIKKAWA, M. OZALESI, E. MOTOYAMA, M. KAIBARA, C. ZIGAS, AND C. COOK. The effect of thyroxine on the maturation of fetal rabbit lungs. *Biol. Neonat.* 22: 161–168, 1973.

INDEX

Index

Respiratory Mechanics

DISCARD

Main Symbols

C	compliance (capacity in symbols for subdivisions of lung volume)
E	elastance
f	frequency
G	conductance
I	inertance
P	pressure
R	resistance
sG	specific conductance
t	time
V	volume
W	work
$\dot{W}$	power
Z	impedance
$\dot{X}$	dot above any symbol indicates first time derivative; e.g., $\dot{V}$ is flow of gas
$\ddot{X}$	two dots above symbol indicate second time derivative; e.g., $\ddot{V}$ is acceleration of volume

Modifiers

A	alveolar
ab	abdomen
am	ambient
ao	airway opening
aw	airway
B	barometric
bs	body surface
ca	convective acceleration
di	diaphragm
ds	downstream
dyn	dynamic
E	expiratory
el	elastic
es	esophageal
fr	frictional or flow resistive
ga	gastric
I	inspiratory
ia	intercostal/accessory muscles

L	transpulmonary or lung or pulmonary
lam	laminar
m	mouth
max	maximum
mus	muscle
pl	pleural
rc	rib cage
rel	relaxed or relaxation
rs	respiratory system
st	static
ti	tissue
tm	transmural
tur	turbulence
us	upstream
w	chest wall

Subdivisions of Lung Volume

CC	closing capacity
CV	closing volume
ERV	expiratory reserve volume
FRC	functional residual capacity
IC	inspiratory capacity
IRV	inspiratory reserve volume
RV	residual volume
TLC	total lung capacity
VC	vital capacity
VT	tidal volume

Measurements on Forced Respiratory Maneuvers

EPP	equal pressure points
FEF_{x-y}	mean forced expiratory flow between two designated volume points in $FVC = (V_x - V_y)/t$
FET_x	time required to forcibly expire percent of VC, x, from TLC

FEV_t	forced expiratory volume in time interval t
$FEV_t/FVC\%$	percent of FVC expired in time interval t
FVC	forced vital capacity
IVPF curve	isovolume pressure-flow curve
MEFV curve	maximum expiratory flow-volume curve
MFSR curve	maximum flow–static recoil curve
MIFV curve	maximum inspiratory flow-volume curve
MVV	maximum voluntary ventilation
MVV_t	maximum voluntary ventilation in time interval t
PEF	peak expiratory flow
PEFV curve	partial expiratory flow-volume curve
$\dot{V}max_{xx}$	maximum expiratory flow at xx% of VC (note: 100% VC is at TLC; 0% VC is at RV)
$\dot{V}max_{xx,TLC}$	maximum expiratory flow at xx% of TLC

Examples of Combinations

C_L	lung compliance
$C_{st,L}$	static lung compliance
P_A	alveolar pressure
P_{ao}	pressure at the airway opening
$P_{E,m,max_{xx,TLC}}$	maximum expiratory mouth pressure at xx% of TLC
sG_{aw}	specific airway conductance
$\dot{W}_{di}$	diaphragmatic power
$W_{I,el,L}$	elastic work performed on the lung during inspiration